Mathematics B

Edward P. Keenan
Ann Xavier Gantert
Isidore Dressler

AMSCO

AMSCO SCHOOL PUBLICATIONS, INC.
315 HUDSON STREET, NEW YORK, N.Y. 10013

Portions of this book were adapted from the following Amsco publications:
Integrated Mathematics, Course II, Third Edition
     Revised by Edward P. Keenan and Ann Xavier Gantert
Integrated Mathematics, Course III, Third Edition
     by Edward P. Keenan and Ann Xavier Gantert
Algebra Two and Trigonometry
     by Isidore Dressler and Barnett Rich
AP Statistics
     by James F. Bohan
Preparing for the SOL Algebra I Test
     by Helen Benyard Luster

Amsco gratefully acknowledges Texas Instruments' generosity and assistance in the preparation of this book.

Please visit our Web site at: www.amscopub.com

When ordering this book, please specify:
R 729 P *or* MATHEMATICS B, *Paperback*
or
R 729 H *or* MATHEMATICS B, *Hardbound*

     ISBN 1-56765-551-3/NYC Item 56765-551-2 (Softbound edition)
     ISBN 1-56765-550-5/NYC Item 56765-550-4 (Hardbound edition)

Preface

Amsco's **Mathematics B** is a new compilation of the material that has been a leader in presenting high school mathematics in a contemporary, integrated manner. Over the last decade, this approach has undergone further changes and refinements, which have evolved into Mathematics B.

This Amsco book parallels the integrated approach to the teaching of high school mathematics that is being promoted by the National Council of Teachers of Mathematics (NCTM) in its *Principles and Standards for School Mathematics* and the New York State Core Curriculum for High School Mathematics B. Moreover, the Amsco book implements the range of suggestions set forth in the NCTM Standards and the Core Curriculum, which are the acknowledged guidelines for achieving a higher level of excellence in the study of mathematics.

In this new edition:

✔ **The graphing calculator** is used throughout the book as a routine tool in the study of mathematics, replacing the need for tables and requiring increased attention to estimation skills.

✔ **Statistics**, cited as one example of new approaches based on the calculator, includes use of the graphing calculator to study summation, mean, standard deviation, box-and-whisker plots, histograms, and frequency polygon graphs.

✔ **Integration** of geometry, algebra, and other branches of mathematics is further expanded by the early introduction of selected topics and the inclusion of challenging problems. Topics such as probability, statistics, transformations, systems, sequences and series, and geometry of the circle are included to provide an effective and unified course of study for mathematics students beyond the traditional study of advanced algebra and trigonometry.

✔ **Algebraic skills** from **Mathematics A** have been maintained, strengthened, and expanded, and *Cumulative Review* sections appear at the end of each chapter to reinforce all concepts learned in this course.

✔ **Enrichment** is stressed both in the book and in the Teacher's Manual where many suggestions are given for teaching strategies and alternative assessment. The Manual includes opportunities for extended tasks, hands-on activities, and even more applications with graphing calculators. Reproducible *Enrichment Activities* that challenge students to explore topics in greater depth are provided in the Manual for each chapter.

✔ **Problem solving**, which is a primary goal in all learning standards, is emphasized throughout the text with fully developed examples, alternative solutions, and procedures to help students. These examples and procedures promote the growth of each student's ability to solve nonroutine problems.

This text has been written to provide effective teaching materials for a unified program appropriate for tenth- and eleventh-grade mathematics students, including all topics contained in the Core Curriculum Key Ideas and Performance Indicators for Mathematics B.

Mathematics B emphasizes extensive use of the calculator in the study of mathematics. Trigonometric, exponential, and logarithmic functions, along with their graphs and applications, have always been important topics at this level, but now, with the existence of negative mantissas on calculators, characteristics such as 9.0000–10 are not used. Irrational numbers, often shown in exact radical form, appear as rational approximations on calculator displays. Other changes are required as well with calculator usage.

Learning standards, whether national in scope such as the NCTM Standards or more regional such as the Core Curriculum of New York State, include goals that are based on clearly defined curriculum content. This text provides that curriculum and gives teachers an opportunity to establish procedures for alternative assessment. As an example, student portfolios may consist of completed copies of the *Enrichment Activities*, Suggested Test Items, and both group and individual reports generated by Extended Tasks in the Teacher's Manual. Writing and communication skills are employed frequently when students are asked to explain their reasoning in exercises throughout the text.

An intent of the authors was to make the material of greatest service to the average student. Since its publication, however, this material has been used successfully with students of all abilities, and this book continues to address that ability range.

Specifically:

✔ Concepts are carefully developed using appropriate language and mathematical symbolism.

✔ General principles are stated clearly and concisely.

✔ Numerous examples are solved as models for students, with detailed explanations and, where appropriate, alternative approaches and calculator solutions.

✔ Varied and carefully graded exercises are given in abundance to test student understanding of mathematical skills and concepts, and additional enrichment materials challenge the most capable students.

This text is offered so that teachers may effectively continue to help students comprehend, master, and enjoy mathematics from an integrated point of view.

Mathematics B is dedicated to Anna Gantert, whose encouragement throughout its writing was a continuation of the loving support she has given to her daughter all her life. This book is also dedicated to Mary, David, Jennifer, and Joanna Keenan, who are a constant source of pride to their father.

The Authors

Contents

Chapter 3
Proving Statements in Geometry   92

Chapter 4
Triangle Congruence   144

Chapter 11
Geometry of the Circle   **435**

Chapter 12
Relations and Functions   **481**

Chapter 16
Exponential Functions

Chapter 17
Logarithmic Functions

Chapter 18
Trigonometric Applications

Chapter 19
Trigonometric Equations and Identities   **857**

Chapter 20
The Complex Numbers   **920**

Chapter 1

Introducing Geometry and Coordinates

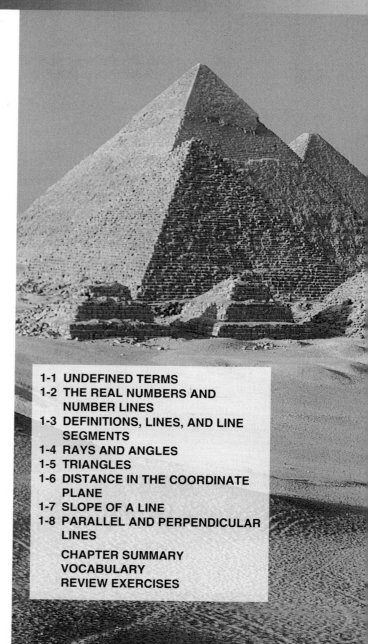

For thousands of years, civilized people have needed to know how to work with the sizes, shapes, and positions of things. Ancient Egyptians used geometry to solve many practical problems involving landmarks, boundaries, and land areas.

Greek scholars such as Thales, Pythagoras, Plato, Aristotle, and Euclid, together with the bands of followers who learned from them and expanded their teachings, sought explanations for the geometric facts that they had learned. About 300 B.C., Euclid organized the geometry of his day into a single logical system, now known as **Euclidean geometry**, which became the basis for the study of geometry in the Western world.

In the seventeenth century, a French mathematician, René Descartes, applied algebraic principles and methods to geometry. This blending of algebra and geometry is known as **coordinate geometry** or **analytic geometry**.

In this chapter, we will establish the foundations of both Euclidean and coordinate geometry.

I-I UNDEFINED TERMS

Language always plays an important role in the development of any area of knowledge. Before we can discuss a topic, it is necessary to agree on the meanings of the words that we will use.

We ordinarily define a term by using a simpler or a previously defined term, which is then defined by using a still simpler term. But this process cannot go on endlessly. There comes a time when the definition must use a term whose meaning is assumed to be clear. Because its meaning is accepted without definition, such a term is called an **undefined term**.

The word *set*, which we use in the study of arithmetic and algebra, is one such undefined term. When a collection of distinct objects is so clearly described that we can always tell whether or not an object belongs to it, we call the collection a **set**. For example, the odd counting numbers less than 10 form a set. The numbers 1, 3, 5, 7, and 9 belong to this set, but −5, 6, and 13 do not.

In geometry, we are concerned with such ideas as *point*, *line*, and *plane*. Since we cannot give satisfactory definitions of these words using simpler defined words, we will consider them as undefined terms.

Although the words *point*, *line*, and *plane* are undefined terms, we still must make clear the properties and characteristics they possess.

A **point** may be represented as a dot on a piece of paper, and is usually named by a capital letter. The dot shown, for example, represents a point, which we call *point P*. A geometric point has no length, width, or thickness; it merely indicates a place or position.

A **line** is a set of points. A set of points may form a curved line or it may form a straight line, as shown. We understand what a straight line is by considering the set of points that can be arranged along the edge of a ruler or along a stretched string.

Curved Line

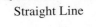

Straight Line

Unless otherwise stated, the term *line* will mean **straight line**.

While a ruler or a stretched string is limited in length, a line is an infinite set of points that extends endlessly in both directions. Arrowheads are sometimes used in a geometric drawing that represents a line to emphasize the fact that there are no endpoints.

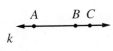

To name a line, we usually use two capital letter that name two points on the line. The line shown may be named *line AB*, written as $\overleftrightarrow{AB}$. It may also be named *line AC* or *line BC*, written as $\overleftrightarrow{AC}$ or $\overleftrightarrow{BC}$. The line may also be named by a single lowercase letter; thus, we may call it *line k* or simply *k*.

A **plane** is a set of points that forms a completely flat surface extending indefinitely in all directions. The figure represents a plane, called *plane R*. This four-sided figure shows only part of the plane, however, because a plane has no boundaries.

A plane may also be named by using letters that identify three points in the plane, provided that they are not on the same line. The plane shown is named *plane ABC*.

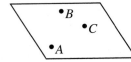

EXERCISES WITH OPEN-RESPONSE PROBLEMS

1. Name something that can be represented by a point.
2. Name something that can be represented by a line.
3. Name something that can be represented by a plane.

In 4–9, is each statement true or false? Explain your choice.

4. A point has no length, width, or thickness.
5. A line is limited in length.
6. A plane has boundaries that are lines.
7. The names $\overleftrightarrow{AB}$ and $\overleftrightarrow{BA}$ refer to the same line.
8. The statement "A line is a set of points" is a definition.
9. A point indicates a place or position.

1-2   THE REAL NUMBERS AND NUMBER LINES

Connecting Numbers and Lines

Numbers, which are an important part of mathematics, help us to understand algebra and to measure and compare geometric figures. In Course I, you learned that the set of real numbers can be associated with the set of points on a ***number line***. Every real number corresponds to a point on a line, and every point on a line corresponds to a real number. The real number line shown below is a partial illustration of this correspondence.

The number that corresponds to a point on a line is called the ***coordinate*** of the point. The coordinate of point A on the number line shown above is 3, and the coordinate of point B is $-\frac{1}{2}$. The point to which a number corresponds is called the ***graph*** of the number. The graph of 5 is C, and the graph of -2 is D.

Pairs of Real Numbers and the Coordinate Plane

To study points in a plane, we use two real number lines that intersect at the point whose coordinate on each line is 0. The two number lines are called the ***coordinate axes***. One of the coordinate axes is a horizontal line called the ***x-axis***; the other is a vertical line called the ***y-axis***. The point O at which the two lines intersect is called the ***origin***.

The axes divide the points that are not on the axes into four regions called *quadrants*. These quadrants are numbered in a counter-clockwise direction, starting from the upper right, as Quadrant I, Quadrant II, and so on.

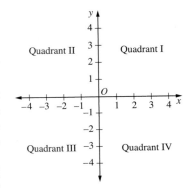

On the *x*-axis, coordinates to the right of *O* are positive, and coordinates to the left of *O* are negative. On the *y*-axis, coordinates above *O* are positive, and coordinates below *O* are negative.

As shown in the figure below, we will use the two number lines to determine a pair of numbers that is associated with a point *P* in the plane. Through *P*, we draw a vertical line to the *x*-axis. This line intersects the *x*-axis at 2. The number 2 is called the *x-coordinate*, or the *abscissa*, of point *P*. Now, through *P*, we draw a horizontal line to the *y*-axis. This line intersects the *y*-axis at 4. The number 4 is called the *y-coordinate*, or the *ordinate*, of point *P*. The *x*-coordinate, 2, and the *y*-coordinate, 4, are called the *co-ordinates* of point *P*, written as (2, 4).

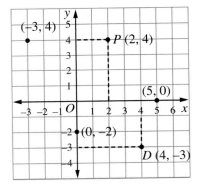

To designate the coordinates of any point, we agree to write the abscissa as the first element and the ordinate as the second element, forming an *ordered pair of numbers*. In general, the coordinates of a point are represented by (*x*, *y*).

Point *D* on the figure above is the graph of the ordered pair of numbers (4, −3) because the abscissa of the pair is 4 and the ordinate of the pair is −3. The pair (4, −3) is not the same as the pair (−3, 4).

For every point on the *x*-axis, *y* = 0, and for every point on the *y*-axis, *x* = 0. In the figure above, note that points on the axes are identified as (5, 0) and (0, −2). The origin, point *O*, represents the ordered pair of numbers (0, 0).

This coordinate system is also called a *rectangular coordinate system*, or the *Cartesian coordinate system* in honor of its originator, Descartes.

EXAMPLE

Of the points *A*, *B*, *C*, and *D* shown in the figure, which point represents the graph of the ordered pair of real numbers $(\sqrt{5}, 1)$?

Solution   Since $(x, y) = (\sqrt{5}, 1)$, the abscissa, or x-value, is $\sqrt{5}$, and the ordinate, or y-value, is 1. We know that $\sqrt{5}$ is greater than $\sqrt{4}$ and less than $\sqrt{9}$; that is, $2 < \sqrt{5} < 3$. Only point B shows an abscissa between 2 and 3, and an ordinate of 1.

Answer: B

EXERCISES WITH OPEN-RESPONSE PROBLEMS

In 1–3, refer in each case to the number line given below, and write the answer for each question as indicated.

Ex. 1–3

1. On the number line, A is the ___(a)___ of -1 and 2 is the ___(b)___ of B.
2. On the number line, 6 is the coordinate of ___(a)___ and C is the graph of ___(b)___.
3. Locate point E on the number line if E is the graph of 0.

In 4–8, refer in each case to the graph shown.

4. Write as an ordered pair of numbers the coordinates of each point:
   A, B, C, D, E, F, G, H, and O.
5. Name the abscissa of each point:
   P, R, and F.
6. Name the ordinate of each point:
   Q, T, and G.
7. Which point represents the graph of $(-2, \sqrt{2})$?
8. Which point represents the graph of $(\sqrt{2}, -2)$?

Ex. 4–8

9. On graph paper, draw and label a pair of coordinate axes. Then plot and label each of the following points.

   $A(4, 5)$ $B(-2, 5)$ $C(3, -4)$ $D(-3, -5)$ $E(6, 0)$

   $F(-3, 0)$ $G(0, -4)$ $H(0, 4)$ $J\left(5, -1\frac{1}{2}\right)$ $K(-1, 2.5)$

   $L\left(-\frac{3}{4}, -6\right)$ $M(0, -2)$ $P(3, 0)$ $Q(\sqrt{3}, 2)$ $R(-5, \sqrt{5})$

10. What are the coordinates of the origin?
11. If a point is on the x-axis, what is the value of its ordinate?
12. What is the value of the abscissa of every point on the y-axis?

1-3 DEFINITIONS, LINES, AND LINE SEGMENTS

Qualities of a Good Definition

A *definition* is a statement of the precise meaning of a term. We must define a word or a term so that it will be understood by all people in exactly the same way.

As stated in Section 1-1, a good definition must be expressed in words that have already been defined or in words that have been accepted as undefined. It must state the class to which the defined word belongs, and it must distinguish the defined word from other members of that class. Also, it must be reversible.

Collinear Points

● **DEFINITION.** A *collinear set of points* is a set of points all of which lie on the same straight line.

This definition has the properties of a good definition:

1. It is expressed in words that have already been defined or accepted as undefined.
   Set, *point*, and *line* are undefined terms.
2. It states the class to which the defined term belongs.
   The class is a set of points.
3. It distinguishes the defined term from other members of the class.
   The points must be on the same straight line.
4. It is reversible.
   A set of points all of which lie on the same straight line is a collinear set of points.

A, *B*, and *C* are collinear points, whereas *D*, *E*, and *F* are not collinear points. *D*, *E*, and *F* are called *noncollinear points*.

● **DEFINITION.** A *noncollinear set of points* is a set of three or more points that do not all lie on the same straight line.

The distance between two points   To find the distance between any two points on a number line, we find the difference between the coordinates assigned to these points. For example, the distance between *G* and *C*, written as *GC*, is 4 units, found by subtracting the coordinates of these points: $GC = 5 - 1 = 4$. The distance *CG* must equal the distance *GC*. Therefore, we make use of ***absolute value*** in finding distance so that the difference of the coordinates will be independent of the order in which they are subtracted. Thus, we write:

$$GC = |5 - 1| = |4| = 4 \qquad \text{and} \qquad CG = |1 - 5| = |-4| = 4$$

Recall that:

1. The absolute value of a positive number p is p. Thus, $|6| = 6$.
2. The absolute value of a negative number n is $-n$. If $n = -5$, then $-n = -(-5) = 5$. Thus, $|-5| = 5$.
3. The absolute value of 0 is 0. Hence, $|0| = 0$.

We can now state the following definition:

● **DEFINITION.** The ***distance between any two points on the real number line*** is the absolute value of the difference of the coordinates of the two points.

Hence, on the real number line, the distance between point A, whose coordinate is a, and point B, whose coordinate is b, can be represented by

$$AB = |a - b| \quad \text{or} \quad AB = |b - a|$$

In the coordinate plane, when two points are on the same horizontal line, they have the same y-coordinate. For example, points $A(2, 1)$ and $B(6, 1)$ have the same ordinate, 1. The distance AB between A and B, two points with the same ordinate, is the absolute value of the difference between their x-coordinates.

$$AB = |6 - 2| = |4| = 4$$
and
$$AB = |2 - 6| = |-4| = 4$$

When two points are on the same vertical line, they have the same x-coordinate. For example, points $C(2, 4)$ and $D(2, -1)$ have the same abscissa, 2. The distance CD between C and D, two points with the same abscissa, is the absolute value of the difference between their y-coordinates.

$$CD = |4 - (-1)| = |4 + 1| = |5| = 5$$
and $$CD = |-1 - 4| = |-5| = 5$$

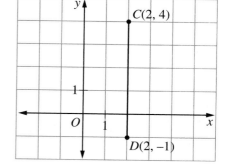

Betweenness of points on a line In the study of arithmetic and algebra, we saw that, since 3 is less than 4, denoted by $3 < 4$, and 4 is less than 6, denoted by $4 < 6$, we wrote $3 < 4 < 6$, and we said that 4 is ***between*** 3 and 6. In general, if a, b, and c are real numbers such that $a < b$ and $b < c$, we write $a < b < c$, and we say that b is between a and c.

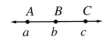

Note that the position of point B with respect to points A and C is different from the position of point D with respect to points A and C for the following reasons:

1. Points A, B, and C are collinear, whereas points A, D, and C are not collinear.

2. The sum of the distance between A and B and the distance between B and C is equal to the distance from A to C; that is, $AB + BC = AC$. However, the sum of the distance between A and D and the distance between D and C is not equal to the distance between A and C; that is, $AD + DC \neq AC$.

These considerations guide us in formulating the following definition:

- **DEFINITION.** *B is between A and C* if and only if A, B, and C are distinct collinear points and $AB + BC = AC$.

We can represent a line on which B is between A and C by the symbol $\overleftrightarrow{ABC}$ It can be shown that, if point B is between point A and point C, then b, the coordinate of point B, is between a, the coordinate of point A, and c, the coordinate of point C. In the diagram, $a < b < c$.

Line Segment

A line segment is a subset, or part of, a line. In the figure, A and B are two points on line m. Points A and B determine *line segment AB*, or *segment AB*, denoted by the symbol $\overline{AB}$.

- **DEFINITION.** A *line segment*, or *segment*, is a set of points consisting of two points on a line, called *endpoints*, and all points on the line between the endpoints.

Segment AB is a set of points consisting of the union of points A and B and all points on line AB between points A and B.

Note. Although a line may be named by any two of its points, a line segment is always named by its two endpoints.

To indicate that C is a point on $\overline{AB}$, but is not one of its endpoints, we use the symbol $\overline{ACB}$.

Measuring a line segment When we measure a line segment, we determine the distance between its endpoints.

- **DEFINITION.** The *length or measure of a line segment* is the distance between its endpoints.

The length of every segment whose endpoints are distinct points is a unique positive number.

Note: $\overleftrightarrow{AB}$ represents *line AB*.
$\overline{AB}$ represents *segment AB*.
AB represents *the measure of* $\overline{AB}$.

Congruence of line segments   The line segments shown have the same length or measure. We say that $\overline{AB}$ and $\overline{CD}$ are *congruent segments*.

● **DEFINITION. *Congruent segments*** are segments that have the same measure.

To indicate that segments AB and CD are congruent to each other, we write $\overline{AB} \cong \overline{CD}$, read as *segment AB is congruent to segment CD*.

If $\overline{AB} \cong \overline{CD}$, then AB, the length of $\overline{AB}$, and CD, the length of $\overline{CD}$, are the same number. Hence, $\overline{AB} \cong \overline{CD}$ implies that $AB = CD$. We say that the congruence $\overline{AB} \cong \overline{CD}$ is equivalent to the equality $AB = CD$. We may use either notation at any time.

Correct Symbolism

$\overline{AB} \cong \overline{CD}$ The segments are congruent.
$AB = CD$ The measures or distances are the same.

We would not write $\overline{AB} = \overline{CD}$ because this would indicate that $\overline{AB}$ and $\overline{CD}$ represent the same set of points.

If we were to move $\overline{AB}$ and $\overline{CD}$ by folding the paper on which they appear, we could fit one segment on top of the other—that is, we could make the segments ***coincide***. Sometimes, congruent line segments are thought of as line segments that can be made to coincide.

When two or more segments are known to be congruent, or their lengths to be equal, we note this fact on the diagram by marking each segment with the same number of strokes.

Midpoint of a line segment

● **DEFINITION.** The ***midpoint of a line segment*** is the point of that line segment that divides the segment into two congruent segments.

If M is the midpoint of $\overline{AB}$, then $\overline{AM} \cong \overline{MB}$ or $AM = MB$.

It is also true that $AM = \frac{1}{2} AB$, that $MB = \frac{1}{2} AB$, that $AB = 2AM$, and that $AB = 2MB$.

Bisector of a line segment

● **DEFINITION.** The ***bisector of a line segment*** is any line or subset of a line that intersects the segment at its midpoint.

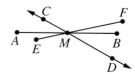

Segment AB is bisected at point M if M is the midpoint of $\overline{AB}$. Therefore, $\overline{AM} \cong \overline{MB}$ or $AM = MB$.

Any line, such as $\overleftrightarrow{CD}$, or any segment, such as $\overline{EF}$, that is distinct from $\overline{AB}$ and that contains point M is a bisector of $\overline{AB}$ or *bisects* $\overline{AB}$ at M.

Note that a line, unlike a line segment, cannot be bisected since a line extends indefinitely in two opposite directions and, therefore, does not have a midpoint.

Adding and subtracting line segments

- **DEFINITION.** A line segment RS is the ***sum of two line segments*** $\overline{RP}$ and $\overline{PS}$ if point P is between points R and S. Thus, $\overline{RS} = \overline{RP} + \overline{PS}$. Recall that, if P is between R and S, then P, R, and S are collinear.

Observe that point P divides $\overline{RS}$ into two segments, $\overline{RP}$ and $\overline{PS}$, such that the following relations are true for the length of the segments:

$$RS = RP + PS \qquad RP = RS - PS \qquad PS = RS - RP$$

EXAMPLES

1. Find the distance between the points whose coordinates on the real number line are -4 and 3.

Solution   Let A be the point on the number line whose coordinate is -4.
Let B be the point on the number line whose coordinate is 3.
Then distance $AB = |a - b| = |(-4) - 3| = |-7| = 7$

Answer: The distance is 7 units.

---

2. In the coordinate plane, the endpoints of $\overline{AB}$ are $A(-3, 2)$ and $B(5, 2)$. The endpoints of $\overline{CD}$ are $C(1, 0)$ and $D(1, 6)$. Segments $\overline{AB}$ and $\overline{CD}$ intersect at $M(1, 2)$.
  a. Find AB, AM, MB, CD, CM, and MD.
  b. Is $\overline{AM}$ congruent to $\overline{MB}$? Explain.
  c. Is M the midpoint of $\overline{AB}$? Explain.
  d. Is M between A and B? Explain.
  e. Is $\overline{CD}$ a bisector of $\overline{AB}$? Explain.
  f. Is $\overline{AB}$ a bisector of $\overline{CD}$? Explain.

Answers:

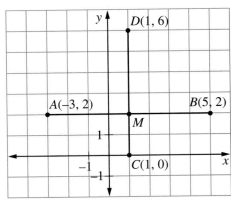

  a. $AB = |5 - (-3)| = |5 + 3| = 8$
    $AM = |1 - (-3)| = |1 + 3| = 4$
    $MB = |5 - 1| = 4$
    $CD = |6 - 0| = |6| = 6$
    $CM = |2 - 0| = |2| = 2$
    $MD = |6 - 2| = |4| = 4$
  b. $\overline{AM}$ is congruent to $\overline{MB}$ because the two segments have the same measure.
  c. M is the midpoint of $\overline{AB}$ because M is a point on $\overline{AB}$ that divides $\overline{AB}$ into two congruent segments.

d. *M* is between *A* and *B* because *M*, *A*, and *B* are distinct collinear points and
$\overline{AM} + \overline{MB} = AB$.

e. $\overline{CD}$ is a bisector of $\overline{AB}$ because $\overline{CD}$ is a line segment that intersects $\overline{AB}$ at its
midpoint.

f. $\overline{AB}$ is not a bisector of $\overline{CD}$ because, since $CM \neq MD$, $\overline{AB}$ does not intersect
CD at its midpoint.

EXERCISES WITH OPEN-RESPONSE PROBLEMS

In 1–6, in each case, use the figure shown.

1. Name a set of three or more points that are collinear.
2. Name a point between *P* and *Q*.
3. Name a point between *R* and *T*, and also between *S* and *Q*.
4. Is *U* between *S* and *P*? Explain your answer.
5. Name the segment whose endpoints are *R* and *Q*.
6. Name two segments that are subsets of $\overleftrightarrow{ST}$.

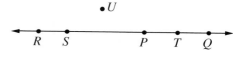

Ex. 1–6

In 7–18, represent each number by the simplest numeral, without using an absolute value symbol.

7. $|7|$ **8.** $|-2|$ **9.** $|3 + (-9)|$ **10.** $|0|$
11. $|3 + 7|$ **12.** $|(-2) + (-3)|$ **13.** $|5 - 12|$ **14.** $|4 - (-2)|$
15. $|0 - (3)|$ **16.** $|(-6) - 0|$ **17.** $|(-3) - (-1)|$ **18.** $|(-9) - 6|$

In 19–28, use the number line below to find the distance between the points in each pair.

Ex. 19–28

19. *E* and *H*   **20.** *E* and *B*   **21.** *E* and *A*   **22.** *G* and *H*   **23.** *A* and *F*
24. *F* and *I*   **25.** *D* and *C*   **26.** *B* and *I*   **27.** *J* and *D*   **28.** *B* and *H*

In 29–38, find on a number line the distance between the points in each pair that have the indicated
coordinates.

29. 0 and 6   **30.** −6 and 0   **31.** 7 and 2   **32.** 2 and 10   **33.** 8 and −3
34. 5 and −3   **35.** −8 and 4   **36.** −10 and −5   **37.** 15 and −5   **38.** −1 and −4

In 39–42, find each required distance if A, B, and C are collinear points and B is between A and C.

39. $AB = 5$, $BC = 7$, $AC = ?$

40. $BC = 10$, $AB = 7$, $AC = ?$

41. $AB = 3$, $AC = 12$, $BC = ?$

42. $AC = 30$, $BC = 12$, $AB = ?$

In 43–48, find the distance between each pair of points that have the indicated coordinates in the coordinate plane.

43. $(2, 6)$ and $(2, 1)$

44. $(5, 4)$ and $(0, 4)$

45. $(0, 3)$ and $(0, 7)$

46. $(-1, 3)$ and $(4, 3)$

47. $(-1, 3)$ and $(-1, -2)$

48. $(-2, 5)$ and $(-6, 5)$

49. $DE = 8$ and $EF = 12$.   **a.** Does DF always equal 20?   **b.** Draw a diagram or diagrams to justify your answer.

50. $DF = 35$ and $EF = 20$.   **a.** Does DE always equal 15?   **b.** Draw a diagram or diagrams to justify your answer.

51. Is the midpoint of a line segment always on the line segment? Explain your reasoning.

52. Does a line have a midpoint? Explain your reasoning.

53. a. Graph points $A(-2, -1)$, $B(3, -1)$, and $C(5, -1)$ in the coordinate plane.
   b. Find AB, BC, and AC.   **c.** Explain why $AC = AB + BC$.

54. a. Graph points $D(-1, 2)$, $E(5, 2)$, and $F(5, -3)$ in the coordinate plane.
   b. Find DE and EF.   **c.** If $DEFG$ is a rectangle, what are the coordinates of G?

55. If $\overline{XY}$ is the bisector of $\overline{RS}$, must $\overline{RS}$ be the bisector of $\overline{XY}$? Explain your answer with a diagram.

56. If $\overline{AM} \cong \overline{MB}$, does this necessarily mean that M is the midpoint of $\overline{AB}$? Explain your answer with a diagram.

57. Use the markings in the diagram to tell which of the following statements is incorrect:

   (1) $\overline{AB} \cong \overline{CD}$ (2) $AB = CD$ (3) $\overline{AC} \cong \overline{BD}$ (4) $\overline{AC} \cong \overline{CD}$

In 58–61, state two conclusions that can be drawn from the given data for each figure. In one conclusion, use the symbol $\cong$; in the other, use the symbol $=$.

Ex. 58

Ex. 59

Ex. 60

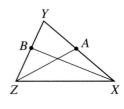

Ex. 61

58. T is the midpoint of $\overline{AC}$.

60. E is the midpoint of $\overline{AD}$.

59. $\overline{MN}$ bisects $\overline{RQ}$.

61. $\overline{XB}$ bisects $\overline{ZY}$.

In 62 and 63, use the figure in Exercise 58 to complete each statement.

62. $AT + TC = $ ___

63. $AC - AT = $ ___

1-4 RAYS AND ANGLES

Half-Line and Ray

- **DEFINITION.** Two points, *A* and *B*, are *on one side of* point *P* if *A*, *B*, and *P* are collinear and *P* is not between *A* and *B*.

Every point on a line divides the line into two opposite sets of points called *half-lines*. A **half-line** consists of the set of all points on one side of the point of division. The point of division itself does not belong to the half-line. In the figure, point *P* divides $\overleftrightarrow{MB}$ into two half-lines.

- **DEFINITION.** A *ray* is a part of a line that consists of a point on the line, called an *endpoint*, and all the points on one side of the endpoint.

Thus, a ray is a set of all the points in a half-line, *plus* the dividing point, which is called the endpoint of the ray.

A ray is named by placing an arrow pointing to the right over two capital letters. The first letter must be the letter that names the endpoint of the ray. The second letter may be the name of any other point on the ray. The figure shows ray *AB*, written as $\overrightarrow{AB}$ which starts at endpoint *A*, contains point *B*, and extends indefinitely in one direction.

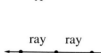

Thus, a point on a line creates two **opposite rays**, each with the same endpoint. In the figure, $\overrightarrow{AB}$ and $\overrightarrow{AC}$ are opposite rays because points *A*, *B*, and *C* are collinear and points *B* and *C* are not on one side of point *A*, but are on opposite sides of point *A*.

- **DEFINITION.** *Opposite rays* are two rays of the same line with a common endpoint and no other point in common.

Note in the figure that the ray whose endpoint is *O* may be named $\overrightarrow{OA}$ or $\overrightarrow{OB}$. However, it may not be named $\overrightarrow{AB}$ since the first capital letter in the name of a ray must represent its endpoint.

Angle

- **DEFINITION.** An **angle** is a set of points that is the union of two rays having the same endpoint.

In the figure, $\overrightarrow{AB}$ and $\overrightarrow{AC}$, which form an angle, are called the *sides* of the angle. *A*, the endpoint of each ray, is called the **vertex** of the angle. The symbol for angle is ∠.

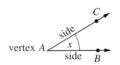

An angle, such as the one illustrated at the left, may be named in any of the following ways:

1. By a capital letter that names its vertex. Example: $\angle A$

2. By a lowercase letter or by a number placed inside the angle. Example: $\angle x$

3. By three capital letters, the middle letter naming the vertex and each of the other letters naming a point on a different ray. Example: $\angle BAC$ or $\angle CAB$

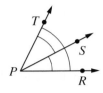

Note. When a diagram shows several angles with the same vertex, we avoid confusion by using three letters to name each angle. For example, in the figure, the smaller angles are $\angle RPS$ and $\angle SPT$; the large angle is $\angle RPT$.

Straight angle

● **DEFINITION.** A *straight angle* is an angle that is the union of opposite rays.

$\overrightarrow{OA}$ and $\overrightarrow{OB}$ are opposite rays of $\overleftrightarrow{AB}$ because they have a common endpoint O, and no other points in common. Thus, $\angle AOB$ is a straight angle because it is the union of the opposite rays $\overrightarrow{OA}$ and $\overrightarrow{OB}$.

The sides of a straight angle belong to the same straight line, and any point on the line may be considered the vertex of the straight angle.

Interior and exterior regions of an angle that is not a straight angle   An angle divides the points of a plane that are not on the angle into two sets of points called *regions*. One region is called the *interior of the angle*; the other region is called the *exterior of the angle*. In the figure, if M is any point on one side of the angle and N is any point on the other side of the angle, neither M nor N being the vertex of the angle, then any point P on $\overline{MN}$ between points M and N belongs to the interior region of the angle. The region

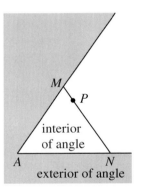

consisting of all points such as P is called the *interior of the angle*. All other points of the plane, except the points in the angle itself, form the region called the *exterior of the angle*.

Measuring an angle   To measure an angle, we must select a unit of measure and know how this unit is to be applied. In geometry, the unit used to measure an angle is usually a *degree*. The number of degrees in an angle is called its *degree measure*.

Since the degree measure of a straight angle is 180, a *degree* is, therefore, the measure of an angle that is $\frac{1}{180}$ of a straight angle. A *protractor* is an instrument that is used to measure angles.

It is possible to use units other than the degree to measure angles, which will be discussed later in this book. Here, when we write that m∠*HRC* = 45, we mean that the measure of ∠*HRC* is 45 degrees.

Classifying angles according to their measures

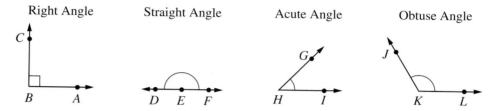

Right Angle   Straight Angle   Acute Angle   Obtuse Angle

- **DEFINITION.** A *right angle* is an angle whose degree measure is 90.

In the figure above, ∠*ABC* is a right angle. Therefore, we know that m∠*ABC* = 90. The symbol ⌐ at *B* is used to show that ∠*ABC* is a right angle.

A *straight angle*, previously defined as the union of opposite rays, is an angle whose degree measure is 180.

In the figure above, ∠*DEF* is a straight angle. Thus, m∠*DEF* = 180. Note that $\overrightarrow{ED}$ and $\overrightarrow{EF}$, the sides of ∠*DEF*, are opposite rays and form a straight line.

- **DEFINITION.** An *acute angle* is an angle whose degree measure is greater than 0 and less than 90. In the figure above, ∠*GHI* is an acute angle.

- **DEFINITION.** An *obtuse angle* is an angle whose degree measure is greater than 90 and less than 180. In the figure above, ∠*JKL* is an obtuse angle.

Congruent angles

- **DEFINITION.** *Congruent angles* are angles that have the same measure.

In the figures at the left, ∠*ABC* and ∠*DEF* have the same measure. This is written as m∠*ABC* = m∠*DEF*. We may also say that these angles are congruent, symbolized as ∠*ABC* ≅ ∠*DEF*. We may use either notation at any time.

Correct Symbolism

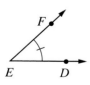

∠*ABC* ≅ ∠*DEF*   The angles are congruent.

m∠*ABC* = m∠*DEF*   The measures of the angles are the same.

We would not write ∠*ABC* = ∠*DEF* because this would indicate that ∠*ABC* and ∠*DEF* represent the same set of points.

When the representations of congruent angles such as ∠*ABC* and ∠*DEF* are drawn on paper, we can fold the paper on which they appear to fit one angle on top of the other; that is, we can make the congruent angles coincide.

When two angles are known to be congruent, we may mark each one with the same number of strokes, as shown in the figures above, where each angle is marked with a single stroke.

Bisector of an angle

- **DEFINITION.** A *bisector of an angle* is a ray whose endpoint is the vertex of the angle, and divides that angle into two congruent angles.

For example, if $\overrightarrow{OC}$ is the bisector of $\angle AOB$, then $\angle AOC \cong \angle COB$ or m$\angle AOC = $ m$\angle COB$.

Since line OC contains ray OC, and since segment OC is part of ray OC, then $\overrightarrow{OC}$, $\overleftrightarrow{OC}$, and $\overline{OC}$ all *bisect* $\angle AOB$.

Note. If $\overrightarrow{OC}$ bisects $\angle AOB$, we may say that m$\angle AOC = \frac{1}{2}$ m$\angle AOB$, m$\angle COB = \frac{1}{2}$ m$\angle AOB$, m$\angle AOB = 2$m$\angle AOC$, and m$\angle AOB = 2$m$\angle COB$.

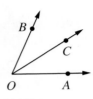

Let C be any point on $\overleftrightarrow{AB}$. If $\overrightarrow{CD}$ is the bisector of $\angle ACB$, each of the two congruent angles, $\angle ACD$ and $\angle DCB$, has degree measure 90 and is therefore a right angle. The ray, $\overrightarrow{CD}$, the line that contains the ray, $\overleftrightarrow{CD}$, or any segment containing C, such as $\overline{CD}$, that is a subset of $\overleftrightarrow{CD}$ is said to be perpendicular to $\overleftrightarrow{AB}$ at C.

- **DEFINITION.** *Perpendicular lines* are two lines that intersect to form right angles.

Since rays and line segments are contained in lines, any rays or line segments that intersect to form right angles are also perpendicular.

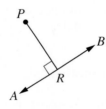

- **DEFINITION.** The *distance from a point to a line* is the length of the perpendicular from the point to the line.

P is a point *not on* $\overleftrightarrow{AB}$, and $\overline{PR} \perp \overleftrightarrow{AB}$. The segment $\overline{PR}$ is called the *perpendicular* from P to $\overleftrightarrow{AB}$. The point R at which the perpendicular meets the line is called the *foot* of the perpendicular. The distance from P to $\overleftrightarrow{AB}$ is PR (the length of $\overline{PR}$).

Adding and subtracting angles

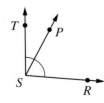

- **DEFINITION.** A nonstraight angle RST is the *sum* of *two angles RSP and PST* if point P is in the interior of $\angle RST$. Thus, $\angle RST = \angle RSP + \angle PST$.

In the figure, $\overrightarrow{SP}$ divides $\angle RST$ into two angles, $\angle RSP$ and $\angle PST$, such that the following relations are true for the measures of the angles:

$$m\angle RST = m\angle RSP + m\angle PST$$
$$m\angle RSP = m\angle RST - m\angle PST$$
$$m\angle PST = m\angle RST - m\angle RSP$$

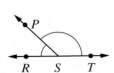

Note. Angle RST may be a straight angle with P any point not on $\angle RST$.

EXAMPLES

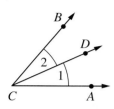

1. In the diagram, $\overrightarrow{CD}$ bisects $\angle ACB$.
  a. Name $\angle 1$ in two other ways.
  b. Write a conclusion that states that two angles are congruent.
  c. Write a conclusion that states that two angles have equal measures.

Answers: **a.** $\angle ACD$ and $\angle DCA$.
  b. $\angle ACD \cong \angle BCD$ or $\angle 1 \cong \angle 2$.
  c. $m\angle ACD = m\angle BCD$ or $m\angle 1 = m\angle 2$.

---

2. H is a point in the interior of $\angle EFG$, $m\angle EFH = 15$, and $m\angle HFG = 90$.
  a. Find $m\angle EFG$.
  b. Name an acute angle.
  c. Name a right angle.
  d. Name an obtuse angle.

Answers: **a.** $m\angle EFG = m\angle EFH + m\angle HFG = 15 + 90 = 105$
  b. $\angle EFH$ is an acute angle.
  c. $\angle HFG$ is a right angle.
  d. $\angle EFG$ is an obtuse angle.

EXERCISES WITH OPEN-RESPONSE PROBLEMS

1. For the figure shown:
  a. Name two rays.
  b. Name the vertex of the angle.
  c. Name the sides of the angle.
  d. Name the angle in four ways.

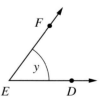

2. a. Name the vertex of $\angle BAD$ in the figure.
  b. Name the sides of $\angle BAD$.
  c. Name all the angles with A as vertex.
  d. Name the angle whose sides are $\overrightarrow{AB}$ and $\overrightarrow{AC}$.
  e. Name the ray that is a side of both $\angle BAD$ and $\angle BAC$.
  f. Name two angles in whose interior regions point R lies.
  g. Name the angle in whose exterior region point S lies.
  h. Are $\overrightarrow{AB}$ and $\overrightarrow{AC}$ opposite rays? Explain your answer.
  i. Is $\angle BAC$ a straight angle? Explain your answer.

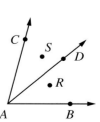

3. For the figure shown:

  a. Name ∠1 in four other ways.
  b. Name ∠2 in two other ways.
  c. Name ∠3 in two other ways.
  d. Name the point of intersection of $\overline{AC}$ and $\overline{BD}$.
  e. Name two pairs of opposite rays.
  f. Name two straight angles each of which has its vertex at *E*.
  g. Name two angles whose sum is ∠*ABC*.

In 4–9, if an angle contains the given number of degrees, state whether the angle is an acute angle, a right angle, an obtuse angle, or a straight angle.

4. 18   **5.** 98   **6.** 110   **7.** 90   **8.** 64   **9.** 180

In 10–12, find the measure of each of the following:

10. $\frac{1}{2}$ of a right angle   **11.** $\frac{2}{3}$ of a right angle   **12.** $\frac{3}{5}$ of a straight angle

In 13 and 14, in each case, use the information about the figure shown:

  a. Write a conclusion that states the congruence of two angles.
  b. Write a conclusion that states the equality of the measures of two angles.

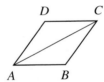

13. $\overline{CD}$ bisects ∠*ACB*.   **14.** $\overrightarrow{AC}$ is the bisector of ∠*DAB*.

15. If a straight angle is bisected, what type of angle is each of the resulting angles?
16. If an obtuse angle is bisected, what type of angle is each of the resulting angles?

In 17–19, complete each statement, which refers to the figure shown.

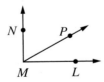

17. m∠*LMN* = m∠*LMP* + m∠_____
18. m∠*LMP* = m∠*LMN* − m∠_____
19. m∠*PMN* = m∠_____ − m∠*LMP*

Ex. 17–19

In 20–23, use the figure shown to answer each question.

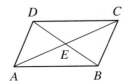

20. m∠*ABE* + m∠*EBC* = m∠_____
21. m∠*BEC* + m∠*CED* = m∠_____
22. m∠*ADC* − m∠*CDE* = m∠_____
23. m∠*AEC* − m∠*AEB* = m∠_____

Ex. 20–23

24. Every horizontal line is perpendicular to every vertical line. Draw a horizontal line *ACB* and vertical line *DCF*.

   a. Name four congruent angles in your diagram.

   b. What is the measure of each of the angles that you named in part **a**?

   c. Name two rays that bisect ∠*ACB*.

   d. Name two rays that bisect ∠*DCF*.

1-5 TRIANGLES

● **DEFINITION.** A *polygon* is a closed figure in a plane that is the union of line segments such that the segments intersect only at their endpoints and no segments sharing a common endpoint are collinear.

A polygon consists of three or more line segments, each of which is a side of the polygon. For example, a triangle has three sides, a quadrilateral has four sides, a pentagon has five sides, and so on.

In the definition of a polygon, we will consider the word *closed* as an undefined term. We understand by the word *closed* that, if we start at any point on the figure and trace along the sides, we will at some time arrive back at the starting point. At the left, we see a figure that is not a closed figure and is, therefore, not a polygon.

● **DEFINITION.** A *triangle* is a polygon that has exactly three sides.

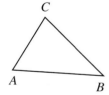

The polygon shown is triangle *ABC*, written as △*ABC*. In △*ABC*, each of the points *A*, *B*, and *C* is a vertex of the triangle. $\overline{AB}$, $\overline{BC}$, and $\overline{CA}$ are the sides of the triangle.

The three sides and the three angles (∠*A*, ∠*B*, and ∠*C*) are called the six *parts* of the triangle.

Included Sides and Included Angles in a Triangle

If a line segment is the side of a triangle, the endpoints of that segment are the vertices of two angles. For example, in △*ABC*, the endpoints of $\overline{AB}$ are the vertices of ∠*A* and ∠*B*. We say that the side, $\overline{AB}$, is *included* between the angles, ∠*A* and ∠*B*. In △*ABC*:

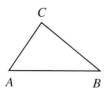

   1. $\overline{AB}$ is included between ∠*A* and ∠*B*.

   2. $\overline{BC}$ is included between ∠*B* and ∠*C*.

   3. $\overline{CA}$ is included between ∠*C* and ∠*A*.

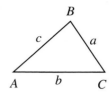

In a similar way, two sides of a triangle are subsets of the rays of an angle, and we say that the angle is ***included*** between those sides. In $\triangle ABC$:

1. $\angle A$ is included between $\overline{AC}$ and $\overline{AB}$.
2. $\angle B$ is included between $\overline{BA}$ and $\overline{BC}$.
3. $\angle C$ is included between $\overline{CA}$ and $\overline{CB}$.

Opposite Sides and Opposite Angles in a Triangle

For each side of a triangle, there is one vertex of the triangle that is not an endpoint of that side. For example, in $\triangle ABC$, C is not an endpoint of $\overline{AB}$. We say that $\overline{AB}$ is the side ***opposite*** $\angle C$ and that $\angle C$ is the angle ***opposite*** side $\overline{AB}$. Similarly, $\overline{AC}$ is opposite $\angle B$ and $\angle B$ is opposite $\overline{AC}$; also $\overline{BC}$ is opposite $\angle A$ and $\angle A$ is opposite $\overline{BC}$.

The length of a side of a triangle may be represented by the lowercase form of the letter naming the opposite vertex. For example, in $\triangle ABC$, $BC = a$, $CA = b$, and $AB = c$.

Classifying Triangles According to Sides

Scalene Triangle	Isosceles Triangle	Equilateral Triangle

- **DEFINITION.** A *scalene triangle* is a triangle that has no congruent sides.
- **DEFINITION.** An *isosceles triangle* is a triangle that has two congruent sides.
- **DEFINITION.** An *equilateral triangle* is a triangle that has three congruent sides.

Parts of an Isosceles Triangle

In isosceles triangle *RST*, the two congruent sides, $\overline{TR}$ and $\overline{TS}$, are called the ***legs*** of the triangle. The third side, $\overline{RS}$, is called the ***base***.

The angle formed by the two congruent sides of the triangle, $\angle T$, which is the angle opposite the base, is called the ***vertex angle*** of the isosceles triangle.

The angles whose vertices are the endpoints of the base of the triangle, $\angle R$ and $\angle S$, which are the angles opposite the congruent sides, are called the ***base angles*** of the isosceles triangle.

Classifying Triangles According to Angles

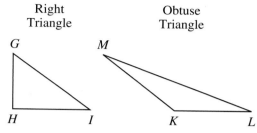

Acute Triangle

Equiangular Triangle

Right Triangle

Obtuse Triangle

- **DEFINITION.** An *acute triangle* is a triangle that has three acute angles.
- **DEFINITION.** An *equiangular triangle* is a triangle that has three congruent angles.
- **DEFINITION.** A *right triangle* is a triangle that has a right angle.
- **DEFINITION.** An *obtuse triangle* is a triangle that has an obtuse angle.

Parts of a Right Triangle

In right triangle *GHI*, the two sides of the triangle that form the right angle, $\overline{GH}$ and $\overline{HI}$, are called the **legs** of the right triangle. The third side of the triangle, $\overline{GI}$, which is the side opposite the right angle, is called the **hypotenuse**.

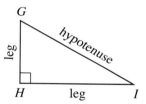

EXAMPLE

In △*DEF*, m∠*E* = 90 and *EF* = *ED*.

a. Classify the triangle according to sides.
b. Classify the triangle according to angles.
c. What sides are the legs of the triangle?
d. What side is opposite the right angle?
e. What angle is opposite $\overline{EF}$?
f. What angle is included between $\overline{EF}$ and $\overline{FD}$?

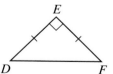

Answers: **a.** The triangle is an isosceles triangle.
b. The triangle is a right triangle.
c. The legs of the triangle are $\overline{EF}$ and $\overline{ED}$.
d. $\overline{FD}$ is opposite the right angle.
e. Angle *D* is opposite $\overline{EF}$.
f. Angle *F* is between $\overline{EF}$ and $\overline{FD}$.

EXERCISES

In 1 and 2, name the legs and the hypotenuse in the right triangle shown.

1. △ABC

2. △JKL

In 3 and 4, name the legs, the base, the vertex angle, and the base angles in the isosceles triangle shown.

3. △LMN

4. △RST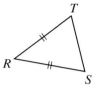

In 5–8, use a ruler and a protractor to draw each of the following.

5. An acute triangle that is isosceles

6. An obtuse triangle that is isosceles

7. A right triangle that is isosceles

8. An obtuse triangle that is scalene

In 9–11, write the *numeral* preceding the choice that best completes each sentence.

9. The vertex angle in an isosceles triangle is ∠ABC. The base angles of this triangle are
   (1) ∠A and ∠B   (2) ∠A and ∠C   (3) ∠B and ∠C

10. In △DEF, $\overline{DE}$ is included between
   (1) ∠D and ∠E   (2) ∠D and ∠F   (3) ∠E and ∠F

11. In △RST, ∠S is included between
   (1) $\overline{RT}$ and $\overline{RS}$ (2) $\overline{TR}$ and $\overline{ST}$ (3) $\overline{ST}$ and $\overline{SR}$

1-6 DISTANCE IN THE COORDINATE PLANE

In section 1-3, we defined the distance between two points and found, in the coordinate plane, the distance between two points on the same vertical line (points that have the same abscissa) and the distance between two points on the same horizontal line (points that have the same ordinate). The method that we used in these special cases can help us to find the distance between any two points.

First, recall the Pythagorean Theorem, which you studied in Math A. This theorem, which will be proved later in this book, applies only to right triangles.

For example, in the accompanying diagram, $\triangle ABC$ is a right triangle in which the right angle is $\angle C$, the longest side, or the hypotenuse, is $\overline{AB}$, and the legs are $\overline{BC}$ and $\overline{AC}$. Let $BC = a$, $AC = b$, and $AB = c$. The theorem is stated here, first in words and then in symbols.

- **Pythagorean Theorem.** If a triangle is a right triangle, then the square of the length of the longest side (the hypotenuse) is equal to the sum of the squares of the lengths of the other two sides (the legs).

$$\text{In symbols: } (AB)^2 = (BC)^2 + (AC)^2$$
$$\text{or} \qquad c^2 = a^2 + b^2$$

Now, to find the distance d from $A(2, 3)$ to $B(5, 7)$, two points that have different abscissas and different ordinates, first draw a horizontal line through A and a vertical line through B. These two lines intersect at point $C(5, 3)$. The distance from $A(2, 3)$ to $C(5, 3)$ is the absolute value of the difference of their abscissas:

$$AC = |5 - 2| = 3$$

Also, the distance from $B(5, 7)$ to $C(5, 3)$ is the absolute value of the difference of their ordinates:

$$BC = |7 - 3| = 4$$

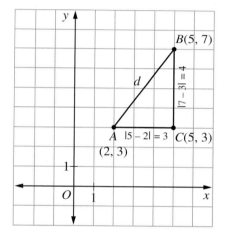

Since $\triangle ABC$ is a right triangle whose hypotenuse is $\overline{AB}$, we can use the Pythagorean Theorem to find AB.

$$
\begin{aligned}
c^2 &= a^2 + b^2 \\
(AB)^2 &= (BC)^2 + (AC)^2 \\
&= 4^2 + 3^2 \\
&= 16 + 9 \\
&= 25 \\
AB &= 5
\end{aligned}
$$

Repeat the steps that you used to find AB to derive a formula for the distance d between any two points $R(x_1, y_1)$ and $S(x_2, y_2)$. It is possible to use the Pythagorean Theorem to derive the distance formula only because the axes that were chosen for the coordinate system are perpendicular to each other, and the scales on the axes are the same.

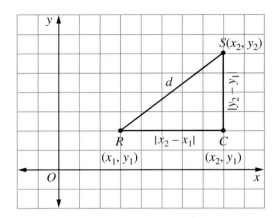

1. Form right triangle RCS by drawing a vertical line through S and a horizontal line through R with the two lines intersecting at C.

2. The coordinates of C are (x_2, y_1).

3. Therefore, $RC = |x_2 - x_1|$ and $CS = |y_2 - y_1|$. Let $RS = d$.

4. $(RS)^2 = \quad (RC)^2 \quad + \quad (CS)^2$
$$d^2 = |x_2 - x_1|^2 + |y_2 - y_1|^2$$
$$= (x_2 - x_1)^2 + (y_2 - y_1)^2$$

5. Take the positive square root of each member of the equation:
$$d = \sqrt{(x_2 - x_1)^2 + (y_2 - y_1)^2}$$

We can now state the ***distance formula*** in general terms:

- The distance d between any two points (x_1, y_1) and (x_2, y_2) in the coordinate plane is given by the formula
$$d = \sqrt{(x_2 - x_1)^2 + (y_2 - y_1)^2}$$

EXAMPLES

1. Find the distance between $A(-4, -2)$ and $B(8, 3)$.

Solution   Use the distance formula.

Let $A = (x_1, y_1)$.   Then $x_1 = -4$, $y_1 = -2$.

Let $B = (x_2, y_2)$.   Then $x_2 = 8$, $y_2 = 3$.

$$d = \sqrt{(x_2 - x_1)^2 + (y_2 - y_1)^2}$$

$$AB = \sqrt{[8 - (-4)]^2 + [3 - (-2)]^2}$$

$$= \sqrt{(8 + 4)^2 + (3 + 2)^2}$$

$$= \sqrt{12^2 + 5^2}$$

$$= \sqrt{144 + 25}$$

$$= \sqrt{169}$$

$$= 13$$

Answer: $AB = 13$

Calculator Solution   The calculation can be done on a graphing calculator by using the following sequence of keys:

Enter: 2nd   √   (8 − (−) 4) ∧ 2 +
(3 − (−) 2) ∧ 2)   ENTER

Display: 13.

---

2. Express the length of $\overline{CD}$ in radical form if the coordinates of C are $(-4, 2)$ and the coordinates of D are $(-3, 5)$.

Solution   Let $C = (x_1, y_1)$. Then $x_1 = -4$, $y_1 = 2$.
Let $D = (x_2, y_2)$. Then $x_2 = -3$, $y_2 = 5$.

$$CD = \sqrt{(x_2 - x_1)^2 + (y_2 - y_1)^2}$$

$$= \sqrt{[-3 - (-4)]^2 + [5 - 2]^2}$$

$$= \sqrt{(-3 + 4)^2 + (5 - 2)^2}$$

$$= \sqrt{(1)^2 + (3)^2} = \sqrt{1 + 9} = \sqrt{10}$$

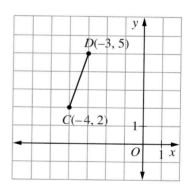

Answer: $CD = \sqrt{10}$

Note. The only acceptable answer for this question is $\sqrt{10}$. Recall that $\sqrt{10}$ is an irrational number whose exact value is shown by the radical. Any solution found by using a calculator will be a *rational approximation* of $\sqrt{10}$.

EXERCISES WITH OPEN-RESPONSE PROBLEMS

Throughout this section, answers that are not whole numbers should be left in radical form.

In 1–12, find the distance between each pair of points.

1. (2, 7) and (12, 7)

2. $(-3, 4)$ and (5, 4)

3. $(-1, -2)$ and $(-1, 4)$

4. (0, 0) and (4, 3)

5. $(-6, -8)$ and (0, 0)

6. (1, 4) and (4, 8)

7. (4, 2) and $(-2, 10)$

8. (6, 4) and (3, 6)

9. $(-5, 0)$ and $(-9, 6)$

10. (0, 0) and $(-2, 5)$

11. $(0, c)$ and $(b, 0)$

12. (0, 0) and (a, b)

In 13–16, find in each case the length of the line segment joining the points whose coordinates are:

13. (5, 2) and (8, 6)   **14.** $(-5, 1)$ and (7, 6)   **15.** (0, 5) and $(-3, 3)$ **16.** $(-4, -5)$ and $(1, -2)$

In 17–22, find in each case the lengths of the sides of a triangle whose vertices are:

17. (0, 0), (8, 0), (4, 3)

18. (1, 5), (5, 5), (5, 1)

19. (3, 6), $(-1, 3)$, $(5, -5)$

20. $(6, -3)$, (0, 4), $(8, -1)$

21. $(-1, 7)$, (0, 0), (8, 4)

22. $(-4, 2)$, $(-1, 6)$, (5, 4)

23. Find the length of the shortest side of the triangle whose vertices are $R(-2, -1)$, $S(1, 3)$, and $T(1, 10)$.

In 24–27, show in each case that points A, B, and C are collinear; that is, they lie on the same straight line. [*Hint.* Show that $AB + BC = AC$.]

24. $A(0, 0)$, $B(5, 12)$, $C(10, 24)$

25. $A(-1, -2)$, $B(2, 2)$, $C(8, 10)$

26. $A(-2, -2)$, $B(0, 2)$, $C(1, 4)$

27. $A(-1, 2)$, $B(2, -1)$, $C(4, -3)$

In 28–31, show that each triangle with the given vertices is isosceles.

28. (2, 3), (5, 7), (1, 4)

29. (1, 0), (5, 0), (3, 4)

30. $(7, -1)$, $(2, -2)$, (3, 3)

31. $(4, -7)$, $(-3, -4)$, (7, 0)

32. Points $A(-1, 2)$ and $B(-1, -3)$ have the same abscissa.
  a. Find AB by using the absolute value of the difference of the ordinates.
  b. Find AB by using the distance formula.
  c. Can the distance formula be used to find the distance between two points that have the same abscissa or two points that have the same ordinate? Explain your answer.
  d. Does $\sqrt{(x_2 - x_1)^2}$ always equal $|x_2 - x_1|$? Explain your answer.

1-7 SLOPE OF A LINE

 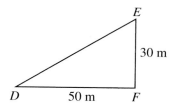

Of the two roads, $\overline{AB}$ and $\overline{DE}$, which is steeper? To answer this question, compare the slopes of the two roads. Recall that a *slope* is a ratio of the change in the vertical distance to the change in the horizontal distance. Therefore:

$$\text{Slope of road } \overline{AB} = \frac{\text{change in vertical distance, } CB}{\text{change in horizontal distance, } AC} = \frac{10 \text{ m}}{50 \text{ m}} = \frac{1}{5}$$

$$\text{Slope of road } \overline{DE} = \frac{\text{change in vertical distance, } FE}{\text{change in horizontal distance, } DF} = \frac{30 \text{ m}}{50 \text{ m}} = \frac{3}{5}$$

Since $\frac{3}{5} > \frac{1}{5}$, slope $\overline{DE}$ is greater than slope $\overline{AB}$, and road $\overline{DE}$ is steeper than road $\overline{AB}$. Let us state a more precise definition of slope.

● **DEFINITION.** The *slope, m, of a line,* $\overleftrightarrow{AB}$*,* where A has coordinates (x_1, y_1) and B has coordinates (x_2, y_2) and $x_1 \neq x_2$, is the ratio of the difference of the y-values to the corresponding x-values; that is:

$$m = \frac{y_2 - y_1}{x_2 - x_1} \quad \textbf{or} \quad m = \frac{y_1 - y_2}{x_1 - x_2}$$

By letting $\Delta x = x_2 - x_1$, that is, delta x equals the difference in x-values, and $\Delta y = y_2 - y_1$, that is, delta y equals the difference in y-values, you may also represent the slope of a line as follows:

$$\textbf{Slope} = m = \frac{\Delta y}{\Delta x}$$

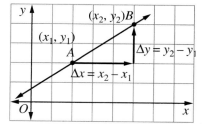

Replace the general terms with specific values given for coordinates of points on line $\overleftrightarrow{AB}$. Since $A(x_1, y_1) = (2, 2)$ and $B(x_2, y_2) = (5, 4)$, you can determine the slope by using the formulas noted above.

$$m = \frac{y_2 - y_1}{x_2 - x_1} = \frac{4 - 2}{5 - 2} = \frac{2}{3} \quad \text{or} \quad m = \frac{\Delta y}{\Delta x} = \frac{2}{3}$$

Also,

$$m = \frac{y_1 - y_2}{x_1 - x_2} = \frac{2 - 4}{2 - 5} = \frac{-2}{-3} = \frac{2}{3}$$

Either formula may be used to determine the slope of a line. Also, either of two points may be identified by the coordinates (x_1, y_1).

Every line is classified as having either a positive slope, a negative slope, a zero slope, or no slope.

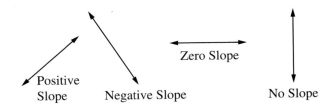

- **As a point moves from left to right along a line that is rising, y increases as x increases, and the slope of the line is positive.**
- **As a point moves from left to right along a line that is falling, y decreases as x increases, and the slope of the line is negative.**
- **A horizontal line has a slope of 0.**
- **A vertical line has no slope.**

The figure shows three *noncollinear* points: $A(2, 1)$, $B(4, 2)$, and $C(5, 5)$. Two distinct lines, $\overleftrightarrow{AB}$ and $\overleftrightarrow{BC}$, pass through the same point B.

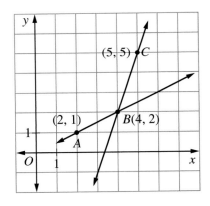

$$\text{Slope of } \overleftrightarrow{AB} = \frac{\Delta y}{\Delta x} = \frac{2 - 1}{4 - 2} = \frac{1}{2}$$

$$\text{Slope of } \overleftrightarrow{BC} = \frac{\Delta y}{\Delta x} = \frac{5 - 2}{5 - 4} = \frac{3}{1}$$

This example illustrates the fact that:

- **Two distinct lines that pass through the same point must have unequal slopes.**

The figure shows three *collinear* points: $D(2, 2)$, $E(4, 3)$, and $F(8, 5)$. We note that the slope of a segment whose endpoints are any two distinct points on this line is always the same value.

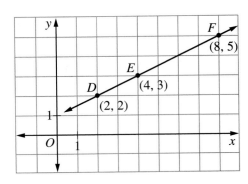

$$\text{Slope of } \overleftrightarrow{DE} = \frac{\Delta y}{\Delta x} = \frac{3 - 2}{4 - 2} = \frac{1}{2}$$

$$\text{Slope of } \overleftrightarrow{EF} = \frac{\Delta y}{\Delta x} = \frac{5 - 3}{8 - 4} = \frac{2}{4} = \frac{1}{2}$$

$$\text{Slope of } \overleftrightarrow{DF} = \frac{\Delta y}{\Delta x} = \frac{5 - 2}{8 - 2} = \frac{3}{6} = \frac{1}{2}$$

This example illustrates the fact that:

● **Three points are collinear if the slope determined by the first point and the second point is equal to:**

　(*a*) **the slope determined by the second point and the third point,**

　　　　　　　　　　or

　(*b*) **the slope determined by the first point and the third point.**

EXAMPLES

1. Find the slope of the line that passes through points $C(-2, 1)$ and $D(0, 4)$.

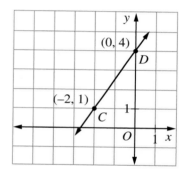

Solution　Let $C(-2, 1) = (x_1, y_1)$.

Then $x_1 = -2$, $y_1 = 1$.

Let $D(0, 4) = (x_2, y_2)$.

Then $x_2 = 0$, $y_2 = 4$.

$$\text{Slope of } \overleftrightarrow{CD} = m = \frac{y_2 - y_1}{x_2 - x_1} = \frac{4 - 1}{0 - (-2)} = \frac{4 - 1}{0 + 2} = \frac{3}{2}$$

Answer:　Slope of $\overleftrightarrow{CD} = \frac{3}{2}$.

---

2. Find the value of k so that the slope of the line passing through points $(2, 3)$ and $(k, 4)$ will be $\frac{1}{3}$.

Solution　(1)　Let $(x_1, y_1) = (2, 3)$ and $(x_2, y_2) = (k, 4)$. The slope $m = \frac{1}{3}$. Then $x_1 = 2$, $y_1 = 3$, $x_2 = k$, and $y_2 = 4$.

(2)　Write the slope formula:　　　　$m = \frac{y_2 - y_1}{x_2 - x_1}$　　│　*Check:*

(3)　Substitute the given values:　　$\frac{1}{3} = \frac{4 - 3}{k - 2}$　　│　If $k = 5$, find the slope of the line passing through $(2, 3)$

(4)　Simplify and solve:　　　　　$\frac{1}{3} = \frac{1}{k - 2}$　　│　and $(5, 4)$.

　　　　　　　　　　　　　　　$k - 2 = 3$　　│　$\frac{1}{3} \overset{?}{=} \frac{4 - 3}{5 - 2}$

　　　　　　　　　　　　　　　$k = 5$　　　│　$\frac{1}{3} = \frac{1}{3}$　(True)

Answer: $k = 5$

---

3. Show that points $A(1, 4)$, $B(3, 3)$, and $C(7, 1)$ are collinear.
Plan: Show that the slope of $\overleftrightarrow{AB}$ is equal to the slope of $\overleftrightarrow{AC}$.

Solution   (1) Let $A(1, 4) = (x_1, y_1)$
and $B(3, 3) = (x_2, y_2)$.

$$\text{Slope of } \overleftrightarrow{AB} = \frac{y_2 - y_1}{x_2 - x_1}$$

$$= \frac{3 - 4}{3 - 1} = \frac{-1}{2} = -\frac{1}{2}$$

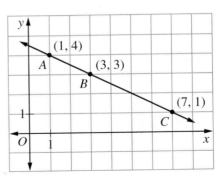

(2) Let $A(1, 4) = (x_1, y_1)$
and $C(7, 1) = (x_2, y_2)$.

$$\text{Slope of } \overleftrightarrow{AC} = \frac{y_2 - y_1}{x_2 - x_1} = \frac{1 - 4}{7 - 1} = \frac{-3}{6} = \frac{-1}{2} = -\frac{1}{2}$$

(3) Since A is a point on $\overleftrightarrow{AB}$ as well as on $\overleftrightarrow{AC}$, and since the slope of $\overleftrightarrow{AB}$ is equal to the slope of $\overleftrightarrow{AC}$, points A, B, and C all lie on the same line and are therefore collinear.

EXERCISES WITH OPEN-RESPONSE PROBLEMS

1. For each line in the diagram, $\overleftrightarrow{AB}$, $\overleftrightarrow{CD}$, $\overleftrightarrow{EF}$, $\overleftrightarrow{GH}$, $\overleftrightarrow{JK}$, $\overleftrightarrow{LM}$, $\overleftrightarrow{PQ}$, $\overleftrightarrow{RS}$, $\overleftrightarrow{TU}$, and $\overrightarrow{VW}$:
a. Tell whether the line has a positive slope, a negative slope, a slope of 0, or no slope.
b. If the line has a slope, find the slope of the line.

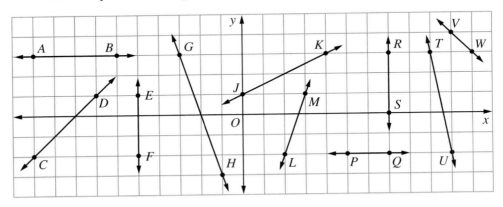

In 2–13, in each case, plot both points on graph paper, draw the line determined by these points, and find the slope of the line.

2. $(0, 0)$ and $(9, 3)$
3. $(0, 0)$ and $(-2, 4)$
4. $(-2, -6)$ and $(0, 0)$
5. $(0, 4)$ and $(2, 8)$
6. $(-5, 6)$ and $(-1, 0)$
7. $(0, -3)$ and $(-6, 0)$
8. $(1, 5)$ and $(3, 9)$
9. $(2, 3)$ and $(4, 15)$
10. $(5, 8)$ and $(4, 3)$
11. $(2, 7)$ and $(6, 9)$
12. $(4, 6)$ and $(-5, 9)$
13. $(5, -2)$ and $(7, -8)$

14. Find the slope of the line that passes through points (3, 5) and (8, 5).

15. Find the value of k so that the slope of the line passing through points (5, 3) and (k, 6) will be 1.

16. Find the value of t so that the slope of the line passing through points (2, t) and (6, 10) will be $\frac{1}{2}$.

17. Find the value of y so that the slope of the line passing through points (-8, -2) and (4, y) will be 0.

18. Find the value of x so that the line passing through points (-4, 8) and (x, -2) will have no slope.

In 19–24, determine in each case whether the points are collinear.

19. (1, 2), (4, 5), (6, 7)   **20.** (-1, -4), (2, -2), (8, 2)   **21.** (1, 1), (3, 4), (6, 5)

22. (-2, 6), (0, 2), (1, 1)   **23.** (0, 0), (-8, -2), (4, 1)   **24.** (-3, 4), (-1, 1), (1, -3)

25. Given points $A(1, 1)$, $B(3, 2)$, and $C(k, 4)$:
  a. Using the coordinates of A and B, find the slope of $\overleftrightarrow{AB}$.
  b. Using the coordinates of B and C, express the slope of $\overleftrightarrow{BC}$ in terms of k.
  c. If A, B, and C are collinear, write an equation that can be used to find the value of k.
  d. Find k.

26. Given points $D(1, 3)$, $E(5, 5)$, and $F(7, d)$:
  a. Find the slope of $\overleftrightarrow{DE}$.
  b. Express the slope of $\overleftrightarrow{EF}$ in terms of d.
  c. If D, E, and F are collinear points, find the value of d.

27. $\overleftrightarrow{CD}$ passes through points (-4, -2) and (8, 7).
  a. Find the slope of $\overleftrightarrow{CD}$.
  b. *True* or *False*: $\overleftrightarrow{CD}$ passes through point (0, 1).
  c. *True* or *False*: $\overleftrightarrow{CD}$ passes through point (11, 11).

1-8 PARALLEL AND PERPENDICULAR LINES

Parallel Lines

Two lines in the same plane are either intersecting lines or parallel lines.

● **DEFINITION.** *Parallel lines* are lines in the same plane that have no points in common or that have all points in common.

We indicate that $\overleftrightarrow{AB}$ is parallel to $\overleftrightarrow{CD}$ by writing $\overleftrightarrow{AB} \parallel \overleftrightarrow{CD}$. These parallel lines, extended indefinitely, will never intersect and therefore have no points in common. However, using the fact that lines are parallel if they have all points in common, we may also write $\overleftrightarrow{AB} \parallel \overleftrightarrow{AB}$ and $\overleftrightarrow{CD} \parallel \overleftrightarrow{CD}$. The word *lines* in the definition means straight lines that extend indefinitely in both directions. Segments and rays are also said to be parallel if the lines that contain them are parallel.

The Slopes of Parallel Lines

In the figure, $\overleftrightarrow{AB} \parallel \overleftrightarrow{CD}$. Use the coordinates given in the diagram to write:

$$\text{Slope of } \overleftrightarrow{AB} = \frac{y_2 - y_1}{x_2 - x_1}$$

$$= \frac{6 - 2}{4 - 2} = \frac{4}{2} = \frac{2}{1}$$

$$\text{Slope of } \overleftrightarrow{CD} = \frac{y_2 - y_1}{x_2 - x_1}$$

$$= \frac{6 - 4}{7 - 6} = \frac{2}{1}$$

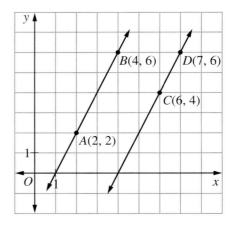

This example illustrates the following statement:

● **Two nonvertical lines are parallel if and only if their slopes are equal.**

In other words:
When the slope of $\overleftrightarrow{AB} = m_1$, and the slope of $\overleftrightarrow{CD} = m_2$, $\overleftrightarrow{AB}$ is *parallel* to $\overleftrightarrow{CD}$ if and only if:

$$m_1 = m_2$$

Perpendicular Lines

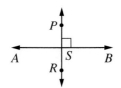

Recall that **perpendicular lines** are two lines that intersect to form right angles. For example, in the diagram, $\overleftrightarrow{AB}$ and $\overleftrightarrow{PR}$ intersect at S to form four right angles: $\angle BSP$, $\angle PSA$, $\angle ASR$, and $\angle RSB$. Therefore, $\overleftrightarrow{PR} \perp \overleftrightarrow{AB}$.

The Slopes of Perpendicular Lines

In the figure, $\overleftrightarrow{AB} \perp \overleftrightarrow{BC}$. Use the coordinates of A, B, and C to write:

$$\text{Slope of } \overleftrightarrow{AB} = \frac{y_2 - y_1}{x_2 - x_1}$$

$$= \frac{5 - 2}{4 - 2} = \frac{3}{2}$$

$$\text{Slope of } \overleftrightarrow{BC} = \frac{y_2 - y_1}{x_2 - x_1}$$

$$= \frac{3 - 5}{7 - 4} = \frac{-2}{3} = -\frac{2}{3}$$

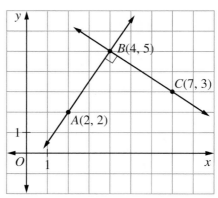

In this example, where $\overleftrightarrow{AB} \perp \overleftrightarrow{BC}$, the product of the slopes of the lines is -1, that is, $\left(\frac{3}{2}\right)\left(-\frac{2}{3}\right) = -1$.

One number is the ***negative reciprocal*** of another if the product of the two numbers is -1.

In general terms, if $a \neq 0$ and $b \neq 0$, we may say that $-\frac{b}{a}$ is the negative reciprocal of $\frac{a}{b}$ since $\left(\frac{a}{b}\right)\left(-\frac{b}{a}\right) = -1$.

Thus, to find the negative reciprocal of a fraction, we simply invert the fraction and change its sign.

● **Two nonvertical lines are perpendicular if and only if the slope of one line is the negative reciprocal of the slope of the other line.**

In other words:

When the slope of $\overleftrightarrow{AB} = m_1$, and the slope of $\overleftrightarrow{CD} = m_2$, $\overleftrightarrow{AB}$ is *perpendicular* to $\overleftrightarrow{CD}$ if and only if:

$$m_1 = -\frac{1}{m_2} \qquad \text{or} \qquad m_2 = -\frac{1}{m_1} \qquad \text{or} \qquad m_1 \cdot m_2 = -1$$

The Slopes of Vertical and Horizontal Lines

We can extend the rules for the slopes of parallel and perpendicular lines to apply to horizontal lines and to vertical lines.

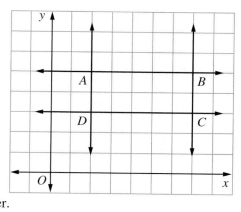

1. Horizontal lines are parallel and have the same slope, 0.
   Here, $\overleftrightarrow{AB} \parallel \overleftrightarrow{DC}$.

2. Vertical lines are parallel and have no slope.
   Here, $\overleftrightarrow{AD} \parallel \overleftrightarrow{BC}$.

3. A vertical line (having no defined slope) and a horizontal line (having a slope of 0) are perpendicular to each other.
   Here, $\overleftrightarrow{AB} \perp \overleftrightarrow{AD}$, $\overleftrightarrow{AB} \perp \overleftrightarrow{BC}$, $\overleftrightarrow{DC} \perp \overleftrightarrow{AD}$, $\overleftrightarrow{DC} \perp \overleftrightarrow{BC}$.

EXAMPLES

1. A rectangle is a four-sided polygon with two pairs of parallel sides and four right angles. In the diagram, *ABCD* is a rectangle.
   a. Name two pairs of parallel lines.
   b. Name four pairs of perpendicular lines.

   Answers: **a.** $\overleftrightarrow{AB} \parallel \overleftrightarrow{CD}$, $\overleftrightarrow{AD} \parallel \overleftrightarrow{BC}$

   b. $\overleftrightarrow{AB} \perp \overleftrightarrow{BC}$, $\overleftrightarrow{BC} \perp \overleftrightarrow{CD}$, $\overleftrightarrow{CD} \perp \overleftrightarrow{DA}$, $\overleftrightarrow{DA} \perp \overleftrightarrow{AB}$

2. Show by means of slopes that quadrilateral $ABCD$ with vertices $A(2, 1)$, $B(4, -2)$, $C(4, 1)$, and $D(2, 4)$ has two pairs of parallel sides.

Solution   Find the slope of each side of the quadrilateral.

Slope of $\overline{AB} = \frac{-2-1}{4-2} = \frac{-3}{2} = -\frac{3}{2}$

$\overline{BC}$ is a vertical line and has no slope.

Slope of $\overline{CD} = \frac{4-1}{2-4} = \frac{3}{-2} = -\frac{3}{2}$

$\overline{DA}$ is a vertical line and has no slope.

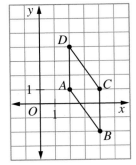

Answer: $\overline{AB}$ and $\overline{CD}$ have the same slope and are parallel.
$\overline{BC}$ and $\overline{DA}$ are vertical lines and are parallel.

---

3. Show, by means of slopes, that the triangle whose vertices are $A(0, 2)$, $B(2, 3)$, and $C(1, 5)$ is a right triangle.

Solution   Show that two sides of the triangle are perpendicular by finding two slopes that are negative reciprocals.

Slope of $\overline{AB} = \frac{3-2}{2-0} = \frac{1}{2}$

Slope of $\overline{BC} = \frac{5-3}{1-2} = \frac{2}{-1} = -2$

The slope of $\overline{AB}$ is the negative reciprocal of the slope of $\overline{BC}$ because $\left(\frac{1}{2}\right)(-2) = -1$.

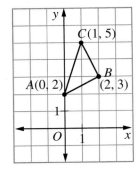

Therefore, $\overline{AB} \perp \overline{BC}$ and $\angle ABC$ is a right angle.

Answer: Triangle ABC is a right triangle because it has a right angle.

EXERCISES WITH OPEN-RESPONSE PROBLEMS

In 1–6, in each case the coordinates of A, B, C, and D are given. Use slope to determine whether or not $\overline{AB} \parallel \overline{CD}$.

1. $A(1, 5)$, $B(3, 9)$, $C(2, 2)$, $D(4, 6)$
3. $A(1, -5)$, $B(3, 3)$, $C(2, 6)$, $D(4, -2)$
5. $A(-1, 5)$, $B(1, 1)$, $C(1, 2)$, $D(3, -2)$

2. $A(1, 1)$, $B(3, 7)$, $C(2, 0)$, $D(5, 9)$
4. $A(1, 5)$, $B(3, 6)$, $C(2, 2)$, $D(4, 6)$
6. $A(1, 3)$, $B(1, 9)$, $C(2, 2)$, $D(2, 6)$

In 7–12, in each case the coordinates of A, B, C, and D are given. Use slope to determine whether or not $\overline{AB} \perp \overline{CD}$.

7. $A(1, 5)$, $B(3, 9)$, $C(2, 3)$, $D(8, 0)$

8. $A(1, 1)$, $B(3, 3)$, $C(5, 0)$, $D(0, 5)$

9. $A(1, -5)$, $B(1, 3)$, $C(2, 6)$, $D(-4, 6)$

10. $A(1, 5)$, $B(3, 4)$, $C(2, 2)$, $D(3, 0)$

11. $A(-1, 1)$, $B(3, 0)$, $C(1, 0)$, $D(-1, 8)$

12. $A(1, 7)$, $B(4, 9)$, $C(4, 0)$, $D(0, 6)$

13. A parallelogram is a quadrilateral with two pairs of parallel sides. Show that $ABCD$ is a parallelogram if the coordinates of the vertices are $A(-2, 3)$, $B(2, 7)$, $C(8, 5)$, and $D(4, 1)$.

14. A rectangle is a quadrilateral with four right angles. Show that $EFGH$ is a rectangle if the coordinates of the vertices are $E(-3, -5)$, $F(3, -1)$, $G(1, 2)$, and $H(-5, -2)$.

CHAPTER SUMMARY

The study of geometry begins with undefined terms—set, point, line, plane—that can be used to define other terms. A *definition* consists of the class to which the term belongs and the characteristic that distinguishes it from others in the class.

A *line segment* is a subset of a line. Its measure is the absolute value of the difference of the coordinates of its endpoints.

In a coordinate plane, the *distance formula* is used to find the measure of any line segment:

$$AB = d = \sqrt{(x_2 - x_1)^2 + (y_2 - y_1)^2}$$

Slope, which is the measure of the slant or steepness of a line, is determined by the formula

$$\text{Slope of } \overline{AB} = m = \frac{\Delta y}{\Delta x} = \frac{y_2 - y_1}{x_2 - x_1}$$

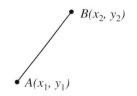

Parallel lines have equal slopes. If two *nonvertical lines* are perpendicular, the slope of one is the negative reciprocal of the slope of the other.

An *angle* is the union of two rays with a common endpoint. In geometry, an angle is usually measured in degrees.

VOCABULARY

1-1 Undefined term   Set   Point   Line   Straight line   Plane

1-2 Number line   Coordinate   Graph   Coordinate axes x-axis y-axis   Origin   Quadrant x-coordinate   Abscissa y-coordinate   Ordinate   Coordinates   Ordered pair of numbers   Rectangular coordinate system   Cartesian coordinate system

1-3 Definition Collinear set of points Noncollinear set of points
Absolute value Distance Between Line segment
Measure of a line segment Congruent Coincide Midpoint
Bisector of a line segment

1-4 Half-line Ray Opposite rays Angle Vertex Straight angle
Interior of an angle Exterior of an angle Degree Protractor
Right angle Acute angle Obtuse angle Perpendicular lines
Congruent angles Bisector of an angle Sum of two angles

1-5 Polygon Triangle Included side Included angle Opposite side
Opposite angle Scalene triangle Isosceles triangle
Equilateral triangle Leg of an isosceles triangle
Base of an isosceles triangle Vertex angle Base angle
Acute triangle Equiangular triangle Right triangle Obtuse triangle
Leg of a right triangle Hypotenuse

1-6 Pythagorean Theorem Distance formula

1-7 Slope

1-8 Parallel Negative reciprocal

REVIEW EXERCISES WITH OPEN-RESPONSE PROBLEMS

1. Which is *not* an undefined term?
(1) point (2) line (3) segment (4) plane

In 2–6, use the number line shown.

2. Find the distance between points B and D.

3. Name the midpoint of $\overline{BE}$.

Ex. 2–6

In 4–6, write the numeral that best answers the question.

4. Which segment has a length of 5?
(1) $\overline{AC}$ (2) $\overline{AD}$ (3) $\overline{BD}$ (4) $\overline{BE}$

5. Which segment is congruent to $\overline{AB}$?
(1) $\overline{AC}$ (2) $\overline{BC}$ (3) $\overline{CE}$ (4) $\overline{DE}$

6. Since A, B, and C are collinear points and B is between A and C, which statement is true?
(1) $\overline{AC} \cong \overline{BC}$ (2) $AB + BC = AC$
(3) $AB = BC$ (4) B is the midpoint of $\overline{AC}$.

7. If R, S, and T are collinear points such that S is between R and T, and if $RS = 12$ and $RT = 15$, find ST.

8. a. Graph points $A(-1, 8)$, $B(-1, -2)$, and $C(3, 0)$ in the coordinate plane. Draw $\triangle ABC$.
b. Find AB, BC, and AC.

    c. Find the slopes of $\overline{AB}$, $\overline{BC}$, and $\overline{AC}$.

    d. What kind of triangle is $\triangle ABC$? Explain your answer.

In 9–13, use polygon $ABCD$, in which $\overline{AC}$ and $\overline{BD}$ intersect at E, and $\overline{AC}$ bisects $\overline{BD}$.

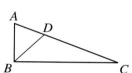

9. Name two straight angles, each having a vertex at E.

10. What angle is the sum of $\angle ADE$ and $\angle EDC$?

11. Name two congruent segments.

12. Complete this statement: $AE + EC =$ _____

13. Complete this statement: $m\angle DEA + m\angle AEB =$ _____

Ex. 9–13

In 14–17, use $\triangle ABC$, in which $\overrightarrow{AB} \perp \overline{BC}$ and $\overrightarrow{BD}$ bisects $\angle ABC$.

14. Name two congruent angles.

15. What is the measure of $\angle ABD$?

16. Does $AB + BC = AC$? Explain your answer.

17. Name a pair of angles the sum of whose measures is 180.

Ex. 14–17

18. In $\triangle PQR$, which of the following statements must be true?
    (1) $\angle P$ is included between $\overline{QR}$ and $\overline{RP}$.
    (2) $\overline{QR}$ is included between $\angle Q$ and $\angle P$.
    (3) $\angle P$ is included between $\overline{QP}$ and $\overline{RP}$.
    (4) $\overline{QP}$ is included between $\angle Q$ and $\angle R$.

19. In isosceles triangle ABC, if $AC = BC$, name the vertex angle.

20. Find $m\angle DBE$ if $\overleftrightarrow{AB} \perp \overleftrightarrow{CD}$ at B and $\overleftrightarrow{BE}$ bisects $\angle ABC$.

21. The coordinates of $ABCD$ are $A(-2, -5)$, $B(2, 0)$, $C(2, 5)$, and $D(-2, 0)$.
    a. Find AB, BC, CD, and DA.
    b. Find the slopes of $\overline{AB}$ and $\overline{CD}$.
    c. Name two pairs of parallel lines and explain why they are parallel.
    d. Show that $O(0, 0)$ is the midpoint of $\overline{AC}$ and $\overline{BD}$.

22. How many triangles are there in the figure?

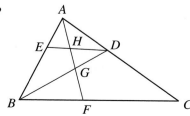

Chapter 2

Logic

Persons who feel strongly about an idea or a proposed course of action often seek to convince others of its truth or its value. To do this, they assemble all the known facts that will support their point of view and try to present a logical argument that shows how these facts lead to the idea or action that they are presenting.

Logic is that branch of mathematics that tells whether an argument is valid or invalid and is the foundation of sound thinking and correct proof.

Many games and riddles such as the following are based on logic. Three friends, Augustus, Brutus, and Caesar, play a game in which each decides to be either a liar or a truth teller. A liar must always lie, and a truth teller must always tell the truth. When you met these three friends, you asked Augustus which he had chosen to be. You didn't hear his answer, but Brutus volunteered, "Augustus said that he is a liar." Caesar added, "If one of us is a liar, then we're all liars." Can you determine, for each person, whether he is a liar or a truth teller?

2-1   SENTENCES, STATEMENTS, AND TRUTH VALUES

A ***mathematical sentence*** is a sentence that states a fact or contains a complete idea. Some sentences have uncertain ***truth values*** since they are *true* for some people and *false* for others. Other mathematical sentences, called ***open sentences***, contain variables. We usually cannot assign a truth value to an open sentence until we choose replacements for the variable. Examples of such sentences follow.

1. Liver really tastes good.   Sentence with *uncertain* truth value.
2. $3x + 2 = 17$ *Open* sentence; the variable is x.
3. He is my friend.   *Open* sentence; the variable is *he*.

A sentence that can be judged to be either true or false is called a ***statement***, or a ***closed sentence***. A statement contains no variables. For example:

1. The degree measure of a right angle is 90.   *True* statement
2. $3(3) + 2 = 17$ *False* statement
3. $3(5) + 2 = 17$ *True* statement

EXERCISES WITH OPEN-RESPONSE PROBLEMS

1. **a.** Write 10 mathematical sentences, including both open sentences and statements.
   b. Which of the sentences that you wrote are open sentences?
   c. For each open sentence that you wrote, give one replacement of the variable that will make the sentence true and one that will make the sentence false.
   d. Which of the sentences that you wrote are statements?
   e. For each statement that you wrote, tell whether the statement is true or false.

In 2–6, give the truth value of each statement.

2. *Line segment* is an undefined term.
3. Every angle has a bisector.
4. Points $A(2, -1)$ and $B(5, -1)$ lie on a line parallel to the x-axis.
5. A line segment has two endpoints.
6. The sum of $\overline{RS}$ and $\overline{ST}$ is always $\overline{RT}$.

2-2   NEGATION AND CONNECTIVES IN LOGIC

In logic, we study the truth values of statements, that is, whether a given statement is true or false.

In Math A, you learned that a letter can be used to represent a single complete thought, or a simple statement. For example, let p represent "A triangle is a polygon containing exactly three sides."

Connectives, such as *and, or, if . . . then*, and *if and only if*, are words or phrases that allow us to form compound statements that contain two or more thoughts. Each of these new statements will be either true or false.

Negation

The **negation** of a statement is usually formed by inserting the word **not** into the original, or given, statement. There are many ways of placing the word *not* in a statement to form its negation.

To show the negation of a simple statement in symbolic form, we place the symbol ~ before the letter that represents the original or given statement. In the following examples, truth values are listed to the right of the statements. The symbolic form is written first in each example.

1. p: There are 7 days in every week.   (True)

    $\sim p$: There are *not* 7 days in every week.   (False)

    $\sim p$: It is *not* the case that there are 7 days in every week.   (False)

2. q: $8 + 9 = 10$ (False)

    $\sim q$: $8 + 9 \neq 10$ (True)

● **A statement and its negation have opposite truth values.**

Conjunction

In logic, a **conjunction** is a compound sentence formed by using the word **and** to combine two simple sentences. The symbol for *and* is $\wedge$. Thus, when p and q represent simple sentences, the conjunction **p and q** is written symbolically as **p $\wedge$ q**. For example:

> p: Fred likes math.
>
> q: Dorothy likes science.
>
> $p \wedge q$: Fred likes math *and* Dorothy likes science.

● **The conjunction p and q is true only when both parts are true:** p must be true, and q must be true.

If p is false, or if q is false, or if both are false, then the conjunction p *and* q must be false.

Disjunction

In logic, a **disjunction** is a compound sentence formed by using the word **or** to combine two simple sentences. The symbol for *or* is $\vee$. Thus, when p and q represent simple sentences, the disjunction **p or q** is written symbolically as **p $\vee$ q**. For example:

> p: The clock is fast.
>
> q: The time is correct.
>
> $p \vee q$: The clock is fast *or* the time is correct.

● **The disjunction *p or q* is true when any part of the compound sentence is true:** *p* is true, or *q* is true, or both *p* and *q* are true.

The disjunction *p or q* is false when both *p* and *q* are false.

In the example used above, "The clock is fast or the time is correct" is false only when both parts are false.

The Conditional

In logic, a ***conditional*** is a compound sentence usually formed by using the words ***if . . . then*** to combine two simple sentences. When *p* and *q* represent simple sentences, the conditional ***if p then q*** is written in symbols as $p \rightarrow q$.

A conditional is sometimes called an ***implication***. Thus, we may also read the symbols for the conditional $p \rightarrow q$ as ***p implies q***. For example:

$$p: \overline{AB} \cong \overline{CD}$$
$$q: AB = CD$$
$$p \rightarrow q: \text{If } \overline{AB} \cong \overline{CD}, \text{ then } AB = CD.$$
$$p \rightarrow q: \overline{AB} \cong \overline{CD} \text{ implies that } AB = CD.$$

The parts of the conditional ***if p then q*** can be identified by name.

p is called the ***hypothesis*** or the ***antecedent***. It is an assertion or a sentence that begins an argument. The antecedent usually follows the word *if*.

q is called the ***conclusion*** or the ***consequent***. It is an ending or a sentence that closes an argument. The consequent usually follows the word *then*.

There are many ways to write the conditional $p \rightarrow q$ in words. Notice that the antecedent *p* follows the word *if* in both of the following examples:

$p \rightarrow q$:   If you are hungry, then you should eat.

   antecedent   consequent
       or   or
   hypothesis   conclusion

$p \rightarrow q$:   You should eat if you are hungry.

   consequent   antecedent
       or   or
   conclusion   hypothesis

● **The conditional *if p then q*, or *p implies q*, is false when a true hypothesis *p* leads to a false conclusion *q*.**

In all other cases, the conditional *if p then q* will be true.

A ***truth table*** is a compact way of listing symbols to show all possible truth values for a set of sentences. The letters T and F represent "True" and "False."

p	*q*	$p \rightarrow q$
T	T	T
T	F	F
F	T	T
F	F	T

Truth Table for the Conditional

The Biconditional

A *biconditional* is a compound sentence formed by using the conjunction *and* to combine the two conditionals $p \to q$ and $q \to p$. Thus, the biconditional tells us that ***p implies q and q implies p***, written symbolically as $(p \to q) \land (q \to p)$.

p	q	$p \to q$	$q \to p$	$(p \to q) \land (q \to p)$
T	T	T	T	T
T	F	F	T	F
F	T	T	F	F
F	F	T	T	T

Although the more common ways of reading $p \to q$ are *if p then q* and *p implies q*, other ways are also correct; for example, *p only if q* and *q if p*. Thus, the conjunction $(p \to q) \land (q \to p)$ can be read as *p only if q and p if q*.

This is abbreviated in writing the *biconditional*:

in words: ***p if and only if q***

in symbols: ***p ↔ q***

- **The biconditional *p if and only if q* is true when *p* and *q* are both true or both false.**

In other words, $p \leftrightarrow q$ is true when *p* and *q* have the ***same truth values***. When *p* and *q* have different truth values, the biconditional is false.

p	q	$p \leftrightarrow q$
T	T	T
T	F	F
F	T	F
F	F	T

Truth Table for the Biconditional

Compound Statements and Truth Values

A compound sentence can contain more than one connective. When the truth value of every simple sentence is certain within the compound being formed, we have a *compound statement*.

PROCEDURE.   To find the truth value of a compound sentence:
1. Substitute the given truth values into the compound sentence.
2. Simplify the truth values within parentheses or other groupings, always working from the innermost group first.
3. Simplify negations.
4. Simplify other connectives, working from left to right.

For example, to find the truth value of the compound sentence $(p \rightarrow \sim q) \wedge \sim r$ when p, q, and r are all true, we proceed as follows:

(1) First, substitute the truth values: $(T \rightarrow \sim T) \quad \wedge \sim T$

(2) Within parentheses, simplify the negation: $(T \rightarrow F) \quad \wedge \sim T$

(3) Simplify parentheses: $F \qquad\qquad \wedge \sim T$

(4) Simplify the negation: $F \qquad\qquad \wedge \; F$

(5) Simplify the conjunction: F

The compound sentence is false.

EXAMPLES

In 1–6: Let s represent "We go to school on Labor Day."   (False)
           Let h represent "Labor Day is a holiday."   (True)
           Let w represent "We work on Labor Day."   (False)

a. Write each given statement in symbolic form.   **b.** Tell whether the statement is true or false, based on the truth values listed above.

Answers

1. We work on Labor Day or Labor Day is a holiday.
    a. $w \vee h$
    b. $F \vee T$ True

2. Labor Day is a holiday and we do not work on Labor Day.
    a. $h \wedge \sim w$
    b. $T \wedge \sim F = T \wedge T$ True

3. If we go to school on Labor Day, then we work on Labor Day.
    a. $s \rightarrow w$
    b. $F \rightarrow F$ True

4. We do not go to school on Labor Day implies that we work on Labor Day.
    a. $\sim s \rightarrow w$
    b. $\sim F \rightarrow F = T \rightarrow F$ False

5. We work on Labor Day if and only if we go to school on Labor Day.
    a. $w \leftrightarrow s$
    b. $F \leftrightarrow F$ True

6. If we do not go to school on Labor Day and Labor Day is a holiday, then we do not work on Labor Day.
    a. $(\sim s \wedge h) \rightarrow \sim w$
    b. $(\sim F \wedge T) \rightarrow \sim F$
    $= (T \wedge T) \rightarrow \sim F$
    $= T \rightarrow \sim F$
    $= T \rightarrow T$ True

EXERCISES WITH OPEN-RESPONSE PROBLEMS

In 1–12 in each case: **a.** Tell whether the sentence is true, false, or open.   **b.** If the sentence is an open sentence, identify the variable.

1. Canada is a country in North America.

2. He went to Canada for a vacation.

3. A triangle is a four-sided polygon.

4. Two is odd or prime.

5. A ray has one endpoint and a segment has two endpoints.

6. A three-sided polygon is called a triangle or a quadrilateral.

7. Perpendicular lines do not meet to form right angles.

8. An angle is a right angle if and only if the angle measures 90 degrees.

9. $x > 1$ and $x < 5$.

10. If $1 + 2 = 3$, then $2 + 3 = 4$.

11. $2^4 = 4^2$ if and only if $1^3 = 3^1$.

12. $7 \geq 0$ or $7 < 0$.

In 13–24, use the domain of real numbers to find the truth set or solution set for each open sentence; that is, find the elements of the domain which, when used as replacements for x, make true sentences.

13. $x + 7 = 16$

14. $x - 5 = 19$

15. $\frac{3x}{5} = 30$

16. $2x - 3 = 57$

17. $x + 3x = 12$

18. $2x + 1 = 2$

19. $0.3x = 6$

20. $5x + 30 = 0$

21. $\frac{x}{6} = \frac{2}{3}$

22. $x + \frac{1}{3} = 5$

23. $x + 7 = 3x$

24. $6 + 0.1x = 5$

In 25–32, use the domain of whole numbers to find the truth set for each compound open sentence. If no replacements make true sentences, write { }.

25. $(x > 6) \wedge (x < 9)$

26. $(x > 3) \wedge (x \leq 5)$

27. $(x > 7) \wedge (x < 5)$

28. $(x < 3) \wedge (x < 4)$

29. $(x < 3) \vee (x < 4)$

30. $(x < 2) \vee (x \leq 5)$

31. $(3x \geq 2x + 3) \wedge (2x - 1 < 7)$

32. $(x + x = 10) \vee (3 + x < 5)$

In 33–38, choose the word *true* or the word *false* to replace the blank to make each resulting sentence true.

33. When p is true and q is false, then $p \wedge q$ is _____.

34. When p and q are both true, then $p \vee \sim q$ is _____.

35. When p and q have different truth values, then $p \leftrightarrow q$ is _____.

36. If both p and q are false, then $\sim p \wedge q$ is _____.

37. When the hypothesis p is false, then $p \rightarrow q$ is _____.

38. When the conclusion q is true, then $p \rightarrow q$ is _____.

In 39–44, select the *numeral* preceding the choice that best answers the question.

39. Let p represent "x is an even number," and let q represent "x is divisible by 4." Which is true when $x = 10$?

(1) $p \wedge q$ (2) $p \vee q$ (3) $\sim p$ (4) q

40. Let p represent "$2x + 5 = 17$," and let q represent "$2x + 3x = 20$." Which is true when $x = 6$?

(1) $p \wedge q$ (2) $p \rightarrow q$ (3) $p \leftrightarrow q$ (4) $p \vee q$

41. If p represents "the polygon has four sides" and q represents "all sides of the polygon are congruent," then which is true when the polygon is an isosceles triangle?

(1) $p \wedge q$ (2) $p \vee q$ (3) $p \rightarrow q$ (4) $\sim p \leftrightarrow q$

42. If the conjunction $p \wedge q$ is true, which statement must be false?

(1) $p \vee q$ (2) $p \rightarrow q$ (3) $\sim p$ (4) $p \leftrightarrow q$

43. If the conditional $p \rightarrow q$ is false, which statement must be true?

(1) q (2) $p \wedge q$ (3) $q \rightarrow p$ (4) $p \leftrightarrow q$

44. If the biconditional $p \leftrightarrow q$ is false, which statement must be true?

(1) $p \wedge q$ (2) $p \vee q$ (3) $\sim p \leftrightarrow \sim q$ (4) $\sim p \wedge \sim q$

In 45–54: Let M represent "May has 31 days."   (True)
              Let J represent "June has 31 days."   (False)
              Let F represent "June follows May." (True)

a. Write each given statement in symbolic form.
b. Tell whether the statement is true or false.
c. Explain your answer.

45. May does not have 31 days.   **46.** May or June has 31 days.
47. May has 31 days and June has 31 days.   **48.** If June follows May, then May has 31 days.

49. If May has 31 days, then June has 31 days.
50. June follows May if and only if June has 31 days.
51. If June does not follow May, then June does not have 31 days.
52. June has 31 days if June follows May.
53. If May and June have 31 days, then June does not follow May.
54. June does not have 31 days implies that May has 31 days.

In 55–66, use the symbols assigned to represent the four true statements.

Let m represent "A segment is bisected at its midpoint."
Let s represent "Congruent segments are equal in length."
Let b represent "An angle bisector forms two congruent angles."
Let a represent "Congruent angles are equal in measure."

For each compound sentence in symbolic form:

a. Write a complete sentence in words to show what the symbols represent.
b. Tell whether the compound sentence is true or false.
c. Explain your answer.

55. $m \wedge s$ **56.** $a \wedge s$ **57.** $m \rightarrow s$ **58.** $\sim m \vee \sim s$
59. $s \leftrightarrow a$ **60.** $b \rightarrow \sim a$ **61.** $\sim a \rightarrow \sim s$ **62.** $(m \wedge b) \rightarrow (s \wedge a)$
63. $m \rightarrow \sim s$ **64.** $\sim b \vee m$ **65.** $\sim m \leftrightarrow \sim s$ **66.** $(b \vee \sim a) \rightarrow \sim s$

In 67–78, let p and q be *true* statements, and let r and s be *false* statements. Tell whether each compound sentence is true or false. Explain your answers.

67. $p \rightarrow r$ **68.** $(p \wedge q) \wedge r$ **69.** $(q \vee r) \vee s$ **70.** $(p \vee r) \wedge s$

71. $q \leftrightarrow s$ **72.** $(p \wedge q) \rightarrow s$ **73.** $(q \vee s) \leftrightarrow p$ **74.** $p \wedge \sim r$

75. $\sim p \vee r$ **76.** $q \rightarrow (p \vee r)$ **77.** $(q \rightarrow p) \vee r$ **78.** $(\sim r \vee s) \rightarrow \sim s$

In 79–88, find the truth values for m and k that would make each statement *false*.

79. $m \vee k$ **80.** $m \rightarrow k$ **81.** $m \rightarrow \sim k$ **82.** $\sim m \rightarrow k$ **83.** $\sim (m \wedge k)$

84. $\sim m \rightarrow \sim k$ **85.** $m \vee \sim k$ **86.** $\sim (m \wedge \sim k)$ **87.** $\sim m \vee \sim k$ **88.** $\sim (\sim m \wedge k)$

2-3 TAUTOLOGIES AND LOGICALLY EQUIVALENT STATEMENTS

When the simple sentences used to form a compound sentence can assume different truth values, we must consider cases where the sentences are true and cases where they are false. As stated in Section 2-2, a truth table shows all possible truth values.

Tautologies

In logic, a ***tautology*** is a compound sentence that is *always true*, no matter what truth values are assigned to the simple sentences that form the compound sentence. For example, let us study the truth value of $(p \wedge q) \rightarrow (p \vee q)$ by building a truth table.

p	q	$p \wedge q$	$p \vee q$	$(p \wedge q) \rightarrow (p \vee q)$
T	T	T	T	T
T	F	F	T	T
F	T	F	T	T
F	F	F	F	T

Tautology

Every entry in the last column is true; that is, $(p \wedge q) \rightarrow (p \vee q)$ is true for all possible truth values of p and of q. Therefore, we know that $(p \wedge q) \rightarrow (p \vee q)$ is a tautology, or a basic truth in logic.

Not every truth table represents a tautology. For example, suppose we reverse the hypothesis and the conclusion in the conditional statement just made and look at the truth table of $(p \lor q) \to (p \land q)$.

p	q	$p \lor q$	$p \land q$	$(p \lor q) \to (p \land q)$
T	T	T	T	T
T	F	T	F	F
F	T	T	F	F
F	F	F	F	T

Not a Tautology

We note that $(p \lor q) \to (p \land q)$ is *not* a tautology because *not* every element in the last column is true.

Remember that p and q can be any statements at all. Therefore, let p represent "Eric is handsome" and let q represent "Heidi is beautiful." The two preceding truth tables show us that:

1. A conjunctive statement will always imply a disjunctive statement since $(p \land q) \to (p \lor q)$ is a tautology. Thus, if "Eric is handsome *and* Heidi is beautiful," it follows that "Eric is handsome *or* Heidi is beautiful." This compound statement is true.

2. A disjunctive statement can*not* imply a conjunctive statement since $(p \lor q) \to (p \land q)$ is *not* a tautology. Thus, if "Eric is handsome *or* Heidi is beautiful," we can*not* conclude that "Eric is handsome *and* Heidi is beautiful."

Logically Equivalent Statements

When two statements always have the same truth value, we say that the statements are **logically equivalent**. To show that an **equivalence** exists between two statements, we use the biconditional *if and only if*. If the statements always have the same truth value, then the biconditional statement will be true in every case, resulting in a tautology.

Let p represent "I study."

Let q represent "I'll pass the test."

The two statements being tested for an equivalence follow:

$p \to q$: If I study, then I'll pass the test.

$\sim p \lor q$: I don't study or I'll pass the test.

Using the biconditional, we wish to test the truth of this statement:

$$(p \rightarrow q) \leftrightarrow (\sim p \vee q)$$

			Col. 4	Col. 5	Col. 6
p	*q*	$\sim p$	$\sim p \vee q$	$p \rightarrow q$	$(p \rightarrow q) \leftrightarrow (\sim p \vee q)$
T	T	F	T	T	T
T	F	F	F	F	T
F	T	T	T	T	T
F	F	T	T	T	T

We note that the truth values of $\sim p \vee q$ in column 4 match exactly with the truth values of $p \rightarrow q$ in column 5. Thus $\sim p \vee q$ and $p \rightarrow q$ are logically equivalent statements. In fact, $\sim p \vee q$ is sometimes called the ***conditional equivalence*** because the statement $\sim p \vee q$ can be used to replace the conditional statement $p \rightarrow q$. This equivalence is verified by the tautology written as a biconditional statement in column 6.

EXAMPLES

Let *c* represent "Simone takes chorus."
Let *s* represent "Simone takes Spanish."

a. Using *c*, *s*, and the proper logic connectives, express each of the following sentences in symbolic form.

If Simone takes chorus, then she cannot take Spanish.
If Simone takes Spanish, then she cannot take chorus.

b. Prove that the two statements are logically equivalent, or give a reason why they are not equivalent.

Solutions

a. $c \rightarrow \sim s$ and $s \rightarrow \sim c$

b. To test for logical equivalence of these two statements, construct a truth table, using the following biconditional: $(c \rightarrow \sim s) \leftrightarrow (s \rightarrow \sim c)$

				Col. 5	Col. 6	Col. 7
c	*s*	$\sim c$	$\sim s$	$c \rightarrow \sim s$	$s \rightarrow \sim c$	$(c \rightarrow \sim s) \leftrightarrow (s \rightarrow \sim c)$
T	T	F	F	F	F	T
T	F	F	T	T	T	T
F	T	T	F	T	T	T
F	F	T	T	T	T	T

The statements $c \rightarrow \sim s$ and $s \rightarrow \sim c$ are logically equivalent, as proved by their matching truth values in columns 5 and 6, or by the biconditional that is shown to be a tautology in column 7.

EXERCISES WITH OPEN-RESPONSE PROBLEMS

In 1–6, prove in each case that the two statements denoted as (*1*) and (*2*) are logically equivalent or give a reason why they are not equivalent.

1. (*1*) $q \rightarrow p$ (*2*) $p \lor \sim q$ **2.** (*1*) $p \land \sim q$ (*2*) $\sim(\sim p \lor q)$
3. (*1*) $p \land \sim q$ (*2*) $\sim(p \rightarrow q)$ **4.** (*1*) $p \rightarrow q$ (*2*) $q \rightarrow p$
5. (*1*) $p \rightarrow q$ (*2*) $\sim p \rightarrow \sim q$ **6.** (*1*) $p \lor q$ (*2*) $p \lor (q \land \sim p)$

In 7–11 in each case: **a.** Using the letters given to represent sentences and the proper logic connectives, express each of the two compound sentences in symbolic form.   **b.** Prove that the two compound sentences are logically equivalent or give a reason why they are not equivalent.

7. Let f represent "I eat the right foods."
Let s represent "I get sick."
Sentences: If I eat the right foods, then I don't get sick.
           I don't get sick or I don't eat the right foods.

8. Let m represent "Michael likes math."
Let s represent "Michael likes science."
Sentences: It is not true that Michael likes both math and science.
           Michael does not like math or Michael does not like science.

9. Let t represent "Ms. Wu is a teacher."
Let e represent "Ms. Wu is an engineer."
Sentences: If Ms. Wu is a teacher, then she is not an engineer.
           If Ms. Wu is not an engineer, then she is a teacher.

10. Let s represent "You succeed."
Let t represent "You try again."
Sentences: If you don't succeed, then you try again.
           You succeed or you try again.

11. Let p represent "Lines are perpendicular."
Let r represent "Right angles are formed by the lines."
Sentences: Right angles are formed by the lines if the lines are perpendicular.
           The lines are not perpendicular or right angles are formed by the lines.

2-4   THE LAW OF DETACHMENT

There are many laws of reasoning that allow us to present a convincing argument or a formal proof in logic. Before developing a formal proof in logic, we need first to understand what is meant by a convincing argument.

An *argument* consists of a series of statements called *premises* and a final statement called the *conclusion*. We say that the premises lead to the conclusion, or that the conclusion follows from the premises. For example:

Premise:	If I play baseball, then I need a bat.
Premise:	I play baseball.
Conclusion:	I need a bat.

We have drawn a line to separate the premises from the conclusion. If we let p represent "I play baseball" and q represent "I need a bat," we can write this argument in symbolic form as:

Premise:	$p \to q$
Premise:	p
Conclusion:	q

A Test of Validity by Truth Values

An argument is called a *valid argument* if and only if (1) its premises are *true* and (2) by the laws of reasoning these premises force the conclusion to be *true*. You can test the validity of any argument by examining the possible truth values of the variables given in the premises.

1. Since all premises must be true, start by assigning T for true to the simplest premise in the argument. Here, indicate that the premise p is true by writing T above the variable p.

$$p \to q$$
$$\overset{\text{T}}{p}$$
$$\overline{}$$
$$q$$

2. Since p is true in the second premise, we must also label p as true in the first premise.

$$\overset{\text{T}}{p} \to q$$
$$\overset{\text{T}}{p}$$
$$\overline{}$$
$$q$$

3. The conditional premise $p \rightarrow q$ must also be true. From the truth table for conditional, we know that $\mathsf{T} \rightarrow \mathsf{F}$ is a false statement. Therefore, we cannot label q as false because the premise $p \rightarrow q$ would then be false. Since $\mathsf{T} \rightarrow \mathsf{T}$ is a true statement, we label q as true to keep the premise $p \rightarrow q$ true.

$$\begin{array}{c} ⓣ\ \ ⓣ \\ p \rightarrow q \\ ⓣ \\ p \\ \hline q \end{array}$$

4. Finally, since q is true in the first premise, we must also label q as true in the conclusion. In this way, we see that the set of true premises has led to a true conclusion. Therefore, we have a valid argument.

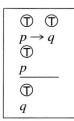

Defining the Law of Detachment

The argument you have just tested, by assigning truth values to show its validity, is called the *Law of Detachment*. This law is the first of many *laws of reasoning*, or inference laws, that you will study. This is called a *law of inference* because, when the given premises are true, you can *infer* that the conclusion is true.

- The *Law of Detachment* states that, when two given premises are true, one a conditional and the other the hypothesis of that conditional, it then follows that the conclusion of the conditional is true.

The Law of Detachment can also be identified by its Latin name, *Modus Ponens*. In this law of reasoning, and in other inference laws to follow, we use the symbol $\therefore$ to mean the word *therefore*. We will use the symbol $\therefore$ or the word *therefore* only when we reach a conclusion.

The Law of Detachment may be written symbolically in either of two ways:

$$\begin{array}{c} p \rightarrow q \\ p \\ \hline \therefore q \end{array} \qquad \text{or} \qquad [(p \rightarrow q) \wedge p] \rightarrow q$$

Note. In the example just given, q is called a valid conclusion. A *valid conclusion* is a true statement that is deduced from a set of true premises by using the laws of reasoning.

Hidden Conditionals

In an argument, a conditional statement is sometimes given in a form that does not use the words *if . . . then* or the word *implies*. Such a statement is called a **hidden conditional**. In such cases, it is helpful to change the hidden conditional to a statement using the words *if . . . then*. Here are four examples:

1. Hidden conditional: A polygon with three sides is called a triangle.
   If . . . then form: If a polygon has three sides, then the
                polygon is called a triangle.

2. Hidden conditional: What's good for Bill is good for me.
   If . . . then form: If it's good for Bill, then it's good for me.

3. Hidden conditional: I'll get a job when I graduate.
   If . . . then form: If I graduate, then I'll get a job.

4. Hidden conditional: Drink milk to stay healthy.
   If . . . then form: If you drink milk, then you will stay healthy.

EXAMPLES

1. Let *r* represent "It is raining."
   Let *m* represent "I have to mow the lawn."

   Premises: If it is raining, then I don't have to mow the lawn.
        It is raining.

   a. Using *r*, *m*, and the proper logic connectives, express the premises of this argument in symbolic form.
   b. Write a conclusion in symbolic form.
   c. Translate the conclusion into words.

Solutions **a.** $r \rightarrow \sim m$
        r

   b. Compare these premises to the general form used in the Law of Detachment to see that the conclusion must be $\sim m$.

$$p \rightarrow q \qquad r \rightarrow \sim m$$
$$\underline{p \qquad} \qquad \underline{r \qquad}$$
$$\therefore q \qquad \therefore \sim m$$

   c. $\sim m$ represents "I don't have to mow the lawn."

   Answers: **a.** $r \rightarrow \sim m$ **b.** $\sim m$ **c.** I don't have to mow the lawn.
          r

2. Write a valid conclusion for the given premises, or indicate that no conclusion is possible.

Premises: If two rays are rays of the same line with a common endpoint and no other points in common, then the rays are opposite rays.

$\overrightarrow{BC}$ and $\overrightarrow{BA}$ are rays of the same line.

$\overrightarrow{BC}$ and $\overrightarrow{BA}$ have a common endpoint and no other points in common.

Solution   The diagram shows $\overrightarrow{BC}$ and $\overrightarrow{BA}$ to be rays of the same line with a common endpoint and no other points in common.

Let ℓ represent "The rays are rays of the same line."
Let c represent "The rays have a common endpoint and no other points in common."
Let p represent "The rays are opposite rays."

In the first premise, the hypothesis is a conjunction $(\ell \wedge c)$ and the conclusion is p. Therefore the first premise can be written as $(\ell \wedge c) \rightarrow p$. The second and third premises can be written as a conjunction. Use the Law of Detachment.

$(\ell \wedge c) \rightarrow p$: If two rays are rays of the same line with a common endpoint and no other points in common, then the rays are opposite rays.

$(\ell \wedge c)$: $\overrightarrow{BC}$ and $\overrightarrow{BA}$ are rays of the same line and have a common endpoint and no other points in common.

$\therefore p$: $\overrightarrow{BC}$ and $\overrightarrow{BA}$ are opposite rays.   *Answer*

3. Write a valid conclusion for the given premises or indicate that no conclusion is possible.

Premises: If two rays are rays of the same line with a common endpoint and no other points in common, then the rays are opposite rays.

$\overrightarrow{BC}$ and $\overrightarrow{BA}$ have a common endpoint and no other points in common.

Solution   The diagram shows $\overrightarrow{BC}$ and $\overrightarrow{BA}$ to be rays with a common endpoint and no other points in common.

Let ℓ represent "The rays are rays of the same line."
Let c represent "The rays have a common endpoint and no other points in common."
Let p represent "The rays are opposite rays."

In the first premise, the hypothesis is a conjunction $(\ell \wedge c)$ and the conclusion is p. Therefore the first premise can be written as $(\ell \wedge c) \rightarrow p$.

Note that, since $\overrightarrow{BC}$ and $\overrightarrow{BA}$ are not rays of the same line, the second premise fails to meet all conditions stated in the hypothesis of the first premise.

$(\ell \wedge c) \rightarrow p$: If two rays are rays of the same line with a common endpoint and no other points in common, then the rays are opposite rays.

c: $\overrightarrow{BC}$ and $\overrightarrow{BA}$ have a common endpoint and no other points in common.

∴ No conclusion is possible.   *Answer*

---

4. Write a valid conclusion for the given premises or indicate that no conclusion is possible.

Premises: Reading will give a person knowledge.
Mrs. Walker is an avid reader.

Solution   The first premise is a hidden conditional that can be restated in the *if . . . then* form. The premises are rewritten, both in symbols and in words, as follows:

$p \rightarrow q$: If a person reads, then the reader gains knowledge.

p: Mrs. Walker reads.

By the Law of Detachment, we conclude q. We write this conclusion by including Mrs. Walker's name as the reader:

∴ q: Mrs. Walker gains knowledge.   *Answer*

EXERCISES WITH OPEN-RESPONSE PROBLEMS

In 1–4, in each case use the Law of Detachment to state a correct conclusion from the given premises.

1. $p \rightarrow q$ **2.** $k \rightarrow \sim t$ **3.** $\sim a \rightarrow x$ **4.** $p \rightarrow (r \wedge s)$

$\underline{p\quad\quad}$ $\underline{k\quad\quad}$ $\underline{\sim a\quad\quad}$ $\underline{p\quad\quad\quad}$

In 5–7, identify the premises and the conclusion in each argument.

5. If n is an even number, then n is exactly divisible by 2.
n is an even number.
Therefore, n is exactly divisible by 2.

6. If an event is a certainty, then its probability is 1.
The event that I am alive is a certainty.
The probability that I am alive is 1.

7. Fredda watches TV if she has nothing better to do.
Fredda has nothing better to do.
Fredda watches TV.

In 8–12, express each hidden conditional in a sentence using the words *if . . . then.*

8. When points are on the same line, they are called collinear points.

9. I'll do my homework when I'm good and ready.

10. What Jack doesn't see, he doesn't believe exists.

11. The complement of an angle measuring x degrees is an angle measuring $(90 - x)$ degrees.

12. Flowers grow when given sun and water.

13. Given the premises $a \rightarrow b$ and a, which is a logical conclusion?
   (1) a (2) $\sim a$ (3) b (4) $\sim b$

14. Given the premises $p \rightarrow \sim q$ and p, which is a logical conclusion?
   (1) p (2) $\sim p$ (3) q (4) $\sim q$

In 15–18:   Let r represent "It rains."
            Let s represent "It snows."
            Let v represent "Vegetables grow."

   a. Using r, s, v, and the proper logic connectives, express the given premises of each argument in symbolic form.

   b. Write the conclusion of the argument in symbolic form.

   c. Translate the conclusion into words.

15. If it rains, then vegetables grow.
       It rains.

16. If it snows, then vegetables do not grow.   **17.** It does not snow if it rains.
       It snows.   It rains.

18. If it rains and it does not snow, then vegetables grow.
       It rains and it does not snow.

In 19–24, write a valid conclusion for each given set of premises.

19. If you deserve a break today, then you should have lunch.
       Mr. Willig deserves a break today.

20. If two points are given, then a straight line can be drawn containing the points.
       Points A and B are given.

21. Tom will get an A if his essay is handed in on time.
       Tom's essay is handed in on time.

22. When x is an integer, then x is a real number.
       x is the integer 5.

23. The person who is late for supper will get into trouble.
       Matthew is late for supper.

24. Any friend of Jim Kavanagh is a friend of mine.
       Alex is a friend of Jim Kavanagh.

In 25–28, state whether or not each conclusion is *valid* based on the Law of Detachment. Explain your answer.

25. When football season ends, we start baseball practice.
Football season has ended.
Conclusion: We have started baseball practice.

26. You can use the machine if you have exact change.
You use the machine.
Conclusion: You have exact change.

27. If I understand logic, then I can reason correctly.
I understand logic.
Conclusion: I can reason correctly.

28. A square is a rectangle.
If a figure is a rectangle, then it has four right angles.
Conclusion: A square has four right angles.

In 29–36, write a valid conclusion for each given set of premises or tell why no conclusion is possible.

29. If she is in love, then her head is in the clouds.
Mary is in love.

30. You can buy a luxury car if you are rich.
Mr. Lopez is rich.

31. If a point is a midpoint of a line segment, then that point divides the line segment into two congruent segments.
M is the midpoint of $\overline{AB}$.

32. If two angles are both right angles, then the angles are congruent.
$\angle A$ and $\angle B$ are congruent angles.

33. If two angles are congruent, then the angles have the same measure.
$\angle C \cong \angle D$.

34. If I had the time and the energy, then I'd walk to work.
I have the time.

35. When a polygon is regular, all sides of the polygon are congruent.
A square is a regular polygon.

36. If a sentence has a truth value, then it is a statement.
"$3 + 8 = 11$" is true.

2-5 THE LAW OF THE CONTRAPOSITIVE AND PROOF IN LOGIC

The conditional *if p then q* is the connective most often used in reasoning. In Math A, we studied three related conditionals, each of which was formed by making some changes in the original conditional. These conditionals are called the *inverse*, the *converse*, and the *contrapositive*.

Let us examine these related conditionals both in symbolic form and in words. For an example, let *p* represent "It's −5°" and let *q* represent "It's cold."

Conditional ($p \rightarrow q$): If it's $-5°$, then it's cold. Certainly, we can agree that this statement is *true*.

Inverse ($\sim p \rightarrow \sim q$): If it's *not* $-5°$, then it's *not* cold. Here we are uncertain of the truth value of this statement. Perhaps it's 30° Celsius and the statement is true, or perhaps it's $-10°$ and the statement is false. In any event, we know that this statement could *possibly be false*.

Converse ($q \rightarrow p$): If it's cold, then it's $-5°$. Again we are uncertain of the truth value of this statement. If it is cold, the temperature could be $-5°$ or it could be some other low temperature. We know that this statement could *possibly be false*.

Contrapositive ($\sim q \rightarrow \sim p$): If it's *not* cold, then it's *not* $-5°$. Knowing that it is not cold does imply that the temperature cannot be $-5°$. Thus, we can agree that this statement is *true*.

To convince ourselves that the conditional statement and its contrapositive are *logically equivalent statements*, we can construct a truth table for the expression $(p \rightarrow q) \leftrightarrow (\sim q \rightarrow \sim p)$.

				Col. 5	Col. 6	Col. 7
p	q	$\sim q$	$\sim p$	$p \rightarrow q$	$\sim q \rightarrow \sim p$	$(p \rightarrow q) \leftrightarrow (\sim q \rightarrow \sim p)$
T	T	F	F	T	T	T
T	F	T	F	F	F	T
F	T	F	T	T	T	T
F	F	T	T	T	T	T

The truth values for the conditional in column 5 match the truth values for the contrapositive in column 6, resulting in a tautology in column 7.

Defining the Law of the Contrapositive

The truth table we have just constructed verifies our second law of reasoning, or inference law, called the *Law of the Contrapositive*.

● The *Law of the Contrapositive* states that, when a conditional premise is true, it follows that the contrapositive of the premise is also true.

The Law of the Contrapositive may be written symbolically in either of two ways:

$$\frac{p \rightarrow q}{\therefore \sim q \rightarrow \sim p} \qquad \text{or} \qquad (p \rightarrow q) \leftrightarrow (\sim q \rightarrow \sim p)$$

We recall that a contrapositive is formed by taking any conditional statement, negating its hypothesis, negating its conclusion, and then reversing the roles of these negated statements. Therefore, in the contrapositive: (1) the hypothesis is the negated conclusion of the original conditional and (2) the conclusion is the negated hypothesis of the original conditional. Thus, we can see that:

1. The contrapositive of $a \rightarrow \sim b$ is $b \rightarrow \sim a$.
2. The contrapositive of $\sim c \rightarrow d$ is $\sim d \rightarrow c$.
3. The contrapositive of $\sim e \rightarrow \sim f$ is $f \rightarrow e$.

The Inverse and the Converse

It is possible to construct truth tables to show that:

1. A conditional $p \rightarrow q$ and its inverse $\sim p \rightarrow \sim q$ are *not* logically equivalent statements.
2. A conditional $p \rightarrow q$ and its converse $q \rightarrow p$ are *not* logically equivalent statements.
3. However, the inverse $\sim p \rightarrow \sim q$ and the converse $q \rightarrow p$ are logically equivalent statements. By examining the tautology, $(\sim p \rightarrow \sim q) \leftrightarrow (q \rightarrow p)$, we realize that this statement is merely another form of the Law of the Contrapositive.

A Proof in Logic

When we are given a series of premises that are true and we apply the laws of reasoning to reach a conclusion that is true, we say that we are proving an argument by means of a ***formal proof***. This is a preparation for proofs in geometry.

The most commonly used proof in logic involves two columns. The first column consists of **statements**, and the second column consists of **reasons** that allow us to make the statements. Let us study an example.

Given the premises: If Joanna saves enough money, then she can buy a bike.
Joanna cannot buy a bike.

Prove the conclusion: Joanna did not save enough money.

To simplify this proof, we will assign variables to the statements and rewrite the premises and the conclusion in symbolic form.

Let m represent "Joanna saves enough money."
Let b represent "Joanna can buy a bike."

Given: $m \rightarrow b$
$\sim b$

Prove: $\sim m$

Statements	Reasons
1. $m \rightarrow b$	1. Given.
2. $\sim b$	2. Given.
3. $\sim b \rightarrow \sim m$	3. Law of the Contrapositive (step 1).
4. $\sim m$	4. Law of Detachment (steps 2 and 3).

The proof just presented starts by listing the premises that are given and the conclusion that must be proved. In the statements that follow, we number the steps. Thus, steps 1 and 2 are the given premises. In step 3, we apply the Law of the Contrapositive to step 1, allowing us to say that, when $m \rightarrow b$ is true, then $\sim b \rightarrow \sim m$ is also true. In step 4, we apply the Law of Detachment to steps 2 and 3. Thus, $\sim b \rightarrow \sim m$ and $\sim b$ lead to the conclusion $\sim m$, which must be true.

Note. Whenever we use a law of reasoning to make a statement in the first column, we must write in the second column *both* the name of the law of reasoning and the steps used to reach this new statement.

EXAMPLES

1. Which is logically equivalent to the statement "If I live in Brooklyn, then I live in New York"?
(1) If I live in New York, then I live in Brooklyn.
(2) If I do not live in New York, then I do not live in Brooklyn.
(3) If I do not live in New York, then I live in Brooklyn.
(4) If I do not live in Brooklyn, then I do not live in New York.

Solution   A conditional statement $B \rightarrow N$ is logically equivalent to its contrapositive $\sim N \rightarrow \sim B$. The contrapositive of the given statement is choice (2).

Answer: (2)

---

2. *Given the premises:*   If Al does not study, then he will fail.
                                Al did not fail.
      Prove the conclusion: Al studied.

Solution   A formal proof is given here, after assigning variables to the statements and rewriting our premises and conclusion in symbolic form.

Let s represent "Al studied."
Let f represent "Al failed."

Given: $\sim s \rightarrow f$
         $\sim f$

Prove: s

Statements	Reasons
1. $\sim s \rightarrow f$	1. Given
2. $\sim f$	2. Given.
3. $\sim f \rightarrow s$	3. Law of the Contrapositive (step 1).
4. s	4. Law of Detachment (steps 2 and 3).

Therefore, we have proved s: Al studied.

EXERCISES WITH OPEN-RESPONSE PROBLEMS

In 1–10, write the contrapositive of each given conditional statement.

1. $p \rightarrow q$ **2.** $k \rightarrow m$ **3.** $\sim r \rightarrow t$ **4.** $x \rightarrow \sim y$

5. If winter is here, then spring will soon follow.
6. If it is not raining, then Leah will not take her umbrella.
7. Rick feels good if he jogs every morning.
8. If Ali is sick, then she will not go to school.
9. Linda is not happy if people are late to dinner.
10. The presence of too many cooks implies that the broth is spoiled.

In 11–15, select the *numeral* preceding the choice that best answers the question.

11. Which statement is logically equivalent to $\sim p \rightarrow r$?
(1) $p \rightarrow r$ (2) $p \rightarrow \sim r$ (3) $\sim r \rightarrow p$ (4) $r \rightarrow p$

12. Which statement is logically equivalent to $p \rightarrow \sim q$?
(1) $q \rightarrow \sim p$ (2) $\sim p \rightarrow q$ (3) $\sim q \rightarrow p$ (4) $q \rightarrow p$

13. Which is logically equivalent to the statement "If it's cold, then we go skiing"?
(1) If we go skiing, then it's cold.   (2) If we do not go skiing, then it's cold.
(3) If it is not cold, then we do not go skiing.   (4) If we do not go skiing, then it is not cold.

14. Which is logically equivalent to the statement "If I eat, then I live"?
(1) If I do not eat, then I do not live.   (2) If I do not live, then I do not eat.
(3) If I live, then I eat.   (4) If I eat, then I do not live.

15. Which is logically equivalent to the statement "You will get sick if you eat green apples"?
(1) If you get sick, then you have eaten green apples.
(2) If you don't get sick, then you have not eaten green apples.
(3) If you don't eat green apples, then you won't get sick.
(4) You've eaten green apples if you have gotten sick.

In 16–28, tell in each case whether the two given statements are logically equivalent or are not equivalent.

16. $r \rightarrow t$ **17.** $k \rightarrow m$ **18.** $t \rightarrow \sim b$ **19.** $\sim d \rightarrow \sim h$
$\quad \sim r \rightarrow \sim t$ $\quad m \rightarrow k$ $\quad b \rightarrow \sim t$ $\quad h \rightarrow d$

20. $p \rightarrow \sim b$ **21.** $\sim n \rightarrow e$ **22.** $r \rightarrow \sim p$ **23.** $\sim p \rightarrow t$
$\quad \sim b \rightarrow p$ $\quad \sim e \rightarrow n$ $\quad \sim r \rightarrow p$ $\quad t \rightarrow \sim p$

24. If a triangle is isosceles, then it has exactly two congruent sides.
If a triangle does not have exactly two congruent sides, then it is not isosceles.

25. If $x + 2 = 5$, then $x \neq 4$.   **26.** If $x + 2 = 5$, then $x = 3$.
If $x + 2 \neq 5$, then $x = 4$.   If $x \neq 3$, then $x + 2 \neq 5$.

27. If two angles are vertical angles, then they are congruent.
   If two angles are congruent, then they are vertical angles.
28. Dick will reach home plate if Doug hits a triple.
   If Dick does not reach home plate, then Doug did not hit a triple.

In 29 and 30, copy each given proof and provide the reason needed for each step.

29. *Given:* $a \rightarrow \sim b$
            b
   Prove: $\sim a$

Statements	Reasons
1. $a \rightarrow \sim b$	1. _____
2. b	2. _____
3. $b \rightarrow \sim a$	3. _____
4. $\sim a$	4. _____

30. *Given:* $\sim p \rightarrow \sim t$
            t
   Prove: p

Statements	Reasons
1. $\sim p \rightarrow \sim t$	1. _____
2. $t \rightarrow p$	2. _____
3. t	3. _____
4. p	4. _____

In 31–36, write in each case a formal proof to show that the conclusion must follow from the given set of premises. (In 34–36, write all statements in symbolic form, using the given variables.)

31. *Given:* $p \rightarrow r$
            p
   Prove: r

32. *Given:* $\sim k \rightarrow e$
            $\sim e$
   Prove: k

33. *Given:* $q \rightarrow t$
            $\sim t$
   Prove: $\sim q$

34. *Given:* If two lines intersect, the lines meet at only one point.
            Lines k and m do not meet at one point.

   Prove: Lines k and m do not intersect.
      (Let I represent "Two lines intersect.")
      (Let P represent "Lines meet at one point.")

35. *Given:* Gabe went to medical school if he is a doctor.
            Gabe is a doctor.

   Prove: Gabe went to medical school.
      (Let M represent "Gabe went to medical school.")
      (Let D represent "Gabe is a doctor.")

36. *Given:* Lights will go off if there is a power failure.
            The lights do not go off.

   Prove: There is no power failure.
      (Let O represent "Lights go off.")
      (Let P represent "There is a power failure.")

2-6 THE LAW OF MODUS TOLLENS

In Ruritania, when Juliet is no longer the queen, her son Prince Charles will take the throne as the new king. We will use these facts to present a third law of reasoning. Let *p* represent "Charles is the prince," and let *q* represent "Juliet is the queen."

Premise ($p \rightarrow q$):	If Charles is still the prince, then Juliet is still the queen.
Premise ($\sim q$):	Juliet is no longer the queen.
Conclusion ($\sim p$):	Charles is no longer the prince.

A Test of Validity by Truth Values

We can test the validity of this argument by assigning truth values to show us that true premises must lead to a true conclusion.

1. The simplest premise in this argument is $\sim q$. We show that $\sim q$ is true by writing T above the premise $\sim q$.

2. When $\sim q$ is true, *q* must be false. Since *q* is false in the second premise, we must label *q* as false in the first premise.

3. The conditional premise $p \rightarrow q$ must also be true. From the truth table, we know that T → F is a false statement. Therefore, we cannot label *p* as true because the premise $p \rightarrow q$ would then be false. Since F → F is a *true* statement, we label *p* as false to keep the premise $p \rightarrow q$ true.

4. Finally, since *p* is false in the first premise, we know that $\sim p$ is true. This true conclusion tells us that we have a valid argument.

Defining the Law of Modus Tollens

The argument we have just tested is known by its Latin name, *Modus Tollens*. This is our third law of inference or law of reasoning.

- The *Law of Modus Tollens* states that, when two given premises are true, one a conditional and the other the negation of the conclusion of that conditional, it then follows that the negation of the hypothesis of the conditional is true. This means that, if a conditional is true and its conclusion is false, then its hypothesis is false.

The Law of Modus Tollens may be written symbolically in either of two ways:

$$\begin{array}{c} p \to q \\ \sim q \\ \hline \therefore \sim p \end{array}$$
   or $$[(p \to q) \land \sim q] \to \sim p$$

An Equivalence in Logic

The following two examples reveal an interesting equivalence in logic. In both cases, we start with the premises $p \to q$ and $\sim q$.

	Step 1 Contrapositive	Step 2 Detachment		Modus Tollens
$p \to q$ $\sim q$	$\sim q \to \sim p$ $\sim q$	$\sim q \to \sim p$ $\sim q$ $\therefore \sim p$	or	$p \to q$ $\sim q$ $\therefore \sim p$

- Applying the Law of Modus Tollens is equivalent to applying both the Law of the Contrapositive and the Law of Detachment to a set of premises.

Thus, in a logic proof, Modus Tollens can be used as a single step to replace the two steps taken when applying *both* the Law of the Contrapositive and the Law of Detachment.

EXAMPLE

Given the premises: If Al does not study, then he will fail.
                         Al did not fail.

Prove the conclusion: Al studied.

Solution A formal proof is given here, after assigning variables to the statements and rewriting our premises and conclusion in symbolic form.

Let s represent "Al studied."
Let f represent "Al failed."

Given: $\sim s \rightarrow f$
$\sim f$

Prove: s

Statements	Reasons
1. $\sim s \rightarrow f$	1. Given.
2. $\sim f$	2. Given.
3. s	3. Law of Modus Tollens (steps 1 and 2).

Thus, we have proved s: "Al studied."

Compare this example with Example 2 in Section 2-5 to see that there are different ways to do the same proof.

EXERCISES WITH OPEN-RESPONSE PROBLEMS

In 1–4, apply the Law of Modus Tollens to each given set of premises to reach a valid conclusion.

1. $a \rightarrow b$
$\underline{\sim b}$

2. $\sim p \rightarrow t$
$\underline{\sim t}$

3. $k \rightarrow \sim n$
$\underline{n}$

4. $\sim r \rightarrow \sim q$
$\underline{q}$

In 5–7, select the *numeral* preceding the choice that best answers the question.

5. "If I am tired, then I sleep. I am not sleeping." Which is a valid conclusion from this given set of premises?
(1) I am tired.   (2) I am sleeping.   (3) I am not tired.   (4) I just woke up.

6. "If the temperature in my room is above 80°, the air conditioner will go on. The air conditioner is not on." Which best describes the temperature in my room?
(1) It is going up.   (2) It is going down.   (3) It is above 80°.   (4) It is not above 80°.

7. *Premises:* Perpendicular lines form right angles.
$\angle ABC$ is an obtuse angle.

Which of the following statements is a valid conclusion?
(1) $\overline{AB}$ is perpendicular to $\overline{CB}$.
(2) $\angle ABC$ is a right angle.
(3) $\overline{AB}$ is not perpendicular to $\overline{CB}$.
(4) There is no valid conclusion.

In 8–11, write a valid conclusion for each given set of premises.

8. If I am smart, then I like chemistry.
   I do not like chemistry.
9. If both pairs of opposite sides of a quadrilateral are parallel, then the quadrilateral is a parallelogram.
   Quadrilateral *ABCD* is not a parallelogram.
10. Stacey will come to the party if her mother lets her.
   Stacey does not come to the party.
11. If *x* is an even prime number, then *x* = 2.
   x = 3.

In 12–16, write a valid conclusion for each given set of premises or indicate that no conclusion is possible.

12. If it doesn't rain, then Kristen will go swimming this weekend.
   Kristen does not go swimming this weekend.
13. I'll be there when you call my name.
   I'm not there.
14. If Bob wakes up early, then he will walk to school.
   Bob did not wake up early.
15. If I fill up this notebook, then I must buy another notebook.
   I must buy another notebook.
16. If today is Friday, then tomorrow is not a school day.
   Today is Friday.

In 17–21, in each case write a formal proof involving statements and reasons to show that the conclusion must follow from the given set of premises. (In 19–21, write all statements in symbolic form using the given variables.)

17. *Given:* $r \rightarrow t$
   $\sim t$
   Prove: $\sim r$

18. *Given:* $\sim m \rightarrow e$
   $\sim e$
   Prove: m

19. *Given:* If the tickets are sold out, then we'll wait for the next show.
   We do not wait for the next show.

   Prove: The tickets were not sold out.
   (Let *t* represent "The tickets are sold out.")
   (Let *w* represent "We'll wait for the next show.")

20. *Given:* The scale is broken if Sal weighs less than 150 pounds.
   The scale is not broken.

   Prove: Sal does not weigh less than 150 pounds.
   (Let *b* represent "The scale is broken.")
   (Let *w* represent "Sal weighs less than 150 pounds.")

21. *Given:* You can take driver's education if you're a senior.

You can't take driver's education this year.

Prove: You are not a senior this year.

(Let *D* represent "You can take driver's education.")

(Let *S* represent "You are a senior.")

2-7 INVALID ARGUMENTS

At times, we may be confronted with an argument in which all of the premises are *true* but these premises do *not* always lead to a conclusion that is *true*. The conclusion could be *true* or *false*. Such an argument is called an **invalid argument**.

We will study two examples of invalid arguments only to point out that these are *incorrect* forms of reasoning.

The First Invalid Argument

We start with the premises $p \rightarrow q$ and q, both of which must be true. Therefore, we label the second premise q as true and we must also label q as true in the first premise, $p \rightarrow q$.

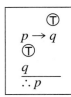

What truth value does p have? When p is true, then the premise $p \rightarrow q$ becomes T → T, which is true. However, when p is false, the premise $p \rightarrow q$ becomes F → T, which is also true. Thus, the premise $p \rightarrow q$ is true *both* when p is true and when p is false.

Since we cannot state that p is true nor can we state that it is false, this argument is invalid.

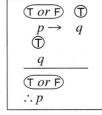

Invalid Argument

Let us consider an example of this *invalid* argument.

$p \rightarrow q$:	If I oversleep, then I'll be late for school.
q:	I am late for school.
$\therefore p$:	I overslept.

While it is possible that I did oversleep, it is also possible that I did *not* oversleep. Perhaps I was late because the bus was delayed or I took too long to walk to school. In other words, we cannot conclude that "I overslept" is true.

The Second Invalid Argument

We start with the premises $p \rightarrow q$ and $\sim p$, both of which must be true. Since $\sim p$ is true, it follows that p must be false. We label p as false in the first premise and $\sim p$ as true in the second premise.

What truth value does q have? Since F $\rightarrow$ T is true and F $\rightarrow$ F is true, we realize that the premise $p \rightarrow q$ will be true *both* when q is true and when q is false. If q can be true or false, then $\sim q$ can also be true or false.

Since we cannot state that $\sim q$ is true nor can we state that it is false, this argument is invalid.

Invalid Argument

Let us consider an example of this *invalid* argument.

$p \rightarrow q$:	"If $x = 10$, then x is greater than 5."
$\sim p$:	"$x \neq 10$."
$\therefore \sim q$:	"x is not greater than 5."

The second premise tells us only that $x \neq 10$. If $x = 3$, it is *true* that 3 is not greater than 5. But if $x = 8$, it is *false* that 8 is not greater than 5. In other words, we cannot conclude that $\sim q$, which means x is not greater than 5, is true nor can we conclude that it is false.

EXAMPLES

In 1–4, if the argument is valid, state in each case the law of reasoning that tells why the conclusion is true. If the argument is invalid, write *Invalid*.

1. $p \rightarrow q$	**2.** $p \rightarrow q$	**3.** $p \rightarrow q$	**4.** $p \rightarrow q$
p	$\sim p$	q	$\sim q$
$\therefore q$	$\therefore \sim q$	$\therefore p$	$\therefore \sim p$

Answers:

1. Valid by the Law of Detachment

2. Invalid

3. Invalid

4. Valid by the Law of Modus Tollens

EXERCISES WITH OPEN-RESPONSE PROBLEMS

In 1–12, if the argument is valid, state in each case the law of reasoning that tells why the conclusion is true. If the argument is not valid, write *Invalid*.

1. $r \rightarrow t$
$\underline{r}$
$\therefore t$

2. $k \rightarrow m$
$\underline{\sim k}$
$\therefore \sim m$

3. $a \rightarrow b$
$\underline{b}$
$\therefore a$

4. $p \rightarrow k$
$\underline{\sim k}$
$\therefore \sim p$

5. $\sim p \rightarrow q$
$\underline{\sim p}$
$\therefore q$

6. $\sim p \rightarrow q$
$\underline{q}$
$\therefore \sim p$

7. $\sim p \rightarrow \sim q$
$\underline{q}$
$\therefore p$

8. $\sim p \rightarrow \sim q$
$\underline{\sim q}$
$\therefore \sim p$

9. $k \rightarrow t$
$\underline{\sim k}$
$\therefore \sim t$

10. $k \rightarrow t$
$\underline{\sim t}$
$\therefore \sim k$

11. $k \rightarrow \sim t$
$\underline{t}$
$\therefore \sim k$

12. $k \rightarrow \sim t$
$\underline{k}$
$\therefore \sim t$

In 13–17, select the *numeral* preceding the choice that best answers the question. Explain your answers.

13. Which of the following is an *invalid* argument?
  (1) $[(a \rightarrow b) \wedge b] \rightarrow a$
  (3) $[(e \rightarrow f) \wedge e] \rightarrow f$
  (2) $[(c \rightarrow d) \wedge \sim d] \rightarrow \sim c$
  (4) $[(g \rightarrow \sim h) \wedge h] \rightarrow \sim g$

14. Which of the following is an *invalid* argument?
  (1) $[(p \rightarrow \sim t) \wedge p] \rightarrow \sim t$
  (3) $[(p \rightarrow \sim t) \wedge t] \rightarrow \sim p$
  (2) $[(p \rightarrow \sim t) \wedge \sim t] \rightarrow p$
  (4) $[(\sim p \rightarrow t) \wedge \sim t] \rightarrow p$

15. Given these true statements: "If Fred catches fish today, then he will give me some" and "Fred will give me some fish." Which statement must be true?
  (1) Fred will not give me some fish.
  (3) Fred will catch some fish today.
  (2) Fred will not catch some fish today.
  (4) No conclusion is possible.

16. Assume that the statement "People who read well get good grades in school" is true. Which true statement leads to a valid conclusion?
  (1) Kathy gets good grades in school. Therefore, Kathy reads well.
  (2) Jeanne does not read well. Therefore, Jeanne does not get good grades in school.
  (3) Debbie reads well. Therefore, Debbie gets good grades in school.
  (4) If Jimmy gets good grades in school, then Jimmy reads well.

17. Assume that the statement "All geniuses have studied geometry" is true. Which true statement leads to a valid conclusion?
  (1) Karla has studied geometry; therefore, Karla is a genius.
  (2) Lou has not studied geometry; therefore, Lou is not a genius.
  (3) Jonathon is not a genius; therefore, Jonathon has not studied geometry.
  (4) If David studies geometry, then David is a genius.

In 18–24, state whether each argument is valid or invalid. Explain your reasoning.

18. The winner of the Most Valuable Player award gets a trophy.
Cathy Florio won a trophy.
Conclusion: Cathy Florio won the Most Valuable Player award.

19. If x is an integer, then it is a real number.
x is a real number.
Conclusion: x is an integer.

20. If x is an integer, then it is a real number.
x is not an integer.
Conclusion: x is not a real number.

21. A shopper saves money if he uses coupons at the store.
Tom Hunter uses coupons at the store.
Conclusion: Tom Hunter saves money.

22. If the radio is loud, then you cannot hear the phone ring.
The radio is not loud.
Conclusion: You can hear the phone ring.

23. An acute angle has a degree measure between 0 and 90.
$m\angle ABC = 130$.
Conclusion: $\angle ABC$ is not an acute angle.

24. I take off my shoes when I get home.
I am not home.
Conclusion: I do not take off my shoes.

In 25–34, write a valid conclusion for the given set of premises. If no valid conclusion is possible, write *No conclusion.* Explain your reasoning.

25. If you are honest, then you'll keep your word.
You are not honest.
26. If David auditions, then he will get a role in the play.
David auditions.
27. If Jennifer practices, then she will be a good musician.
Jennifer is a good musician.
28. If Joe gets sick, then he will visit the doctor.
Joe does not get sick.
29. If Joe gets sick, then he will visit the doctor.
Joe does not visit the doctor.
30. If two angles are straight angles, then they are congruent.
$\angle ABC$ and $\angle RST$ are not straight angles.
31. If two angles are straight angles, then they are congruent.
$\angle ABC$ is congruent to $\angle RST$.

32. If two angles are straight angles, then they are congruent.

∠*ABC* and ∠*RST* are both straight angles.

33. You can use a pencil if your pen runs out of ink.

You use a pencil.

34. Thrifty people save money.

Mrs. Melendy does not save money.

2-8 THE CHAIN RULE

A common form of reasoning uses *many* conditional statements in an argument. We will limit our premises to two conditional statements in the following example.

Let *p* represent "It's spring," let *q* represent "Flowers blossom," and let *r* represent "I get allergies."

Premise ($p \rightarrow q$):	If it's spring, then flowers blossom.
Premise ($q \rightarrow r$):	If flowers blossom, then I get allergies.
Conclusion ($p \rightarrow r$):	If it's spring, then I get allergies.

It is difficult to demonstrate the validity of this argument by assigning truth values to the variables *p*, *q*, and *r* because there are many possible arrangements. The validity of this argument may be demonstrated by constructing a truth table. Here, a truth table of eight lines is necessary to show all possible assignments of truth values to *p*, *q*, and *r*. To test the validity of the argument we are considering:

$$\text{If } (p \rightarrow q) \text{ and } (q \rightarrow r), \text{ then } (p \rightarrow r),$$

we must show that $[(p \rightarrow q) \wedge (q \rightarrow r)] \rightarrow (p \rightarrow r)$ is a tautology. Once the truth table is constructed as an exercise, we may conclude that the argument is valid.

Defining the Chain Rule

The argument we have just discussed is our fourth law of inference, commonly known as the *Chain Rule*.

- *The Chain Rule* states that, when two given premises are true conditionals such that the consequent of the first is the antecedent of the second, it follows that the conclusion, a conditional formed using the antecedent of the first and the consequent of the second premise, is true.

The Chain Rule may be written symbolically in either of two ways:

$$\begin{array}{l} p \rightarrow q \\ \underline{q \rightarrow r} \\ \therefore p \rightarrow r \end{array}$$

or

$$[(p \rightarrow q) \wedge (q \rightarrow r)] \rightarrow (p \rightarrow r)$$

The Chain Rule is sometimes referred to as the *Law of the Syllogism*.

Applications of the Chain Rule

The Chain Rule not only plays an important role in everyday thinking but also is vital to every branch of mathematics.

In *algebra*, we use the Chain Rule to solve equations.

$p \rightarrow q$:   If $2x + 5 = 13$, then $2x = 8$.

$\underline{q \rightarrow r\text{:}\quad \text{If } 2x = 8, \text{ then } x = 4.}$

$\therefore p \rightarrow r$:   If $2x + 5 = 13$, then $x = 4$.

We use the Chain Rule when doing any process involving multiple steps, such as this example in *statistics*.

$p \rightarrow q$:   If given 5, 8, and 14, then their sum is 27.

$\underline{q \rightarrow r\text{:}\quad \text{If the sum of three numbers is 27, then their mean average is 9.}}$

$\therefore p \rightarrow r$:   If given 5, 8, and 14, then their mean average is 9.

We will use the Chain Rule in almost every *geometry* proof in later chapters. Here is one example.

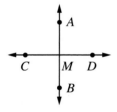

$p \rightarrow q$:   If $\overleftrightarrow{AB} \perp \overleftrightarrow{CD}$ at point M, then $\angle AMC$ and $\angle AMD$ are right angles.

$\underline{q \rightarrow r\text{:}\quad \text{If } \angle AMC \text{ and } \angle AMD \text{ are right angles, then } \angle AMC \cong \angle AMD.}$

$\therefore p \rightarrow r$:   If $\overleftrightarrow{AB} \perp \overleftrightarrow{CD}$ at point M, then $\angle AMC \cong \angle AMD$.

EXAMPLES

1. Given the premises: If I am invited, then I will go to the party.
                         If I do not buy a gift, then I will not go to the party.

Write *two* logical conclusions for this set of premises.

Solution   We assign variables to represent the statements made.

Let i represent "I am invited."
Let p represent "I will go to the party."
Let g represent "I buy a gift."

The premises written in symbolic form are:

$$i \rightarrow p$$
$$\sim g \rightarrow \sim p$$

In our first argument we change the second premise, $\sim g \rightarrow \sim p$, to its contrapositive, $p \rightarrow g$. Then, using the Chain Rule with the premises $i \rightarrow p$ and $p \rightarrow g$, we conclude $i \rightarrow g$.

$i \rightarrow p$	$i \rightarrow p$
$\sim g \rightarrow \sim p$	$p \rightarrow g$
	$\therefore i \rightarrow g$

In our next argument, we change the first premise, $i \rightarrow p$, to its contrapositive, $\sim p \rightarrow \sim i$. Then, using the Chain Rule with the premises $\sim g \rightarrow \sim p$ and $\sim p \rightarrow \sim i$, we conclude $\sim g \rightarrow \sim i$.

$i \rightarrow p$	$\sim p \rightarrow \sim i$
$\sim g \rightarrow \sim p$	$\sim g \rightarrow \sim p$
	$\therefore \sim g \rightarrow \sim i$

Answer: $(i \rightarrow g)$ means "If I am invited, then I will buy a gift."

$(\sim g \rightarrow \sim i)$ means "If I do not buy a gift, then I am not invited."

Note that the conclusions are logically equivalent.

---

2. Given the premises: $a \rightarrow c$
$\sim a \rightarrow b$
$\sim c$

Prove the conclusion: b

Solution   There are many different ways to prove the conclusion b. Two proofs are presented here. Can you find other proofs?

Statements	*Reasons*
1. $a \rightarrow c$	1. Given.
2. $\sim a \rightarrow b$	2. Given.
3. $\sim c$	3. Given.
4. $\sim c \rightarrow \sim a$	4. Law of the Contrapositive (1).
5. $\sim c \rightarrow b$	5. Chain Rule (4, 2).
6. b	6. Law of Detachment (5, 3).

Statements	Reasons
1. $a \rightarrow c$	1. Given.
2. $\sim a \rightarrow b$	2. Given.
3. $\sim c$	3. Given.
4. $\sim a$	4. Law of Modus Tollens (1, 3).
5. b	5. Law of Detachment (2, 4).

EXERCISES WITH OPEN-RESPONSE PROBLEMS

In 1–10, apply the Chain Rule to each given set of premises to write a valid conclusion.

1. $a \rightarrow b$
$\underline{b \rightarrow c}$

2. $e \rightarrow f$
$\underline{f \rightarrow \sim g}$

3. $p \rightarrow q$
$\underline{t \rightarrow p}$

4. $\sim r \rightarrow m$
$\underline{p \rightarrow \sim r}$

5. If today is Monday, then I go to school.
If I go to school, then I have homework.

6. If $9 - 2x > 3$, then $-2x > -6$.
If $-2x > -6$, then $x < 3$.

7. If Edgar is tired, then he sleeps.
If Edgar works hard, then he is tired.

8. If Phil is not on time, then he will be fired.
If Phil is fired, then Trude will get his job.

9. My parents are happy when I get good grades.
I go out on weekends when my parents are happy.

10. If I live in New York City, then I live in New York State.
If I live in New York State, then I live near the Atlantic Ocean.

In 11–17, state whether each argument is valid or invalid. Explain your answers.

11. $p \rightarrow \sim t$
$\underline{\sim t \rightarrow \sim q}$
$\therefore p \rightarrow \sim q$

12. $r \rightarrow k$
$\underline{k \rightarrow m}$
$\therefore m \rightarrow r$

13. $a \rightarrow \sim p$
$\underline{\sim b \rightarrow p}$
$\therefore a \rightarrow b$

14. $a \rightarrow x$
$\underline{b \rightarrow x}$
$\therefore a \rightarrow b$

15. If Carissa Sue is a child, then she will grow taller.
If Carissa Sue will grow taller, then she is not an adult.
Conclusion: If Carissa Sue is a child, then she is not an adult.

16. If Gary is tall, then regular clothes do not fit him.
If regular clothes do not fit Gary, then he goes to a special clothing store.
Conclusion: If Gary goes to a special clothing store, then he is tall.

17. If a plant blooms, it is well nourished.
If a plant is not watered, it is not well nourished.
Conclusion: If a plant blooms, it has been watered.

In 18–21, select the *numeral* preceding the choice that best answers the question or completes the statement.

18. If $a \to b$ and $d \to \sim b$, then it logically follows that

    (1) $a \to d$ (2) $b \to a$ (3) $d \to a$ (4) $a \to \sim d$

19. Given $r \to t$ and $\sim s \to \sim t$. Which is a valid conclusion?

    (1) $r \to s$ (2) $\sim s \to r$ (3) $\sim t \to r$ (4) $r \to \sim s$

20. Which is logically concluded from the true statements "If I drive a smaller car, I will use less gas" and "If I use less gas, I will save money"?

    (1) If I use less gas, I will drive a smaller car.

    (2) If I drive a smaller car, I will save money.

    (3) If I save money, then I drive a smaller car.

    (4) If I do not drive a smaller car, I will not use less gas.

21. Which conclusion logically follows from the true statements "If we ruin our rivers, the fish will die" and "If we pollute, we ruin our rivers"?

    (1) If the fish die, then we pollute.

    (2) If we do not pollute, the fish will not die.

    (3) If we pollute, the fish will die.

    (4) If we do not pollute, we do not ruin our rivers.

In 22–27, write a valid conclusion for each given set of premises.

22. $r \to q$ **23.** $p \to t$ **24.** $\sim r \to s$ **25.** $k \to q$

   $\underline{q \to p}$ $\underline{\sim r \to \sim t}$ $\underline{m \to \sim s}$ $\underline{p \to \sim q}$

26. If I take math, then I will study logic.

    If I study logic, then I can think clearly.

27. If Mr. Beller is late, then he drives to work.

    If Mr. Beller is not late, then he walks to work.

In 28–34, for each given set of premises, write a valid conclusion in the form of a conditional statement, or write *No conclusion* to indicate that a valid conclusion is not possible.

28. $p \to q$ **29.** $p \to q$ **30.** $p \to q$ **31.** $\sim p \to r$

   $\underline{r \to p}$ $\underline{r \to q}$ $\underline{p \to r}$ $\underline{\sim r \to t}$

32. If it's period 3, then I have history.

    If I have English, then I don't have history.

33. I bleed if I get cut.

    If I get cut, then I need a bandage.

34. Ricardo buys a pumpkin if it's Halloween.

    If it's Election Day, Ricardo does not buy a pumpkin.

35. On a separate paper, copy the proof shown and provide the reasons needed for each step.

		Statements		Reasons
Given:	$b \to c$	1. $b \to c$	1.	_____
	$\sim d \to \sim c$	2. $\sim d \to \sim c$	2.	_____
	$\sim d$	3. $\sim d$	3.	_____
Prove:	$\sim b$	4. $c \to d$	4.	_____
		5. $b \to d$	5.	_____
		6. $\sim b$	6.	_____

In 36–38, in each case write a formal proof to show that the conclusion must follow from the given set of premises. Include statements and reasons.

36. *Given:* $a \to m$
        $m \to t$
        a
Prove: t

37. *Given:* $h \to w$
        $x \to \sim w$
        x
Prove: $\sim h$

38. *Given:* $p \to q$
        $r \to p$
        $q \to k$
Prove: $r \to k$

In 39–42, let w represent "I walk," let r represent "I run," let c represent "I collapse," and let b represent "I am out of breath."

  a. Using $w, r, c, b,$ and the proper logic connectives, express each of the given premises in symbolic form.

  b. Using laws of inference, present a formal proof to show that each conclusion is true.

39. When I walk, I do not run.
When I do not run, I do not get out of breath.
Conclusion: When I walk, I do not get out of breath.

40. When I don't walk, I run.
I get out of breath if I run.
I am not out of breath.
Conclusion: I am walking.

41. If I run, I collapse.
If I am not out of breath, then I do not collapse.
I run.
Conclusion: I am out of breath.

42. If I walk, then I don't run.
I do not collapse if I don't run.
I collapse if I am out of breath.
Conclusion: If I walk, then I am not out of breath.

2-9 THE LAW OF DISJUNCTIVE INFERENCE

In the first four laws of inference presented, one (or more) of the premises was in the form of a conditional statement, $p \rightarrow q$. In this next inference law, there are no conditional statements in the given premises.

As we watch a mystery show on television, we believe that the criminal is either the butler or the strange neighbor. We then discover a clue that rules out the neighbor. We can now infer that the butler did it!

Let b represent "The butler is the criminal," and let n represent "The neighbor is the criminal." In words and in symbols, we say:

Premise $(b \lor n)$: The butler is the criminal, or the neighbor is the criminal.
Premise $(\sim n)$: The neighbor is not the criminal.

Conclusion (b): The butler is the criminal.

A Test of Validity by Truth Values

We start with the premises $b \lor n$ and $\sim n$, both of which must be true. Since $\sim n$ is true, it follows that n must be false. We label n as false in the first premise and $\sim n$ as true in the second premise.

The first premise $b \lor n$ is a disjunction. We realize that b cannot be false since $F \lor F$ would give us a false premise. Since $b \lor n$ is true, we must label b as true in the first premise. It follows that b is also true in our conclusion.

Defining the Law of Disjunctive Inference

This fifth law of reasoning, or inference law, is called the *Law of Disjunctive Inference* because a disjunction is one of the premises.

● The *Law of Disjunctive Inference* states that, when two given premises are true, one a disjunction and the other the negation of one of the disjuncts, it then follows that the other disjunct is true.

The Law of Disjunctive Inference is written symbolically in either of two ways:

$p \lor q$	$p \lor q$
$\sim q$	$\sim p$
$\therefore p$	$\therefore q$

or

$$[(p \lor q) \land \sim q] \rightarrow p$$
$$[(p \lor q) \land \sim p] \rightarrow q$$

EXAMPLES

1. Given the premises: $p \lor {\sim}q$
$${\sim}p$$

Write a valid conclusion for this set of premises.

Solution   Since ${\sim}p$ is true, we know that p is false. Apply the Law of Disjunctive Inference, using the premise $p \lor {\sim}q$, and conclude ${\sim}q$ is true.

Answer: ${\sim}q$

---

2. Given the following sentences:
(*1*) Either Peter joined the baseball team or he sings in the chorus.
(*2*) If he sings in the chorus, he will need a white shirt.
(*3*) If he needs a white shirt, then he cannot save his money.
(*4*) He saves his money.

Let B represent: "Peter joined the baseball team."
Let C represent: "He sings in the chorus."
Let W represent: "He needs a white shirt."
Let M represent: "He saves his money."

a. Using B, C, W, M, and the proper logic connectives, express each sentence in symbolic form.
b. Using laws of inference, show that Peter joined the baseball team.

Solutions   **a.** (*1*) $B \lor C$ (*2*) $C \rightarrow W$ (*3*) $W \rightarrow {\sim}M$ (*4*) M
b. Many proofs are possible. One is presented here.

Statements	*Reasons*
1. $B \lor C$	1. Given.
2. $C \rightarrow W$	2. Given.
3. $W \rightarrow {\sim}M$	3. Given.
4. M	4. Given.
5. $C \rightarrow {\sim}M$	5. Chain Rule (2, 3).
6. ${\sim}C$	6. Modus Tollens (5, 4).
7. B	7. Law of Disjunctive Inference (1, 6).

Therefore, we have proved B: Peter joined the baseball team.

EXERCISES WITH OPEN-RESPONSE PROBLEMS

In 1–7, apply the Law of Disjunctive Inference to each given set of premises to write a valid conclusion.

1. $a \lor b$ **2.** $k \lor \sim m$ **3.** $k \lor \sim m$ **4.** $\sim p \lor q$

$\underline{\sim a}$ $\underline{\sim k}$ $\underline{m}$ $\underline{\sim q}$

5. We'll go to the movies or we'll go bowling.
We won't go to the movies.
6. Mrs. McGurn has coffee or tea at every meal.
Mrs. McGurn does not have coffee at dinner.
7. Grace studies or she does not pass her test.
Grace passes her test.

In 8–14, state whether each argument is valid or invalid. Explain your answers.

8. $r \lor k$ **9.** $r \lor k$ **10.** $\sim p \lor t$ **11.** $\sim p \lor t$

$\underline{\sim r}$ $\underline{r}$ $\underline{\sim t}$ $\underline{p}$

$\therefore k$ $\therefore \sim k$ $\therefore p$ $\therefore t$

12. Either Abbie or Kate will win the award.
Abbie will not win the award.
Conclusion: Kate will win the award.
13. Ted hits a home run or his team does not win the game.
Ted's team does not win the game.
Conclusion: Ted did not hit a home run.
14. The stereo was defective or you were not careful in handling it.
The stereo was defective.
Conclusion: You were careful in handling the stereo.

In 15–18, write a valid conclusion for each given set of premises. Explain your answers.

15. Either the key fits or we won't get in.
The key does not fit.
16. The shoes I buy hurt my feet or they don't look good.
I just bought shoes that look good.
17. Points are on the same line or they are noncollinear.
Points A, B, and C are not on the same line.
18. An integer is even or odd.
3 is not an even integer.

In 19–22, write a valid conclusion for each given set of premises or write *No conclusion* to indicate that no conclusion is possible. Explain your answers.

19. Paul is tall or Mort is short.
Paul is not tall.

20. Either it rains in April or flowers will not grow in May.
It did not rain in April.

21. Carl listens to the radio or he cannot do his homework.
Carl cannot do his homework.

22. In isosceles $\triangle ABC$, $AB = BC$ or $AB = AC$.
In isosceles $\triangle ABC$, $AB \neq AC$.

In 23–25, use laws of inference to prove that each conclusion is true. Include statements and reasons in your formal proofs.

23. *Given:* $q \rightarrow r$
  $p \vee q$
  $\sim p$
Prove: r

24. *Given:* $c \rightarrow b$
  $a \vee \sim b$
  c
Prove: a

25. *Given:* $p \rightarrow (q \vee t)$
  p
  $\sim q$
Prove: t

26. Four persons are standing on line. The following facts are true:
Don is first or Nancy is second.
If Nancy is second, then Chris is third.
If Chris is third, then Pattie is fourth.
Pattie is not fourth.

Let D represent "Don is first," let N represent "Nancy is second," let C represent "Chris is third," and let P represent "Pattie is fourth."

a. Using D, N, C, P, and proper logic connectives, express each of the four facts as a sentence in symbolic form.
b. Using laws of inference, prove that Don is first.

27. Given the following statements:
Ron diets or he spends money.
If Ron diets, he loses weight.
If Ron goes to restaurants, he does not lose weight.
Ron goes to restaurants.

Let D represent "Ron diets," let S represent "Ron spends money," let L represent "Ron loses weight," and let R represent "Ron goes to restaurants."

a. Using D, S, L, R, and proper connectives, express each of the statements in symbolic form.
b. Using laws of inference, prove that Ron spends money.

28. Given the following sentences:

John will buy a stereo or a tape unit.

If John buys a stereo, he will build a cabinet for it.

John will quit his job if he builds a stereo cabinet.

If John buys a tape unit, he will need cassettes.

John does not quit his job.

Let *S* represent "John buys a stereo," let *T* represent "John buys a tape unit," let *B* represent "John builds a stereo cabinet," let *J* represent "John quits his job," and let *C* represent "John will need cassettes."

a. Using *S*, *T*, *B*, *J*, *C*, and proper connectives, express each of the sentences in symbolic form.

b. Using laws of inference, prove that John will need cassettes.

2-10 NEGATIONS AND DE MORGAN'S LAWS

In many of the arguments we have studied, we have made use of a law of inference without actually stating it by name. Let us compare the first form of each argument to the second (and much easier) form that we have been using.

1. By the Contrapositive, $\sim p \rightarrow q$ implies that $\sim q \rightarrow \sim(\sim p)$.
We have been saying that $\sim p \rightarrow q$ implies that $\sim q \rightarrow p$.

2. By Modus Tollens, $[(\sim p \rightarrow q) \wedge \sim q]$ implies $\sim(\sim p)$.
We have been saying that $[(\sim p \rightarrow q) \wedge \sim q]$ implies p.

In preceding work, we have simply said that, when $\sim p$ is false, it follows that p is true. We may also say that, when $\sim p$ is false, then $\sim(\sim p)$ is true. These examples illustrate our sixth law of inference, the *Law of the Double Negation*.

The Law of the Double Negation

● The *Law of the Double Negation* states that $\sim(\sim p)$ and p are logically equivalent statements.

Thus, given $\sim(\sim p)$ as a premise, we can conclude p. Or, given p as a premise, we can conclude $\sim(\sim p)$. Since $[\sim(\sim p) \rightarrow p]$ and $[p \rightarrow \sim(\sim p)]$, we can write the biconditional statement $\sim(\sim p) \leftrightarrow p$, which displays the logical equivalence.

The truth table below verifies that $\sim(\sim p)$ and p are logically equivalent by showing that $\sim(\sim p) \leftrightarrow p$ is a tautology.

p	$\sim p$	$\sim(\sim p)$	$\sim(\sim p) \leftrightarrow p$
T	F	T	T
F	T	F	T

In this book, the Law of the Double Negation is not required as a reason in a proof. We simply follow the easier forms we have been using by writing p in place of $\sim(\sim p)$.

De Morgan's Laws

The next two laws of inference were discovered by an English mathematician named De Morgan, and they bear his name. These inference rules tell how to negate a conjunction and how to negate a disjunction. Consider this example of a conjunction and its negation.

$(m \wedge s)$: Sy studies math *and* science.

$\sim(m \wedge s)$: It is *not* true that Sy studies math *and* science.

Is there a simpler way to express the second statement involving the negation? We know that Sy does not study both subjects. However, we cannot say that Sy does not study math *and* that he does not study science. It is possible that he does study one of these subjects. We can say only that Sy does not study math *or* he does not study science.

$\sim m \vee \sim s$: Sy does not study math *or* he does not study science.

Let us demonstrate that the statements $\sim(m \wedge s)$ and $\sim m \vee \sim s$ are logically equivalent by constructing a truth table.

			Col. 4			Col. 7	Col. 8
m	s	$m \wedge s$	$\sim(m \wedge s)$	$\sim m$	$\sim s$	$\sim m \vee \sim s$	$\sim(m \wedge s) \leftrightarrow [\sim m \vee \sim s]$
T	T	T	F	F	F	F	T
T	F	F	T	F	T	T	T
F	T	F	T	T	F	T	T
F	F	F	T	T	T	T	T

By examining the truth values for $\sim(m \wedge s)$ in column 4 and the truth values for $\sim m \vee \sim s$ in column 7, we see that the statements are logically equivalent. We also see that the biconditional statement $\sim(m \wedge s) \leftrightarrow [\sim m \vee \sim s]$ in column 8 is a tautology.

A similar equivalence can be found for the negation of a disjunction. Consider the following example.

$(G \vee P)$: I will take Gloria *or* Patricia to the dance.

$\sim(G \vee P)$: It is *not* true that I will take Gloria *or* Patricia to the dance.

$\sim G \wedge \sim P$: I will *not* take Gloria to the dance *and* I will *not* take Patricia to the dance.

If I am not taking Gloria *or* Patricia to the dance, it follows that I am not taking Gloria *and* I am not taking Patricia. The statements $\sim(G \vee P)$ and $\sim G \wedge \sim P$ are logically equivalent. This can be verified by a truth table, the construction of which is left to the student as an exercise.

- **De Morgan's Laws** state that:

1. The negation of a conjunction of two statements is logically equivalent to the disjunction of the negation of each of the two statements.
2. The negation of a disjunction of two statements is logically equivalent to the conjunction of the negation of each of the two statements.

These laws of inference are more easily understood in symbolic form:

$$1. \ \sim(p \wedge q) \leftrightarrow (\sim p \vee \sim q)$$
$$2. \ \sim(p \vee q) \leftrightarrow (\sim p \wedge \sim q)$$

EXAMPLES

1. What is the negation of $\sim p \vee q$?

Solution   Indicate the negation of the compound sentence as $\sim(\sim p \vee q)$.
Apply De Morgan's Law by negating both $\sim p$ and q, and by changing the disjunction to a conjunction:

Answer: $p \wedge \sim q$

---

2. Given the statements: If x is positive and $x^2 = 9$, then $x = 3$.

$$x \neq 3$$
$$x^2 = 9$$

Prove the conclusion: x is not positive.

Solution   Let q represent "x is positive."

r represent "$x^2 = 9$."

p represent "$x = 3$."

Many proofs are possible. One proof is given here.

	Statements		*Reasons*
1.	$(q \land r) \to p$	1.	Given.
2.	$\sim p$	2.	Given.
3.	r	3.	Given.
4.	$\sim(q \land r)$	4.	Modus Tollens (1, 2).
5.	$\sim q \lor \sim r$	5.	De Morgan's Law (4).
6.	$\sim q$	6.	Disjunctive Inference (5, 3).

Therefore, x is not positive.   *Answer*

EXERCISES WITH OPEN-RESPONSE PROBLEMS

In 1–13, tell in each case whether the two given statements are logically equivalent or are not equivalent.

1. $\sim(\sim q)$
q

2. $\sim(\sim r)$
$\sim r$

3. $\sim(p \lor q)$
$\sim p \lor \sim q$

4. $\sim(p \land q)$
$\sim p \lor \sim q$

5. $\sim(p \land \sim q)$
$\sim p \lor q$

6. $\sim(\sim p \lor q)$
$p \land \sim q$

7. $\sim(p \land \sim q)$
$\sim p \land q$

8. $\sim p \lor \sim q$
$\sim(p \lor q)$

9. $\sim p \land \sim q$
$\sim(p \lor q)$

10. $\sim p \land q$
$\sim(p \lor \sim q)$

11. It is not true that Alice likes both vanilla and chocolate.
Alice does not like vanilla and Alice does not like chocolate.

12. It is not true that either $x = 5$ or $x > 5$.
$x \neq 5$ and x is not greater than 5.

13. I don't exercise and I am healthy.
It is false that either I exercise or I am not healthy.

In 14–17, select the *numeral* preceding the choice that best completes the statement or answers the question.

14. The statement $\sim(r \lor \sim t)$ is logically equivalent to
(1) $\sim r \lor t$ (2) $\sim r \land t$ (3) $\sim r \lor \sim t$ (4) $\sim r \land \sim t$

15. The negation of $\sim p \land k$ is
(1) $p \lor \sim k$ (2) $p \lor k$ (3) $p \land \sim k$ (4) $\sim p \lor \sim k$

16. The negation of $\sim k \lor \sim m$ is
(1) $k \land m$ (2) $k \lor m$ (3) $\sim(k \lor m)$ (4) $k \to m$

17. What is the negation of "Fred is old and Paul is not young"?
(1) Fred is not old and Paul is young.   (2) Fred is not old or Paul is not young.
(3) Fred is old or Paul is young.   (4) Fred is not old or Paul is young.

In 18–22, negate each given statement.

18. $p \land q$ **19.** $\sim p \lor q$ **20.** $\sim p \land \sim q$ **21.** $\sim(\sim p)$ **22.** $\sim p \lor \sim q$

In 23–27, write a valid conclusion for each given set of premises.

23. $\sim(\sim p \wedge t)$
$\underline{\sim p \qquad}$

24. $\sim(s \wedge \sim r)$
$\underline{\sim r \qquad}$

25. $\sim(\sim k \wedge \sim g)$
$\underline{\sim g \qquad\quad}$

26. $\sim(s \wedge t)$
$\underline{t \qquad}$

27. It is not true that I chew gum and whistle at the same time.
I am whistling.

In 28 and 29, in each case write a formal proof to show that the conclusion must follow from the given premises.

28. *Given:* $(\sim a \wedge b) \rightarrow c$
$\qquad\quad \sim c$
$\qquad\quad b$
Prove: a

29. *Given:* $t \rightarrow p$
$\qquad\quad p \rightarrow \sim(q \wedge r)$
$\qquad\quad t$
$\qquad\quad q$

$\qquad$ *Prove:* $\sim r$

30. Given the following statements:
   If I had the talent and the energy, then I could be rich.
   I am not rich.
   I have the energy.
Let T represent "I have the talent," let E represent "I have the energy," and let R represent "I am rich."

   a. Using T, E, R, and proper connectives, express each of the given statements in symbolic form.
   b. Use laws of inference to prove "I do not have the talent."

31. Given the following statements:
   If Jay earns money and is not thrifty, then he will waste money.
   If Jay saves money, then he does not waste money.
   Jay earns money.
   Jay saves money.
Let E represent "Jay earns money," let T represent "Jay is thrifty," let W represent "Jay wastes money," and let S represent "Jay saves money."

   a. Using E, T, W, S, and proper connectives, express each of the given statements in symbolic form.
   b. Use laws of inference to prove "Jay is thrifty."

2-11 THE LAWS OF SIMPLIFICATION, CONJUNCTION, AND DISJUNCTIVE ADDITION

The three laws of reasoning that we will study in this section are relatively easy to understand. Tests of validity are left to the student.

The Law of Simplification

- The *Law of Simplification* states that, when a single conjunctive premise is true, it follows that each of the individual conjuncts must be true.

The Law of Simplification is written symbolically in either of two ways:

$$\begin{array}{c|c} p \wedge q & p \wedge q \\ \hline \therefore p & \therefore q \end{array} \qquad \text{or} \qquad \boxed{\begin{array}{l} (p \wedge q) \to p \\ (p \wedge q) \to q \end{array}}$$

For example, from the premise "Mel likes to read and to play basketball," we may conclude "Mel likes to read." From this same premise, we may also conclude "Mel likes to play basketball."

The Law of Conjunction

- The *Law of Conjunction* states that, when two given premises are true, it follows that the conjunction of these premises is true.

The Law of Conjunction is written symbolically in either of two ways:

$$\boxed{\begin{array}{l} p \\ q \\ \hline \therefore p \wedge q \end{array}} \qquad \text{or} \qquad \boxed{(p) \wedge (q) \to (p \wedge q)}$$

For example, from the premises "$\overleftrightarrow{AB}$ is perpendicular to $\overline{CD}$" and "$\overleftrightarrow{AB}$ is a bisector of $\overline{CD}$," we may conclude "$\overleftrightarrow{AB}$ is perpendicular to $\overline{CD}$ *and* $\overleftrightarrow{AB}$ is a bisector of $\overline{CD}$." In later chapters this conjunctive statement will be simplified to "$\overleftrightarrow{AB}$ is the perpendicular bisector of $\overline{CD}$."

The Law of Disjunctive Addition

- The *Law of Disjunctive Addition* states that, when a single premise is true, it follows that any disjunction that has this premise as one of its disjuncts must also be true.

The Law of Disjunctive Addition is written symbolically in either of two ways:

$$\boxed{\begin{array}{l} p \\ \hline \therefore p \vee q \end{array}} \qquad \text{or} \qquad \boxed{p \to (p \vee q)}$$

For example, we solve an equation and see that the premise $x = 5$ is true. We may conclude that the statement "$x = 5$ *or* $x > 5$" is also true. In fact, any statement may be added by a disjunction to the true statement "$x = 5$." Thus, "$x = 5$ *or* I have two left feet" is also true.

EXAMPLES

1. Given the statement r, which is a valid conclusion?
  (1) $r \wedge k$ (2) $r \vee k$ (3) $r \rightarrow k$ (4) $r \leftrightarrow k$

Solution   In all four choices, r is true but the truth value of k is not known. When k is true, all four choices are correct. However, when k is false, only choice (2) remains true. This demonstrates the Law of Disjunctive Addition; that is, we may "add" a statement k to a given statement r only by using disjunction.

Answer: (2) $r \vee k$

---

2. *Given:* $p \rightarrow t$
        $p \wedge q$

   Prove: t

Solution   In the proof that follows, we must use the Law of Simplification to extract the single statement p from the conjunction $(p \wedge q)$. Then, having p by itself, we can use this premise with the conditional $(p \rightarrow t)$ to prove t.

Statements	*Reasons*
1. $p \rightarrow t$	1. Given.
2. $p \wedge q$	2. Given.
3. p	3. Law of Simplification (2).
4. $\therefore t$	4. Law of Detachment (1, 3).

EXERCISES WITH OPEN-RESPONSE PROBLEMS

In 1–4, select the *numeral* preceding the choice that best completes the statement or answers the question.

1. Given p and q, the Law of Conjunction leads to the conclusion
  (1) $p \vee q$ (2) $p \wedge q$ (3) $p \rightarrow q$ (4) $p \leftrightarrow q$

2. If $\sim m$ is the given premise, which is a valid conclusion?
  (1) $\sim m \wedge t$ (2) $\sim m \vee t$ (3) $\sim m \rightarrow t$ (4) m

3. Given $p \wedge r$, we can conclude that
  (1) $\sim p$ (2) $\sim p \wedge r$ (3) r (4) $\sim r$

4. From the premise k, a valid conclusion is
  (1) $\sim k$ (2) $k \wedge b$ (3) $k \vee b$ (4) $\sim k \vee b$

5. Use the Law of Conjunction to write a valid conclusion for the premises "Carrie likes ice cream" and "Carrie likes cookies."

6. If the given premise is "13 is odd and prime," use the Law of Simplification to write two conclusions.

7. If the given premise is "Bob grows lettuce," use the Law of Disjunctive Addition to write a conclusion.

In 8–18, tell whether each argument is valid or invalid. Explain your answers.

8. $p \rightarrow (p \wedge d)$

9. $d \rightarrow (p \vee d)$

10. $d \rightarrow (p \wedge d)$

11. $(\sim r \vee k) \rightarrow k$

12. $(\sim r \wedge k) \rightarrow k$

13. $(\sim r \wedge k) \rightarrow r$

14. $\sim(r \vee k) \rightarrow \sim k$

15. $\sim(r \wedge k) \rightarrow \sim k$

16. x is a rational number.
Conclusion: The number x is rational or irrational.

17. Mabel is famous for baking brownies or coffee cake.
Conclusion: Mabel is famous for baking brownies.

18. Mr. Bancheri is a chemistry teacher.
Conclusion: Mr. Bancheri teaches chemistry or homemaking.

In 19–22, use laws of inference to prove that each conclusion is true.

19. *Given:* $r \rightarrow t$

$r \wedge m$

$t \rightarrow k$

Prove: k

20. *Given:* $b \rightarrow c$

$c \rightarrow r$

$p \wedge \sim r$

Prove: $\sim b$

21. *Given:* $c \rightarrow p$

$\sim c \rightarrow a$

$\sim(p \vee t)$

Prove: a

22. *Given:* $p \rightarrow q$

$(r \vee s) \rightarrow p$

$\sim q$

Prove: $\sim r$

23. Given the following statements:
   If Janet will go to college, then she will get a summer job.
   If Janet goes to the beach daily, she will not get a summer job.
   Janet will go to college and medical school.

Let C represent "Janet will go to college," let S represent "Janet will get a summer job," let B represent "Janet goes to the beach daily," and let M represent "Janet will go to medical school."

   a. Using C, S, B, M, and proper logic connectives, express each given statement in symbolic form.
   b. Using laws of inference, prove that Janet does not go to the beach daily.

24. Given the following statements:
   Jesse likes baseball or football.
   Jesse likes hockey and not baseball.

Let B represent "Jesse likes baseball," let F represent "Jesse likes football," and let H represent "Jesse likes hockey."

   a. Using B, F, H, and proper logic connectives, express each given statement in symbolic form.
   b. Using laws of inference, prove that Jesse likes football.

CHAPTER SUMMARY

Logic is the study of reasoning. Logic uses the **negation** *not* and the **connectives** *and*, *or*, *if . . . then*, and *if and only if* to form new statements from simple statements that are either true or false.

A *tautology* is a statement that is always true no matter what truth values are assigned to the simple statements used to form it. The following tautologies lead to logical conclusions:

The Law of Detachment: $[(p \rightarrow q) \wedge p] \rightarrow q$

The Law of the Contrapositive: $(p \rightarrow q) \leftrightarrow (\sim q \rightarrow \sim p)$

The Law of Modus Tollens: $[(p \rightarrow q) \wedge \sim q] \rightarrow \sim p$

The Chain Rule: $[(p \rightarrow q) \wedge (q \rightarrow r)] \rightarrow (p \rightarrow r)$

The Law of Disjunctive Inference: $[(p \vee q) \wedge \sim p] \rightarrow q$ and $[(p \vee q) \wedge \sim q] \rightarrow p$

The Law of the Double Negation: $\sim(\sim p) \leftrightarrow p$

De Morgan's Laws: $\sim(p \wedge q) \leftrightarrow (\sim p \vee \sim q)$ and $\sim(p \vee q) \leftrightarrow (\sim p \wedge \sim q)$

The Law of Simplification: $(p \wedge q) \rightarrow p$ and $(p \wedge q) \rightarrow q$

The Law of Conjunction: $(p) \wedge (q) \rightarrow (p \wedge q)$

The Law of Disjunctive Addition: $p \rightarrow (p \vee q)$

VOCABULARY

2-1	Mathematical sentence	Truth value	Open sentence	Statement
	Closed sentence			
2-2	Connectives	Negation	Conjunction	Disjunction Conditional
	Biconditional	Compound statement		
2-3	Tautology	Logically equivalent	Equivalence	
	Conditional equivalence			
2-4	Argument	Premise	Conclusion	Valid argument
	Law of Detachment	Modus Ponens	Hidden conditional	
2-5	Inverse	Converse	Contrapositive	Law of the Contrapositive
	Formal proof			
2-6	Law of Modus Tollens			
2-7	Invalid argument			
2-8	Chain Rule	Law of the Syllogism		
2-9	Law of Disjunctive Inference			
2-10	Law of the Double Negation	De Morgan's Laws		
2-11	Law of Simplification	Law of Conjunction		
	Law of Disjunctive Addition			

REVIEW EXERCISES WITH OPEN-RESPONSE PROBLEMS

In 1–12, name the *inference law* that tells why each argument is valid, or state that the argument is *invalid*.

1. $p \rightarrow \sim r$
$\underline{p }$
$\therefore \sim r$

2. $q \rightarrow \sim t$
$\underline{t }$
$\therefore \sim q$

3. $b \rightarrow d$
$\underline{\sim b }$
$\therefore \sim d$

4. $a \rightarrow b$
$\underline{b \rightarrow h}$
$\therefore a \rightarrow h$

5. $r \rightarrow d$
$\underline{\sim d }$
$\therefore \sim r$

6. $m \rightarrow \sim p$
$\underline{\sim p }$
$\therefore m$

7. $p \vee t$
$\underline{\sim p }$
$\therefore t$

8. $\sim r \rightarrow k$
$\underline{\sim k }$
$\therefore \sim r$

9. $\sim q \vee p$
$\underline{q }$
$\therefore p$

10. $\underline{\sim(\sim p \wedge t)}$
$\therefore p \wedge \sim t$

11. $(r \rightarrow m) \leftrightarrow (\sim m \rightarrow \sim r)$

12. $\sim(p \vee \sim q) \leftrightarrow (\sim p \wedge q)$

In 13–20, write a valid conclusion for each given set of premises, or write *No conclusion* to indicate that a valid conclusion is not possible. Explain your answers.

13. If you live in the United States, then you do not live in Canada.
   Louise Arsena lives in the United States.
14. If you live in the United States, then you do not live in Canada.
   Pat McEntee lives in Canada.
15. If you live in the United States, then you do not live in Canada.
   Joe Fernandes does not live in Canada.
16. My mind wanders if I watch TV.
   I don't watch TV.
17. If Tyrone gets a good report card, then he can go out.
   If Tyrone fails science, then he cannot go out.
18. Mr. Cavallaro's favorite color is blue or brown.
   Mr. Cavallaro does not like the color blue.
19. If Johanna has a toothache, then she visits the dentist.
   Johanna does not have a toothache.
20. Lines that intersect at one point are not parallel lines.
   Lines k and m intersect at point P only.

In 21–28, write the *numeral* preceding the choice that best completes the statement or answers the question.

21. What is the negation of $\sim a \wedge b$?
   (1) $\sim a \vee b$ (2) $a \vee \sim b$ (3) $a \wedge \sim b$ (4) $a \wedge b$
22. What is the negation of "I run or I walk"?
   (1) I run and I walk   (2) I don't run or I don't walk.
   (3) I don't run and I walk.   (4) I don't run and I don't walk.

23. If $P \to Q$ and $\sim R \to \sim Q$, which is a valid conclusion?
    (1) $P \to R$ (2) $P \to \sim R$ (3) $\sim P \to R$ (4) $\sim P \to \sim R$

24. If $a \to b$ and $g \to \sim b$, it can be shown that
    (1) $a \to g$ (2) $g \to a$ (3) $g \to \sim a$ (4) $a \to \sim b$

25. Which is logically equivalent to $\sim K \to M$?
    (1) $K \to \sim M$ (2) $M \to \sim K$ (3) $\sim M \to \sim K$ (4) $\sim M \to K$

26. Which statement is logically equivalent to "I run if I'm late"?
    (1) If I don't run, I'm not late.   (2) I'm late if I run.
    (3) If I'm not late, I don't run.   (4) If I run, I'm late.

27. *Premises:* Every line segment has a midpoint.
                 $\overleftrightarrow{AB}$ does not have a midpoint.
    What conclusion can be inferred?
    (1) $\overleftrightarrow{AB}$ is not a line segment.
    (2) $\overleftrightarrow{AB}$ has a midpoint.
    (3) Some line segment has no midpoint.
    (4) There is no conclusion.

28. It is true that Brad likes eggs. It must then be true that
    (1) Brad likes bacon and eggs.
    (2) Brad likes bacon or eggs.
    (3) If Brad likes eggs, then he likes bacon.
    (4) If Brad likes eggs, then he does not like bacon.

29. Given the following statements:
    I can do this proof or I cannot think clearly.
    If I know logic, then I can think clearly.
    If I don't know logic, then I need help.
    I don't need help.

Let P represent "I can do this proof," let T represent "I can think clearly," let L represent "I know logic," and let H represent "I need help."

    a. Using P, T, L, H, and proper logic connectives, express each statement in symbolic form.
    b. Using laws of inference, show that I can do this proof.

30. An engineer's brother married, but the man who married had no brother. How is this possible?

31. Mrs. Brown, Mrs. White, and Mrs. Gray are a teacher, a doctor, and a lawyer, not necessarily in that order. Each has a horse. One horse is white, one is brown, and one is gray. From the following clues, determine the occupation of each woman and the color of her horse.
    No one's name is the same as the color of her horse.
    The teacher owns a brown horse.
    Mrs. Gray is a doctor.

CUMULATIVE REVIEW WITH OPEN-RESPONSE PROBLEMS

1. When Carlos turned on to the expressway, he noted that his five-digit odometer registered a palindrome. (A palindrome is a sequence of numbers or letters that reads the same from left to right as from right to left.) After driving for two hours, his odometer again registered a palindrome. During that time the odometer reading passed 36,000.
   a. What was Carlos' odometer reading at the beginning of the two hours?
   b. What was his odometer reading after two hours?
   c. What was his average speed for the two hours?

2. Choose one of the four following numbers, and explain how it is different from the others: 121   123   125   127
3. On the real number line, the coordinate of A is -2 and the coordinate of B is 6. What is the coordinate of the midpoint of $\overline{AB}$?
4. If $\overline{AB} + \overline{BC} = \overline{AC}$, what is the measure of $\angle ABC$?
5. **a.** Graph the points $A(-3, 0)$, $B(5, 0)$, and $C(1, 4)$. Draw $\triangle ABC$.
   b. Locate D, the midpoint of $\overline{AB}$ on the graph, and write its coordinates.
   c. Find AB, AC, BC, AD, DB, and CD.
   d. What kind of triangle is $\triangle ABC$?
   e. What kind of triangle is $\triangle ADC$?

Exploration

Write a logic statement that is the negation of $p \to q$. (*Hint:* Since $p \to q$ is true in three cases and false in one, the negation must be false in three cases and true in one.)

Chapter 3

Proving Statements in Geometry

A good cook prepares a meal by assembling the ingredients and then using a recipe to combine these ingredients into the desired dish.

We follow a similar plan in preparing a proof. First we assemble the ingredients—the definitions, postulates, and theorems—that will be used in the proof. Then we use a recipe—the principles of logic—to combine these ingredients into a convincing proof. Careful attention to each step is necessary for both successful cooking and successful proof. Overlooking even a minor detail can lead to poor results.

Midori was doing her homework, which involved inequalities using the squares of numbers. She made the following table:

Number	1	2	3	4	5
Square of Number	1	4	9	16	25

Midori reasoned as follows: "Since the square of the number is greater than or equal to the number and the squares are increasing faster than the numbers, I can conclude that the square of a number is always greater than or equal to the number."

Is Midori's reasoning correct? Can you find a counterexample to prove that the square of a number is not always greater than or equal to the number?

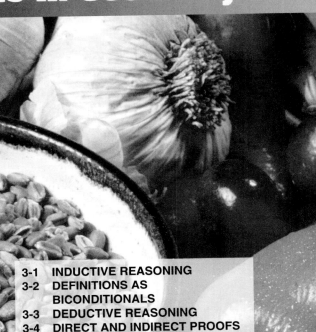

3-1 INDUCTIVE REASONING

When you study science in school, you usually perform experiments in a laboratory. By doing the experiment once, twice, even many times, you hope to arrive at a conclusion that will be a true statement. This method of reasoning, in which a series of particular examples leads to a general truth, is called *inductive reasoning*.

In geometry, you can also perform experiments that may help you to discover properties of geometric figures and to determine geometric relationships. Most of these experiments involve measurements. Because all direct measurements are *approximate*, however, results can also be only approximate. This is the first weakness in attempting to reach conclusions by inductive reasoning.

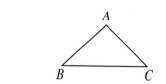

If you look at isosceles triangle *ABC*, in which the vertex angle, $\angle A$, is acute, and $\overline{AB} \cong \overline{AC}$, you may observe that the base angles, $\angle B$ and $\angle C$, appear to be congruent. To check your observation, measure $\angle B$ and $\angle C$ with a protractor. When you do, you will discover that $\angle B$ and $\angle C$ have the same degree measure. Therefore, $\angle B \cong \angle C$.

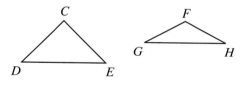

To convince yourself that this relationship is true in other isosceles triangles, draw other isosceles triangles and measure their base angles. The figures show isosceles triangle *DCE*, in which the vertex angle, $\angle C$, is a right angle, and isosceles triangle *FGH*, in which the vertex angle, $\angle F$, is obtuse. Using a protractor, you will again discover that the base angles have the same degree measure and are, therefore, congruent: $\angle D \cong \angle E$ and $\angle G \cong \angle H$.

Draw even more isosceles triangles by changing the number of degrees in the vertex angle. However, in each experiment you will find that the base angles have the same degree measure. From these experiments, you can arrive at a general conclusion: The base angles of an isosceles triangle are congruent. This is an example of *inductive reasoning* in geometry.

Suppose a student, after examining several isosceles triangles, made the generalization "all isosceles triangles are acute triangles." Here, a single *counterexample*, such as isosceles triangle *DCE*, in which $\angle C$ is a right angle, is sufficient to show that the general conclusion that the student reached is false.

When we use inductive reasoning, we must use extreme care because we are arriving at a general conclusion before we have examined every possible example. This is the second weakness in attempting to reach conclusions by inductive reasoning.

When a general conclusion is reached by inductive reasoning alone, it can at best be called probably true. Furthermore, although inductive reasoning may be a powerful aid in discovering new facts, it does not help to explain or prove them.

EXERCISES WITH OPEN-RESPONSE PROBLEMS

1. **a.** Using a computer program or a pencil, ruler, and protractor, draw three right triangles that have different sizes and shapes.
   b. In each right triangle, measure the two acute angles and find the sum of their measures.
   c. Using inductive reasoning based on the experiments just made, write a general statement about the sum of the measures of the acute angles of a right triangle.

In 2–7, plan and perform a series of experiments to investigate whether each statement is *probably true* or *false*.

2. If two lines intersect, at least one pair of congruent angles is formed.
3. The sum of the degree measures of the angles of a triangle is 180.

4. If $\frac{a}{b} < 1$, then $a < b$.

5. In any rectangle *ABCD*, such as the one shown here, $AC = BD$.
6. In any quadrilateral *DEFG*, such as the one shown here, $\overline{DF}$ bisects $\angle D$ and $\angle F$.
7. The length of the line segment that joins the midpoints of two sides of a triangle is equal to one-half the length of the third side of the triangle.

Ex. 5   **Ex. 6**

8. Adam made the following statement: "For any counting number *n*, the expression $n^2 + n + 41$ will always be equal to some prime number." He reasoned:

   When $n = 1$, then $n^2 + n + 41 = 1 + 1 + 41 = 43$, a prime number.
   When $n = 2$, then $n^2 + n + 41 = 4 + 2 + 41 = 47$, a prime number.

   Use inductive reasoning, by letting *n* be many different counting numbers, to show that Adam's generalization is probably true, or find a counterexample to show that Adam's generalization is false.

In 9–12, state in each case whether the conclusion drawn was justified.

9. One day, Ed drove home on Sunrise Highway and found traffic very heavy. He decided never again to drive on this highway on his way home.
10. Doris received an A on each of her first two math tests this term. She concluded that she would get A on every math test during the term.

11. From the angles shown, we conclude that, if the sum of two angles is a right angle, then the sum of the degree measures of the two angles is 90.
12. From the angles shown, we conclude that, if an angle is the sum of two angles, then it is a right angle.

Ex. 11–12

3-2 DEFINITIONS AS BICONDITIONALS

Inductive reasoning that is based on the examination of individual cases may contain weaknesses. The type of reasoning that is more often used combines definitions and general statements that are known to be true to prove assumptions. Before we discuss this type of reasoning, we will review the definitions from Chapter 1 that are used in the study of Euclidean geometry. We recall that Euclid did *not* use coordinates in his systematic approach to geometry.

Basic Definitions in Euclidean Geometry

A *collinear set of points* is a set of points all of which lie on the same straight line.

A *noncollinear set of points* is a set of three or more points that do not all lie on the same straight line.

The *distance between two points on the real number line* is the absolute value of the difference of the coordinates of the two points.

B is between A and C if and only if A, B, and C are distinct collinear points and $AB + BC = AC$.

A *line segment*, or *segment*, is a set of points consisting of two points on a line, called *endpoints*, and all points on the line between the endpoints.

The *length or measure of a line segment* is the distance between the endpoints.

Congruent segments are segments that have the same measure.

The *midpoint of a line segment* is the point of that line segment that divides the segment into two congruent segments.

The *bisector of a line segment* is any line or subset of a line that intersects the segment at its midpoint.

A line segment, $\overline{RS}$, is the sum of *two line segments*, $\overline{RP}$ and $\overline{PS}$, if point P is between points R and S.

Two points, A and B, are *on one side* of point P if A, B, and P are collinear and P is not between A and B.

A *ray* is a part of a line that consists of a point on the line, called an *endpoint*, and all the points on one side of the endpoint.

Opposite rays are two rays of the same line with a common endpoint and no other point in common.

An *angle* is a set of points that is the union of two rays having the same endpoint.

A *straight angle* is an angle that is the union of opposite rays.

An *acute angle* is an angle whose degree measure is greater than 0 and less than 90.

A *right angle* is an angle whose degree measure is 90.

An *obtuse angle* is an angle whose degree measure is greater than 90 and less than 180.

Congruent angles are angles that have the same measure.

A *bisector of an angle* is a ray whose endpoint is the vertex of the angle and that divides the angle into two congruent angles.

A nonstraight angle, $\angle RST$, is the sum of two angles, $\angle RSP$ and $\angle PST$, if point P is in the interior of $\angle RST$.

A *polygon* is a closed figure in a plane that is the union of line segments such that the segments intersect only at their endpoints and no segments sharing a common endpoint are collinear.

A *triangle* is a polygon that has exactly three sides.

A *scalene triangle* is a triangle that has no congruent sides.

An *isosceles triangle* is a triangle that has two congruent sides.

An *equilateral triangle* is a triangle that has three congruent sides.

An *acute triangle* is a triangle that has three acute angles.

An *equiangular triangle* is a triangle that has three congruent angles.

A *right triangle* is a triangle that has a right angle.

An *obtuse triangle* is a triangle that has an obtuse angle.

Parallel lines are lines in the same plane that have no points in common or have all points in common.

Perpendicular lines are two lines that intersect to form right angles.

Definitions and Logic

Each of the definitions listed above can be written in the form of a conditional. For example:

● **DEFINITION.** A *triangle* is a polygon that has exactly three sides.

Using the definition of a triangle, we know that:

1. The definition contains a hidden *conditional statement* and can be rewritten using the words *If . . . then* as follows:
   t: A polygon is a triangle.
   p: A polygon has exactly three sides.
   $t \to p$:   If a polygon is a triangle, then it has exactly three sides.

2. In general, the converse of a true statement is not necessarily true. However, the converse of the conditional form of a definition is always true. For example, the following converse is a true statement:
   $p \to t$: If a polygon has exactly three sides, then it is a triangle.

3. When a conditional and its converse are both true, the conjunction of these statements can be combined to write a true biconditional statement. Thus, $(t \to p) \wedge (p \to t)$ is equivalent to the biconditional $(t \leftrightarrow p)$.

Therefore, since both the conditional statement and its converse are true, we can rewrite the above definition as a biconditional statement, using the words *if and only if*, as follows:

● **DEFINITION ($t \leftrightarrow p$).** A polygon is a triangle if and only if it has exactly three sides.

The *if* tells what we must include, that is, "exactly three sides," and the *only if* tells what we must exclude, that is, "all cases that do not have exactly three sides."

This example shows us that:

●   A precise definition in mathematics is a biconditional statement.

We have taken the time to reexamine definitions from a logical viewpoint because, as we will soon see, definitions play an important role in helping to prove statements in geometry.

We can conclude that:

1. Every definition is equivalent to a conditional statement, $p \rightarrow q$, that is true, and the converse of the conditional statement, $q \rightarrow p$, that is also true.

2. Every definition may be expressed as a biconditional statement, $p \leftrightarrow q$.

EXAMPLE

Given this definition: An angle is a set of points that is the union of two rays having the same endpoint.

a. Write the definition in conditional form.
b. Write the converse of the statement given as an answer in part **a**.
c. Write the biconditional form of the definition.

Solutions   **a.** *Conditional:* If a set of points is an angle, then it is the union of two rays having the same endpoint.
b. *Converse:* If a set of points is the union of two rays having the same endpoint, then it is an angle.
c. *Biconditional:* A set of points is an angle if and only if it is the union of two rays having the same endpoint.

EXERCISES WITH OPEN-RESPONSE PROBLEMS

In 1–5:   **a.** Write each definition in conditional form.   **b.** Write the converse of the statement given as an answer in part **a**.   **c.** Write the biconditional form of the definition.

1. An *isosceles triangle* is a triangle that has two congruent sides.
2. A *bisector of an angle* is a ray whose endpoint is the vertex of the angle and that divides the angle into two congruent angles.
3. An *obtuse angle* is an angle whose degree measure is greater than 90 and less than 180.
4. An *acute triangle* is a triangle that has three acute angles.
5. A *collinear set of points* is a set of points all of which lie on the same straight line.

In 6–10, write the biconditional form of each given definition.

6. A point B *is between A and C* if A, B, and C are distinct collinear points and $AB + BC = AC$.
7. *Congruent segments* are segments that have the same length.
8. The *midpoint of a line segment* is the point of that line segment that divides the segment into two congruent segments.

9. A *scalene triangle* is a triangle that has no congruent sides.

10. A *right angle* is an angle whose degree measure is 90.

In 11–13, write the biconditional form of the definition of each given term.

11. equilateral triangle   **12.** congruent angles   **13.** perpendicular lines

3-3 DEDUCTIVE REASONING

Most proofs in geometry are very much like the proofs in logic. They are based on a series of statements that are assumed to be true, called the **premises** or the **hypotheses**.

When the laws of inference are used to link together the premises and any other true statements to arrive at a true conclusion, **deductive reasoning** is being applied. Thus, proofs in logic are all examples of deductive reasoning. The **conclusion** is sometimes called the **deduction** or the deduced statement.

Since definitions are true statements, they are used in a geometric proof. In the examples that follow, notice how the inference laws of logic are used in the proofs of geometric statements.

Comparing a Geometry Proof to a Logic Proof

Given the premise: In $\triangle ABC$, $\overline{AB} \perp \overline{BC}$.

Prove the conclusion: $\angle ABC$ is a right angle.

In this proof, use the following definition: Perpendicular lines are two lines that intersect to form right angles. This definition contains a hidden conditional and can be rewritten as follows: *If* two lines are perpendicular, *then* they intersect to form right angles.

Recall that this definition is true for perpendicular line segments as well as for perpendicular lines. Using the specific information cited above, let p represent "$\overline{AB} \perp \overline{BC}$," and let r represent "$\angle ABC$ is a right angle."

The proof is shown by the reasoning that follows:

Statements		Reasons
1. p	$(\overline{AB} \perp \overline{BC}.)$	1. Given.
2. $p \rightarrow r$	(If $\overline{AB} \perp \overline{BC}$, then $\angle ABC$ is a right angle.)	2. Definition of perpendicular lines.
3. $\therefore r$	($\angle ABC$ is a right angle.)	3. Law of Detachment (1, 2).

In the logic proof above, notice that the Law of Detachment is cited as a reason for reaching our conclusion. In a typical geometry proof, however, inference laws are used to deduce the conclusion but the inference laws are *not* listed among the reasons.

Let us restate this proof in the format used most often in Euclidean geometry.

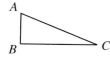

Given: In $\triangle ABC$, $\overline{AB} \perp \overline{BC}$.

Prove: $\angle ABC$ is a right angle.

Statements	Reasons
1. $\overline{AB} \perp \overline{BC}$.	1. Given.
2. $\angle ABC$ is a right angle.	2. Definition of perpendicular lines.

Notice how the Law of Detachment was used in this geometry proof. By combining statement 1 with reason 2, the conclusion is written here as statement (2), just as p and $p \to r$ led us to the conclusion r in the logic proof.

How Geometry Proofs Are Connected to Logic Proofs

Given the premise: $\overrightarrow{BD}$ is the bisector of $\angle ABC$.

Prove the conclusion: $m\angle ABD = m\angle CBD$.

In this proof, use two definitions. Write each definition as a conditional.

1. *Definition:* A bisector of an angle is a ray whose endpoint is the vertex of the angle and that divides the angle into two congruent angles.
Conditional form: If a ray is the bisector of an angle, then the ray divides the angle into two congruent angles.

2. *Definition:* Congruent angles are angles that have the same measure.
Conditional form: If angles are congruent, then they have the same measure.

Using specific information from the given problem, let P represent "$\overrightarrow{BD}$ is the bisector of $\angle ABC$," let Q represent "$\angle ABD \cong \angle CBD$," and let R represent "$m\angle ABD = m\angle CBD$."

In logic, we would state this proof as follows:

Statements		Reasons
1. P	($\overrightarrow{BD}$ is the bisector of $\angle ABC$.)	1. Given.
2. $P \to Q$	(If $\overrightarrow{BD}$ is the bisector of $\angle ABC$, then $\angle ABD \cong \angle CBD$.)	2. Definition of angle bisector.
3. Q	($\angle ABD \cong \angle CBD$.)	3. Law of Detachment (1, 2).
4. $Q \to R$	(If $\angle ABD \cong \angle CBD$, then $m\angle ABD = m\angle CBD$.)	4. Definition of congruent angles.
5. $\therefore R$	($m\angle ABD = m\angle CBD$.)	5. Law of Detachment (3, 4).

Here, we used the Law of Detachment twice: first with P and $P \to Q$ to infer Q, then again with Q and $Q \to R$ to infer R.

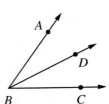

Let us restate this proof in the format used most often in geometry.

Given: $\overrightarrow{BD}$ is the bisector of $\angle ABC$.

Prove: $m\angle ABD = m\angle CBD$.

Statements	Reasons
1. $\overrightarrow{BD}$ is the bisector of $\angle ABC$.	1. Given.
2. $\angle ABD \cong \angle CBD$.	2. Definition of angle bisector.
3. $m\angle ABD = m\angle CBD$.	3. Definition of congruent angles.

Again, we notice that the Law of Detachment was not cited in the reasons of this geometry proof. However, the diagram in the box below shows how this inference law was used.

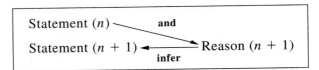

Thus, we see that:

From statement 1 and reason 2, we infer statement 2, just as from P and $(P \rightarrow Q)$, we infer Q in the logic proof.

From statement 2 and reason 3, we infer statement 3, just as from Q and $(Q \rightarrow R)$, we infer R in the logic proof.

The given premises and true statements used in this argument, namely P, $P \rightarrow Q$, and $Q \rightarrow R$, would allow us to use the Chain Rule in a logic proof by inferring the statement $P \rightarrow R$. A geometry proof is essentially a chain of reasoning in which we link the given premises and true statements to arrive at the conclusion.

These examples allow us to observe the following:

1. The laws of inference are *listed* as reasons in a ***logic proof***.

2. The laws of inference are *not listed* as reasons in a ***geometry proof***, but these inference laws are used to develop the proof.

EXAMPLES

1. *Given:* In $\triangle DEF$, $\overline{DE} \cong \overline{DF}$.
   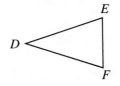
   a. State the given premise.
   b. After identifying a word or phrase from the given premise whose definition may be used in a proof, write the definition in a conditional form.
   c. From the given premise and the definition involved, draw a specific conclusion.

Solutions   **a.** The given premise states that two segments are congruent: $\overline{DE} \cong \overline{DF}$.

b. The definition of congruent segments, in a conditional form, is as follows: *If two segments are congruent, then they have the same length.*

c. The given *premise* states: $\overline{DE} \cong \overline{DF}$.

The *definition* can be rewritten to include the specific information in the statement: If $\overline{DE} \cong \overline{DF}$, then $DE = DF$.

By the Law of Detachment, the specific conclusion is: $DE = DF$.

$A \quad M \quad B$

2. *Given:* M is the midpoint of $\overline{AB}$.

Prove: $AM = MB$.

Definition: The midpoint of a line segment is the point that divides the segment into two congruent segments.

Definition: Congruent segments are segments that have the same length.

a. Let M represent "M is the midpoint of $\overline{AB}$."
Let C represent "$\overline{AM} \cong \overline{MB}$."
Let E represent "$AM = MB$."
   Using M, C, E, conditional forms of the definitions, and laws of inference, write a logic proof to show that $AM = MB$.

b. Using the given premise and definitions, write a geometry proof to show that $AM = MB$.

c. Write the geometric proof in paragraph form.

Solutions   **a.** The conditional form of the first definition can be written as follows: If a point is a midpoint of a line segment, then the point divides the segment into two congruent segments. Using M as the midpoint of $\overline{AB}$, we can write the specific conditional:

$$M \to C: \text{If } M \text{ is the midpoint of } \overline{AB}, \text{ then } \overline{AM} \cong \overline{MB}.$$

The conditional form of the second definition can be written as follows: If segments are congruent, then these segments have the same length. Using the segments $\overline{AM}$ and $\overline{MB}$ and their lengths, we can write:

$$C \to E: \text{If } \overline{AM} \cong \overline{MB}, \text{ then } AM = MB.$$

The given premise is M. The conditional forms of the definitions are $M \to C$ and $C \to E$. The *logic proof* now follows:

	Statements		*Reasons*

1. M (M is the midpoint of $\overline{AB}$.)   1. Given.

2. $M \rightarrow C$ (If M is the midpoint of $\overline{AB}$, then $\overline{AM} \cong \overline{MB}$.)   2. Definition of midpoint of a segment.

3. C ($\overline{AM} \cong \overline{MB}$.)   3. Law of Detachment (1, 2).

4. $C \rightarrow E$ (If $\overline{AM} \cong \overline{MB}$, then $AM = MB$.)   4. Definition of congruent segments.

5. $\therefore E$ ($AM = MB$.)   5. Law of Detachment (3, 4).

b. The *geometry proof* can be stated as follows:

Statements

1. M is the midpoint of $\overline{AB}$.

2. $\overline{AM} \cong \overline{MB}$.

3. $AM = MB$.

Reasons

1. Given.

2. Definition of midpoint of a segment.

3. Definition of congruent segments.

Note. Compare the use of the Law of Detachment in this geometry proof and in the logic proof presented in part **a**. In the geometry proof, we observe that:

From statement 1 and reason 2, we infer statement 2, just as from M and $M \rightarrow C$, we infer C in the logic proof.

From statement 2 and reason 3, we infer statement 3, just as from C and $C \rightarrow E$, we infer E in the logic proof.

c. If a proof is written in *paragraph form*, all statements and reasons are written as sentences. The sentences in the paragraph, as shown below, include the same definitions that were used in the two-column proof to reach the required conclusion. The paragraph form of this geometric proof may be stated as follows:

We are given that M is the midpoint of $\overline{AB}$. Therefore, $\overline{AM} \cong \overline{MB}$ since the midpoint of a line segment separates the segment into two congruent segments. Then, since congruent segments are segments that have the same measure, $\overline{AM}$ and $\overline{MB}$ have the same measure, or $AM = MB$.

EXERCISES WITH OPEN-RESPONSE PROBLEMS

In 1–10, in each case: **a.** State the given premise. **b.** After identifying a word or phrase from the given premise whose definition may be used in a proof, write the definition in a conditional form. **c.** From the premise and the definition involved, draw a specific conclusion.

1.

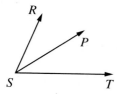

Given: $\overrightarrow{SP}$ bisects $\angle RST$.

2.

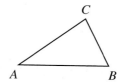

Given: $\triangle ABC$ is a scalene triangle.

3.

Given: $\angle 1 \cong \angle 2$.

4.

Given: $\overline{AB} \cong \overline{CD}$.

5.

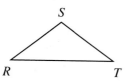

Given: In $\triangle RST$, $\overline{RS} \perp \overline{ST}$.

6.

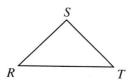

Given: In $\triangle RST$, $\angle R \cong \angle T$.

7.

Given: $\angle ABC$ is a right angle.

8.

Given: $\overleftrightarrow{AB}$ bisects $\overline{RS}$ at point M.

9.

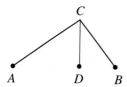

Given: D is in the interior of $\angle ACB$.

10.

Given: $\overline{AB} \cong \overline{BC}$.

11. Given: In △ABC, M is the midpoint of $\overline{AB}$.
  Prove: $\overline{AM} \cong \overline{MB}$.

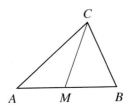

  a. Let P represent "M is the midpoint of $\overline{AB}$."
    Let Q represent "$\overline{AM} \cong \overline{MB}$."

  Copy the following *logic proof*, filling in all missing
  statements in word form and all missing reasons:

Statements		Reasons
1. P	(M is the midpoint of $\overline{AB}$.)	1. _____
2. P → Q	(_____)	2. Definition of midpoint of a segment.
3. ∴ Q	(_____)	3. _____

  b. Copy the following *geometry proof*, filling in the missing statement and the missing reason:

Statements	Reasons
1. M is the midpoint of $\overline{AB}$.	1. _____
2. _____	2. Definition of midpoint of a segment.

  c. Write the proof in paragraph form.

12. Given: △RST.
       $\overline{RS} \cong \overline{ST}$.
  Prove: ∠RST is the vertex angle of △RST.

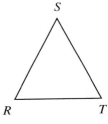

  a. Let P represent "$\overline{RS} \cong \overline{ST}$."
    Let Q represent "∠RST is the vertex angle of △RST."

  Copy the following *logic proof*, filling in all missing
  statements in word form and all missing reasons:

Statements		Reasons
1. P	($\overline{RS} \cong \overline{ST}$.)	1. _____
2. P → Q	(_____)	2. Definition of vertex angle of an isosceles triangle.
3. ∴ Q	(_____)	3. _____

  b. Copy the following *geometry proof*, filling in the missing reasons:

Statements	Reasons
1. In △RST, $\overline{RS} \cong \overline{ST}$.	1. _____
2. ∠RST is the vertex angle of isosceles triangle RST.	2. _____

  c. Write the proof in paragraph form.

13. *Given:* In $\triangle ABC$, $\overrightarrow{CE}$ bisects $\angle ACB$.
   Prove: $m\angle ACE = m\angle BCE$.

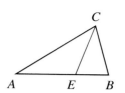

a. Let P represent "$\overrightarrow{CE}$ bisects $\angle ACB$."
   Let Q represent "$\angle ACE \cong \angle BCE$."
   Let R represent "$m\angle ACE = m\angle BCE$."

Copy the *logic proof*, filling in all missing statements in word form and all missing reasons:

Statements		Reasons
1. P	($\overrightarrow{CE}$ bisects $\angle ACB$.)	1. _____
2. $P \rightarrow Q$	(_____)	2. Definition of angle bisector.
3. Q	(_____)	3. _____
4. $Q \rightarrow R$	(_____)	4. Definition of congruent angles.
5. $\therefore R$	(_____)	5. _____

b. Copy the following *geometry proof*, filling in all missing statements. In reasons 2 and 3, write the definitions as biconditionals.

Statements	Reasons
1. _____	1. Given.
2. _____	2. Definition of angle bisector.
3. _____	3. Definition of congruent angles.

c. Write the proof in paragraph form.

14. *Given:* $\triangle ABC$ is an equilateral triangle.
   Prove: $AB = BC = CA$.

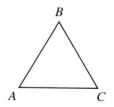

a. Let E represent "$\triangle ABC$ is equilateral."
   Let S represent "$\overline{AB} \cong \overline{BC} \cong \overline{CA}$."
   Let L represent "$AB = BC = CA$."

Copy the *logic proof*, filling in all missing statements in word form and all missing reasons:

Statements		Reasons
1. E	($\triangle ABC$ is equilateral.)	1. _____
2. $E \rightarrow S$	(_____)	2. Definition of equilateral triangle.
3. S	(_____)	3. _____
4. $S \rightarrow L$	(_____)	4. Definition of congruent segments.
5. $\therefore L$	(_____)	5. _____

b. Using the given premise and definitions, write a *geometry proof* to show $AB = BC = CA$.
c. Write the proof in paragraph form.

3-4 DIRECT AND INDIRECT PROOFS

There are basically two types of proof, called *direct proof* and *indirect proof*. In both types, we use deductive reasoning to prove a valid conclusion based upon the given premises. Let us see how these two types of proof differ.

Direct Proof

All proofs seen in Section 3-3 are direct proofs. In a **direct proof**, we use laws of inference to link together true premises and statements that lead *directly* to a true conclusion.

The following is an example of a direct proof.

Given: △*ABC* is equiangular.

Prove: ∠*A* ≅ ∠*B* ≅ ∠*C*.

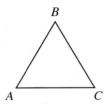

In this proof, we will use the following definition: An equiangular triangle is a triangle that has three congruent angles. We can restate this definition in the conditional form: If a triangle is equiangular, then the triangle has three congruent angles.

Let *E* represent the statement "△*ABC* is equiangular," and let *C* represent the statement "∠*A* ≅ ∠*B* ≅ ∠*C*." Both the logic form and the geometric form of a direct proof follow.

Direct Proof in Logic

	Statements		Reasons
1. *E*	(△*ABC* is equiangular.)	1. Given.
2. *E* → *C*	(If △*ABC* is equiangular, then ∠*A* ≅ ∠*B* ≅ ∠*C*.)	2. Definition of equiangular triangle.
3. ∴ *C*	(∠*A* ≅ ∠*B* ≅ ∠*C*.)	3. Law of Detachment (1, 2).

Direct Proof in Geometry

Statements	Reasons
1. △*ABC* is equiangular.	1. Given.
2. ∠*A* ≅ ∠*B* ≅ ∠*C*.	2. Definition of equiangular triangle.

Indirect Proof

You learned in Chapter 2 that, when a statement is false, then the negation of this statement must be true. In an indirect proof, laws of inference are used to prove that a statement is false, leading *indirectly* to the conclusion that the negation of the statement must be true.

In an ***indirect proof***, take the following steps to show that the conclusion q is true:

1. Start with the true premise p.

2. Assume that the negation of the conclusion q is true; that is, assume that $\sim q$ is true.

3. Use p and $\sim q$ and the laws of inference to prove $\sim p$.

4. But $\sim p$ is false.

5. From this contradiction, it follows that the assumption $\sim q$ is false, and we conclude that q is true.

Let us use the same premise and conclusion stated above for the direct proof. However, this time we will reach the conclusion by means of an indirect proof.

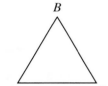

Given: $\triangle ABC$ is equiangular.

Prove: $\angle A \cong \angle B \cong \angle C$.

We again let E represent "$\triangle ABC$ is equiangular," and let C represent "$\angle A \cong \angle B \cong \angle C$." In the proof, we must assume that the negation of the conclusion C is true, namely, that $\sim C$ is true.

Indirect Proof in Logic

Statements		Reasons
1. E	($\triangle ABC$ is equiangular.)	1. Given.
2. $\sim C$	(It is *not* the case that $\angle A \cong \angle B \cong \angle C$.)	2. Assumed.
3. $E \rightarrow C$	(If $\triangle ABC$ is equiangular, then $\angle A \cong \angle B \cong \angle C$.)	3. Definition of equiangular triangle.
4. $\sim E$	($\triangle ABC$ is *not* equiangular.)	4. Modus Tollens (2, 3).
5. $E \wedge \sim E$	($\triangle ABC$ is equiangular and $\triangle ABC$ is *not* equiangular.)	5. Conjunction (1, 4).
6. $\therefore C$	(It is the case that $\angle A \cong \angle B \cong \angle C$.)	6. Contradiction in (5), $\therefore$ assumption in (2) is false.

Indirect Proof in Geometry

	Statements	Reasons
	1. $\triangle ABC$ is equiangular.	1. Given.
	2. It is *not* the case that $\angle A \cong \angle B \cong \angle C$.	2. Assumption.
	3. $\triangle ABC$ is *not* equiangular.	3. If three angles of a triangle are not congruent, then the triangle is not equiangular. (Contrapositive of the conditional form of the definition of equiangular triangle.)
	4. $\angle A \cong \angle B \cong \angle C$.	4. Contradiction in (1) and (3). $\therefore$ assumption in (2) is false.

In both proofs, we assume that the conclusion C is false by writing $\sim C$ as an assumption. From this assumption that the three angles of the triangle are not congruent, we deduce that the triangle is not equiangular (a contradiction to the given premise). Thus, the assumption $\sim C$ must be false and its negation, which is the conclusion C, must be true.

Note. To learn how an indirect proof works, it will be necessary for you to prove some simple statements indirectly in this section. Thereafter, you should follow the general guidelines for proof, which are stated below.

KEEP IN MIND ──────────────────────────────────

1. Wherever possible, a statement in geometry should be proved by means of a direct proof.
2. An indirect proof should be used only when there is no clear way to prove the statement directly.

EXAMPLES

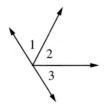

In 1 and 2, information is given regarding a proof. In each case: **a.** Write the statement that is to be proved.   **b.** Write the assumption that must appear in an indirect proof of the statement.

1. *Given:* $\angle 1 \cong \angle 2$.
$\angle 2 \cong \angle 3$.

Prove: $\angle 1 \cong \angle 3$.

Solutions   **a.** The conclusion to be proved is $\angle 1 \cong \angle 3$.
b. In an indirect proof, we must assume the negation of the conclusion, namely: $\angle 1$ is *not* congruent to $\angle 3$, or $\angle 1 \not\cong \angle 3$.

2. *Given:* In $\triangle ABC$, $\overline{AB} \cong \overline{BC}$ and $\overline{BD}$ bisects $\angle ABC$.

Prove: $\overline{BD} \perp \overline{AC}$ and $AD = DC$.

Solutions **a.** The conclusion to be proved consists of two statements: $\overline{BD} \perp \overline{AC}$ and $AD = DC$.

b. In an indirect proof, we must assume the negation of the conclusion. Since there are two statements in the conclusion, we think of the negation in terms of De Morgan's Law. We assume:

$\sim(P \wedge Q)$:   It is *not* the case that $\overline{BD} \perp \overline{AC}$ **and** $AD = DC$,

or

$\sim P \vee \sim Q$: $\overline{BD}$ is *not* $\perp$ to $\overline{AC}$ **or** $AD \neq DC$.

EXERCISES WITH OPEN-RESPONSE PROBLEMS

In 1–8, information is given regarding a proof. In each case: **a.** Write the statement that is to be proved. **b.** Write the assumption that must appear in an indirect proof of the statement.

Ex. 1   Ex. 2

Ex. 3

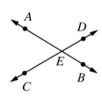

Ex. 4

1. *Given:* In $\triangle RST$, $\angle R \cong \angle T$.
   Prove: $RS = ST$.

2. *Given:* Points A, B, and C are collinear;
   B is between A and C.
   Prove: $AB + BC = AC$.

3. *Given:* $\triangle DEF$.
   Prove: $m\angle D + m\angle E + m\angle F = 180$.

4. *Given:* $\overleftrightarrow{AB}$ and $\overleftrightarrow{CD}$ intersect at E.
   Prove: $\angle AED \cong \angle BEC$ and $\angle AEC \cong \angle BED$.

5. *Given:* Parallel lines ℓ and m are cut by transversal k.
   Prove: $\angle 1 \cong \angle 2$.

6. *Given:* Lines ℓ and m are cut by transversal k; $\angle 1 \cong \angle 2$.
   Prove: $\ell \parallel m$.

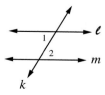

Ex. 5–6

7. *Given:* In parallelogram *ABCD*, diagonals $\overline{AC}$ and $\overline{BD}$
intersect at *M*.
   Prove: *AM* = *MC* and *DM* = *MB*.

8. *Given:* Square *PQRS* with diagonals $\overline{RP}$ and $\overline{QS}$.
   Prove: $\overline{RP} \cong \overline{QS}$ and $\overline{RP} \perp \overline{QS}$.

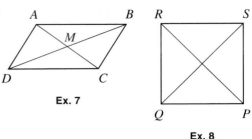

Ex. 7

Ex. 8

In 9 and 10, in each case use an indirect proof.

9. *Given:* $\overrightarrow{BA}$ is not perpendicular to $\overrightarrow{BC}$.
   Prove: $\angle ABC$ is not a right angle.

10. *Given:* $\angle DEF$ is not a straight angle.
   Prove: $\overrightarrow{ED}$ and $\overrightarrow{EF}$ are not opposite rays.

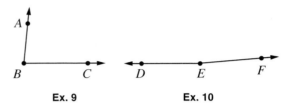

Ex. 9

Ex. 10

3-5 UNDERSTANDING THE NATURE OF A POSTULATIONAL SYSTEM

In reasoning, we saw that the premises of an argument must be taken as true statements in order to reach a conclusion that we are convinced is also true. In Chapter 1, we listed both undefined terms and definitions that we accept as being true.

At times, statements are made in geometry that are neither undefined terms nor definitions, and yet we know these are true statements. There are two such types of statements in geometry: one is called a *postulate* or an **axiom**, and the other is called a *theorem*.

A postulate, or axiom, is a statement whose truth is assumed without any proof whatsoever. Some mathematicians use the term *axiom* for a *general statement* whose truth is assumed without proof, and the term *postulate* for a *geometric statement* whose truth is assumed without proof. We will use the term *postulate* for both types of assumptions.

● **DEFINITION.** A *postulate* is a statement whose truth is accepted without proof.

In a **postulational system**, the *undefined terms*, the *defined terms*, and the *postulates* are the seeds from which the tree of knowledge in the subject grows. They, together with the laws of reasoning, become the instruments with which we prove the truth of new statements, called *theorems*.

● **DEFINITION.** A *theorem* is a statement that is proved by **deductive reasoning**.

Postulational thinking, which is the instrument used to make deductions in geometry, is a powerful technique for several reasons including:

1. It makes it possible to arrive at a conclusion in situations where observation and measurement are not practicable or possible.

2. Observation and measurement may help us to discover a fact, but they never explain the reason for the truth of that fact. Postulational thinking explains why the reasoning used in arriving at a conclusion is valid or invalid.

3. In a postulational system, the entire body of knowledge known as geometry can be discovered and explained by continually proving new theorems. These theorems are proved by applying the laws of reasoning to *undefined terms* and to statements that are known to be true, namely, *definitions*, *postulates*, and *previously proved theorems*.

EXERCISES

In 1–4, answer *True* or *False* in each case.

1. In a postulational system, all terms are defined.
2. A postulate is a true statement accepted without proof.
3. A theorem is a true statement that must be proved.
4. Every statement in geometry is a postulate or a definition.

5. Name the elements in a postulational system that are used to prove a new theorem.

3-6   THE FIRST POSTULATES USED IN PROVING STATEMENTS

We have seen that deductive reasoning is based upon the use of undefined terms, defined terms, and postulates. Now, we will examine some of these postulates and learn how to use them in deductive reasoning.

When we state the relation "*a* is equal to *b*," symbolized as "$a = b$," we mean that *a* and *b* are two different names for the same element of a set, usually a number. For example:

1. When we write $RS = LM$, we mean that $\overline{RS}$ and $\overline{LM}$ have the same length.
2. When we write $m\angle A = m\angle B$, we mean that $\angle A$ and $\angle B$ contain the same number of degrees.

The following three *equality postulates* are also referred to as the *properties of equality*.

The Reflexive Property of Equality

$$a = a$$

This property is stated in words as follows:

- **POSTULATE. A quantity is equal to itself.**

For example: In $\triangle ABC$, observe that:

1. The length of a segment is equal to itself:

   $AB = AB$ $BC = BC$ $AC = AC$

2. The measure of an angle is equal to itself:

   $m\angle A = m\angle A$ $m\angle B = m\angle B$ $m\angle C = m\angle C$

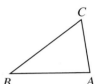

The Symmetric Property of Equality

If $a = b$, then $b = a$.

This property is stated in words as follows:

- **POSTULATE. An equality may be expressed in either order.**

For example:

1. If $AB = CD$, then $CD = AB$.

2. If $m\angle R = m\angle S$, then $m\angle S = m\angle R$.

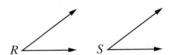

The Transitive Property of Equality

If $a = b$ and $b = c$, then $a = c$.

This property states that, if a and b have the same value, and b and c have the same value, it follows that a and c have the same value. This property is stated in words as follows:

- **POSTULATE. If quantities are equal to the same quantity, they are equal to each other.**

Let us now see how these postulates of equality can be used in deductive reasoning.

Proofs with Postulates of Equality

From this point on, proofs will be presented in only one format. To arrange a geometry proof formally in two columns, we will proceed as follows:

1. We state the premises or the hypothesis, which is also called the *given*, because the premises are the given facts.

2. We state the conclusion, which is also called the *prove*, because the conclusion contains what is to be proved. (Note that the *drawing of a figure*, properly lettered, helps in stating the *given* premises and the conclusion that we are to *prove*.)

3. We present the *proof*, the deductive reasoning, which is the series of logical arguments used in the demonstration. Each step in the proof should consist of a *statement* in one column and its *reason* in the other column. A reason may be the *given*, a *definition*, a *postulate*, or, as we will see later, a *previously proved theorem*.

EXAMPLES

1. *Given:* $m\angle x = 40$.
   $m\angle y = 40$.

   Prove: $m\angle x = m\angle y$.

Statements	Reasons
1. $m\angle x = 40$.	1. Given.
2. $m\angle y = 40$.	2. Given.
3. $40 = m\angle y$.	3. The symmetric property of equality. (*Or:* An equality may be written in either order.)
4. $m\angle x = m\angle y$.	4. The transitive property of equality. (*Or:* If quantities are equal to the same quantity, they are equal to each other.)

Note. In the future, we will abbreviate the proof by eliminating step 3 and reason 3, the step that makes use of the symmetric property of equality. After presenting steps 1 and 2, we will immediately deduce the conclusion that $m\angle x = m\angle y$.

2. *Given:* $AB = LM$.
$\qquad\quad CD = RS$.
$\qquad\quad LM = RS$.

Prove: $AB = CD$.

A •———————• B   L •————————• M

C •————————• D   R •———————• S

Statements	Reasons
1. $AB = LM$.	1. Given.
2. $LM = RS$.	2. Given.
3. $AB = RS$.	3. The transitive property of equality.
4. $CD = RS$.	4. Given.
5. $AB = CD$.	5. The transitive property of equality.

In Example 2, we proved an illustration of the statement "If quantities are equal to equal quantities, they are equal to each other." In the future, we will feel free to use this statement, which is an expanded version of the transitive property of equality, as a reason in a proof.

EXERCISES WITH OPEN-RESPONSE PROBLEMS

In 1–3, in each case: **a.** State the postulate that can be used to show that the conclusion is valid.
b. Write a formal proof.

1.

C •———————• D
X •———————• Y

Given:
$\quad CD = 2$ in.
$\quad XY = 2$ in.

Prove:
$\quad CD = XY$.

2.

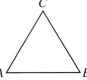

Given:
$\quad m\angle A = m\angle B$.
$\quad m\angle C = m\angle B$.

Prove:
$\quad m\angle A = m\angle C$.

3.

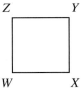

Given:
$\quad WZ = XY$.
$\quad ZY = WX$.
$\quad WZ = ZY$.

Prove:
$\quad XY = WX$.

3-7 EQUIVALENCE RELATIONS

In the reflexive, symmetric, and transitive properties of equality, our examples indicated that the relation *is equal to* acted upon some set of numbers such as lengths of line segments or measures of angles. To discuss any relation R, we must clearly define a set S upon whose elements this relation will act.

For example:

Let S = the set of real numbers (since these numbers are used to describe the lengths of line segments and the measures of angles).

Let R = the relation *is equal to*, symbolized as =.

Then, for the set of real numbers whose elements are represented as a, b, and c, and for the relation =, the following properties hold:

1. Reflexive property: $a = a$.
2. Symmetric property: If $a = b$, then $b = a$.
3. Transitive property: If $a = b$ and $b = c$, then $a = c$.

Because all three properties are true, we say that the relation = is an *equivalence relation* on the set of real numbers. To restate this, we say:

Equality of real numbers is an equivalence relation.

Using more general terms, we now define an equivalence relation:

● **DEFINITION.** A relation R is an ***equivalence relation*** on some set S when the relation R is reflexive, symmetric, and transitive.

Let us investigate other relations to see whether they form equivalence relations on sets in geometry.

Congruence of Line Segments

Let S = the set of all line segments, and let R = the relation *is congruent to*, symbolized as ≅.

Since $\overline{AB} \cong \overline{CD}$ is equivalent to $AB = CD$, and $\overline{CD} \cong \overline{EF}$ is equivalent to $CD = EF$, it follows that the congruence of line segments has the same three properties as the equality of numbers:

1. Reflexive property: $\overline{AB} \cong \overline{AB}$.
2. Symmetric property: If $\overline{AB} \cong \overline{CD}$, then $\overline{CD} \cong \overline{AB}$.
3. Transitive property: If $\overline{AB} \cong \overline{CD}$, and $\overline{CD} \cong \overline{EF}$, then $\overline{AB} \cong \overline{EF}$.

Therefore, congruence of line segments is an equivalence relation.

Congruence of Angles

Let S = the set of all angles, and let R = the relation *is congruent to*, symbolized as ≅.

Since $\angle ABC \cong \angle DEF$ is equivalent to m$\angle ABC$ = m$\angle DEF$, and $\angle DEF \cong \angle XYZ$ is equivalent to m$\angle DEF$ = m$\angle XYZ$, it follows that the congruence of angles has the same three properties as the equality of numbers:

1. Reflexive property: $\angle ABC \cong \angle ABC$.
2. Symmetric property: If $\angle ABC \cong \angle DEF$, then $\angle DEF \cong \angle ABC$.
3. Transitive property: If $\angle ABC \cong \angle DEF$, and $\angle DEF \cong \angle XYZ$, then $\angle ABC \cong \angle XYZ$.

Therefore, congruence of angles is an equivalence relation.

Perpendicularity of Lines

Let S = the set of all lines, and let R = the relation *is perpendicular to*, symbolized as $\perp$. Let a, b, and c represent any lines.
In this case:

1. Reflexive property: $a \perp a$. (False)
   In the figure, line a is *not* perpendicular to itself.

2. Symmetric property: If $a \perp b$, then $b \perp a$. (True)
   The figure shows that this property holds.

3. Transition property: If $a \perp b$ and $b \perp c$, then $a \perp c$. (False)
   Although the hypothesis that $a \perp b$ and $b \perp c$ is true, the figure shows that a is *not* perpendicular to c.

Thus, perpendicularity of lines is *not* an equivalence relation.
At other points in this book, as we begin to work with a new relation, we will test to see whether an equivalence relation exists.

EXERCISES WITH OPEN-RESPONSE PROBLEMS

In 1–8, in each case name the property that justifies the statement.

1. $\overline{AC} \cong \overline{AC}$.

2. If $\angle RST \cong \angle XYZ$, then $\angle XYZ \cong \angle RST$.

3. $\angle ABC \cong \angle ABC$.

4. If $\overline{LM} \cong \overline{XY}$, then $\overline{XY} \cong \overline{LM}$.

5. If $\overline{AB} \cong \overline{CD}$, and $\overline{CD} \cong \overline{ST}$, then $\overline{AB} \cong \overline{ST}$.

6. If $\angle XYZ \cong \angle RST$, and $\angle RST \cong \angle ABC$, then $\angle XYZ \cong \angle ABC$.

7. If $\overleftrightarrow{AB} \perp \overleftrightarrow{CD}$, then $\overleftrightarrow{CD} \perp \overleftrightarrow{AB}$.

8. If $AB = CD$ and $CD = EF$, then $AB = EF$.

In 9–15, tell in each case which of the three properties of an equivalence relation is (are) true for the given relation and the set given in parentheses.

9. is greater than (for natural numbers)

10. $\leq$ (for integers)

11. is a factor of (for natural numbers)

12. $\neq$ (for real numbers)

13. is the father of (for people)

14. is older than (for people)

15. lives in the same house as (for people)

16. Let the set S = a set of statements (namely, p, q, and r), and let the relation R = the relation *implies*, symbolized as $\rightarrow$. Notice that this relation is the one used to write conditional statements in logic.
   a. Is this relation reflexive; that is, will the statements $p \rightarrow p$, $q \rightarrow q$, and $r \rightarrow r$ always be true? Explain your answer.

b. Is this relation symmetric; that is, if $p \rightarrow q$, does it follow that $q \rightarrow p$? Explain your answer.

c. Is this relation transitive; that is, if $p \rightarrow q$ and $q \rightarrow r$, does it follow that $p \rightarrow r$? Explain your answer.

d. Is this relation an equivalence relation? Explain your answer.

3-8 THE SUBSTITUTION POSTULATE

The substitution postulate allows us to replace one quantity, number, or measure with its equal. The postulate is stated in words as follows:

- **POSTULATE. A quantity may be substituted for its equal in any expression.**

EXAMPLES

1. *Given:* $AB = 2AD$.
$AD = DB$.

Prove: $AB = 2DB$.

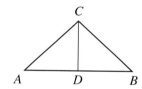

Statements	*Reasons*
1. $AB = 2AD$.	1. Given.
2. $AD = DB$.	2. Given.
3. $AB = 2DB$.	3. Substitution postulate. (*Or:* A quantity may be substituted for its equal in any expression.)

2. *Given:* $m\angle a + m\angle b = 90$.
$m\angle a = m\angle c$.

Prove: $m\angle c + m\angle b = 90$.

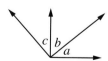

Statements	*Reasons*
1. $m\angle a + m\angle b = 90$.	1. Given.
2. $m\angle a = m\angle c$.	2. Given.
3. $m\angle c + m\angle b = 90$.	3. Substitution postulate.

EXERCISES WITH OPEN-RESPONSE PROBLEMS

In 1–3, in each case write a formal proof to show that the conclusion is valid.

1.

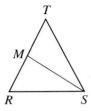

Given:

$MT = \frac{1}{2} RT$.

$RM = MT$.

Prove:

$RM = \frac{1}{2} RT$.

2.

Given:

$AD + DE = AE$.

$AD = EB$.

Prove:

$EB + DE = AE$.

3.

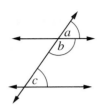

Given:

$m\angle a + m\angle b = 180$.

$m\angle a = m\angle c$.

Prove:

$m\angle c + m\angle b = 180$.

3-9 POSTULATES CONCERNING ADDITION AND SUBTRACTION

The Partition Postulate

- **POSTULATE. A whole is equal to the sum of all its parts.**

This postulate applies to segments or to their lengths.

$$AD = AB + BC + CD.$$
$$\text{Also, } \overline{AD} = \overline{AB} + \overline{BC} + \overline{CD}.$$

This postulate also applies to angles or their measures.

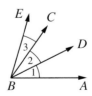

$$\angle ABE = \angle 1 + \angle 2 + \angle 3.$$
$$\text{Also, } m\angle ABE = m\angle 1 + m\angle 2 + m\angle 3.$$

The Addition Postulate

The addition postulate may be stated in symbols or in words as follows:

- **POSTULATE. If $a = b$, and $c = d$, then $a + c = b + d$.**
- **POSTULATE. If equal quantities are added to equal quantities, the sums are equal.**

Let us consider the following proof, which uses the addition postulate. We recall that the notation $\overleftrightarrow{ABC}$ tells us that B is a point on $\overleftrightarrow{AC}$ between A and C.

Given: $\overleftrightarrow{ABC}$ and $\overleftrightarrow{DEF}$ with $AB = DE$ and $BC = EF$.

Prove: $AC = DF$.

Statements	Reasons
1. $AB = DE$.	1. Given.
2. $BC = EF$.	2. Given.
3. $AB + BC = DE + EF$.	3. Addition postulate. (*Or:* If equal quantities are added to equal quantities, the sums are equal.)
4. $AB + BC = AC$ and $DE + EF = DF$.	4. Partition postulate. (*Or:* A whole is equal to the sum of all its parts.)
5. $AC = DF$.	5. Substitution postulate.

Since $AB = DE$ indicates that $\overline{AB} \cong \overline{DE}$, and $BC = EF$ indicates that $\overline{BC} \cong \overline{EF}$, we can add congruent line segments in the same way that we add lengths that are equal. Therefore, we can restate the addition postulate as follows:

- **POSTULATE. If congruent segments are added to congruent segments, the sums are congruent.**

The proof just demonstrated can be rewritten in terms of the congruence of segments.

Given: $\overleftrightarrow{ABC}$ and $\overleftrightarrow{DEF}$ with $\overline{AB} \cong \overline{DE}$ and $\overline{BC} \cong \overline{EF}$.

Prove: $\overline{AC} \cong \overline{DF}$.

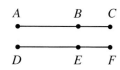

Statements	Reasons
1. $\overline{AB} \cong \overline{DE}$.	1. Given.
2. $\overline{BC} \cong \overline{EF}$.	2. Given.
3. $\overline{AB} + \overline{BC} \cong \overline{DE} + \overline{DF}$ or $\overline{AC} \cong \overline{DF}$.	3. Addition postulate. (*Or:* If congruent segments are added to congruent segments, the sums are congruent segments.)

The addition postulate can also be stated for congruent angles.

- **POSTULATE. If congruent angles are added to congruent angles, the sums are congruent.**

The Subtraction Postulate

The subtraction postulate may also be stated in symbols or in words.

- **POSTULATE. If** $a = b$, **and** $c = d$, **then** $a - c = b - d$.
- **POSTULATE. If equal quantities are subtracted from equal quantities, the differences are equal.**

Just as the addition postulate was restated for congruent segments and congruent angles, so too may we restate the subtraction postulate. In Example 2, measures are subtracted. In Example 3, congruent lengths are subtracted.

EXAMPLES

1. *Given:* $\angle ABG \cong \angle DEH$.
$\angle GBC \cong \angle HEF$.

Prove: $\angle ABC \cong \angle DEF$.

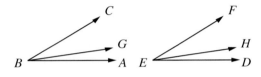

Statements	Reasons
1. $\angle ABG \cong \angle DEH$.	1. Given.
2. $\angle GBC \cong \angle HEF$.	2. Given.
3. $\angle ABG + \angle GBC \cong \angle DEH + \angle HEF$ or $\angle ABC \cong \angle DEF$.	3. Addition postulate.

Note. By the definition of the sum of two angles, $\angle ABC$ is another name for $\angle ABG + \angle GBC$ only when G is an interior point of $\angle ABC$; similarly, $\angle DEF$ is another name for $\angle DEH + \angle HEF$.

2. *Given:* $m\angle DAC = m\angle ECA$.
$m\angle 1 = m\angle 2$.

Prove: $m\angle 3 = m\angle 4$.

Statements	Reasons
1. $m\angle DAC = m\angle ECA$.	1. Given.
2. $m\angle 1 = m\angle 2$.	2. Given.
3. $m\angle DAC - m\angle 1 = m\angle ECA - m\angle 2$ or $m\angle 3 = m\angle 4$.	3. Subtraction postulate.

3. *Given:* $\overline{AB} \cong \overline{AC}$.
$\overline{DB} \cong \overline{EC}$.

Prove: $\overline{AD} \cong \overline{AE}$.

Statements	Reasons
1. $\overline{AB} \cong \overline{AC}$.	1. Given.
2. $\overline{DB} \cong \overline{EC}$.	2. Given.
3. $\overline{AB} - \overline{DB} \cong \overline{AC} - \overline{EC}$ or $\overline{AD} \cong \overline{AE}$.	3. Subtraction postulate.

EXERCISES WITH OPEN-RESPONSE PROBLEMS

In 1–12, in each case write a formal proof to show that the conclusion is valid.

1.

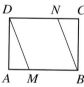

Given:
 $AM = CN$.
 $MB = ND$.

Prove:
 $AB = CD$.

2.

Given:
 $m\angle 1 = m\angle 2$.
 $m\angle 3 = m\angle 4$.

Prove:
 $m\angle QPS = m\angle QRS$.

3.

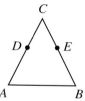

Given:
 $\overline{CD} \cong \overline{CE}$.
 $\overline{DA} \cong \overline{EB}$.

Prove:
 $\overline{CA} \cong \overline{CB}$.

4.

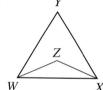

Given:
 $\angle XWZ \cong \angle WXZ$.
 $\angle ZWY \cong \angle ZXY$.

Prove:
 $\angle XWY \cong \angle WXY$.

5.

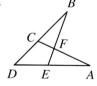

Given:
 $\overline{AF} \cong \overline{BF}$.
 $\overline{FC} \cong \overline{FE}$.

Prove:
 $\overline{AC} \cong \overline{BE}$.

6.

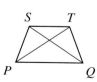

Given:
 $\angle QST \cong \angle PTS$.
 $\angle QSP \cong \angle PTQ$.

Prove:
 $\angle PST \cong \angle QTS$.

7.

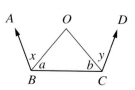

Given:
 $m\angle ABC = m\angle DCB$.
 $m\angle a = m\angle b$.

Prove:
 $m\angle x = m\angle y$.

8.

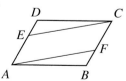

Given:
 $AD = BC$.
 $AE = CF$.

Prove:
 $DE = BF$.

9.

Given:
$\overline{DA} \cong \overline{CB}$.
$\overline{DE} \cong \overline{CF}$.

Prove:
$\overline{EA} \cong \overline{FB}$.

10.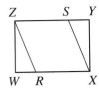

Given:
$\angle WZY \cong \angle WXY$.
$\angle RZY \cong \angle RXS$.

Prove:
$\angle WZR \cong \angle YXS$.

11.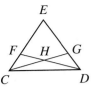

Given:
$\overline{FD} \cong \overline{GC}$.
$\overline{FH} \cong \overline{GH}$.

Prove:
$\overline{CH} \cong \overline{DH}$.

12.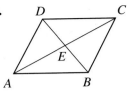

Given:
$\angle DEB \cong \angle AEC$.
$\angle DEA \cong \angle BEC$.

Prove:
$\angle AEB \cong \angle DEC$.

3-10   POSTULATES CONCERNING MULTIPLICATION AND DIVISION

All of the postulates in this section may be stated in symbols or in words.

The Multiplication Postulate

- **POSTULATE. If $a = b$, and $c = d$, then $ac = bd$.**
- **POSTULATE. If equal quantities are multiplied by equal quantities, the products are equal.**

When each of two equal quantities is multiplied by 2, we have a special case of this postulate, which is stated as follows:

- **Doubles of equal quantities are equal.**

The Division Postulate

- **POSTULATE. If $a = b$, and $c = d$, then $\frac{a}{c} = \frac{b}{d}$ (c is not 0 and d is not 0).**
- **POSTULATE. If equal quantities are divided by nonzero equal quantities, the quotients are equal.**

When each of two equal quantities is divided by 2, we have a special case of this postulate, which is stated as follows:

- **Halves of equal quantities are equal.**

We will deal with doubles and halves of congruent segments and of congruent angles in the same way that we deal with doubles and halves of segments whose lengths are equal and of angles whose measures are equal. This procedure is illustrated in Examples 1–3.

Powers Postulate

- **POSTULATE. If $a = b$, then $a^2 = b^2$.**
- **POSTULATE. The squares of equal quantities are equal.**

If $AB = 10$, then $(AB)^2 = (10)^2$, or $(AB)^2 = 100$.

Roots Postulate

- **POSTULATE. If $a = b$, then $\sqrt{a} = \sqrt{b}$.**
- **POSTULATE. Positive square roots of equal quantities are equal.**

If $(AB)^2 = 25$, then $\sqrt{(AB)^2} = \sqrt{25}$, or $AB = 5$.

EXAMPLES

1. *Given: $AB = CD$.*
$RS = 2AB$.
$LM = 2CD$.

A •—→ B   R •—→ S
C •—→ D   L •—→ M

Prove: $RS = LM$.

Statements	*Reasons*
1. $AB = CD$.	1. Given.
2. $RS = 2AB$.	2. Given.
3. $LM = 2CD$.	3. Given.
4. $RS = LM$.	4. Multiplication postulate. (*Or:* Doubles of equal quantities are equal.)

2. *Given: $\angle r \cong \angle s$.*
$m\angle BAD = 2\,m\angle r$.
$m\angle BCD = 2\,m\angle s$.

Prove: $\angle BAD \cong \angle BCD$.

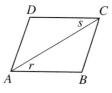

Statements	*Reasons*
1. $\angle r \cong \angle s$.	1. Given.
2. $m\angle BAD = 2\,m\angle r$.	2. Given.
3. $m\angle BCD = 2\,m\angle s$.	3. Given.
4. $\angle BAD \cong \angle BCD$.	4. Doubles of congruent angles are congruent.

3. *Given:* $\overline{AB} \cong \overline{DC}$.

$AF = \frac{1}{2} AB$.

$EC = \frac{1}{2} DC$.

Prove: $\overline{AF} \cong \overline{EC}$.

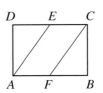

Statements	Reasons
1. $\overline{AB} \cong \overline{DC}$.	1. Given.
2. $AF = \frac{1}{2} AB$.	2. Given.
3. $EC = \frac{1}{2} DC$.	3. Given.
4. $\overline{AF} \cong \overline{EC}$.	4. Division postulate. (*Or:* Halves of congruent segments are congruent segments.)

EXERCISES WITH OPEN-RESPONSE PROBLEMS

In 1–10, in each case write a formal proof to show that the conclusion is valid.

1.

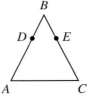

Given: $BD = BE$.

$BA = 3BD$.

$BC = 3BE$.

Prove: $BA = BC$.

2.

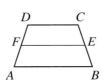

Given: $AF = BE$.

$AD = 2AF$.

$BC = 2BE$.

Prove: $AD = BC$.

3.

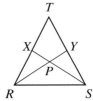

Given: $\overline{PX} \cong \overline{PY}$.

$SP = 2PX$.

$RP = 2PY$.

Prove: $\overline{SP} \cong \overline{RP}$.

4.

Given: $m\angle x = m\angle y$.

$m\angle CBA = 2\ m\angle x$.

$m\angle BCD = 2\ m\angle y$.

Prove: $m\angle CBA = m\angle BCD$.

5.

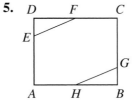

Given: $\overline{DF} \cong \overline{HB}$.

$DC = 2DF$.

$AB = 2HB$.

Prove: $\overline{DC} \cong \overline{AB}$.

6.

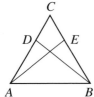

Given: $\angle EBD \cong \angle EAD$.

$m\angle ABE = 2\ m\angle EBD$.

$m\angle BAD = 2\ m\angle EAD$.

Prove: $\angle ABE \cong \angle BAD$.

7.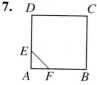

Given: $AD = AB$.

$AE = \frac{AD}{3}$.

$AF = \frac{AB}{3}$.

Prove: $AE = AF$.

8.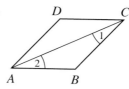

Given: $m\angle DAB = m\angle DCB$.

$m\angle 2 = \frac{1}{2} m\angle DAB$.

$m\angle 1 = \frac{1}{2} m\angle DCB$.

Prove: $m\angle 1 = m\angle 2$.

9.

Given: $\angle SRX \cong \angle RSY$.

$m\angle SRY = \frac{1}{2} m\angle SRX$.

$m\angle RSX = \frac{1}{2} m\angle RSY$.

Prove: $\angle SRY \cong \angle RSX$.

10.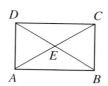

Given: $\overline{BD} \cong \overline{AC}$.

$BE = \frac{1}{2} BD$.

$AE = \frac{1}{2} AC$.

Prove: $\overline{BE} \cong \overline{AE}$.

3-11 POSTULATES INVOLVING LINES, LINE SEGMENTS, AND ANGLES

- **POSTULATE. A line segment can be extended to any length in either direction.**

The line segment, $\overline{AB}$, can be extended indefinitely to the right and to the left. The line, $\overleftrightarrow{AB}$, however, is *not* the original segment, $\overline{AB}$.

- **POSTULATE. Through two given points, one and only one line can be drawn. [Two points determine a line.]**

Through given points C and D, one and only one line can be drawn.

- **POSTULATE. Two lines cannot intersect in more than one point.**

If $\overleftrightarrow{AEB}$ and $\overleftrightarrow{CED}$ intersect, they cannot intersect in more than the one point, E.

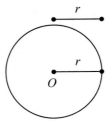

● **POSTULATE. One and only one circle can be drawn with any given point as a center and the length of any given line segment as a radius.**

Only one circle can be drawn that has point O as its center and a radius equal in length to segment r.

We make use of this postulate in constructions when we use compasses.

● **POSTULATE. At a given point on a given line, one and only one perpendicular can be drawn to the line.**

At point P on $\overleftrightarrow{APB}$, only one line, $\overleftrightarrow{PD}$, can be drawn perpendicular to $\overleftrightarrow{APB}$.

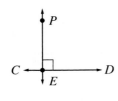

● **POSTULATE. From a given point not on a given line, one and only one perpendicular can be drawn to the line.**

From point P not on $\overleftrightarrow{CD}$, only one line, $\overleftrightarrow{PE}$, can be drawn perpendicular to $\overleftrightarrow{CD}$.

● **POSTULATE. For any two distinct points, there is only one positive real number that is called the *length* of the line segment joining the two points.**

For the distinct points A and B, there is only one positive real number, represented by AB, which is the length of $\overline{AB}$.

Since AB is also called the *distance* from A to B, we refer to this postulate as the *distance postulate*.

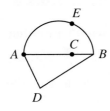

● **POSTULATE. The shortest path between two points is the line segment joining these two points.**

The figure shows three paths that can be taken in going from A to B. The length of $\overline{AB}$ (the path through C, a point collinear with A and B) is less than the length of the path through D or the path through E. The measure of the shortest path from A to B is the distance, AB.

● **POSTULATE. A line segment has one and only one midpoint.**

$\overline{AB}$ has one and only one midpoint, point M.

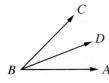

● **POSTULATE. An angle has one and only one bisector.**

Angle ABC has one and only one bisector, ray BD.

Conditional Statements as They Relate to Proof

> *Given:* $\angle A \cong \angle B$.
> $\angle B \cong \angle C$.
>
> *Prove:* $\angle A \cong \angle C$.

At the left is the format normally used to present a proof. The "given" statements form the *hypothesis* that we assume to be true. From this hypothesis, we are asked to "prove" that another statement, called the *conclusion*, is true.

In logic, we learned that a conditional statement "If *p*, then *q*" contains the hypothesis *p* and the conclusion *q*. Thus, it is possible to state the "given" hypothesis and the conclusion that we are to "prove" in a conditional form. For example, we can write:

> If $\underbrace{\angle A \cong \angle B, \text{and } \angle B \cong \angle C,}_{\text{"given" hypothesis}}$ then $\underbrace{\angle A \cong \angle C.}_{\substack{\text{conclusion} \\ \text{"to prove"}}}$

When the information needed for a proof is presented in a conditional statement, we are to:

1. Assume the truth of the hypothesis, or the "given" statement.
2. Prove the truth of the conclusion, or the "prove" statement.

Numerical and Algebraic Applications

In geometry, we are interested in proving that statements are true. These true statements can then be used to help solve numerical and algebraic problems, as in Example 2.

EXAMPLES

1. Rewrite the conditional statement in the *Given* and *Prove* format:

   If $AB + BC = AC$ and $\overline{BC} \cong \overline{PR}$, then $AB + PR = AC$.

   Solution

   > *Given:* $AB + BC = AC$.
   > $\overline{BC} \cong \overline{PR}$.
   >
   > *Prove:* $AB + PR = AC$.

2. **a.** If $\angle ABD \cong \angle DBE$, m$\angle ABD = 4x - 10$, and m$\angle DBE = 2x + 30$, find m$\angle ABD$ and m$\angle DBE$.

   b. If $\angle DBC$ is a right angle, use an answer from part **a** to find m$\angle EBC$.

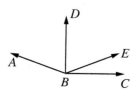

Solutions   **a.** This is an *algebraic application* of a geometric relationship.

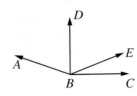

(1) Since congruent angles have equal measures:

$$m\angle ABD = m\angle DBE$$

(2) Substitute the given algebraic expressions:

$$4x - 10 = 2x + 30$$

(3) Solve for x:

$$2x = 40$$
$$x = 20$$

(4) Let $x = 20$ in the given algebraic expressions to find the measures of the angles:

$$m\angle ABD = 4x - 10 = 4(20) - 10 = 80 - 10 = 70 \quad Answer$$
$$m\angle DBE = 2x + 30 = 2(20) + 30 = 40 + 30 = 70 \quad Answer$$

b. This is a *numerical application* of a geometric relationship.

(1) The whole is equal to the sum of its parts:

$$m\angle DBE + m\angle EBC = m\angle DBC$$

(2) The measure of a right angle is 90, and, from part **a**, $m\angle DBE = 70$:

$$70 + m\angle EBC = 90$$

(3) Use subtraction.

$$\underline{-70 \qquad\qquad = -70}$$
$$m\angle EBC = 20 \quad Answer$$

Note. In both parts of this question, we are asked to *find* numerical quantities. We are *not* asked to prove geometric statements.

EXERCISES WITH OPEN-RESPONSE PROBLEMS

In 1–14, in each case: **a.** Rewrite the conditional statement in the *Given* and *Prove* format.   **b.** Write a formal proof.

Ex. 1

Ex. 2

Ex. 3

Ex. 4

1. If $AB = AD$ and $DC = AD$, then $AB = DC$.
2. If $m\angle 1 + m\angle 2 = 90$ and $m\angle A = m\angle 2$, then $m\angle 1 + m\angle A = 90$.
3. If $\overline{AD} \cong \overline{CD}$ and $\overline{BD} \cong \overline{CD}$, then $\overline{AD} \cong \overline{BD}$.
4. If $\angle TRS \cong \angle TSR$ and $\angle PRT \cong \angle PST$, then $\angle PRS \cong \angle PSR$.

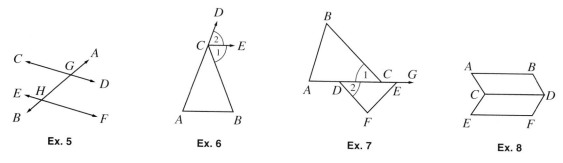

| Ex. 5 | Ex. 6 | Ex. 7 | Ex. 8 |

5. If m∠AGH = 180, m∠EHF = 180, and m∠AGD = m∠GHF, then m∠DGH = m∠GHE.

6. If m∠A = m∠B, m∠1 = m∠B, and m∠2 = m∠A, then m∠1 = m∠2.

7. If ∠ACG ≅ ∠ADE, and ∠BCG ≅ ∠ADF, then ∠1 ≅ ∠2.

8. If $\overline{AB} \cong \overline{CD}$, and $\overline{EF} \cong \overline{CD}$, then $\overline{AB} \cong \overline{EF}$.

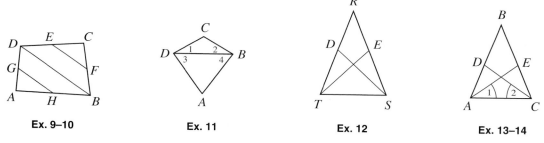

| Ex. 9–10 | Ex. 11 | Ex. 12 | Ex. 13–14 |

9. If $EF = \frac{1}{2} DB$ and $GH = \frac{1}{2} DB$, then EF = GH.

10. If CE = CF, CD = 2CE, and CB = 2CF, then CD = CB.

11. If ∠1 ≅ ∠2 and ∠3 ≅ ∠4, then ∠CDA ≅ ∠CBA.

12. If RT = RS, $RD = \frac{1}{2} RT$, and $RE = \frac{1}{2} RS$, then RD = RE.

13. If AD = CE and DB = EB, then AB = CB.

14. If m∠BAC = m∠BCA, $m\angle 1 = \frac{1}{2} m\angle BAC$, and $m\angle 2 = \frac{1}{2} m\angle BCA$, then m∠1 = m∠2.

In 15–17, $\overleftrightarrow{RST}$, $\overrightarrow{SQ}$, and $\overrightarrow{SP}$ are given.

15. If ∠QSR ≅ ∠PST and m∠QSP = 96, find m∠QSR.

16. If m∠QSR = 40 and $\overrightarrow{SQ} \perp \overrightarrow{SP}$, find m∠PST.

17. If m∠PSQ is twice m∠QSR and $\overrightarrow{SQ} \perp \overrightarrow{SP}$, find m∠PST.

Ex. 15–17

3-12 USING POSTULATES AND DEFINITIONS IN PROOFS

Often, it is necessary to use a combination of definitions and postulates in order to prove a theorem. A carefully drawn figure can be very helpful in deciding upon the steps to use in the proof. However, we may not assume special relationships that appear to be true in the figure drawn for a particular problem. For example, we may not assume that two line segments are congruent or are perpendicular because they appear to be so in the figure.

On the other hand, unless otherwise stated, we will assume that lines that appear to be straight lines in a figure actually are straight lines and that points that appear to be on a given line actually are on that line in the order shown.

EXAMPLES

1. *Given:* $\overleftrightarrow{ABCD}$ *with* $\overline{AB} \cong \overline{CD}$.

Prove: $\overline{AC} \cong \overline{BD}$.

$A \bullet\!\!-\!\!\bullet\!\!-\!\!-\!\!\bullet\!\!-\!\!\bullet D$
    B C

Statements	*Reasons*
1. A, B, C, and D are collinear with B between A and C and C between B and D.	1. Given.
2. $\overline{AB} + \overline{BC} = \overline{AC}$. $\overline{BC} + \overline{CD} = \overline{BD}$.	2. Definition of the sum of two segments.
3. $\overline{AB} \cong \overline{CD}$.	3. Given.
4. $\overline{BC} \cong \overline{BC}$.	4. Reflexive property.
5. $\overline{AB} + \overline{BC} \cong \overline{CD} + \overline{BC}$.	5. Addition postulate.
6. $\overline{AC} \cong \overline{BD}$.	6. Substitution postulate.

2. *Given:* M is the midpoint of $\overline{AB}$.

Prove: $AM = \frac{1}{2}AB$ and $MB = \frac{1}{2}AB$.

$\bullet\!\!-\!\!-\!\!-\!\!\bullet\!\!-\!\!-\!\!-\!\!\bullet$
A M B

Statements	*Reasons*
1. M is the midpoint of $\overline{AB}$.	1. Given.
2. $\overline{AM} \cong \overline{MB}$.	2. Definition of midpoint.
3. $AM = MB$.	3. Definition of congruent segments.
4. $AM + MB = AB$.	4. Partition postulate.
5. $AM + AM = AB$ or $2AM = AB$.	5. Substitution postulate.
6. $AM = \frac{1}{2}AB$.	6. Halves of equal quantities are equal.
7. Also, $MB + MB = AB$ or $2MB = AB$.	7. Substitution postulate.
8. $MB = \frac{1}{2}AB$.	8. Halves of equal quantities are equal.

EXERCISES WITH OPEN-RESPONSE PROBLEMS

In 1–10, in each case: **a.** Rewrite the conditional statement in the *Given* and *Prove* format.   **b.** Write a formal proof that demonstrates that the conclusion is valid.

Ex. 1

Ex. 2

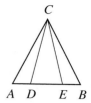

Ex. 3

1. If $\overline{AB} \cong \overline{CB}$, $\overline{FD}$ bisects $\overline{AB}$, and $\overline{FE}$ bisects $\overline{CB}$, then $\overline{AD} \cong \overline{CE}$.
2. If $\overrightarrow{CA}$ bisects both $\angle DCB$ and $\angle DAB$, and $\angle DCB \cong \angle DAB$, then $\angle r \cong \angle s$.
3. If $\overline{AD} \cong \overline{BE}$, then $\overline{AE} \cong \overline{BD}$.

Ex. 4

Ex. 5

Ex. 6

4. If $\overrightarrow{AD}$ bisects $\angle CAB$, $\overrightarrow{EB}$ bisects $\angle CBA$, and $\angle CAB \cong \angle CBA$, then $\angle 1 \cong \angle 2$.
5. If $\overline{DF} \cong \overline{BE}$, then $\overline{DE} \cong \overline{BF}$.
6. If $\angle LQM \cong \angle NQP$, then $\angle LQN \cong \angle MQP$.

Ex. 7

Ex. 8

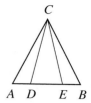

Ex. 9

7. If $\overline{AD} \cong \overline{BC}$, E is the midpoint of $\overline{AD}$, and F is the midpoint of $\overline{BC}$, then $\overline{AE} \cong \overline{FC}$.
8. If $\overline{AC} \cong \overline{DB}$ and $\overline{AC}$ and $\overline{DB}$ bisect each other at E, then $\overline{AE} \cong \overline{EB}$.
9. If $\overrightarrow{DR}$ bisects $\angle CDA$, $\angle 3 \cong \angle 1$, and $\angle 4 \cong \angle 2$, then $\angle 3 \cong \angle 4$.

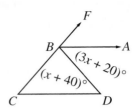

10. If m∠1 + m∠3 + m∠C = 180,
m∠2 + m∠4 + m∠C = 180,
and m∠3 = m∠4,
then m∠1 = m∠2.

11. If $\overrightarrow{BA}$ bisects ∠FBD and m∠ABD = m∠BDC:
   a. Prove that m∠ABF = m∠BDC.
   b. Find the number of degrees in ∠ABF when
   m∠ABD = 3x + 20 and m∠BDC = x + 40.

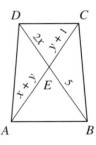

Ex. 12   **Ex. 13**

12. If ∠EFG ≅ ∠ABC and ∠EFH ≅ ∠ABD:
   a. Prove that ∠HFG ≅ ∠DBC.
   b. Solve for x and y when m∠EFH = x − y, m∠HFG = 50, m∠ABD = 30, and m∠DBC = x + y.

13. If $\overline{DB} ≅ \overline{AC}$ and $\overline{AE} ≅ \overline{EB}$:
   a. Prove that $\overline{DE} ≅ \overline{EC}$.
   b. Find lengths DE, EC, DB, and AC when AE = x + y, EB = 5, DE = 2x, and EC = y + 1.

3-13 PROVING SIMPLE THEOREMS ABOUT ANGLES

In Section 3-5 a theorem was defined as a statement proved by deductive reasoning. In this section we will use definitions and postulates to prove some simple angle theorems. The theorems proved in this section will be used in later chapters to prove other theorems.

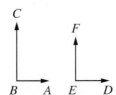

● **THEOREM 1. If two angles are right angles, then they are congruent.**

Given: ∠ABC and ∠DEF are right angles.

Prove: ∠ABC ≅ ∠DEF.

Statements	Reasons
1. ∠ABC and ∠DEF are right angles.	1. Given.
2. m∠ABC = 90, m∠DEF = 90.	2. Definition of right angle.
3. m∠ABC = m∠DEF.	3. Transitive postulate of equality.
4. ∠ABC ≅ ∠DEF.	4. Definition of congruent angles.

- **THEOREM 2. If two angles are straight angles, then they are congruent.**

The proof of this theorem is left to the student. However, here and for other theorems not proved in this book, clues are provided so that the student can understand the hypothesis and the conclusion.

Given ∠ABC and ∠DEF, which are both straight angles, prove that ∠ABC ≅ ∠DEF. The proof of this theorem is similar to the proof of Theorem 1.

Definitions Involving Pairs of Angles

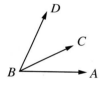

- **DEFINITION.** *Adjacent angles* are two angles in the same plane that have a common vertex and a common side but do not have any interior points in common.

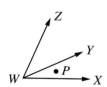

As shown here, ∠ABC and ∠CBD are adjacent angles because they have B as their common vertex and $\overrightarrow{BC}$ as their common side, with no interior points in common. However, ∠XWY and ∠XWZ are not adjacent angles because, although they have W as their common vertex and $\overrightarrow{WX}$ as their common side, they do have interior points in common. For example, point P is in the interior of both ∠XWY and ∠XWZ.

- **DEFINITION.** *Complementary angles* are two angles the sum of whose degree measures is 90.

Each angle is called the *complement* of the other.

If m∠c = 40 and m∠d = 50, then ∠c and ∠d are complementary angles. If m∠a = 35 and m∠b = 55, then ∠a and ∠b are complementary angles. Complementary angles may be adjacent, as in the case of ∠c and ∠d, or they may be nonadjacent, as in the case of ∠a and ∠b.

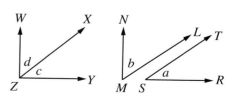

Since m∠c + m∠d = 90, we say that ∠c is the complement of ∠d, and that ∠d is the complement of ∠c. We can represent the degree measure of the complement of an angle whose degree measure is k by (90 − k) because k + (90 − k) = 90.

- **DEFINITION.** *Supplementary angles* are two angles the sum of whose degree measures is 180.

Each angle is called the *supplement* of the other.

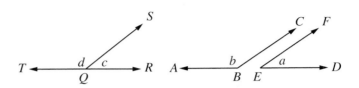

If m∠c = 40 and m∠d = 140, then ∠c and ∠d are supplementary angles. If m∠a = 35 and m∠b = 145, then ∠a and ∠b are supplementary angles. Supplementary angles may be adjacent, as in the case of ∠c and ∠d, or they may be nonadjacent, as in the case of ∠a and ∠b.

Since m∠c + m∠d = 180, we say that ∠c is the supplement of ∠d and that ∠d is the supplement of ∠c. We can represent the degree measure of the supplement of an angle whose degree measure is k by (180 − k) because k + (180 − k) = 180.

Theorems Involving Pairs of Angles

- **THEOREM 3. If two angles are complements of the same angle, then they are congruent.**

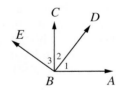

Given: ∠1 is complementary to ∠2.
　　　　∠3 is complementary to ∠2.

Prove: ∠1 ≅ ∠3.

Statements	*Reasons*
1. ∠1 is the complement of ∠2.	1. Given.
2. m∠1 + m∠2 = 90.	2. Complementary angles are two angles the sum of whose degree measures is 90. (*Or:* Definition of complementary angles.)
3. ∠3 is the complement of ∠2.	3. Given.
4. m∠3 + m∠2 = 90.	4. Definition of complementary angles.
5. m∠1 + m∠2 = m∠3 + m∠2.	5. Transitive property of equality.
6. m∠2 = m∠2.	6. Reflexive property of equality.
7. m∠1 = m∠3.	7. Subtraction postulate of equality.
8. ∠1 ≅ ∠3.	8. Congruent angles are angles that have the same measure. (*Or:* Definition of congruent angles.)

Note. In a proof, there are two acceptable ways to indicate a definition as a reason. In reason 2 of the proof above, the definition of complementary angles is stated in its complete form. It is also acceptable to indicate this reason by the phrase "Definition of complementary angles," as in reason 4 of the same proof.

The figure shows an algebraic explanation for the theorem just proved. Here, $m\angle CBD = x$. Both $\angle ABD$ and $\angle CBE$ are complements to $\angle CBD$. Thus, $m\angle ABD = 90 - x$ and $m\angle CBE = 90 - x$, and we conclude $\angle ABD \cong \angle CBE$.

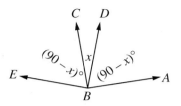

- **THEOREM 4. If two angles are congruent, their complements are congruent.**

If $\angle ABD \cong \angle EFH$, $\angle CBD$ is complementary to $\angle ABD$, and $\angle GFH$ is complementary to $\angle EFH$, then $\angle CBD \cong \angle GFH$. This proof is similar to the proof of Theorem 3 but requires the use of the substitution postulate.

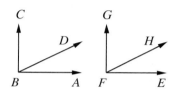

- **THEOREM 5. If two angles are supplements of the same angle, then they are congruent.**

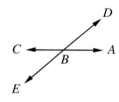

If $\angle ABD$ is supplementary to $\angle DBC$, and $\angle EBC$ is supplementary to $\angle DBC$, then $\angle ABD \cong \angle EBC$.

- **THEOREM 6. If two angles are congruent, then their supplements are congruent.**

If $\angle ABD \cong \angle EFH$, $\angle CBD$ is supplementary to $\angle ABD$, and $\angle GFH$ is supplementary to $\angle EFH$, then $\angle CBD \cong \angle GFH$.

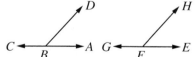

More Definitions and Theorems Involving Pairs of Angles

- **DEFINITION.** A *linear pair of angles* are two adjacent angles whose sum is a straight angle.

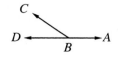

In the figure, $\angle ABD$ is a straight angle and C is not on $\angle ABD$. Therefore, $\angle ABC + \angle CBD = \angle ABD$. Note that $\angle ABC$ and $\angle CBD$ are adjacent angles whose common side is $\overrightarrow{BC}$ and whose remaining sides are opposite rays that together form a straight line, $\overleftrightarrow{AD}$. The term *linear* tells us that a *line* is part of the figure.

- **THEOREM 7. If two angles form a linear pair, they are supplementary.**

In the figure, $\angle ABC$ and $\angle CBD$ form a linear pair. They share a common side, $\overrightarrow{BC}$, and their remaining sides, $\overrightarrow{BA}$ and $\overrightarrow{BD}$, are opposite rays. Thus $\angle ABC$ and $\angle CBD$ are supplementary.

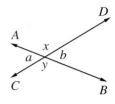

- **DEFINITION.** *Vertical angles* are two angles in which the sides of one angle are opposite rays to the sides of the second angle.

In the figure, $\angle a$ and $\angle b$ are a pair of vertical angles; $\angle x$ and $\angle y$ are also a pair of vertical angles. In each pair of vertical angles, the opposite rays, which are the sides of the angles, form straight lines, $\overleftrightarrow{AB}$ and $\overleftrightarrow{CD}$. Also, when two straight lines intersect, two pairs of vertical angles are formed.

- **THEOREM 8. If two angles are vertical angles, then they are congruent.**

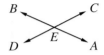

Given: $\angle BEC$ and $\angle AED$ are vertical angles.

Prove: $\angle BEC \cong \angle AED$.

Statements	*Reasons*
1. $\angle BEC$ and $\angle AED$ are vertical angles.	1. Given.
2. $\overrightarrow{EB}$ and $\overrightarrow{EA}$ are opposite rays. $\overrightarrow{ED}$ and $\overrightarrow{EC}$ are opposite rays.	2. Definition of vertical angles.
3. $\overleftrightarrow{AEB}$ and $\overleftrightarrow{CED}$ are lines.	3. Definition of opposite rays.
4. $\angle BEC$ and $\angle AEC$ are a linear pair. $\angle AED$ and $\angle AEC$ are a linear pair.	4. Definition of a linear pair.
5. $\angle BEC$ and $\angle AEC$ are supplementary. $\angle AED$ and $\angle AEC$ are supplementary.	5. If two angles form a linear pair, they are supplementary.
6. $\angle BEC \cong \angle AED$.	6. If two angles are supplements of the same angle, they are congruent.

In the proof above, reasons 5 and 6 demonstrate how previously proved theorems can be used as reasons in deducing statements in a proof.

How to Present a Formal Proof

In this chapter, we have seen the steps to be taken in presenting a formal proof in geometry using deductive reasoning.

1. As an aid, carefully draw a good *figure* which pictures the data of the theorem or the problem. Letter the figure.
2. State the *given*, which is the hypothesis of the theorem, in terms of the lettered figure.
3. State the *prove*, which is the conclusion of the theorem, in terms of the lettered figure.
4. Present the *proof*, which is a series of logical arguments used in the demonstration. Each step in the proof should consist of a *statement* and its *reason*. A reason may be the *given*, a *definition*, a *postulate*, or a *previously proved theorem*. The proof may be presented in a two-column format or in paragraph form.

EXAMPLES

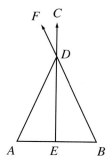

1. Write a formal proof: If $\overleftrightarrow{CE}$ bisects $\angle ADB$, and $\overleftrightarrow{FDB}$ and $\overleftrightarrow{CDE}$ intersect, then $\angle ADE \cong \angle FDC$.

Given: $\overleftrightarrow{CD}$ bisects $\angle ADB$.
$\overrightarrow{FDB}$ and $\overrightarrow{CDE}$ intersect.

Prove: $\angle ADE \cong \angle FDC$.

Statements	*Reasons*
1. $\overleftrightarrow{CE}$ bisects $\angle ADB$.	1. Given.
2. $\angle ADE \cong \angle BDE$.	2. Definition of a bisector of an angle.
3. $\overleftrightarrow{FDB}$ and $\overleftrightarrow{CDE}$ intersect.	3. Given.
4. $\angle BDE$ and $\angle FDC$ are vertical angles.	4. Definition of vertical angles.
5. $\angle BDE \cong \angle FDC$.	5. If two angles are vertical angles, then they are congruent.
6. $\angle ADE \cong \angle FDC$.	6. Transitive property of equality.

2. Find the measure of an angle if its measure is 20 degrees more than the measure of its complement.

Solution   Let x = measure of complement of angle.

Then $x + 20$ = measure of angle.

The sum of the degree measures of an angle and its complement is 90.

$$x + x + 20 = 90$$
$$2x + 20 = 90$$
$$2x = 70$$
$$x = 35$$
$$x + 20 = 55$$

Answer: The measure of the angle is 55 degrees.

3. In the coordinate plane, the vertices of $\triangle ABC$ are $A(1, -1)$, $B(6, -1)$, and $C(3, 3)$.

   a. Find AB, AC, and BC.
   b. Find the slope of $\overline{AB}$, of $\overline{AC}$, and of $\overline{BC}$.
   c. Using the answer to part **a** as the *given*, explain why $\triangle ABC$ is an isosceles triangle.
   d. Using the answer to part **b** as the *given*, explain why $\triangle ABC$ is *not* a right triangle.

Solutions This is a *coordinate application* in geometry. Information about the sides of a triangle is obtained using coordinates. This information, combined with the definitions of Euclidean geometry, allows us to draw conclusions about the triangle.

a. When two points are on the same horizontal line, we find the length of the line segment joining the points by finding the absolute value of the difference of their x-coordinates:

$$AB = |6 - 1| = 5$$

When two points are not on the same horizontal or vertical line, we find the length of the line segment joining them by using the distance formula,

$$d = \sqrt{(x_2 - x_1)^2 + (y_2 - y_1)^2}:$$
$$AC = \sqrt{(3 - 1)^2 + (3 - (-1))^2} = \sqrt{2^2 + 4^2} = \sqrt{4 + 16} = \sqrt{20}$$
$$BC = \sqrt{(3 - 6)^2 + (3 - (-1))^2} = \sqrt{(-3)^2 + 4^2} = \sqrt{9 + 16} = \sqrt{25} = 5$$

b. Slope of $\overline{AB} = \dfrac{-1 - (-1)}{6 - 1} = \dfrac{0}{5} = 0$

Slope of $\overline{AC} = \dfrac{3 - (-1)}{3 - 1} = \dfrac{4}{2} = 2$

Slope of $\overline{BC} = \dfrac{3 - (-1)}{3 - 6} = \dfrac{4}{-3} = -\dfrac{4}{3}$

c. From part **a**, $AB = BC$. Therefore, $\overline{AB} \cong \overline{BC}$ because congruent line segments are segments that have the same measure. Since an isosceles triangle is a triangle with two congruent sides, $\triangle ABC$ is isosceles.

d. In the coordinate plane, two line segments are perpendicular if either of these conditions is met: (1) one line is horizontal and has a slope of 0 while the second line is vertical and has no slope, or (2) the slopes of the two lines are negative reciprocals, that is, the product of their slopes is -1.

   From part **b**. (1) $\overline{AB}$ is horizontal and has a slope of 0, but neither $\overline{AC}$ nor $\overline{BC}$ is vertical since each segment has a slope. Therefore $\overline{AB}$ and $\overline{AC}$ are not perpendicular, and $\overline{AB}$ and $\overline{BC}$ are not perpendicular. (2) The product of the slopes of $\overline{AC}$ and $\overline{BC} = 2\left(-\dfrac{4}{3}\right) \neq -1$. Thus, $\overline{AC}$ and $\overline{BC}$ are not perpendicular.

   Since no two sides of the triangle are perpendicular, the triangle does not contain a right angle. We conclude that $\triangle ABC$ is not a right triangle.

EXERCISES WITH OPEN-RESPONSE PROBLEMS

In 1–9, in each case write a formal proof, using the *given*, definitions, postulates, and theorems as the reasons for the statements used.

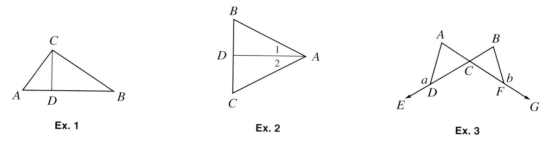

Ex. 1   **Ex. 2**   **Ex. 3**

1. If ACB is a triangle with $\angle ACB$ a right angle and $\overline{CD} \perp \overline{AB}$, then $\angle ACB \cong \angle ADC$.
2. If $\angle 1 \cong \angle 2$, $\angle B$ is complementary to $\angle 1$, and $\angle C$ is complementary to $\angle 2$, then $\angle B \cong \angle C$.
3. If $\overrightarrow{ACFG}$ and $\overrightarrow{BCDE}$ intersect and $\angle a \cong \angle b$, then $\angle ADC \cong \angle BFC$.

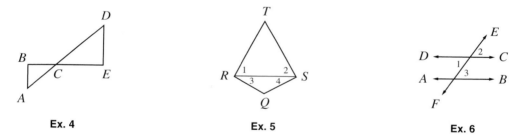

Ex. 4   **Ex. 5**   **Ex. 6**

4. If $\overrightarrow{BE}$ and $\overline{AD}$ intersect at C, $\angle BAC$ is complementary to $\angle ACB$, and $\angle EDC$ is complementary to $\angle ECD$, then $\angle BAC \cong \angle EDC$.
5. If $\overline{TR} \perp \overline{RQ}$, $\overline{TS} \perp \overline{SQ}$, and $\angle 3 \cong \angle 4$, then $\angle 1 \cong \angle 2$.
6. If $\overleftrightarrow{EF}$ intersects $\overleftrightarrow{AB}$ and $\overleftrightarrow{DC}$, and $\angle 3 \cong \angle 2$, then $\angle 1 \cong \angle 3$.

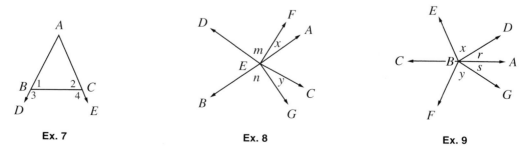

Ex. 7   **Ex. 8**   **Ex. 9**

7. If $\overrightarrow{ABD}$ and $\overrightarrow{ACE}$ intersect, and $\angle 1 \cong \angle 2$, then $\angle 3 \cong \angle 4$.
8. If $\overleftrightarrow{AEB}$ and $\overleftrightarrow{CED}$ intersect at E, and $\angle x \cong \angle y$, then $\angle m \cong \angle n$.
9. Given $\overleftrightarrow{ABC}$, $\angle r \cong \angle s$, $\overrightarrow{BE}$ bisects $\angle CBD$, and $\overrightarrow{BF}$ bisects $\angle CBG$, prove $\angle x \cong \angle y$.

Numerical, Algebraic, and Coordinate Applications

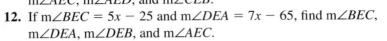

In 10–13, $\overleftrightarrow{AEB}$ and $\overleftrightarrow{CED}$ intersect at E.

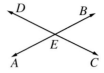

10. If m∠BEC = 70, find m∠AED, m∠DEB, and m∠AEC.
11. If m∠DEB = 2x + 20 and m∠AEC = 3x − 30, find m∠DEB, m∠AEC, m∠AED, and m∠CEB.
12. If m∠BEC = 5x − 25 and m∠DEA = 7x − 65, find m∠BEC, m∠DEA, m∠DEB, and m∠AEC.
13. If m∠BEC = y, m∠DEB = 3x, and m∠DEA = 2x − y, find m∠CEB, m∠BED, m∠DEA, and m∠AEC.

14. Two angles are supplementary. The measure of the smaller angle is one-half the measure of the larger angle. Find the degree measure of the larger angle.
15. The measure of the supplement of an angle is 60 degrees more than twice the measure of the angle. Find the degree measure of the angle.
16. The difference between the degree measures of two supplementary angles is 80. Find the degree measure of the larger angle.
17. Two angles are complementary. The measure of the larger angle is 5 times the measure of the smaller angle. Find the degree measure of the larger angle.
18. Two angles are complementary. The degree measure of the smaller angle is 50 less than the degree measure of the larger. Find the degree measure of the larger angle.
19. The measure of the complement of an angle exceeds the measure of the angle by 24 degrees. Find the degree measure of the angle.
20. $\overleftrightarrow{RS}$ intersects $\overleftrightarrow{LM}$ at P, m∠RPL = x + y, m∠LPS = 3x + 2y, m∠MPS = 3x − 2y.
    a. Solve for x and y.
    b. Find m∠RPL, m∠LPS, and m∠MPS.

21. In the coordinate plane, $A(3, 5)$, $B(-1, 2)$, and $C(1, 1)$ are the vertices of △ABC.
    a. Find AB, AC, and BC.
    b. Find the slope of $\overline{AC}$.
    c. Find the slope of $\overline{BC}$.
    d. What do the answers to parts **b** and **c** tell you about $\overline{AC}$ and $\overline{BC}$?
    e. Using the answers to part **a** as the *given*, explain why △ABC is a scalene triangle.
    f. Using the answer to part **d** as the *given*, explain why △ABC is a right triangle.

CHAPTER SUMMARY

Geometric statements can be proved by using ***deductive*** or ***inductive*** reasoning. Deductive reasoning draws a general conclusion from particular examples. Inductive reasoning applies the ***laws of inference*** to a series of true statements to arrive at a conclusion. The true statements used in deductive reasoning may be the *given*, *definitions*, *postulates*, or *theorems* that have been previously proved.

A *proof* using deductive reasoning may be either *direct* or *indirect*. In direct reasoning, a series of statements that include the given statement lead to the desired conclusion. In indirect reasoning, the negation of the desired conclusion leads to a statement that contradicts a given statement.

VOCABULARY

3-1   Inductive reasoning   Counterexample

3-3   Premise   Hypothesis   Deductive reasoning   Conclusion

3-4   Direct proof   Indirect proof

3-5   Postulate   Axiom   Theorem   Postulational system

3-6   Reflexive property   Symmetric property   Transitive property

3-7   Equivalence relation

3-13   Adjacent angles   Complementary angles   Supplementary angles
        Linear pair of angles   Vertical angles

REVIEW EXERCISES WITH OPEN-RESPONSE PROBLEMS

In 1–3, in each case: **a.** Write the given definition in a conditional form using the words *If . . . then.*   **b.** Write the converse of the statement given as an answer to part **a.**   **c.** Write the biconditional form of the definition.

1. An *obtuse triangle* is a triangle that has one obtuse angle.

2. *Congruent angles* are angles that have the same measure.

3. *Perpendicular lines* are two lines that intersect to form right angles.

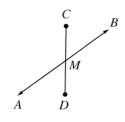

4. *Given:* $\overleftrightarrow{AB}$ bisects $\overline{CD}$ at M.

    Prove: $CM = MD$.

    a. Let P represent "$\overleftrightarrow{AB}$ bisects $\overline{CD}$ at M," let Q represent "$\overline{CM} \cong \overline{MD}$," and let R represent "$CM = MD$." Write a *direct proof in logic*, listing statements in both symbols and words, and citing reasons, to show that $CM = MD$.

    b. Write a *direct geometry proof* to show that $CM = MD$.

    c. To prove that $CM = MD$ by *indirect methods*, what assumption must be made in the proof? (Do not write an indirect proof.)

5. Explain the difference between a postulate and a theorem.

6. Write the property that justifies the statement:
If $AB = CD$, then $CD = AB$.

In 7–10, in each case tell which property or properties of an equivalence relation are true for the given relation and the set given in parentheses.

7. ≅ (for angles)

8. is as tall as (for people)

9. ≠ (for integers)

10. is the sister of (for people)

In 11–17, in each case write a formal proof to show that the conclusion is valid.

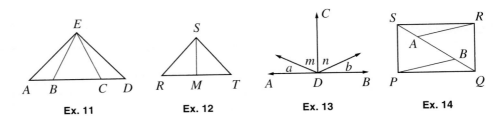

Ex. 11   Ex. 12   Ex. 13   Ex. 14

11. If $\overline{AC} \cong \overline{BD}$, then $\overline{AB} \cong \overline{CD}$.

12. If $\overline{RM} \cong \overline{MS}$ and $\overline{MS} \cong \overline{MT}$, then $\overline{RM} \cong \overline{MT}$.

13. If $\overleftrightarrow{CD} \perp \overleftrightarrow{AB}$ and $\angle m \cong \angle n$, then $\angle a \cong \angle b$.

14. If $SA = BQ$, then $SB = AQ$.

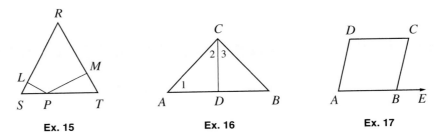

Ex. 15   Ex. 16   Ex. 17

15. If $\overline{PL} \perp \overline{RS}$ and $\overline{PM} \perp \overline{RT}$, then m$\angle PLS$ = m$\angle PMT$.

16. If $\angle ACB$ is a right angle and $\angle 1$ is complementary to $\angle 3$, then $\angle 1 \cong \angle 2$.

17. Given $\overleftrightarrow{ABE}$ and $\angle CBE$ is supplementary to $\angle ADC$, then $\angle ADC \cong \angle ABC$.

In 18–20, $\overleftrightarrow{AEB}$ and $\overleftrightarrow{CED}$ intersect at E.

18. If m$\angle BEC$ = 125, find m$\angle BED$ and m$\angle AED$.

19. If m$\angle BEC$ = $3x + 10$ and m$\angle AED$ = $4x - 30$, find m$\angle BEC$.

20. If m$\angle BEC$ = $9x - 10$ and m$\angle CEA$ = $4x - 5$, find m$\angle BEC$.

21. If $\angle A$ and $\angle B$ are complementary, and $\angle A \cong \angle B$, find m$\angle A$.

22. If $\overline{AB} \cong \overline{CD}$ and $\overline{CD} \cong \overline{EF}$, and if $AB = 2x + 3$ and $CD = 4x - 5$, find EF.

23. The measure of the larger angle of a linear pair is 27 degrees more than twice the measure of the smaller. Find the degree measure of each angle.

24. The measure of the supplement of an angle is 3 times the measure of the complement of the angle. Find the degree measure of the angle.

25. A student wrote the following proof:

Given: $\overline{AB} \cong \overline{CD}$.
$\overline{AB} \perp \overline{BC}$.

Prove: $\overline{CD} \perp \overline{BC}$.

Statements	Reasons
1. $\overline{AB} \cong \overline{CD}$.	1. Given.
2. $AB = CD$.	2. Congruent segments are segments that have the same measures.
3. $\overline{AB} \perp \overline{BC}$.	3. Given.
4. $\overline{CD} \perp \overline{BC}$.	4. A quantity may be substituted for its equal.

What is the error in this proof?

CUMULATIVE REVIEW WITH OPEN-RESPONSE PROBLEMS

1. Definition: A *palindrome* is a sequence of numbers or letters that reads the same from left to right as from right to left.
   a. Write the definition of a palindrome as a conditional statement.
   b. Write the converse of the conditional statement in **a**.
   c. Write the definition as a biconditional.
2. Write a statement that is logically equivalent to $\sim(p \wedge \sim s)$.

Exploration

The following "proof" leads to the statement that twice a number is equal to the number. This would mean, for example, that if $b = 1$, then $2(1) = 1$, which is obviously incorrect. What is the error in the proof?

Given: $a = b$.

Prove: $b = 2b$.

Statements	Reasons
1. $a = b$.	1. Given.
2. $a^2 = ab$.	2. Multiplication postulate.
3. $a^2 - b^2 = ab - b^2$.	3. Subtraction postulate.
4. $(a + b)(a - b) = b(a - b)$.	4. Substitution postulate.
5. $a + b = b$.	5. Division postulate.
6. $b + b = b$.	6. Substitution postulate.
7. $2b = b$.	7. Substitution postulate.

Chapter 4

Triangle Congruence

Alfie and Saniqua were building a base for a birdfeeder. They constructed the base out of metal rods fastened at the ends, forming the edges of a rectangular solid. When they finished, their support was not sturdy enough and they decided to add extra metal rods for strength.

At first they tried to reinforce the base with rods parallel to the four vertical posts but found that the result was still wobbly. Their mother suggested that they look at the way in which the supports for power lines were constructed. The next day, Alfie and Saniqua rode their bicycles to the edge of town, where the power station was located, and studied the structures that supported the incoming power lines. As a result, they decided to remove the extra vertical rods that they had added and replace them with rods that joined opposite corners of each quadrilateral.

Why was this change an improvement? What geometric figure occurs most frequently in weight-bearing structures?

4-1 CONGRUENT POLYGONS AND CORRESPONDING PARTS

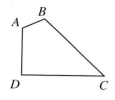

When two polygons are drawn on separate pieces of paper, and these figures can be placed on top of one another in such a way that the sides and angles of one polygon fit exactly on the sides and angles of the other, we call these figures ***congruent polygons***. In other words, congruent polygons have the same size and shape.

In the diagram, polygon *ABCD* is congruent to polygon *EFGH*. Note that the congruent polygons are named in such a way that the order of their vertices indicates a ***one-to-one correspondence*** of points.

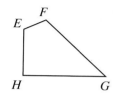

ABCD ≅ *EFGH* indicates that:

A corresponds to *E*; *E* corresponds to *A*.

B corresponds to *F*; *F* corresponds to *B*.

C corresponds to *G*; *G* corresponds to *C*.

D corresponds to *H*; *H* corresponds to *D*.

Congruent polygons should always be named so as to indicate the correspondences between the vertices of the polygons.

Corresponding Parts of Congruent Polygons

Corresponding angles   In congruent polygons *ABCD* and *EFGH* shown above, vertex *A* corresponds to vertex *E*. Angles *A* and *E* are called ***corresponding angles***, and ∠*A* ≅ ∠*E*.

In this example, there are four pairs of such corresponding angles:

$$\angle A \cong \angle E \qquad \angle B \cong \angle F \qquad \angle C \cong \angle G \qquad \angle D \cong \angle H$$

In congruent polygons, *corresponding angles are congruent.*

Corresponding sides   In congruent polygons *ABCD* and *EFGH*, since *A* corresponds to *E* and *B* corresponds to *F*, $\overline{AB}$ and $\overline{EF}$ are ***corresponding sides***, and $\overline{AB} \cong \overline{EF}$.

In this example, there are four pairs of such corresponding sides:

$$\overline{AB} \cong \overline{EF} \qquad \overline{BC} \cong \overline{FG} \qquad \overline{CD} \cong \overline{GH} \qquad \overline{DA} \cong \overline{HE}$$

In congruent polygons, *corresponding sides are congruent.*

The pairs of congruent angles and the pairs of congruent sides are called the *corresponding parts of congruent polygons.* We can now present the formal definition for congruent polygons.

● **DEFINITION.** *Two polygons are congruent* if and only if there is a one-to-one correspondence between their vertices such that:

1. Corresponding angles are congruent.

2. Corresponding sides are congruent.

Let us consider this definition in symbolic form, where

a represents "the angles of each pair of corresponding angles are congruent";
s represents "the sides of each pair of corresponding sides are congruent"; and
p represents "the two polygons are congruent."

Observe that the definition, which is stated in biconditional form, contains the conjunction $(a \wedge s)$; that is:

$(a \wedge s) \rightarrow p$: If the angles of each pair of corresponding angles are congruent and the sides of each pair of corresponding sides are congruent, then the two polygons are congruent;

and

$p \rightarrow (a \wedge s)$: If two polygons are congruent, then the angles of each pair of corresponding angles are congruent and the sides of each pair of corresponding sides are congruent.

By the Law of Simplification, $(a \wedge s) \rightarrow a$
and $(a \wedge s) \rightarrow s$.

By the Chain Rule, from $p \rightarrow (a \wedge s)$ and $(a \wedge s) \rightarrow a$
we may conclude $p \rightarrow a$,
and from $p \rightarrow (a \wedge s)$ and $(a \wedge s) \rightarrow s$
we may conclude $p \rightarrow s$.

Thus, we may write:

$p \rightarrow a$: If two polygons are congruent, then the angles of each pair of corresponding angles are congruent.
$p \rightarrow s$: If two polygons are congruent, then the sides of each pair of corresponding sides are congruent.

These statements can be written more simply as follows:

- **Corresponding parts of congruent polygons are congruent.**

Congruent Triangles

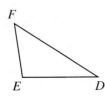

The simplest possible polygon is the triangle, a polygon with exactly three sides. In the figure, $\triangle ABC$ and $\triangle DEF$ are congruent triangles.

From the correspondence established, we can list six facts about these triangles: three facts about corresponding sides and three facts about corresponding angles. In the table that follows, these six facts are stated as equalities in the column at the right.

Congruences	**Equalities**
$\overline{AB} \cong \overline{DE}.$	$AB = DE.$
$\overline{BC} \cong \overline{EF}.$	$BC = EF.$
$\overline{AC} \cong \overline{DF}.$	$AC = DF.$
$\angle A \cong \angle D.$	$m\angle A = m\angle D.$
$\angle B \cong \angle E.$	$m\angle B = m\angle E.$
$\angle C \cong \angle F.$	$m\angle C = m\angle F.$

Since each congruence statement is equivalent to an equality statement, we will use whichever notation serves our purpose better in a particular situation.

For example, in one proof, we may prefer to write $\overline{AC} \cong \overline{DF}$, and in another proof, to write $AC = DF$. In the same way, we might write $\angle C \cong \angle F$ or we might write $m\angle C = m\angle F$. From the definition, we may now say:

- **Corresponding parts of congruent triangles are equal in measure.**

In two congruent triangles, pairs of corresponding sides are always opposite pairs of corresponding angles. The preceding figure, where $\triangle ABC \cong \triangle DEF$, shows that:

1. $\angle C$ and $\angle F$ are corresponding congruent angles.
2. $\overline{AB}$ is opposite $\angle C$, and $\overline{DE}$ is opposite $\angle F$.
3. $\overline{AB}$ and $\overline{DE}$ are corresponding congruent sides.

Equivalence Relation of Congruence

In Section 3-7 we saw that the relation *is congruent to* is an equivalence relation for the set of angles, and is also an equivalence relation for the set of line segments. Let us test this relation for the set of all triangles.

1. Reflexive property: $\triangle ABC \cong \triangle ABC.$
2. Symmetric property: If $\triangle ABC \cong \triangle DEF$, then $\triangle DEF \cong \triangle ABC.$
3. Transitive property: If $\triangle ABC \cong \triangle DEF$ and $\triangle DEF \cong \triangle RST$, then $\triangle ABC \cong \triangle RST.$

By referring to the congruence of corresponding angles and corresponding sides of triangles, we can prove that the congruence of triangles is an equivalence relation. In addition, these examples suggest that the congruence of geometric figures in general will be an equivalence relation. Therefore, we state these properties of congruence as three postulates.

- **POSTULATE. Any geometric figure is congruent to itself. (Reflexive property.)**
- **POSTULATE. A congruence may be expressed in either order. (Symmetric property.)**
- **POSTULATE. Two geometric figures congruent to the same geometric figure are congruent to each other. (Transitive property.)**

EXERCISES

In 1–3, in each case name three pairs of corresponding angles and three pairs of corresponding sides in the given congruent triangles. Use the symbol $\cong$ to indicate that the angles named and also the sides named in your answers are congruent.

1.

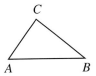

$\triangle ADC \cong \triangle BDC$

2.

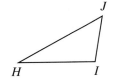

$\triangle AEC \cong \triangle BEC$

3.

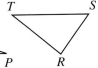

$\triangle CDE \cong \triangle ABF$

4. Referring to the four triangles that follow: **a.** Name the figures that appear to be congruent, using the correct order of their vertices and the symbol $\cong$.   **b.** Use the symbol $=$ to indicate the corresponding parts whose measures are equal.

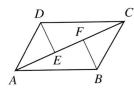

In 5–10, *ABCD* is a square and $\overline{AC}$ intersects $\overline{BD}$ at *E*. Name the property that justifies each statement.

5. $\triangle CAD \cong \triangle CAD$.

6. If $\triangle DBA \cong \triangle DBC$, then $\triangle DBC \cong \triangle DBA$.

7. Square *ABCD* $\cong$ square *ABCD*.

8. If $\triangle AED \cong \triangle CED$ and $\triangle CED \cong \triangle CEB$, then $\triangle AED \cong \triangle CEB$.

9. If $DB = AC$, then $AC = DB$.

10. If $\triangle CAD \cong \triangle CAB$ and $\triangle CAB \cong \triangle BDC$, then $\triangle CAD \cong \triangle BDC$.

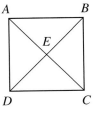

4-2 PROVING TRIANGLES CONGRUENT USING SIDE, ANGLE, SIDE

In Math A, you saw that it was possible to prove two triangles congruent by proving that fewer than three pairs of sides and three pairs of angles were congruent. For example, the diagrams and the explanation that follow show how to use a ruler and a protractor to copy a triangle by drawing only two sides and the angle *included* between these sides.

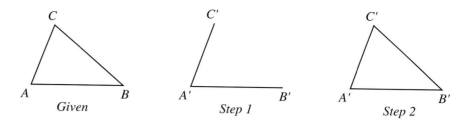

Given   *Step 1*   *Step 2*

Given $\triangle ABC$. In step 1, copy $\overline{AB}$ to form $\overline{A'B'}$, copy the included $\angle A$ to form the included $\angle A'$, and copy $\overline{AC}$ to form $\overline{A'C'}$. Although only two sides and their included angle were copied, note in step 2 that the only way to complete the triangle is to connect B' and C'. Triangle $A'B'C'$ is formed, and $\triangle A'B'C' \cong \triangle ABC$.

This experiment, repeated several times, leads to the following statement, whose truth will be assumed without proof:

- **POSTULATE. Two triangles are congruent if two sides and the included angle of one triangle are congruent, respectively, to two sides and the included angle of the other. [s.a.s. $\cong$ s.a.s.]**

Thus, in $\triangle ABC$ and $\triangle A'B'C'$ above, if $\overline{AB} \cong \overline{A'B'}$, $\angle A \cong \angle A'$, and $\overline{AC} \cong \overline{A'C'}$, it follows that $\triangle ABC \cong \triangle A'B'C'$.

Note. When congruent sides and angles are listed, a correspondence is established. Since $\angle A \cong \angle A'$, A and A' are corresponding vertices. Then, since $\overline{AB} \cong \overline{A'B'}$ and A corresponds to A', B must correspond to B'; and since $\overline{AC} \cong \overline{A'C'}$, C must correspond to C'. This establishes the correspondence that is used in writing the triangle congruence as $\triangle ABC \cong \triangle A'B'C'$.

EXAMPLE

In $\triangle ABC$, if $\overline{AC} \cong \overline{BC}$ and $\overline{CD}$ is the bisector of $\angle ACB$, prove that $\triangle ACD \cong \triangle BCD$.

Given: $\triangle ABC$ with $\overline{AC} \cong \overline{BC}$.
$\overline{CD}$ bisects $\angle ACB$.

Prove: $\triangle ACD \cong \triangle BCD$.

Plan: Prove the triangles congruent by showing that s.a.s. $\cong$ s.a.s.

Statements	*Reasons*
1. In △ABC, $\overline{AC} \cong \overline{BC}$. (s. ≅ s.)	1. Given
2. $\overline{CD}$ bisects ∠ACB.	2. Given.
3. ∠1 ≅ ∠2. (a. ≅ a.)	3. Definition of angle bisector.
4. $\overline{CD} \cong \overline{CD}$. (s. ≅ s.)	4. Reflexive property of congruence.
5. △ACD ≅ △BCD.	5. s.a.s. ≅ s.a.s.

Note. In steps 1, 3, and 4, we wrote (s. ≅ s.) next to pairs of congruent sides and (a. ≅ a.) next to pairs of congruent angles to help identify the corresponding parts that prove the triangles are congruent.

As an additional aid, you may mark corresponding parts of the diagram with the same number of strokes or arcs. For example, in the diagram above:

∠1 and ∠2 are marked by single arcs to show ∠1 ≅ ∠2.

$\overline{AC}$ and $\overline{BC}$ are marked by single strokes to show $\overline{AC} \cong \overline{BC}$.

$\overline{CD}$ is marked with an X to show $\overline{CD} \cong \overline{CD}$.

EXERCISES WITH OPEN-RESPONSE PROBLEMS

In 1–6: Pairs of line segments marked with the same number of strokes are congruent. Pairs of angles marked with the same number of arcs are congruent. A line segment or an angle marked with X is congruent to itself by the reflexive property of congruence.

In each case, is the given information sufficient to prove congruent triangles?

1.

2.

3.

4.

5.

6.

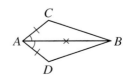

In 7–9, in each case name the pair of corresponding sides or the pair of corresponding angles that would have to be proved congruent (in addition to those pairs marked congruent) in order to prove that the triangles are congruent by s.a.s. ≅ s.a.s.

7.

8.

9.

Ex. 10

Ex. 11

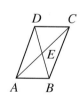

Ex. 12

10. *Given:* $\overline{DE} \cong \overline{AB}$, $\overline{EF} \cong \overline{BC}$, ∠E and ∠B are right angles.
  Prove: △DEF ≅ △ABC.

11. *Given:* $\overline{AE} \cong \overline{BC}$, ∠E ≅ ∠C, D is the midpoint of $\overline{EC}$.
  Prove: △ADE ≅ △BDC.

12. *Given:* $\overline{RS}$ bisects $\overline{PQ}$ at T. $\overline{PQ}$ bisects $\overline{RS}$ at T.
  Prove: △PTS ≅ △QTR.

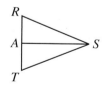

Ex. 13   **Ex. 14**   **Ex. 15**   **Ex. 16**

13. *Given:* $\overline{AB} \cong \overline{AD}$, $\overline{AC}$ bisects ∠BAD.
  Prove: △ABC ≅ △ADC.

14. *Given:* $\overline{AS} \perp \overline{RT}$, A is the midpoint of $\overline{RT}$.
  Prove: △RAS ≅ △TAS.

15. If $\overline{AP} \cong \overline{CP}$, ∠x ≅ ∠y, and $\overleftrightarrow{BPD}$, prove that △ABP ≅ △CBP.

16. If $\overline{DB}$ and $\overline{AC}$ bisect each other at E, prove that △AEB ≅ △CED.

17. In the coordinate plane, the vertices of △ABC and △DEB are A(−2, 5), B(2, 2), C(−2, 2), D(5, 2), and E(2, −2).
  a. Draw △ABC and △DEB.
  b. Find m∠ACB and m∠DBE.
  c. Find AC, CB, DB, and BE.
  d. Are △ABC and △DEB congruent? Explain your answer.

4-3 PROVING TRIANGLES CONGRUENT USING ANGLE, SIDE, ANGLE

In Math A, you saw that a triangle can be copied, using a ruler and protractor, by drawing only two angles and the side *included* between these angles. The diagrams and the explanation that follow show how this is done.

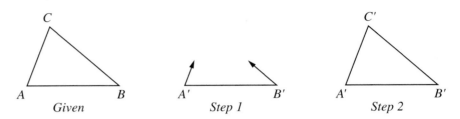

Start with △*ABC*. In step 1, copy ∠*A* to form ∠*A′*, copy the included side $\overline{AB}$ to form the included side $\overline{A'B'}$, and copy ∠*B* to form ∠*B′*. Although only two angles and their included side were copied, note in step 2 that, to extend the rays at *A′* and *B′*, these rays must be made to meet at a point that we call *C′*. Triangle *A′B′C′* is formed such that △*A′B′C′* ≅ △*ABC*.

This experiment, repeated several times, leads to the following statements, whose truth will be assumed without proof:

• **POSTULATE. Two triangles are congruent if two angles and the included side of one triangle are congruent, respectively, to two angles and the included side of the other. [a.s.a. ≅ a.s.a.]**

Thus, in △*ABC* and △*A′B′C′*, if ∠*A* ≅ ∠*A′*, $\overline{AB} ≅ \overline{A'B'}$, and ∠*B* ≅ ∠*B′*, it follows that △*ABC* ≅ △*A′B′C′*. We will now use this postulate to prove two triangles congruent.

EXAMPLE

Given: $\overleftrightarrow{CD}$ and $\overleftrightarrow{AB}$ intersect at *E*.
$\overline{BA}$ bisects $\overline{CD}$.
$\overline{AC} ⊥ \overline{CD}, \overline{BD} ⊥ \overline{CD}$.

Prove: △*ACE* ≅ △*BDE*.

Plan: Prove the triangles congruent by showing that a.s.a. ≅ a.s.a. (Insert numbers for easy reference to angles.)

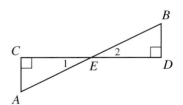

Statements	*Reasons*
1. $\overleftrightarrow{CD}$ and $\overleftrightarrow{AB}$ intersect E.	1. Given.
2. $\angle 1$ and $\angle 2$ are vertical angles.	2. Definition of vertical angles.
3. $\angle 1 \cong \angle 2$. (a. $\cong$ a.)	3. If two angles are vertical angles, they are congruent.
4. $\overline{BA}$ bisects $\overline{CD}$.	4. Given.
5. $\overline{CE} \cong \overline{ED}$. (s. $\cong$ s.)	5. Definition of bisector of a line segment.
6. $\overline{AC} \perp \overline{CD}$, $\overline{BD} \perp \overline{CD}$.	6. Given.
7. $\angle C$ and $\angle D$ are right angles.	7. Definition of perpendicular lines.
8. $\angle C \cong \angle D$. (a. $\cong$ a.)	8. If two angles are right angles, they are congruent.
9. $\triangle ACE \cong \triangle BDE$.	9. a.s.a. $\cong$ a.s.a.

EXERCISES WITH OPEN-RESPONSE PROBLEMS

In 1–3, tell whether the triangles in each pair can be proved congruent by the a.s.a. $\cong$ a.s.a. postulate, using only the marked congruent parts in establishing the congruence. Give the reason for your answer.

1.

2.

3.
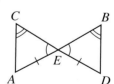

In 4–6, in each case name the pair of corresponding sides or the pair of corresponding angles that would have to be proved congruent (in addition to those pairs marked congruent) in order to prove that the triangles are congruent by a.s.a. $\cong$ a.s.a.

4.

5.

6.

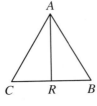

Ex. 7   **Ex. 8**   **Ex. 9**   **Ex. 10**

7. *Given:* ∠1 ≅ ∠2, *D* is the midpoint of $\overline{EC}$, ∠3 ≅ ∠4.
   Prove: △*AED* ≅ △*BCD*.
8. *Given:* $\overrightarrow{DB}$ bisects ∠*ADC*, $\overrightarrow{BD}$ bisects ∠*ABC*.
   Prove: △*ADB* ≅ △*CDB*.
9. *Given:* $\overline{AR}$ ⊥ $\overline{CB}$, $\overrightarrow{AR}$ bisects ∠*CAB*.
   Prove: △*ACR* ≅ △*ABR*.
10. *Given:* $\overline{DCFA}$, ∠*E* ≅ ∠*B*, $\overline{ED}$ ≅ $\overline{AB}$, $\overline{FD}$ ⊥ $\overline{DE}$, $\overline{CA}$ ⊥ $\overline{AB}$.
    Prove: △*DEF* ≅ △*ABC*.

4-4 PROVING TRIANGLES CONGRUENT USING SIDE, SIDE, SIDE

In Math A, you used compasses to construct a triangle by copying the three sides of the triangle. The diagram and explanation that follow show how this is done.

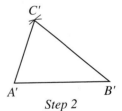

Given   *Step 1*   *Step 2*

Given △*ABC*. In step 1, copy side $\overline{AB}$ to form side $\overline{A'B'}$. In step 2, using *A'* as the center of a circle, mark off an arc whose radius is *AC*. Also, using *B'* as the center of a different circle, mark off an arc whose radius is *BC*. The arcs intersect at point *C'*, forming △*A'B'C'*. [You can measure the angles to see that ∠*A* ≅ ∠*A'*, ∠*B* ≅ ∠*B'*, and ∠*C* ≅ ∠*C'*.] Thus, using only three sides, we see that △*ABC* ≅ △*A'B'C'*. Repeated experiments lead to the next statement, whose truth is assumed without proof.

● **POSTULATE. Two triangles are congruent if the three sides of one triangle are congruent, respectively, to the three sides of the other. [s.s.s. ≅ s.s.s.]**

Thus, in △*ABC* and △*A'B'C'*, if $\overline{AB}$ ≅ $\overline{A'B'}$, $\overline{BC}$ ≅ $\overline{B'C'}$, and $\overline{CA}$ ≅ $\overline{C'A'}$, it follows that △*ABC* ≅ △*A'B'C'*. We will now use this postulate to prove two triangles congruent.

EXAMPLE

Given: Isosceles triangle *ABC* with $\overline{CA} \cong \overline{CB}$.
D is the midpoint of base $\overline{AB}$.

Prove: $\triangle ACD \cong \triangle BCD$.

Plan: Prove the triangles congruent by showing that s.s.s. $\cong$ s.s.s.

Statements	*Reasons*
1. In isosceles triangle *ABC*, $\overline{CA} \cong \overline{CB}$. (s. $\cong$ s.)	1. Given.
2. *D* is the midpoint of base $\overline{AB}$.	2. Given.
3. $\overline{AD} \cong \overline{DB}$. (s. $\cong$ s.)	3. Definition of midpoint.
4. $\overline{CD} \cong \overline{CD}$. (s. $\cong$ s.)	4. Reflexive property of congruence.
5. $\triangle ACD \cong \triangle BCD$.	5. s.s.s. $\cong$ s.s.s.

EXERCISES WITH OPEN-RESPONSE PROBLEMS

In 1–3, in each case tell whether the triangles can be proved congruent using only the marked congruent parts in establishing the congruence. Give the reason for your answer.

1.

2.

3.
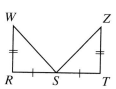

In 4–6, in each case name the pair of corresponding sides that would have to be proved congruent (in addition to those pairs marked congruent) in order to prove that the triangles are congruent by s.s.s. $\cong$ s.s.s.

4.

5.

6.

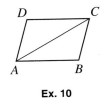

| Ex. 7 | Ex. 8 | Ex. 9 | Ex. 10 |

7. *Given:* $\overline{AB} \cong \overline{AD}$, $\overline{CB} \cong \overline{CD}$.
   Prove: $\triangle ABC \cong \triangle ADC$.
8. *Given:* T is the midpoint of $\overline{PQ}$, $\overline{PQ}$ bisects $\overline{RS}$, $\overline{RQ} \cong \overline{SP}$.
   Prove: $\triangle RTQ \cong \triangle STP$.
9. *Given:* $\overline{AC}$ and $\overline{DF}$ bisect each other at E, $\overline{AD} \cong \overline{CF}$.
   Prove: $\triangle DEA \cong \triangle FEC$.

10. If both pairs of opposite sides of quadrilateral $ABCD$ are congruent, prove that
    $\triangle ABC \cong \triangle CDA$.

4-5 LINE SEGMENTS ASSOCIATED WITH TRIANGLES

Altitude of a Triangle

● **DEFINITION.** An *altitude of a triangle* is a line segment drawn from any vertex of the triangle, perpendicular to and ending in the line that contains the opposite side.

In $\triangle ABC$, if $\overline{CD}$ is perpendicular to $\overline{AB}$, then $\overline{CD}$ is the altitude from vertex C to the opposite side. In $\triangle EFG$, if $\overline{GH}$ is perpendicular to $\overleftrightarrow{EF}$, the line that contains $\overline{EF}$, then $\overline{GH}$ is the altitude from vertex G to the opposite side. In an obtuse triangle such as EFG above, the altitude from each of the acute angles lies outside the triangle.

In $\triangle TSR$, if $\overline{RS}$ is perpendicular to $\overline{TS}$, then $\overline{RS}$ is the altitude from vertex R to the opposite side. In a right triangle such as $\triangle TSR$ above, the altitude from each of the acute angles is a leg of the triangle.

Every triangle has three altitudes as shown in $\triangle JKL$.

Median of a Triangle

- **DEFINITION.** A *median of a triangle* is a line segment that joins any vertex of the triangle to the midpoint of the opposite side.

In $\triangle ABC$, if D is the midpoint of $\overline{AB}$, then $\overline{CD}$ is the median drawn from vertex C to side $\overline{AB}$. We may also draw a median from vertex A to the midpoint of side $\overline{BC}$, and a median from vertex B to the midpoint of side $\overline{AC}$. Thus, every triangle has three medians.

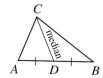

Angle Bisector of a Triangle

- **DEFINITION.** An *angle bisector of a triangle* is a line segment that bisects any angle of the triangle and terminates in the side opposite that angle.

In $\triangle PQR$, if $\angle PRD \cong \angle QRD$ and D is a point on side $\overline{PQ}$, then $\overline{RD}$ is the bisector of $\angle PRQ$ in $\triangle PQR$. We may also draw an angle bisector from the vertex of $\angle P$ to some point on $\overline{RQ}$, and an angle bisector from the vertex of $\angle Q$ to some point on $\overline{PR}$. Thus, every triangle has three angle bisectors.

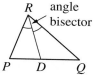

- **In a scalene triangle, the *altitude*, the *median*, and the *angle bisector* drawn from any common vertex are three distinct line segments.**

In $\triangle ABC$, from the common vertex B, three line segments are drawn:

1. $\overline{BD}$ is the *altitude* from B because $\overline{BD} \perp \overline{AC}$.
2. $\overline{BE}$ is the *angle bisector* from B because $\angle ABE \cong \angle EBC$.
3. $\overline{BF}$ is the *median* from B because F is the midpoint of $\overline{AC}$.

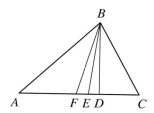

In some special triangles, such as the isosceles triangle and the equilateral triangle, some of these segments *coincide*, that is, fall on the same line. We will consider these examples later.

EXAMPLE

In the coordinate plane, $A(3, 4)$, $B(-5, 4)$, and $C(1, -3)$ are the vertices of $\triangle ABC$.

a. Draw $\overline{CD}$, the altitude from C to $\overline{AB}$.
b. State the coordinates of D.
c. Draw $\overline{CM}$, the median from C to $\overline{AB}$.
d. State the coordinates of M.

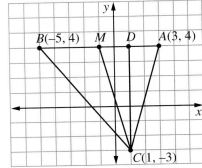

Solutions   a. Draw $\triangle ABC$. Since $\overline{AB}$ is a horizontal line, a line perpendicular to $\overline{AB}$ is a vertical line. Draw the vertical line through C. The point at which this line intersects $\overline{AB}$ is D.

b. The coordinates of D are $(1, 4)$.
c. $AB = |3 - (-5)| = 8$. Therefore, the midpoint of $\overline{AB}$ is the point of $\overline{AB}$ that is 4 units from A and 4 units from B. Label this point M, and draw $\overline{CM}$.
d. The coordinates of M are $(-1, 4)$.

EXERCISES WITH OPEN-RESPONSE PROBLEMS

In 1–4, for each triangle, name the type of line segment that $\overline{CD}$ is.

1.

2.

3.

4.
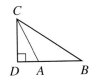

5. Polygon ABC is a triangle. $\overline{CD}$ is an altitude. $\overline{CE}$ is an angle bisector. $\overline{CF}$ is a median.
   a. State two congruent angles, each of which has its vertex at C.
   b. State two line segments that are congruent.
   c. State two line segments that are perpendicular to each other.
   d. State two angles that are right angles.

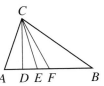

6. Use pencil, ruler, and protractor, or use a computer program, to draw several triangles. Include acute, obtuse, and right triangles.
   a. Draw three altitudes for each triangle.
   b. What do you observe about the intersection(s) of these altitudes? (In an obtuse triangle, it may be necessary to extend the altitude.)

7. Use pencil, ruler, and protractor, or use a computer program, to draw several triangles. Include acute, obtuse, and right triangles.
   a. Draw three medians for each triangle.
   b. What do you observe about the intersection(s) of these medians?

8. Use pencil, ruler, and protractor, or use a computer program, to draw several triangles. Include acute, obtuse, and right triangles.
   a. Draw three angle bisectors for each triangle.
   b. What do you observe about the intersection(s) of these angle bisectors?

9. In the coordinate plane, $A(-2, -1)$, $B(4, -1)$, and $C(2, 3)$ are the vertices of $\triangle ABC$.
   a. Draw $\overline{CD}$, the altitude from C to $\overline{AB}$.
   b. State the coordinates of D.
   c. Draw $\overline{CM}$, the median from C to $\overline{AB}$.
   d. State the coordinates of M.

4-6   PRACTICE IN PROVING TRIANGLES CONGRUENT

Methods of Proving Triangles Congruent

To prove that two triangles are congruent, you must prove that any one of the following statements is true:

1. Two sides and the included angle of one triangle are congruent, respectively, to two sides and the included angle of the other. [s.a.s. $\cong$ s.a.s.]

2. Two angles and the included side of one triangle are congruent, respectively, to two angles and the included side of the other. [a.s.a. $\cong$ a.s.a.]

3. Three sides of one triangle are congruent, respectively, to the three sides of the other. [s.s.s. $\cong$ s.s.s.]

Analyzing a Congruence Problem

A process of *analysis* can help to determine which of the three congruence postulates can be used to prove that two triangles are congruent. Examples 1 and 2 show how to perform such an analysis.

EXAMPLES

1. *Given:* $\overleftrightarrow{ABE}$ bisects $\angle CAD$.
   $\angle CBE \cong \angle DBE$.

   Prove: $\triangle ACB \cong \triangle ADB$.

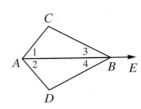

Since A, B, and E lie on a line, we know that $\angle 3$ and $\angle CBE$ form a linear pair and are supplementary and also that $\angle 4$ and $\angle DBE$ form a linear pair and are supplementary. Therefore, we can show that $\angle 3$ must be congruent to $\angle 4$ since they are the supplements of congruent angles.

We prove $\triangle ACB \cong \triangle ADB$ by the a.s.a. postulate as follows:

Statements	Reasons
1. $\overleftrightarrow{ABE}$ bisects $\angle CAD$.	1. Given.
2. $\angle 1 \cong \angle 2$. (a. $\cong$ a.)	2. Definition of angle bisector.
3. $\overline{AB} \cong \overline{AB}$. (s. $\cong$ s.)	3. Reflexive property of congruence.
4. $\overleftrightarrow{ABE}$.	4. Given.
5. $\angle CBE \cong \angle DBE$.	5. Given.
6. $\angle 3$ is supplementary to $\angle CBE$. $\angle 4$ is supplementary to $\angle DBE$.	6. If two angles form a linear pair, the angles are supplementary.
7. $\angle 3 \cong \angle 4$. (a. $\cong$ a.)	7. If two angle are supplements of congruent angles, they are congruent.
8. $\triangle ACB \cong \triangle ADB$.	8. a.s.a. $\cong$ a.s.a.

2. *Given:* $\overline{ABCD}$.
$\overline{AE} \cong \overline{DF}$.
$\angle A \cong \angle D$.
$\overline{AC} \cong \overline{DB}$.

Prove: $\triangle AEB \cong \triangle DFC$.

Plan: Prove the triangles congruent by showing that s.a.s. $\cong$ s.a.s. To do this, it is necessary to prove that $\overline{AB} \cong \overline{DC}$.

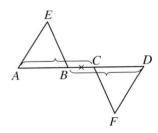

Statements	Reasons
1. $\overline{AE} \cong \overline{DF}$. (s. $\cong$ s.)	1. Given.
2. $\angle A \cong \angle D$. (a. $\cong$ a.)	2. Given.
3. $\overline{ABCD}$.	3. Given.
4. $\overline{AC} \cong \overline{DB}$.	4. Given.
5. $\overline{BC} \cong \overline{BC}$.	5. Reflexive property of congruence.
6. $\overline{AC} - \overline{BC} \cong \overline{DB} - \overline{BC}$, or $\overline{AB} \cong \overline{DC}$. (s. $\cong$ s.)	6. Subtraction postulate of congruent segments.
7. $\triangle AEB \cong \triangle DFC$.	7. s.a.s. $\cong$ s.a.s.

EXERCISES WITH OPEN-RESPONSE PROBLEMS

Ex. 1

Ex. 2

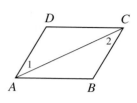

Ex. 3

1. *Given:* $\overleftrightarrow{ABCDE}$ and $\overrightarrow{FCG}$, C is the midpoint of $\overline{BD}$, $\angle 1 \cong \angle 2$.
   Prove: $\triangle BFC \cong \triangle DGC$.
2. *Given:* $ABCD$, $\overline{FA} \perp \overline{AD}$, $\overline{ED} \perp \overline{AD}$, $\overline{AF} \cong \overline{DE}$, $\overline{AC} \cong \overline{DB}$.
   Prove: $\triangle ABF \cong \triangle DCE$.
3. *Given:* In quadrilateral $ABCD$, $\overline{AD} \cong \overline{CB}$ and $\angle 1 \cong \angle 2$.
   Prove: $\triangle ADC \cong \triangle CBA$.
4. *Given:* Isosceles triangle RST with $\overline{RT} \cong \overline{ST}$,
   $\overline{TP}$ is a median to base $\overline{RS}$.
   Prove: $\triangle RTP \cong \triangle STP$.
5. *Given:* In $\triangle ABC$, $\overline{CD}$ is a median to $\overline{AB}$, $\overline{CE} \cong \overline{CF}$, $\overline{EA} \cong \overline{FB}$.
   Prove: $\triangle ACD \cong \triangle BCD$.

Ex. 4

Ex. 5

Ex. 6

Ex. 7

Ex. 8

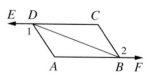

Ex. 9

6. *Given:* Points D and E divide $\overline{AB}$ into three congruent parts, $\overline{CD} \cong \overline{CE}$, $\angle x \cong \angle y$.
   Prove: $\triangle ACD \cong \triangle BCE$.
7. *Given:* E is the midpoint of $\overline{BC}$, $\angle ACB \cong \angle FBC$, $\overline{AD} \cong \overline{CD}$, $\overline{FB} \cong \overline{AD}$.
   Prove: $\triangle CDE \cong \triangle BFE$.
8. *Given:* $\overrightarrow{MS}$ is the perpendicular bisector of $\overline{LP}$, $\overline{RM} \cong \overline{QM}$, $\angle a \cong \angle b$.
   Prove: $\triangle RLM \cong \triangle QPM$.
9. *Given:* $\overleftrightarrow{CDE}$ and $\overrightarrow{ABF}$, $\angle 1 \cong \angle 2$, $\angle EDB \cong \angle FBD$.
   Prove: $\triangle ADB \cong \triangle CBD$.

10. *Prove:* Two right triangles are congruent if the legs of one triangle are congruent to the legs of the other triangle.

4-7   USING CONGRUENT TRIANGLES TO PROVE LINE SEGMENTS CONGRUENT AND ANGLES CONGRUENT

Recall that, when two triangles are congruent, their corresponding sides are congruent and their corresponding angles are congruent.

Thus, to prove that two line segments are congruent or two angles are congruent:

1. Choose two triangles that contain the segments or angles that are to be proved congruent.

2. Prove that the chosen triangles are congruent.

3. Show that the segments or angles that are to be proved congruent are corresponding parts of congruent triangles. Thus, these parts are congruent.

EXAMPLE

In $\triangle ABC$, if $\overline{BD}$ bisects $\angle ABC$, and $\overline{BD} \perp \overline{AC}$, prove that $\overline{AD} \cong \overline{CD}$.

Given: In $\triangle ABC$, $\overline{BD}$ bisects $\angle ABC$.
$\overline{BD} \perp \overline{AC}$.

Prove: $\overline{AD} \cong \overline{CD}$.

Plan: To prove that $\overline{AD} \cong \overline{CD}$, show that the triangles that contain these segments are congruent, namely, $\triangle ABD \cong \triangle CBD$. Then, $\overline{AD} \cong \overline{CD}$ because these are corresponding parts of congruent triangles.

Statements	Reasons
1. $\overline{BD}$ bisects $\angle ABC$.	1. Given.
2. $\angle 3 \cong \angle 4$. (a. $\cong$ a.)	2. Definition of angle bisector.
3. $\overline{BD} \perp \overline{AC}$.	3. Given.
4. $\angle 1$ and $\angle 2$ are right angles.	4. Definition of perpendicular lines.
5. $\angle 1 \cong \angle 2$. (a. $\cong$ a.)	5. If two angles are right angles, they are congruent.
6. $\overline{BD} \cong \overline{BD}$. (s. $\cong$ s.)	6. Reflexive property of congruence.
7. $\triangle ABD \cong \triangle CBD$.	7. a.s.a. $\cong$ a.s.a.
8. $\overline{AD} \cong \overline{CD}$	8. Corresponding parts of congruent triangles are congruent.

EXERCISES WITH OPEN-RESPONSE PROBLEMS

In 1–6, the figures have been marked to indicate pairs of congruent angles and pairs of congruent segments.

   a. In each figure, name two triangles that are congruent.

   b. State the reason why the triangles are congruent.

   c. For each pair of triangles, name three additional pairs of parts that are congruent because they are corresponding parts of congruent triangles.

1.

2.

3.

4.

5.

6.

Ex. 7

Ex. 8

Ex. 9

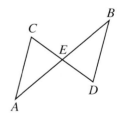

Ex. 10

7. $\overline{CA} \cong \overline{CB}$ and $\overline{AD} \cong \overline{BD}$. **a.** Prove that $\triangle ADC \cong \triangle BDC$. **b.** Find three pairs of congruent angles in $\triangle ADC$ and $\triangle BDC$.

8. $\overline{AD} \cong \overline{AB}$ and $\angle 1 \cong \angle 2$. **a.** Prove that $\triangle ADC \cong \triangle ABC$. **b.** Find three more pairs of congruent parts in $\triangle ADC$ and $\triangle ABC$.

9. $\overline{BD}$ bisects $\angle ABC$, and $\overline{DB}$ bisects $\angle ADC$.
   a. Prove that $\triangle ABD \cong \triangle CBD$.
   b. Find three more pairs of congruent parts in $\triangle ABD$ and $\triangle CBD$.

10. If $\overline{AB}$ and $\overline{CD}$ bisect each other at E, prove that $\angle C \cong \angle D$.

Ex. 11

Ex. 12

Ex. 13

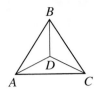

Ex. 14

11. If $\overline{AB} \cong \overline{CD}$ and $\overline{BC} \cong \overline{DA}$, prove that $\angle B \cong \angle D$.
12. If $\angle 1 \cong \angle 2$ and $\angle 3 \cong \angle 4$, prove that $\overline{DC} \cong \overline{BA}$.
13. If $\overline{AEC}$ and $\overline{BFC}$ intersect at C, $\angle 1 \cong \angle 2$, $\overline{CE} \cong \overline{CF}$ and $\overline{EA} \cong \overline{FB}$, prove that $\angle 3 \cong \angle 4$.
14. If $\overline{BA} \cong \overline{BC}$ and $\overline{DA} \cong \overline{DC}$, prove that $\overline{BD}$ bisects $\angle ABC$.

Ex. 15

Ex. 16

Ex. 17

Ex. 18

15. If $\overline{TQ}$ bisects $\angle RTS$ and $\overline{TQ} \perp \overline{RS}$, prove that $\overline{TQ}$ bisects $\overline{RS}$.
16. If $\overline{DC} \cong \overline{DE}$, $\angle x \cong \angle y$, and $\angle z \cong \angle w$, prove that $\overline{AE} \cong \overline{AC}$.
17. If $\overrightarrow{AB}$ is the perpendicular bisector of $\overline{CF}$, $\angle 1 \cong \angle 2$, and $\overline{AD} \cong \overline{AE}$, prove that $\angle D \cong \angle E$.
18. If F is the midpoint of $\overline{GH}$, E is the midpoint of $\overline{AD}$, $\overline{FC} \cong \overline{ED}$, $\overline{BF} \cong \overline{AE}$, and $\overline{BFC}$ and $\overline{HFG}$ intersect at F, prove that $\overline{GC} \cong \overline{HB}$.

19. Triangle ABC is congruent to $\triangle A'B'C'$. If $m\angle C$ is represented by $2x - 10$ and $m\angle C'$ is represented by $x + 30$:
  a. Find x.   **b.** Find $m\angle C$.   **c.** Find $m\angle B$ if it is represented by $x - 25$.
20. Triangle DEF is congruent to $\triangle D'E'F'$. If EF is represented by $3x + 2$, $E'F'$ is represented by $x + 10$, and ED is represented by $x + 2$:
  a. Find x.   **b.** Find ED.   **c.** Find $E'D'$.

21. *Given:* $\overline{AD} \cong \overline{CB}$, $\angle 1 \cong \angle 2$.
  a. *Prove:* $\triangle ADB \cong \triangle CBD$.
  b. *Prove:* $\overline{AB} \cong \overline{CD}$.
  c. If $AB = 5x - 30$, $CD = 3x + 10$, and $BC = 2x + 5$, write an equation to solve for x.
  d. Find the lengths of $\overline{AB}$, $\overline{CD}$, and $\overline{BC}$.
22. If all sides of polygon $ABCDE$ are congruent and $\angle E \cong \angle C$, find AD and BD.

Ex. 21

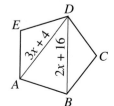

Ex. 22

23. Triangle ABC is congruent to $\triangle A'B'C'$. If AB is represented by $2x + y$, $A'B' = 7$, $BC = 11$, and $B'C'$ is represented by $4x + y$, find x and y.

Miscellaneous Exercises

In 24–28, select the *numeral* preceding the choice that best completes the statement or answers the question.

24. If, in $\triangle ABC$, $\overline{BD}$ is the median to side $\overline{AC}$, and $\triangle ABD \cong \triangle CBD$, then $\triangle ABC$ must be
(1) scalene   (2) isosceles   (3) right   (4) equilateral

25. Two right triangles must be congruent if (1) the hypotenuse of one triangle is congruent to the hypotenuse of the other (2) an acute angle of one triangle is congruent to an acute angle of the other (3) two legs of one triangle are congruent to two legs of the other (4) each triangle contains a right angle

26. Two isosceles triangles are congruent if (1) the vertex angle of one triangle is congruent to the vertex angle of the other (2) a base angle of one triangle is congruent to a base angle of the other (3) a leg of one triangle is congruent to a leg of the other (4) a leg and the vertex angle of one triangle are congruent to a leg and the vertex angle of the other

27. In $\triangle ABC$, D is a point on $\overline{BC}$ such that $\overline{AD}$ is both an angle bisector and an altitude. Which statement may be *false*?
(1) $BD = CD$ (2) $AB = AC$ (3) $AC = BC$ (4) $m\angle B = m\angle C$

28. In isosceles right triangle ABC, $\angle B$ is a right angle, $\overline{AB} \cong \overline{BC}$, and BD is a median. Which segment is *not* an altitude for $\triangle ABC$?
(1) $\overline{BD}$ (2) $\overline{AD}$ (3) $\overline{AB}$ (4) $\overline{BC}$

4-8 ISOSCELES AND EQUILATERAL TRIANGLES

Properties of an Isosceles Triangle

When working with triangles, we observed that when two sides of a triangle are congruent, two angles of the triangle are also congruent. This observation can be stated as a theorem in either of two ways and proved to be always true.

- **THEOREM 9. If two sides of a triangle are congruent, the angles opposite these sides are congruent.**

Or:

- **THEOREM 9. The base angles of an isosceles triangle are congruent.**

Given: $\triangle ACB$ with $\overline{CA} \cong \overline{CB}$.

Prove: $\angle A \cong \angle B$.

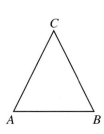

To begin our proof, we draw an isosceles triangle and letter the vertices so that we can identify the congruent sides, namely, $\overline{CA} \cong \overline{CB}$. To prove Theorem 9, it will be necessary to draw an additional line segment in the triangle.

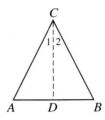

Plan: To prove that $\angle A \cong \angle B$, show that $\angle A$ and $\angle B$ are corresponding angles of two congruent triangles. Draw the bisector of the vertex angle to separate $\triangle ABC$ into two triangles, $\triangle ACD$ and $\triangle BCD$, which can be proved congruent by s.a.s. $\cong$ s.a.s. From these congruent triangles, show that $\angle A \cong \angle B$.

Statements	Reasons
1. Draw the bisector of vertex $\angle ACB$. Let D be the point at which the bisector intersects $\overline{AB}$.	1. Every angle has one and only one bisector.
2. $\angle 1 \cong \angle 2$. (a. $\cong$ a.)	2. A bisector of an angle divides the angle into two congruent angles.
3. $\overline{CA} \cong \overline{CB}$. (s. $\cong$ s.)	3. Given.
4. $\overline{CD} \cong \overline{CD}$. (s. $\cong$ s.)	4. Reflexive property of congruence.
5. $\triangle ACD \cong \triangle BCD$.	5. s.a.s. $\cong$ s.a.s.
6. $\angle A \cong \angle B$.	6. Corresponding angles of congruent triangles are congruent.

Theorem 9 is called the Isosceles Triangle Theorem.

- **DEFINITION.** A *corollary* is a theorem that can easily be deduced from another theorem.

    From Theorem 9 we can prove two other statements that are called corollaries of Theorem 9 because the statements are related to an isosceles triangle.

- **COROLLARY 9-1. The bisector of the vertex angle of an isosceles triangle bisects the base.**

    From the preceding proof that $\triangle ACD \cong \triangle BCD$, we can also conclude that $\overline{AD} \cong \overline{BD}$ since they, too, are corresponding parts of congruent triangles. Thus, $\overline{CD}$ bisects base $\overline{AB}$.

- **COROLLARY 9-2. The bisector of the vertex angle of an isosceles triangle is perpendicular to the base.**

    Again, from $\triangle ACD \cong \triangle BCD$, we can say that $\angle CDA \cong \angle CDB$ because they are corresponding parts of congruent triangles. Since the noncommon sides of these adjacent congruent angles form a line, $\angle CDA$ and $\angle CDB$ are both right angles, and $\overline{CD} \perp \overline{AB}$.

Properties of an Equilateral Triangle

Theorem 9 has shown that in an isosceles triangle, where two sides are congruent, the angles opposite these sides are congruent. We may prove another corollary to this theorem for any equilateral triangle, where three sides are congruent.

● **COROLLARY 9-3. Every equilateral triangle is equiangular.**

Given $\triangle ABC$, where $\overline{BC} \cong \overline{CA} \cong \overline{AB}$. It then follows that $\angle A \cong \angle B \cong \angle C$, or that $\triangle ABC$ is equiangular.

EXAMPLE

Given: Isosceles triangle ABC with $\overline{CA} \cong \overline{CB}$.
M is the midpoint of $\overline{AB}$.
$\overline{AD} \cong \overline{BE}$.

Prove: $\overline{MD} \cong \overline{ME}$.

Plan: To prove $\overline{MD} \cong \overline{ME}$, prove that $\triangle ADM \cong \triangle BEM$ since these two triangles have $\overline{MD}$ and $\overline{ME}$ as corresponding sides. To prove that $\triangle ADM \cong \triangle BEM$, use s.a.s. $\cong$ s.a.s.

Statements	*Reasons*
1. $\overline{CA} \cong \overline{CB}$.	1. Given.
2. $\angle A \cong \angle B$. (a. $\cong$ a.)	2. If two sides of a triangle are congruent, the angles opposite these sides are congruent.
3. $\overline{AD} \cong \overline{BE}$. (s. $\cong$ s.)	3. Given.
4. M is the midpoint of $\overline{AB}$.	4. Given.
5. $\overline{AM} \cong \overline{BM}$. (s. $\cong$ s.)	5. A midpoint divides a line segment into two congruent parts.
6. $\triangle ADM \cong \triangle BEM$.	6. s.a.s. $\cong$ s.a.s.
7. $\overline{MD} \cong \overline{ME}$.	7. Corresponding parts of congruent triangles are congruent.

EXERCISES WITH OPEN-RESPONSE PROBLEMS

Numerical and Algebraic Applications

1. In $\triangle ABC$, if $\overline{CA} \cong \overline{CB}$ and m$\angle A = 50$, find m$\angle B$.
2. In $\triangle ABC$, $\overline{AB} \cong \overline{BC}$. If $AB = 5x$ and $BC = 2x + 18$, find AB and BC.
3. In isosceles triangle ABC, $\overline{AB} \cong \overline{BC}$. If $AB = 5x + 10$, $BC = 3x + 40$, and $AC = 2x + 30$, find the length of each side of the triangle.

4. In $\triangle ABC$, $\overline{AB} \cong \overline{BC}$. If $m\angle A = 7x$ and $m\angle C = 2x + 50$, find $m\angle A$ and $m\angle C$.
5. In $\triangle EFG$, $\overline{EF} \cong \overline{FG}$. If $m\angle E = 4x + 50$, $m\angle F = 2x + 60$, and $m\angle G = 14x + 30$, find $m\angle E$, $m\angle F$, and $m\angle G$.

Ex. 6

Ex. 7

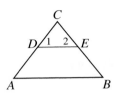

Ex. 8

6. *Given:* $\triangle ABC$ with $\overline{CA} \cong \overline{CB}$ and $\overleftrightarrow{DABE}$.
   Prove: $\angle CAD \cong \angle CBE$.
7. *Given:* Isosceles triangles ABC and ADC have common base $\overline{AC}$.
   Prove: $\angle BAD = \angle BCD$.
8. If $\overline{CA} \cong \overline{CB}$, and $\overline{DA} \cong \overline{EB}$, prove that $\angle 1 \cong \angle 2$.

Ex. 9

Ex. 10

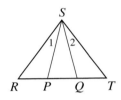

Ex. 11

9. *Given:* In $\triangle ABC$, $\overline{CA} \cong \overline{CB}$, $\overline{AR} \cong \overline{BS}$, $\overline{DR} \perp \overline{AC}$, and $\overline{DS} \perp \overline{BC}$.
   Prove: $\overline{DR} \cong \overline{DS}$.
10. In isosceles triangle ABC, D and F are midpoints of the congruent legs, and E and G are the trisection points of the base ($\overline{AE} \cong \overline{EG} \cong \overline{GB}$). Prove that $\overline{DE} \cong \overline{FG}$.
11. Given $\overline{RPQT}$, $\overline{SR} \cong \overline{ST}$, and $\angle 1 \cong \angle 2$, prove that $\triangle PSQ$ is an isosceles triangle.

Ex. 12

Ex. 13

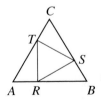

Ex. 14

12. In $\triangle ABC$, $\overline{AB} \cong \overline{AC}$, $\overline{DE} \perp \overline{BC}$, $\overline{FG} \perp \overline{BC}$, and $\overline{BG} \cong \overline{CE}$. Prove that $\overline{BD} \cong \overline{CF}$.
13. Given $\overline{AD} \cong \overline{BE}$, $\overline{CD} \cong \overline{CE}$, and $\overline{ADEB}$, prove that $\overline{AC} \cong \overline{BC}$.
14. If $\triangle ABC$ is an equilateral triangle and $\overline{CT} \cong \overline{AR} \cong \overline{BS}$, prove:
    a. $\overline{TA} \cong \overline{RB} \cong \overline{SC}$ **b.** $\triangle TAR \cong \triangle RBS \cong \triangle SCT$
    c. $\overline{TR} \cong \overline{RS} \cong \overline{ST}$ **d.** $\triangle TRS$ is an equilateral triangle.

15. *Prove:* The line segments joining the midpoint of the base of an isosceles triangle to the midpoints of the legs are congruent.

16. **a.** Prove the Isosceles Triangle Theorem (If two sides of a triangle are congruent, the angles opposite these sides are congruent.) by drawing the median to the base of the isosceles triangle.

   b. Can this theorem be proved by drawing the altitude to the base of the isosceles triangle? Explain your answer.

4-9   USING TWO PAIRS OF CONGRUENT TRIANGLES

Sometimes, it is impossible to use the *given* in order to prove immediately that a particular pair of triangles are congruent. In such cases, however, the *given* may contain enough information to first prove another pair of triangles congruent. Then, we may use corresponding congruent parts of these congruent triangles to prove the original pair of triangles congruent. The following example shows how this is done.

EXAMPLE

Given: $\overline{AEB}$.
  $\overline{AC} \cong \overline{AD}$.
  $\overline{BC} \cong \overline{BD}$.

Prove: $\overline{CE} \cong \overline{DE}$.

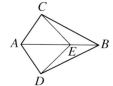

From the *given*, we can*not* prove immediately that $\triangle ACE \cong \triangle ADE$ nor can we prove that $\triangle CEB \cong \triangle DEB$.

However, we can prove that $\triangle CAB \cong \triangle DAB$. Using corresponding parts of these larger congruent triangles, we can then prove that either pair of the smaller triangles mentioned earlier are congruent. Thus, $\overline{CE} \cong \overline{DE}$ because they are corresponding parts of the smaller congruent triangles.

Plan: Prove $\triangle CAB \cong \triangle DAB$. Then, use corresponding parts of these congruent triangles to prove that $\triangle ACE \cong \triangle ADE$, resulting in $\overline{CE} \cong \overline{DE}$.

	Statements	*Reasons*

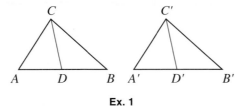

Statements	*Reasons*
1. $\overline{AC} \cong \overline{AD}$. (s. $\cong$ s.)	1. Given.
2. $\overline{BC} \cong \overline{BD}$. (s. $\cong$ s.)	2. Given.
3. $\overline{AB} \cong \overline{AB}$. (s. $\cong$ s.)	3. Reflexive property of congruence.
4. $\triangle CAB \cong \triangle DAB$.	4. s.s.s. $\cong$ s.s.s.
5. $\angle CAB \cong \angle DAB$, *or* $\angle CAE \cong \angle DAE$.	5. Corresponding parts of congruent triangles are congruent.
6. For $\triangle ACE$ and $\triangle ADE$, $\angle CAE \cong \angle DAE$. (a. $\cong$ a.)	6. Proved in step 5.
7. $\overline{AC} \cong \overline{AD}$. (s. $\cong$ s.)	7. Given.
8. $\overline{AE} \cong \overline{AE}$. (s. $\cong$ s.)	8. Reflexive property of congruence.
9. $\triangle ACE \cong \triangle ADE$.	9. s.a.s. $\cong$ s.a.s.
10. $\overline{CE} \cong \overline{DE}$.	10. Corresponding parts of congruent triangles are congruent.

Note that steps 6 and 7 repeat steps 5 and 1. Steps 6 and 7 could be omitted from the proof.

EXERCISES WITH OPEN-RESPONSE PROBLEMS

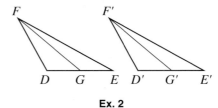

Ex. 1   Ex. 2

1. *Given:* $\triangle ABC \cong \triangle A'B'C'$, $\overline{CD}$ bisects $\angle C$, $\overline{C'D'}$ bisects $\angle C'$.
   Prove: $\overline{CD} \cong \overline{C'D'}$.
2. *Given:* $\triangle DEF \cong \triangle D'E'F'$, $\overline{FG}$ and $\overline{F'G'}$ are medians.
   Prove: $\overline{FG} \cong \overline{F'G'}$.

3. *Given:* $\overline{AEC}$, $\overline{BED}$, and $\overline{GEF}$; $\overline{AE} \cong \overline{CE}$, $\overline{FE} \cong \overline{GE}$.
   Prove: **a.** $\triangle FEC \cong \triangle GEA$.
         b. $\angle C \cong \angle A$.
         c. $\triangle DEC \cong \triangle BEA$.

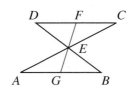

Ex. 3

4. *Given:* $\overline{AC}$ and $\overline{BD}$ bisect each other at G; $\overline{EGF}$.
   Prove: **a.** $\triangle DGC \cong \triangle BGA$.
          b. $\angle D \cong \angle B$.
          c. $\overline{GE} \cong \overline{GF}$.

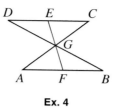

Ex. 4

5. *Given:* $\overline{AD} \cong \overline{CB}$, $\overline{DC} \cong \overline{BA}$, $\overline{EF}$ bisects $\overline{BD}$ at G.
   Prove: **a.** $\triangle ADB \cong \triangle CBD$.
          b. $\angle ABD \cong \angle CDB$.
          c. $\overline{FG} \cong \overline{EG}$.

Ex. 5

Ex. 6

Ex. 7

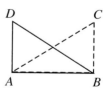

Ex. 8

6. *Given:* $\overline{AC} \cong \overline{AD}$, $\overline{BC} \cong \overline{BD}$, $\overline{AB}$ intersects $\overline{CD}$ at E.
   Prove: $\angle 1 \cong \angle 2$.

7. *Given:* $\overline{RP} \cong \overline{RQ}$, $\overline{SP} \cong \overline{SQ}$.   **8.** *Given:* $\overline{PQ}$, $\overline{PAB}$, $\overline{PCD}$, $\overline{AQD}$, and $\overline{CQB}$, $\angle 1 \cong \angle 2$, $\overline{AP} \cong \overline{CP}$.
   Prove: $\overline{RT}$ bisects $\overline{PQ}$.   *Prove:* $\overline{QB} \cong \overline{QD}$.

4-IO PROVING OVERLAPPING TRIANGLES CONGRUENT

    If we are given that $\overline{AD} \cong \overline{BC}$ and $\overline{DB} \cong \overline{CA}$, can we prove that $\triangle DAB \cong \triangle CBA$?

    Since these two triangles overlap, we may find it easier to visualize them by using one of the following devices:

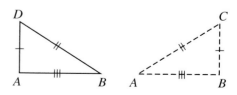

1. Outline one triangle with a solid line and the other with a dotted line, as shown *or*

2. Separate the triangles, as shown at the right.

    Then $\overline{AB} \cong \overline{AB}$ allows us to prove that $\triangle DAB \cong \triangle CBA$ by s.s.s. $\cong$ s.s.s.

EXAMPLES

1. *Given:* In $\triangle ABC$, $\overline{AB} \cong \overline{AC}$.
$\overline{CD}$ and $\overline{BE}$ are medians.

Prove: $\overline{BE} \cong \overline{CD}$.

Plan: Separate the triangles. Prove $\triangle ABE \cong \triangle ACD$ by s.a.s. $\cong$ s.a.s. Then, $\overline{BE}$ and $\overline{CD}$ are corresponding parts of these congruent triangles.

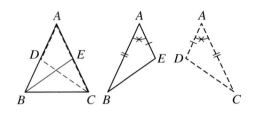

Statements	*Reasons*
1. $\overline{AB} \cong \overline{AC}$. (s. $\cong$ s.)	1. Given.
2. $\angle A \cong \angle A$. (a. $\cong$ a.)	2. Reflexive property of congruence.
3. $\overline{CD}$ and $\overline{BE}$ are medians.	3. Given.
4. D is the midpoint of $\overline{AB}$. E is the midpoint of $\overline{AC}$.	4. Definition of median of a triangle.
5. $AD = \frac{1}{2} AB$. $AE = \frac{1}{2} AC$.	5. Definition of midpoint.
6. $AD = AE$.	6. Halves of equal quantities are equal.
7. $\overline{AD} \cong \overline{AE}$. (s. $\cong$ s.)	7. Definition of congruent segments.
8. $\triangle ABE \cong \triangle ACD$.	8. s.a.s. $\cong$ s.a.s.
9. $\overline{BE} \cong \overline{CD}$.	9. Corresponding parts of congruent triangles are congruent.

2. Using the results of Example 1, find the length of $\overline{BE}$ if $BE = 5x - 8$ and $CD = 3x + 12$.

Solution

(1) Since we proved the segments were congruent, they are equal in length:

$$BE = CD$$

(2) Substitute the given expressions:

$$5x - 8 = 3x + 12$$

(3) Solve for x:

$$2x = 20$$
$$x = 10$$

(4) Thus, $BE = 5x - 8 = 5(10) - 8 = 42$.   *Answer*

EXERCISES WITH OPEN-RESPONSE PROBLEMS

Ex. 1

Ex. 2

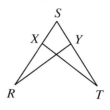

Ex. 3

1. *Given:* $\overline{AFEC}$, $\overline{DC} \cong \overline{BA}$, $\overline{DF} \cong \overline{BE}$, $\overline{CE} \cong \overline{AF}$.
   Prove: $\triangle AEB \cong \triangle CFD$.
2. *Given:* $\overline{AEFB}$, $\overline{CE} \cong \overline{DF}$, $\angle 1 \cong \angle 2$, $\overline{AE} \cong \overline{BF}$.
   Prove: $\triangle AFD \cong \triangle BEC$.
3. *Given:* $\overline{SXR}$, $\overline{SYT}$, $\overline{SX} \cong \overline{SY}$, $\overline{XR} \cong \overline{YT}$.
   Prove: $\triangle RSY \cong \triangle TSX$.

Ex. 4

Ex. 5

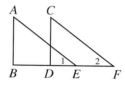

Ex. 6

4. *Given:* $\overline{DA} \cong \overline{CB}$, $\overline{DA} \perp \overline{AB}$, $\overline{CB} \perp \overline{AB}$.
   Prove: $\triangle DAB \cong \triangle CBA$.
5. *Given:* $\overline{AFEC}$, $\overline{AF} \cong \overline{EC}$, $\angle 3 \cong \angle 4$, $\angle 1 \cong \angle 2$.
   Prove: $\triangle ABE \cong \triangle CDF$.
6. *Given:* $\overline{AB} \perp \overline{BF}$, $\overline{CD} \perp \overline{BF}$, $\overline{BD} \cong \overline{FE}$, $\angle 1 \cong \angle 2$.
   Prove: $\triangle ABE \cong \triangle CDF$.

Ex. 7

Ex. 8

Ex. 9

7. *Given:* $\overline{LP} \perp \overline{PN}$, $\overline{MN} \perp \overline{PN}$, $\overline{LP} \cong \overline{MN}$, $\overline{PR} \cong \overline{NS}$, $\overline{PRSN}$.
   Prove: $\triangle LPS \cong \triangle MNR$.
8. *Given:* $\angle BAC \cong \angle BCA$, $\overline{CD}$ bisects $\angle BCA$, $\overline{AE}$ bisects $\angle BAC$.
   Prove: $\triangle ADC \cong \triangle CEA$.
9. *Given:* $\overline{TR} \cong \overline{TS}$, $\overline{MR} \cong \overline{NS}$.
   Prove: $\triangle RTN \cong \triangle STM$.

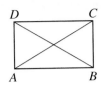

Ex. 10   **Ex. 11**   **Ex. 12**

10. *Given:* $\overline{AB} \cong \overline{DB}$, $\angle A \cong \angle D$, $\angle DBA \cong \angle CBE$.
   Prove: $\triangle ABE \cong \triangle DBC$.
11. *Given:* $\overline{DA} \cong \overline{EC}$, $\overline{DC} \cong \overline{EA}$.
   Prove: **a.** $\triangle CAD \cong \triangle ACE$.   **b.** $\angle DCA \cong \angle EAC$.
12. *Given:* $\overline{DA} \perp \overline{AB}$, $\overline{CB} \perp \overline{AB}$, $\overline{AD} \cong \overline{BC}$.
   Prove: **a.** $\triangle DAB \cong \triangle CBA$.   **b.** $\overline{AC} \cong \overline{BD}$.

Ex. 13   **Ex. 14**   **Ex. 15**

13. *Given:* $\overline{ADB}$, $\overline{BEC}$, $\overline{BD} \cong \overline{BE}$, $\overline{DA} \cong \overline{EC}$.
   Prove: **a.** $\triangle DBC \cong \triangle EBA$.   **b.** $\angle A \cong \angle C$.
14. *Given:* $\overline{ADEB}$, $\overline{AC} \cong \overline{BC}$, $\overline{CE} \cong \overline{CD}$, $\overline{AE} \cong \overline{BD}$.
   Prove: **a.** $\triangle ACE \cong \triangle BCD$.   **b.** $\angle 1 \cong \angle 2$.
15. If $\overline{RT} \cong \overline{ST}$ and median $\overline{RB} \cong$ median $\overline{SA}$, prove that $\angle RAS \cong \angle SBR$.

Ex. 16   **Ex. 17**   **Ex. 18**

16. Given $\overrightarrow{BFA}$, $\overline{CFD}$, $\angle ECF \cong \angle CFA$, $\overline{CF} \cong \overline{FD}$, and $\overline{CE} \cong \overline{FB}$, prove that $\overline{EF} \cong \overline{BD}$.
17. Given $\overline{ADB}$, $\overline{BEC}$, $\overline{BD} \cong \overline{BE}$, and $\overline{DA} \cong \overline{EC}$, prove that $\angle 1 \cong \angle 2$.
18. If $\overline{AC}$ and $\overline{BD}$ intersect at E, $\angle D \cong \angle C$, M is the midpoint of $\overline{DC}$, and $\angle 1 \cong \angle 2$, prove that $\overline{DB} \cong \overline{CA}$.

19. *Prove:* The medians to the legs of an isosceles triangle are congruent.

In 20–23, select the *numeral* preceding the choice that best completes the statement.

20. It can be proved that $\angle YWX \cong \angle ZXW$ if it is known that
   (1) $\overline{ZW} \cong \overline{YX}$ (2) $\overline{YW} \cong \overline{YX}$
   (3) $\overline{PW} \cong \overline{PX}$ (4) $\overline{PW} \cong \overline{YX}$

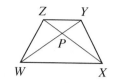

21. If $\triangle ZPW \cong \triangle YPX$, it can be proved that
   (1) $\triangle ZPW$ is isosceles   (2) $\triangle YPX$ is isosceles
   (3) $\triangle PWX$ is isosceles   (4) $\triangle YWX$ is isosceles

Ex. 20–21

22. If $\overline{AB} \cong \overline{AC}$, it can be proved that $\overline{CD} \cong \overline{BE}$ if it is also known that
   (1) $\angle 1 \cong \angle 2$ (2) $\angle 3 \cong \angle 4$
   (3) $\angle 3 \cong \angle 5$ (4) $\angle 4 \cong \angle 6$

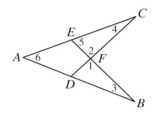

23. If $\angle 3 \cong \angle 4$, it can be proved that $\overline{EC} \cong \overline{DB}$ if it is also known that
   (1) $\overline{CF} \cong \overline{BF}$ (2) $\overline{CD} \cong \overline{BE}$
   (3) $\overline{CA} \cong \overline{BA}$ (4) $\overline{EA} \cong \overline{DA}$

Ex. 22–23

CHAPTER SUMMARY

Triangles can be proved to be congruent by using one of the following postulates:

Postulate. Two triangles are congruent if two sides and the included angle of one triangle are congruent, respectively, to two sides and the included angle of the other. (s.a.s. $\cong$ s.a.s.)

Postulate. Two triangles are congruent if two angles and the included side of one triangle are congruent, respectively, to two angles and the included side of the other. (a.s.a. $\cong$ a.s.a.)

Postulate. Two triangles are congruent if the three sides of one triangle are congruent, respectively, to the three sides of the other. (s.s.s. $\cong$ s.s.s.)

Two line segments or two angles are congruent if they are ***corresponding parts of congruent triangles***.

Congruence is an ***equivalence relation***; that is, the reflexive, symmetric, and transitive properties are true for the relation *is congruent to*.

In a scalene triangle, the ***altitude***, the ***median***, and the ***angle bisector*** drawn from a common vertex are three distinct line segments.

VOCABULARY

4-1	Congruent polygons	One-to-one correspondence		Corresponding angles
	Corresponding sides			
4-5	Altitude of a triangle	Median of a triangle		Angle bisector of a triangle
4-8	Corollary			

REVIEW EXERCISES WITH OPEN-RESPONSE PROBLEMS

In 1–8, in each case: **a.** Tell whether the triangles can be proved congruent by using only the marked congruent parts. **b.** If the triangles are congruent, give the reason for your answer.

1. **2.** **3.** **4.**

5. **6.** **7.** **8.**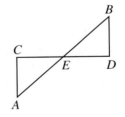

9. In $\triangle RST$, $\overline{SA}$ is a median, $\overline{SB}$ is an angle bisector, and $\overline{SC}$ is an altitude.
   a. Name two perpendicular line segments.
   b. Name two congruent line segments.
   c. Name two right angles.
   d. Name two congruent angles, each with vertex at S.
   e. If $\overline{SA}$, $\overline{SB}$, and $\overline{SC}$ should coincide, then $\triangle RST$ would have to be
      (*1*) right   (*2*) isosceles   (*3*) scalene   (*4*) equilateral

Ex. 9

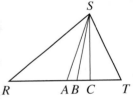

Ex. 10   **Ex. 11**   **Ex. 12**   **Ex. 13**

10. *Given:* $\overline{DA} \perp \overline{AB}$, $\overline{CB} \perp \overline{AB}$, $\overline{DA} \cong \overline{CB}$, M is the midpoint of $\overline{AB}$.
   Prove: $\triangle ADM \cong \triangle BCM$.
11. *Given:* $\overline{SR} \cong \overline{ST}$, $\overline{RP} \cong \overline{TP}$.
   Prove: **a.** $\triangle SRP \cong \triangle STP$.   **b.** $\angle RSP \cong \angle TSP$.
12. *Given:* $\overline{AB}$ and $\overline{CD}$ intersect at E, $\overline{BA}$ bisects $\overline{CD}$, $\overline{CA} \perp \overline{CD}$, $\overline{BD} \perp \overline{CD}$.
   Prove: **a.** $\triangle ACE \cong \triangle BDE$.   **b.** $\overline{AE} \cong \overline{BE}$.
13. If $\overline{LR} \cong \overline{LS}$ and $\overline{RK} \cong \overline{SM}$, prove that $\triangle RML \cong \triangle SKL$.

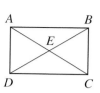

Ex. 14   **Ex. 15**   **Ex. 16**   **Ex. 17**

14. If $\overline{TR} \cong \overline{TS}$, $\overline{RN}$ bisects $\angle R$, and $\overline{SM}$ bisects $\angle S$, prove that $\angle NRS \cong \angle MSR$.

15. Given $\overrightarrow{ADE}$, $\angle r \cong \angle s$, and $\overline{BD} \cong \overline{CD}$, prove that $\overline{AB} \cong \overline{AC}$.

16. If $\overline{RT} \cong \overline{ST}$ and $\angle 1 \cong \angle 2$: **a.** Prove $\overline{RK} \cong \overline{MS}$ **b.** Prove $\overline{RM} \cong \overline{KS}$.

17. In quadrilateral $ABCD$, diagonals $\overline{AC}$ and $\overline{BD}$ bisect each other at E.
   a. Prove that $\triangle AEB \cong \triangle CED$.   **b.** If $AB = 4x + 2$ and $CD = 7x - 19$, find AB.

18. In isosceles triangle ABC, $\overline{AB} \cong \overline{BC}$, $m\angle A = x + 10$, and $m\angle C = 2x - 20$.
   a. Find the value of x.   **b.** Find $m\angle A$.

19. a. $A(2, 1)$, $B(8, 1)$, and $C(8, 5)$ are three points in the coordinate plane. Find the coordinates of D such that $\triangle ABC \cong \triangle BAD$.
   b. Based on your answer to part **a**, which postulate proves that $\triangle ABC \cong \triangle BAD$?

20. To keep a pasture gate from sagging, a board is nailed diagonally from one corner of the four-sided gate to the opposite corner. What theorem or postulate is illustrated?

CUMULATIVE REVIEW WITH OPEN-RESPONSE PROBLEMS

1. Let $p \rightarrow q$ be "If two triangles are congruent, then each pair of corresponding angles of the two triangles are congruent."
   a. Write the converse of $p \rightarrow q$.
   b. Write the inverse of $p \rightarrow q$.
   c. Write the contrapositive of $p \rightarrow q$.
   d. Which of the four statements, $p \rightarrow q$, its converse, inverse, and contrapositive, are always true?

2. *Given:* $m\angle ABC = 90$ and $m\angle DBE = 90$.
   Prove: $\angle ABD \cong \angle CBE$.

Exploration

   Cut six congruent triangles. Arrange the six triangles to form a hexagon. Is the hexagon a regular hexagon? What qualities does this hexagon have?

Chapter *5*

Geometric Inequalities

Not everything in our world consists of equalities and congruences. In fact, we live in a world of inequalities where we routinely use words such as *greater*, *less*, *more*, and *fewer*.

Consider the field of sports. Athletes strive to achieve new records for faster speeds, greater distances, and shorter times. Some sports records remain untouched for decades. In the 1927 baseball season, Babe Ruth hit 60 home runs. It was not until the 1961 season, 34 years later, that Roger Maris surpassed Ruth's record by hitting 61 home runs. Maris' record stood for 37 years until it was broken in 1998 by Mark McGwire who hit 70 home runs. McGwire's record was broken in 2001 by Barry Bonds who hit 73 home runs.

In the Olympics, however, records are broken more frequently. As a *research project*, select any Olympic event and produce a chart that shows the dates when records were set, and the length of time each record stood before being surpassed.

In this chapter, we will see how familiar inequalities from arithmetic, algebra, and our world can be applied to geometric figures.

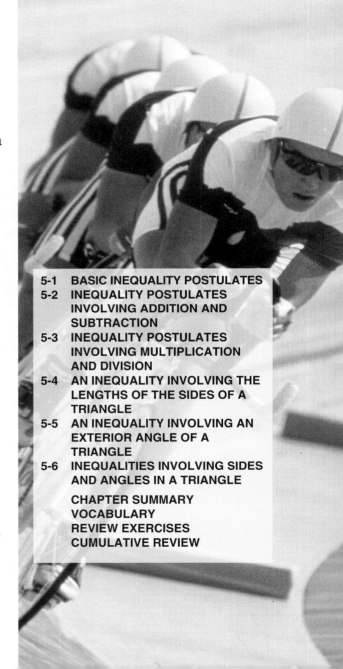

5-1 BASIC INEQUALITY POSTULATES

In an *equality*, the left-hand member of an equation is *equal* to the right-hand member of the equation.

In an *inequality*, the left-hand and right-hand members are *not* equal, and this fact is usually indicated by one of two phrases: *is greater than* ($>$) or *is less than* ($<$). Examples of inequalities exist in geometry just as they exist in arithmetic and in algebra.

	Equality	*Inequalities*	
In arithmetic:	$3 + 5 = 8$	$3 + 5 > 2$	$3 + 5 < 10$
In algebra:	$x + x = 2x$	$x + 1 > x$	$x - 5 < x$
In geometry:	$AB = CD$	$AB > BC$	$AB < CE$
	$m\angle A = m\angle B$	$m\angle A > m\angle C$	$m\angle A < m\angle D$

Postulate Relating a Whole Quantity and Its Parts

The following postulate involving an inequality is related to the postulate we accepted in Section 3-9: *A whole is equal to the sum of all its parts.*

● **POSTULATE. A whole is greater than any of its parts.**

In arithmetic: Since $12 = 7 + 5$, then $12 > 7$ and $12 > 5$.

In algebra: If a, b, and c represent positive numbers such that $a = b + c$, then $a > b$ and $a > c$.

In geometry: The lengths of line segments and the measures of angles are positive numbers.

Consider these two applications:

Since $AB = AC + CB$,   Since $m\angle ABC = m\angle 1 + m\angle 2$,

then $AB > AC$ then $m\angle ABC > m\angle 1$

and $AB > CB$.   and $m\angle ABC > m\angle 2$.

Let us state some other postulates involving inequalities. Each postulate will be stated in two forms: (1) using symbols that represent real numbers and (2) using words.

Uniqueness of Order (the Trichotomy Postulate)

- **POSTULATE. If *a* and *b* are real numbers, then exactly one of the following relations is true: $a < b$, $a = b$, $a > b$, or**
- **POSTULATE. Given any two quantities, exactly one of the following relations is true:**

  1. **The first quantity is less than the second.**
  2. **The first quantity is equal to the second.**
  3. **The first quantity is greater than the second.**

Transitive Property of Inequality

- **POSTULATE. If *a*, *b*, and *c* are real numbers such that $a > b$ and $b > c$, then $a > c$, or**
- **POSTULATE. If the first of three quantities is greater than the second and the second is greater than the third, then the first is greater than the third.**

Arithmetic Application: If $10 > 8$ and $8 > 5$, then $10 > 5$.

Geometric Application:

If $BA > BD$ and $BD > BC$,

then $BA > BC$.

Also, if $BC < BD$ and $BD < BA$,

then $BC < BA$.

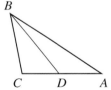

Substitution Postulate for Inequalities

- **POSTULATE. If *a*, *b*, and *c* are real numbers such that $a > b$ and $c = b$, then $a > c$, or**
- **POSTULATE. A quantity may be substituted for its equal in any inequality.**

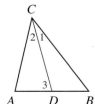

Algebraic Application: *Geometric Application:*

If $x > 7$ If $m\angle 3 > m\angle 1$

and $y = x$,   and $m\angle 2 = m\angle 1$,

then $y > 7$.   then $m\angle 3 > m\angle 2$.

EXAMPLES

1. *Given:* In $\triangle ABC$,
$m\angle ABC = m\angle 1 + m\angle 2$,
$m\angle 2 > m\angle 3$.

Prove: $m\angle ABC > m\angle 3$.

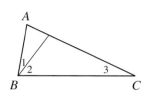

Statements	*Reasons*
1. $m\angle ABC = m\angle 1 + m\angle 2$.	1. Given.
2. $m\angle ABC > m\angle 2$.	2. A whole is greater than any of its parts.
3. $m\angle 2 > m\angle 3$.	3. Given.
4. $m\angle ABC > m\angle 3$.	4. Transitive property of inequality.

---

2. *Given:* $CB < CA$.
$CD = CB$.

Prove: $CD < CA$.

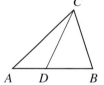

Statements	*Reasons*
1. $CB < CA$.	1. Given.
2. $CD = CB$.	2. Given.
3. $CD < CA$.	3. Substitution postulate for inequalities.

EXERCISES WITH OPEN-RESPONSE PROBLEMS

In 1–5, which refer to the figure, each statement is true. In each case write the inequality postulate that justifies the true statement.

1. $m\angle ACB > m\angle ACD$.

2. $AB > BD$.

3. Given the premises: $AC > CD$ and $CD > DA$.
We deduce the true statement: $AC > DA$.

4. Given the premises: $CD < CB$ and $CB = CA$.
We deduce the true statement: $CD < CA$.

5. Given the premises:
$m\angle BDC > m\angle A$ and $m\angle A = m\angle B$.
We deduce the true statement: $m\angle BDC > m\angle B$.

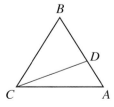

Ex. 1–5

In 6–8, in each case what inequality property justifies the conclusion?

6. If Mike is taller than Jeff, and Jeff and John are the same height, then Mike is taller than John.

7. If Joe is older than Carolyn, and Carolyn is older than Larry, then Joe is older than Larry.

8. If Alice earns more than Roberta, and Roberta earns more than Nancy, then Alice earns more than Nancy.

Ex. 9

Ex. 10

Ex. 11

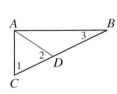

Ex. 12

9. If $AT > AS$ and $AS > AR$, prove that $AT > AR$.

10. If m$\angle 1 >$ m$\angle 2$ and m$\angle 2 >$ m$\angle 3$, prove that m$\angle 1 >$ m$\angle 3$.

11. If $SR > KR$ and $SR = TR$, prove that $TR > KR$.

12. If m$\angle 3 <$ m$\angle 2$ and m$\angle 2 =$ m$\angle 1$, prove that m$\angle 3 <$ m$\angle 1$.

Ex. 13

Ex. 14

Ex. 15

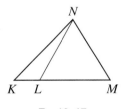

Ex. 16–17

13. *Given:* m$\angle ABD =$ m$\angle ABC +$ m$\angle CBD$; m$\angle ABC =$ m$\angle DBE$.
Prove: **a.** m$\angle ABD >$ m$\angle ABC$. **b.** m$\angle ABD >$ m$\angle DBE$.

14. *Given:* $\overline{PQRS}$, where $PR = PQ + QR$ and $PQ = RS$.
Prove: **a.** $PR > PQ$. **b.** $PR > RS$.

15. *Given:* $\triangle ABC$ is isosceles, $\overline{AC} \cong \overline{BC}$, m$\angle 1 >$ m$\angle A$.
Prove: m$\angle 1 >$ m$\angle B$.

16. Given $\overline{KLM}$ and $\overline{LM} \cong \overline{NM}$, prove that $KM > NM$.

17. If $KM > KN$, $KN > NM$, and $NM = NL$, prove that $KM > NL$.

18. Explain why the relation $>$ is not an equivalence relation for the set of real numbers.

5-2   INEQUALITY POSTULATES INVOLVING ADDITION AND SUBTRACTION

Examples of inequalities involving the numbers of arithmetic can help us to understand the three inequality postulates presented here. Again, we will state each postulate in symbols and in words.

- **POSTULATE. If a, b, c, and d are real numbers such that $a > b$ and $c = d$, then $a + c > b + d$, or**
- **POSTULATE. If equal quantities are added to unequal quantities, the sums are unequal in the same order.**

Arithmetic Application:

If $5 < 8$ and $4 = 4$,
then $5 + 4 < 8 + 4$
or $9 < 12$.

Geometric Application:

If $AB > CD$ and $BE = DF$,
then $AB + BE > CD + DF$
or $AE > CF$.

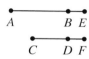

- **POSTULATE. If a, b, c, and d are real numbers such that $a > b$ and $c > d$, then $a + c > b + d$, or**
- **POSTULATE. If unequal quantities are added to unequal quantities of the same order, the sums are unequal in the same order.**

Arithmetic Application:

If $6 > 4$ and $8 > 5$,
then $6 + 8 > 4 + 5$
or $14 > 9$.

Geometric Application:

If $CD < AB$ and $DF < BE$,
then $CD + DF < AB + BE$
or $CF < AE$.

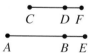

- **POSTULATE. If a, b, c, and d are real numbers such that $a > b$ and $c = d$, then $a - c > b - d$, or**
- **POSTULATE. If equal quantities are subtracted from unequal quantities, the differences are unequal in the same order.**

Arithmetic Application:

If $15 > 12$ and $5 = 5$,
then $15 - 5 > 12 - 5$
or $10 > 7$.

Geometric Application:

If $AC < AB$ and $EC = DB$,
then $AC - EC < AB - DB$
or $AE < AD$.

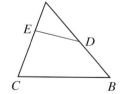

Note that, if unequal quantities are subtracted from unequal quantities, the differences are not necessarily unequal in the same order. For example, $5 > 4$ and $3 > 1$, but it does not follow that $5 - 3 > 4 - 1$.

EXAMPLE

Given: m∠ABG < m∠DEH.
        m∠GBC = m∠HEF.

Prove: m∠ABC < m∠DEF.

Statements	*Reasons*
1. m∠ABG < m∠DEH.	1. Given.
2. m∠GBC = m∠HEF.	2. Given.
3. m∠ABG + m∠GBC < m∠DEH + m∠HEF, or m∠ABC < m∠DEF.	3. If equal quantities are added to unequal quantities, the sums are unequal in the same order.

EXERCISES WITH OPEN-RESPONSE PROBLEMS

In 1–8, in each case use an inequality postulate to prove the conclusion.

1. If 10 > 7, then 18 > 15.
2. If 4 < 14, then 15 < 25.
3. If $x + 3 > 12$, then $x > 9$.
4. If $y - 5 < 5$, then $y < 10$.
5. If 8 > 6 and 5 > 3, then 13 > 9.
6. If 7 < 12, then 5 < 10.
7. If $y > 8$, then $y - 1 > 7$.
8. If $a = b$, then $180 - a > 90 - b$.

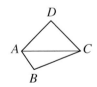

Ex. 9	Ex. 10	Ex. 11	Ex. 12

9. *Given:* $AB = AD$, $BC < DE$.
    Prove: $AC < AE$.

10. *Given:* $AE > BD$, $AF = BF$.
     Prove: $FE > FD$.

11. *Given:* m∠DAC > m∠DBC, $\overline{AE} \cong \overline{EB}$.
     Prove: **a.** m∠EAB = m∠EBA.
            b. m∠DAB > m∠CBA.

12. *Given:* m∠DCB < m∠DAB, $\overline{AD} \cong \overline{DC}$.
     Prove: m∠ACB < m∠CAB.

13. Find values of p, q, r, and s such that, when $p > q$ and $r > s$, then:
    a. $p - r > q - s$ **b.** $p - r = q - s$ **c.** $p - r < q - s$

5-3   INEQUALITY POSTULATES INVOLVING MULTIPLICATION AND DIVISION

Care must be taken when using inequality postulates involving multiplication and division because multiplying or dividing by a *negative* number will reverse the order of the inequality. Each of the two postulates in this section is stated first in symbols and then in words.

- **POSTULATE. If *a* and *b* are numbers such that $a > b$, and if *c* is a *positive* number, then $ac > bc$, or**
- **POSTULATE. If unequal quantities are multiplied by equal *positive* quantities, the products are unequal in the same order.**

[A special case of this postulate is as follows: *Doubles of unequal quantities are unequal in the same order.*]

Arithmetic Application:

If $9 > 7$ and $4 = 4$,
then $9(4) > 7(4)$
   or $36 > 28$.

Geometric Application:

If $AB > DE$, $AC = 2AB$, and $DF = 2DE$, then $AC > DF$ because doubles of unequal quantities are unequal in the same order.

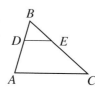

- **POSTULATE. If *a* and *b* are numbers such that $a > b$, and if *c* is a *positive* number, then $\frac{a}{c} > \frac{b}{c}$, or**
- **POSTULATE. If unequal quantities are divided by equal *positive* quantities, the quotients are unequal in the same order.**

[A special case of this postulate is as follows: *Halves of unequal quantities are unequal in the same order.*]

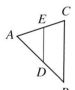

Arithmetic Application:

If $12 > 8$ and $4 = 4$,
then $\frac{12}{4} > \frac{8}{4}$
   or $3 > 2$.

Geometric Application:

If $AC < AB$, $AE = \frac{1}{2} AC$, and $AD = \frac{1}{2} AB$, then $AE < AD$ because halves of unequal quantities are unequal in the same order.

EXAMPLES

1. *Given:* $BA = 3BD$.
          $BC = 3BE$.
          $BE > BD$.

   Prove: $BC > BA$.

Statements	*Reasons*
1. $BE > BD$.	1. Given.
2. $3BE > 3BD$.	2. Unequal quantities multiplied by equal positive quantities are unequal in the same order.
3. $BC = 3BE$, $BA = 3BD$.	3. Given.
4. $BC > BA$.	4. Substitution postulate for inequalities.

---

2. *Given:* $m\angle ABC > m\angle DEF$.
$\overrightarrow{BG}$ bisects $\angle ABC$.
$\overrightarrow{EH}$ bisects $\angle DEF$.

Prove: $m\angle ABG > m\angle DEH$.

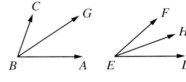

Statements	*Reasons*
1. $m\angle ABC > m\angle DEF$.	1. Given.
2. $\frac{1}{2} m\angle ABC > \frac{1}{2} m\angle DEF$.	2. Halves of unequal quantities are unequal in the same order.
3. $\overrightarrow{BG}$ bisects $\angle ABC$, $\overrightarrow{EH}$ bisects $\angle DEF$.	3. Given.
4. $m\angle ABG = \frac{1}{2} m\angle ABC$. $m\angle DEH = \frac{1}{2} m\angle DEF$.	4. Definition of angle bisector.
5. $m\angle ABG > m\angle DEH$.	5. Substitution postulate for inequalities.

EXERCISES WITH OPEN-RESPONSE PROBLEMS

In 1–6, in each case use an inequality postulate to prove the conclusion.

1. If $8 > 6$, then $24 > 18$.

2. If $30 < 35$, then $6 < 7$.

3. If $8 > 6$, then $4 > 3$.

4. If $3x > 15$, then $x > 5$.

5. If $\frac{x}{2} > 6$, then $x > 12$.

6. If $\frac{y}{5} < 4$, then $y < 20$.

In 7–12: If a, b, and c are positive integers such that $a > b$, tell whether each relationship is *True* or *False*.

7. $ac > bc$

8. $a + c > b + c$

9. $c - a > c - b$

10. $a - c > b - c$

11. $\frac{c}{a} > \frac{c}{b}$

12. $\frac{a}{c} > \frac{b}{c}$

Ex. 13

Ex. 14

Ex. 15

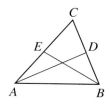

Ex. 16

13. *Given:* $BD < BE$, D is the midpoint of $\overline{BA}$, E is the midpoint of $\overline{BC}$.
Prove: $BA < BC$.

14. *Given:* $m\angle DBA > m\angle CAB$, $m\angle CBA = 2m\angle DBA$, $m\angle DAB = 2m\angle CAB$.
Prove: $m\angle CBA > m\angle DAB$.

15. *Given:* $AB > AD$, $AE = \frac{1}{2}AB$, $AF = \frac{1}{2}AD$.
Prove: $AE > AF$.

16. *Given:* $m\angle CAB < m\angle CBA$, $\overline{AD}$ bisects $\angle CAB$, $\overline{BE}$ bisects $\angle CBA$.
Prove: $m\angle DAB < m\angle EBA$.

5-4   AN INEQUALITY INVOLVING THE LENGTHS OF THE SIDES OF A TRIANGLE

- **THEOREM 10. The sum of the lengths of two sides of a triangle is greater than the length of the third side.**

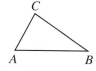

The proof of Theorem 10 is based upon an earlier postulate, which states that the shortest path between two points is the line segment joining the two points. Using $\triangle ABC$ and the lengths of its sides, we apply this theorem to state the following inequalities:

$$AC + CB > BA \qquad CB + BA > AC \qquad BA + AC > CB$$

EXAMPLES

1. Which of the following may be the lengths of the sides of a triangle?
    (1) 2, 3, 5   (2) 4, 4, 8   (3) 3, 4, 8   (4) 5, 6, 7

Solution   If the greatest length is added to either of the two smaller lengths, this sum will always be greater than the remaining length. Therefore, we need to add *only* the two shorter lengths to see whether their sum is greater than the third (or largest) length.
    (1) Is $2 + 3 > 5$? No.   (3) Is $3 + 4 > 8$? No.
    (2) Is $4 + 4 > 8$? No.   (4) Is $5 + 6 > 7$? Yes.

Answer: Choice (4)

2. Two sides of a triangle have lengths 2 and 5. Find all possible lengths of the third side.

Solution   (1) Let s = length of third side of triangle.

(2) Of the lengths 2, 5, and s, the longest side is either 5 or s.

(3) Assume the longest side of the triangle is 5.

(4) Assume the longest side of the triangle is s.

Then, $2 + s > 5$
$s > 5 - 2$
or $s > 3$

Then, $2 + 5 > s$
$7 > s$
or $s < 7.$

Answer: Length s is greater than 3 and less than 7.

Note that the solution $(s > 3) \land (s < 7)$ may be rewritten as $(3 < s) \land (s < 7)$, which becomes $(3 < s < 7)$.

EXERCISES WITH OPEN-RESPONSE PROBLEMS

In 1–12, tell in each case whether the given lengths can be the measures of the sides of a triangle.

1. 3, 4, 5   **2.** 5, 8, 13   **3.** 6, 7, 10   **4.** 3, 9, 15
5. 2, 2, 3   **6.** 1, 1, 2   **7.** 3, 4, 4   **8.** 5, 8, 11
9. 6, 2, 3   **10.** 5, 3, 7   **11.** 9, 4, 5   **12.** 4, 6, 3

In 13–16, select the numeral that precedes the set of numbers that can represent the lengths of the sides of a triangle.

13. (1) $\{2, 4, 6\}$ (2) $\{2, 4, 4\}$ (3) $\{4, 4, 8\}$ (4) $\{4, 6, 12\}$
14. (1) $\{3, 5, 7\}$ (2) $\{5, 8, 14\}$ (3) $\{5, 10, 15\}$ (4) $\{4, 4, 10\}$
15. (1) $\{1, 2, 4\}$ (2) $\{1, 2, \sqrt{2}\}$ (3) $\{2, 2, 4\}$ (4) $\{8, 4, 3\}$
16. (1) $\{2, 5, \sqrt{50}\}$ (2) $\{1, 3, \sqrt{20}\}$ (3) $\{2, 3, \sqrt{20}\}$ (4) $\{1, 5, \sqrt{40}\}$

In 17–19, select the numeral preceding the choice that best answers the question or completes the sentence.

17. The lengths of two sides of a triangle are 6 and 3. The length of the third side may be
(1) 12   (2) 9   (3) 3   (4) 6

18. The lengths of two sides of a triangle are 10 and 14. The length of the third side may be
(1) 24   (2) 2   (3) 22   (4) 4

19. If the lengths of two sides of a triangle are 3 and 8, which best describes the length s of the third side of the triangle?

(1) $3 < s < 8$ (2) $3 < s < 11$ (3) $5 < s < 8$ (4) $5 < s < 11$

In 20–23, using the two given lengths of the sides of a triangle, find all possible lengths for the third side, s.

20. 2 and 4   **21.** 4 and 7   **22.** 5 and 6   **23.** 3 and 9

24. The coordinates of $\triangle ABC$ are $A(4, 1)$, $B(-1, 3)$, and $C(0, -2)$. Name the side of $\triangle ABC$ that has:
a. the greatest length   **b.** the smallest length.

25. Triangle RST is an isosceles right triangle, where $R = (1, 3)$ and $S = (1, -1)$. Find all possible coordinates of point T so that the longest side of $\triangle RST$ is:
a. $\overline{ST}$ **b.** $\overline{RT}$ **c.** $\overline{RS}$

5-5   AN INEQUALITY INVOLVING AN EXTERIOR ANGLE OF A TRIANGLE

Exterior Angle of a Polygon

- **DEFINITION.** An *exterior angle of a polygon* is an angle that forms a linear pair with one of the interior angles of the polygon.

We have learned that the angles in a linear pair are supplementary. Also, we note that an exterior angle lies outside the polygon.

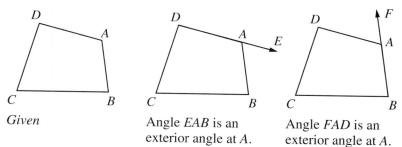

Given   Angle *EAB* is an exterior angle at *A*.   Angle *FAD* is an exterior angle at *A*.

The figure above shows that we can form an exterior angle of polygon *ABCD* at vertex *A* by using either of two methods:

1. Draw $\overrightarrow{DA}$, of which $\overline{DA}$ is a subset, to some point E, where E is not on $\overline{DA}$. Since $\angle EAB$ forms a linear pair with $\angle DAB$, $\angle EAB$ is an exterior angle at vertex *A*.

2. Draw $\overrightarrow{BA}$, of which $\overline{BA}$ is a subset, to some point F, where F is not on $\overline{BA}$. Since $\angle FAD$ forms a linear pair with $\angle DAB$, $\angle FAD$ is an exterior angle at vertex *A*.

Angle *EAB* and ∠*FAD* are each supplementary to ∠*DAB*. Since two angles that are supplementary to the same angle must be congruent, ∠*EAB* ≅ ∠*FAD*. Thus, we may use *either* ∠*EAB* or ∠*FAD* as the exterior angle at vertex *A*.

Exterior Angle of a Triangle

An exterior angle of a triangle is formed outside the triangle by extending a side of the triangle.

In the figure at the right, △*ABC* has three *interior* angles, namely, ∠*a*, ∠*b*, and ∠*c*. By extending the sides of △*ABC*, three *exterior* angles are formed, namely, ∠1, ∠2, and ∠3.

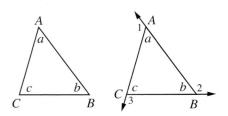

For each exterior angle, there are one **adjacent interior angle** and two **nonadjacent interior angles**. For △*ABC*, these angles are as follows:

Exterior Angle	Adjacent Interior Angle	Nonadjacent Interior Angles
∠1	∠*a*	∠*b* and ∠*c*
∠2	∠*b*	∠*a* and ∠*c*
∠3	∠*c*	∠*a* and ∠*b*

With these facts in mind, we are now ready to prove another theorem about *inequalities* in geometry.

● **THEOREM 11. The measure of an exterior angle of a triangle is greater than the measure of either nonadjacent interior angle.**

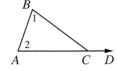

Given: △*ABC* with exterior ∠*BCD* at vertex *C*; ∠1 and ∠2 are nonadjacent interior angles to ∠*BCD*.

Prove: m∠*BCD* > m∠1.
  m∠*BCD* > m∠2.

Plan: Since we must prove two inequalities, we present the proof in two parts. Each part requires drawing additional lines in the diagram. We use congruent triangles and substitution to show that ∠1 and ∠2 are each congruent to only a part of the whole exterior ∠*BCD*.

PART 1:
Prove that m∠*BCD* > m∠1.

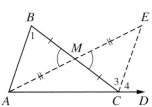

Statements	*Reasons*
1. Let M be the midpoint of $\overline{BC}$.	1. Every line segment has one and only one midpoint.
2. Draw $\overrightarrow{AM}$, extending the ray through M to point E so that $\overline{AM} \cong \overline{EM}$.	2. Two points determine a line, and a segment may be copied.
3. Draw $\overline{EC}$.	3. Through two given points, one and only one line can be drawn.
4. For exterior $\angle BCD$, let $m\angle BCD = m\angle 3 + m\angle 4$.	4. A whole is equal to the sum of its parts.
5. $\overline{BM} \cong \overline{CM}$. (s. $\cong$ s.)	5. Definition of midpoint.
6. $\overline{AM} \cong \overline{EM}$. (s. $\cong$ s.)	6. By the construction in step 2.
7. $\angle AMB \cong \angle EMC$. (a. $\cong$ a.)	7. Vertical angles are congruent.
8. $\triangle AMB \cong \triangle EMC$.	8. s.a.s. $\cong$ s.a.s.
9. $\angle 1 \cong \angle 3$.	9. Corresponding parts of congruent triangles are congruent.
10. $m\angle BCD > m\angle 3$.	10. A whole is greater than any of its parts.
11. $m\angle BCD > m\angle 1$.	11. Substitution postulate.

PART 2:
Prove that $m\angle BCD > m\angle 2$.

Plan: Draw $\overline{BG}$ through midpoint N of $\overline{AC}$, such that $BN = GN$.
$\triangle ABN \cong \triangle CGN$ by s.a.s. $\cong$ s.a.s., and $\angle 2 \cong \angle 5$.

Since $m\angle ACF > m\angle 5$, and $m\angle BCD = m\angle ACF$, then $m\angle BCD > m\angle 5$ and $m\angle BCD > m\angle 2$ by substitution.

Because of its length, you are not expected to remember the steps in this proof of the theorem that the measure of an exterior angle of a triangle is greater than the measure of either nonadjacent interior angle. You should, however, have followed the reasoning.

Example 2 illustrates how this theorem is used in a proof.

EXAMPLES

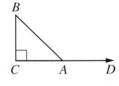

1. Refer to given triangle *ABC*, where *D* is a point on $\overline{AB}$.

Answers

a. Name the exterior angle of △*DCB* at vertex *D*.

a. ∠*ADC* (or ∠*CDA*)

b. Name the two nonadjacent interior angles of △*DCB* for the exterior angle given as an answer in part **a**.

b. ∠*DCB* and ∠*DBC*

c. Write the theorem that allows us to say:
m∠*ADC* > m∠*DCB*.

c. The measure of an exterior angle of a triangle is greater than the measure of either nonadjacent interior angle.

d. Write the postulate that allows us to say:
m∠*ACB* > m∠*DCB*.

d. A whole is greater than any of its parts.

e. Using the postulate stated as an answer in part **d**, give two illustrations of the postulate applied to lengths of line segments in the figure.

e. *AB* > *AD*
AB > *DB*

---

2. *Given:* Right triangle *ABC*, m∠*C* = 90, ∠*BAD* is an exterior angle at *A*.

Prove: ∠*BAD* is obtuse.

Plan: Use Theorem 11 to prove that m∠*BAD* > m∠*C* and therefore greater than 90. Then use the linear pair of angles at *A* to show that m∠*BAD* < 180.

Statements	*Reasons*
1. ∠*BAD* is an exterior angle.	1. Given.
2. m∠*BAD* > m∠*C*.	2. The measure of an exterior angle of a triangle is greater than the measure of either nonadjacent interior angle.
3. m∠*C* = 90.	3. Given.
4. m∠*BAD* > 90.	4. Substitution.
5. m∠*BAD* + m∠*BAC* = 180.	5. If two angles form a linear pair, they are supplementary.

6. $180 > $ m$\angle BAD$.   6. The whole is greater than any of its parts.

7. $180 > $ m$\angle BAD > 90$.   7. Steps 4 and 6.

8. $\angle BAD$ is obtuse.   8. Definition of an obtuse angle.

EXERCISES WITH OPEN-RESPONSE PROBLEMS

In 1–4:   **a.** Name the given exterior angle of $\triangle ABC$.   **b.** Name the two nonadjacent interior angles to that exterior angle.

1.   **2.**   **3.**   **4.**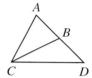

In 5–14, $\triangle ABC$ is scalene and $\overline{CM}$ is a median to side $\overline{AB}$.

a. Tell whether each given statement is *True* or *False*.
b. If the statement is true, indicate the postulate or theorem that justifies your answer.

5. $AM = MB$.
7. m$\angle AMC > $ m$\angle ABC$.
9. m$\angle CMB > $ m$\angle ACM$.
11. $BA > MB$.
13. m$\angle BCA > $ m$\angle MCA$.

6. m$\angle ACB > $ m$\angle ACM$.
8. $AB > AM$.
10. m$\angle CMB > $ m$\angle CAB$.
12. m$\angle ACM = $ m$\angle BCM$.
14. m$\angle BMC > $ m$\angle AMC$.

Ex. 5–14

Ex. 15

Ex. 16

Ex. 17

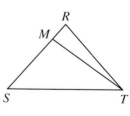

Ex. 18

15. $\overrightarrow{BD}$ and $\overrightarrow{BE}$ are interior rays of $\angle ABC$; $\overrightarrow{BD}$ is in the interior of $\angle ABE$, and $\overrightarrow{BE}$ is in the interior of $\angle DBC$; $\angle ABD \cong \angle EBC$. Prove that m$\angle ABE > $ m$\angle EBC$.

16. In $\triangle RST$, if Q is a point on $\overline{RT}$ and P is a point on $\overline{ST}$ such that $\overline{QT} \cong \overline{PT}$, prove that m$\angle SPQ > $ m$\angle QPT$.

17. In $\triangle ABC$, D is a point on $\overline{AC}$. If $\overline{AD} \cong \overline{BD}$, prove that m$\angle ABC > $ m$\angle A$.

18. If $\triangle RST$ is isosceles with $\overline{RS} \cong \overline{RT}$ and M is a point on $\overline{RS}$, prove that m$\angle RMT > $ m$\angle STR$.

Ex. 19

Ex. 20

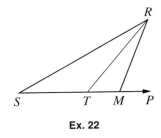

Ex. 21   Ex. 22

19. In $\triangle ABC$, $\overline{AD}$ is drawn to $\overline{BC}$ and $\angle ABC \cong \angle 2$.
Prove that m$\angle 1 >$ m$\angle 2$.

20. In isosceles triangle PQR, $\overline{PS}$ bisects vertex $\angle RPQ$ and $\overline{RSQ}$ is extended through Q to T.
Prove: **a.** m$\angle PQT >$ m$\angle QPS$.   **b.** m$\angle PQT >$ m$\angle RPS$.

21. In quadrilateral $ABCD$, $\overline{AC}$ is drawn, and $\overline{CB}$ is extended through B to E. If $\overline{AB} \cong \overline{CD}$ and $\overline{BC} \cong \overline{DA}$, prove:
a. $\triangle ABC \cong \triangle CDA$.   **b.** m$\angle EBA >$ m$\angle CAD$.

22. In $\triangle RSM$, T is on $\overline{SM}$, which is extended through M to P. Prove that m$\angle RMP >$ m$\angle SRT$.

5-6 INEQUALITIES INVOLVING SIDES AND ANGLES IN A TRIANGLE

There are two other major inequality theorems involving the measures of the angles and sides of a triangle.

● **THEOREM 12. If the lengths of two sides of a triangle are unequal, the measures of the angles opposite these sides are unequal and the greater angle lies opposite the greater side.**

Given: $\triangle ABC$ with $AB > BC$.

Prove: m$\angle 1 >$ m$\angle 2$.

Plan: On the line containing the shorter side, $\overline{BC}$, we locate point D so that $BD = BA$, and C is between B and D. By drawing $\overline{AD}$, we form a series of angles. Applying the transitive property of inequality to the measures of these angles, we can show that m$\angle 1 >$ m$\angle 2$.

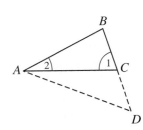

Statements	*Reasons*
1. $\triangle ABC$ with $AB > BC$.	1. Given.
2. Extend $\overline{BC}$ through C to point D so that $BD = BA$.	2. A line segment may be extended to a given length.
3. Draw $\overline{AD}$.	3. A line segment may be drawn joining two points.
4. $\triangle ABD$ is isosceles.	4. Definition of isosceles triangle.
5. $m\angle BAD = m\angle BDA$	5. Base angles of an isosceles triangle are equal in measure.
6. For $\triangle ACD$, $m\angle 1 > m\angle BDA$.	6. The measure of an exterior angle of a triangle is greater than the measure of either nonadjacent interior angle.
7. $m\angle 1 > m\angle BAD$.	7. Substitution postulate.
8. $m\angle BAD > m\angle 2$.	8. A whole is greater than any of its parts.
9. $m\angle 1 > m\angle 2$.	9. Transitive property of inequality.

Let us apply this theorem to $\triangle RST$, where $RT = 7$, $TS = 5$, and $SR = 4$.

Since $\overline{RT}$ has the greatest length and $\angle S$ is opposite $\overline{RT}$, then $\angle S$ is the angle with the greatest measure. Also, since $\overline{SR}$ has the smallest length and $\angle T$ is opposite $\overline{SR}$, then $\angle T$ is the angle with the smallest measure. In summary:

1. We can order the lengths of the three sides, from the largest to the smallest:

2. By looking at the angles opposite these three sides in the same given order, we can order the measures of the three angles from the largest to the smallest:

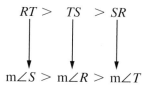

The converse of this theorem, which follows, is also true. The proof is presented using an indirect method.

- **THEOREM 13. If the measures of two angles of a triangle are unequal, the lengths of the sides opposite these angles are unequal and the greater side lies opposite the greater angle.**

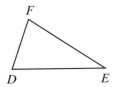

Given: △DEF with m∠D > m∠E.

Prove: FE > FD.

Plan: In an indirect proof, we must assume the negation of the conclusion and show that this assumption leads to a contradiction. Instead of listing all the steps in this proof, we will simply indicate five general concepts (along with appropriate reasons) that form the outline of a paragraph proof.

Paragraph Proof:

1. By the trichotomy postulate: *FE > FD* or *FE = FD* or *FE < FD*.

2. We assume the negation of the conclusion; that is, we assume *FE ⊁ FD*. Therefore, we assume either *FE = FD* or *FE < FD*.

3. If *FE = FD*, then m∠D = m∠E because base angles of an isosceles triangle are equal in measure. This contradicts the given premise, m∠D > m∠E. Thus, *FE = FD* is a false assumption.

4. If *FE < FD*, then, by Theorem 12, we must conclude that m∠D < m∠E. This also contradicts the given premise, that is, m∠D > m∠E. Thus, *FE < FD* is also a false assumption.

5. Since *FE = FD* and *FE < FD* are both false, *FE > FD* must be true.

If we apply Theorem 13 to △ABC, where m∠A = 40, m∠B = 80, and m∠C = 60, then:

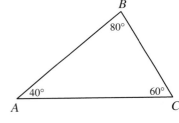

1. We can order the angle measures, from the largest to the smallest:

2. By looking at the sides opposite these angles in the same given order, we can order the lengths of the three sides from the largest to the smallest:

EXAMPLES

1. In △ABD, C is between A and D, and $\overline{BC}$ is drawn. If m∠D = 50, m∠CBD = 55, and m∠BCA = 105, which is the longest side of △BCD?

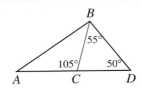

Solution   (1) Since $\angle BCA$ and $\angle BCD$ are a linear
pair, $m\angle BCD = 180 - 105 = 75$.

(2) The longest side of a triangle is
opposite the angle with the greatest
measure. Therefore, the longest side
of $\triangle BCD$ is $\overline{BD}$ because it is opposite $\angle BCD$, whose degree measure
is 75.

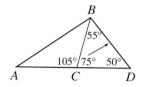

Answer: $\overline{BD}$ is the longest side of $\triangle BCD$.

---

2. *Given:* In $\triangle ACD$, $\overline{CB}$ is drawn to
$\overline{ABD}$ so that $\overline{CB} \cong \overline{CA}$.

Prove: $CD > CA$.

Plan: To prove that $CD > CA$ in
$\triangle ACD$, show that $m\angle 3$
(opposite $\overline{CD}$) is greater than
$m\angle 1$ (opposite $\overline{CA}$).

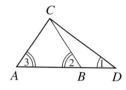

Statements	Reasons
1. In $\triangle CBD$, $m\angle 2 > m\angle 1$.	1. The measure of an exterior angle of a triangle is greater than the measure of either nonadjacent interior angle.
2. $\overline{CB} \cong \overline{CA}$.	2. Given.
3. $m\angle 3 = m\angle 2$.	3. Base angles of an isosceles triangle are equal in measure.
4. $m\angle 3 > m\angle 1$.	4. A quantity may be substituted for its equal in any inequality.
5. $CD > CA$.	5. If the measures of two angles of a triangle are unequal, the lengths of the sides opposite these angles are unequal, and the greater side lies opposite the greater angle.

---

3. Given $\triangle ABC$ with coordinates $A(4, 1)$,
$B(4, 5)$, and $C(0, 2)$. Which angle of
$\triangle ABC$ has the largest measure?

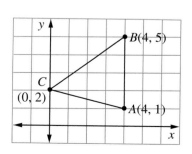

How to Proceed	*Solution*

(1) Find the length of each side of $\triangle ABC$.

(1) $AB = |y_2 - y_1| = |5 - 1| = |4| = 4$
$BC = \sqrt{(x_2 - x_1)^2 + (y_2 - y_1)^2}$
$= \sqrt{(4 - 0)^2 + (5 - 2)^2}$
$= \sqrt{4^2 + 3^2} = \sqrt{16 + 9} = \sqrt{25} = 5$
$CA = \sqrt{(0 - 4)^2 + (2 - 1)^2}$
$= \sqrt{(-4)^2 + 1^2} = \sqrt{16 + 1} = \sqrt{17}$

(2) Find the longest side of $\triangle ABC$.

(2) Since $5 > \sqrt{17} > 4$, then $BC > CA > AB$. The longest side is $\overline{BC}$.

(3) Find the angle with the greatest measure.

(3) In a triangle, the angle with the greatest measure is opposite the longest side. Here, $\angle A$ is opposite the longest side, $\overline{BC}$.

Answer: Angle A has the greatest measure.

EXERCISES WITH OPEN-RESPONSE PROBLEMS

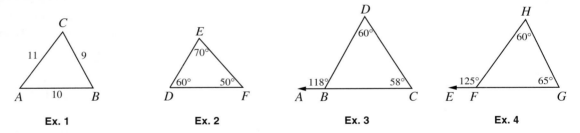

Ex. 1   Ex. 2   Ex. 3   Ex. 4

1. If $AB = 10$, $BC = 9$, and $CA = 11$, name the largest angle of $\triangle ABC$.
2. If $m\angle D = 60$, $m\angle E = 70$, and $m\angle F = 50$, name the shortest side of $\triangle DEF$.
3. Given: $\overrightarrow{CBA}$, $m\angle ABD = 118$, $m\angle D = 60$, $m\angle C = 58$. Name the longest side of $\triangle BCD$.
4. Given: $\overrightarrow{GFE}$, $m\angle EFH = 125$, $m\angle G = 65$, $m\angle H = 60$. Name the shortest side of $\triangle FGH$.

In 5 and 6, name the shortest side of $\triangle ABC$, using the given information.

5. In $\triangle ABC$, $m\angle C = 90$, $m\angle B = 35$, and $m\angle A = 55$.
6. In $\triangle ABC$, $m\angle A = 74$, $m\angle B = 58$, and $m\angle C = 48$.

In 7 and 8, name the smallest angle of $\triangle ABC$, using the given information.

7. In $\triangle ABC$, $AB = 7$, $BC = 9$, and $AC = 5$.
8. In $\triangle ABC$, $AB = 5$, $BC = 12$, and $AC = 13$.

9. In $\triangle RST$, an exterior angle at R measures 80 degrees. If $m\angle S > m\angle T$, name the shortest side of the triangle.

In 10–13, select the numeral preceding the choice that best completes the sentence.

10. In isosceles triangle ABC, $\overline{AC} \cong \overline{CB}$. If D is a point on base $\overline{AB}$ lying between A and B, and $\overline{CD}$ is drawn, then
   (1) $AC > CD$ (2) $CD > AC$ (3) $m\angle A > m\angle ADC$ (4) $m\angle B > m\angle BDC$

Ex. 11

Ex. 12

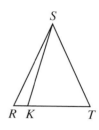

Ex. 13

11. In $\triangle ABD$, $\overline{AB} \cong \overline{BC}$, and points A, C, and D are collinear. It is true that
   (1) $m\angle 1 > m\angle 2$ (2) $m\angle 1 > m\angle 4$ (3) $m\angle 3 > m\angle 4$ (4) $m\angle 4 > m\angle 2$
12. In quadrilateral $ABCD$, $\overline{BD}$ and $\overrightarrow{BAE}$ are drawn. It is true that
   (1) $m\angle 1 > m\angle 2$ (2) $m\angle 1 > m\angle 3$ (3) $m\angle 2 > m\angle 4$ (4) $m\angle 4 > m\angle 3$
13. In isosceles triangle RST, $\overline{SR} \cong \overline{ST}$, and K is a point lying between R and T on base $\overline{RT}$. If $\overline{SK}$ is drawn, it is true that
   (1) $RS > SK$ (2) $SK > RS$ (3) $m\angle R > m\angle RKS$ (4) $m\angle T > m\angle TKS$

Ex. 14

Ex. 15

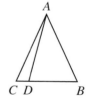

Ex. 16

14. *Given:* $m\angle DEB = m\angle DAB$, points B, E, and C are collinear.
   Prove: $m\angle DAB > m\angle BCD$.
15. *Given:* $\overline{RTW}$, $m\angle RST > m\angle RTS$.
   Prove: $m\angle RST > m\angle RWS$.
16. *Given:* $\triangle ABC$, $\overline{AB} \cong \overline{AC}$, D is a point between B and C.
   Prove: $AB > AD$.

17. In a right triangle, the hypotenuse is the longest side. For any right triangle:
   a. What is the measure of its largest angle? Explain your reasoning.
   b. What type of angles are the two remaining angles? Explain your answer.
18. In $\triangle DEF$, $m\angle D$ is twice $m\angle E$, and $m\angle D$ is 3 times $m\angle F$. Which side of $\triangle DEF$ has the shortest length?

In 19–22, the coordinates of the vertices of △*ABC* are given. In each case:

a. Graph △*ABC*.   **b.** Find the lengths of its sides: $\overline{AB}$, $\overline{BC}$, and $\overline{CA}$.

c. Determine which angle of △*ABC* has the largest measure.

19. *A*(1, −1), *B*(−1, 2), *C*(−2, −1)   **20.** *A*(2, 2), *B*(−3, 1), *C*(0, −2)
21. *A*(−1, −2), *B*(−4, 2), *C*(5, 6)   **22.** *A*(0, 2), *B*(0, −4), *C*(−5, 0)

23. *Given:* △*ABC* ≅ △*CDA*, *AD* > *DC*.
    Prove: **a.** m∠*ACD* > m∠*CAD*.
        b. $\overline{AC}$ does *not* bisect ∠*A*.

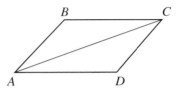

24. In isosceles triangle *ABC*, $\overline{CA}$ ≅ $\overline{CB}$. If *D* is a point on $\overline{AC}$ between *A* and *C*, prove that *DB* > *DA*.

CHAPTER SUMMARY

Since **angle measures** and **lengths** of **line segments** are real numbers, many postulates that apply to arithmetic and algebra can also be applied to geometric figures. These **postulates** include:

1. A **whole** is greater than any of its parts.

2. The **Trichotomy Postulate:** For real numbers *a* and *b*, exactly one of these relationships is true: *a* < *b*, *a* = *b*, or *a* > *b*.

3. **Addition Postulates:**   If *a* > *b* and *c* = *d*, then *a* + *c* > *b* + *d*.
                 If *a* > *b* and *c* > *d*, then *a* + *c* > *b* + *d*.

4. **Subtraction Postulate:**   If *a* > *b* and *c* = *d*, then *a* − *c* > *b* − *d*.

5. **Multiplication/Division Postulates:**   If *a* > *b* and *c* > 0, then *ac* > *bc*.
    (where *c* is a positive number)   If *a* > *b* and *c* > 0, then $\frac{a}{c} > \frac{b}{c}$.

The **inequality postulates** are used to prove theorems that compare the measures of the sides and angles of a triangle, such as:

1. The sum of the lengths of two sides of a triangle is greater than the length of the third side.

2. If the lengths of two sides of a triangle are unequal, the measures of the angles opposite these sides are unequal in the same order, and conversely.

VOCABULARY

5-1   Equality   Inequality
5-5   Exterior angle of a polygon   Adjacent interior angle (of a polygon)
      Nonadjacent interior angles (of a polygon)

REVIEW EXERCISES WITH OPEN-RESPONSE PROBLEMS

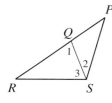

In 1–6, △*PRS* is given, and *Q* is a point on $\overline{PR}$. State the inequality postulate or theorem that justifies each of the following true statements.

1. m∠*PSR* > m∠2. **2.** m∠1 > m∠2.
3. *RS* + *SP* > *PR*. **4.** *PR* > *PQ*.
5. m∠2 > m∠3, or m∠2 = m∠3, or m∠2 < m∠3.
6. If *RP* > *PS* and *PS* > *SQ*, then *RP* > *SQ*.

In 7–10, select the numeral preceding the choice that best answers the question or completes the statement.

7. The lengths of the sides of a triangle may be
(1) 4, 9, 13 (2) 5, 8, 12 (3) 5, 5, 13 (4) 5, 5, 10

8. Which set of numbers could represent the lengths of the sides of an isosceles triangle?
(1) {3, 4, 5} (2) {3, 3, 8} (3) {3, 8, 8} (4) {3, 3, 6}

9. In isosceles triangle *RST*, $\overline{SR} \cong \overline{ST}$, and *K* is a point between *R* and *T* on $\overline{RT}$. Which must be true?
(1) *SK* > *SR* (2) *ST* > *SK*
(3) m∠*R* > m∠*SKR* (4) m∠*T* > m∠*SKT*

10. In △*ABC*, $\overline{BD}$ is drawn to $\overline{AC}$. Which must be true?
(1) m∠1 > m∠3 (2) m∠2 > m∠4
(3) m∠2 > m∠3 (4) m∠3 > m∠4

Ex. 10

11. In △*PQR*, if *PQ* = 7, *QR* = 9, and *RP* = 12, which angle of the triangle has the smallest measure?

12. In △*ABC*, m∠*A* is 20 more than m∠*B*, and m∠*C* is the average of m∠*A* and m∠*B*. Which side of △*ABC* has the greatest length?

In 13–18, ∠*ACE* is an exterior angle to △*ABC* at vertex *C*, *D* is a point on $\overline{BC}$, and $\overline{AD}$ is drawn. **a.** Tell whether each statement is always true or not necessarily true. **b.** If the statement is always true, indicate the postulate or theorem that justifies it.

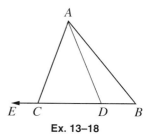

Ex. 13–18

13. m∠*ACE* > m∠*CAD*. **14.** *CB* > *CD*.
15. m∠*ACE* > m∠*ABC*. **16.** *BC* > *CE*.
17. m∠*CAB* > m∠*CAD*. **18.** m∠*ACE* > m∠*ACD*.

19. The coordinates of the vertices of △*PAM* are *P*(−1, −1), *A*(−1, 4), and *M*(4, 1). Which angle of △*PAM* has the greatest measure?

Ex. 20

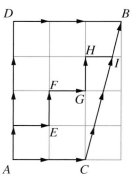

Ex. 21

20. *Given:* $\overline{ABC}$, $\overline{CDE}$, $AB > ED$, $BC > DC$.
    Prove: $AC > EC$.

21. *Given:* $\angle BDA$ is an exterior angle to $\triangle BCD$ at D, $\overline{BD} \cong \overline{BC}$.
    Prove: $m\angle BDA > m\angle BDC$.

22. Point B is 4 blocks north and
    3 blocks east of A. All streets run
    north and south or east and west
    except a street that slants from C to
    B. Of the three paths from A and B
    that are marked:
    a. Which path is shortest?
    b. Which path is longest?

CUMULATIVE REVIEW WITH OPEN-RESPONSE PROBLEMS

1. In $\triangle ABC$, $\overline{AD}$ is the median, $\overline{AE}$ is the altitude, and $\overline{AF}$ is the angle bisector, all
   drawn from vertex A to $\overleftrightarrow{BC}$. Of $\overline{AD}$, $\overline{AE}$, and $\overline{AF}$, which must lie in the interior of
   $\triangle ABC$?

2. If $\overleftrightarrow{AEB}$ and $\overleftrightarrow{CED}$ intersect at E, $m\angle AEC = x + 30$, and $m\angle CEB = 2x$, find:
   a. x **b.** $m\angle AEC$ **c.** $m\angle CEB$ **d.** $m\angle AED$ **e.** $m\angle BED$

3. On the real number line, the length of $\overline{BC}$ is twice the length of $\overline{AB}$ and B lies
   between A and C. If $A = -7$ and $C = 2$, find the coordinate of B.

Exploration

   The longest side of a triangle has a length of 6. The lengths of the other two sides
are integers that may be less than or equal to 6. List the ordered triples that can be the
lengths of the sides of *all* triangles that meet the conditions stated here. For example,
(6, 3, 5) is the triple for one such triangle.

Chapter 6

Perpendicular and Parallel Lines

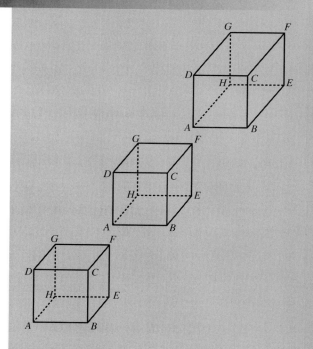

The study of parallel lines has intrigued and challenged scholars from earliest times. Since parallel lines never meet, it is reasonable to believe that they are everywhere equidistant. Nevertheless, when we are depicting a three-dimensional object in a drawing, parallel lines that are receding from the eye are shown as if they are getting closer to one another.

Often our eyes play tricks on us when we look at drawings that include parallel lines. The illustration at the right shows three rectangular solids, and all lines represent either parallel or perpendicular lines. Of the three drawings, which looks most like a cube, that is, a rectangular solid with all edges equal in length? Without measuring, choose the drawing in which you think that $AB = BE$. Now measure the line segments in each drawing. Did you select the correct drawing? Find other examples of optical illusions with parallel lines. Can you draw some representations of these illusions?

6-1 PROVING LINES PERPENDICULAR

Perpendicular lines were defined as lines that intersect to form right angles. Since a definition is a biconditional, we may look at the figure shown in two ways:

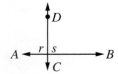

1. If $\overleftrightarrow{CD} \perp \overleftrightarrow{AB}$, then $\angle r$ and $\angle s$ are right angles.

2. If $\angle r$ and $\angle s$ are right angles formed by intersecting lines, then $\overleftrightarrow{CD} \perp \overleftrightarrow{AB}$.

Let us look at the figure in a third way. We start with the premise that the lines intersect so that $\angle r$ and $\angle s$ are congruent adjacent angles. Since $\angle r$ and $\angle s$ are supplementary angles with a common vertex C on $\overleftrightarrow{AB}$, we know that m$\angle r$ + m$\angle s$ = 180. It follows that m$\angle r$ = 90 and m$\angle s$ = 90, or $\angle r$ and $\angle s$ are right angles. Thus, $\overleftrightarrow{CD} \perp \overleftrightarrow{AB}$.

Proof of the following theorem, using the steps suggested in this discussion, is left to the student.

- **THEOREM 14. If two intersecting lines form congruent adjacent angles, the lines are perpendicular.**

Perpendicular Bisector of a Line Segment

When M is the midpoint of AB, any line or subset of a line that intersects $\overline{AB}$ at M is a bisector of $\overline{AB}$. Therefore, in the diagram below, $\overrightarrow{PM}$, $\overrightarrow{NM}$, $\overline{QM}$, and $\overrightarrow{MR}$ are all bisectors of $\overline{AB}$. Note that a line segment may have many bisectors.

   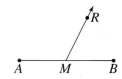

If $\angle AMN \cong \angle NMB$, the line $\overleftrightarrow{MN}$ forms congruent adjacent angles with $\overline{AB}$, and is therefore perpendicular to $\overline{AB}$. Since $\overleftrightarrow{MN}$ is a bisector of $\overline{AB}$ and $\overleftrightarrow{MN}$ is perpendicular to $\overline{AB}$, we say that $\overleftrightarrow{MN}$ is the perpendicular bisector of $\overline{AB}$. A line segment may have only one perpendicular bisector since, through a given point (the midpoint), only one line can be drawn perpendicular to a given line.

- **DEFINITION.** The perpendicular bisector of a line segment is a line, a line segment, or a ray that is perpendicular to the line segment and bisects it.

The Meaning of *Equidistant*

If $PX = PY$, we say that the distance from P to X is equal to the distance from P to Y, or, more simply, that P is *equidistant* from X and Y.

If $MX = MY$, M is also equidistant from X and Y. Therefore, P and M are each equidistant from X and Y.

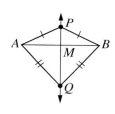

The diagram shows how to construct the *perpendicular bisector*, $\overleftrightarrow{PM}$, of a line segment, $\overline{XY}$. Notice that $PX = PY$ and $MX = MY$. We say that $\overleftrightarrow{PM}$ is the perpendicular bisector of $\overline{XY}$ because $\overleftrightarrow{PM} \perp \overline{XY}$ and $\overleftrightarrow{PM}$ bisects $\overline{XY}$. From this information, we will state two more theorems.

- **THEOREM 15. If two points are each equidistant from the endpoints of a line segment, the points determine the perpendicular bisector of the line segment.**

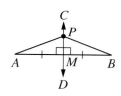

Given: $\overline{PA} \cong \overline{PB}, \overline{QA} \cong \overline{QB}$.

Prove: $\overleftrightarrow{PQ} \perp \overline{AB}$.

$\overleftrightarrow{PQ}$ bisects $\overline{AB}$.

Plan: Prove $\triangle PQA \cong \triangle PQB$ by s.s.s. $\cong$ s.s.s.
Then prove $\triangle PMA \cong \triangle PMB$ by s.a.s. $\cong$ s.a.s.

- **THEOREM 16. Any point on the perpendicular bisector of a line segment is equidistant from the endpoints of the line segment.**

Given: $\overleftrightarrow{CPD} \perp \overline{AB}$.

M is the midpoint of $\overline{AB}$.

Prove: $\overline{PA} \cong \overline{PB}$.

Plan: Prove $\triangle PMA \cong \triangle PMB$ by s.a.s. $\cong$ s.a.s.

Methods of Proving Lines or Line Segments Perpendicular

To prove that two intersecting lines or line segments are perpendicular, prove that one of the following statements is true:

1. When the two lines or line segments intersect, they form right angles.

2. When the two lines or line segments intersect, they form congruent adjacent angles.

3. Each of two points on the line or line segment is equidistant from the endpoints of the other line segment.

EXAMPLE

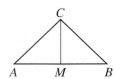

Prove that the median to the base of an isosceles triangle is perpendicular to the base.

Given: △*ABC* with $\overline{CA} \cong \overline{CB}$.
$\overline{CM}$ is the median to base $\overline{AB}$.

Prove: $\overline{CM} \perp \overline{AB}$.

Plan: Prove that points *C* and *M* are each equidistant from the endpoints of $\overline{AB}$.

Statements	*Reasons*
1. $\overline{CA} \cong \overline{CB}$, or *C* is equidistant from *A* and *B*.	1. Given.
2. $\overline{CM}$ is a median.	2. Given.
3. *M* is the midpoint of $\overline{AB}$.	3. Definition of a median of a triangle.
4. $\overline{AM} \cong \overline{MB}$, or *M* is equidistant from *A* and *B*.	4. Definition of the midpoint of a line segment.
5. $\overline{CM} \perp \overline{AB}$.	5. If two points are each equidistant from the endpoints of a line segment, the points determine the perpendicular bisector of the line segment.

EXERCISES WITH OPEN-RESPONSE PROBLEMS

1. List four different objects or places in the classroom that could be represented by perpendicular lines.

Ex. 2

Ex. 3

Ex. 4

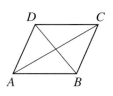

Ex. 5

2. Given $\overleftrightarrow{ADB}$, $\angle 1 \cong \angle 4$, and $\angle 2 \cong \angle 3$, prove that $\overrightarrow{DC} \perp \overleftrightarrow{AB}$.

3. If $\overline{AC} \cong \overline{BC}$ and $\overrightarrow{CD}$ bisects $\angle ACB$, prove that $\overline{CD} \perp \overline{AB}$.

4. If $\overline{PR} \cong \overline{PS}$ and $\overline{QR} \cong \overline{QS}$, prove that $\overline{PQ} \perp \overline{RS}$.

5. If polygon *ABCD* is equilateral ($AB = BC = CD = DA$), prove that $\overline{DB} \perp \overline{AC}$.

6. Given $\overline{CED}$, $\angle 1 \cong \angle 2$, and $\angle 3 \cong \angle 4$, prove that $\overline{CD}$ is the perpendicular bisector of $\overline{AB}$.

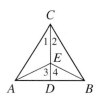

Ex. 6

7. *Prove:* The bisector of the vertex angle of an isosceles triangle is perpendicular to the base of the triangle.

In 8–10, let D be a point on $\overleftrightarrow{AB}$ between A and B.

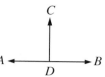

Ex. 8–10

8. Given $m\angle ADC = 3x + 18$ and $m\angle CDB = 4x - 6$.
   a. Find the value of x.   **b.** Show that $\overleftrightarrow{CD} \perp \overleftrightarrow{AB}$.

9. If $\overleftrightarrow{CD} \perp \overleftrightarrow{AB}$, $m\angle ADC = 3x - y$, and $m\angle CDB = 2x + y$, find the value of x and the value of y.

10. If $\overleftrightarrow{CD} \perp \overleftrightarrow{AB}$, $m\angle CDA = 7x + y$, and $m\angle CDB = x + 4y$, find the value of x and the value of y.

11. $\overleftrightarrow{AB}$ intersects $\overleftrightarrow{CD}$ at E, $m\angle AEC = 3x$, and $m\angle AED = 5x - 60$.
   a. Find x.   **b.** Show that $\overleftrightarrow{AB}$ is perpendicular to $\overleftrightarrow{CD}$.

12. In $\triangle ABC$, a line drawn from vertex A intersects $\overline{BC}$ in D. If $m\angle ADB = 6x$ and $m\angle ADC = 9x - 45$, show that $\overline{AD} \perp \overline{BC}$.

13. In $\triangle RST$, a line drawn from vertex R intersects $\overline{ST}$ in B. If $m\angle SBR = \frac{3}{2}x + 30$ and $m\angle TBR = 4x - 70$, show that $\overline{RB}$ is an altitude in $\triangle RST$.

14. In the coordinate plane, the vertices of polygon $ABCD$ are $A(2, 1)$, $B(4, 1)$, $C(4, 3)$, and $D(2, 3)$. The intersection of $\overline{AC}$ and $\overline{BD}$ is $E(3, 2)$.
   a. Show that $\overline{AC}$ is the perpendicular bisector of $\overline{BD}$ by using a theorem from this section.
   b. Show that $\overline{AC}$ is the perpendicular bisector of $\overline{BD}$ by using slopes and the distance formula.

6-2 PROVING LINES PARALLEL

You have already studied many situations involving intersecting lines that lie in the same plane. When all the points or lines in a set lie in a single plane, we say that these points or these lines are *coplanar*. Let us now consider situations involving coplanar lines that do not intersect.

- **DEFINITION.** *Parallel lines* are coplanar lines that have no points in common, or have all points in common and, therefore, coincide.

We indicate that $\overleftrightarrow{AB}$ is parallel to $\overleftrightarrow{CD}$ by writing $\overleftrightarrow{AB} \parallel \overleftrightarrow{CD}$. These parallel lines extended indefinitely will never intersect and thus have no points in common. However, using the concept of lines having all points in common, we may also say that a line is parallel to itself. Thus, $\overleftrightarrow{AB} \parallel \overleftrightarrow{AB}$, and $\overleftrightarrow{CD} \parallel \overleftrightarrow{CD}$.

The word *lines* in the definition means straight lines of unlimited extent. We say that segments and rays are parallel if the lines that contain them are parallel.

Recall that a definition can be written in the form of a true conditional with a true converse:

$p \rightarrow q$:   If coplanar lines are parallel, then they have no points in common or all points in common.

$q \rightarrow p$:   If coplanar lines have no points in common or all points in common, then they are parallel lines.

The conditional and its converse may be written as a biconditional:

$p \leftrightarrow q$:   Coplanar lines are parallel if and only if they have no points in common or all points in common.

- **THEOREM 17. If coplanar lines are not parallel lines, then they are intersecting lines.**

The proof of this theorem uses the contrapositive of the converse of the definition of parallel lines: If coplanar lines are not parallel lines, then they have a point in common and do not have all points in common.

Given $\overleftrightarrow{AB}$ and $\overleftrightarrow{CD}$ as two coplanar lines, we observe that one of the following situations may exist:

$\overleftrightarrow{AB}$ intersects $\overleftrightarrow{CD}$ $\overleftrightarrow{AB} \parallel \overleftrightarrow{CD}$ $\overleftrightarrow{AB} \parallel \overleftrightarrow{CD}$

Equivalence Relation of Parallelism

Let us now consider whether the relation *parallelism* is an equivalence relation.

1. **Reflexive property:** $m \parallel m$, $p \parallel p$, and $t \parallel t$. (This property is true by reason of our definition.)
2. **Symmetric property:** If $m \parallel p$, then $p \parallel m$.
3. **Transitive property:** If $m \parallel p$ and $p \parallel t$, then $m \parallel t$.

From these examples, we sense that parallelism of lines is an equivalence relation because all three properties appear to be true. We will restate these properties of parallelism as follows:

- **POSTULATE. A line is parallel to itself.** (Reflexive property.)
- **POSTULATE. A parallelism of lines may be expressed in either order.** (Symmetric property.)
- **POSTULATE. Two lines each parallel to the same line are parallel to each other.** (Transitive property.)

Angles Formed by a Transversal

- **DEFINITION. A *transversal* is a line that intersects two other lines in two different points.**

When two lines are cut by a transversal, two sets of angles, each containing four angles, are formed. In Math A, we learned names to identify special sets of these angles:
Interior angles: angles 3, 4, 5, 6
Exterior angles: angles 1, 2, 7, 8
Alternate interior angles are a pair of interior angles on opposite sides of the transversal, not sharing a common vertex: angles 3 and 6; also angles 4 and 5.

Alternate exterior angles are a pair of exterior angles on opposite sides of the transversal, not sharing a common vertex: angles 1 and 8; also angles 2 and 7.

Interior angles on the same side of the transversal: angles 3 and 5; also angles 4 and 6.

Corresponding angles are a pair of angles on the same side of the transversal, not sharing a common vertex, one exterior and one interior: angles 1 and 5; angles 2 and 6; angles 3 and 7; and angles 4 and 8.

In the diagram shown, the two lines cut by the transversal are not parallel lines. However, when two lines are parallel, many statements may be postulated or proved.

● **POSTULATE. Through a given point not on a given line, there exists one and only one line parallel to the given line.**

Given a line, $\overleftrightarrow{AB}$, and a point P, which is not on $\overleftrightarrow{AB}$. Through P, there exists one and only one line, $\overleftrightarrow{LM}$, which can be drawn parallel to $\overleftrightarrow{AB}$.

For each of the next two theorems, we will use indirect proof, assuming the negation of the conclusion and showing that the assumption leads to a contradiction.

● **THEOREM 18. If a line intersects one of two parallel lines, it intersects the other.**

Given: $\overleftrightarrow{AB} \parallel \overleftrightarrow{CD}$.
$\overleftrightarrow{EF}$ intersects $\overleftrightarrow{AB}$.

Prove: $\overleftrightarrow{EF}$ intersects $\overleftrightarrow{CD}$.

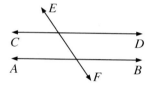

Plan: Use an indirect proof and the transitive property.

Proof: Assume $\overleftrightarrow{EF}$ does not intersect $\overleftrightarrow{CD}$. Then $\overleftrightarrow{EF} \parallel \overleftrightarrow{CD}$. By the transitive property, if $\overleftrightarrow{EF} \parallel \overleftrightarrow{CD}$ and $\overleftrightarrow{CD} \parallel \overleftrightarrow{AB}$, then $\overleftrightarrow{EF} \parallel \overleftrightarrow{AB}$. But we are given that $\overleftrightarrow{EF}$ intersects $\overleftrightarrow{AB}$. Thus, we have a contradiction and our assumption must be false. Therefore, $\overleftrightarrow{EF}$ intersects $\overleftrightarrow{CD}$.

● **THEOREM 19. If two coplanar lines are cut by a transversal so that the alternate interior angles formed are congruent, then the two lines are parallel.**

Given: $\overleftrightarrow{AB}$ and $\overleftrightarrow{CD}$ are cut by transversal $\overleftrightarrow{EF}$ at points E and F, respectively; $\angle 1 \cong \angle 2$.

Prove: $\overleftrightarrow{AB} \parallel \overleftrightarrow{CD}$.

Plan: Use an indirect proof. Assume that the negation of the conclusion is true, namely, that $\overleftrightarrow{AB}$ is *not* parallel to $\overleftrightarrow{CD}$. Show that $\overleftrightarrow{AB} \nparallel \overleftrightarrow{CD}$ implies that $\angle 1$ and $\angle 2$ are *not* congruent. Thus, the assumption is false and $\overleftrightarrow{AB} \parallel \overleftrightarrow{CD}$.

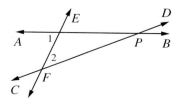

Statements	Reasons
1. $\overleftrightarrow{AB}$ and $\overleftrightarrow{CD}$ are cut by transversal $\overleftrightarrow{EF}$ at points E and F, respectively.	1. Given.
2. $\overleftrightarrow{AB}$ is not parallel to $\overleftrightarrow{CD}$.	2. Assumption.
3. $\overleftrightarrow{AB}$ and $\overleftrightarrow{CD}$ intersect at some point P, forming $\triangle EFP$.	3. If coplanar lines are not parallel, then they are intersecting lines.
4. $m\angle 1 > m\angle 2$.	4. The measure of an exterior angle of a triangle is greater than the measure of either nonadjacent interior angle.
5. But $\angle 1 \cong \angle 2$.	5. Given.
6. $m\angle 1 = m\angle 2$.	6. Congruent angles are equal in measure.
7. $\overleftrightarrow{AB} \parallel \overleftrightarrow{CD}$.	7. Contradiction in steps 4 and 6. Therefore, the assumption in step 2 is false.

Now that we have proved Theorem 19, we can use it in other theorems that also prove that two lines are parallel.

● **THEOREM 20. If two coplanar lines are cut by a transversal so that the corresponding angles are congruent, then the two line are parallel.**

Given: $\overleftrightarrow{EF}$ intersects $\overleftrightarrow{AB}$ and $\overleftrightarrow{CD}$.
  $\angle 1 \cong \angle 5$.
Prove: $\overleftrightarrow{AB} \parallel \overleftrightarrow{CD}$.
Plan: Show that $\angle 1 \cong \angle 3$ and $\angle 3 \cong \angle 5$.

● **THEOREM 21. If two coplanar lines are cut by a transversal so that the interior angles on the same side of the transversal are supplementary, then the lines are parallel.**

Given: $\overleftrightarrow{EF}$ intersects $\overleftrightarrow{AB}$ and $\overleftrightarrow{CD}$.
  $\angle 5$ is the supplement of $\angle 4$.
Prove: $\overleftrightarrow{AB} \parallel \overleftrightarrow{CD}$.
Plan: Show that $\angle 3$ is the supplement of $\angle 4$. Since $\angle 3$ and $\angle 5$ are supplements of the same angle, $\angle 3 \cong \angle 5$.

● **THEOREM 22. If two coplanar lines are perpendicular to the same line, then they are parallel.**

Given: $\overleftrightarrow{CD} \perp \overleftrightarrow{AB}$, $\overleftrightarrow{EF} \perp \overleftrightarrow{AB}$.

Prove: $\overleftrightarrow{CD} \parallel \overleftrightarrow{EF}$.

Plan: Show that $\angle ADC \cong \angle DFE$.

The proofs of these theorems are left to the student.

Methods of Proving Lines Parallel

To prove that two coplanar lines that are cut by a transversal are parallel, prove that any one of the following statements is true:

1. A pair of alternate interior angles are congruent.

2. A pair of corresponding angles are congruent.

3. A pair of interior angles on the same side of the transversal are supplementary.

Also, two coplanar lines may be proved parallel by proving:

4. Both lines are perpendicular to the same line.

5. Both lines are parallel to the same line.

EXAMPLES

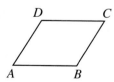

1. If $m\angle A = 100 + 3x$ and $m\angle B = 80 - 3x$, tell why $\overline{AD} \parallel \overline{BC}$.

Solution $m\angle A + m\angle B = 100 + 3x + 80 - 3x = 180$. Thus, $\angle A$ and $\angle B$ are supplementary. Since $\overline{AD}$ and $\overline{BC}$ are cut by transversal $\overline{AB}$ to form supplementary interior angles on the same side of the transversal, the segments are parallel, namely, $\overline{AD} \parallel \overline{BC}$.

2. If $\overline{BD}$ bisects $\angle ABC$, and $\overline{BC} \cong \overline{CD}$, prove $\overleftrightarrow{CD} \parallel \overrightarrow{BA}$.

Given: $\overline{BD}$ bisects $\angle ABC$, $\overline{BC} \cong \overline{CD}$.

Prove: $\overleftrightarrow{CD} \parallel \overrightarrow{BA}$.

Plan: Think of $\overleftrightarrow{CD}$ and $\overrightarrow{BA}$ as two lines cut by transversal $\overline{BD}$.
If $\angle 2 \cong \angle 3$, these congruent alternate interior angles make $\overleftrightarrow{CD} \parallel \overrightarrow{BA}$.

	Statements	*Reasons*

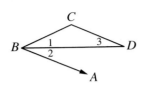

1. $\overline{BC} \cong \overline{CD}$.

2. $\angle 3 \cong \angle 1$.

3. $\overrightarrow{BD}$ bisects $\angle ABC$.

4. $\angle 1 \cong \angle 2$.

5. $\angle 3 \cong \angle 2$.

6. $\overrightarrow{CD} \parallel \overrightarrow{BA}$.

1. Given.

2. If two sides of a triangle are congruent, the angles opposite these sides are congruent.

3. Given.

4. Definition of angle bisector.

5. Transitive property of congruence.

6. If two lines are cut by a transversal forming a pair of congruent alternate interior angles, the two lines are parallel.

EXERCISES WITH OPEN-RESPONSE PROBLEMS

1. In the figure $\overleftrightarrow{AB}$ and $\overleftrightarrow{CD}$ are cut by transversal $\overleftrightarrow{EF}$, forming eight angles. For each of the following, state the theorem or theorems that prove $\overleftrightarrow{AB} \parallel \overleftrightarrow{CD}$.
   a. $m\angle 3 = 70$ and $m\angle 5 = 70$.
   b. $m\angle 2 = 140$ and $m\angle 6 = 140$.
   c. $m\angle 3 = 60$ and $m\angle 6 = 120$.
   d. $m\angle 2 = 150$ and $m\angle 5 = 30$.
   e. $m\angle 2 = 160$ and $m\angle 8 = 160$.

Ex. 2–3

Ex. 4

Ex. 5

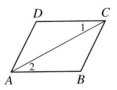

Ex. 6

2. In quadrilateral $ABCD$, if $m\angle A = 120 + 5x$ and $m\angle B = 60 - 5x$, show that $\overline{AD} \parallel \overline{BC}$.
3. In quadrilateral $ABCD$, $\overline{DC} \perp \overline{BC}$ and $m\angle ADC = 90$. Prove $\overline{AD} \parallel \overline{BC}$.
4. If $\overline{AB}$ and $\overline{CD}$ bisect each other at point E, prove:
   a. $\triangle CEA \cong \triangle DEB$.　　　b. $\angle ECA \cong \angle EDB$.　　　c. $\overline{CA} \parallel \overline{DB}$.
5. If $\overrightarrow{CD} \perp \overline{BC}$, $\overrightarrow{BA} \perp \overline{BC}$, $\overrightarrow{CE}$ bisects $\angle BCD$, and $\overrightarrow{BF}$ bisects $\angle ABC$, prove that $\overrightarrow{CE} \parallel \overrightarrow{BF}$.
6. If $\overline{AB} \cong \overline{CD}$ and $\angle 1 \cong \angle 2$, prove:
   a. $\triangle CAB \cong \triangle ACD$.　　　b. $\overline{BC} \parallel \overline{DA}$.

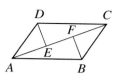

Ex. 7   **Ex. 8**   **Ex. 9**   **Ex. 10**

7. Given $\overrightarrow{ACD}$, $\overline{CA} \cong \overline{CB}$, and $\angle ECB \cong \angle CAB$, prove $\overrightarrow{CE} \parallel \overline{AB}$.
8. If $\angle 1$ is supplementary to $\angle 2$ and $\angle 3 \cong \angle 1$, prove $\overline{AD} \parallel \overline{BC}$.
9. If $\overline{BA} \cong \overline{BC}$ and $\angle BDE \cong \angle BCA$, prove $\overline{DE} \parallel \overline{AC}$.
10. If $\overline{DE} \perp \overline{AC}$, $\overline{BF} \perp \overline{AC}$, $\overline{AF} \cong \overline{CE}$, and $\overline{DE} \cong \overline{BF}$, prove:
   a. $\triangle ADE \cong \triangle CBF$.   b. $\overline{DA} \parallel \overline{BC}$.

11. *Prove:* If two coplanar lines are cut by a transversal, forming a pair of alternate exterior angles that are congruent, then the two lines are parallel.

6-3 PROPERTIES OF PARALLEL LINES

Logic has shown that, when a conditional statement $p \to q$ is true, the *converse* $q \to p$ may be true or it may be false. Each converse statement must be judged on its own merits before assigning a truth value.

In Section 6-2, starting with given premises of angle relations, we were able to prove that lines were parallel. *Conversely*, starting with given premises that lines are parallel, we will now prove that certain angle relations exist.

● **THEOREM 23. If two parallel lines are cut by a transversal, then the alternate interior angles formed are congruent.**

Given: $\overleftrightarrow{AB} \parallel \overleftrightarrow{CD}$.

The lines are cut by transversal $\overleftrightarrow{EF}$ at points E and F, respectively. *Note.* As shown in the figure, arrowheads on the lines indicate that the lines are parallel.

Prove: $\angle 1 \cong \angle 2$.

Plan: Use an indirect proof. Assume $\angle 1 \not\cong \angle 2$. Construct $\overrightarrow{EH}$ so that $\angle HEF \cong \angle 2$. Since $\angle HEF$ and $\angle 2$ are congruent alternate interior angles, $\overleftrightarrow{HE} \parallel \overleftrightarrow{CD}$. But $\overleftrightarrow{AB}$ is a line through E, and we are given $\overleftrightarrow{AB} \parallel \overleftrightarrow{CD}$. This contradicts the

postulate that states that, through a given point not on a given line, there exists one and only one line parallel to the given line. Thus, the assumption is false and $\angle 1 \cong \angle 2$.

Note that Theorem 23 is the converse of Theorem 19, proved in Section 6-2: *If two coplanar lines are cut by a transversal so that the alternate interior angles formed are congruent, then the two lines are parallel.* Therefore, we may state the two theorems in biconditional form:

Two coplanar lines cut by a transversal are parallel if and only if the alternate interior angles formed are congruent.

Therefore, let $\overleftrightarrow{AB}$ and $\overleftrightarrow{CD}$ be two coplanar lines cut by transversal $\overleftrightarrow{EF}$, forming alternate interior angles, $\angle 1$ and $\angle 2$.

If $\angle 1 \cong \angle 2$, then $\overleftrightarrow{AB} \parallel \overleftrightarrow{CD}$.
If $\overleftrightarrow{AB} \parallel \overleftrightarrow{CD}$, then $\angle 1 \cong \angle 2$.

Each of the next two theorems is also a *converse* of a theorem stated in Section 6-2.

● **THEOREM 24. If two parallel lines are cut by a transversal, then the corresponding angles are congruent (converse of Theorem 20).**

Given: $\overleftrightarrow{AB} \parallel \overleftrightarrow{CD}$.
$\qquad\quad$ $\overleftrightarrow{EF}$ intersects $\overleftrightarrow{AB}$ and $\overleftrightarrow{CD}$.

Prove: $\angle 1 \cong \angle 5$.

Plan: Show that $\angle 1 \cong \angle 3$ and $\angle 3 \cong \angle 5$. Then use the transitive property.

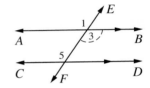

● **THEOREM 25. If two parallel lines are cut by a transversal, then two interior angles on the same side of the transversal are supplementary (converse of Theorem 21).**

Given: $\overleftrightarrow{AB} \parallel \overleftrightarrow{CD}$.
$\qquad\quad$ $\overleftrightarrow{EF}$ intersects $\overleftrightarrow{AB}$ and $\overleftrightarrow{CD}$.

Prove: $\angle 4$ is the supplement of $\angle 5$.

Plan: Show that $\angle 4$ is the supplement of $\angle 3$, and $\angle 3 \cong \angle 5$. Then use substitution.

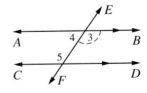

● **THEOREM 26. If a line is perpendicular to one of two parallel lines, it is perpendicular to the other.**

Given: $\overleftrightarrow{AB} \parallel \overleftrightarrow{CD}$, $\overleftrightarrow{EF} \perp \overleftrightarrow{AB}$.

Prove: $\overleftrightarrow{EF} \perp \overleftrightarrow{CD}$.

Plan: Show that $\angle 6 \cong \angle 7$, and $m\angle 6 = 90$. Therefore, $m\angle 7 = 90$ or $\angle 7$ is a right angle. Use the definition of perpendicular lines.

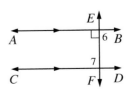

The proofs of these theorems are left to the student.

Summary of Properties of Parallel Lines

If two lines cut by a transversal are parallel:

1. Their alternate interior angles are congruent.
2. Their corresponding angles are congruent.
3. Two interior angles on the same side of the transversal are supplementary.

Also, if two lines are parallel:

4. A line perpendicular to one of them is also perpendicular to the other.
5. A line parallel to one of them is also parallel to the other.

EXAMPLES

1. Transversal $\overleftrightarrow{EF}$ intersects $\overleftrightarrow{AB}$ and $\overleftrightarrow{CD}$ at G and H, respectively. If $\overleftrightarrow{AB} \parallel \overleftrightarrow{CD}$, $m\angle BGH = 3x - 20$ and $m\angle GHC = 2x + 10$:
a. Find the value of x.   **b.** Find $m\angle DHF$.

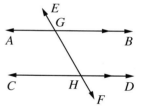

Solutions **a.** Since $\overleftrightarrow{AB} \parallel \overleftrightarrow{CD}$ and these lines are cut by transversal $\overleftrightarrow{EF}$, the alternate interior angles are congruent. Thus:

Check:

$m\angle BGH = m\angle GHC.$ $3x - 20 = \quad 2x + 10$

$3x - 20 = 2x + 10$ $3(30) - 20 \overset{?}{=} 2(30) + 10$

$3x - 2x = 10 + 20$ $90 - 20 \overset{?}{=} \quad 60 + 10$

$x = 30$ *Answer* $70 = \quad 70$ ✔

Note. A check can be made by substituting $x = 30$ in both given angle measures.

b. Here, $\angle DHF$ is a corresponding angle to $\angle BGH$. Since parallel lines cut by a transversal form congruent corresponding angles, first find $m\angle BGH$.

$$m\angle BGH = 3x - 20 = 3(30) - 20 = 90 - 20 = 70$$

Then: $m\angle DHF = m\angle BGH = 70$ *Answer*

2. *Given:* Quadrilateral *ABCD*.
$\overline{BC} \cong \overline{DA}$, $\overline{BC} \parallel \overline{DA}$.

Prove: $\overline{AB} \parallel \overline{CD}$.

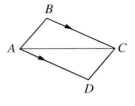

Plan: Show that alternate interior angles formed by transversal $\overline{AC}$ are congruent, namely, $\angle BAC \cong \angle DCA$. First prove that the triangles containing the angles are congruent. Use s.a.s. $\cong$ s.a.s.

Statements	Reasons
1. $\overline{BC} \cong \overline{DA}$. (s. $\cong$ s.)	1. Given.
2. $\overline{BC} \parallel \overline{DA}$.	2. Given.
3. $\angle BCA \cong \angle DAC$. (a. $\cong$ a.)	3. If two parallel lines are cut by a transversal, the alternate interior angles are congruent.
4. $\overline{AC} \cong \overline{AC}$. (s. $\cong$ s.)	4. Reflexive property of congruence.
5. $\triangle BAC \cong \triangle DCA$.	5. s.a.s. $\cong$ s.a.s.
6. $\angle BAC \cong \angle DCA$.	6. Corresponding parts of congruent triangles are congruent.
7. $\overline{AB} \parallel \overline{CD}$.	7. If two lines cut by a transversal form alternate interior angles that are congruent, the lines are parallel.

EXERCISES WITH OPEN-RESPONSE PROBLEMS

In 1–3: **a.** Write the converse of each given statement. **b.** State whether the converse is true or false. **c.** Explain your answer.

1. If two coplanar lines are cut by a transversal forming a pair of alternate interior angles that are congruent, then the two lines are parallel.

2. If two coplanar lines are cut by a transversal forming a pair of corresponding angles that are congruent, then the two lines are parallel.

3. If two coplanar lines are cut by a transversal forming a pair of interior angles on the same side of the transversal that are supplementary, then the two lines are parallel.

4. In the figure, if $\overleftrightarrow{AB} \parallel \overleftrightarrow{CD}$, find:

    a. m$\angle 5$ when m$\angle 3 = 80$.
    b. m$\angle 2$ when m$\angle 6 = 150$.
    c. m$\angle 4$ when m$\angle 5 = 60$.
    d. m$\angle 7$ when m$\angle 1 = 75$.
    e. m$\angle 8$ when m$\angle 3 = 65$.

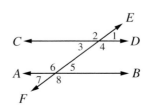

In 5–10, $\overleftrightarrow{AB} \parallel \overleftrightarrow{CD}$ and these lines are cut by transversal $\overleftrightarrow{EF}$ at G and H, respectively.

5. If m$\angle BGH = 3x$ and m$\angle GHC = 60$, find x.
6. If m$\angle EGA$ is $2x$ and m$\angle GHC$ is $5x - 54$, find x.
7. If m$\angle AGH = x + 90$ and m$\angle DHG = 3x - 10$, find x.
8. If m$\angle AGH$ is twice the measure of $\angle GHC$, find m$\angle GHC$.
9. If the ratio of the measure of $\angle BGH$ to the measure of $\angle GHD$ is $2:3$, find: **a.** m$\angle BGH$ **b.** m$\angle GHD$
10. If m$\angle AGH = 3x - 40$ and m$\angle CHG = x + 20$, find:
    a. the value of x **b.** m$\angle AGH$ **c.** m$\angle CHG$ **d.** m$\angle BGH$

Ex. 5–10

Ex. 11

Ex. 12

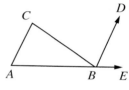

Ex. 13

11. If $\overleftrightarrow{AB} \parallel \overleftrightarrow{CD}$, m$\angle 5 = 40$, and m$\angle 4 = 30$, find the measures of the remaining angles in the figure.
12. If $\overrightarrow{AE} \parallel \overline{DC}$, $\overline{BC} \parallel \overline{AD}$, and m$\angle CBE = 80$, find m$\angle 1$, m$\angle 2$, and m$\angle 3$.
13. Given $\overrightarrow{ABE}$, $\overline{BD} \parallel \overline{AC}$, m$\angle A = 65$, and m$\angle C = 80$, find m$\angle CBE$.

14. If $\overline{AB} \parallel \overline{CD}$ and $\overline{BC} \parallel \overline{AD}$, find m$\angle 1$ and m$\angle 2$.

15. If $\overrightarrow{BA} \parallel \overrightarrow{DC}$, m$\angle B = 39$, and m$\angle D = 65$, find m$\angle DEB$.
    (*Hint.* Through E, draw $\overleftrightarrow{GEF} \parallel \overrightarrow{BA}$.)

Ex. 14

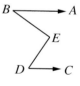

Ex. 15

16. Two parallel lines, $\overleftrightarrow{AB}$ and $\overleftrightarrow{CD}$, are cut at E and F, respectively, by transversal $\overleftrightarrow{GEFH}$. If $\angle AEG$ and $\angle CFH$ are exterior angles on the same side of $\overleftrightarrow{GH}$, and m$\angle AEG = 130$, find m$\angle CFH$.
17. Two parallel lines, $\overleftrightarrow{AB}$ and $\overleftrightarrow{CD}$, are cut by transversal $\overleftrightarrow{EF}$, where E is on $\overleftrightarrow{AB}$ and F is on $\overleftrightarrow{CD}$. The bisector of $\angle AEF$ meets $\overleftrightarrow{CD}$ at point P. If m$\angle AEF = 64$, find m$\angle EPF$.
18. Transversal $\overleftrightarrow{GH}$ cuts two parallel lines, $\overleftrightarrow{AB}$ and $\overleftrightarrow{CD}$, at E and F, respectively. If exterior angle AEG and interior angle DFE are on opposite sides of $\overleftrightarrow{GH}$, and if m$\angle AEG = 35$, find m$\angle DFE$.
19. Two parallel lines are cut by a transversal. The degree measures of two interior angles on the same side of the transversal are represented by x and $4x$. Find the measure of the smaller angle.
20. Two parallel lines are cut by a transversal. One of the two interior angles on the same side of the transversal contains $15°$ more than the other. Find the degree measure of the smaller angle.

In 21–24, $\overleftrightarrow{AB} \parallel \overleftrightarrow{CD}$.

21. If m$\angle 3 = 2x + 40$ and m$\angle 7 = 3x + 20$, find m$\angle 3$.

22. If m$\angle 4 = 4x - 10$ and m$\angle 5 = 2x - 20$, find the measure of the smaller of the two angles.

23. If m$\angle 4 = 3x + 40$ and m$\angle 7 = 2x$, find m$\angle 7$.

24. If m$\angle 3 = 2y$, m$\angle 4 = x + y$, and m$\angle 5 = 2x - y$, find m$\angle 3$, m$\angle 4$, and m$\angle 5$.

Ex. 21–24

  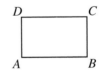

Ex. 25	**Ex. 26**	**Ex. 27**

25. If $\overline{AB} \parallel \overline{DC}$ and $\overline{AB} \cong \overline{CD}$, prove that $\overline{AD} \cong \overline{CB}$ and $\overline{AD} \parallel \overline{BC}$.

26. If $\overleftrightarrow{DCE} \parallel \overline{AB}$ and $\angle 1 \cong \angle 2$, prove that $\angle A \cong \angle B$.

27. Given $\overrightarrow{ABD}$ and $\overrightarrow{BE} \parallel \overline{AC}$, prove that m$\angle CBD = $ m$\angle A + $ m$\angle C$.

 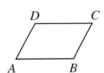

Ex. 28	**Ex. 29**	**Ex. 30**

28. If $\overrightarrow{CE}$ bisects $\angle DCB$ and $\overrightarrow{CE} \parallel \overline{AB}$, prove that $\angle A \cong \angle B$.

29. If $\overline{AB} \parallel \overline{DC}$ and $\overline{BC} \parallel \overline{AD}$, prove that $\angle B \cong \angle D$.

30. If $\overline{AB} \parallel \overline{DC}$, $\overline{BC} \parallel \overline{AD}$, and $\angle A$ is a right angle, prove that $\angle B$, $\angle C$, and $\angle D$ are also right angles.

31. *Prove:* If two lines cut by a transversal are parallel, the bisectors of a pair of alternate interior angles are parallel.

6-4 THE SUM OF THE MEASURES OF THE ANGLES OF A TRIANGLE

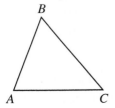

● **THEOREM 27. The sum of the degree measures of the angles of a triangle is 180.**

Given: $\triangle ABC$.

Prove: m$\angle A + $ m$\angle B + $ m$\angle C = 180$.

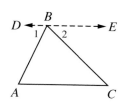

Plan: Draw $\overleftrightarrow{DE}$ through B so that $\overleftrightarrow{DE} \parallel \overline{AC}$. Since $\angle DBE$ is a straight angle, $m\angle DBE = 180$, or $m\angle 1 + m\angle B + m\angle 2 = 180$. Show that $m\angle 1 = m\angle A$, and $m\angle 2 = m\angle C$, so that $m\angle A + m\angle B + m\angle C = 180$.

Statements	*Reasons*
1. Let $\overleftrightarrow{DE}$ be the line through B that is parallel to $\overline{AC}$.	1. Through a given point, not on a given line, there exists one and only one line parallel to the given line.
2. $m\angle DBE = 180$.	2. A straight angle is an angle whose degree measure is 180.
3. $m\angle 1 + m\angle B + m\angle 2 = 180$.	3. The whole is equal to the sum of all its parts.
4. $\angle A \cong \angle 1$; $\angle C \cong \angle 2$.	4. If two parallel lines are cut by a transversal, the alternate interior angles are congruent.
5. $m\angle A = m\angle 1$; $m\angle C = m\angle 2$.	5. Congruent angles are equal in measure.
6. $m\angle A + m\angle B + m\angle C = 180$.	6. Substitution postulate.

Many corollaries to this important theorem exist.

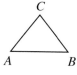

● **COROLLARY 27-1. If two angles of one triangle are congruent to two angles of another triangle, then the third angles are congruent.**

In $\triangle ABC$ and $\triangle A'B'C'$, $\angle A \cong \angle A'$ and $\angle B \cong \angle B'$. Since the sum of the degree measures of the angles of a triangle is 180, $m\angle A + m\angle B + m\angle C = m\angle A' + m\angle B' + m\angle C'$. We use substitution and the subtraction postulate to prove that $m\angle C = m\angle C'$, and therefore $\angle C \cong \angle C'$.

● **COROLLARY 27-2. The acute angles of a right triangle are complementary.**

When we are given right triangle ABC with $\angle C$ as the right angle, we can prove that $m\angle A + m\angle B = 90$, or that $\angle A$ and $\angle B$ are complementary.

● **COROLLARY 27-3. Each acute angle of an isosceles right triangle measures 45°.**

In isosceles right triangle ABC, $m\angle C = 90$ and $\overline{AC} \cong \overline{BC}$. Therefore, $m\angle A = m\angle B$. We substitute $m\angle A$ for $m\angle B$ and 90 for $m\angle C$ in the equation $m\angle A + m\angle B + m\angle C = 180$, and then solve the resulting equation for $m\angle A$.

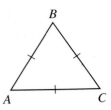

● **COROLLARY 27-4. Each angle of an equilateral triangle measures 60°.**

In equilateral triangle ABC, $m\angle A = m\angle B = m\angle C$. We substitute $m\angle A$ for $m\angle B$ and $m\angle C$ in the equation $m\angle A + m\angle B + m\angle C = 180$, and then solve the resulting equation for $m\angle A$.

● **COROLLARY 27-5. The sum of the degree measures of the angles of a quadrilateral is 360.**

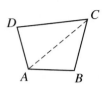

In quadrilateral $ABCD$, we draw $\overline{AC}$, forming two triangles. The sum of the measures of the angles of quadrilateral $ABCD$ is the sum of the measures of the angles of the two triangles.

EXAMPLES

1. The measure of the vertex angle of an isosceles triangle exceeds the measure of each base angle by 30 degrees. Find the degree measure of each angle of the triangle.

Solution   Let x = measure of each base angle.

Let $x + 30$ = measure of vertex angle.

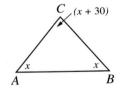

The sum of the degree measures of the angles of a triangle is 180.

$$x + x + x + 30 = 180$$
$$3x + 30 = 180$$
$$3x = 150$$
$$x = 50, \text{ and } x + 30 = 80.$$

Answer: The angle measures are 50°, 50°, and 80°.

---

2. In $\triangle ABC$, the measures of the three angles are represented by $9x$, $3x - 6$, and $11x + 2$. Show that $\triangle ABC$ is a right triangle.

Solution   Triangle ABC will be a right triangle if one of the angles is a right angle. Since the sum of the degree measures of the three angles of $\triangle ABC$ is 180:

$$9x + 3x - 6 + 11x + 2 = 180$$
$$23x - 4 = 180$$
$$23x = 184$$
$$x = 8$$

Substitute $x = 8$ in the representations of the angle measures.

$$9x = 9(8) = 72$$
$$3x - 6 = 3(8) - 6 = 24 - 6 = 18$$
$$11x + 2 = 11(8) + 2 = 88 + 2 = 90$$

Answer: Triangle *ABC* is a right triangle because the degree measure of one of its angles is 90.

EXERCISES WITH OPEN-RESPONSE PROBLEMS

1. In each of the following, determine whether the numbers given can represent the degree measures of the three angles of a triangle.
   a. 20, 100, 60   **b.** 55, 45, 90   **c.** 30, 110, 40   **d.** 35, 125, 10

2. Find the degree measure of the third angle of a triangle if the first two angles measure:
   a. 60°, 40°   **b.** 130°, 20°   **c.** 45°, 55°   **d.** 102°, 34°   **e.** 97°, 59°

3. In $\triangle ABC$, $\overline{AB} \cong \overline{BC}$ and $m\angle A = 40$. Find $m\angle B$.
4. In $\triangle DEF$, $\overline{DE} \perp \overline{EF}$ and $m\angle D = 30$. Find $m\angle F$.
5. In $\triangle PQR$, $\overline{PQ} \cong \overline{QR}$ and $\overline{PQ} \cong \overline{RP}$. Find $m\angle P$.
6. If the degree measures of the angles of a triangle are represented by $2x$, $x + 10$, and $3x - 10$, find:
   a. the value of x **b.** the degree measures of the three angles
7. Find the degree measure of the vertex angle of an isosceles triangle if each base angle measures:
   a. 70°   **b.** 35°   **c.** 54°   **d.** $37\frac{1}{2}°$ **e.** 72.5°

8. Find the degree measure of each base angle of an isosceles triangle if the vertex angle measures:
   a. 50°   **b.** 70°   **c.** 82°   **d.** 100°   **e.** 75°

9. Each base angle of an isosceles triangle has a measure that is 20° more than 3 times the measure of the vertex angle. Find the measure of the vertex angle. Show your work.
10. In $\triangle ABC$, $m\angle A = 40$ and $m\angle C = 30$. If $\overline{CD}$ is drawn so that it is the bisector of $\angle C$, and D is a point on $\overline{AB}$, find:
    a. $m\angle B$ **b.** $m\angle ACD$ **c.** $m\angle ADC$ **d.** $m\angle BDC$

11. Find the degree measure of the *smallest* angle of a triangle if the ratio of the measures of the three angles is:
    a. 1:2:3   **b.** 1:3:5   **c.** 1:4:7   **d.** 1:2:6   **e.** 1:4:5

12. Find the degree measure of each angle of a triangle if the ratio of the measures of the three angles is:
    a. 4:3:2   **b.** 2:5:8   **c.** 2:5:2   **d.** 3:4:5   **e.** 3:5:7

13. In $\triangle RST$, $m\angle T = 90$ and $m\angle R = 35$. If $\overline{TH}$ is drawn perpendicular to $\overline{RS}$, find:

    a. $m\angle S$ **b.** $m\angle HTS$

14. In $\triangle RST$, P is a point on $\overline{RT}$ such that $\overline{RS} \cong \overline{SP}$. If $m\angle RSP = 40$ and $m\angle STP = 50$, find:

    a. $m\angle R$ **b.** $m\angle RPS$ **c.** $m\angle TPS$ **d.** $m\angle PST$

15. Each of the congruent angles of an isosceles triangle measures 9° less than 4 times the vertex angle. Find the measures of the angles of the triangle.

16. The degree measures of the angles of a triangle are represented by $2x + 10$, $x - 10$, and $2x - 20$. Show that the triangle is a right triangle.

17. The degree measures of the angles of $\triangle ABC$ are represented by $x + 30$, $2x$, and $3x - 30$. Show that $\triangle ABC$ is equiangular.

18. Find the degree measure of the fourth angle of a quadrilateral if the first three angles measure:

    a. 60°, 130°, 90°   **b.** 90°, 90°, 140°   **c.** 120°, 110°, 60°

19. Find the degree measure of each angle of a quadrilateral if the measures of its angles are represented by $3x + 20$, $2x + 40$, $4x - 50$, $x - 10$.

20. *Prove:* A triangle can contain no more than one right angle.

21. *Prove:* A triangle can contain no more than one obtuse angle.

22. *Prove:* If $\overline{CD}$ is the altitude drawn to hypotenuse $\overline{AB}$ of right triangle ABC, then $\angle BCD$ is congruent to $\angle A$.

23. *Prove:* If the measure of one angle of a triangle is equal to the sum of the measures of the other two, the triangle is a right triangle.

24. **a.** In the coordinate plane, graph points $A(5, 2)$, $B(2, 2)$, $C(2, -1)$, $D(-1, -1)$.

    b. Draw $\overleftrightarrow{AB}$ and $\triangle BDC$.

    c. Explain how you know that $\triangle BDC$ is an isosceles right triangle.

    d. What is the measure of $\angle BDC$? Write the corollary that proves your answer.

    e. What is the measure of $\angle DBA$? Write the postulate that proves your answer.

6-5 PROVING TRIANGLES CONGRUENT BY ANGLE, ANGLE, SIDE

When two angles of one triangle are congruent to two angles of another triangle, the third angles are congruent, but this is not enough to prove that the two triangles are congruent. If, however, we also know that the sides opposite a pair of congruent angles are congruent, then we can prove that the triangles are congruent.

- **THEOREM 28. Two triangles are congruent if two angles and a side opposite one of the angles in one triangle are congruent to the corresponding two angles and side of the other. [a.a.s. $\cong$ a.a.s.]**

Given: $\triangle ABC$ and $\triangle A'B'C'$.
$\angle A \cong \angle A'$, $\angle C \cong \angle C'$.
$\overline{AB} \cong \overline{A'B'}$.

Prove: $\triangle ABC \cong \triangle A'B'C'$.

Plan: To prove that two triangles are congruent by the statement a.a.s. $\cong$ a.a.s., it will be necessary to show that the triangles can be proved congruent by one of the accepted postulates. Here, we will show $\triangle ABC \cong \triangle A'B'C'$ by a.s.a. $\cong$ a.s.a.

Statements	*Reasons*
1. In $\triangle ABC$ and $\triangle A'B'C'$, $\angle C \cong \angle C'$.	1. Given.
2. $\angle A \cong \angle A'$. (a. $\cong$ a.)	2. Given.
3. $\overline{AB} \cong \overline{A'B'}$. (s. $\cong$ s.)	3. Given.
4. $\angle B \cong \angle B'$. (a. $\cong$ a.)	4. If two angles of one triangle are congruent to two angles of another triangle, then the third angles are congruent.
5. $\triangle ABC \cong \triangle A'B'C'$.	5. a.s.a. $\cong$ a.s.a.

Therefore, from this point on, when two angles and a side opposite one of these angles in one triangle are congruent to the corresponding two angles and side of a second triangle (a.a.s. $\cong$ a.a.s.), we may say that the triangles are congruent.

KEEP IN MIND _____

You now have four ways to prove two triangles congruent:

$$\text{s.s.s.} \cong \text{s.s.s.} \qquad \text{s.a.s.} \cong \text{s.a.s.}$$
$$\text{a.s.a.} \cong \text{a.s.a.} \qquad \text{a.a.s.} \cong \text{a.a.s.}$$

The following corollary can now be proved using a.a.s. $\cong$ a.a.s. Note that in each triangle the hypotenuse is the side opposite the right angle.

● **COROLLARY 28-1. Two right triangles are congruent if the hypotenuse and an acute angle of one right triangle are congruent to the hypotenuse and an acute angle of the other right triangle.**

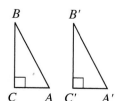

Given: $\triangle ABC$ and $\triangle A'B'C'$ are right triangles with $\angle C$ and $\angle C'$ right angles. $\overline{AB} \cong \overline{A'B'}$; $\angle A \cong \angle A'$.

Prove: $\triangle ABC \cong \triangle A'B'C'$.

The proof is left to the student as Exercise 11, page 226.

Two Other Cases Involving the Angles and Sides of Triangles

In addition to the four ways to prove two triangles congruent, let us consider two other cases.

CASE I. Must two triangles be congruent when three angles of one triangle are congruent to three angles of the other triangle?

In the figure, while a.a.a. $\cong$ a.a.a. in $\triangle ABC$ and $\triangle GHI$, the corresponding sides are not congruent. Thus, $\triangle ABC$ is *not* congruent to $\triangle GHI$.

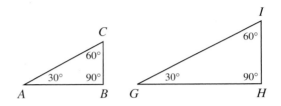

CASE II. Must two triangles be congruent when two sides and an angle opposite one of these sides of one triangle are congruent to the corresponding two sides and the corresponding angle of the other triangle?

Consider the triangles in the figures below. In $\triangle ABC$, imagine that compasses are placed at vertex C and an arc, BD, is swung. Thus, $\overline{CB} \cong \overline{CD}$ and $CB = CD$. Let $m\angle A = 30$, $AC = 20$, $CB = 15$, and $CD = 15$.

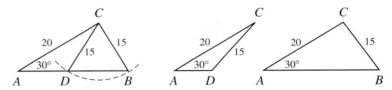

Here, while s.s.a. $\cong$ s.s.a. in $\triangle ACD$ and $\triangle ACB$, one pair of corresponding sides are not congruent: $\overline{AD}$ is not congruent to $\overline{AB}$. Thus, $\triangle ACD$ is *not* congruent to $\triangle ACB$.

KEEP IN MIND ———————————————————————————

Two triangles can*not* be proved to be congruent by

$$\text{a.a.a.} \cong \text{a.a.a.} \qquad \text{or} \qquad \text{s.s.a.} \cong \text{s.s.a.}$$

Here, two sides and the angle opposite one of them in $\triangle ADC$ are congruent to the corresponding sides and angle in $\triangle ABC$.

$$\overline{AC} \cong \overline{AC} \qquad \overline{CD} \cong \overline{CB} \qquad \angle A \cong \angle A$$

But $\overline{AD}$ is not congruent to $\overline{AB}$, $\angle ACD$ is not congruent to $\angle ACB$, and $\angle ADC$ is not congruent to $\angle ABC$. Therefore, $\triangle ADC$ is not congruent to $\triangle ABC$. Thus we see that s.s.a. $\cong$ s.s.a. is not sufficient to prove that two triangles are congruent.

EXAMPLES

1. Prove that the altitudes drawn to the legs of an isosceles triangle from the endpoints of the base are congruent.

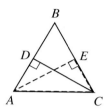

Given: Isosceles triangle ABC with $\overline{BA} \cong \overline{BC}$. $\overline{CD} \perp \overline{BA}$, $\overline{AE} \perp \overline{BC}$.

Prove: $\overline{CD} \cong \overline{AE}$.

Plan: Prove $\triangle DAC \cong \triangle ECA$ by a.a.s. $\cong$ a.a.s.

Statements	*Reasons*
1. In $\triangle ABC$, $\overline{BA} \cong \overline{BC}$.	1. Given.
2. $\angle BAC \cong \angle BCA$. (a. $\cong$ a.)	2. If two sides of a triangle are congruent, the angles opposite these sides are congruent.
3. $\overline{AE} \perp \overline{BC}$, $\overline{CD} \perp \overline{BA}$.	3. Given.
4. $\angle CDA$ and $\angle AEC$ are right angles.	4. Definition of perpendicular lines.
5. $\angle CDA \cong \angle AEC$. (a. $\cong$ a.)	5. All right angles are congruent.
6. $\overline{AC} \cong \overline{AC}$. (s. $\cong$ s.)	6. Reflexive property of congruence.
7. $\triangle DAC \cong \triangle ECA$.	7. a.a.s. $\cong$ a.a.s.
8. $\overline{CD} \cong \overline{AE}$.	8. Corresponding parts of congruent triangles are congruent.

2. In $\triangle ABC$ and $\triangle DEF$, $\angle A \cong \angle D$, $\angle B \cong \angle E$, and $\overline{AB} \cong \overline{EF}$. Can we prove that $\triangle ABC \cong \triangle DEF$?

Solution Sketch the triangles and mark congruent parts. If we use the congruence of angles to set up a correspondence, then

$\angle A$ corresponds to $\angle D$;
$\angle B$ corresponds to $\angle E$;
$\angle C$ corresponds to $\angle F$.

Therefore, $\overline{AB}$ and $\overline{EF}$ are not corresponding sides. Since we do not know a pair of congruent corresponding sides, we *cannot* prove that the triangles are congruent.

EXERCISES WITH OPEN-RESPONSE PROBLEMS

In 1–6, the figures have been marked to indicate the *given* premises. In each case, tell whether the triangles must always be congruent, and give your reason.

1.

2.

3.

4.

5.

6.

Ex. 7

Ex. 8

Ex. 9

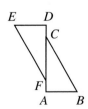

Ex. 10

7. *Given:* $\overline{BD}$ bisects $\angle B$, $\angle A \cong \angle C$.
   Prove: $\triangle ADB \cong \triangle CDB$.

8. *Given:* $\overline{RMP}$ bisects $\overline{AMB}$ at M, $\angle R \cong \angle P$.
   Prove: $\overline{RM} \cong \overline{PM}$.

9. *Given:* In $\triangle ACB$, $\overline{AC} \cong \overline{BC}$ and $\angle ADB \cong \angle BEA$.
   Prove: $\overline{AE} \cong \overline{BD}$.

10. *Given:* $\overline{AFCD}$, $\overline{ED} \perp \overline{DA}$, $\overline{BA} \perp \overline{DA}$, $\overline{DC} \cong \overline{AF}$, $\angle E \cong \angle B$.
   Prove: $\overline{EF} \cong \overline{BC}$.

11. Prove Corollary 28-1, using the figures on page 223.

12. In $\triangle ABC$ and $\triangle DEF$, $m\angle A = 50$, $m\angle B = 70$, $AC = 12$ centimeters, $m\angle D = 50$, $m\angle F = 60$, and $DF = 12$ centimeters. Is $\triangle ABC \cong \triangle DEF$? Explain your answer.

13. In $\triangle ABC$ and $\triangle DEF$, $m\angle A = 45$, $m\angle B = 90$, $AB = 27$ centimeters, $m\angle E = 90$, $m\angle F = 45$, and $EF = 27$ centimeters. Is $\triangle ABC \cong \triangle DEF$? Explain your answer.

6-6   THE CONVERSE OF THE ISOSCELES TRIANGLE THEOREM

The Isosceles Triangle Theorem, proved in Section 4-8 of this book, is restated here in its conditional form.

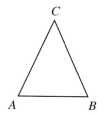

● **THEOREM 9. If two sides of a triangle are congruent, then the angles opposite these sides are congruent.**

When we proved the Isosceles Triangle Theorem, its converse would have been very difficult to prove with the postulates and theorems that we had available at that time. Now that we can prove two triangles congruent by a.a.s. ≅ a.a.s., however, this converse is relatively easy to prove.

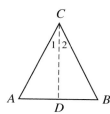

● **THEOREM 29. If two angles of a triangle are congruent, then the sides opposite these angles are congruent.**

Given: △ABC with ∠A ≅ ∠B.

Prove: $\overline{CA} \cong \overline{CB}$.

Plan: By drawing bisector $\overline{CD}$ of vertex ∠ACB, two triangles are formed. Prove △ACD ≅ △BCD and, therefore, $\overline{CA} \cong \overline{CB}$.

Statements	*Reasons*
1. Let $\overline{CD}$, the bisector of vertex ∠ACB, intersect $\overline{AB}$ at D.	1. Every angle has one and only one bisector.
2. ∠1 ≅ ∠2. (a. ≅ a.)	2. Definition of angle bisector.
3. $\overline{CD} \cong \overline{CD}$. (s. ≅ s.)	3. Reflexive property of congruence.
4. ∠A ≅ ∠B. (a. ≅ a.)	4. Given.
5. △ACD ≅ △BCD.	5. a.a.s. ≅ a.a.s.
6. $\overline{CA} \cong \overline{CB}$.	6. Corresponding sides of congruent triangles are congruent.

The statement of the Isosceles Triangle Theorem (Theorem 9) and its converse (Theorem 29) can now be written in biconditional form:

Two angles of a triangle are congruent if and only if the sides opposite these angles are congruent.

To prove that a triangle is isosceles, we may now prove that either of the following two statements is true:

1. Two sides of the triangle are congruent.

2. Two angles of the triangle are congruent.

● **COROLLARY 29-1. If a triangle is equiangular, then it is equilateral.**

If we are given △ABC, where ∠A ≅ ∠B ≅ ∠C, we can then prove that $\overline{BC} \cong \overline{CA} \cong \overline{AB}$ by using Theorem 29. Therefore, △ABC is equilateral.

EXAMPLES

1. In $\triangle PQR$, $\angle Q \cong \angle R$. If $PQ = 5x - 7$ and $PR = 2x + 11$, find:
a. the value of x **b.** PQ **c.** PR.

Solutions   **a.** Since two angles of $\triangle PQR$ are congruent, the sides opposite these angles are congruent. Thus, $PQ = PR$.

$$5x - 7 = 2x + 11$$
$$5x - 2x = 11 + 7$$
$$3x = 18$$
$$x = 6 \quad Answer$$

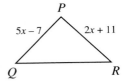

b. $PQ = 5x - 7 = 5(6) - 7 = 30 - 7 = 23$ *Answer*

c. $PR = 2x + 11 = 2(6) + 11 = 12 + 11 = 23$ *Answer*

---

2. If the degree measures of the three angles of a triangle are represented by $x + 20$, $2x - 5$, and $3x + 15$, which of the following choices most completely describes the triangle?
(1) scalene and right
(2) isosceles and acute
(3) isosceles and right
(4) equiangular

Solution   The sum of the degree measures of the angles of a triangle is 180.

$$x + 20 + 2x - 5 + 3x + 15 = 180$$
$$6x + 30 = 180$$
$$6x = 150$$
$$x = 25$$

Substitute $x = 25$ in the representations given for the three angle measures.

$$x + 20 = 25 + 20 = 45$$
$$2x - 5 = 2(25) - 5 = 50 - 5 = 45$$
$$3x + 15 = 3(25) + 15 = 75 + 15 = 90$$

Since each of two angles measures 45°, the triangle is isosceles. Also, since one angle measures 90°, the triangle is right.

Answer: Choice (3)

3. *Given:* In △ABC, $\overline{DHE}$, $\overline{FHG}$,
$\overline{GH} \cong \overline{EH}$, and ∠1 ≅ ∠2.

Prove: △ABC is isosceles.

Plan: Prove that ∠A ≅ ∠C in
△ADE and △CFG, which are
separated and shown below.

Statements	*Reasons*
1. $\overline{GH} \cong \overline{EH}$.	1. Given.
2. In △GHE, ∠3 ≅ ∠4. (a. ≅ a.)	2. If two sides of a triangle are congruent, the angles opposite these sides are congruent.
3. ∠1 ≅ ∠2.	3. Given.
4. ∠5 ≅ ∠6. (a. ≅ a.)	4. Supplements of congruent angles are congruent.
5. ∠A ≅ ∠C.	5. If two angles of one triangle are congruent to two angles of another triangle, then the third angles are congruent.
6. $\overline{BC} \cong \overline{BA}$.	6. If two angles of a triangle are congruent, the sides opposite these angles are congruent.
7. △ABC is isosceles.	7. Definition of an isosceles triangle.

EXERCISES WITH OPEN-RESPONSE PROBLEMS

In 1–4, in each case the degree measures of two angles of a triangle are given.

a. Find the degree measure of the third angle of the triangle.
b. Tell whether the triangle is isosceles or is not isosceles.

1. 70, 40   **2.** 30, 120   **3.** 35, 65   **4.** 100, 50

5. In △ABC, ∠A ≅ ∠C, AB = 5x + 6, and BC = 3x + 14. Find the value of x.
6. In △PQR, ∠Q ≅ ∠P, PR = 3x, and RQ = 2x + 7. Find PR and RQ.

7. In $\triangle MNR$, $\angle M \cong \angle R$, $MN = 3x + 2$, $NR = x + 8$, and $MR = 2x$.
   Find: **a.** the value of x **b.** MN **c.** NR **d.** MR

8. In $\triangle ABC$, $m\angle A = 80$ and $m\angle B = 50$. If $AB = 4x - 4$ and $AC = 2x + 16$, find AB and AC.

9. The degree measures of the angles of $\triangle ABC$ are represented by $2x$, $x + 10$, and $2x - 30$.
   a. Express the sum of the measures of the angles in terms of x.
   b. Find the value of x.   **c.** Show that $\triangle ABC$ is an isosceles triangle.

10. The degree measures of the angles of $\triangle ABC$ are represented by $x + 35$, $2x + 10$, and $3x - 15$.
   a. Find the value of x.   **b.** Show that $\triangle ABC$ is an equilateral triangle.

11. The degree measures of the angles of $\triangle ABC$ are represented by $3x + 18$, $4x + 9$, and $10x$.
   a. Find the value of x.   **b.** Show that $\triangle ABC$ is an isosceles right triangle.

   In 12–17, the given expressions represent the degree measures of the three angles of a triangle. In each case, which of the following choices most completely describes the triangle?
   (1) scalene and right   (2) isosceles and acute
   (3) isosceles and right   (4) equiangular

12. x, $2x$, $3x$ **13.** x, x, $2x$ **14.** $x + 30$, $4x + 30$, $10x - 30$

15. $3x$, $4x - 20$, $2x + 20$ **16.** $x + 15$, $2x - 15$, $3x$ **17.** x, $2x$, $3x - 36$

Ex. 18

Ex. 19

Ex. 20

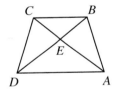
Ex. 21

18. Given $\overleftrightarrow{DBCE}$ and $\angle 1 \cong \angle 2$, prove that $\triangle ABC$ is isosceles.

19. If $\overline{AB} \cong \overline{BC}$ and $\angle 3 \cong \angle 4$, prove that $\triangle ADC$ is isosceles.

20. If $\overline{SD} \perp \overline{MR}$, and $\overline{SD}$ bisects $\overline{MR}$, prove that $\triangle MRS$ is isosceles.

21. If $\overline{AB} \cong \overline{DC}$ and $\overline{AC} \cong \overline{DB}$, prove that:
   a. $\triangle ACD \cong \triangle DBA$.   **b.** $\angle CAD \cong \angle BDA$.
   c. $\triangle DEA$ is isosceles.

22. The vertices of $\triangle ABC$ are $A(k, -2)$, $B(-1, 5)$, and $C(-1, -2)$. If $m\angle A = m\angle B$, find two possible values of k.

23. a. Plot the points $A(0, 0)$, $B(7, 0)$, $C(12, 5)$, and $D(0, 5)$. Draw $\overline{AB}$, $\overline{BC}$, $\overline{AC}$, and $\overline{CD}$.
   b. Find AB and BC.
   c. State the contrapositive of Theorem 29.
   d. Use the answers to parts **b** and **c** to prove that $\overrightarrow{CA}$ does not bisect $\angle DCB$.

Ex. 24

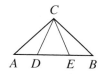

Ex. 25

24. If $\overline{DA} \cong \overline{CB}$ and $\angle DAB \cong \angle CBA$, prove that $\triangle AOB$ is isosceles.

25. *Given:* $\overline{ADEB}, \overline{AD} \cong \overline{BE}, \angle CDE \cong \angle CED.$
  Prove: $\triangle ACB$ is isosceles.

Ex. 26

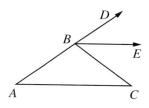

Ex. 27

26. *Given:* $\triangle ABC, \overline{CA} \cong \overline{CB}, \overline{APD}, \overline{BPE}, \angle PAB \cong \angle PBA.$
  Prove: $\overline{PE} \cong \overline{PD}.$

27. *Given:* $\triangle ABC, \overrightarrow{ABD}, \overrightarrow{BE}$ bisects $\angle DBC, \overrightarrow{BE} \parallel \overline{AC}.$
  Prove: $\overline{AB} \cong \overline{CB}.$

28. *Prove:* If a triangle is equiangular, it is equilateral.

6-7 PROVING RIGHT TRIANGLES CONGRUENT BY HYPOTENUSE AND LEG

We showed in Section 6-5 that, when two sides and an angle opposite one of these sides in one triangle are congruent to the corresponding two sides and angle in another triangle, the two triangles may or may not be congruent. When the triangles are right triangles, however, it is possible to prove that they are congruent. The congruent angles are the right angles, and each right angle is opposite the hypotenuse of the triangle.

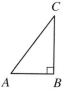

- **THEOREM 30. Two right triangles are congruent if the hypotenuse and a leg of one triangle are congruent to the corresponding parts of the other. [hy. leg ≅ hy. leg]**

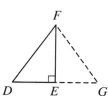

Given: Right triangle ABC with right angle B. Right triangle DEF with right angle E. $\overline{AC} \cong \overline{DF}, \overline{BC} \cong \overline{EF}.$

Prove: Right triangle $ABC \cong$ right triangle DEF.

Plan: Construct a third triangle, $\triangle GEF$. Prove that each of the two given triangles is congruent to $\triangle GEF$ and, thus, to each other.

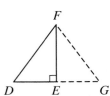

Statements	Reasons
1. Extend $\overline{DE}$ to G so that $\overline{EG} \cong \overline{AB}$. (s. $\cong$ s.)	1. A line segment may be extended any required length.
2. Draw $\overline{FG}$.	2. A line segment can be drawn joining two points.
3. $\overline{BC} \cong \overline{EF}$. (s. $\cong$ s.)	3. Given.
4. $\angle B$ and $\angle DEF$ are right angles.	4. Given.
5. $\overline{DG} \perp \overline{EF}$.	5. Definition of perpendicular lines.
6. $\angle GEF$ is a right angle.	6. Same as reason 5.
7. $\angle B \cong \angle GEF$. (a. $\cong$ a.)	7. All right angles are congruent.
8. $\triangle ABC \cong \triangle GEF$.	8. s.a.s. $\cong$ s.a.s.
9. $\overline{AC} \cong \overline{GF}$.	9. Corresponding sides of congruent triangles are congruent.
10. $\overline{AC} \cong \overline{DF}$.	10. Given.
11. $\overline{DF} \cong \overline{GF}$. (s. $\cong$ s.)	11. Transitive property of congruence.
12. $\angle D \cong \angle G$. (a. $\cong$ a.)	12. If two sides of a triangle are congruent, the angles opposite these sides are congruent.
13. $\angle DEF \cong \angle GEF$. (a. $\cong$ a.)	13. All right angles are congruent.
14. $\triangle DEF \cong \triangle GEF$.	14. a.a.s. $\cong$ a.a.s.
15. $\triangle ABC \cong \triangle DEF$.	15. Transitive property of congruence.

   Therefore, from this point on, when the hypotenuse and a leg of one right triangle are congruent to the corresponding parts of a second right triangle [hy. leg $\cong$ hy. leg], we may say that the triangles are congruent.

EXAMPLE

Given: $\triangle ABC$, $\overline{BD} \perp \overline{AC}$, $\overline{AB} \cong \overline{CB}$.

Prove: $\triangle ADB \cong \triangle CDB$.

Plan: Show that $\triangle ADB$ and $\triangle CDB$ are right triangles. Then use hy. leg $\cong$ hy. leg to prove them congruent.

Statements	Reasons
1. $\overline{BD} \perp \overline{AC}$.	1. Given.
2. $\angle ADB$ and $\angle CDB$ are right angles.	2. Definition of perpendicular lines.
3. $\triangle ADB$ and $\triangle CDB$ are right triangles.	3. Definition of right triangle.
4. $\overline{AB} \cong \overline{CB}$. (hy. $\cong$ hy.)	4. Given.
5. $\overline{BD} \cong \overline{BD}$. (leg $\cong$ leg)	5. Reflexive property of congruence.
6. $\triangle ADB \cong \triangle CDB$.	6. Hy. leg $\cong$ hy. leg.

EXERCISES WITH OPEN-RESPONSE PROBLEMS

Ex. 1

Ex. 2

Ex. 3

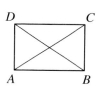

Ex. 4

1. *Given:* Right angle ABD, right angle CDB, $\overline{AD} \cong \overline{CB}$.
   Prove: $\triangle ABD \cong \triangle CDB$.

2. *Given:* $\overrightarrow{PB} \perp \overrightarrow{AC}, \overrightarrow{PD} \perp \overrightarrow{AE}, \overline{AB} \cong \overline{AD}$.
   Prove: $\triangle ABP \cong \triangle ADP$.

3. If M is the midpoint of $\overline{AB}$, $\overline{ME} \perp \overline{AC}$, $\overline{MF} \perp \overline{CB}$, and $\overline{ME} \cong \overline{MF}$, prove that $\angle CAB \cong \angle CBA$.

4. If $\overline{DA} \perp \overline{AB}$, $\overline{CB} \perp \overline{AB}$, and $\overline{AC} \cong \overline{BD}$, prove that: **a.** $\triangle ACB \cong \triangle BDA$. **b.** $\overline{AD} \cong \overline{BC}$.

5. In $\triangle PQR$, $\overline{QS} \perp \overline{PR}$, $\overline{PQ} \cong \overline{RQ}$, $m\angle 1 = 4x$, and $m\angle 2 = 2x + 18$.
   a. Prove $\triangle PQS \cong \triangle RQS$. **b.** Find the value of x.
   c. Find $m\angle 1$.

6. In quadrilateral $ABCD$, $\angle A$ and $\angle C$ are right angles, $\overline{AB} \cong \overline{CD}$.
   a. Prove $\triangle ABD \cong \triangle CDB$.
   b. If $m\angle ABD = 60$, $m\angle DBC = 30$, $m\angle BDA = x - y$, and $m\angle BDC = x + y$, find x and y.

Ex. 5

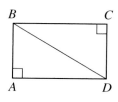

Ex. 6

7. Would it be correct to say that two right triangles are congruent if a leg and an acute angle of one triangle are congruent to a leg and an acute angle of the other triangle? Explain your answer.

6-8 EXTERIOR ANGLES OF A TRIANGLE

In Chapter 5, we proved Theorem 11: *The measure of an exterior angle of a triangle is greater than the measure of either nonadjacent interior angle.* What other relationships between the measure of an exterior angle and the measures of nonadjacent interior angles exist?

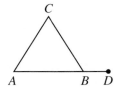

In the diagram, $\angle DBC$ is an exterior angle at vertex B of $\triangle ABC$, $m\angle C = 80$, and $m\angle DBC = 125$. Since $\angle ABC$ and $\angle DBC$ form a linear pair, it is possible to find the measures of $\angle ABC$ and then of $\angle A$.

First: $\quad m\angle ABC + m\angle DBC = 180$

$\qquad\qquad m\angle ABC + \quad 125 \quad = 180$

$\qquad\qquad\qquad\qquad m\angle ABC = 55$

Then: $\quad m\angle A + m\angle ABC + m\angle C = 180$

$\qquad\qquad m\angle A + \quad 55 \quad + \quad 80 \quad = 180$

$\qquad\qquad\qquad\qquad\qquad m\angle A = 45$

We note that $m\angle A + m\angle C = 45 + 80 = 125 = m\angle DBC$.

Since $m\angle DBC = 180 - m\angle ABC$ and $m\angle A + m\angle C = 180 - m\angle ABC$, we can prove the following theorem.

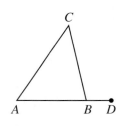

● **THEOREM 31. The measure of an exterior angle of a triangle is equal to the sum of the measures of the two nonadjacent interior angles.**

Given: $\triangle ABC$ with exterior $\angle CBD$ at B, and two nonadjacent interior angles, $\angle A$ and $\angle C$.

Prove: $m\angle CBD = m\angle A + m\angle C$.

Statements	*Reasons*
1. In $\triangle ABC$, $\angle CBD$ is an exterior angle at vertex B.	1. Given.
2. $\angle CBD$ and $\angle CBA$ form a linear pair.	2. A linear pair of angles are two angles whose sum is a straight angle.
3. $m\angle CBD + m\angle CBA = 180$.	3. The degree measure of a straight angle is 180.
4. $m\angle CBD = 180 - m\angle CBA$.	4. Subtraction postulate.
5. $m\angle A + m\angle CBA + m\angle C = 180$.	5. The sum of the degree measures of the angles of a triangle is 180.
6. $m\angle A + m\angle C = 180 - m\angle CBA$.	6. Subtraction postulate.
7. $m\angle CBD = m\angle A + m\angle C$.	7. Substitution postulate and transitive property of equality.

EXAMPLE

In $\triangle ABC$, $\overline{CD}$ is drawn so that $\overline{CD} \cong \overline{CA}$. If $m\angle ACD = 70$, find:

a. $m\angle CAD$ **b.** $m\angle CDB$

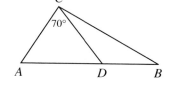

Solutions   **a.** Since $\overline{CD} \cong \overline{CA}$, $\triangle ACD$ is isosceles. Let the degree measures of each base angle equal x: $m\angle CAD = x$, and $m\angle CDA = x$. Then:

$$x + x + 70 = 180$$
$$2x + 70 = 180$$
$$2x = 110$$
$$x = 55$$

Answer: $m\angle CDA = 55$

b. Angle CDB is an exterior angle of $\triangle ACD$ at vertex D. *The measure of an exterior angle of a triangle equals the sum of the measures of the two nonadjacent interior angles.*

$$m\angle CDB = m\angle DCA + m\angle CAD$$
$$= 70 \quad\quad + 55$$
$$= 125$$

Answer: $m\angle CDB = 125$

EXERCISES WITH OPEN-RESPONSE PROBLEMS

In 1–5, in each case find the value of x.

1.   **2.**   **3.**

4.   **5.**

6. In $\triangle RST$, if $m\angle S = 90$ and $m\angle T = 30$, find the degree measure of an exterior angle at R.

7. Find the degree measure of either of the exterior angles formed by extending the base of an isosceles triangle if the vertex angle of the triangle measures:

   a. $20°$ **b.** $40°$ **c.** $82°$ **d.** $120°$ **e.** $135°$

8. An exterior angle at the base of an isosceles triangle measures 140°. Find the number of degrees in the vertex angle.

9. In △*PQR*, the measure of ∠*P* is twice the measure of ∠*Q*. If an exterior angle at vertex *R* has a degree measure of 120, find m∠*Q*.

10. In △*ABC*, m∠*B* is 4 times m∠*A*. An exterior angle at *C* measures 125°. Find the degree measure of ∠*A*.

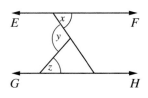

Ex. 11   **Ex. 12–14**

11. In the figure, $\overleftrightarrow{AB} \parallel \overleftrightarrow{CD}$ and $\overleftrightarrow{PQR}$ and $\overline{QS}$ are drawn. If m∠*x* = 44 and m∠*y* = 98, find:
   a. m∠*QRS*   **b.** m∠*RQS*   **c.** m∠*z*

12. If $\overleftrightarrow{EF} \parallel \overleftrightarrow{GH}$, m∠*x* = 68, and m∠*y* = 117, find m∠*z*.

13. If $\overleftrightarrow{EF} \parallel \overleftrightarrow{GH}$, m∠*x* = 70, and m∠*z* = 60, find m∠*y*.

14. If $\overleftrightarrow{EF} \parallel \overleftrightarrow{GH}$, m∠*y* = 123, and m∠*z* = 58, find m∠*x*.

In 15–19, select the *numeral* preceding the choice that best completes the statement.

15. An exterior angle at the base of an isosceles triangle is always
   (1) right   (2) acute   (3) obtuse   (4) equal to the base angle

16. In △*RST*, ∠*S* is a right angle. The exterior angle at vertex *S* is
   (1) right   (2) acute   (3) obtuse   (4) straight

17. For △*ABC*, m∠*A* = 40 and m∠*B* = 60. The degree measure of the exterior angle at ∠*C* is
   (1) 40   (2) 60   (3) 80   (4) 100

18. In △*ABC*, an exterior angle at *C* measures 100° and ∠*B* measures 20°. Triangle *ABC* must be
   (1) isosceles   (2) right   (3) obtuse   (4) equiangular

19. Side $\overline{AC}$ of △*ABC* is extended through *C* to *D*. Angle *BCD* measures 108°, and the measure of ∠*A* is twice the measure of ∠*B*. Triangle *ABC* is
   (1) right   (2) obtuse   (3) isosceles   (4) scalene

20. In △*DEF*, m∠*D* = 2*x* + 4 and m∠*E* = 6*x* − 58. The degree measure of an exterior angle at *F* is represented by 5*x*.
   a. Find the value of *x*.   **b.** Show that △*DEF* is a right triangle.

21. *Prove:* If the two exterior angles formed by extending the line that contains one side of a triangle in both directions are congruent, the triangle is isosceles.

22. In △*RST*, $\overline{RS} \cong \overline{ST}$. Prove that the bisector of an exterior angle at *S* is parallel to $\overline{RT}$.

6-9   INTERIOR ANGLES AND EXTERIOR ANGLES OF A POLYGON

You have learned that a polygon is a closed figure that is the union of line segments in a plane. The figure at the left is polygon *ABCDE*. You have already studied the properties of a triangle, a polygon that is the union of three sides. Other polygons that you will study are defined as follows:

- **DEFINITION.** A *quadrilateral* is a polygon that is the union of four sides.
- **DEFINITION.** A *pentagon* is a polygon that is the union of five sides.
- **DEFINITION.** A *hexagon* is a polygon that is the union of six sides.
- **DEFINITION.** An *octagon* is a polygon that is the union of eight sides.
- **DEFINITION.** A *decagon* is a polygon that is the union of ten sides.
- **DEFINITION.** A *convex polygon* is a polygon each of whose interior angles measures less than 180 degrees.

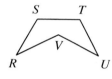

In the figure above, *ABCDE* is a convex polygon. When a polygon has at least one interior angle measuring more than 180 degrees, as in *RSTUV*, shown at the left, we call this figure a **concave polygon.** In this text, we will not deal with concave polygons.

Polygon *JKLMN* is shown at the left. A polygon is named by listing its vertices in order so that each consecutive pair of letters names the endpoints of a side of the polygon. Polygon *JKLMN* could also be named polygon *JNMLK* by listing the vertices in the opposite order, or polygon *LMNJK* by starting at a different vertex, but not polygon *LNKMJ* since *L* and *N* are not the endpoints of a side. A pair of sides with a common endpoint are called *adjacent or consecutive sides.*

A pair of angles whose vertices are the endpoints of a common side are called *consecutive angles*, and the vertices of consecutive angles are called *consecutive or adjacent vertices.*

For example, in polygon *JKLMN*:

$\overline{JK}$ and $\overline{KL}$ are adjacent or consecutive sides with common endpoint *K*; $\angle J$ and $\angle K$ are consecutive angles, and *J* and *K* are consecutive or adjacent vertices, because *J* and *K* are endpoints of side $\overline{JK}$.

A *diagonal* of a polygon is a line segment whose endpoints are two nonadjacent vertices of the polygon. Polygon *JKLMN* has five diagonals: $\overline{JL}$, $\overline{JM}$, $\overline{KM}$, $\overline{KN}$, and $\overline{LN}$.

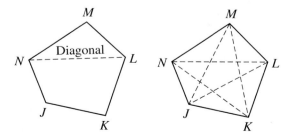

● **DEFINITION.** A *regular polygon* is a polygon that is both equilateral and equiangular.

For regular hexagon *ABCDEF*:

$$\overline{AB} \cong \overline{BC} \cong \overline{CD} \cong \overline{DE} \cong \overline{EF} \cong \overline{FA}$$
and
$$\angle A \cong \angle B \cong \angle C \cong \angle D \cong \angle E \cong \angle F$$

For *regular polygons only*, the measures of interior and exterior angles are indicated in the four simplest regular polygons as follows:

In these four examples, the following rules are true:

1. The sum of the degree measures of the interior angles of a polygon of *n* sides is 180(*n* − 2).

2. The sum of the degree measures of the exterior angles of a polygon is 360.

These rules are true for *any* polygon. In the figures at the right, diagonals are drawn from a single vertex so that, in quadrilateral *PQRS*, two triangles are formed and 180 · 2 = 360. Also, in pentagon *ABCDE*, three triangles are formed and 180 · 3 = 540. In a polygon of *n* sides, *n* − 2 triangles are formed by drawing the diagonals from a single vertex. This fact can be used to prove the following theorem.

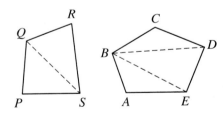

● **THEOREM 32. The sum of the degree measures of the interior angles of any polygon of *n* sides is 180(*n* − 2).**

Also, for any polygon, we can prove the following:

● **THEOREM 33. The sum of the degree measures of the exterior angles of any polygon of *n* sides, taking one exterior angle at each vertex, is 360.**

EXAMPLES

1. A *regular* polygon has 10 sides.   **a.** Find the measure of one exterior angle. **b.** Find the measure of one interior angle.   **c.** Find the sum of the measures of all interior angles of this polygon.

Solutions   **a.** The sum of the degree measures of the exterior angles of any polygon is 360. Since this *regular* polygon contains 10 sides, it also has 10 congruent exterior angles. The measure of one exterior angle is $\frac{360}{10} = 36°$.   *Answer*

b. An interior angle is supplementary to an exterior angle. Thus, the measure of one of the 10 congruent interior angles is $180 - 36 = 144°$.   *Answer*

c. The sum of the degree measures of the 10 interior angles can be found by either of two methods.

METHOD 1. The measure of each interior angle is 144. Therefore, the measure of 10 interior angles is $10(144) = 1,440°$.   *Answer*

METHOD 2. Use the rule $180(n - 2)$, where $n = 10$ sides. The sum of the degree measures of the interior angles is $180(10 - 2) = 180(8) = 1,440°$.   *Answer*

---

2. Find n, the number of sides of a *regular* polygon, if:
  a. Each exterior angle contains 72°.
  b. Each interior angle contains 150°.
  c. The sum of the degree measures of all the interior angles is 2,880.

Solutions   **a.** The sum of the degree measures of the n exterior angles is 360.

$$72 + 72 + 72 + \ldots = 360$$

n terms

$$72n = 360$$
$$n = 5 \quad \textit{Answer}$$

b. For each interior angle of 150°, there is a supplementary exterior angle of $180 - 150$ or 30°. The sum of the degree measures of the n exterior angles is 360.

$$30n = 360$$
$$n = 12 \quad \textit{Answer}$$

c. The sum of the degree measures of the interior angles of any polygon of n sides is $180(n - 2)$.

$$180(n - 2) = 2,880$$
$$180n - 360 = 2,880$$
$$180n = 3,240$$
$$n = 18 \quad \textit{Answer}$$

EXERCISES WITH OPEN-RESPONSE PROBLEMS

1. Find the sum of the degree measures of the interior angles of a polygon that has:
   a. 3 sides **b.** 7 sides **c.** 9 sides
2. Find the sum of the degree measures of the interior angles of:
   a. a hexagon **b.** an octagon **c.** a pentagon **d.** a quadrilateral
3. Find the sum of the measures of the exterior angles of a polygon that has:
   a. 4 sides **b.** 8 sides **c.** 10 sides **d.** 36 sides

   In 4–11, for each *regular* polygon with the given number of sides, find the degree measures of:
   a. one exterior angle **b.** one interior angle

4. 4 sides **5.** 5 sides **6.** 6 sides **7.** 8 sides
8. 9 sides **9.** 12 sides **10.** 20 sides **11.** 36 sides

12. Find the number of sides of a *regular* polygon each of whose exterior angles contains:
    a. 30° **b.** 45° **c.** 60° **d.** 120°
13. Find the number of sides of a *regular* polygon each of whose interior angles contains:
    a. 90° **b.** 120° **c.** 140° **d.** 160°
14. Find the number of sides a polygon has if the sum of the degree measures of its interior angles is:
    a. 180 **b.** 360 **c.** 540 **d.** 900 **e.** 1,440 **f.** 2,700 **g.** 1,800 **h.** 3,600
15. The measure of each exterior angle of a regular polygon is twice the measure of each interior angle. How many sides does the polygon have? Explain your reasoning.
16. The angles of a quadrilateral are in the ratio $3:4:5:6$. Find the number of degrees contained in the largest angle of the quadrilateral. Clearly show your work.

CHAPTER SUMMARY

Two intersecting lines are ***perpendicular*** when:

1. The lines intersect to form right angles.
2. The lines intersect to form congruent adjacent angles.
3. There are two points on one line, each of which is equidistant from the endpoints of a line segment of the other line.

Two coplanar lines that are cut by a transversal are ***parallel*** if and only if:

1. A pair of alternate interior angles are congruent.
2. A pair of corresponding angles are congruent.
3. A pair of interior (or a pair of exterior) angles on the same side of the transversal are supplementary.

Also, coplanar lines are parallel when:

4. Both lines are perpendicular to the same line.
5. Both lines are parallel to the same line.

The ***sum of the degree measures of the angles of a triangle*** is 180.

Triangles can be proven congruent by:

1. s.s.s. $\cong$ s.s.s.   **2.** s.a.s. $\cong$ s.a.s.

3. a.s.a. $\cong$ a.s.a.   **4.** a.a.s. $\cong$ a.a.s.

The ***Isosceles Triangle Theorem*** and its proven converse may be stated in biconditional form: Two angles of a triangle are congruent if and only if the sides opposite these angle are congruent.

VOCABULARY

6-1 Perpendicular bisector

6-2 Coplanar   Parallel lines   Transversal   Interior angles
Exterior angles   Alternate interior angles   Alternate exterior angles
Interior angles on the same side of the transversal   Corresponding angles

6-9 Quadrilateral   Pentagon   Hexagon   Octagon   Decagon
Convex polygon   Concave polygon   Diagonal   Regular polygon

REVIEW EXERCISES WITH OPEN-RESPONSE PROBLEMS

In 1–5, $\overleftrightarrow{AB} \parallel \overleftrightarrow{CD}$ and these lines are cut by transversal $\overleftrightarrow{GH}$ at points E and F, respectively.

1. If m$\angle AEF = 5x$ and
m$\angle DFE = 75$, find x.

2. If m$\angle CFE = 3y + 20$ and
m$\angle AEG = 4y - 10$, find y.

3. If m$\angle BEF = 5x$ and
m$\angle CFE = 7x - 48$, find x.

4. If m$\angle DFE = y$ and
m$\angle BEF = 3y - 40$, find m$\angle DFE$.

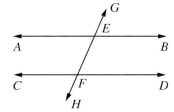

Ex. 1–5

5. If m$\angle AEF = 4x$ and m$\angle EFD = 3x + 18$, find:
a. the value of x **b.** m$\angle AEF$ **c.** m$\angle EFD$ **d.** m$\angle BEF$ **e.** m$\angle CFH$

6. The degree measure of the vertex angle of an isosceles triangle is 120.
Find the measure of a base angle of the triangle.

7. In $\triangle ABC$, $\angle A \cong \angle C$. If $AB = 8x + 4$ and $CB = 3x + 34$, find x.

8. In an isosceles triangle, if the measure of the vertex angle is 3 times the measure of a base angle, find the degree measure of a base angle.

9. In a triangle, the degree measures of the three angles are represented by x, $x + 35$, and $x - 5$. Find the angle measures.

10. In $\triangle PQR$, if m$\angle P = 35$ and m$\angle Q = 85$, what is the degree measure of an exterior angle of the triangle at vertex R?

11. An exterior angle at the base of an isosceles triangle measures 130°. Find the measure of the vertex angle.

12. In $\triangle ABC$, if $\overline{AB} \cong \overline{AC}$ and m$\angle A = 70$, find m$\angle B$.

13. In $\triangle DEF$, if $\overline{DE} \cong \overline{DF}$ and m$\angle E = 70$, find m$\angle D$.

14. In $\triangle PQR$, $\overline{PQ}$ is extended through Q to point T, forming exterior $\angle RQT$. If m$\angle RQT = 70$ and m$\angle R = 10$, find m$\angle P$.

Ex. 15   Ex. 16

15. In the figure, $\overleftrightarrow{AB} \parallel \overleftrightarrow{CD}$, m$\angle x = 70$, and m$\angle y = 102$. Find m$\angle z$.

16. In $\triangle ABC$, $\overline{AC} \cong \overline{BC}$. The degree measure of an exterior angle at vertex C is represented by $5x + 10$. If m$\angle A = 30$, find x.

17. $\overleftrightarrow{AB}$ intersects $\overleftrightarrow{CD}$ at E; m$\angle AEC = 2x + 10$; m$\angle AED = 3x - 30$.
   a. Find x.   **b.** Show that $\overleftrightarrow{AB}$ is perpendicular to $\overleftrightarrow{CD}$.

In 18–24, select the *numeral* preceding the choice that best completes the statement or answers the question.

18. The measures of the angles of a triangle are in the ratio $2:3:5$. The degree measure of the smallest angle of the triangle is
   (1) 9   (2) 18   (3) 36   (4) 40

19. If the degree measures of the angles of a triangle are represented by $x - 10$, $2x + 20$, and $3x - 10$, the triangle must be
   (1) isosceles   (2) right   (3) equilateral   (4) scalene

20. If the degree measures of the angles of a triangle are represented by x, y, and $x + y$, the triangle must be
   (1) isosceles   (2) right   (3) equilateral   (4) scalene

21. If parallel lines are cut by a transversal so that the degree measures of two corresponding angles are represented by $2x + 50$ and $3x + 20$, then x equals
   (1) 22   (2) 30   (3) 94   (4) 110

22. If $\angle 1$ and $\angle 2$ are supplementary, which *must* be true?
(1) $k \perp p$ (2) $k \perp m$
(3) $k \parallel m$ (4) $p \parallel m$

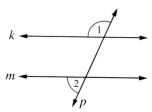

23. The measure of one exterior angle of a *regular* polygon is 60°. How many sides does the regular polygon contain?
(1) 8   (2) 6   (3) 3   (4) 4

24. What is the sum of the degree measures of the interior angles of a pentagon?
(1) 360   (2) 540   (3) 900   (4) 1,260

Ex. 25

Ex. 26

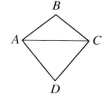

Ex. 27

25. If E is the midpoint of $\overline{BC}$ and E is the midpoint of $\overline{DF}$, prove:
 a. $\triangle BED \cong \triangle CEF$.   **b.** $\angle DBE \cong \angle FCE$.   **c.** $\overline{AB} \parallel \overline{FC}$.

26. If $\angle 1 \cong \angle 3$ and $\angle 3 \cong \angle 2$, prove $\overrightarrow{BH} \parallel \overleftrightarrow{EG}$.

27. If $\overline{BA} \cong \overline{BC}$, $\overline{DA} \perp \overline{AB}$, and $\overline{DC} \perp \overline{CB}$, prove $\triangle ADC$ is an isosceles triangle.

Ex. 28

Ex. 29

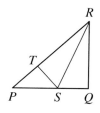

Ex. 30

28. If, in $\triangle RST$, $\angle R \cong \angle T$, $\overline{RM} \cong \overline{TN}$, and $\overline{RMNT}$, prove $\triangle MSN$ is an isosceles triangle.

29. *Given:* $\overline{AFEC}$, $\overline{DF} \perp \overline{AC}$, $\overline{BE} \perp \overline{AC}$, $\angle 1 \cong \angle 2$, $\overline{AF} \cong \overline{CE}$.
 Prove: $\triangle ABE \cong \triangle CDF$.

30. *Given:* In $\triangle PQR$, $\angle Q$ is a right angle, $\overline{ST} \perp \overline{PR}$, $\overline{RT} \cong \overline{RQ}$.
 Prove: $\triangle TRS \cong \triangle QRS$.

31. *Given:* Right triangle ABC with $\angle C$ the right angle.
 Prove: $AB > AC$.

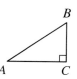

32. In polygon $ABCD$, $\overline{AD}$ is perpendicular to $\overline{AB}$ and to $\overline{CD}$; $\overline{BC}$ is perpendicular to $\overline{AB}$ and to $\overline{CD}$. Separate $ABCD$ into two congruent polygons in four different ways.

33. Given points $A(0, -2)$, $B(2, 0)$, $C(0, 2)$, and $D(-2, 0)$.
  a. Graph polygon $ABCD$.
  b. Find the lengths of the sides: AB, BC, CD, DA.
  c. Find the measures of the angles: $m\angle A$, $m\angle B$, $m\angle C$, $m\angle D$.
  d. Is $ABCD$ a regular polygon? Explain your answer.

CUMULATIVE REVIEW WITH OPEN-RESPONSE PROBLEMS

1. Herbie wanted to draw a triangle with a perimeter of 51 centimeters, one side of length 9 centimeters, and the lengths of the other two sides in the ratio $5:9$. Is such a triangle possible? Explain your answer.

2. The vertices of $\triangle ABC$ are $A(-4, -3)$, $B(-2, 4)$, and $C(4, 1)$. Which angle is the largest angle of the triangle?

3. *Given:* If a is greater than 0, then a is greater than b.
      If a is not greater than 0, then b is less than c.
      It is false that b is less than c.
   Is it true that a is greater than b? Explain how you arrived at your answer.

4. In the diagram, $\overleftrightarrow{AEB}$ and $\overleftrightarrow{CED}$ intersect at E, and $\overline{EF} \perp \overline{AE}$. If $m\angle CEF = 35$, find:
  a. $m\angle CEA$ **b.** $m\angle AED$
  c. $m\angle DEB$ **d.** $m\angle BEF$

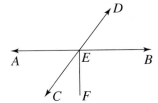

5. *Given:* $\overline{AB} \cong \overline{BC} \cong \overline{CD} \cong \overline{DE}$.
      $\overline{FB} \cong \overline{FD}$.

   Prove: $\overline{AF} \cong \overline{EF}$.

Exploration

   Investigate a non-Euclidean geometry. How do the postulates of a non-Euclidean geometry differ from the postulates of Euclid? What theorems from this chapter are not valid in the non-Euclidean geometry that you investigated?

Chapter 7
Quadrilaterals

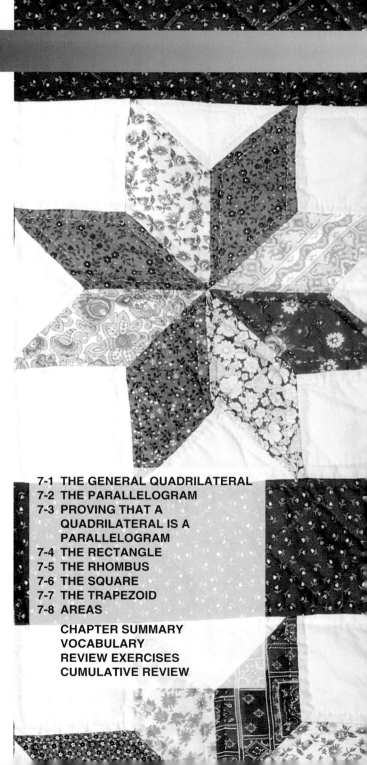

Polygons are often used to produce artistic patterns for decorative and practical purposes. The variety of effects that can be produced by an imaginative combination of colors and textures is as limitless as the human imagination.

One quilt pattern that has been popular since early pioneer days is the Lone Star. This pattern consists of eight large equilateral quadrilaterals placed so that one vertex of each meets in the center, forming an eight-pointed star as shown in the diagram. Each of the large quadrilaterals is itself formed of 64 smaller congruent equilateral quadrilaterals.

What must be the measures of the angles of the quadrilaterals that form this pattern? What other polygons are used to complete the quilt?

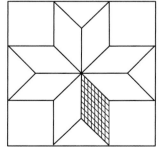

Could you use a similar pattern to make a six-pointed star? If so, what must the measure of the acute angle of the quadrilateral be?

7-1 THE GENERAL QUADRILATERAL

A *quadrilateral* is a polygon with four sides. In this chapter we will study the various special quadrilaterals and the properties of each. Let us first name the general parts of any quadrilateral, using *PQRS* as an example.

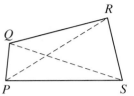

Consecutive vertices or *adjacent vertices* are vertices that are endpoints of the same side such as *P* and *Q*, *Q* and *R*, *R* and *S*, *S* and *P*.

Consecutive sides or *adjacent sides* are sides that have a common endpoint, such as $\overline{PQ}$ and $\overline{QR}$, $\overline{QR}$ and $\overline{RS}$, $\overline{RS}$ and $\overline{SP}$, $\overline{SP}$ and $\overline{PQ}$.

Opposite sides of a quadrilateral are sides that do not have a common endpoint, such as $\overline{PQ}$ and $\overline{RS}$, $\overline{PS}$ and $\overline{QR}$.

Consecutive angles of a quadrilateral are angles whose vertices are consecutive, such as $\angle P$ and $\angle Q$, $\angle Q$ and $\angle R$, $\angle R$ and $\angle S$, $\angle S$ and $\angle P$.

Opposite angles of a quadrilateral are angles whose vertices are not consecutive, such as $\angle P$ and $\angle R$, $\angle Q$ and $\angle S$.

A *diagonal of a quadrilateral* is a line segment whose endpoints are two nonadjacent vertices of the quadrilateral, such as $\overline{PR}$ and $\overline{QS}$.

7-2 THE PARALLELOGRAM

● **DEFINITION.** A *parallelogram* is a quadrilateral in which two pairs of opposite sides are parallel.

Quadrilateral *ABCD* is a parallelogram because $\overline{AB} \parallel \overline{DC}$ and $\overline{AD} \parallel \overline{BC}$. The symbol for parallelogram *ABCD* is $\square ABCD$.

Note the use of arrowheads, pointing in the same direction, to show sides that are parallel in the figure.

● **THEOREM 34. A diagonal divides a parallelogram into two congruent triangles.**

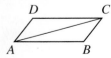

Given: Parallelogram *ABCD* with diagonal $\overline{AC}$.

Prove: $\triangle ABC \cong \triangle CDA$.

Plan: Since opposite sides of a parallelogram are parallel, alternate interior angles can be proved congruent using $\overline{AC}$ as the transversal. The triangles will be proved congruent by a.s.a. $\cong$ a.s.a.

Statements	*Reasons*
1. *ABCD* is a parallelogram; $\overline{AC}$ is a diagonal.	1. Given.
2. $\overline{AD} \parallel \overline{CB}$, $\overline{AB} \parallel \overline{CD}$.	2. A parallelogram is a quadrilateral in which two pairs of opposite sides are parallel.
3. $\angle BAC \cong \angle DCA$, $\angle BCA \cong \angle DAC$.	3. If two parallel lines are cut by a transversal, alternate interior angles are congruent.
4. $\overline{AC} \cong \overline{AC}$.	4. Reflexive property of congruence.
5. $\triangle ABC \cong \triangle CDA$.	5. a.s.a. $\cong$ a.s.a.

Now that we have proved that a diagonal divides a parallelogram into two congruent triangles, many corollaries can be proved.

- **COROLLARY 34-1. Opposite sides of a parallelogram are congruent.**

  In $\square ABCD$, $\overline{AB} \cong \overline{DC}$ and $\overline{BC} \cong \overline{AD}$.

- **COROLLARY 34-2. Opposite angles of a parallelogram are congruent.**

  In $\square ABCD$, $\angle B \cong \angle D$ and $\angle A \cong \angle C$.

- **COROLLARY 34-3. Two consecutive angles of a parallelogram are supplementary.**

  In $\square ABCD$, $\angle A$ is supplementary to $\angle B$, $\angle B$ is supplementary to $\angle C$, $\angle C$ is supplementary to $\angle D$, and $\angle D$ is supplementary to $\angle A$.

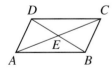

- **COROLLARY 34-4. The diagonals of a parallelogram bisect each other.**

  In $\square ABCD$, $\overline{AC}$ bisects $\overline{BD}$ so that $\overline{BE} \cong \overline{DE}$; also, $\overline{BD}$ bisects $\overline{AC}$ so that $\overline{AE} \cong \overline{CE}$.

- **DEFINITION. The *distance between two parallel lines* is the perpendicular distance from any point on one line to the other line.**

Given $\overleftrightarrow{AB} \parallel \overleftrightarrow{CD}$. The distance between these lines is *LM* or *PQ* or *RS* since each distance is determined by a segment perpendicular to the parallel lines.

- **COROLLARY 34-5. Two distinct parallel lines are everywhere equidistant.**

  If $\overleftrightarrow{AB} \parallel \overleftrightarrow{CD}$, $\overline{LM} \perp \overleftrightarrow{AB}$, $\overline{PQ} \perp \overleftrightarrow{AB}$, and $\overline{RS} \perp \overleftrightarrow{AB}$, we can use Corollary 34-1: *Opposite sides of a parallelogram are congruent* to prove $LM = PQ = RS$.

Properties of a Parallelogram

1. Opposite sides are parallel.
2. A diagonal divides a parallelogram into two congruent triangles.
3. Opposite sides are congruent.
4. Opposite angles are congruent.
5. Consecutive angles are supplementary.
6. The diagonals bisect each other.

EXAMPLE

In $\square ABCD$, if m$\angle B$ exceeds m$\angle A$ by 50, find the degree measure of $\angle B$.

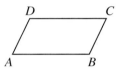

Solution

Let x = degree measure of $\angle A$.

Then $x + 50$ = degree measure of $\angle B$.

Two consecutive angles of a parallelogram are supplementary.

$$
\begin{aligned}
\text{m}\angle A + \quad \text{m}\angle B &= 180 \\
x \ + \ x + 50 &= 180 \\
2x + 50 &= 180 \\
2x &= 130 \\
x &= 65 \\
x + 50 &= 115
\end{aligned}
$$

Answer: m$\angle B = 115$

EXERCISES

1. Find the degree measures of the other three angles of a parallelogram if one angle measures:
   a. 60 **b.** 68 **c.** 73 **d.** 110 **e.** 138 **f.** 160

2. In $\square ABCD$, the degree measure of $\angle A$ is represented by $2x$ and the degree measure of $\angle B$ by $2x + 60$. Find the value of x.

3. In $\square ABCD$, $\angle A$ measures x degrees and $\angle B$ measures $(2x - 30)$ degrees. Find the degree measure of $\angle A$.

4. The measures of angles A and B of $\square ABCD$ are in the ratio $2:7$. Find the degree measure of $\angle A$.

5. In $\square ABCD$, the measure of $\angle A$ exceeds the measure of $\angle B$ by 30. Find the degree measure of $\angle B$.

6. The degree measures of two opposite angles of a parallelogram are represented by $3x + 40$ and $x + 70$.   **a.** Find x.   **b.** Find the degree measure of one of the angles.

7. In $\square ABCD$, $m\angle ABC = 3x - 12$ and $m\angle CDA = x + 40$. Find $m\angle ABC$, $m\angle CDA$, $m\angle BCD$, and $m\angle DAB$.

8. In $\square ABCD$, $AB = 7x - 4$ and $CD = 2x + 21$. Find AB and CD.

9. In $\square ABCD$, $BC = 9y + 10$, $AD = 6y + 40$, and $AB = \frac{1}{2}y + 50$. Find BC, AD, AB, and DC.

Exercises 10–18 refer to parallelogram $ABCD$.

10. If $m\angle DAB = 4x - 60$ and $m\angle DCB = 30 - x$, find $m\angle DAB$, $m\angle DCB$, and $m\angle ABC$.

11. If $m\angle DCB = a + 12$ and $m\angle CDA = 4a + 18$, find the degree measures of the angles of the parallelogram.

Ex. 10–18

12. If $AB = 4x + y$, $BC = y + 4$, $CD = 3x + 6$, $DA = 2x + y$, find the lengths of the sides of the parallelogram.

13. If $AE = 5x - 3$ and $EC = 15 - x$, find AC.

14. If $DE = 4y + 1$ and $EB = 5y - 1$, find DB.

In 15–18, select the *numeral* preceding the choice that best answers the question.

15. In $\square ABCD$, which is *always* true?
   (1) $AB = AD$ (2) $AB = DC$ (3) $\overline{AB} \parallel \overline{AD}$ (4) $\angle A \cong \angle B$

16. If the diagonals of $\square ABCD$ are $\overline{AC}$ and $\overline{BD}$, which is *always* true?
   (1) $\overline{AC} \cong \overline{BD}$ (2) $\overline{AC} \perp \overline{BD}$ (3) $\angle DAC \cong \angle BAC$ (4) $\triangle DAC \cong \triangle BCA$

17. In $\square ABCD$, diagonals $\overline{AC}$ and $\overline{BD}$ meet at E. Which is *always* true?
   (1) $\overline{AE} \cong \overline{EC}$ (2) $\overline{AE} \cong \overline{DE}$ (3) $\overline{AE} \perp \overline{DE}$ (4) $\triangle AEB \cong \triangle AED$

18. In $\square ABCD$, diagonals $\overline{AC}$ and $\overline{BD}$ meet at E. Which is *always* true?
   (1) $\triangle AED$ is an isosceles triangle.   (2) $\triangle ABD$ is a right triangle.
   (3) $\triangle ABD \cong \triangle CDB$.   (4) $\triangle AEB$ is a right triangle.

7-3   PROVING THAT A QUADRILATERAL IS A PARALLELOGRAM

If we wish to prove that a certain quadrilateral is a parallelogram, we can do so by proving its *opposite sides are parallel*, thus satisfying the definition of a parallelogram. There are also other conditions, however, that are sufficient to show that a quadrilateral is a parallelogram.

- **THEOREM 35. If both pairs of opposite sides of a quadrilateral are congruent, the quadrilateral is a parallelogram.**

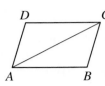

Given: $\overline{AB} \cong \overline{CD}$, $\overline{AD} \cong \overline{BC}$.

Prove: $ABCD$ is a parallelogram.

Plan: Draw $\overline{AC}$. Prove $\triangle ABC \cong \triangle CDA$ by s.s.s. $\cong$ s.s.s. Then use congruent corresponding angles to prove that the opposite sides of $ABCD$ are parallel.

- **THEOREM 36. If one pair of opposite sides of a quadrilateral is both congruent and parallel, the quadrilateral is a parallelogram.**

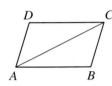

Given: $\overline{AB} \parallel \overline{CD}$, $\overline{AB} \cong \overline{CD}$.

Prove: $ABCD$ is a parallelogram.

Plan: Draw $\overline{AC}$. Prove $\triangle ABC \cong \triangle CDA$ by s.a.s. $\cong$ s.a.s. Therefore, $\overline{BC} \cong \overline{DA}$. Then use Theorem 35.

- **THEOREM 37. If both pairs of opposite angles of a quadrilateral are congruent, the quadrilateral is a parallelogram.**

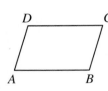

Given: $\angle A \cong \angle C$, $\angle B \cong \angle D$.

Prove: $ABCD$ is a parallelogram.

Plan: Show that $m\angle A + m\angle B + m\angle C + m\angle D = 360$.

Use substitution and the division postulate to show that $\angle A$ is the supplement of $\angle B$ and $\angle A$ is the supplement of $\angle D$. Then use Theorem 21: *If two coplanar lines are cut by a transversal so that the interior angles on the same side of the transversal are supplementary, the lines are parallel.*

- **THEOREM 38. If the diagonals of a quadrilateral bisect each other, the quadrilateral is a parallelogram.**

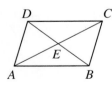

Given: $\overline{AC}$ and $\overline{BD}$ intersect at E.
$\overline{AE} \cong \overline{EC}$, $\overline{BE} \cong \overline{ED}$.

Prove: $ABCD$ is a parallelogram.

Plan: Prove $\triangle AEB \cong \triangle CED$ by s.a.s. $\cong$ s.a.s. Therefore, $\overline{AB} \cong \overline{DC}$.

Also, $\angle ABE \cong \angle CDE$ and, thus, $\overline{AB} \parallel \overline{DC}$. Then use Theorem 36: *If one pair of opposite sides of a quadrilateral is both congruent and parallel, the quadrilateral is a parallelogram.*

- **Summary.** To prove that a quadrilateral is a parallelogram, prove that any one of the following statements is true:

1. Both pairs of opposite sides are parallel.
2. Both pairs of opposite sides are congruent.

3. One pair of opposite sides are both congruent and parallel.
4. Both pairs of opposite angles are congruent.
5. The diagonals bisect each other.

EXAMPLE

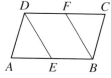

Given: *ABCD* is a parallelogram.
  E is the midpoint of $\overline{AB}$, *F* is the midpoint of $\overline{DC}$.

Prove: *EBFD* is a parallelogram.

Plan: Show that one pair of opposite sides, $\overline{EB}$ and $\overline{DF}$, are both congruent and parallel.

Statements	*Reasons*
1. *ABCD* is a parallelogram.	1. Given.
2. $\overline{AB} \cong \overline{DC}$.	2. Opposite sides of a parallelogram are congruent.
3. *E* is the midpoint of $\overline{AB}$, *F* is the midpoint of $\overline{DC}$.	3. Given.
4. $\overline{EB} \cong \overline{DF}$.	4. Halves of congruent segments are congruent.
5. $\overline{EB} \parallel \overline{DF}$.	5. A parallelogram is a quadrilateral in which two pairs of opposite sides are parallel.
6. *EBFD* is a parallelogram.	6. If one pair of opposite sides of a quadrilateral are both congruent and parallel, the quadrilateral is a parallelogram.

EXERCISES WITH OPEN-RESPONSE PROBLEMS

In 1–5, in each case, the *given* is marked on the figure. Tell why each quadrilateral *ABCD* is a parallelogram.

1.   **2.**   **3.**   **4.**   **5.**

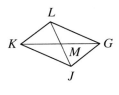

Ex. 6   **Ex. 7**   **Ex. 8**   **Ex. 9**

6. *Given:* ABCD is a quadrilateral, $\overline{AB} \cong \overline{CD}$, $\angle 1 \cong \angle 2$.
   Prove: ABCD is a parallelogram.
7. *Given:* PQRS is a quadrilateral, $\angle 1 \cong \angle 2$, $\angle 3 \cong \angle 4$.
   Prove: PQRS is a parallelogram.
8. *Given:* $\square ABCD$, $\overline{EAB}$, $\overline{DCF}$, $\overline{CF} \cong \overline{AE}$.
   Prove: EBFD is a parallelogram.
9. *Given:* In $\triangle GKL$, $\overline{LM}$ is a median; $\overline{LM}$ is extended to J so that $\overline{LM} \cong \overline{MJ}$; $\overline{JK}$ and $\overline{JG}$ are drawn.
   Prove: GJKL is a parallelogram.

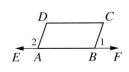

Ex. 10   **Ex. 11**   **Ex. 12**

10. *Given:* $\square ABCD$, $\overline{FDEC}$, $\overline{BE} \perp \overline{FC}$, $\overline{AF} \perp \overline{FC}$.
    Prove: ABEF is a parallelogram.
11. *Given:* PQRS is a parallelogram, $\overline{PT} \cong \overline{RM}$.
    Prove: TQMS is a parallelogram.
12. *Given:* $\overleftrightarrow{EABF}$, $\angle 2$ is supplementary to $\angle 1$, $\angle C \cong \angle 1$.
    Prove: ABCD is a parallelogram.
13. *Given:* $\square ABCD$ and $\square CDFE$.
    Prove: **a.** ABEF is a parallelogram.
    b. $\overline{FA} \cong \overline{EB}$ and $\overline{FA} \parallel \overline{EB}$.

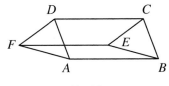

Ex. 13

14. *Prove:* The line segment joining the midpoints of two opposite sides of a parallelogram is parallel to the other two sides.

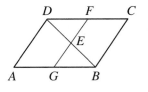

Ex. 15   **Ex. 16**   **Ex. 17**

15. *Given:* $\square ABCD$, E is the midpoint of $\overline{DC}$, F is the midpoint of $\overline{AB}$.
    Prove: $\overline{AE} \cong \overline{CF}$.
16. *Given:* $\square PQRS$, $\overline{PE} \perp \overline{SQ}$, $\overline{RF} \perp \overline{SQ}$.
    Prove: $\overline{SE} \cong \overline{QF}$.
17. *Given:* $\square ABCD$, $\overline{FG}$ bisects $\overline{DB}$.
    Prove: $\overline{DB}$ bisects $\overline{FG}$.

18. *Given:* $\overline{AC}$ is a diagonal in $\square ABCD$,
$\overline{AF} \cong \overline{CE}$.

Prove: $\overline{DE} \parallel \overline{BF}$.

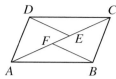

19. If *ABCD* is a parallelogram with $AB > AD$, and $\overline{AC}$ is a diagonal, prove that $m\angle DAC > m\angle CAB$.

20. The coordinates of three points in the coordinate plane are $A(-2, -3)$, $B(5, -3)$, $C(2, 2)$.

    a. Find the coordinates of *D* if *ABCD* is a parallelogram.

    b. Show that $\overline{BC} \parallel \overline{AD}$ and $\overline{AB} \parallel \overline{CD}$.

    c. Find the coordinates of D' if $ABD'C$ is a parallelogram.

    d. Show that $\overline{BD'} \parallel \overline{AC}$ and $\overline{AB} \parallel \overline{D'C}$.

7-4 THE RECTANGLE

- **DEFINITION.** A *rectangle* is a parallelogram one of whose angles is a right angle.

If one angle, $\angle A$, of a parallelogram *ABCD* is a right angle, then $\square ABCD$ is a rectangle.

Any side of a rectangle may be called the *base* of the rectangle. Thus, if side $\overline{AB}$ is taken as the base, then either consecutive side, $\overline{AD}$ or $\overline{BC}$, is called the *altitude* of the rectangle.

Since a rectangle is a special kind of parallelogram, a rectangle has *all the properties of a parallelogram*. In addition, we can prove two special properties for the rectangle.

- **THEOREM 39. All angles of a rectangle are right angles.**

Given: Rectangle *ABCD* with $\angle A$ a right angle.

Prove: $\angle B$, $\angle C$, and $\angle D$ are right angles.

Plan: Use Theorem 26: *If a line is perpendicular to one of two parallel lines, it is perpendicular to the other.* Then use the definition of perpendicular lines.

- **THEOREM 40. The diagonals of a rectangle are congruent.**

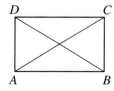

Given: *ABCD* is a rectangle.

Prove: $\overline{AC} \cong \overline{BD}$.

Plan: Prove $\triangle DAB \cong \triangle CBA$ by s.a.s. $\cong$ s.a.s.

Properties of a Rectangle

1. A rectangle has all the properties of a parallelogram.

2. A rectangle contains four right angles and is therefore equiangular.

3. The diagonals of a rectangle are congruent.

Methods of Proving That a Quadrilateral Is a Rectangle

We prove that a quadrilateral is a rectangle by showing that it has the special properties of a rectangle. For example:

- **THEOREM 41. If the diagonals of a parallelogram are congruent, the parallelogram is a rectangle.**

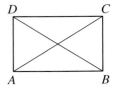

Given: Parallelogram $ABCD$.
$\overline{AC} \cong \overline{BD}$.

Prove: $ABCD$ is a rectangle.

Plan: Show that $\triangle DAB \cong \triangle CBA$ by s.s.s. $\cong$ s.s.s. Therefore, $\angle DAB \cong \angle CBA$. Then, use Corollary 34-3: *Two consecutive angles of a parallelogram are supplementary* (here, $\angle DAB$ and $\angle CBA$).

- **Summary.** To prove that a quadrilateral is a rectangle, prove that any one of the following statements is true:

1. The quadrilateral is a parallelogram with one right angle.

2. The quadrilateral is equiangular.

3. The quadrilateral is a parallelogram whose diagonals are congruent.

EXAMPLES

1. *Given:* $ABCD$ is a parallelogram.
$\overline{DE} \perp \overline{AB}, \overline{CF} \perp \overline{AB}$.

Prove: $DEFC$ is a rectangle.

Plan: Prove that $DEFC$ is a parallelogram that contains a right angle at E.

Statements	*Reasons*
1. $ABCD$ is a parallelogram.	1. Given.
2. $\overline{DC} \parallel \overline{AB}$.	2. A parallelogram is a quadrilateral in which two pairs of opposite sides are parallel.
3. $\overline{DE} \perp \overline{AB}, \overline{CF} \perp \overline{AB}$.	3. Given.
4. $\overline{DE} \parallel \overline{CF}$.	4. Two lines perpendicular to the same line are parallel.
5. $DEFC$ is a parallelogram.	5. Reason 2.
6. $\angle DEB$ is a right angle.	6. Definition of perpendicular lines.
7. $DEFC$ is a rectangle.	7. A rectangle is a parallelogram one of whose angles is a right angle.

2. The lengths of diagonals $\overline{PR}$ and $\overline{QS}$ of rectangle $PQRS$ can be represented by $3x - 7$ centimeters and $5x - 19$ centimeters, respectively. Find the length of each diagonal.

Solution   *The diagonals of a rectangle are congruent.*

$$3x - 7 = 5x - 19$$
$$-2x = -12$$
$$x = 6$$
$$PR = 3(6) - 7 = 11$$
$$QS = 5(6) - 19 = 11$$

Answer: The length of each diagonal is 11 centimeters.

EXERCISES WITH OPEN-RESPONSE PROBLEMS

1. In rectangle $ABCD$, $CB = 6$, $AB = 8$, and $AC = 10$.
Find the missing lengths:
a. AD **b.** CD **c.** EC **d.** AE
e. DE **f.** EB **g.** DB

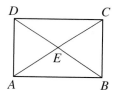

2. In rectangle $PQRS$, diagonals $\overline{PR}$ and $\overline{QS}$ meet at T. If $PT = 4$, find the length of:
a. $\overline{TR}$ **b.** $\overline{TQ}$ **c.** $\overline{PR}$ **d.** $\overline{QS}$

3. In **a** and **b**, the *given* is marked on the figure. Tell why each parallelogram $ABCD$ is a rectangle.

a.   **b.**

4. In quadrilateral $DEFG$, diagonals $\overline{DF}$ and $\overline{EG}$ are drawn. Let $DE = 5$, $FG = 5$, $EF = 12$, $DG = 12$, $EG = 13$, and $DF = 13$. Prove that $DEFG$ is a rectangle.

5. In $\square ABCD$, $AE = 7x - 1$, and $EC = 5x + 5$.
a. Find x.
b. Find AC.
c. If $DB = 10x + 10$, find DB.
d. What kind of parallelogram is $ABCD$? Explain your answer.

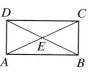

6. In rectangle $ABCD$, the length of diagonal $\overline{AC}$ is represented by $6x - 2$ and the length of diagonal $\overline{BD}$ is represented by $4x + 2$.
a. Find the value of x.   **b.** Find AC and BD.

7. In rectangle $ABCD$, diagonals $\overline{AC}$ and $\overline{BD}$ intersect in E. If $AE = 3x + y$, $BE = 4x - 2y$, and $CE = 20$, find x and y.

In 8–11, tell whether each argument is *valid* or *invalid*.

8. In a parallelogram, opposite sides are congruent.
   A rectangle is a parallelogram.
   Conclusion: In a rectangle, opposite sides are congruent.
9. In a parallelogram, the diagonals bisect each other.
   A rectangle is a parallelogram.
   Conclusion: In a rectangle, the diagonals bisect each other.
10. In a rectangle, the diagonals are congruent.
    A rectangle is a parallelogram.
    Conclusion: In a parallelogram, the diagonals are congruent.
11. All four angles of a rectangle are right angles.
    A rectangle is a parallelogram.
    Conclusion: All four angles of a parallelogram are right angles.

Ex. 12

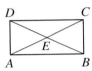

Ex. 13

12. *Given:* $ABCD$ is a rectangle, M is the midpoint of $\overline{AB}$.
    Prove: $\overline{DM} \cong \overline{CM}$.
13. *Given:* $ABCD$ is a rectangle, diagonals $\overline{AC}$ and $\overline{BD}$ intersect at E.
    Prove: $\triangle AEB$ is isosceles.

14. In rectangle $ABCD$, diagonals $\overline{BD}$ and $\overline{AC}$ are drawn. Prove that $\angle DBA \cong \angle CAB$.
15. *Given:* $\triangle ABC$, where $\angle ABC$ is a right angle and $\overline{BE}$ is the median drawn to $\overline{AC}$. Extend $\overline{BE}$ through E to point D so that $\overline{BE} \cong \overline{DE}$. Draw $\overline{AD}$ and $\overline{DC}$.
    Prove: $ABCD$ is a rectangle.
16. *Prove:* If the diagonals of a parallelogram are congruent, then the parallelogram is a rectangle.

17. Use an indirect method of proof to prove: If the diagonals of a parallelogram are not congruent, the parallelogram is *not* a rectangle.
18. In the coordinate plane, $A(-1, -2)$, $B(1, 2)$, $C(-1, 3)$, and $D(-3, -1)$ are the vertices of a quadrilateral.
    a. Find AB and CD.
    b. Find the slope of $\overline{AB}$ and the slope of $\overline{CD}$.
    c. What does the answer to part **b** tell you about $\overline{AB}$ and $\overline{CD}$?
    d. Based on the answers to **a** and **b**, which theorem proves that $ABCD$ is a parallelogram?

e. Find the slope of $\overline{AD}$.

f. What do the answers to parts **b** and **e** tell you about $\overline{AB}$ and $\overline{AD}$?

g. Based on the answers to parts **d** and **f**, which definition proves that *ABCD* is a rectangle?

7-5   THE RHOMBUS

- **DEFINITION.** A *rhombus* is a parallelogram that has two congruent consecutive sides.

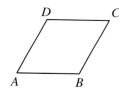

If the consecutive sides $\overline{AB}$ and $\overline{AD}$ of parallelogram *ABCD* are congruent (that is, if $\overline{AB} \cong \overline{AD}$), then $\square ABCD$ is a rhombus.

Since a rhombus is a special kind of parallelogram, a rhombus has *all the properties of a parallelogram*. In addition, we can prove three special properties for the rhombus.

- **THEOREM 42. All sides of a rhombus are congruent.**

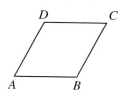

Given: *ABCD* is a rhombus with $\overline{AB} \cong \overline{AD}$.

Prove: $\overline{AB} \cong \overline{BC} \cong \overline{CD} \cong \overline{DA}$.

Plan: Use Corollary 34-1: *Opposite sides of a parallelogram are congruent*, and the transitive property.

- **THEOREM 43. The diagonals of a rhombus are perpendicular to each other.**

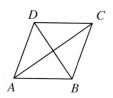

Given: Rhombus *ABCD*.

Prove: $\overline{AC} \perp \overline{BD}$.

Plan: Use Theorem 42: *All sides of a rhombus are congruent.*
Then use Theorem 15: *If two points are each equidistant from the endpoints of a line segment, the points determine the perpendicular bisector of the line segment.*

- **THEOREM 44: The diagonals of a rhombus bisect its angles.**

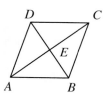

Given: Rhombus *ABCD*.

Prove: $\overline{AC}$ bisects $\angle DAB$ and $\angle DCB$.
$\overline{DB}$ bisects $\angle CDA$ and $\angle CBA$.

Plan: Show that $\triangle ABE \cong \triangle CBE \cong \triangle CDE \cong \triangle ADE$ by s.s.s. $\cong$ s.s.s.
Then $\angle ABE \cong \angle CBE$, $\angle CDE \cong \angle ADE$, $\angle DCE \cong \angle BCE$,
and $\angle DAE \cong \angle BAE$.

Properties of a Rhombus

1. A rhombus has all the properties of a parallelogram.

2. A rhombus is equilateral.

3. The diagonals of a rhombus are perpendicular to each other.

4. The diagonals of a rhombus bisect its angles.

Methods of Proving That a Quadrilateral Is a Rhombus

We prove that a quadrilateral is a rhombus by showing that it has the special properties of a rhombus. For example:

● **THEOREM 45. If a quadrilateral is equilateral, then it is a rhombus.**

Given: Quadrilateral $ABCD$.
$\overline{AB} \cong \overline{BC} \cong \overline{CD} \cong \overline{DA}$.

Prove: $ABCD$ is a rhombus.

Plan: Use Theorem 35: *If both pairs of opposite sides of a quadrilateral are congruent, the quadrilateral is a parallelogram.* Then use the definition of a rhombus.

● **THEOREM 46. If the diagonals of a parallelogram are perpendicular to each other, the parallelogram is a rhombus.**

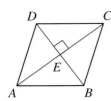

Given: Parallelogram $ABCD$.
$\overline{AC} \perp \overline{BD}$.

Prove: $ABCD$ is a rhombus.

Plan: Show that $\triangle AEB \cong \triangle AED$ by s.a.s. $\cong$ s.a.s.
Then use the fact that corresponding parts of congruent triangles are congruent to show that parallelogram $ABCD$ has two congruent consecutive sides $(\overline{AB} \cong \overline{AD})$.

● **Summary.** To prove that a quadrilateral is a rhombus, prove that any one of the following statements is true:

1. The quadrilateral is a parallelogram with two congruent consecutive sides.

2. The quadrilateral is equilateral.

3. The quadrilateral is a parallelogram whose diagonals are perpendicular to each other.

4. The quadrilateral is a parallelogram, and a diagonal bisects the angles whose vertices it joins.

EXAMPLES

1. *PQRS* is a rhombus. The shorter diagonal, $\overline{PR}$, measures 12 units and m∠*PQR* = 60. Find the length of a side of the rhombus.

Solution   Since all sides of a rhombus are congruent, we know that $\overline{PQ} \cong \overline{RQ}$. Thus, △*PQR* is isosceles and its base angles are equal in measure.

$$\text{Let m}\angle PRQ = \text{m}\angle RPQ = x.$$
$$x + x + 60 = 180$$
$$2x + 60 = 180$$
$$2x = 120$$
$$x = 60$$

Therefore, m∠*PRQ* = 60, m∠*RPQ* = 60, and m∠*PQR* = 60. Since an equiangular triangle is also equilateral, if *PR* = 12, then *PQ* = 12 and *RQ* = 12.

Answer: The length of any side of rhombus *PQRS* is 12.

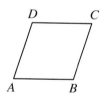

2. *Given:* *ABCD* is a parallelogram.
   $AB = 2x + 1, DC = 3x - 11, AD = x + 13.$

   Show: *ABCD* is a rhombus.

   Plan: Show that two consecutive sides are congruent ($\overline{AB} \cong \overline{AD}$).

Solution   *Step 1.* Since *ABCD* is a parallelogram, opposite sides are equal in length.

$$DC = AB$$
$$3x - 11 = 2x + 1$$
$$3x - 2x = 1 + 11$$
$$x = 12$$

Step 2. Substitute $x = 12$ to find the lengths of sides $\overline{AB}$ and $\overline{AD}$:

$$AB = 2x + 1 = 2(12) + 1 = 25$$
$$AD = x + 13 = (12) + 13 = 25$$

Thus, $\overline{AB} \cong \overline{AD}$. Since *ABCD* is a parallelogram in which two consecutive sides are congruent, *ABCD* is a rhombus.

EXERCISES WITH OPEN-RESPONSE PROBLEMS

In 1–5, refer to rhombus $ABCD$, where diagonals $\overline{AC}$ and $\overline{BD}$ intersect at E. In each case, tell which one of the four given statements is *false*.

1. (1) $\overline{AB} \cong \overline{DC}$ (2) $\overline{AB} \cong \overline{BC}$ (3) $\overline{AB} \cong \overline{AC}$ (4) $\overline{AB} \cong \overline{AD}$

2. (1) $\overline{AC} \perp \overline{DB}$ (2) $\overline{AC} \cong \overline{DB}$
   (3) $\angle DAB \cong \angle DCB$ (4) $\angle ADB \cong \angle CDB$

3. (1) $AE = EC$ (2) $DE = EB$ (3) $AE = DE$ (4) $\overline{AE} \perp \overline{DE}$

4. (1) $\angle DEA \cong \angle DEC$ (2) $m\angle DEA = 90$
   (3) $\angle DCA \cong \angle BAC$ (4) $m\angle DCA = 90$

5. (1) $\triangle ADC$ is isosceles.   (2) $\triangle ADE$ is a right triangle.
   (3) $\triangle ADB$ is a right triangle.   (4) $\triangle ADE \cong \triangle ABE$.

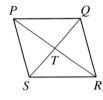

Ex. 1–5

6. In $\square PQRS$, $PQ = x + 4$ and $SR = 3x - 36$.
   a. Find x.   **b.** Find PQ and SR.
   c. If $QR = 2x - 16$, show that $PQRS$ is a rhombus.

7. In $\square PQRS$, $m\angle SQP = 4x - 2$ and $m\angle QSR = 3x + 6$.
   a. Find x.   **b.** Find $m\angle SQP$ and $m\angle QSR$.
   c. If $m\angle QPT = 8x - 4$, show that $PQRS$ is a rhombus.

Ex. 6–7

8. If the length of the shorter diagonal, $\overline{AC}$, of rhombus $ABCD$ is 7 and $m\angle ABC = 60$, find the length of a side of the rhombus.

9. In rhombus $ABCD$, $AB = 8$ and $m\angle ABC = 120$. Find the length of the shorter diagonal $\overline{BD}$.

In 10–13, tell whether each argument is *valid* or *invalid*.

10. In a parallelogram, opposite sides are parallel.
    A rhombus is a parallelogram.
    Conclusion: In a rhombus, opposite sides are parallel.

11. In a rhombus, diagonals are perpendicular to each other.
    A rhombus is a parallelogram.
    Conclusion: In a parallelogram, diagonals are perpendicular to each other.

12. The diagonals of a rhombus bisect its angles.
    A rhombus is a parallelogram.
    Conclusion: The diagonals of a parallelogram bisect its angles.

13. Opposite angles of a parallelogram are congruent.
    A rhombus is a parallelogram.
    Conclusion: Opposite angles of a rhombus are congruent.

14. Prove that, when the diagonals of a rhombus intersect, four congruent triangles are formed.

15. In rhombus $ABCD$, diagonal $\overline{BD} \cong$ side $\overline{AB}$.
    a. Prove that $\triangle ADB$ is equilateral.
    b. Find the measure of each angle of the rhombus.

16. *Prove:* If a quadrilateral is equilateral, it is a rhombus.

17. *Prove:* If the diagonals of a parallelogram are perpendicular to each other, the parallelogram is a rhombus.

Ex. 18

Ex. 19

Ex. 20

18. *Given:* $ABCD$ is a rhombus, $\overline{AE} \cong \overline{CE}$.
   Prove: $\angle ADE \cong \angle CDE$.

19. *Given:* $AECB$ is a rhombus, $\overline{AED}$, $\overline{FEC}$, $\angle FAB \cong \angle DCB$.
   Prove: **a.** $\triangle FAE \cong \triangle DCE$. **b.** $\overline{FE} \cong \overline{DE}$.

20. *Given:* $\overrightarrow{BF}$ bisects $\angle CBA$, $\overline{DE} \parallel \overrightarrow{BA}$, $\overrightarrow{GE} \parallel \overrightarrow{BC}$.
   Prove: $GEDB$ is a rhombus.

21. Use an indirect method of proof to prove: If a diagonal of a parallelogram does not bisect the angles through whose vertices the diagonal is drawn, the parallelogram is *not* a rhombus.

22. If $ABCD$ is a rhombus and m$\angle B >$ m$\angle A$, prove that $AC > BD$. (*Hint:* Use one of the four congruent triangles formed by the diagonals.)

23. In the coordinate plane, $A(-1, 0)$, $B(3, -3)$, $C(3, 2)$, and $D(-1, 5)$ are the vertices of a quadrilateral. $\overline{AC}$ and $\overline{BD}$ intersect at $M(1, 1)$.
   a. Show that $\overline{AC}$ and $\overline{BD}$ bisect each other.
   b. Based on the answer to part **a**, which theorem proves that $ABCD$ is a parallelogram?
   c. Show that $\overline{AC} \perp \overline{BD}$.
   d. Based on the answers to parts **b** and **c**, which theorem proves that $ABCD$ is a rhombus?

7-6 THE SQUARE

- **DEFINITION.** A *square* is a rectangle that has two congruent consecutive sides.

   If consecutive sides $\overline{AB}$ and $\overline{AD}$ of rectangle $ABCD$ are congruent (that is, if $\overline{AB} \cong \overline{AD}$), then rectangle $ABCD$ is a square.

- **THEOREM 47. A square is an equilateral quadrilateral.**

   Given: $ABCD$ is a square with $\overline{AB} \cong \overline{BC}$.

   Prove: $\overline{AB} \cong \overline{BC} \cong \overline{CD} \cong \overline{DA}$.

   Plan: Use Corollary 34-1: *Opposite sides of a parallelogram are congruent*, and the transitive property.

● **THEOREM 48. A square is a rhombus.**

Given: Square *ABCD*.

Prove: *ABCD* is a rhombus.

Plan: Use Theorem 47: *A square is an equilateral quadrilateral.* Then use Theorem 45: *If a quadrilateral is equilateral, then it is a rhombus.*

Properties of a Square

1. A square has all the properties of a rectangle.

2. A square has all the properties of a rhombus.

Methods of Proving That a Quadrilateral Is a Square

We prove that a quadrilateral is a square by showing that it has the special properties of a square. For example:

● **THEOREM 49. If one of the angles of a rhombus is a right angle, then the rhombus is a square.**

Given: *ABCD* is a rhombus with ∠*A* a right angle.

Prove: *ABCD* is a square.

Plan: Show that *ABCD* is a rectangle and that $\overline{AB} \cong \overline{BC}$.

● **Summary.** To prove that a quadrilateral is a square, prove either of the following statements:

1. The quadrilateral is a rectangle in which two consecutive sides are congruent.

2. The quadrilateral is a rhombus one of whose angles is a right angle.

EXAMPLES

1. In the coordinate plane, $A(4, -2)$, $B(5, 5)$, $C(-2, 6)$, and $D(-3, -1)$ are the vertices of a parallelogram.
   a. Find *AC* and *BD*.
   b. Based on the answer to part **a**, which theorem proves that *ABCD* is a rectangle?
   c. Find *AB* and *BC*.
   d. Based on the answers to parts **b** and **c**, what definition proves that *ABCD* is a square?

Solutions **a.** $AC = \sqrt{(-2 - 4)^2 + (6 - (-2))^2}$
$$= \sqrt{(-6)^2 + 8^2} = \sqrt{36 + 64} = \sqrt{100} = 10$$
$$BD = \sqrt{(-3 - 5)^2 + (-1 - 5)^2}$$
$$= \sqrt{(-8)^2 + (-6)^2} = \sqrt{64 + 36} = \sqrt{100} = 10$$

Answer: $AC = BD = 10$.

b. The diagonals of *ABCD* are congruent.

Answer: Theorem 41: *If the diagonals of a parallelogram are congruent, the parallelogram is a rectangle.*

c. $AB = \sqrt{(5-4)^2 + (5-(-2))^2} = \sqrt{(1)^2 + 7^2} = \sqrt{1+49} = \sqrt{50}$

$BC = \sqrt{(-2-5)^2 + (6-5)^2} = \sqrt{(-7)^2 + (1)^2} = \sqrt{49+1} = \sqrt{50}$

Answer: $AB = BC = \sqrt{50}$.

d. *Answer:* A square is a rectangle that has two congruent consecutive sides.

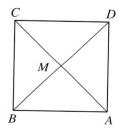

2. *Given:* Quadrilateral *ABCD*.
$\overline{AM} \cong \overline{MC}, \overline{DM} \cong \overline{MB}, \overline{AB} \cong \overline{AD}$, and $\angle ABC$ is a right angle.

Prove: *ABCD* is a square.

Plan: First prove that *ABCD* is a rectangle. Then use the fact that $\overline{AB} \cong \overline{AD}$ to show that rectangle *ABCD* is a square.

Statements	*Reasons*
1. $\overline{AM} \cong \overline{MC}, \overline{DM} \cong \overline{MB}$.	1. Given.
2. *ABCD* is a parallelogram.	2. If the diagonals of a quadrilateral bisect each other, the quadrilateral is a parallelogram.
3. $\angle ABC$ is a right angle.	3. Given.
4. *ABCD* is a rectangle.	4. A rectangle is a parallelogram one of whose angles is a right angle.
5. $\overline{AB} \cong \overline{AD}$.	5. Given.
6. *ABCD* is a square	6. A square is a rectangle that has two congruent consecutive sides.

EXERCISES WITH OPEN-RESPONSE PROBLEMS

Exercises 1–4 refer to square *ABCD* with diagonal $\overline{BD}$. In each case, tell which statement is *false*.

1. (1) $\overline{AB} \cong \overline{BC}$ (2) $\overline{AB} \perp \overline{BC}$
    (3) $\overline{AB} \cong \overline{BD}$ (4) $\overline{AB} \cong \overline{CD}$

2. (1) $\angle 1 \cong \angle 2$ (2) $\angle 2 \cong \angle 3$
    (3) $\angle 1 \cong \angle 3$ (4) $\angle A \cong \angle 4$

3. (1) $\overline{AB} \perp \overline{AD}$ (2) $\angle A \cong \angle CBA$
    (3) $\overline{BC} \parallel \overline{AD}$ (4) $\overline{BD} \perp \overline{AD}$

4. (1) $\triangle ABD$ is isosceles.   (2) $\triangle ABD$ is equilateral.
    (3) $\triangle ABD$ is a right triangle.   (4) $\triangle ABD \cong \triangle CDB$.

Ex. 1–4

In 5–9, tell whether each conclusion is *valid* or *invalid*.

5. In a rhombus, all sides are congruent.
A square is a rhombus.
Conclusion: In a square, all sides are congruent.

6. The diagonal of a parallelogram separates the parallelogram into two congruent triangles.
A square is a parallelogram.
Conclusion: The diagonal of a square separates the square into two congruent triangles.

7. In a square, all angles are right angles.
A square is a rhombus.
Conclusion: In a rhombus, all angles are right angles.

8. If a quadrilateral is a square, then it is a rhombus.
If a quadrilateral is a rhombus, then it is a parallelogram.
Conclusion: If a quadrilateral is a square, then it is a parallelogram.

9. A square is equilateral.
A square is a rectangle.
Conclusion: A rectangle is equilateral.

10. In square $ABCD$, diagonal $\overline{AC}$ is drawn. Find m$\angle ACB$ and m$\angle DCA$.

11. *Prove:* The diagonals of a square are perpendicular to each other.

12. *Prove:* The diagonals of a square divide the square into four congruent isosceles triangles.

13. *Prove:* If the midpoints of the sides of a square are joined in order, another square is formed.

14. *Given:* $PQRS$ is a rectangle, $\overline{QR} \cong \overline{RS}$.   **15.** *Given:* $ABCD$ is a rhombus, $\overline{CD} \perp \overline{DA}$.
Prove: $PQRS$ is a square.   *Prove:* $ABCD$ is a square.

16. *Given:* $\triangle ABC$ is an isosceles right triangle; $\angle ABC$ is a right angle; $\overline{BA} \cong \overline{BC}$; $\overline{BM}$, a median of $\triangle ABC$, is extended to D so that $\overline{BM} \cong \overline{DM}$; $\overline{DC}$ and $\overline{DA}$ are drawn.
Prove: $ABCD$ is a square.

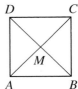

17. In the coordinate plane, $A(1, -4)$, $B(3, 0)$, $C(-1, 2)$, and $D(-3, -2)$ are the vertices of a quadrilateral.
   a. Show that $AB = BC = CD = DA$.
   b. Based on the answer to part **a**, what theorem proves that $ABCD$ is a rhombus?
   c. Show that $\overline{AB} \perp \overline{BC}$.
   d. Based on the answer to part **c**, what theorem proves that the rhombus is a square?

18. The diagonals of square $ABCD$ intersect at M. Another square, $PQRS$, is placed so that P is at M and Q is on $\overleftrightarrow{MA}$ but not necessarily at A.
   a. Will S lie on $\overleftrightarrow{MB}$? Explain your answer.
   b. If Q lies on a point on $\overline{MA}$, which of the following is true? Explain your answer.
      (1) $PQ < AB$ (2) $PQ = AB$ (3) $PQ > AB$
   c. If $PQ = AB$, will the midpoint of $\overline{PQ}$ lie on A? Explain your answer.

7-7 THE TRAPEZOID

- **DEFINITION.** A *trapezoid* is a quadrilateral in which two and only two sides are parallel.

If $\overline{AB} \parallel \overline{DC}$ and $\overline{AD}$ is not parallel to $\overline{BC}$, then quadrilateral $ABCD$ is a trapezoid. The parallel sides, $\overline{AB}$ and $\overline{DC}$, are called the *bases* of the trapezoid; the nonparallel sides, $\overline{AD}$ and $\overline{BC}$, are called the *legs* of the trapezoid.

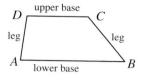

The Isosceles Trapezoid and Its Properties

- **DEFINITION.** An *isosceles trapezoid* is a trapezoid in which the nonparallel sides are congruent.

If $\overline{QT} \cong \overline{RS}$ and $\overline{TS} \parallel \overline{QR}$, then $QRST$ is an isosceles trapezoid. The angles at the ends of a base are called *base angles*. Here, $\angle Q$ and $\angle R$ are one pair of base angles because they are at the ends of base $\overline{QR}$. Also, $\angle T$ and $\angle S$ are a second pair of base angles because they are at the ends of base $\overline{TS}$.

Methods of Proving That a Quadrilateral Is an Isosceles Trapezoid

We prove that a quadrilateral is an isosceles trapezoid by showing that it has the special properties of an isosceles trapezoid: Only two sides are parallel; the nonparallel sides are congruent.

We may also prove special theorems for an isosceles trapezoid.

- **THEOREM 50. If a trapezoid is isosceles, then the base angles are congruent, and conversely.**

Conditional

Given: Isosceles trapezoid $QRST$ with $\overline{TQ} \cong \overline{SR}$.

Prove: $\angle Q \cong \angle R$.

Plan: Draw $\overline{SP} \parallel \overline{TQ}$ to form $\square SPQT$. Thus, $\overline{SP} \cong \overline{TQ}$. Since $\overline{TQ} \cong \overline{SR}$ is given, then $\overline{SP} \cong \overline{SR}$ by the transitive property. Therefore, in $\triangle PSR$, $\angle SPR \cong \angle R$. Also, $\angle SPR \cong \angle Q$ because they are corresponding angles of parallel lines. Use the transitive property again to prove that $\angle Q \cong \angle R$.

Converse

Given: Trapezoid $QRST$ with $\angle Q \cong \angle R$.

Prove: $\overline{QT} \cong \overline{RS}$.

Plan: Draw $\overline{TA} \perp \overline{QR}$ and $\overline{SB} \perp \overline{QR}$. Since parallel lines are everywhere equidistant, $\overline{TA} \cong \overline{SB}$. First, prove $\triangle QTA \cong \triangle RSB$ by a.a.s. $\cong$ a.a.s. Then, by corresponding parts of congruent triangles, $\overline{QT} \cong \overline{RS}$.

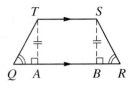

- **THEOREM 51. If a trapezoid is isosceles, then the diagonals are congruent, and conversely.**

Conditional

Given: Trapezoid $ABCD$ with $\overline{AD} \cong \overline{BC}$.

Prove: $\overline{AC} \cong \overline{BD}$.

Plan: Prove $\triangle DAB \cong \triangle CBA$ by s.a.s. $\cong$ s.a.s. Then, by corresponding parts of congruent triangles, $\overline{AC} \cong \overline{BD}$.

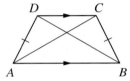

Converse

Given: Trapezoid $ABCD$ with $\overline{AC} \cong \overline{BD}$.

Prove: $\overline{AD} \cong \overline{BC}$.

Plan: Draw $\overline{DE}$, the altitude of $\triangle ADB$, and $\overline{CF}$, the altitude of $\triangle ACB$. Prove $\triangle ACF \cong \triangle BDE$ by hy. leg $\cong$ hy. leg. Therefore, $\angle CAB \cong \angle DBA$. Now, prove that $\triangle ACB \cong \triangle BDA$ by s.a.s. $\cong$ s.a.s. Then, by corresponding parts of congruent triangles, $\overline{AD} \cong \overline{BC}$.

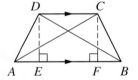

EXAMPLE

Given: Quadrilateral $ABCD$.
$m\angle ABD = 30$, $m\angle BDC = 30$,
$m\angle ADB = 40$, $m\angle BCD = 70$.
$AD = x + 5$, $BC = 3x - 21$.

a. Show that $ABCD$ is an isosceles trapezoid.
b. Find lengths AD and BC.

Solutions **a.** (1) Since $m\angle ABD = 30$ and $m\angle BDC = 30$, we know that $\overline{AB}$ and $\overline{DC}$ are cut by transversal $\overline{DB}$ to form congruent alternate interior angles. Thus, $\overline{AB} \parallel \overline{DC}$.

(2) Since m∠*ADC* = m∠*ADB* + m∠*BDC* = 40 + 30 = 70, and m∠*BCD* = 70, the base angles of *ABCD* are equal in measure.

(*Note.* Since ∠*BCD* and ∠*ADC* are interior angles on the same side of transversal $\overline{DC}$ and they are *not* supplementary, we know $\overline{AD} \not\parallel \overline{BC}$.)

Thus, *ABCD* is an isosceles trapezoid.

b. The nonparallel sides are congruent in an isosceles trapezoid.

Thus: *AD* = *BC*   Substitute $x = 13$ to find *AD* and *BC*:

$x + 5 = 3x - 21$ $AD = x + 5 = (13) + 5 = 18$

$5 + 21 = 3x - x$ $BC = 3x - 21 = 3(13) - 21 = 39 - 21 = 18$

$26 = 2x$

$13 = x$

Answer: *AD* = 18 and *BC* = 18.

EXERCISES WITH OPEN-RESPONSE PROBLEMS

In 1–6, *ABCD* is an isosceles trapezoid, $\overline{AB} \parallel \overline{DC}$, and $\overline{AD} \cong \overline{BC}$.

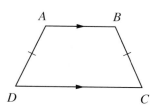

Ex. 1–6

1. If m∠*ADC* = 80, find: **a.** m∠*BCD*
   b. m∠*DAB*
2. If *AD* = 3x + 4 and *BC* = 22, find the value of *x*.
3. If *AD* = 2y − 7 and *BC* = y + 5, find *AD*.
4. If m∠*ADC* = 4x − 5 and m∠*BCD* = 3x + 15, find the value of *x*.
5. If m∠*ADC* = 4x + 20 and m∠*DAB* = 8x − 20, find:
   a. the value of *x*   **b.** m∠*ADC*   **c.** m∠*DAB*   **d.** m∠*BCD*   **e.** m∠*ABC*
6. If *AD* = 2x + y, *BC* = 7y − 2x, and x = 3, find *AD*.

In 7–12, answer *true* or *false* in each case.

7. In an isosceles trapezoid, nonparallel sides are congruent.
8. In a trapezoid, at least two sides must be congruent.
9. In a trapezoid, base angles are always congruent.
10. The diagonals of a trapezoid are congruent only if the nonparallel sides of the trapezoid are congruent.
11. A trapezoid is a special kind of parallelogram.
12. In a trapezoid, two consecutive angles that are not angles on the same base must be supplementary.

In 13–16, *ABCD* is a trapezoid with $\overline{AB} \parallel \overline{DC}$. When *ABCD* is isosceles, sides $\overline{AD}$ and $\overline{BC}$ are marked as congruent. In each case, find the measures of the angles indicated by arcs in the diagram.

13.
14.
15.
16.

Ex. 17

Ex. 18

Ex. 19

17. *Given:* *ABCD* is an isosceles trapezoid, $\overline{DC} \parallel \overline{AB}$, $\overleftrightarrow{EABF}$.
   Prove: $\angle 1 \cong \angle 2$.

18. *Given:* $\overline{ADE}$, $\overline{BCE}$, $\overline{AE} \cong \overline{BE}$, $\overline{DE} \cong \overline{CE}$, $\overline{DC} \parallel \overline{AB}$.
   Prove: *ABCD* is an isosceles trapezoid.

19. *Given:* *ABCD* is a parallelogram, $\overline{ABE}$, $\angle CBE \cong \angle CEB$.
   Prove: **a.** $\angle DAE \cong \angle CEA$.   **b.** *AECD* is an isosceles trapezoid.

20. Prove by an indirect method of proof: If a quadrilateral is a trapezoid, then its diagonals cannot bisect each other.

7-8 AREAS

Area Formulas

In Math A, the formulas for the areas of certain polygons were presented.

1. Rectangle:	2. Square:	3. Parallelogram:
$A = bh$ or $A = \ell w$	$A = s^2$	$A = bh$

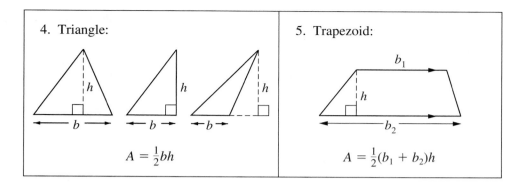

4. Triangle:

$$A = \tfrac{1}{2}bh$$

5. Trapezoid:

$$A = \tfrac{1}{2}(b_1 + b_2)h$$

Since a rhombus is a parallelogram, it is possible to find the area of a rhombus by using this formula: Area = base · height, or $A = bh$. However, another formula may be developed for the area of a rhombus.

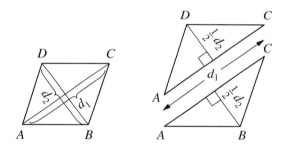

In rhombus $ABCD$, the length of diagonal $\overline{AC}$ is d_1, and the length of diagonal $\overline{BD}$ is d_2. The diagonals of a rhombus are perpendicular bisectors to each other. Therefore, rhombus $ABCD$ can be separated into two congruent triangles, $\triangle ACD$ and $\triangle ACB$, each with a base of d_1, and an altitude of $\tfrac{1}{2}d_2$. Since the area of the rhombus is equal to the sum of the areas of the two triangles, we can say:

Area of rhombus $ABCD$ = area of $\triangle ACD$ + area of $\triangle ACB$

$$= \tfrac{1}{2} \text{ base} \cdot \text{height} + \tfrac{1}{2} \text{ base} \cdot \text{height}$$

$$= \tfrac{1}{2}(d_1) \cdot \left(\tfrac{1}{2}d_2\right) \quad + \tfrac{1}{2}(d_1) \cdot \left(\tfrac{1}{2}d_2\right)$$

$$= \tfrac{1}{4}d_1 d_2 \qquad\qquad + \tfrac{1}{4}d_1 d_2$$

$$= \tfrac{1}{2}d_1 d_2$$

Therefore, we add to our list the formula for the area of a rhombus:

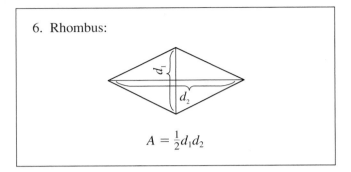

6. Rhombus:

$$A = \frac{1}{2}d_1 d_2$$

Areas and Coordinates

To find the areas of polygons in coordinate geometry, we use the area formulas. When the base of a figure is parallel to one axis, the altitude is parallel to the other axis.

EXAMPLES

1. Points $A(-4, -2)$, $B(2, -2)$, $C(4, 3)$, and $D(-2, 3)$ are the vertices of quadrilateral $ABCD$.
   a. Plot these points on graph paper, and draw the quadrilateral.
   b. What kind of quadrilateral is $ABCD$?
   c. Find the area of quadrilateral $ABCD$.

Solutions **a.** See graph.

   b. (1) $\overline{AB}$ is parallel to $\overline{DC}$.
      (2) $AB = 6$, and $DC = 6$.
         Hence, $\overline{AB} \cong \overline{DC}$.
      (3) Since opposite sides $\overline{AB}$ and $\overline{DC}$ are both parallel and congruent, quadrilateral $ABCD$ is a parallelogram.

   c. (1) In $\square ABCD$, draw altitude $\overline{DE}$ to side $\overline{AB}$. Here, $DE = 5$.
      (2) Area of $\square ABCD$
         $= \text{base} \times \text{altitude}$
         $= AB \times DE = (6)(5) = 30$

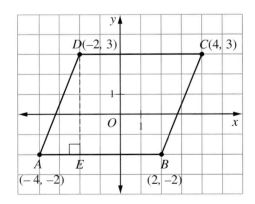

Answers: **a.** See graph.
      b. Parallelogram
      c. 30 square units

2. The vertices of rhombus $ABCD$ are $A(1, 5)$, $B(-1, 2)$, $C(1, -1)$, and $D(3, 2)$. Graph rhombus $ABCD$ and find its area.

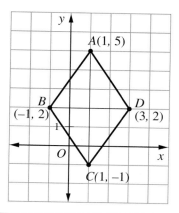

Solution (1) Find the lengths of the diagonals of $ABCD$.
$d_1 = AC = 6$, $d_2 = BD = 4$.

(2) Area of rhombus $= \frac{1}{2} d_1 d_2$

$= \frac{1}{2} \cdot 6 \cdot 4$

$= 12$

Answer: The area of rhombus $ABCD$ is 12 square units.

---

3. Find the area of a triangle whose vertices are $A(-2, 3)$, $B(1, 5)$, and $C(4, 2)$.

Solution METHOD 1. Enclose the figure in a rectangle.

Through the uppermost and lowermost points, here B and C, draw lines EF and CD parallel to the x-axis. Through the points farthest to the left and farthest to the right, here A and C, draw lines DE and CF parallel to the y-axis. Thus, rectangle $CDEF$ is formed.

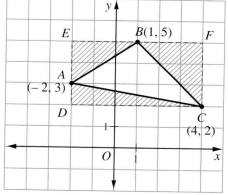

The area of $\triangle ABC$ is equal to the area of rectangle $CDEF$ minus the sum of the areas of right triangles CDA, BEA, and BFC.

Since each side of rectangle $CDEF$ is parallel to one of the axes, the legs of each right triangle are also parallel to these axes. By counting units, base $DC = 6$ and height $DE = 3$ for the rectangle. The legs of the right triangles have these measures: $DC = 6$, $DA = 1$, $BE = 3$, $EA = 2$, $BF = 3$ and $FC = 3$.

(1) Area of rectangle $CDEF = DC \times DE = 6 \times 3 = 18$

(2) Area of right triangle $CDA = \frac{1}{2} DC \times DA = \frac{1}{2}(6)(1) = 3$

(3) Area of right triangle $BEA = \frac{1}{2} BE \times EA = \frac{1}{2}(3)(2) = 3$

(4) Area of right triangle $BFC = \frac{1}{2} BF \times FC = \frac{1}{2}(3)(3) = 4.5$

(5) Area of $\triangle ABC = \left(\begin{array}{c} \text{area of} \\ \text{rect. } CDEF \end{array} \right) - \left(\begin{array}{ccc} \text{area of} & \text{area of} & \text{area of} \\ \triangle CDA & + \triangle BEA & + \triangle BFC \end{array} \right)$

$= \qquad 18 \qquad - (\quad 3 \ + \ 3 \ + \ 4.5 \ )$

$= \qquad 18 \qquad - \quad 10.5$

$= \qquad 7.5$

METHOD 2: Create trapezoids.

Draw a series of lines parallel to one of the axes. Here, $\overleftrightarrow{AD} \parallel \overleftrightarrow{BE} \parallel \overleftrightarrow{CF} \parallel$ the y-axis. Thus, $\overline{AD}$, $\overline{BE}$, and $\overline{CF}$ are the bases of trapezoids $ADEB$, $BEFC$, and $DACF$.

The area of $\triangle ABC$ is equal to the sum of the areas of trapezoids $ADEB$ and $BEFC$ minus the area of trapezoid $DACF$.

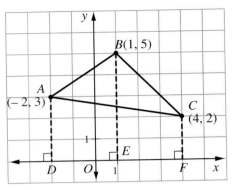

(1) Area of $ADEB = \frac{1}{2}(DE)(DA + EB) = \frac{1}{2}(3)(3 + 5) = \frac{1}{2}(3)(8) = 12$

(2) Area of $BEFC = \frac{1}{2}(EF)(EB + FC) = \frac{1}{2}(3)(5 + 2) = \frac{1}{2}(3)(7) = 10.5$

(3) Area of $DACF = \frac{1}{2}(DF)(AD + FC) = \frac{1}{2}(6)(3 + 2) = \frac{1}{2}(6)(5) = 15$

(4) Area of $\triangle ABC = \left(\begin{array}{c}\text{area of} \\ ADEB\end{array} + \begin{array}{c}\text{area of} \\ BEFC\end{array}\right) - \left(\begin{array}{c}\text{area of} \\ DACF\end{array}\right)$

$$= (12 \quad + 10.5 \quad) - \quad 15$$

$$= \quad 22.5 \quad\quad - \quad 15$$

$$= \quad 7.5$$

Answer: The area of $\triangle ABC$ is 7.5 square units.

EXERCISES WITH OPEN-RESPONSE PROBLEMS

1. Find the area of a rectangle whose vertices are:
   a. $(0, 0), (8, 0), (0, 5), (8, 5)$ **b.** $(-2, 3), (4, 3), (-2, 8), (4, 8)$
2. Find the area of a parallelogram whose vertices are:
   a. $(0, 0), (4, 0), (2, 3), (6, 3)$ **b.** $(-2, 8), (-3, 4), (5, 8), (4, 4)$
3. Find the area of a triangle whose vertices are:
   a. $(0, 0), (12, 0), (2, 8)$ **b.** $(0, 8), (0, -3), (4, 5)$
   c. $(2, -2), (8, -2), (4, -6)$ **d.** $(0, 0), (6, 0), (0, 5)$
4. Find the area of a trapezoid whose vertices are:
   a. $(0, 0), (12, 0), (2, 6), (7, 6)$ **b.** $(0, 4), (0, -8), (3, 1), (3, -4)$
5. Points $Q(8, 2), R(14, 6), S(4, 6), T(-2, 2)$ are the vertices of quadrilateral $QRST$.
   a. Plot these points on graph paper, and draw the quadrilateral.
   b. What kind of quadrilateral is $QRST$?   **c.** Find the area of quadrilateral $QRST$.
6. Points $C(1, -4), D(9, -4), E(9, 2), F(1, 3)$ are the vertices of quadrilateral $CDEF$.
   a. Plot these points on graph paper, and draw the quadrilateral.
   b. Find the lengths of $\overline{CD}$, $\overline{DE}$, and diagonal $\overline{CE}$.
   c. What kind of quadrilateral is $CDEF$?   **d.** Find the area of the quadrilateral.

7. Find the area of a rhombus whose diagonals measure:
   a. 6 and 8   **b.** 4 and 5   **c.** 8 and 15   **d.** 13 and 17
8. Find the area of a rhombus whose vertices are:
   a. (2, 0), (0, 4), (−2, 0), (0, −4)   **b.** (1, 2), (5, 7), (9, 2), (5, −3)
   c. (1, 1), (4, 2), (1, 3), (−2, 2)   **d.** (1, 4), (−1, 2), (1, 0), (3, 2)
   e. (0, 5), (1.5, 0), (3, 5), (1.5, 10)   **f.** (0, 0), (5, 10), (16, 12), (11, 2)
9. Find the area of a triangle whose vertices are:
   a. (2, 4), (8, 8), (16, 6)   **b.** (6, −2), (8, −10), (12, −6)
   c. (6, 4), (9, 2), (13, 6)   **d.** (−5, 4), (2, 1), (6, 5)
   e. (0, 6), (3, 0), (5, 2)   **f.** (2, 2), (7, 6), (4, −2)
10. Plot points $A(2, 5)$, $B(11, 2)$, $C(9, 8)$, and $D(4, 8)$. Draw $\overline{AB}$, $\overline{BC}$, $\overline{CD}$, and $\overline{DA}$. Find the area of quadrilateral $ABCD$.
11. Find the area of a quadrilateral whose vertices are:
    a. (1, 7), (2, 4), (8, 6), (4, 10)   **b.** (−4, 2), (3, −4), (6, 2), (1, 4)
    c. (−3, 0), (4, 0), (1, 4), (−3, 1)   **d.** (1, 2), (5, 4), (8, −2), (4, −4)
12. The coordinates of the vertices of $\triangle RST$ are $R(4, 5)$, $S(12, 5)$, and $T(8, 11)$.
    a. Find the length of the altitude of $\triangle RST$ drawn to side $\overline{RS}$.   **b.** Find the area of $\triangle RST$.
13. The coordinates of the vertices of $\triangle ABC$ are $A(−2, −5)$, $B(7, −2)$, and $C(−2, 1)$.
    a. Find the length of the altitude of $\triangle ABC$ drawn to side $\overline{AC}$.
    b. Find the area of $\triangle ABC$.
14. The vertices of $\triangle RST$ are $R(4, 4)$, $S(12, 10)$, and $T(6, 13)$.
    a. Find the area of $\triangle RST$.   **b.** Find the length of side $\overline{RS}$.
    c. Using the results of parts **a** and **b**, find the length of the altitude drawn from T to $\overline{RS}$.
15. The coordinates of the vertices of $\triangle DEF$ are $D(1, 5)$, $E(5, 8)$, and $F(11, 0)$.
    a. Find the area of $\triangle DEF$.   **b.** Show that $\triangle DEF$ is a right triangle.
    c. Find the lengths of sides $\overline{DE}$ and $\overline{EF}$.
    d. Show how the lengths found in part **c** can be used to find the area of $\triangle DEF$ by a second method.
16. The coordinates of the vertices of $\triangle ABC$ are $A(4, 4)$, $B(15, 2)$, and $C(12, 8)$.
    a. Draw $\triangle ABC$ on a graph paper.   **b.** Show that $\triangle ABC$ is a right triangle.
    c. Find the area of $\triangle ABC$.

17. **a.** Starting with the formula $A = \frac{1}{2}d_1d_2$ for the area of a rhombus with diagonals d_1 and d_2, show that the area of a square with diagonal d can be found by using the formula $A = \frac{1}{2}d^2$.
    b. Find the area of a square whose diagonal measures:
       (1) 4   *(2)* 8   *(3)* 5   *(4)* $\sqrt{2}$ *(5)* $4\sqrt{2}$
18. In a square, s is the length of a side and d is the length of a diagonal.
    a. If $s = 3$, find d.   **b.** Using $A = s^2$, find the area of the square.
    c. Using $A = \frac{1}{2}d^2$, find the area of the square.
19. The vertices of square $ABCD$ are $A(1, 1)$, $B(−1, 3)$, $C(−3, 1)$, and $D(−1, −1)$.
    a. Find the length of $\overline{AB}$.   **b.** Using AB, find the area of the square.
    c. Find the length of $\overline{AC}$.   **d.** Using AC, find the area of the square.

CHAPTER SUMMARY

A *quadrilateral* is a four-sided polygon. A *diagonal of a quadrilateral* is a line segment whose endpoints are two nonadjacent vertices of the quadrilateral.

A *parallelogram* is a quadrilateral in which two pairs of opposite sides are parallel.

1. Opposite sides of a parallelogram are parallel.
2. Opposite sides of a parallelogram are congruent.
3. Opposite angles of a parallelogram are congruent.
4. Consecutive angles of a parallelogram are supplementary.
5. A diagonal divides the parallelogram into two congruent triangles.
6. The diagonals of a parallelogram bisect each other.

A *rectangle* is a parallelogram one of whose angles is a right angle.

1. A rectangle has all the properties of a parallelogram.
2. A rectangle is equiangular.
3. A rectangle has four right angles.
4. A rectangle has congruent diagonals.

A *rhombus* is a parallelogram that has two congruent consecutive sides.

1. A rhombus has all the properties of a parallelogram.
2. A rhombus is equilateral.
3. The diagonals of a rhombus are perpendicular.
4. The diagonals of a rhombus bisect the angles of the rhombus.

A *square* is a rectangle that has two congruent consecutive sides.

1. A square has all the properties of a rectangle.
2. A square has all the properties of a rhombus.

A *trapezoid* is a quadrilateral in which two and only two sides are parallel. An *isosceles trapezoid* is a trapezoid in which the nonparallel sides are congruent.

1. The base angles of an isosceles trapezoid are congruent.
2. The diagonals of an isosceles trapezoid are congruent.

When b is the measure of a base of a triangle, parallelogram, or trapezoid, h is the measure of an altitude to the base. Other measures include diagonal d, length ℓ and width w of a rectangle, and side s of a square.

The following formulas can be used to find the areas of polygons:

Area of a triangle: $A = \frac{1}{2}bh$

Area of a parallelogram: $A = bh$

Area of a rectangle: $A = bh$ or $A = \ell w$

Area of a square: $A = s^2$

Area of a rhombus: $A = bh$ or $A = \frac{1}{2}d_1 d_2$

Area of a trapezoid: $A = \frac{1}{2}(b_1 + b_2)h$

VOCABULARY

7-1 Consecutive vertices   Adjacent vertices   Consecutive sides
Adjacent sides   Opposite sides of a quadrilateral   Consecutive angles
Opposite angles of a quadrilateral   Diagonals of a quadrilateral

7-2 Parallelogram

7-4 Rectangle

7-5 Rhombus

7-6 Square

7-7 Trapezoid   Isosceles trapezoid

REVIEW EXERCISES WITH OPEN-RESPONSE PROBLEMS

1. Copy the table that follows. In the columns headed **a** through **g**, answer *yes* or *no* to the following questions for each of the five given quadrilaterals:
   a. Are opposite sides congruent and parallel?
   b. Are opposite angles congruent?
   c. Are the diagonals congruent?
   d. Do the diagonals bisect each other?
   e. Are the diagonals perpendicular to each other?
   f. Are all angles congruent?
   g. Are any two consecutive sides congruent?

	a	b	c	d	e	f	g
Parallelogram							
Rectangle							
Rhombus							
Square							
Trapezoid							

2. In parallelogram $ABCD$, $m\angle A = 3x$ and $m\angle B = 2x + 60$. Find x.
3. In parallelogram $ABCD$, $AB = 3y - 7$ and $CD = y + 15$. Find y.

4. The degree measures of two opposite angles of a parallelogram are represented by $2n + 30$ and $n + 45$. Find n.
5. The degree measures of two consecutive angles of a rhombus are represented by $5x + 10$ and $3x + 50$. Find x.
6. In rhombus $PQSR$, $PQ = y + 8$ and $QS = 4y - 7$. Find PQ.
7. In rectangle $ABCD$, $AB = x + 15$, $BC = x - 8$, and $CD = 2x + 3$.
   Find: **a.** x **b.** AB **c.** BC
8. In rhombus $DEFG$, if m$\angle DEF = 60$ and the shorter diagonal, $\overline{DF}$, has a length of 7, find the length of a side of the rhombus.

Ex. 9   Ex. 10

9. In trapezoid $ABCD$, $\overline{AB} \parallel \overline{DC}$ and diagonal $\overline{BD}$ is drawn. If m$\angle ABD = 20$ and m$\angle C = 70$, find: **a.** m$\angle BDC$ **b.** m$\angle DBC$
10. In isosceles trapezoid $DEFG$, $\overline{DE} \parallel \overline{GF}$ and $\overline{DG} \cong \overline{EF}$. Using the two angle measures given in the diagram, find all remaining angle measures.

In 11–18, select the *numeral* preceding the choice that best answers the question or completes the statement.

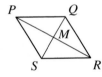

11. In parallelogram $PQRS$, diagonals $\overline{PR}$ and $\overline{QS}$ intersect at M. Which is always true?
    (1) $\overline{PR} \perp \overline{QS}$ (2) $\overline{PM} \cong \overline{RM}$
    (3) $\overline{PQ} \cong \overline{QR}$ (4) $\triangle PMS \cong \triangle PMQ$

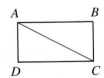

12. In rectangle $ABCD$, $\overline{AC}$ is a diagonal. Which is *always* true?
    (1) $\overline{AB} \cong \overline{AC}$ (2) $\overline{AB} \cong \overline{AD}$
    (3) m$\angle DAC = $ m$\angle BAC$ (4) $\triangle DAC \cong \triangle BCA$

13. A quadrilateral whose diagonals are congruent but are not perpendicular to each other is
    (1) a rectangle   (2) a rhombus
    (3) a parallelogram   (4) a square

14. A quadrilateral whose diagonals are perpendicular to each other is
    (1) a rectangle   (2) a rhombus
    (3) a parallelogram   (4) a trapezoid

15. A quadrilateral that is equiangular but not equilateral is
    (1) a rectangle   (2) a rhombus
    (3) a square   (4) a parallelogram

16. A quadrilateral that is not a parallelogram is
    (1) a rectangle   (2) a rhombus   (3) a square   (4) a trapezoid

17. Which of the following statements is *false*?
  (1) A square is a rhombus.   (2) A rhombus is a square.
  (3) A square is a rectangle.   (4) A rhombus is a parallelogram.

18. The diagonals of a rectangle are *always*
  (1) congruent   (2) perpendicular to each other
  (3) parallel   (4) bisectors of the angles of the rectangle

In 19–22, tell whether each argument is *valid* or *invalid*.

19. In a rectangle, diagonals are congruent.
  A square is a rectangle.
  Conclusion: In a square, diagonals are congruent.

20. The diagonals of a parallelogram bisect each other.
  A rhombus is a parallelogram.
  Conclusion: The diagonals of a rhombus bisect each other.

21. A rhombus is equilateral.
  A rhombus is a parallelogram.
  Conclusion: A parallelogram is equilateral.

22. Two consecutive angles of a parallelogram are supplementary.
  A rectangle is a parallelogram.
  Conclusion: Two consecutive angles of a rectangle are supplementary.

In 23–27, write *true* if the statement is *always* true; write *false* if the statement is *not always* true.

23. If one angle of a parallelogram is a right angle, all the other angles of the parallelogram are also right angles.
24. If a quadrilateral is equilateral, the quadrilateral is a square.
25. A trapezoid has at least one acute angle.
26. The diagonals of a parallelogram divide it into four congruent triangles.
27. If the diagonals of a quadrilateral are congruent, the quadrilateral is a rectangle.

Ex. 28

Ex. 29

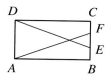

Ex. 30

28. *Given:* In quadrilateral *PQRS*, ∠1 ≅ ∠2 and ∠3 ≅ ∠4.
  Prove: *PQRS* is a parallelogram.

29. *Given:* $\overline{DB}$ bisects $\overline{AC}$ at *E*, ∠1 ≅ ∠2.
  Prove: *ABCD* is a parallelogram.

30. *Given:* *ABCD* is a rectangle, $\overline{BE} \cong \overline{CF}$.
  Prove: $\overline{DE} \cong \overline{AF}$.

31. *Given:* $ABCD$ is a square, $\overline{BAE}$, $\overline{DAF}$, $\overline{AE} \cong \overline{AF}$.
    Prove: **a.** $\triangle BAF \cong \triangle DAE$.
           b. $\angle CBF \cong \angle CDE$.

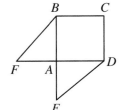

32. Two of the vertices of $\triangle ABC$ are $B(-3, -2)$ and $C(5, 4)$. The midpoint of $\overline{AB}$ is $M(-3, 2)$. Find:
    a. the coordinates of A
    b. the coordinates of D, the altitude from C to $\overline{AB}$
    c. the area of $\triangle ABC$

33. a. Show that a quadrilateral whose vertices are $A(2, 1)$, $B(6, -2)$, $C(10, 1)$, and $D(6, 4)$ is a rhombus.
    b. Find the area of the rhombus.
    c. Find the length of an altitude of the rhombus.

34. a. Show that the quadrilateral whose vertices are $A(-7, 3)$, $B(-1, -5)$, $C(5, 3)$, and $D(-1, 11)$ is a rhombus.
    b. Find the area of the rhombus.
    c. Find the length of an altitude of the rhombus.

35. Equilateral triangle, rhombus, square, rectangle
Of the four polygons listed above, which is different from the others? Explain your answer.

36. *ABCD* is an isosceles trapezoid; *AMCD* and *MBCD* are parallelograms; m$\angle DMC$ is 30.
    a. Find the measure of every other angle in the diagram.
    b. Is M the midpoint of $\overline{AB}$? Explain your answer.

Ex. 36

37. Gus wants to cut out a trapezoid. His brother told him to cut out a triangle and then cut off its top. If Gus did this, would the quadrilateral that resulted be a trapezoid? If not, what other instruction does Gus need to make the quadrilateral be a trapezoid?

38. A set of four quadrilaterals consists of a parallelogram, a rectangle, a rhombus, and a square. One of the four quadrilaterals is selected at random. Find the *probability* that this quadrilateral:
    a. is both equiangular and equilateral.
    b. is equiangular.
    c. is equilateral.
    d. has congruent diagonals.
    e. has diagonals that are congruent and perpendicular to each other.
    f. has diagonals that bisect each other.
    g. has only one pair of parallel lines.
    h. has a diagonal that divides the quadrilateral into two congruent triangles.

39. Prove that any line through the midpoint of a diagonal of a parallelogram separates the parallelogram into two congruent polygons. (To prove two polygons congruent, show that each pair of corresponding sides and angles are congruent.)

40. A dressmaker has a length of cloth. She knows that the cloth is woven with the selvage edges (the woven edges on two opposite sides) parallel. By folding the cloth and cutting along the fold, then folding and cutting again, she can cut a square of cloth. Using diagrams, explain precisely how this can be done.

CUMULATIVE REVIEW WITH OPEN-RESPONSE PROBLEMS

1. *Given:* If polygon $ABCD$ is a rhombus and has a right angle, then polygon $ABCD$ is a square.
Polygon $ABCD$ is not a square.
Polygon $ABCD$ has a right angle.

Let R represent "Polygon $ABCD$ is a rhombus."
Let A represent "Polygon $ABCD$ has a right angle."
Let S represent "Polygon $ABCD$ is a square."
Use a logic proof to prove that polygon $ABCD$ is not a rhombus.

2. In the diagram, $\ell_1 \parallel \ell_2$, $m\angle 1 = 2x + 18$, and $m\angle 2 = 3x + 12$.
  a. Find x.   **b.** Find $m\angle 1$.   **c.** Find $m\angle 2$.

3. Given $\overleftrightarrow{AB}$ is the perpendicular bisector of $\overline{CD}$.
Prove: $\angle ACD \cong \angle ADC$

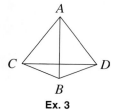

Ex. 3

4. Sylvia and Tim are studying quadrilaterals. Sylvia says that if you draw a diagonal, the quadrilateral is divided into two triangles. Therefore the sum of the measures of the angles of a quadrilateral is 2(180) or 360 degrees. Tim says that if you draw two diagonals, the quadrilateral is divided into four triangles. Therefore the sum of the measures of the angles of a quadrilateral is 4(180) or 720 degrees. Who is correct? What is the error in the incorrect method? Explain how the incorrect method could lead to the correct answer.

Exploration

   Make a list of objects or surfaces that are in the shape of a quadrilateral. Classify each shape as a trapezoid, square, rhombus, rectangle, parallelogram, or none of these. Which shape occurs most frequently in your list?

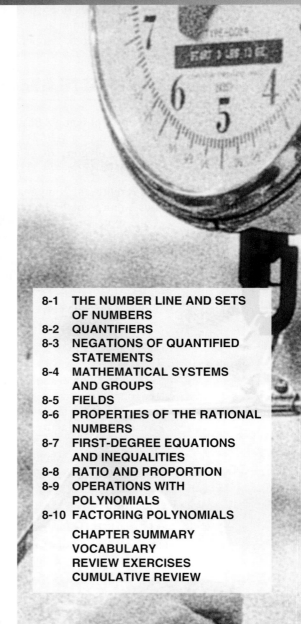

Chapter *8*

The Rational Numbers

In a fabric store, a yardstick or tape measure is used to determine the length of a piece of cloth to be purchased. The yardstick or tape measure is marked in inches divided into halves, quarters, and eighths.

As we drive or ride, the odometer of the car measures, in miles and tenths of a mile, the distance traveled.

In a hardware store, sets of wrenches that are calibrated in fractional parts of an inch or in millimeters can be purchased.

In the produce department of a grocery store, fruits and vegetables are sold by the pound and are weighed to the nearest tenth or hundredth of a pound.

In short, measurement is one of the many applications of numbers that we encounter repeatedly in daily life. Each of the measurements described above is expressed as a rational number. In this chapter we will reexamine the set of rational numbers and the properties that determine the ways in which we work with these numbers.

8-1   THE NUMBER LINE AND SETS OF NUMBERS

The numbers stamped onto a ruler are the first numbers we learned as children, namely, 1, 2, 3, and so on. This set of numbers, called the **counting numbers** or the **natural numbers**, is written in set notation as {1, 2, 3, 4, 5, 6, 7, 8, 9, . . .}. The three dots indicate that the numbers continue in the same pattern without end.

By combining 0 with the counting numbers, we form the set of **whole numbers**, represented as {0, 1, 2, 3, 4, 5, . . .}.

The Real Number Line

The ruler is a model of a **number line**. Once we have assigned to any two distinct points on a straight line the values 0 and 1, we have determined a segment whose length is the **unit measure**. By continuing in the direction of 1 from 0, it is possible to mark off equally spaced points and to assign to these points the numbers 2, 3, 4, and so on, as seen on the ruler.

Since, however, a line extends infinitely in both directions, we can begin at 0 to mark off even more equally spaced points in the direction opposite to that used to assign the whole numbers. We assign the numbers -1, -2, -3, and so on to these points.

The set of numbers assigned to equally spaced points on the number line is the set of **integers**, written symbolically as {. . . , -3, -2, -1, 0, 1, 2, 3, . . .}.

A number line can go in any direction and can have any length as its unit measure. However, once the values 0 and 1 have been assigned to points on the line, we cannot change the direction and we cannot change the unit measure or the scale for the remainder of the line. Arrowheads indicate that a line has no beginning and no end, just as the set of integers has no beginning and no end.

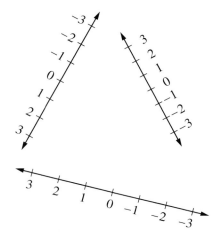

Of all the possible directions that can be used for number lines, two directions are seen most often in daily life. A *vertical* number line is used in thermometers to show temperature and in rulers to measure height. In a vertical line, we agree that numbers increase as we move up the line and decrease as we move down the line.

A *horizontal* line, such as the ruler first shown, is drawn so that numbers increase as we move to the right and decrease as we move to the left. Thus we agree that the *positive integers* 1, 2, 3, . . . lie to the right of 0, and the **negative integers** −1, −2, −3, . . . to the left of 0. Since every point on the line is the graph of a real number and every real number is the coordinate of a point on the line, the line is called the **real number line**.

Every real number is either a rational number or an irrational number. We will study rational numbers in this chapter and irrational numbers in Chapter 10.

The Rational Numbers

Once the integers have been assigned to points on a number line, it is possible to divide the segments whose endpoints represent the integers into halves, thirds, quarters, tenths, and so on. In this way, we can assign fractions, decimals, and mixed numbers to specific points on the number line.

All numbers indicated on the line above, including the integers, are examples of rational numbers.

- **DEFINITION.** A number is a **rational number** if and only if it can be expressed in the form $\frac{a}{b}$, where a and b are integers and $b \neq 0$.

We can see that every integer x is a rational number because the integer can be written in the form $\frac{x}{1}$. Using examples from the number line above, we notice how decimals and mixed numbers are written in the required form:

$$0.21 = \frac{21}{100} \qquad 2\frac{1}{6} = \frac{13}{6} \qquad 3.4 = 3\frac{4}{10} = \frac{34}{10}$$

$$-0.9 = \frac{-9}{10} \qquad -4\frac{1}{4} = \frac{-17}{4} \qquad -3.13 = -3\frac{13}{100} = \frac{-313}{100}$$

To express a rational number that is written as the ratio of integers in decimal form, we divide the numerator by the denominator.

Enter: 3 ÷ 8 =   *Enter:*   1 ÷ 3 =

Display: ⌐ 0.375 ⌐   *Display:*   ⌐ 0.33333333 ⌐

$\frac{3}{8} = 0.375$ $\frac{1}{3} = 0.33333\ldots$

Enter: 2 ⊞ 5 ÷ 11 ⊟   *Enter:*   7 ÷ 22 ⊟
Display: | 2.45454545 | *Display:* | 0.31818182 |

$$2\frac{5}{11} = 2.454545\ldots$$ $$\frac{7}{22} = 0.3181818\ldots$$

In three of these calculator displays, we see that, when the division is performed, the quotient at some point begins to consist of a group of digits that repeat, in the same order, as many times as the size of the display will allow. Then, in the quotient for $\frac{7}{22}$, the calculator rounded the fourth repetition of the digits 18 to 2. A decimal that, from some point onward, repeats a sequence of digits without end is called a ***repeating decimal***, or ***periodic decimal***. A repeating decimal may be written in abbreviated form by placing a bar ($^-$) over the group of digits that repeat. For example:

$$0.33333\ldots = 0.\overline{3}   \qquad 2.454545\ldots = 2.\overline{45}   \qquad 0.3181818\ldots = 0.3\overline{18}$$

In some cases, such as $\frac{3}{8} = 0.375$, the decimal value is called a ***terminating decimal*** because a point is reached where the division appears to end or to be completed. After this point is reached, however, it can be seen that 0's will repeat endlessly in the quotient of every terminating decimal. For this reason, every terminating decimal can be expressed as a repeating decimal. For example:

$$0.375 = 0.375000\ldots = 0.375\overline{0}$$

Therefore, we make the following important observation:

- Every rational number can be expressed as a repeating decimal.

In Math A, we learned a procedure by which a repeating decimal can be changed to a ratio of integers. The examples that follow review this procedure and illustrate the truth of the following statement, which is the converse of the observation given above.

- Every repeating decimal represents a rational number.

Since both the original observation and its converse are true, we know from our study of logic that a *biconditional* statement can be made:

- A number is a rational number if and only if it can be represented as a repeating decimal.

EXAMPLES

1. Find a fraction that names 0.13333 . . . as a repeating decimal.

How to Proceed:

(1) Let $N = 0.13333. \ldots$

(2) Multiply both sides of the equation in step 1 by 10, because a one-digit repetition appears in the number.

(3) Subtract the equation in step 1 from the equation in step 2.

(4) Solve the resulting equation for N.

Answer: $0.13333 \ldots = \frac{2}{15}$

Solution:

$10N = 1.33333 \ldots$

$$\begin{array}{r} - \ N = 0.13333 \ldots \\ \hline 9N = 1.2 \end{array}$$

$N = \frac{1.2}{9.0} = \frac{12}{90} = \frac{2}{15}$

---

2. Find a fraction that names 0.606060 . . . as a repeating decimal.

(1) Let $N = 0.606060. \ldots$

(2) Multiply both sides of the equation in step 1 by 100, because a two-digit repetition appears in the number.

(3) Subtract the equation in step 1 from the equation in step 2.

(4) Solve the resulting equation for N.

Answer: $0.606060 \ldots = \frac{20}{33}$

$100N = 60.606060 \ldots$

$$\begin{array}{r} - \ N = \ \ 0.606060 \ldots \\ \hline 99N = 60 \end{array}$$

$N = \frac{60}{99} = \frac{20}{33}$

EXERCISES WITH OPEN-RESPONSE PROBLEMS

In 1–8, tell whether each statement is true or false. Explain your answer.

1. Every counting number is a rational number.
2. Every whole number is an integer.
3. Every integer is a whole number.
4. The smallest whole number is 0.
5. The smallest natural number is 0.
6. Every rational number can be expressed as a repeating decimal.
7. Every repeating decimal is a rational number.
8. If a and b are integers, then $\frac{a}{b}$ is a rational number.

In 9–20, express each rational number as a repeating decimal. (Note that 0's repeat in all terminating decimals.)

9. $\frac{4}{9}$ **10.** $\frac{4}{11}$ **11.** $-\frac{2}{3}$ **12.** $\frac{4}{5}$ **13.** $1\frac{1}{3}$ **14.** $-1\frac{1}{6}$

15. $-2\frac{3}{4}$ **16.** $\frac{7}{60}$ **17.** $-\frac{4}{15}$ **18.** $\frac{1}{90}$ **19.** $1\frac{1}{20}$ **20.** $3\frac{1}{7}$

In 21–40, express each rational number as a fraction.

21. 5 **22.** -3 **23.** $3\frac{1}{2}$ **24.** 0 **25.** $-2\frac{5}{7}$

26. 0.7 **27.** 0.23 **28.** -0.8 **29.** 4.1 **30.** 0.666 . . .

31. $0.\overline{7}$ **32.** $0.\overline{23}$ **33.** $0.2\overline{2}$ **34.** $0.0\overline{2}$ **35.** $0.2\overline{7}$

36. $8.\overline{3}$ **37.** $0.8\overline{3}$ **38.** $0.08\overline{3}$ **39.** $0.3\overline{6}$ **40.** $0.\overline{142857}$

41. Does 0.999 . . . = 1? Explain your answer.

42. Kayse evaluated $\frac{5}{11}$ and $\frac{9,090,909}{20,000,000}$ on a calculator that could display no more than eight decimal places of the quotient. In each case, the display read 0.45454545. Kayse is confused because she knows that the two fractions are not equal. Explain to Kayse: **a.** the difference in the quotients **b.** how each should be written to express its decimal form exactly **c.** how she can tell which fraction is equivalent to each form.

8-2 QUANTIFIERS

Consider these sentences and their related truth values.

p: Integers are rational numbers. (True)
q: Negative numbers are greater than 0. (False)
r: Integers are primes. (Uncertain)

We know that p is true because *all* integers are rational numbers. We know that q is false because *no* negative number is greater than 0. We are uncertain of the truth value of r because *some* integers are primes and *some* integers are not primes. The words we have just used, namely, *all*, *no*, and *some*, are called *quantifiers*.

By using the proper quantifier in a given sentence, we can form a quantified statement that is always true. Thus:

All integers are rational numbers. (True)
No negative number is greater than 0. (True)
Some integers are primes. (True)

● **DEFINITION.** A *domain* is a set of all possible replacements for a given variable. For example, in statements p and r, above, the domain is the set of integers.

In statement q, the domain is the set of negative numbers. Thus, a given sentence that involves a variable may be written using a quantifier.

● **DEFINITION.** A *quantifier* is a word or phrase that describes in general terms the part of the domain for which a sentence is true.

The Universal Quantifier

Whenever a sentence has the same truth value for all replacements from the domain, we can write this sentence as a *universally quantified statement*.

The word *all* is the commonly used expression for the *universal quantifier*, represented symbolically as $\forall_x$. This symbol is formed by writing a capital letter A upside down and by adding a subscript x to indicate the variable. The symbol $\forall_x$ can be read in many ways, as shown in the box to the right.

$\forall_x$:	All
	For all x
	Every
	For every x

Universal Quantifier

Let us consider two types of sentences in which the universal quantifier is used.

1. *Sentences that are always true.*

Let b represent the sentence "$x + x = 2x$."

When the domain is the set of rational numbers, every replacement for the variable x results in a true statement: $5 + 5 = 2(5)$, $3.1 + 3.1 = 2(3.1)$, and so on. Thus, we can attach the universal quantifier, $\forall_x$, to the sentence and form a true statement. Although the statement is expressed symbolically in only one way, it may be expressed in words in many ways. For example:

$\forall_x: b$ | For *all* values of x, $x + x = 2x$.
| For *every* x, $x + x = 2x$.

In the same way, consider the sentence studied earlier in this section, namely, "p: Integers are rational numbers." Here the domain is the set of integers. Since the statement is always true, we can use the universal quantifier *all* as follows:

$\forall_x: p$ | *All* integers are rational numbers.
| *Every* integer is a rational number.
| For *all* integers, integers are rational numbers.

2. *Sentences that are always false.*

Let d represent the sentence "$x \cdot x = -1$."

When the domain is the set of rational numbers, there is no number that, when multiplied by itself, results in the product -1. Since the sentence d: $x \cdot x = -1$, is always *false*, it follows that its negation, $\sim d$: $x \cdot x \neq -1$, is always *true*.

Therefore, we quantify a false statement by attaching the universal quantifier, $\forall_x$, to the negation of the statement. In the example below, the words *no* and *not* enter the sentences in various ways.

$\forall_x: \sim d$	For all x, $x \cdot x \neq -1$.
	For all x, it is *not* true that $x \cdot x = -1$.
	There are *no* values of x for which $x \cdot x = -1$.
	For every x, $x \cdot x$ is *not* equal to -1.

In the same way, let us consider another sentence studied earlier in this section, namely, "q: Negative numbers are greater than 0." This statement is always false. To form a true statement, we negate the given sentence and attach a universal quantifier. This statement can be expressed in words by using the quantifier *no*.

$\forall_x: \sim q$	*No* negative number is greater than 0.
	Every negative number is *not* greater than 0.
	All negative numbers are *not* greater than 0.

Therefore we may conclude:

- **DEFINITION.** A *universal quantifier* is a word or phrase that describes a statement as being true for *all* elements of the domain. When a statement is true for all elements of the domain, its negation is true for *no* element of the domain.

The Existential Quantifier

Whenever a sentence is true for at least one replacement from the domain, we may write this sentence as an *existentially quantified statement*.

The words *there exists* or the word *some* are commonly used expressions for the *existential quantifier*, represented symbolically as $\exists_x$. This symbol is formed by writing a capital letter E backwards and by adding a subscript x to indicate the variable. The symbol $\exists_x$ is read in many ways, as shown in the box at the right.

$\exists_x:$	There exists
	At least one
	For some
	There is one
	Some

Existential Quantifier

Let h represent the sentence "$x + 1 = 5$."

When the domain is the set of rational numbers, there is at least one replacement for the variable x that results in a true statement. When $x = 4$, it is true that $x + 1 = 5$. Thus, we can attach the existential quantifier, $\exists_x$, to the sentence and form a true statement.

$\exists_x: h$	*There exists* a value for x such that $x + 1 = 5$.
	For *some* value of x, $x + 1 = 5$.
	There is *at least one* value of x where $x + 1 = 5$.

In the same way, let us consider the third sentence studied earlier in this section, namely, "*r*: Integers are primes." We know that some integers are primes. Therefore, we know that at least one integer exists that is a prime. We attach the existential quantifier to form the following true statement:

$\exists_x$: *r*

There *exists* an integer that is a prime.

There is *at least one* integer that is a prime.

Some integers are primes.

Therefore, we may conclude:

● **DEFINITION.** An *existential quantifier* is a phrase that describes a statement as being true for *at least one* replacement from the domain.

It should be noted that an existential quantifier may be used for a sentence that is universally true. Thus, while all replacements of the domain are true, it is *not false* to say that *at least one* replacement results in a true statement. The following statements are described more accurately by using a universal quantifier, but they are still *true* statements.

$\exists_x$:   *b*

There is an *x* such that $x + x = 2x$.

$\exists_x$: ~*d*

There exists at least one *x* such that $x \cdot x \neq -1$.

$\exists_x$:   *p*

Some integers are rational numbers.

$\exists_x$: ~*q*

There is at least one negative number that is not greater than 0.

EXAMPLES

In 1–4, describe each sentence as being universally quantified, existentially quantified, or not quantified.

1. Some books are written in Greek.

The word *some* indicates existentially quantified.   *Answer*

---

2. This book is Greek to me.

The statement is not quantified.   *Answer*

---

3. Every Greek has a rich cultural heritage.

The word *every* indicates universally quantified.   *Answer*

---

4. No Greeks are wealthy.

This statement is equivalent to "All Greeks are not wealthy." The words *no* and *all* indicate universally quantified.   *Answer*

---

5. Which statement is true for the set of real numbers?

(1) $\exists_x \, x > x + 8$ (2) $\forall_x \, x > x + 8$ (3) $\exists_x \, x = 8$ (4) $\forall_x \, x = 8$

Solution   The open sentence $x > x + 8$ in choices (1) and (2) is never true. The open sentence $x = 8$ in choices (3) and (4) is true for only one value, namely, 8. Thus, the sentence $x = 8$ can be existentially quantified.

Answer: (3)

---

6. Which of the following quantified statements are true?

(1) All squares are rectangles.   (2) No squares are rectangles.
(3) Some squares are rectangles.   (4) All rectangles are squares.

Solution   Since the universally quantified statement "All squares are rectangles" in choice (1) is true, the existentially quantified statement "Some squares are rectangles" in choice (3) must also be true. Choices (2) and (4) are false.

Answer: (1) and (3) are both true.

EXERCISES WITH OPEN-RESPONSE PROBLEMS

In 1–8:   **a.** Describe each sentence as being universally quantified, existentially quantified, or not quantified.   **b.** If the sentence is quantified, name the word or words that act as the quantifiers.

1. All whole numbers are rational numbers.
2. Some angles are obtuse angles.
3. No boy in his right mind brings a camel into the subway.
4. The probability that you are correct is $\frac{1}{3}$.
5. There are certain whole numbers that are divisible by 5.
6. This is a difficult decision for me to make.
7. Every important decision requires careful thought.
8. At least one person is a true friend to me.

In 9–12, write each given sentence in words. Let $x \in \{\text{cars}\}$.

9. $\forall_x$ cars have wheels.
10. $\forall_x$ cars do not fly.
11. $\exists_x$ cars are red.
12. $\exists_x$ cars need tune-ups.

In 13–17, for each statement: **a.** State the domain.   **b.** Write the statement in symbolic form using $\forall_x$ or $\exists_x$.   **c.** Tell whether the statement is true or false.

13. For every integer x, x is less than $x + 5$.
14. For some integer x, x is less than 5.
15. For no integer x, x is equal to $x + 5$.
16. For every rational number x, it is not true that $x + 5 = 8$.
17. There is a rational number x such that $x + 5 = 8$.

In 18–22, in each case use the domain of rational numbers to tell which one of the three given statements is true.

18. (1) $\forall_x: x^2 = 0$ (2) $\forall_x: x^2 > 0$ (3) $\forall_x: x^2 \geq 0$
19. (1) $\exists_x: x^2 = 0$ (2) $\exists_x: x^2 < 0$ (3) $\forall_x: x^2 < 0$
20. (1) $\exists_x: 2x + 1 = 5$ (2) $\forall_x: 2x + 1 = 5$ (3) $\forall_x: 2x + 1 \neq 5$
21. (1) $\forall_x: x - 3 \geq 7$ (2) $\exists_x: x - 3 \geq 7$ (3) $\exists_x: x - 3 \geq x$
22. (1) $\forall_x: x + x \neq x$ (2) $\forall_x: x + x > x$ (3) $\exists_x: x + x < x$

In 23–25, in each case select all quantified statements that are true. Some exercises may have more than one true statement.

23. (1) All people are tall.   (2) No people are tall.
     (3) Some people are tall.   (4) Some people are not tall.

24. (1) All rational numbers are integers.   (2) All integers are rational numbers.
     (3) Some rational numbers are integers.   (4) Some integers are rational numbers.

25. (1) All rectangles are parallelograms.   (2) Some rectangles are not parallelograms.
     (3) No rectangles are parallelograms.   (4) Some rectangles are parallelograms.

26. Emerita says that, since "All isosceles triangles are congruent" is false, then "All isosceles triangles are not congruent" must be true. Do you agree with Emerita? Explain your answer.

8-3 NEGATIONS OF QUANTIFIED STATEMENTS

Negating a Universally Quantified Statement

"Every month has 31 days." We know that this statement is false. To prove that it is false, it is not necessary to consider every month. We need only to name one month that does not have 31 days. For example, since September has 30 days, the statement is not true for every month. The one month, September, that we used to show that the universally quantified statement was false is called a ***counterexample***. In this case, the counterexample shows that there is at least one month that does not have 31 days.

We can express these statements in symbols and in words as follows:

Let $x \in \{$months of the year$\}$.
Let p represent "x has 31 days."

$\forall_x p$: *Every* month has 31 days.   (False)
$\exists_x \sim p$: *Some* months do not have 31 days.   (True)

Let us study another example, starting with a universally quantified statement that is true. We know that all segments have two endpoints. Thus, the statement "At least one segment exists that does not have two endpoints" is false. In symbols and in words, we say:

Let $x \in$ {line segments}.
Let q represent "x has two endpoints."

$\forall_x \, q$: *All* segments have two endpoints.   (True)
$\exists_x \, {\sim}q$: *Some* segments do *not* have two endpoints. (False)

or

There is *at least one* segment that does *not* have two endpoints.   (False)

We may conclude:

- The *negation of a universally quantified statement p* is an existentially quantified statement of the negation of *p*.

In symbolic form:

The negation of $\forall_x \, p$ is expressed as $\exists_x \, {\sim}p$.

Negating an Existentially Quantified Statement

"Some months have 32 days." We know that this statement is false. To prove that it is false, it is necessary to consider every month. After we have shown that every month has fewer than 32 days, we know that no month exists that has 32 days.

We can express these statements in symbols and in words as follows:

Let $x \in$ {months of the year}.
Let p represent "x has 32 days."

$\exists_x \, p$: *Some* months have 32 days.   (False)
$\forall_x \, {\sim}p$: *All* months do not have 32 days.   (True)

or

No month has 32 days.   (True)

In the following example, we start with an existentially quantified statement that is true.

Let $x \in$ {polygons}.
Let t represent "x has five sides."

$\exists_x \, t$: *Some* polygons have five sides.   (True)
$\forall_x \, {\sim}t$: *No* polygon has five sides.   (False)

We may conclude:

- The *negation of an existentially quantified statement p* is a universally quantified statement of the negation of *p*.

In symbolic form:

The negation of $\exists_x \, p$ is expressed as $\forall_x \, {\sim}p$.

The Difference Between *All Are Not* and *Not All Are*

The negation of a quantified statement is sometimes indicated by negating the quantifier. Let us note the differences that occur because of the placement of a negation. The following examples illustrate the difference between the phrases

all are not ($\forall_x \sim p$, where the negation is on p), and
not all are ($\sim \forall_x p$, where the negation is on $\forall$).

Let $x \in \{\text{persons}\}$.   Let p represent "x is honest."

We use *all are not* when the statement p, which is universally quantified, is being negated:

$\forall_x p$: *All* persons are honest.
$\forall_x \sim p$: *All* persons *are not* honest.
or *No* persons are honest.

We use *not all are* when the universal quantifier $\forall$ is being negated:

$\sim \forall_x p$: Not all persons are honest.

Since the negation of a universally quantified statement is an existentially quantified statement, we have:

$\sim \forall_x p \leftrightarrow \exists_x \sim p$: *Not all* persons *are* honest.
or *Some* persons *are not* honest.
or *At least one* person *is not* honest.

EXAMPLES

In 1–4, write the negation of each quantified statement.

1. $\forall_x: x = 2$ **2.** $\exists_x: x > 7$ **3.** $\forall_x \sim k$ **4.** $\exists_x \sim m$

Answers: **1.** $\exists_x: x \neq 2$ **2.** $\forall_x: x \leq 7$ **3.** $\exists_x k$ **4.** $\forall_x m$

Note. In answer 2, the expression $x \leq 7$ is equivalent to the expression $x \not> 7$.

5. Which is the negation of the statement "Some rectangles are squares"?
(1) Some rectangles are not squares.
(2) All rectangles are squares.
(3) All rectangles are not squares.
(4) All squares are rectangles.

Solution   Copy the original statement: "Some rectangles are squares."
Write the statement in symbolic form: $\exists_x p$
Negate this quantified statement: $\forall_x \sim p$
Translate the negation: "All rectangles are not squares."

This is choice (3).   *Answer*

EXERCISES WITH OPEN-RESPONSE PROBLEMS

In 1–22, write the negation of each quantified statement.

1. $\forall_x: x = 3$
2. $\exists_x: x \neq 5$
3. $\exists_x: x > 4$
4. $\forall_x: x < 9$
5. $\exists_x: x \geq 2$
6. $\forall_x: x = x$
7. $\forall_x\ b$
8. $\exists_x\ d$

9. All men are human.
10. Some men are handsome.
11. All women are beautiful.
12. Some women are not rich.
13. Some animals can fly.
14. All roses are not red.
15. Some chairs are not soft.
16. No chairs are tables.
17. All people are not fat.
18. Every frog cannot sing.
19. All segments have a midpoint.
20. No segments are lines.
21. Every segment does not have two midpoints.
22. Some segments do not have a length of 5 meters.

In 23–30, select the *numeral* preceding the statement that best answers the question or completes the sentence.

23. Which is the negation of the statement "All math is fun"?
   (1) No math is fun.
   (2) All math is not fun.
   (3) Some math is fun.
   (4) Some math is not fun.

24. Which is the negation of the statement "Some numbers are odd"?
   (1) All numbers are odd.
   (2) All numbers are not odd.
   (3) Some numbers are even.
   (4) Some numbers are not odd.

25. Which is the negation of $\forall_x\ x > 5$?
   (1) $\exists_x\ x > 5$
   (2) $\forall_x\ x \leq 5$
   (3) $\exists_x\ x \leq 5$
   (4) $\exists_x\ x < 5$

26. The negation of "Some angles are acute" is
   (1) Some angles are not acute.
   (2) No angles are acute.
   (3) All angles are acute.
   (4) No angles are not acute.

27. Which is the negation of "Every triangle has three sides"?
   (1) No triangle has three sides.
   (2) Some triangles do not have three sides.
   (3) All triangles have three sides.
   (4) Some triangles have three sides.

28. Which is the negation of "No flowers are pink"?
   (1) Some flowers are pink.
   (2) All flowers are pink.
   (3) Some flowers are not pink.
   (4) All flowers are not pink.

29. The negation of "No rectangles are trapezoids" is
   (1) All rectangles are trapezoids.
   (2) All rectangles are not trapezoids.
   (3) Some rectangles are trapezoids.
   (4) Some rectangles are not trapezoids.

30. Which is the negation of "There is an n such that $n^2 = n$"?
    (1) For all n, $n^2 = n$.   (2) For some n, $n^2 \neq n$.
    (3) For some n, $n^2 = n$.   (4) For all n, $n^2 \neq n$.

31. Let S be a set that is not the empty set and $x \in S$.
    a. Is it possible for both $\forall_x p$ and $\forall_x \sim p$ to be true? Explain your answer.
    b. Is it possible for both $\exists_x p$ and $\exists_x \sim p$ to be false? Explain your answer.
    c. Is it possible for both $\exists_x p$ and $\exists_x \sim p$ to be true? Explain your answer.

8-4 MATHEMATICAL SYSTEMS AND GROUPS

In geometry, we learned that a ***postulational system*** is one in which definitions and postulates are used to prove theorems, and then definitions, postulates, and proved theorems are used to *deduce* other theorems. This type of ***deductive reasoning*** is not limited to geometry but is used also to develop systems that are numerical or algebraic in nature.

Binary Operations

When we operate on two elements from a set and the result is an element from that set, we are performing a *binary operation*. Addition, subtraction, multiplication, and division are examples of binary operations on the set of rational numbers. Of course we sometimes add columns consisting of more than two numbers, but to do so we add only two numbers at a time.

●   **DEFINITION.** A ***binary operation*** $*$ in a set S is a way of assigning to every ordered pair of elements from S a unique response from S.

In symbolic form, we write:

$$\forall a, b \in S: \quad a * b = c \quad \text{and} \quad c \in S$$

If S is a finite set, a given binary operation may be defined by showing each result in a table. For example:

Let $S = \{0, 1, 2, 3, 4\}$. Let $\oplus$ be the symbol for an operation defined by the table shown at the right. Note that, to every pair of elements from S, there is assigned a unique member of S.

$\oplus$	0	1	2	3	4
0	0	1	2	3	4
1	1	2	3	4	0
2	2	3	4	0	1
3	3	4	0	1	2
4	4	0	1	2	3

We can illustrate these results by using a cyclic arrangement of numbers on a dial. For example:

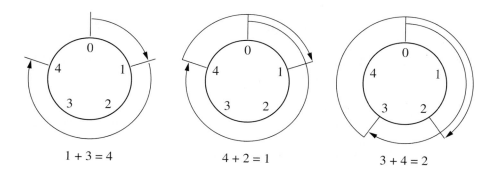

$$1 + 3 = 4 \qquad\qquad 4 + 2 = 1 \qquad\qquad 3 + 4 = 2$$

The operation $\oplus$ could also have been defined by describing each result in terms of ordinary addition and subtraction.

$$a \oplus b = \begin{cases} a + b & \text{if} \quad a + b < 5 \\ a + b - 5 & \text{if} \quad a + b \geq 5 \end{cases}$$

The operation $\oplus$ is often called **clock addition**, or **modular addition**. The set S together with the operation $\oplus$ is a *mathematical system*.

● **DEFINITION.** A **mathematical system** consists of:

1. A known set of elements.
2. One or more operations defined on this set of elements.

In general, the system also includes:

3. Definitions and postulates concerning operations on the set of elements.
4. Theorems that can be deduced from the given definitions and postulates.

The mathematical system consisting of the set of five elements {0, 1, 2, 3, 4} and the operation modular addition, $\oplus$, is written in symbols as (Clock 5, $\oplus$).

Closure

Once a binary operation is defined on all elements of a set, we know that the set is *closed* under the operation. For a set, we may define the property of **closure** as follows:

● **DEFINITION.** The set S is **closed** under operation $*$ if and only if:

$$\forall a, b \in S: \quad a * b = c \quad \text{and} \quad c \in S$$

The following are examples of sets that are closed under an operation.

1. Addition is a binary operation on the set of integers.
   The set of integers is closed under addition.
2. Clock addition is a binary operation on $\{0, 1, 2, 3, 4\}$.
   The set $\{0, 1, 2, 3, 4\}$ is closed under modular addition.
3. Multiplication is a binary operation on the set of integers.
   The set of integers is closed under multiplication.

A binary operation may be defined for some but not all members of a set. For example, division is a binary operation only for nonzero elements of the set of rational numbers. Therefore, under division the set of rational numbers is not closed, but the set of nonzero rational numbers is closed.

Associativity

● **DEFINITION.** The operation $*$ is **associative** on set S if and only if:

$$\forall a, b, c \in S: \quad (a * b) * c = a * (b * c)$$

1. Addition is associative on the set of integers.

$$(-3 + 2) + 5 \overset{?}{=} -3 + (2 + 5)$$
$$-1 + 5 \overset{?}{=} -3 + 7$$
$$4 = 4$$

2. Modular addition is associative on clock 5. We would need to verify $5 \cdot 5 \cdot 5$ or 125 cases in order to prove this statement. Two examples are shown.

$$(2 \oplus 2) \oplus 4 \overset{?}{=} 2 \oplus (2 \oplus 4) \qquad (1 \oplus 3) \oplus 2 \overset{?}{=} 1 \oplus (3 \oplus 2)$$
$$4 \oplus 4 \overset{?}{=} 2 \oplus 1 \qquad\qquad 4 \oplus 2 \overset{?}{=} 1 \oplus 0$$
$$3 = 3 \qquad\qquad\qquad 1 = 1$$

3. Subtraction and division are *not* associative on the set of integers.

$$(5 - 8) - 3 \overset{?}{=} 5 - (8 - 3) \qquad (12 \div 6) \div 2 \overset{?}{=} 12 \div (6 \div 2)$$
$$-3 - 3 \overset{?}{=} 5 - 5 \qquad\qquad 2 \div 2 \overset{?}{=} 12 \div 3$$
$$-6 \neq 0 \qquad\qquad\qquad 1 \neq 4$$

Commutativity

● **DEFINITION.** The operation $*$ is **commutative** on set S if and only if:

$$\forall a, b \in S: \quad a * b = b * a$$

1. Addition and multiplication are commutative on the set of integers.
2. Modular addition is commutative on clock 5. We would need to verify $\frac{5 \cdot 4}{2 \cdot 1}$ or 10 combinations of two different elements in order to prove this statement. Three examples are shown.

$$2 \oplus 3 \overset{?}{=} 3 \oplus 2 \qquad 1 \oplus 2 \overset{?}{=} 2 \oplus 1 \qquad 3 \oplus 4 \overset{?}{=} 4 \oplus 3$$
$$0 = 0 \qquad\qquad\quad 3 = 3 \qquad\qquad\quad 2 = 2$$

3. Subtraction and division are *not* commutative on the set of integers.

$$5 - 3 \neq 3 - 5 \qquad 2 \div 1 \neq 1 \div 2$$

The Identity Element

- **DEFINITION.** For set S and operation $*$, e is the **identity element** if and only if:

$$\exists e \in S, \forall a \in S: \quad a * e = e * a = a$$

We will investigate the existence of an identity element in the following cases:

1. In the set of rational numbers, the identity element for addition is 0 and the identity element for multiplication is 1.
   For all rational numbers a: $a + 0 = 0 + a = a$ and $a \cdot 1 = 1 \cdot a = a$.
2. In (Clock 5, $\oplus$), the identity element is 0.

$$0 \oplus 0 = 0 \qquad 1 \oplus 0 = 0 \oplus 1 = 1 \qquad 2 \oplus 0 = 0 \oplus 2 = 2$$
$$\qquad\qquad 3 \oplus 0 = 0 \oplus 3 = 3 \qquad 4 \oplus 0 = 0 \oplus 4 = 4$$

3. In the set of integers, there is no identity element for subtraction and no identity element for division.

$$12 - 0 = 12 \text{ but } 0 - 12 \neq 12 \qquad\qquad 12 \div 1 = 12 \text{ but } 1 \div 12 \neq 12$$

Inverse Elements

- **DEFINITION.** For set S, an element a has a *unique* **inverse** a^{-1} under the operation $*$ if and only if:

$$\text{there exists an identity } e \text{ for } * \text{ in } S, \text{ and}$$
$$\forall a \in S, \exists a^{-1} \in S: \quad a * a^{-1} = a^{-1} * a = e$$

1. Every integer a has an inverse $-a$ for the operation addition since $a + (-a) = (-a) + a = 0$.
2. In (Clock 5, $\oplus$), every element has an inverse.

$$\begin{aligned}
&0 \text{ is the inverse of } 0: \quad 0 \oplus 0 = 0 \\
&4 \text{ is the inverse of } 1: \quad 1 \oplus 4 = 4 \oplus 1 = 0 \\
&3 \text{ is the inverse of } 2: \quad 2 \oplus 3 = 3 \oplus 2 = 0 \\
&2 \text{ is the inverse of } 3: \quad 3 \oplus 2 = 2 \oplus 3 = 0 \\
&1 \text{ is the inverse of } 4: \quad 4 \oplus 1 = 1 \oplus 4 = 0
\end{aligned}$$

Groups

The properties that we have been using enable us to define an important structure in mathematics called a *group*.

● **DEFINITION.** A *group* is a mathematical system consisting of a set G and an operation $*$ that satisfies four properties:

1. The set G is *closed* under $*$.
2. The operation $*$ is *associative* on the elements of G.
3. There is an element e of G that is the *identity* for $*$.
4. Every element a in G has, for $*$, an *inverse* a^{-1} in G.

This definition can be written in symbolic form.

● **DEFINITION.** $(G, *)$ is a group if and only if:

1. $\forall a, b \in G$: $a * b = c$, $c \in G$. (*Closure*)
2. $\forall a, b, c \in G$: $(a * b) * c = a * (b * c)$. (*Associativity*)
3. $\exists e \in G, \forall a \in G$: $a * e = e * a = a$. (*Identity*)
4. $\forall a \in G, \exists a^{-1} \in G$: $a * a^{-1} = a^{-1} * a = e$. (*Inverses*)

The integers form a group under addition, and the clock 5 numbers form a group under clock addition.

Groups were first defined in the eighteenth century. Examples of groups can be found in algebra, geometry, art, and nature. The properties of groups play an important role in science. For example, the symmetries of crystals of minerals form groups, as do the symmetries of particles and of fields of force.

Although commutativity is not required for a mathematical system to be a group, many groups have operations that are commutative. Such a group is called a *commutative group*, or an *Abelian group*. (Integers, $+$) and (Clock 5, $\oplus$) are commutative groups.

Clock multiplication or *modular multiplication,* which is often indicated by symbol $\odot$, can be described in terms of ordinary multiplication. For the clock 5 system in Examples 1 and 2 below, $a \odot b$ is defined as the remainder when $a \cdot b$ is divided by 5.

EXAMPLES

The system (Clock 5, $\odot$) consists of the set $\{0, 1, 2, 3, 4\}$ and the operation clock multiplication defined by the table.

1. Prove that (Clock 5, $\odot$) is *not* a group.

Solution　(1) *Closure:* Every pair of numbers from clock 5 has a product in clock 5, as seen in the table. Therefore, (Clock 5, $\odot$) is closed.

$\odot$	0	1	2	3	4
0	0	0	0	0	0
1	0	1	2	3	4
2	0	2	4	1	3
3	0	3	1	4	2
4	0	4	3	2	1

(Clock 5, $\odot$)

(2) *Associativity:* We could demonstrate that the associative property holds for all numbers in clock 5. We will agree that all clock additions and multiplications are associative.

(3) *Identity:* The identity is 1 because, for all clock 5 numbers x:
$$x \odot 1 = 1 \odot x = x.$$

(4) *Inverses:* This condition fails.
The inverse of 1 is 1 because $1 \odot 1 = 1$.
The inverse of 2 is 3 because $2 \odot 3 = 3 \odot 2 = 1$.
The inverse of 3 is 2 because $3 \odot 2 = 2 \odot 3 = 1$.
The inverse of 4 is 4 because $4 \odot 4 = 1$.
However, there is no inverse for 0.

Therefore, (Clock 5, $\odot$) is *not* a group.

---

2. Let **clock 5/{0}** be clock 5 after eliminating 0 from the set. The table shows (Clock 5/{0}, $\odot$).
Prove that (Clock 5/{0}, $\odot$) is a group.

$\odot$	1	2	3	4
1	1	2	3	4
2	2	4	1	3
3	3	1	4	2
4	4	3	2	1

(Clock 5/{0}, $\odot$)

Solution   (1) *Closure:* Every pair of numbers from clock 5/{0} has a product of 1, 2, 3, or 4, as seen in the table. Therefore, (Clock 5/{0}, $\odot$) is closed.

(2) *Associativity:* We agreed to accept the associativity of clock multiplication.

(3) *Identity:* The identity is 1 because, for all clock 5 numbers x:
$$x \odot 1 = 1 \odot x = x.$$

(4) *Inverses:* Every element has an inverse.
The inverse of 1 is 1 because $1 \odot 1 = 1$.
The inverse of 2 is 3 because $2 \odot 3 = 3 \odot 2 = 1$.
The inverse of 3 is 2 because $3 \odot 2 = 2 \odot 3 = 1$.
The inverse of 4 is 4 because $4 \odot 4 = 1$.

Therefore, (Clock 5/{0}, $\odot$) is a group.

---

3. Tell why each of the following is *not* a group.
   a. The whole numbers under addition.
   b. The even integers under multiplication.
   c. The odd integers under addition.

Answers:

a. The whole numbers have no additive inverses.
b. The even integers have no multiplicative identity, and, therefore, it is meaningless to discuss inverses.
c. The odd integers are not closed under addition, no identity element exists, and it is meaningless to discuss inverses.

EXERCISES WITH OPEN-RESPONSE PROBLEMS

In 1–10, in each case answer the following questions for the set and operation shown in the accompanying table.

a. Is the set closed under the given operation?
b. Is the operation associative on the given set?
c. Name the identity element for the system.
d. For every element having an inverse, name the element and its inverse.
e. Is the system a group?

1. Set $S = \{pos, neg\}$, to represent positive and negative integers. The operation is multiplication.
2. Set $S = \{-1, 0, 1\}$. The operation is multiplication.

·	pos	neg
pos	pos	neg
neg	neg	pos

Ex. 1

·	−1	0	1
−1	1	0	−1
0	0	0	0
1	−1	0	1

Ex. 2

3. Set $S = $ clock 3 $= \{0, 1, 2\}$. The operation is multiplication.
4. Set $S = $ clock 3/$\{0\} = \{1, 2\}$. The operation is multiplication.

⊙	0	1	2
0	0	0	0
1	0	1	2
2	0	2	1

Ex. 3

⊙	1	2
1	1	2
2	2	1

Ex. 4

5. Set $S = \{odd, even\}$, to represent odd and even integers. The operation is multiplication.
6. Set $S = \{1, 2, 3\}$. The operation is *min*, that is, finding the minimum, or smaller, of two numbers.

·	odd	even
odd	odd	even
even	even	even

Ex. 5

min	1	2	3
1	1	1	1
2	1	2	2
3	1	2	3

Ex. 6

7. Set $S = \{a, b, c, d\}$. The operation ∗ is defined by the table.
8. Set $S = \{w, x, y, z\}$. The operation # is defined by the table.

∗	a	b	c	d
a	c	d	a	b
b	d	a	b	c
c	a	b	c	d
d	b	c	d	a

Ex. 7

#	w	x	y	z
w	x	w	z	y
x	w	x	y	z
y	z	y	x	w
z	y	z	w	x

Ex. 8

9. Set $S = \{e, f, g\}$. The operation @ is defined by the table.
10. Set $S = $ clock 8/$\{0\} = \{1, 2, 3, 4, 5, 6, 7\}$. The operation is multiplication.

@	e	f	g
e	e	f	g
f	f	e	g
g	g	f	g

Ex. 9

⊙	1	2	3	4	5	6	7
1	1	2	3	4	5	6	7
2	2	4	6	0	2	4	6
3	3	6	1	4	7	2	5
4	4	0	4	0	4	0	4
5	5	2	7	4	1	6	3
6	6	4	2	0	6	4	2
7	7	6	5	4	3	2	1

Ex. 10

11. a. Construct the table for (Clock 6, $\oplus$).
  b. Is (Clock 6, $\oplus$) a group?

12. a. Construct the table for (Clock 6, $\odot$).
  b. Is (Clock 6, $\odot$) a group?

13. a. Construct the table for (Clock 6/{0}, $\odot$).
  b. Is (Clock 6/{0}, $\odot$) a group?

14. *True* or *false*: For any counting number n, (Clock n, $\oplus$) is a group.
15. *True* or *false*: For any counting number n, (Clock n/{0}, $\odot$) is a group.
16. *True* or *false*: For any prime number n, (Clock n/{0}, $\odot$) is a group.

17. a. If $S = \{0\}$, is $(S, +)$ a group?
  b. If $S = \{1\}$, is $(S, \cdot)$ a group?
  c. If S contains a single element x, and $x * x = x$, is $(S, *)$ a group?

+	0
0	0

a

$\cdot$	1
1	1

b

*	x
x	x

c

Exercises 18–22 refer to *digital multiplication* with $S = \{1, 3, 5, 7, 9\}$.

18. In digital multiplication, answers are single digits, obtained by writing only the units digit from a product in standard multiplication. Compare the given examples.

Standard:
  $3 \cdot 5 = 15$ $3 \cdot 7 = 21$ $3 \cdot 9 = 27$

Digital:
  $3 \odot 5 = 5$ $3 \odot 7 = 1$ $3 \odot 9 = 7$

$\odot$	1	3	5	7	9
1					
3		5	1	7	
5					
7					
9					

Ex. 18–22

Copy and complete the table shown above for digital multiplication with the set $\{1, 3, 5, 7, 9\}$.

19. a. Compute $(3 \odot 9) \odot 7$.   **b.** Compute $3 \odot (9 \odot 7)$.
  c. Is $(3 \odot 9) \odot 7 = 3 \odot (9 \odot 7)$?
  d. Is digital multiplication associative? Explain your answer.
20. a. Name the identity element for $(\{1, 3, 5, 7, 9\}, \odot)$.
  b. For every element having an inverse, name the element and its inverse.
21. Is the set closed under the operation of digital multiplication?
22. Is the set $\{1, 3, 5, 7, 9\}$ under digital multiplication a group? Explain your answer.

23. a. Construct a table for the set $\{1, 3, 7, 9\}$ under digital multiplication.
  b. Is the set $\{1, 3, 7, 9\}$ under digital multiplication a group? Explain your answer.
  c. How does the table for part **a** compare to the table constructed in Exercise 18?

24. a. Using set $S = \{0, 2, 4\}$ and the operation of *average*, symbolized by *avg*, copy and complete the table shown at the right.
  b. Give three reasons why this system is *not* a group.

avg	0	2	4
0			
2			
4			

8-5 FIELDS

In Math A we studied the ***distributive property*** of multiplication over addition.

$$a(b + c) = ab + ac \qquad \text{and} \qquad ab + ac = a(b + c)$$

The importance of the distributive property is that it links two operations defined on a set of elements. The distributive property is not limited to multiplication over addition; sometimes it holds for other pairs of operations as well.

1. Is multiplication distributive over max?

$$a(b \text{ max } c) \overset{?}{=} ab \text{ max } ac$$
$$-3(5 \text{ max } 7) \overset{?}{=} -3(5) \text{ max } -3(7)$$
$$-3(7) \overset{?}{=} -15 \text{ max } -21$$
$$-21 \neq -15$$

Multiplication is *not* distributive over *max*.

2. Is squaring distributive over multiplication?

$$(ab)^2 \overset{?}{=} a^2 b^2$$

By using the definition of a square and the associative and commutative properties of multiplication we see that:

$$(ab)^2 = (ab)(ab) = (aa)(bb) = a^2 b^2$$

Squaring is distributive over multiplication.

3. Is multiplication distributive over addition in the system (Clock 5, $\oplus$, $\odot$)? Clock addition and clock multiplication are defined on the set of clock 5 numbers $\{0, 1, 2, 3, 4\}$ as shown in the tables below. (Clock 5, $\oplus$, $\odot$) is a mathematical system.

$\oplus$	0	1	2	3	4
0	0	1	2	3	4
1	1	2	3	4	0
2	2	3	4	0	1
3	3	4	0	1	2
4	4	0	1	2	3

$\odot$	0	1	2	3	4
0	0	0	0	0	0
1	0	1	2	3	4
2	0	2	4	1	3
3	0	3	1	4	2
4	0	4	3	2	1

$$3 \odot (2 \oplus 4) \overset{?}{=} 3 \odot 2 \oplus 3 \odot 4$$
$$3 \odot 1 \overset{?}{=} 1 \oplus 2$$
$$3 = 3$$

This is just one case for which the distributive property holds for the given system. By considering all possible sets of numbers from clock 5, we could show that multiplication is distributive over addition in the (Clock 5, $\oplus$, $\odot$) system.

It is possible to write a more general definition of the distributive property of one operation, $*$, over another operation, #, as $a * (b \# c) = (a * b) \# (a * c)$. However, we will limit our definition to the more familiar operations.

- **DEFINITION.** In set S, multiplication is **distributive** over addition if and only if:

$$\forall a, b, c \in S: a(b + c) = ab + ac \qquad \text{and} \qquad ab + ac = a(b + c)$$

A Field

Just as the distributive property links together two operations, there is a mathematical system, called a *field*, that contains two operations. Since most fields consist of the operations of addition and multiplication, we will use these operations in our definition.

- **DEFINITION.** A *field* is a mathematical system consisting of a set F and two operations, normally addition and multiplication, that satisfies eleven properties:

    1–5. The set F is a commutative group under the operation of addition, satisfying five properties: closure, associativity, the existence of an identity for addition (usually 0), the existence of inverses under addition, and commutativity.

    6–10. The set F without the additive identity (usually $F/\{0\}$) is a commutative group under the operation of multiplication, satisfying five properties: closure, associativity, the existence of an identity for multiplication (usually 1), the existence of inverses under multiplication, and commutativity.

    11. The second operation, multiplication, is distributive over the first operation, addition.

Thus, if we know the properties of a group, it becomes relatively easy to remember the definition of a field. We now rewrite the definition in symbolic form. We include *two* operations with the set F by writing $(F, +, \cdot)$.

- **DEFINITION.** $(F, +, \cdot)$ is a *field* if and only if:

    1. $(F, +)$ is a commutative group.
    2. $(F/\{0\}, \cdot)$ is a commutative group.
    3. Multiplication distributes over addition.

EXAMPLES

1. Prove that (Clock 3, $\oplus$, $\odot$) is a field.

Solution   First, establish that (Clock 3, $\oplus$) is a commutative group.
1. (Clock 3, $\oplus$) is closed.
2. (Clock 3, $\oplus$) is associative.
3. In (Clock 3, $\oplus$), the identity is 0.
4. In (Clock 3, $\oplus$):
    The additive inverse of 0 is 0.
    The additive inverse of 1 is 2.
    The additive inverse of 2 is 1.
5. (Clock 3, $\oplus$) is commutative.

$\oplus$	0	1	2
0	0	1	2
1	1	2	0
2	2	0	1

(Clock 3, $\oplus$)

Next, establish that (Clock 3/{0}, $\odot$) is a commutative group.
6. (Clock 3/{0}, $\odot$) is closed.
7. (Clock 3/{0}, $\odot$) is associative.
8. In (Clock 3/{0}, $\odot$), the identity is 1.
9. In (Clock 3/{0}, $\odot$):
    The multiplicative inverse of 1 is 1.
    The multiplicative inverse of 2 is 2.
10. (Clock 3/{0}, $\odot$) is commutative.

$\odot$	1	2
1	1	2
2	2	1

(Clock 3/{0}, $\odot$)

Finally, establish that multiplication distributes over addition.
11. In (Clock 3, $\oplus$, $\odot$), $a \odot (b \oplus c) = a \odot b \oplus a \odot c$.

Here are three examples of the distributive property that can be shown in (Clock 3, $\oplus$, $\odot$):

$$1 \odot (0 \oplus 2) \stackrel{?}{=} 1 \odot 0 \oplus 1 \odot 2 \qquad 2 \odot (2 \oplus 1) \stackrel{?}{=} 2 \odot 2 \oplus 2 \odot 1$$
$$1 \odot 2 \stackrel{?}{=} 0 \oplus 2 \qquad\qquad 2 \odot 0 \stackrel{?}{=} 1 \oplus 2$$
$$2 = 2 \qquad\qquad\qquad 0 = 0$$

$$2 \odot (1 \oplus 1) \stackrel{?}{=} 2 \odot 1 \oplus 2 \odot 1$$
$$2 \odot 2 \stackrel{?}{=} 2 \oplus 2$$
$$1 = 1$$

It can be shown that all possible arrangements of clock 3 numbers in the rule $a \odot (b \oplus c) = a \odot b \oplus a \odot c$ will result in true statements.

2. Prove that (Integers, $+$, $\cdot$) is *not* a field.

Solution Of the eleven field properties, one fails to be satisfied. With the exception of 1 and -1, integers do *not* have multiplicative inverses.

EXERCISES WITH OPEN-RESPONSE PROBLEMS

In 1–6, in each case: **a.** State whether or not the system is a field. **b.** If the system is *not* a field, name one field property that is not satisfied.

1. (Whole numbers, $+$, $\cdot$)
3. (Even integers, $+$, $\cdot$)
5. (Clock 5, $\oplus$, $\odot$)

2. (Positive numbers, $+$, $\cdot$)
4. (Odd integers, $+$, $\cdot$)
6. (Clock 4, $\oplus$, $\odot$)

7. Give a reason why (Rational numbers, $+$) is *not* a field.
8. If $S = \{0\}$, give a reason why $(S, +, \cdot)$ is *not* a field.

Exercises 9–13 refer to the field (Clock 5, $\oplus$, $\odot$). The tables for these operations are given on page 302.

9. What element does not have an inverse under multiplication?
10. What elements are their own inverses under multiplication?
11. What is the additive inverse of 4?
12. Evaluate $3 \oplus 3 \oplus 3$.

13. Evaluate $3 \odot 3 \odot 3$.

In 14–16, in each case, using the field (Clock 5, $\oplus$, $\odot$), evaluate parts **a** and **b**; then answer part **c**.

14. a. $4 \odot (2 \oplus 4)$ **b.** $4 \odot 2 \oplus 4 \odot 4$
    c. Is $4 \odot (2 \oplus 4) = 4 \odot 2 \oplus 4 \odot 4$?

15. a. $2 \odot (3 \oplus 2)$ **b.** $2 \odot 3 \oplus 2 \odot 2$
    c. Is $2 \odot (3 \oplus 2) = 2 \odot 3 \oplus 2 \odot 2$?

16. a. $3 \odot 4 \oplus 3 \odot 2$ **b.** $3 \odot (4 \oplus 2)$
    c. Is $3 \odot 4 \oplus 3 \odot 2 = 3 \odot (4 \oplus 2)$?

17. What field property is being tested in Exercises 14–16?

Exercises 18–27 refer to set $S = \{0, 2, 4, 6, 8\}$ under the operations of digital addition and digital multiplication, shown in the tables.

18. Is $(S, \oplus)$:   **a.** closed?   **b.** associative?   **c.** commutative?
19. Name the identity for $(S, \oplus)$.
20. For every element in $(S, \oplus)$ having an inverse, name the element and its inverse.
21. Is $(S, \oplus)$ a commutative group?

$\oplus$	0	2	4	6	8
0	0	2	4	6	8
2	2	4	6	8	0
4	4	6	8	0	2
6	6	8	0	2	4
8	8	0	2	4	6

22. Is $(S/\{0\}, \odot)$:

    a. closed?   **b.** associative?   **c.** commutative?

23. Name the identity for $(S/\{0\}, \odot)$.

24. For every element in $(S/\{0\}, \odot)$ having an inverse, name the element and its inverse.

25. Is $(S/\{0\}, \odot)$ a commutative group?

26. **a.** Is $4 \odot (2 \oplus 6) = (4 \odot 2) \oplus (4 \odot 6)$?

    b. Is $8 \odot (2 \oplus 4) = (8 \odot 2) \oplus (8 \odot 4)$?

    c. Does the operation $\odot$ distribute over the operation $\oplus$?

27. Is $(S, \oplus, \odot)$ a field?

$\odot$	0	2	4	6	8
0	0	0	0	0	0
2	0	4	8	2	6
4	0	8	6	4	2
6	0	2	4	6	8
8	0	6	2	8	4

Exercises 28–32 refer to the set $S = \{a, b, c\}$ under the operations $\triangle$ and $*$, as shown in the tables.

28. In $(S, \triangle)$, the operation $\triangle$ is associative and the identity element is c. Is $(S, \triangle)$ a commutative group? Explain your answer.

29. In $(S, *)$, which element does *not* have an inverse?

30. By removing c (the identity element under $\triangle$) from the set S, the set $S/\{c\}$ is formed. Is $(S/\{c\}, *)$ a commutative group? Explain your answer.

31. One of the operations distributes over the other operation.

    a. Is $b \triangle (a * c) = (b \triangle a) * (b \triangle c)$?

    b. Is $b * (a \triangle c) = (b * a) \triangle (b * c)$?

    c. Which operation is distributive over the other?

32. Is $(S, \triangle, *)$ a field? Explain your answer.

$\triangle$	a	b	c
a	b	c	a
b	c	a	b
c	a	b	c

$*$	a	b	c
a	b	a	c
b	a	b	c
c	c	c	c

8-6 PROPERTIES OF THE RATIONAL NUMBERS

Field Properties of the Rational Numbers

The set of rational numbers under the operations of addition and multiplication forms a field.

- **(Rational numbers, $+, \cdot$) is a field satisfying eleven properties:**

    1. (Rational numbers, $+$) is closed.

$$\forall_{a,b} \in \text{Rationals:} \quad a + b = c, \text{ where } c \in \text{Rationals.}$$

    2. (Rational numbers, $+$) is associative.

$$\forall_{a,b,c} \in \text{Rationals:} \quad (a + b) + c = a + (b + c).$$

    3. A unique identity element (0) exists for addition.

$$\exists_0 \in \text{Rationals}, \forall_x \in \text{Rationals:} \quad x + 0 = x, \text{ and } 0 + x = x.$$

4. **Every element has an inverse (−x) under addition.**

$$\forall_x \in \text{Rationals}, \exists_{(-x)} \in \text{Rationals:} \quad x + (-x) = 0), \text{ and } (-x) + x = 0.$$

5. **(Rational numbers, +) is commutative.**

$$\forall_{a,b} \in \text{Rationals:} \quad a + b = b + a.$$

6. **(Rational numbers/{0}, ·) is closed.**

$$\forall_{a,b} \in \text{Rationals/}\{0\}: \quad ab = c, \text{ where } c \in \text{Rationals/}\{0\}.$$

7. **(Rational numbers/{0}, ·) is associative.**

$$\forall_{a,b,c} \in \text{Rationals/}\{0\}: \quad (ab)c = a(bc).$$

8. **A unique identity element (1) exists for multiplication.**

$$\exists_1 \in \text{Rationals/}\{0\}, \forall_x \in \text{Rationals/}\{0\}: \quad x \cdot 1 = x, \text{ and } 1 \cdot x = x.$$

9. **Every element in Rationals/{0} has an inverse $\left(\frac{1}{x}\right)$ under multiplication.**

$$\forall_x \in \text{Rationals/}\{0\}, \exists_{1/x} \in \text{Rationals/}\{0\}: \quad x \cdot \tfrac{1}{x} = 1, \text{ and } \tfrac{1}{x} \cdot x = 1.$$

10. **(Rational numbers/{0}, ·) is commutative.**

$$\forall_{a,b} \in \text{Rationals/}\{0\}: \quad ab = ba.$$

11. **Multiplication is distributive over addition.**

$$\forall_{a,b,c} \in \text{Rationals:} \quad a(b + c) = ab + ac, \text{ and } ab + ac = a(b + c).$$

We will use these eleven field properties of the rational numbers to solve equations and to perform computations throughout this chapter.

Properties of Order

Two numbers, a and b, are equal, that is, $a = b$, when they name the same number. For example, the integer 3 is expressed in rational form as $\frac{3}{1}$, and $3 = \frac{3}{1}$.

On a standard horizontal number line, the point assigned to the number 3 is to the right of the point assigned to the number 2. Certainly $3 \neq 2$, read as "3 is not equal to 2." However, it is possible to describe the **order** of these numbers in more specific terms:

$3 > 2$, read as "3 is greater than 2."

or

$2 < 3$, read as "2 is less than 3."

$b \qquad a$

$a > b$

$b < a$

We can state the following generalization: For two rational numbers a and b, $a > b$ and $b < a$ if and only if the graph of a is to the right of the graph of b on the conventional number line.

The number line helps us to understand the following four properties of order, each of which is true for the set of rational numbers.

1. Trichotomy property

Given the numbers a and b, then one and only one of the following sentences is true:

$$a > b \qquad \text{or} \qquad a = b \qquad \text{or} \qquad a < b$$

2. Transitive property of inequalities

For all quantities a, b, and c: **If $a > b$ and $b > c$, then $a > c$.**

$c \quad b \qquad a$

and

If $c < b$ and $b < a$, then $c < a$.

Using the rational numbers, we observe:

If $5 > 3\frac{1}{2}$ and $3\frac{1}{2} > 3$, then $5 > 3$.

3. Addition properties of inequalities

For all quantities a, b, and c: **If $a > b$, then $a + c > b + c$.**

and

If $a < b$, then $a + c < b + c$.

Using the rational numbers, we observe:

If $3\frac{1}{2} > 2$, then $3\frac{1}{2} + 7 > 2 + 7$, or $10\frac{1}{2} > 9$.

If $4 < 6$, then $4 + \frac{1}{2} < 6 + \frac{1}{2}$, or $4\frac{1}{2} < 6\frac{1}{2}$.

4. Multiplication properties of inequalities

For all quantities a and b:

If $a > b$ and $c > 0$ (c is positive), then $ac > bc$.
If $a < b$ and $c > 0$ (c is positive), then $ac < bc$.
If $a > b$ and $c < 0$ (c is negative), then $ac < bc$.
If $a < b$ and $c < 0$ (c is negative), then $ac > bc$.

Using the rational numbers, we observe:

If $8 > 6$ and $\frac{1}{2} > 0$, then $8\left(\frac{1}{2}\right) > 6\left(\frac{1}{2}\right)$, or $4 > 3$.

If $1\frac{1}{2} < 5$ and $2 > 0$, then $1\frac{1}{2}(2) < 5(2)$, or $3 < 10$.

If $8 > 6$ and $-\frac{1}{2} < 0$, then $8\left(-\frac{1}{2}\right) < 6\left(-\frac{1}{2}\right)$, or $-4 < -3$.

If $1\frac{1}{2} < 5$ and $-2 < 0$, then $1\frac{1}{2}(-2) > 5(-2)$, or $-3 > -10$.

- **DEFINITION.** An ***ordered field*** $(F, +, \cdot, >)$ is a mathematical system in which a set F under the usual operations of addition and multiplication satisfies the eleven properties of a field and the four order properties of trichotomy, transitivity, addition of inequalities, and multiplication of inequalities.

Not every field is an ordered field. For example, (Clock 5, $\oplus$, $\odot$) is a field that is not ordered. In Chapter 20 we will study an infinite set of numbers that forms a field that is not ordered.

- **The set of rational numbers is an ordered field.**

The Property of Density

- **DEFINITION.** A set is ***dense*** if and only if there is at least one element of the set between any two given elements of the set.

Between any two given rational numbers, it is always possible to identify at least one more rational number by finding the *average* (avg) of the two given numbers. Thus, the set of rational numbers is a ***dense set***, or a set having the property of ***density***. Consider the following examples:

1. Find a rational number between 1 and $1\frac{1}{2}$.

Solution: $1 \text{ avg } 1\frac{1}{2} = \dfrac{1 + 1\frac{1}{2}}{2} = \dfrac{2\frac{1}{2}}{2} = \dfrac{2.50}{2} = 1.25, \text{ or } 1\frac{1}{4}$ *Answer*

2. Find a rational number between $\frac{1}{7}$ and $\frac{2}{7}$.

Solution: $\frac{1}{7} \text{ avg } \frac{2}{7} = \dfrac{\frac{1}{7} + \frac{2}{7}}{2} = \dfrac{\frac{3}{7}}{2} = \frac{3}{7} \div \frac{2}{1} = \frac{3}{7} \cdot \frac{1}{2} = \frac{3}{14}$ *Answer*

Let us consider another example. We choose any two numbers that can be graphed on a number line, such as 0 and $\frac{1}{2}$,

and we think of these numbers in decimal form as 0.0 and 0.5. Then 0.1, 0.2, 0.3, and 0.4 lie between them on the number line. Now we think of 0.0 and 0.1 written with two decimal places as 0.00 and 0.10. Then 0.01, 0.02, 0.03, . . . , 0.09 all lie between them. We can continue this process indefinitely, finding numbers between 0 and 0.01 by writing the numbers with three, four, and more decimal places.

This example leads us to the following generalization:

- **Between any two rational numbers, there is an infinite number of rational numbers.**

We have seen that every rational number is associated with a point on the number line, but the converse of this statement is not true. For example, between the points associated with 1 and $1\frac{1}{2}$ on the number line, there is an infinite number of points associated with other rational numbers, but there is also a point associated with $\sqrt{2}$, a number that is not rational. We will study irrational numbers such as $\sqrt{2}$ in Chapter 10 of this book. For now, we realize that, no matter how densely packed the points associated with rational numbers are, there are still "holes" in the rational number line.

EXAMPLES

1. Write the negation of the expression $x > 5$ in two ways.

Solution   By the trichotomy property, $x > 5$, $x = 5$, or $x < 5$. If we know that $x \ngtr 5$, then $x = 5$ or $x < 5$, that is, $x \leq 5$.

Answer: $x \ngtr 5$ or $x \leq 5$

---

2. Arrange the numbers $\frac{3}{5}$, $\frac{4}{7}$, and $\frac{1}{2}$ in proper order, using the symbol $<$.

Solution   (1) Change the fractions to decimal form.

Enter:	3 ÷ 5 =	*Display:*	0.6
Enter:	4 ÷ 7 =	*Display:*	0.5714285
Enter:	1 ÷ 2 =	*Display:*	0.5

(2) Since $0.5 < 0.\overline{571428}$ and $0.\overline{571428} < 0.6$, it is now evident that $\frac{1}{2} < \frac{4}{7}$ and $\frac{4}{7} < \frac{3}{5}$. A more compact form of this inequality is $\frac{1}{2} < \frac{4}{7} < \frac{3}{5}$.

Answer: $\frac{1}{2} < \frac{4}{7} < \frac{3}{5}$

EXERCISES WITH OPEN-RESPONSE PROBLEMS

In 1–8, name the property illustrated for each set of rational numbers.

1. $3\frac{1}{2} + 7 = 7 + 3\frac{1}{2}$

2. $\left(17 \cdot \frac{1}{2}\right) \cdot 4 = 17 \cdot \left(\frac{1}{2} \cdot 4\right)$

3. $\frac{3}{2} + \left(-\frac{3}{2}\right) = 0$

4. $\frac{3}{2} \cdot \frac{2}{3} = 1$

5. $6\left(3 + \frac{1}{3}\right) = 6 \cdot 3 + 6 \cdot \frac{1}{3}$

6. $x > 0$ or $x = 0$ or $x < 0$

7. $\frac{2}{5} + 0 = \frac{2}{5}$

8. $4.321(1) = 4.321$

In 9–18, tell whether each statement is true or false.

9. $5 < 8$ **10.** $8 < 7$ **11.** $-3 > 0$ **12.** $12 \geq 2$ **13.** $-6 \leq -1$

14. $\frac{3}{2} > -\frac{5}{2}$ **15.** $\frac{5}{1} \geq 5$ **16.** $\frac{1}{3} > \frac{1}{4}$ **17.** $-\frac{1}{3} > -\frac{1}{4}$ **18.** $-1.6 \leq -2$

In 19–26, in each case replace the question mark with the symbol $>$ or $<$ to make the sentence true.

19. If $x < 9$, then $x + 2 \, ? \, 9 + 2$.

20. If $x > 5$, then $3x \, ? \, 15$.

21. If $x + 3 > -2$, then $x \, ? \, -5$.

22. If $-2 < x$, then $-3 \, ? \, x - 1$.

23. If $7 > 6$ and $x > 0$, then $7x \, ? \, 6x$.

24. If $x < 6$ and $6 < 8$, then $x \, ? \, 8$.

25. If $7 > 6$ and $6 > x$, then $7 \, ? \, x$.

26. If $6 < 8$ and $x < 0$, then $6x \, ? \, 8x$.

In 27–31, write the negation of each given expression in two ways.

27. $x > 2$ **28.** $x < 3$ **29.** $x \leq 12$ **30.** $x \geq -8$ **31.** $x = 4$

In 32–39, in each case arrange the given numbers in proper order, using the symbol $<$.

32. $-2, 5, 1$ **33.** $-4, -2, -7$ **34.** $0.2, 0.12, 0.21$ **35.** $\frac{1}{5}, \frac{1}{10}, \frac{3}{20}$

36. $-\frac{3}{2}, -1, -1.6$ **37.** $\frac{2}{3}, \frac{3}{5}, \frac{5}{8}$ **38.** $\frac{8}{9}, \frac{7}{8}, \frac{9}{11}$ **39.** $1\frac{4}{5}, 1\frac{3}{10}, 1\frac{3}{4}$

In 40–47, in each case: **a.** State whether or not the system is a group.   **b.** If your answer to part **a** is "No," name all group properties that fail.

40. (Counting numbers, $+$)

41. (Integers, $+$)

42. (Integers/{0}, $\cdot$)

43. (Rational numbers, $\cdot$)

44. (Rational numbers, $+$)

45. (Rational numbers/{0}, $\cdot$)

46. (Positive rational numbers, $+$)

47. (Positive rational numbers, $\cdot$)

In 48–57, in each case determine the *average* of the two given rational numbers to find another rational number that lies between the given numbers.

48. $7, 8$ **49.** $0, -3$ **50.** $-8, -7$ **51.** $-5, 2$ **52.** $3, 3.3$

53. $2, 2\frac{1}{2}$ **54.** $\frac{2}{5}, \frac{3}{5}$ **55.** $1.9, 2$ **56.** $\frac{2}{3}, \frac{5}{6}$ **57.** $\frac{3}{4}, \frac{7}{8}$

58. Name three rational numbers that lie between 17.1 and 17.

59. In the system (Clock 5, $\oplus$, $\odot$), assume that $0 < 1 < 2 < 3 < 4$. Explain why (Clock 5, $\oplus$, $\odot$) is *not* an ordered field.

8-7 FIRST-DEGREE EQUATIONS AND INEQUALITIES

In working with the field of rational numbers, as well as other ordered fields, we deal with quantities, operations, and relationships. The addition and multiplication properties for inequalities were stated in Section 8-6. When two quantities are equal, other postulates are needed.

Postulates of Equality

A *postulate* or an **axiom** is a statement that is accepted as being true without proof. Let us recall some postulates of equality, studied in earlier courses, that are used when dealing with equalities and solving equations.

1. **Reflexive property** $\forall_a$: $a = a$.
2. **Symmetric property** $\forall_{a,b}$: If $a = b$, then $b = a$.
3. **Transitive property** $\forall_{a,b,c}$: If $a = b$ and $b = c$, then $a = c$.
4. **Substitution property** $\forall_{a,b}$: If $a = b$, then a may be replaced by b, or b may be replaced by a, in any expression.
5. **Addition property** $\forall_{a,b,c}$: If $a = b$, then $a + c = b + c$.
6. **Multiplication property** $\forall_{a,b,c}$: If $a = b$, then $ac = bc$.

Equations and Inequalities

An *equation* is a sentence that uses the symbol $=$ to state that two quantities are equal; for example, $\frac{2}{4} = \frac{1}{2}$. An *inequality* is a sentence that uses one of the symbols of order, namely, $>$, $<$, $\geq$, or $\leq$, to show the order relationship of two quantities; for example, $\frac{1}{2} < 1$.

Types of Solution Sets

We have learned that sets may be finite, infinite, or empty. This statement is also true for solution sets, as we will now see.

A *finite set* is a set whose elements can be counted. For example:

1. Given the domain of integers and $x + 7 = 3$, the solution set is $\{-4\}$.
2. Given the domain of whole numbers and $x < 4$, the solution set is $\{0, 1, 2, 3\}$.
3. Given the domain of counting numbers and $x \leq 300$, the solution set is then $\{1, 2, 3, \ldots, 300\}$.

An **infinite set** is a set whose elements cannot be counted. Here, the counting process does not come to an end. For example:

1. Given the domain of integers and $x + 7 < 3$, the solution set is then $\{-5, -6, -7, \ldots\}$.

2. Given the domain of rational numbers and $x + 7 < 3$, it is *not* possible to list a pattern of numbers as the solution set. Rather, the solution set is written in *set-builder notation* as follows:

$$\{x \mid x < -4 \text{ and } x \in \text{rational numbers}\}$$

This is read as
"the set of
all elements x
such that
x is less than -4 and x is a rational number."

Set-builder notation may be used to indicate any set. However, if it is possible to list the elements of a set in a simpler form, we should do so. For example, the solution set $\{x \mid x = 4 \text{ and } x \in \text{integers}\}$ can be expressed simply as $\{4\}$.

The *empty set*, or *null set*, is the set that has no elements. For example:

1. Given the domain of integers and $3x + 1 = 2$, the solution set is the empty set, written as $\{\ \}$ or $\emptyset$.

2. Given the domain of whole numbers and $x < -4$, the solution set is again $\{\ \}$ or $\emptyset$.

In an *open sentence*, one or more of the quantities in the relationship contains a variable. For example:

$$\text{Equation: } x + 7 = 3 \qquad \text{Inequality: } x + 7 < 3$$

In each of these open sentences, the left-hand member $(x + 7)$ contains the variable x. The right-hand member (3), as well as the term 7, is called a *constant*. A *variable* is a placeholder that represents a member or an element of a given set. Such a set is called the *domain*, or the *replacement set*, of the variable. The open sentence is neither true nor false until we replace the variable with elements of the domain. For example:

Equation: $x + 7 = 3$

If $x = -6$, then $-6 + 7 = 3$

$\qquad\qquad\qquad 1 = 3$ (False)

If $x = -4$, then $-4 + 7 = 3$

$\qquad\qquad\qquad 3 = 3$ (True)

Inequality: $x + 7 < 3$

If $x = -6$, then $-6 + 7 < 3$

$\qquad\qquad\qquad 1 < 3$ (True)

If $x = -4$, then $-4 + 7 < 3$

$\qquad\qquad\qquad 3 < 3$ (False)

When a sentence can be judged to be true or false, it is called a *statement*, or a *closed sentence*. In a statement there are no variables.

A *solution set* is a subset of the domain consisting of the elements or members of the domain that make the open sentence true. A solution to an equation is sometimes called a *root* of the equation. For example:

☐ Domain = Integers
Solve for x: $x + 7 = 3$.

Solution: Add the inverse of 7 to both members and simplify.

$$x + 7 = 3$$
$$x + 7 + (-7) = 3 + (-7)$$
$$x = -4$$

Answer: $x = -4$, or the solution set = $\{-4\}$

☐ Domain = Integers
Solve for x: $x + 7 < 3$.

Solution: Add the inverse of 7 to both members and simplify.

$$x + 7 < 3$$
$$x + 7 + (-7) < 3 + (-7)$$
$$x < -4$$

Answer: $x < -4$, or the solution set = $\{-5, -6, -7, \ldots\}$

In solving the open sentences above, we used many of the field properties, the properties of equality, and the properties of order. Included were the addition property of equality, the addition property of inequality, the associative property of addition, additive inverses, the additive identity, and closure under addition. Often, however, to simplify the procedure, these properties were not written out as individual steps.

The Graphing Calculator

A graphing calculator will perform all of the operations of a scientific calculator as well as many additional ones. Not all graphing calculators perform the same functions, and on those that have similar functions, the sequence of keystrokes used to make entries may vary from one calculator to the next.

In this text, we will give directions for two widely used graphing calculators (Texas Instruments TI-81 and TI-83 models), but the given sequence of keystrokes may need to be changed for a different make or model of graphing calculator.

Some graphing calculators have the ability to test the truth of an equation or inequality, and this feature can be used to display the solution set of an inequality on the number line.

The ☐ TEST ☐ key of most graphing calculators displays a menu that consists of six symbols of equality and inequality: $=, \neq, >, \geq, <,$ and $\leq$. When an equation or inequality using one of these symbols is entered, the calculator will display 1 when the statement is true and 0 when it is false. Consider the following examples:

1. Is the statement $1,702 \div 37 + 3 = 50$ true or false?

In the test menu, $=$ is the entry numbered 1. Therefore, after displaying the test menu, enter 1 to copy $=$ to the screen on which the equation is being written.

Enter: 1702 ÷ 37 + 3 **2nd** **TEST** 1 50 **ENTER**

Display:

$$1702/37+3=50$$
$$0$$

Since the calculator displayed 0, the statement is false.   *Answer*

2. Is the statement $14 \times 14 > 13 \times 15$ true or false?

This time, after displaying the test menu by entering **2nd** **TEST**, enter 3 because $>$ is the entry numbered 3.

Enter: 14 × 14 **2nd** **TEST** 3 13 × 15 **ENTER**

Display:

$$14*14>13*15$$
$$1$$

Since the calculator displayed 1, the statement is true.   *Answer*

   When we enter an equation or inequality that contains a variable, the calculator will return the truth value, 0 or 1, for the value of the variable currently stored in the calculator.

3. Is $2x + 4 \geq 9$ when $x = 3$?
   (1) Store 3 as the value of x.

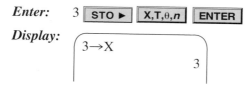

Enter: 3 **STO ▶** **X,T,θ,n** **ENTER**

Display:

$$3 \rightarrow X$$
$$3$$

   (2) Enter the inequality.

Enter: 2 **X,T,θ,n** + 4 **2nd** **TEST** 4 9 **ENTER**

Display:

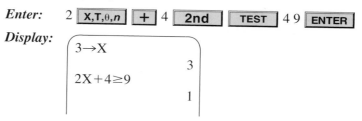

$$3 \rightarrow X$$
$$3$$
$$2X+4 \geq 9$$
$$1$$

Since the calculator displayed 1, the inequality is true when $x = 3$.

When we enter an inequality in the menu, and graph the function, the calculator will display a dot at $y = 1$ for all values of x for which the inequality is true. For example, to draw the graph of $3x + 5 \leq 11$, we use the following steps:

(1) Change the graph from connected to dot mode.

Enter: | MODE | | ▼ | | ▼ | | ▼ | | ▼ | | ▶ | | ENTER |

(2) Select an appropriate range or window. Each graphing calculator will use a unique set of x values to produce specific results. For example, to display values of x as multiples of 0.1, we select x values from -4.7 to 4.8 on the TI-81, and values of x from -4.7 to 4.7 on the TI-83. We will choose y values from -3.1 to 3.1 on both calculators.

On the TI-81:

Enter: | RANGE | | (−) | 4.7 | ENTER | 4.8 | ENTER | 1 | ENTER |
| (−) | 3.1 | ENTER | 3.1 | ENTER | 1 | ENTER |

On the TI-83, the required set of values can be obtained by using the ZDecimal values in the | ZOOM | menu.

Enter: | ZOOM | 4 | ENTER |

(3) Enter the inequality and draw the graph.

Enter: | Y= | 3 | X,T,θ,*n* | | + | 5 | 2nd | | TEST | 6 11 | GRAPH |

Display:

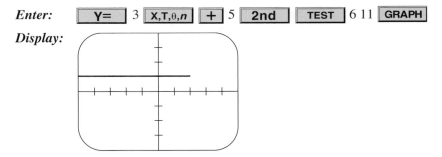

Note the line of points at $y = 1$ for all values of x that are less than or equal to 2. These are the values of x for which the inequality is true. (For values of x for which the inequality is false, there is a line of points at $y = 0$; but since these points lie on the x-axis, they are not apparent on the graph.) Press | TRACE | and use the right and left arrow keys to move through the values of x. For all values of x for which $y = 1$, the inequality $3x + 5 \leq 11$ is true; for all values of x for which $y = 0$, the inequality is false.

EXAMPLES

Unless otherwise noted, assume that the domain for all equations and inequalities in this chapter is the set of rational numbers.

1. Solve and check: $5(x - 1) - 3 = 2x - (3 - x)$.

Procedure for Solving a First-Degree Equation:

Solution:

(1) Write the equation.

$$5(x - 1) - 3 = 2x - (3 - x)$$

(2) Simplify each side.

$$5x - 5 - 3 = 2x - 3 + x$$

$$5x - 8 = 3x - 3$$

(3) Use additive inverses to form an equivalent equation with only variable terms on one side and only constant terms on the other.

$$5x - 8 + 8 = 3x - 3 + 8$$

$$5x = 3x + 5$$

$$5x - 3x = 3x + 5 - 3x$$

$$2x = 5$$

(4) Use the multiplicative inverse to obtain an equivalent equation with only the variable on one side.

$$\frac{1}{2}(2x) = \frac{1}{2}(5)$$

$$x = \frac{5}{2}$$

Procedure for Checking an Equation:

Check:

(1) Write the given equation.

$$5(x - 1) - 3 = 2x - (3 - x)$$

(2) Substitute the solution for the variable.

$$5\left(\frac{5}{2} - 1\right) - 3 \stackrel{?}{=} 2\left(\frac{5}{2}\right) - \left(3 - \frac{5}{2}\right)$$

(3) Evaluate each side.

$$5\left(\frac{3}{2}\right) - 3 \stackrel{?}{=} 2\left(\frac{5}{2}\right) - \left(\frac{1}{2}\right)$$

$$\frac{15}{2} - 3 \stackrel{?}{=} 5 - \frac{1}{2}$$

$$\frac{9}{2} = \frac{9}{2} \quad ✔$$

Answer: $x = \frac{5}{2}$, or $2\frac{1}{2}$, or 2.5; or solution set $= \left\{2\frac{1}{2}\right\}$

2. Solve within the set of rational numbers: $2(5 - x) > 3 + 1$.

How to Proceed:	*Solution:*
(1) Write the inequality.	$2(5 - x) > 3 + 1$
(2) Clear parentheses.	$10 - 2x > 3 + 1$
(3) Combine the like terms on each side of the inequality.	$10 - 2x > 4$
(4) Use additive inverses to form an equivalent inequality with only variable terms on one side and only constant terms on the other.	$\cancel{10} - 2x + (-\cancel{10}) > 4 + (-10)$ $-2x > 4 + (-10)$
(5) Combine like terms.	$-2x > -6$
(6) Use a multiplicative inverse (reciprocal) to isolate the variable.	$-\frac{1}{2}(-2x) < -\frac{1}{2}(-6)$ $x < 3$
(*Note:* When multiplying by a negative number, the order is reversed.)	

Answer: $\{x \mid x < 3 \text{ and } x \in \text{rational numbers}\}$

Since this solution set is infinite, it is not possible to check all values that make the inequality true. However, you may select one or more rational numbers less than 3 and check these values in $2(5 - x) > 3 + 1$, the original open sentence.

EXERCISES WITH OPEN-RESPONSE PROBLEMS

In 1–7, list the elements of each solution set, or indicate that the solution is the empty set.

1. $\{x \mid x + 5 = 16 \text{ and } x \in \text{whole numbers}\}$

2. $\{x \mid x - 3 < 1 \text{ and } x \in \text{counting numbers}\}$

3. $\{y \mid 2y + 5 = 8 \text{ and } y \in \text{rational numbers}\}$

4. $\{y \mid 3 - 4y = 2y \text{ and } y \in \text{natural numbers}\}$

5. $\{x \mid 3(4 + x) \leq 27 \text{ and } x \in \text{whole numbers}\}$

6. $\{x \mid x + 21 = 3 - 2x \text{ and } x \in \text{integers}\}$

7. $\{y \mid 5 - 2y = 4(y - 7) \text{ and } y \in \text{integers}\}$

In 8–36, solve and check each equation. Use the domain of rational numbers.

8. $x - 7 = 10$

9. $y + 8 = 3$

10. $4z = 1$

11. $-3 = 2w$

12. $0.8 = a + 0.5$

13. $2b = \frac{1}{4}$

14. $0.4c = 6$

15. $\frac{5}{3}d = \frac{15}{9}$

16. $-2\frac{1}{3} = -3 + p$

17. $\frac{x}{3} = -2\frac{1}{3}$

18. $r - 0.35 = 0.2$

19. $s + 0.1 = 0.21$

20. $2x + 7 = 1$

21. $4y - 3 = 4$

22. $3z = 20 + z$

23. $\frac{3}{2}m = 12 - \frac{5}{2}m$

24. $2.5k = 11 + 0.3k$

25. $4(t + 3) = 8$

26. $2(x - 1) = -2$

27. $4 = 8(y + 1)$

28. $4(b + 0.2) = 4$

29. $6x - 6 = 3x - 2$

30. $3y - 5 + 2y = 8 - 3$

31. $b - 0.24 = 0.4 - 3b$

32. $2k - 3 = 0.4k + 3.4$

33. $3x - 2(x - 3) = 15$

34. $2y - (y + 10) = 5(y + 6)$

35. $2y - 3(2y - 3) = y + 29$

36. $4 - (x + 0.2) = 2x - 0.1$

In 37–52, solve each inequality within the set of rational numbers. Use set-builder notation to write the solution set. Check your answer by drawing the graph of the solution set on a graphing calculator.

37. $x + 1\frac{1}{2} < 4$ **38.** $3x + 1 > 13$ **39.** $-3x < -18$ **40.** $15 - 2x < 1$

41. $x \geq 7x - 6$ **42.** $25 < 9x - 2$ **43.** $\frac{3}{4}y \geq \frac{3}{8}$ **44.** $\frac{y}{2} \leq 0.15$

45. $3 - x < 11$ **46.** $4x < 3(x + 4)$ **47.** $3(x + 2) \leq 2$ **48.** $2(3 - x) \leq 10$

49. $8 + 3y > 10 - 2y$ **50.** $14 + y \leq 4 + 2y$ **51.** $x - 2(x - 2) \leq 2$ **52.** $x - 3 \leq 3(2x - 1)$

In 53–55, select the *numeral* preceding the expression that best completes the sentence or answers the question.

53. The solution set of $x + 8 = 7$ is { } when the domain is the set of
   (1) integers   (2) whole numbers
   (3) negative numbers   (4) rational numbers

54. For which domain will the solution set of $4x + 1 < 13$ be $\{1, 2\}$?
   (1) integers   (2) whole numbers
   (3) natural numbers   (4) rational numbers

55. The solution set of $3x - 2 = 5$ is *not* empty when the domain is the set of
   (1) integers   (2) whole numbers
   (3) natural numbers   (4) rational numbers

8-8 RATIO AND PROPORTION

The first five letters of the word *rational* form a closely associated mathematical term, *ratio*.

● **DEFINITION.** The ***ratio*** of any two numbers a and b, where b is not 0, is the number $\frac{a}{b}$.

For example, the ratio of 2 and 4 in the order given is the number $\frac{2}{4}$. We recall that any ratio of a to b may also be written in the form $a:b$. Thus, the ratio of 2 to 4 may be written as $\frac{2}{4}$ or as $2:4$.

Either form, $\frac{a}{b}$ or $a:b$, may be used when comparing two numbers.

In our study of geometry, we used ratios to compare lengths of segments and measures of angles. We know that lengths and angle measures are *numbers*. When comparing three or more numbers in a *continued ratio*, we use the form $a:b:c$. For example, the ratio of the angle measure of a 30°-60°-90° triangle is expressed as $30:60:90$.

If M is a midpoint of $\overline{AB}$, and $AB = 4$ centimeters, then $AM = 2$ centimeters and $MB = 2$ centimeters. Thus, the ratio $\frac{AM}{AB}$ is the number $\frac{2}{4}$ or is $2:4$. Since the ratio $\frac{2}{4}$ is equal to the ratio $\frac{1}{2}$, we may write $\frac{2}{4} = \frac{1}{2}$. We may also write $2:4 = 1:2$, which is read as "2 is to 4 as 1 is to 2." Each of these equations is an example of a *proportion*.

● **DEFINITION.** A *proportion* is an equation that states that two ratios are equal.

In general terms, a proportion is written as $\frac{a}{b} = \frac{c}{d}$, or as $a:b = c:d$, where $b \neq 0$ and $d \neq 0$. The first and fourth terms, a and d, are called the **extremes** of the proportion. The second and third terms, b and c, are the **means** of the proportion.

Given any proportion, for example: we may

$$\frac{a}{b} = \frac{c}{d}$$

1. Apply the multiplication property of equality. $\quad \frac{a}{b}(bd) = \frac{c}{d}(bd)$

2. Simplify. $\qquad\qquad\qquad\qquad\qquad\qquad ad = bc$

Conversely, by starting with $ad = bc$, and multiplying each side by $\frac{1}{bd}$, we will obtain $\frac{a}{b} = \frac{c}{d}$. Thus, we observe:

● **A proportion exists if and only if the product of the means is equal to the product of the extremes.**

This statement can be written in symbols as follows:

When $b \neq 0$ and $d \neq 0$, $\frac{a}{b} = \frac{c}{d}$ if and only if $ad = bc$.

For example, given $\frac{6}{15} = \frac{8}{20}$, then $6 \cdot 20 = 15 \cdot 8$, or $120 = 120$.

Using the multiplication property for inequalities, where $b > 0$ and $d > 0$, we can prove that similar relations are true for fractions that are not equal or for terms not in a proportion:

$\frac{a}{b} > \frac{c}{d}$ **if and only if** $ad > bc$ $\qquad$ $\frac{a}{b} < \frac{c}{d}$ **if and only if** $ad < bc$

For example: $\qquad\qquad\qquad\qquad\qquad$ For example:

$\frac{2}{3} > \frac{4}{7}$ if and only if $2 \cdot 7 > 3 \cdot 4$ $\qquad$ $\frac{4}{7} < \frac{8}{9}$ if and only if $4 \cdot 9 < 7 \cdot 8$

Equivalent Fractions

Two fractions, such as $\frac{2}{4}$ and $\frac{1}{2}$, that are different numerals for the same rational number are called ***equivalent fractions***. An equation that states that two equivalent fractions are equal, such as $\frac{2}{4} = \frac{1}{2}$, is a proportion. Conversely, in a proportion, the left and right members of the equation are equivalent fractions.

There are two common methods to find fractions that are equivalent to any given rational number $\frac{a}{b}$:

1. **EXTENSION.** Multiply both numerator and denominator by the same number, x, where $x \neq 0$. Since any nonzero number divided by itself is 1, $\frac{x}{x} = 1$, the identity element for multiplication.

    $$\frac{a}{b} = \frac{a \cdot x}{b \cdot x} = \frac{ax}{bx}$$

    For example, $\frac{3}{4} = \frac{3 \cdot 5}{4 \cdot 5} = \frac{15}{20}$, and $\frac{3}{4} = \frac{3(-2)}{4(-2)} = \frac{-6}{-8}$. Thus, $\frac{3}{4}, \frac{15}{20}$, and $\frac{-6}{-8}$ are all equivalent fractions.

2. **CANCELLATION.** When possible, divide both numerator and denominator by the same number, x, where $x \neq 0$. To determine a number for this division, find a factor common to both parts of the fraction.

    For example, $\frac{8}{12} = \frac{4 \cdot 2}{4 \cdot 3}$. Thus, $\frac{8}{12} = \frac{8 \div 4}{12 \div 4} = \frac{2}{3}$. This procedure is sometimes written in the form of a cancellation: $\frac{8}{12} = \frac{\overset{2}{\cancel{8}}}{\underset{3}{\cancel{12}}} = \frac{2}{3}$. Thus, $\frac{8}{12}$ and $\frac{2}{3}$ are equivalent fractions.

Proportions in Geometry

Let us recall some applications of proportions from geometry. We begin with *similar polygons*.

*   **DEFINITION. *Two polygons are similar*** if and only if there is a one-to-one correspondence between their vertices such that the corresponding angles are congruent, and the ratios of the lengths of corresponding sides are equal.

For example, $\triangle ABC \sim \triangle A'B'C'$ tells us that $\angle A$ corresponds to $\angle A'$, $\angle B$ corresponds to $\angle B'$, and $\angle C$ corresponds to $\angle C'$. Since the ratios of the lengths of the corresponding sides of similar triangles are equal, we may write:

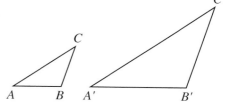

$$\frac{AB}{A'B'} = \frac{BC}{B'C'} \qquad \frac{AB}{A'B'} = \frac{CA}{C'A'} \qquad \frac{BC}{B'C'} = \frac{CA}{C'A'}$$

Note: When the ratios of the lengths of the corresponding sides of two polygons are equal, as just shown, we say that *the corresponding sides of the two polygons are in proportion.* The three ratios $\frac{AB}{A'B'}$, $\frac{BC}{B'C'}$, and $\frac{CA}{C'A'}$ all name the same number and are therefore equivalent fractions.

Some familiar examples involving similar triangles appear in the exercises at the end of the section. For now, let us recall three specific situations.

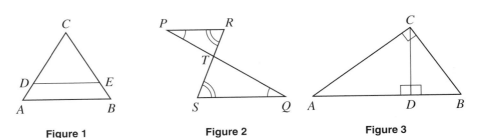

Figure 1   Figure 2   Figure 3

1. In Figure 1, if $\overleftrightarrow{DE} \parallel \overleftrightarrow{AB}$, then $\triangle DEC \sim \triangle ABC$. Many proportions can be formed, including $\frac{CD}{DA} = \frac{CE}{EB}$, $\frac{CD}{CA} = \frac{CE}{CB}$, $\frac{CD}{DE} = \frac{CA}{AB}$.

2. In Figure 2, if $\overleftrightarrow{PR} \parallel \overleftrightarrow{SQ}$, then $\angle P \cong \angle Q$ and $\angle R \cong \angle S$. Since $\triangle PRT \sim \triangle QST$ by a.a. $\cong$ a.a., the proportions include $\frac{PR}{QS} = \frac{RT}{ST}$, $\frac{PR}{QS} = \frac{PT}{QT}$.

3. In Figure 3, if altitude $\overline{CD}$ is drawn to hypotenuse $\overline{AB}$ in right triangle ABC, three similar triangles are formed, $\triangle ABC \sim \triangle ACD \sim \triangle CBD$. Among the proportions are $\frac{DA}{DC} = \frac{DC}{DB}$, $\frac{AD}{AC} = \frac{AC}{AB}$, $\frac{BD}{BC} = \frac{BC}{BA}$.

EXAMPLES

In 1 and 2, replace the question mark between each pair of rational numbers with $>$, $<$, or $=$ to make the statement true.

1. $\frac{4}{7} ? \frac{12}{21}$ **2.** $\frac{8}{15} ? \frac{6}{10}$

Solution   METHOD 1. Change each fraction to an equivalent fraction so that both rational numbers have the same denominator.

1. $\frac{4}{7} ? \frac{12}{21}$ **2.** $\frac{8}{15} ? \frac{6}{10}$

$\frac{4 \cdot 3}{7 \cdot 3} ? \frac{12}{21}$ $\frac{8 \cdot 2}{15 \cdot 2} ? \frac{6 \cdot 3}{10 \cdot 3}$

$\frac{12}{21} = \frac{12}{21}$ $\frac{16}{30} < \frac{18}{30}$

Thus, $\frac{4}{7} = \frac{12}{21}$ Thus, $\frac{8}{15} < \frac{6}{10}$

METHOD 2. Determine the relationship that exists between the product of the means and the product of the extremes.

1. $\frac{4}{7} ? \frac{12}{21}$

$4(21) ? 7(12)$

$84 = 84$

Thus, $\frac{4}{7} = \frac{12}{21}$

2. $\frac{8}{15} ? \frac{6}{10}$

$8(10) ? 15(6)$

$80 < 90$

Thus, $\frac{8}{15} < \frac{6}{10}$

Answers: **1.** $\frac{4}{7} = \frac{12}{21}$ **2.** $\frac{8}{15} < \frac{6}{10}$

These answers can be verified by using the ⬛ **TEST** ⬛ menu on a graphing calculator.

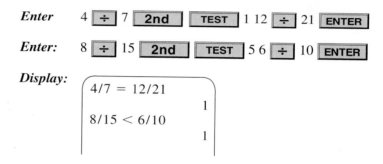

Enter 4 ⬛÷⬛ 7 ⬛ **2nd** ⬛ ⬛ **TEST** ⬛ 1 12 ⬛÷⬛ 21 ⬛ **ENTER** ⬛

Enter: 8 ⬛÷⬛ 15 ⬛ **2nd** ⬛ ⬛ **TEST** ⬛ 5 6 ⬛÷⬛ 10 ⬛ **ENTER** ⬛

Display:

$$\begin{array}{l} 4/7 = 12/21 \\ \qquad\qquad\qquad 1 \\ 8/15 < 6/10 \\ \qquad\qquad\qquad 1 \end{array}$$

The response 1 in both cases indicates that the statements given in the answer are true.

---

3. Given: $\overline{AB}$ intersects $\overline{CD}$ at E.

   $\angle A \cong \angle D$ and $\angle C \cong \angle B$.

If $AC = 36$, $CE = 15$, $EA = 30$, and $DB = 24$:
   a. Explain why $\triangle ACE \sim \triangle DBE$.
   b. Find the lengths of $\overline{DE}$ and $\overline{BE}$.

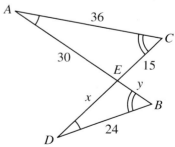

Solution **a.** Since $\angle A \cong \angle D$ and $\angle C \cong \angle B$, it follows that $\triangle ACE \sim \triangle DBE$ by a.a. $\cong$ a.a.

b. (1) Identify the variables.

   (2) The corresponding sides of similar triangles are in proportion.

   (3) Substitute known values.

Let $x = DE$.

$\dfrac{DE}{AE} = \dfrac{DB}{AC}$

$\dfrac{x}{30} = \dfrac{24}{36}$

Let $y = BE$.

$\dfrac{BE}{CE} = \dfrac{BD}{CA}$

$\dfrac{y}{15} = \dfrac{24}{36}$

(4) The product of the means is equal to the product of the extremes.

$36(x) = 30(24)$ $36(y) = 15(24)$

$36x = 720$ $36y = 360$

(5) Solve the equations.

$x = 20$ $y = 10$

Answers: **a.** $\triangle ACE \sim \triangle DBE$ by a.a. $\cong$ a.a.   **b.** $DE = 20$, $BE = 10$

(Note that $\frac{DE}{AE} = \frac{20}{30} = \frac{2}{3}$, $\frac{BE}{CE} = \frac{10}{15} = \frac{2}{3}$, and $\frac{DB}{AC} = \frac{24}{36} = \frac{2}{3}$. The ratios are equivalent fractions because they name the same rational number, $\frac{2}{3}$.)

EXERCISES WITH OPEN-RESPONSE PROBLEMS

In 1–4, if $AB = 6$ and $BC = 9$, state each ratio in simplest (or reduced) form.

Ex. 1–4

1. $\frac{AB}{BC}$ **2.** $\frac{BC}{AB}$ **3.** $\frac{AB}{AC}$ **4.** $\frac{AC}{BC}$

In 5–7, if M is the midpoint of segment $\overline{DE}$, find the rational number represented by each ratio.

5. $\frac{EM}{MD}$ **6.** $\frac{DE}{EM}$ **7.** $\frac{DM}{DE}$

In 8–13, tell whether or not each statement represents a true proportion.

8. $\frac{2}{3} = \frac{8}{12}$ **9.** $\frac{9}{4} = \frac{36}{14}$ **10.** $\frac{16}{10} = \frac{24}{15}$

11. $4:18 = 6:27$ **12.** $6:18 = 4:27$ **13.** $8:72 = 7:63$

In 14–21, replace the question mark between each pair of rational numbers with $>$, $<$, or $=$ to make the statement true.

14. $\frac{9}{20} ? \frac{4}{10}$ **15.** $\frac{3}{6} ? \frac{6}{12}$ **16.** $\frac{20}{30} ? \frac{12}{18}$ **17.** $\frac{14}{16} ? \frac{18}{20}$

18. $\frac{4}{12} ? \frac{5}{15}$ **19.** $\frac{10}{8} ? \frac{9}{7}$ **20.** $\frac{15}{2} ? \frac{-30}{4}$ **21.** $5\frac{1}{3} ? \frac{32}{6}$

In 22–27, $\triangle ABC \sim \triangle A'B'C'$.

22. If $AB = 10$, $BC = 6$, and $A'B' = 15$, find $B'C'$.
23. If $AC = 18$, $AB = 12$, and $A'C' = 30$, find $A'B'$.
24. If $A'B' = 30$, $B'C' = 20$, and $BC = 14$, find AB.
25. If $A'B' = 40$, $B'C' = 30$, and $AB = 26$, find BC.
26. If $AB = 8$, $BC = 6$, $AC = 10$, and $A'B' = 12$, find $B'C'$ and $A'C'$.
27. If $A'B' = 35$, $B'C' = 25$, $C'A' = 40$, and $BC = 15$, find AB and CA.

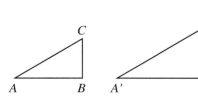

Ex. 22–27

In 28–33, D is a point on $\overline{AC}$ and E is a point on $\overline{BC}$ such that $\overleftrightarrow{DE} \parallel \overleftrightarrow{AB}$.

28. If $AD = 6$, $DC = 8$, and $BE = 12$, find EC.
29. If $DE = 12$, $AB = 18$, and $CA = 12$, find CD.
30. If $CE = 5$, $ED = 5$, and $EB = 3$, find BA.
31. If $CD = 6$, $DE = 12$, and $DA = 5$, find AB.
32. If $CE = 6$, $ED = 10$, and $AB = 15$, find EB.
33. If $AD = 5$, $DC = 10$, and $BC = 24$, find BE and EC.

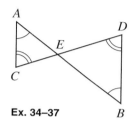

Ex. 28–33

In 34–37, $\overline{AB}$ and $\overline{CD}$ meet at E, $\angle A \cong \angle B$, and $\angle C \cong \angle D$.

34. If $AC = 12$, $CE = 9$, and $ED = 12$, find BD.
35. If $AE = 8$, $EB = 12$, and $DE = 9$, find EC.
36. If $AE = 3$, $EB = 6$, and $DE = 10$, find EC.
37. If $AC = 4$, $CE = 5$, $EA = 6$, and $BD = 6$, find BE and ED.

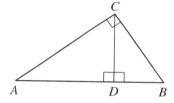

Ex. 34–37

In 38–44, $\overline{CD}$ is the altitude to hypotenuse $\overline{AB}$ in right triangle ACB.

38. If $DB = 3$ and $DC = 6$, find DA.
39. If $DB = 4$ and $BC = 6$, find BA.
40. If $DB = 8$ and $DC = 10$, find DA.
41. If $AB = 10$ and $BC = 4$, find DB.
42. If $AD = 20$ and $DB = 5$, find CD.
43. If $CB = 6$ and $BA = 18$, find BD and DA.
44. If $AD = 16$ and $DB = 9$, find DC, BC, and AC.

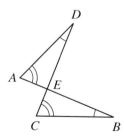

Ex. 38–44

In 45–50, $\overline{AB}$ intersects $\overline{CD}$ at E, $\angle A \cong \angle C$, and $\angle D \cong \angle B$.

45. If $DE = 12$, $EA = 8$, and $BE = 9$, find EC.
46. If $DE = 14$, $BE = 10$, and $EA = 7$, find EC.
47. If $BE = 5$, $EA = 3$, and $CE = 2$, find ED.
48. If $DA = 16$, $AE = 6$, and $EC = 3$, find CB.
49. If $BE = 9$, $EA = 2$, and the ratio of $DE:EC$ is $2:1$, find DE and EC.
50. If $DE = 16$, $EC = 3$, and the ratio of $BE:EA$ is $3:1$, find BE and EA.

Ex. 45–50

51. If a photograph 8 centimeters by 5 centimeters is enlarged so that its longer side measures 20 centimeters, what is the measure of its shorter side?

52. There are 75 calories in a $2\frac{1}{2}$-ounce serving of cottage cheese. How many calories are in an 8-ounce container of cottage cheese?

53. Find three numbers in the ratio of $1:2:4$ whose sum is 35.

54. Doris and Danny play checkers. The ratio of the number of games won by Doris to the number of games won by Danny is $5:3$. If Doris won 6 more games than Danny, find the total number of games of checkers that they played.

8-9 OPERATIONS WITH POLYNOMIALS

We have learned that a rational number can be expressed in the form of a fraction such as $\frac{2}{5}$, $\frac{8}{1}$, or $\frac{-17}{3}$. An ***algebraic fraction***, sometimes called a ***rational expression***, is a quotient of two polynomials. Examples of algebraic fractions include $\frac{3}{x}$, $\frac{x+5}{x-2}$, and $\frac{-4x}{x^2-3x+2}$.

To prepare for operations with algebraic fractions, we will review operations with polynomial expressions.

Algebraic Terms

A ***term*** is a number, a variable, or the indicated product or quotient of numbers and variables. Examples of terms include 8, x, $-5ab$, $\frac{x}{y}$.

In a product, any factor is the ***coefficient*** of the remaining factors. Thus, for the product $2ax$, we say that $2a$ is the coefficient of x, and $2x$ is the coefficient of a. If a numeral only is the coefficient, we call this factor the ***numerical coefficient***. Given $2ax$, we say that 2 is the numerical coefficient of ax.

Let us agree that the word *coefficient*, will, unless otherwise stated, mean "numerical coefficient." Therefore, the coefficient of $7ab$ is 7, and the coefficient of y is 1, since $y = 1y$.

In a term such as x^a, the ***base*** (x) is the quantity that is used as a factor two or more times; the ***exponent*** (a) is the number that tells us how many times the base is used as a factor; and the ***power*** (x^a) is the product. Although x^3 is read as "x to the third power," the power is $x \cdot x \cdot x$, or simply x^3.

Like terms are two or more terms that contain the same variables, with corresponding variables having the same exponents. Terms that are not like are called ***unlike terms***. The differences are apparent in the examples below.

	Numerical Example	
$5^2 = 25$	Base = 5	
	Exponent = 2	
	Power = 5^2 or 25	

	Algebraic Term	
x^3	Base = x	
	Exponent = 3	
	Power = x^3	

LIKE TERMS: $5x$ and $6x$ t^2 and $-2t^2$ $3ab^2$ and ab^2

UNLIKE TERMS: $5x$ and $6y$ t^2 and $-2t$ $3ab^2$ and a^2b

Polynomials

An algebraic expression consisting of one term that is a constant, a variable, or the product of constants and variables is a ***monomial***. Thus, we say:

● **DEFINITION.** A ***polynomial*** is a monomial or any sum of monomials.

Since the prefix *poly-* means "many," we often think of a polynomial as an expression with many terms, but a polynomial may consist of only one term. We have also learned to identify types of polynomials by special names. For example:

1. ***Monomials*** (*mono-* means "one"), such as 8, x, and $-5ab$.
2. ***Binomials*** (*bi-* means "two"), such as $3a - 2b$ and $x + 7$.
3. ***Trinomials*** (*tri-* means "three"), such as $a + b + c$ and $x^2 - x - 6$.

The ***degree of a monomial*** is the sum of the exponents of the variables. For example, the degree of $8a^3bx^2$ is $3 + 1 + 2$, or 6. The ***degree of a polynomial*** is the highest degree in the expression. Thus, the degree of $5a^2x^2 + x$ is 4; the degree of $x^2 - 5x + 8$ is 2; and the degree of $10x - 7$ is 1.

By arranging the terms according to the values of their exponents, we may write a polynomial containing only one variable in *ascending order* ($5 - 2x + x^2$) or in *descending order* ($x^2 - 2x + 5$). The ***standard form*** of a polynomial in one variable uses descending order. Thus, $2x^2 + 8x - 5$ and $5x - 9$ are polynomials in standard form. In general terms, these standard forms are written as

$$ax^2 + bx + c \ (a \neq 0) \qquad \text{and} \qquad ax + b \ (a \neq 0)$$

Addition

We have learned to add like terms, or like monomials, by using the distributive property:

$$8y + 6y = (8 + 6)y = 14y$$

Usually we eliminate the middle step and simply write $8y + 6y = 14y$. Although we can *combine like terms* under addition, the sum of two unlike terms will always be a binomial. For example, the sum of $4a$ and $3b$ is $4a + 3b$. Unlike terms cannot be combined into a single term under addition.

PROCEDURE.   To add polynomials, combine like terms.

Vertical Addition	*Horizontal Addition*
Add: $\quad 3x^2 - 7x - 5$	$(5a - 3b) + (-4a - 2b)$
$\qquad\quad 2x^2 + 5x - 3$	$= \quad 5a - 3b - 4a - 2b$
$\qquad\quad \underline{-x^2 + 2x + 1}$	$= \quad a - 5b \quad$ *Answer*
Answer: $\quad 4x^2 \qquad\quad - 7$	

Subtraction

In $9x - 7x$, the minuend is $9x$ and the subtrahend is $7x$. The opposite, or additive inverse, of $7x$ is $-7x$. Since $9x - 7x = 2x$ and $9x + (-7x) = 2x$, we know that $9x - 7x = 9x + (-7x)$. In general,

$$a - b = x \quad \text{if and only if} \quad a = b + x \quad \text{or} \quad x = a + (-b)$$

Therefore,

$$a - b = a + (-b)$$

PROCEDURE.   To subtract polynomials, add the opposite (additive inverse) of the subtrahend to the minuend.

Vertical Subtraction

Subtract: $3x^2 - 7x$

                $\underline{-2x^2 \qquad + 5}$

Answer: $5x^2 - 7x - 5$

Horizontal Subtraction

   $(5a - 3b) - (4a - 2b)$

$= (5a - 3b) + (-4a + 2b)$

$= 5a - 3b - 4a + 2b$

$= a - b \quad Answer$

Multiplication

We recall the procedures learned in multiplying monomials:

1. When terms with the same base are multiplied, the product contains the same base, but its exponent is the sum of the exponents of the terms. For example, $x^3 \cdot x^2 = (x \cdot x \cdot x) \cdot (x \cdot x) = x^5$. Also, $y \cdot y^6 = y^7$. In general, if a and b are positive integers:

$$x^a \cdot x^b = x^{a+b}$$

2. In repeated multiplication of the same term, sometimes called the power of a power, the product can be found by addition or multiplication of exponents. For example, $(x^3)^4 = x^3 \cdot x^3 \cdot x^3 \cdot x^3 = x^{12}$. Here, $3 + 3 + 3 + 3 = 12$, and $3 \cdot 4 = 12$. In general, if a and c are positive integers:

$$(x^a)^c = x^{ac}$$

3. When monomials are multiplied, we can express the product by a series of factors: first, we multiply the numerical coefficients; then, in alphabetical order, we multiply variable factors that are powers having the same base. For example:

$$(3x)(6x) = (3 \cdot 6)(x \cdot x) = 18x^2$$
$$(5a)(4b) = (5 \cdot 4)(a \cdot b) = 20ab$$
$$(-8a^3b)(ab^2x) = -8a^4b^3x$$

PROCEDURE. To multiply a polynomial by a monomial, use the distributive property to multiply each term of the polynomial by the monomial; then add the resulting products.

For example:

$$2x(x^2 - 3x + 4) = 2x(x^2) + 2x(-3x) + 2x(4)$$
$$= (2x^3) + (-6x^2) + (8x)$$
$$= 2x^3 - 6x^2 + 8x \quad Answer$$

PROCEDURE. To multiply a polynomial by a polynomial, use the distributive property to multiply each term of one polynomial (the multiplicand) by each term of the other polynomial (the multiplier); then combine like terms.

Whenever possible, it is advisable to write each polynomial in standard form before multiplying.

Vertical Multiplication	*Horizontal Multiplication*
Multiply: $x^2 + 8x + 9$	$(x + 2)(3x - 5)$
$\underline{\qquad\qquad x - 4}$	$= x(3x - 5) + 2(3x - 5)$
$x(x^2 + 8x + 9) = x^3 + 8x^2 + 9x$	$= 3x^2 - 5x + 6x - 10$
$-4(x^2 + 8x + 9) = \underline{\quad -4x^2 - 32x - 36}$	$= 3x^2 + x - 10 \quad Answer$
Answer: $\quad x^3 + 4x^2 - 23x - 36$	

Now let us redo the example of horizontal multiplication, using the process to multiply binomials mentally.

1. Multiply the first terms of the binomials.

2. Multiply the first term of each binomial by the last term of the other binomial, and add these products. (Here, $-5x + 6x = x$.)

3. Multiply the last terms of the binomials.

4. Add the results from steps 1, 2, and 3.

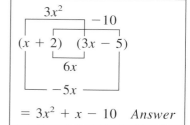

Division

We recall the procedures learned in dividing monomials:

1. When terms with the same base are divided, the quotient contains the same base but its exponent is the difference of the exponents of the terms in the order given. For example:

$$x^5 \div x^3 = \frac{\overset{1}{\cancel{x}} \cdot \overset{1}{\cancel{x}} \cdot \overset{1}{\cancel{x}} \cdot x \cdot x}{\underset{1}{\cancel{x}} \cdot \underset{1}{\cancel{x}} \cdot \underset{1}{\cancel{x}}} = x^2$$

Also, $y^7 \div y = y^7 \div y^1 = y^6$. In general, if a and b are integers, $a > b$, and $x \neq 0$:

$$x^a \div x^b = x^{a-b}$$

2. When monomials are divided, we can express the quotient as a series of factors: first, we divide the numerical coefficients; then, in alphabetical order, we divide variable factors that are powers of the same base. For example:

$$(2x \div 3x) = \frac{2x}{3x} = \frac{2}{3} \qquad 4a^4y^2 \div 8a^3y^2 = \frac{4a^4y^2}{8a^3y^2} = \frac{a}{2}$$

PROCEDURE. To divide a polynomial by a monomial, divide each term of the polynomial by the monomial.

For example:

$$(8x^3 + 6x^2) \div (-2x) = \frac{8x^3}{-2x} + \frac{6x^2}{-2x} = -4x^2 - 3x \quad \textit{Answer}$$

PROCEDURE. To divide a polynomial by a polynomial, follow the process of long division from arithmetic until reaching a remainder of 0 or a remainder whose degree is less than the degree of the divisor.

Before starting the division process, we write each polynomial in standard form. This process is shown with two examples, one from arithmetic and one from algebra, to allow for a comparison.

	In Arithmetic	*In Algebra*
	$1079 \div 43$	$\dfrac{x^2 + 8x + 19}{x + 5}$
How to Proceed:	*Solution:*	*Solution:*
(1) Write the usual division form.	$43\overline{)1079}$	$x + 5\overline{)x^2 + 8x + 19}$
(2) Divide the first term of the dividend by the first term of the divisor.	$\dfrac{2}{43\overline{)1079}}$	$\dfrac{x}{x + 5\overline{)x^2 + 8x + 19}}$
(3) Multiply the entire divisor by the first term of the quotient.	$\dfrac{2}{43\overline{)1079}}$ 86	$\dfrac{x}{x + 5\overline{)x^2 + 8x + 19}}$ $x^2 + 5x$
(4) Subtract this product from the dividend. Bring down the next term to obtain the new dividend.	$\dfrac{2}{43\overline{)1079}}$ $\underline{86}$ 219	$\dfrac{x}{x + 5\overline{)x^2 + 8x + 19}}$ $\underline{x^2 + 5x}$ $3x + 19$

(5) Repeat steps 2 to 4 with the next term of the quotient, and so on, until the remainder is 0 or the degree of the remainder is less than the degree of the divisor.

$$\begin{array}{r} 25 \\ 43\overline{)1079} \\ \underline{86} \\ 219 \\ \underline{215} \\ 4 \end{array}$$

$$\begin{array}{r} x + 3 \\ x + 5\overline{)x^2 + 8x + 19} \\ \underline{x^2 + 5x} \\ 3x + 19 \\ \underline{3x + 15} \\ 4 \end{array}$$

In the algebraic example the remainder 4 has a degree of 0, while the divisor $x + 5$ has a degree of 1.

Answer:

$25\frac{4}{43}$

Answer:

$x + 3 + \dfrac{4}{x + 5}$

Check:

Check:

Check:

To check a division problem, multiply the quotient by the divisor. When the remainder is added to this product, the result should be the dividend.

$$\begin{array}{r} 25 \\ \times\, 43 \\ \hline 75 \\ 100 \\ \hline 1075 \\ +\, 4 \\ \hline 1079 \end{array}$$

$x\ +\ 3$	Quotient
$x\ +\ 5$	Divisor
$x^2 + 3x$	
$+\ 5x\ +\ 15$	
$x^2 + 8x + 15$	
$+\ \ 4$	Remainder
$x^2 + 8x + 19$	Dividend

EXAMPLES

1. Simplify: $3x + 2(3x + 2) + (x - 1)^2$

How to Proceed:

(1) Write the expression.

(2) Multiply (or divide) from left to right.

(3) Add (or subtract) by combining like terms.

Solution:

$3x + 2(3x + 2) + (x - 1)^2$
$= 3x + 2(3x + 2) + (x - 1)(x - 1)$
$= 3x + 6x + 4 + x^2 - 2x + 1$
$= x^2 + (3x + 6x - 2x) + (4 + 1)$
$= x^2 + 7x + 5$ *Answer*

2. Simplify: $4y^2 - [3y + 4y(y - 3)]$

How to Proceed:

If an expression contains one grouping within another, such as parentheses within brackets, work from the innermost grouping first. Clear grouping symbols by using the distributive property.

Solution:

$4y^2 - [3y + 4y(y - 3)]$
$= 4y^2 - [3y + 4y^2 - 12y]$
$= 4y^2 - 3y - 4y^2 + 12y$
$= 9y$ *Answer*

EXERCISES WITH OPEN-RESPONSE PROBLEMS

In 1–5, in each case, add the polynomials.

1. $3ab$
    ab
  $-2ab$

2. $4x^2 - \ x - 3$
   $2x^2 - 3x + 1$
    $x^2 + 4x + 8$

3. $(2a - 3b + c) + (5b - 6c)$
4. $(8m - 7) + (5 - m) + (2 - 7m)$
5. $(3b - a) + (2a - 3c) + (c - b)$

In 6–13, in each case subtract the lower polynomial from the upper polynomial.

6. $18az$
  $12ax$

7. $5by^2$
  $-4by^2$

8. $-3k + 2$
  $-8k + 3$

9. $4c - 3d$
   $c + 2d$

10. $x^2 - 5x - 6$
   $2x^2 - 3x - 6$

11. $4 - 3x - x^2$
   $3 - 4x - 2x^2$

12. $8a \qquad - 4c$
  $-7a + 3b + 6c$

13. $a^2 - 7a$
   $a^2 \qquad + 6$

14. Subtract $x^2 - 8x + 2$ from $3x^2 - 8x + 1$.
15. From the sum of $2x + 8$ and $x - 13$, subtract $4x - 3$.
16. Subtract $3y - y^2$ from the sum of $y^2 - 2$ and $8y - 8$.
17. By how much does $4k - 7$ exceed $3k + 2$?
18. How much greater than $a^2 + a - 3$ is $3a^2 + a + 5$?
19. The sum of two polynomials is $x^2 - 8x + 1$. If one of the polynomials is $2x^2 - x + 1$, what is the other polynomial?
20. a. What polynomial when added to $3a - b$ produces a sum of 0?
   b. What polynomial when subtracted from $3a - b$ produces a difference of 0?
   c. How are the answers to parts **a** and **b** related?

In 21–46, in each case multiply.

21. $3x^3 \cdot 2x^2$
22. $(-m)(8m)$
23. $y^3 \cdot y \cdot y^5$
24. $9ab(2ab^3)$
25. $x^a \cdot x^{3a}$
26. $y^b \cdot y \cdot y$
27. $(-8x^a)(-x^a)$
28. $y^{a+5} \cdot y^{3-a}$
29. $-4(2a - b)$
30. $5x(x + 3)$
31. $-c^2(8c - 3c^2)$
32. $xy(2x^2 - y)$
33. $ab^2(ab - a^2)$
34. $(x + 5)(x + 4)$
35. $(y - 8)(y + 8)$
36. $(k - 1)(k - 6)$
37. $(t - 5)(t - 5)$
38. $(5x + 2)(3x - 1)$
39. $(2y - 3)(2y + 3)$
40. $(2x - 1)(x - 5)$
41. $(3a + b)(a + b)$
42. $(2x - y)(2x - y)$
43. $(x + 3b)(x - 7b)$
44. $(x^2 - 2x + 1)(x - 1)$
45. $(y^2 + y + 1)(y - 1)$
46. $(d^2 + 3d - 4)(2d - 6)$

In 47–64, simplify each expression.

47. $5(x - 2) + 10$
48. $6k - (7 - 6k)$
49. $8x - 2(4x - 1)$
50. $-[x - 2(x - 1)]$
51. $3 - [2 - (1 - x)]$
52. $(y^2)^3 + (y^3)^2$
53. $(2k^2)^3 - k^6$
54. $[(6x - x) + 3]^2$
55. $6x - (x + 3)^2$
56. $(y + 2)^2 - y^2$
57. $3(x - 3)^2 - 27$
58. $[3(x - 2) + 5]^2$

59. $ab(3a - 4c) - bc(2b - 4a)$
60. $x(x - 8) - 2x(x - 3)$
61. $3y[4y - 3(y - 2) - 5]$
62. $k - 3[k - 3(k - 3)]$
63. $(2x + 3)^2 - (2x - 3)^2$
64. $(x^a + 6)(x^a - 6) - (x^2)^a$

In 65–79, in each case divide and check.

65. $(18a - 6b) \div 6$
66. $(3x^2 + 8x) \div x$
67. $(4y^2 - 2ay) \div 2y$
68. $\dfrac{8x^2 - 12x + 4}{4}$
69. $\dfrac{28t^3 - 21t^4}{7t^3}$
70. $\dfrac{6a^2b - 3ab^2 + 3ab}{3ab}$
71. $(y^2 + 9y + 14) \div (y + 7)$
72. $(x^2 - 2x - 15) \div (x + 3)$
73. $(2x^2 + 7x - 4) \div (x + 4)$
74. $(6y^2 + 7y + 2) \div (2y + 1)$
75. $(k^2 - 11k + 30) \div (k - 3)$
76. $(4x^2 + 8x - 19) \div (2x - 3)$
77. $\dfrac{x^2 - 16}{x - 4}$
78. $\dfrac{y^2 + 12y + 36}{y + 6}$
79. $\dfrac{x^2 - 4x - 6}{x - 1}$

80. If the length and width of a rectangle measure $2y + 7$ and $3y - 10$, respectively, express the area of the rectangle as a polynomial.

81. A side of a square measures $7x - 3$. Express the area of the square as a trinomial.

82. If one factor of $x^2 - 8x - 9$ is $x - 9$, find the other factor.

83. In a parallelogram whose area is $5k^2 + 13k - 6$, a base measures $k + 3$. Find the measure of the altitude to that base in terms of k.

84. The measures of the length and width of a rectangle are $3x + 4$ and $2x + 2$, respectively. Copy the diagram of the rectangle shown here.

a. Find the area of each of the four regions into which the rectangle is partitioned. Then add these values to find the area of the rectangle.

b. Show that the area of the rectangle is found by multiplying $(3x + 4)(2x + 2)$.

c. Express the perimeter of the rectangle as a binomial.

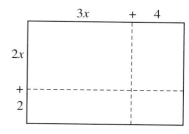

Ex. 84

8-10 FACTORING POLYNOMIALS

To *factor a number*, we find two or more numbers whose product is the given number. Although $20 = \frac{1}{2} \cdot 40$, we restrict factors of integers to numbers that are integers only, as in $20 = 4 \cdot 5$. It is sometimes useful to find all possible pairs of factors for a number. How-

Pairs of Factors	Prime Factors
$20 = 1 \cdot 20$	
$20 = 2 \cdot 10$	$20 = 2 \cdot 2 \cdot 5$
$20 = 4 \cdot 5$	

ever, a number is *factored completely* only when it is expressed as a product of prime factors. We recall that a **prime number**, such as 2 or 5, is a positive integer greater than 1 whose only factors are 1 and the number itself.

To **factor** *a polynomial*, we find two or more algebraic expressions whose product is the given polynomial. When we write $\frac{1}{2}a + \frac{1}{2}b = \frac{1}{2}(a + b)$, we are factoring this polynomial over the set of rational numbers because $\frac{1}{2}$ is a rational number. It is generally understood, however, that polynomials with integral coefficients are factored with respect to the set of integers. In other words, all coefficients of polynomial factors are integers.

In this example: $6x^3 - 12x^2 = 6x^2(x - 2)$, all coefficients of the factors $6x^2$ and $(x - 2)$ are integers. Let us examine these factors carefully:

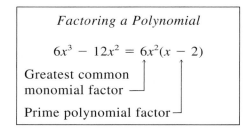

1. The first factor $(6x^2)$ is called the **greatest common monomial factor** of the polynomial because it is the greatest monomial term that is a factor of each term of the polynomial. In writing this greatest common monomial factor, we do not factor its numerical coefficient or any powers of variables; that is, $6x^2$ is not written as $2 \cdot 3 \cdot x \cdot x$.

2. The second factor $(x - 2)$ is called a **prime polynomial** because it has no factors other than 1 and the polynomial itself, with respect to the set of integers.

● **A *polynomial is factored completely* when it is expressed as a product that may include only the greatest common monomial factor and prime polynomial factors.**

Binomial Factors

After the greatest common monomial has been factored from a polynomial expression, or if no common term exists, we next look for binomial factors. In earlier courses, we learned to recognize two polynomial forms having special types of factors. For example:

1. The Difference of Two Squares

$$x^2 - a^2 = (x + a)(x - a)$$

☐ Factor $25y^2 - 4k^2$.

Solution

Since $25y^2 - 4k^2 = (5y)^2 - (2k)^2$, the difference of two squares, we factor the expression to fit the form:

$$25y^2 - 4k^2$$

$$= (5y + 2k)(5y - 2k) \quad \textit{Answer}$$

2. A Perfect Square Trinomial

$$x^2 + 2bx + b^2 = (x + b)(x + b)$$

☐ Factor $4y^2 + 12y + 9$.

Solution

Since the first and last terms are perfect squares, $(2y)^2$ and $(3)^2$, and the middle term $12y = 2(3)(2y)$, we factor the expression to fit the form:

$$4y^2 + 12y + 9$$

$$= (2y + 3)(2y + 3) \quad \textit{Answer}$$

PROCEDURE.   To factor any trinomial of the form $ax^2 + bx + c$ $(a \neq 0)$, find two binomial factors such that:

1. The product of the first terms of the binomials is ax^2.

2. The product of the last terms of the binomials is c.

3. When the first term of each binomial is multiplied by the last term of the other, the sum of the two products is bx.

☐ Factor $2x^2 - x - 6$.

1. The product of the first terms of the binomials must be $2x^2$. Thus, we write: $2x^2 - x - 6 = (2x \quad)(x \quad)$.

2. The product of the last terms of the binomials must be -6. Pairs of factors of -6 are $(1)(-6)$, $(2)(-3)$, $(3)(-2)$, and $(6)(-1)$. Since the order of the placement for these pairs is important, possible factors include:

$$\begin{array}{ll} (2x + 1)(x - 6) & (2x - 6)(x + 1) \\ (2x + 2)(x - 3) & (2x - 3)(x + 2) \\ (2x + 3)(x - 2) & (2x - 2)(x + 3) \\ (2x + 6)(x - 1) & (2x - 1)(x + 6) \end{array}$$

3. When the first term of each binomial is multiplied by the last term of the other, only one pair of binomial factors has products whose sum is the middle term $-x$. The sum of the products $+3x$ and $-4x$ is $-x$.

$(2x + 3) \ (x - 2)$
$+3x$
$-4x$

Answer: $2x^2 - x - 6 = (2x + 3)(x - 2)$

Note: A shortcut could have been taken in step 2 of this example. Since $2x^2 - x - 6$ has no common monomial factors other than 1, we know that the binomial factors of this expression must be prime. Therefore, it was not necessary to include the following possible factors:

$$(2x + 2)(x - 3) \qquad (2x - 6)(x + 1)$$
$$(2x + 6)(x - 1) \qquad (2x - 2)(x + 3)$$

In each case, the first binomial is not prime because it has a common factor of 2.

PROCEDURE.   To factor a polynomial completely:

1. First find the greatest common monomial factor, if one exists.
2. Then factor the remaining expression into binomials or other polynomials until all such factors are prime.

We have learned how to factor a polynomial by finding the greatest common monomial factor. It is sometimes possible, however, to factor a polynomial by finding a common binomial factor. Let us compare the following:

$$3xy - 5y = y(3x - 5)$$
$$3x(x + 2) - 5(x + 2) = (x + 2)(3x - 5)$$

In the first example, y is a common monomial factor. In the second example, $(x + 2)$ is a common binomial factor.

Often it is necessary to factor *pairs* of terms first in order to identify a common binomial factor. For example:

☐ Factor $x^3 - 5x^2 + 2x - 10$.

1. Find a common monomial factor for each pair of terms.
2. Factor out the common binomial.

$$x^3 - 5x^2 + 2x - 10$$
$$= x^2(x - 5) + 2(x - 5)$$
$$= (x - 5)(x^2 + 2) \quad Answer$$

Note: A polynomial with four terms can be factored into two binomials when the product of the first and last terms equals the product of the two middle terms.

EXAMPLES

In 1–5, factor each polynomial completely.

1. $12a^3b + 3a^2b^2 - 6a^2b^3$

Solution   The greatest common monomial factor is $3a^2b$. Once this term has been factored out, the trinomial factor that remains is prime.

$$12a^3b + 3a^2b^2 - 6a^2b^3 = 3a^2b(4a + b - 2b^2) \quad Answer$$

2. $2x^3 + 14x^2 - 60x$

How to Proceed:

(1) Find the greatest common monomial factor.

(2) Factor the trinomial into two prime binomials.

Solution:

$2x^3 + 14x^2 - 60x$

$= 2x(x^2 + 7x - 30)$

$= 2x(x + 10)(x - 3)$ *Answer*

---

3. $y^4 - 81$

Solution:

$y^4 - 81$

$= (y^2 + 9)(y^2 - 9)$

$= (y^2 + 9)(y + 3)(y - 3)$ *Answer*

4. Factor: $x^{b+2} - 16x^b$

Solution:

$x^{b+2} - 16x^b$

$= x^b(x^2 - 16)$

$= x^b(x + 4)(x - 4)$ *Answer*

---

5. $ax^2 - bx - ax + b$

How to Proceed:

(1) Find the greatest common monomial factor for each pair of terms. Note that 1 or -1 may be a factor.

(2) Factor out the common binomial.

Solution:

$ax^2 - bx - ax + b$

$= x(ax - b) - 1(ax - b)$

$= (ax - b)(x - 1)$ *Answer*

Alternative Solution

Change the order of the two middle terms and use the process outlined above. The resulting factors will be equivalent to those in the first solution.

$ax^2 - bx - ax + b$

$= ax^2 - ax - bx + b$

$= ax(x - 1) - b(x - 1)$

$= (x - 1)(ax - b)$ *Answer*

Note: This method can be used to factor a polynomial of four terms into two binomials if the product of the first and last term equals the product of the two middle terms.

EXERCISES WITH OPEN-RESPONSE PROBLEMS

In 1–54, factor each polynomial completely.

1. $3x^2 - 12x$

2. $18 - 6y - 12x$

3. $4ab^2 - 12a^2b$

4. $9y^3 + 3y^2$

5. $x^{b+1} - x^b$

6. $y^{a+2} + 2y^a$

7. $k^2 - 49$

8. $100 - x^2$

9. $a^2b^2 - 144$

10. $x^2 + 10x + 25$

11. $y^2 - 12y + 36$

12. $9x^2 + 6x + 1$

13. $y^2 + 10y + 9$ **14.** $x^2 - 12x + 27$ **15.** $k^2 + 5k - 14$ **16.** $x^2 + 2x - 24$

17. $3y^2 + 4y + 1$ **18.** $2x^2 + 13x + 6$ **19.** $2k^2 - 7k + 6$ **20.** $2x^2 + 7x - 4$

21. $6y^2 - 13y - 5$ **22.** $3y^2 - 12$ **23.** $80 - 5d^2$ **24.** $100 - 4x^2$

25. $7a^2 - 7b^2$ **26.** $x^3 - 121x$ **27.** $3y^3 - 192y$ **28.** $4c^3 - 36cx^2$

29. $y^4 - 1$ **30.** $x^4 - 625$ **31.** $x^3 + 3x^2 - 10x$ **32.** $4x^2 - 20x + 24$

33. $ax^3 - 9ax$ **34.** $2y^3 + 50y$ **35.** $36c^2 - 100d^2$ **36.** $y^{2a} - 1$

37. $x^{2k} - 16$ **38.** $x^{2+k} - 4x^k$ **39.** $x^4 - 5x^2 + 4$

40. $y^4 - 7y^2 - 18$ **41.** $2x^3 + 6x^2 + 2x$ **42.** $4x^2 + 40x + 64$

43. $5x^2 - 5ax - 60a^2$ **44.** $2ax^2 - 8ax - 12a$ **45.** $8y^3 - 60y^2 - 32y$

46. $9ay^2 - 21a^2y + 6a^3$ **47.** $3bx^2 + b^2x^2 - 2b^3x$ **48.** $x^{c+2} - 14x^{c+1} + 24x^c$

49. $x^2 - 2x - 3x + 6$ **50.** $3x^3 - 6x^2 + 2x - 4$ **51.** $4x^5 - 8x^3 - 3x^2 + 6$

52. $b^2y^2 + by^2 + 3b^2 + 3b$ **53.** $c^2x^2 + x^2 - c^2 - 1$ **54.** $4x^2 - 4 - x^2y^2 + y^2$

55. If $3x^2 + 20x + 12$ represents the area of a rectangle, find two binomials that can represent the dimensions of the rectangle. Show your work.

56. If $25x^2 + 20d^2x + 4d^4$ represents the area of a square, express the measure of a side of the square as a binomial. Show your work.

CHAPTER SUMMARY

A number is a ***rational number*** if and only if it can be expressed in the form $\frac{a}{b}$, where a and b are integers and $b \neq 0$. Every rational number can be graphed as a point on the real number line. A number is rational if and only if it can be expressed as a ***repeating*** or ***periodic decimal***.

A ***domain*** is a set of all possible replacements for a given variable. A ***quantifier*** is a phrase that describes in general terms the part of the domain for which the sentence is true. The ***universal quantifier*** ($\forall_x$) indicates that the statement that follows is true for all x's in the domain. The ***existential quantifier*** ($\exists_x$) indicates that the statement that follows is true for at least one x in the domain.

The negation of the universally quantified statement $\forall_x\, p$ is $\exists_x\, \sim p$, and the negation of the existentially quantified statement $\exists_x\, p$ is $\forall_x\, \sim p$.

The mathematical system $(G\, *)$ is a group if and only if:

1. For all a and b in G, $a * b$ is in the set G (closure).

2. For all a, b, and c in G, $(a * b) * c = a * (b * c)$ (associativity).

3. There is an element e in G such that, for all a in G, $a * e = e * a = a$ (identity element).

4. For every a in G, there is an element a^{-1} in G such that $a * a^{-1} = a^{-1} * a = e$ (inverses).

The mathematical system $(F, +, \cdot)$ is a field if and only if:

1. $(F, +)$ is a commutative group.
2. $(F/\{0\}, \cdot)$ is a commutative group.
3. For all a, b, c in F, $a \cdot (b + c) = a \cdot b + a \cdot c$ (distributive property of multiplication over addition).

For two rational numbers a and b, $a > b$ and $b < a$ if and only if a is to the right of b on the real number line. The set of rational numbers under addition and multiplication form an **ordered field**; that is, (Rationals, $+, \cdot, >$) is a field with the following properties of inequality:

1. Trichotomy property. For elements of the field a and b, one and only one of the following is true:
   $a > b$ or $a = b$ or $a < b$.
2. Transitive property. For all elements of the field a, b, and c:
   if $a > b$ and $b > c$, then $a > c$; and
   if $c < b$ and $b < a$, then $c < a$.
3. Addition properties. For all elements of the field a, b, and c:
   if $a > b$, then $a + c > b + c$; and
   if $a < b$, then $a + c < b + c$.
4. Multiplication properties. For all elements of the field a, b, and c:
   if $a > b$ and $c > 0$, then $ac > bc$; if $a < b$ and $c > 0$, then $ac < bc$;
   if $a > b$ and $c < 0$, then $ac < bc$; and if $a < b$ and $c < 0$, then $ac > bc$.

A set is **dense** if and only if there is at least one element of the set between any two given elements of the set. The rational numbers are dense.

The field properties, the properties of equality, and the properties of order are used to find the solution set of an open sentence.

The **ratio** of two numbers a and b, where b is not 0, is the number $\frac{a}{b}$. A **proportion** is an equation that states that two ratios are equal. When $b > 0$ and $d > 0$, $\frac{a}{b} = \frac{c}{d}$ if and only if $ad = bc$, $\frac{a}{b} > \frac{c}{d}$ if and only if $ad > bc$, and $\frac{a}{b} < \frac{c}{d}$ if and only if $ad < bc$.

A polynomial is factored completely when it is expressed as a product that may include the greatest common monomial factor and prime polynomial factors. Two polynomials have special types of factors:

1. The difference of two squares: $x^2 - a^2 = (x + a)(x - a)$.
2. A perfect square trinomial: $x^2 + 2bx + b^2 = (x + b)(x + b) = (x + b)^2$.

VOCABULARY

8-1   Counting numbers   Natural numbers   Whole numbers
Number line   Unit measure   Integers   Positive integers
Negative integers   Real number line   Rational numbers
Repeating (periodic) decimal   Terminating decimal

8-2   Domain   Quantifier   Universal quantifier ($\forall_x$)
Existential quantifier ($\exists_x$)

8-3   Counterexample   Negation

8-4   Postulational system   Deductive reasoning   Binary operation
Clock (modular) addition   Mathematical system   Closure
Associativity   Group   Identity element   Inverse element
Commutativity   Clock multiplication   Modular multiplication

8-5   Distributive property   Field

8-6   Order   Trichotomy property   Transitive property of inequalities
Addition properties of inequalities   Multiplication properties of
inequalities   Ordered field   Dense set

8-7   Postulate   Axiom   Reflexive property of equality   Symmetric
property of equality   Transitive property of equality   Substitution
property of equality   Addition property of equality   Multiplication
property of equality   Equation   Inequality   Finite set
Infinite set   Set-builder notation   Empty (null) set   Open sentence
Constant   Variable   Domain (replacement set)   Solution set
Root

8-8   Ratio   Proportion   Extremes   Means   Equivalent fractions
Similar polygons

8-9   Algebraic fraction (rational expression)   Term   Coefficient
Numerical coefficient   Base   Exponent   Power   Like terms
Unlike terms   Monomial   Polynomial   Degree of a monomial
Degree of a polynomial   Standard form of a polynomial   Binomial
Trinomial

8-10   Factor   Prime number   Greatest common monomial factor
Prime polynomial

REVIEW EXERCISES WITH OPEN-RESPONSE PROBLEMS

In 1–5, express each rational number as a repeating decimal.

1. $\frac{2}{9}$ **2.** $\frac{5}{6}$ **3.** $\frac{6}{11}$ **4.** $3\frac{2}{5}$ **5.** $-\frac{7}{30}$

In 6–10, express each rational number as a fraction.

6. $3\frac{1}{4}$ **7.** -2.8 **8.** 0.05 **9.** $0.\overline{5}$ **10.** $0.\overline{63}$

In 11–14, name the property illustrated for each set of rational numbers.

11. $\frac{3}{7} \cdot \frac{7}{3} = 1$

12. $\frac{1}{2} \cdot 4 + \frac{1}{2} \cdot 12 = \frac{1}{2}(4 + 12)$

13. $\frac{3}{7} + 0 = \frac{3}{7}$

14. $\left(\frac{1}{2} \cdot 4\right) \cdot 12 = \frac{1}{2} \cdot (4 \cdot 12)$

In 15–20, solve each equation and check. Use the domain of rational numbers.

15. $x + 0.2 = 6$

16. $3y - 2 = 20$

17. $k + 0.4 = 3k$

18. $6(b - 2) = 3$

19. $5c + 4 = 3c - 7$

20. $x - 2(x - 2) = -2$

In 21–25, using a domain of rational numbers, write, in set-builder notation, the solution set for each inequality.

21. $\frac{y}{4} > 3\frac{1}{2}$

22. $k \leq 4k - 6$

23. $2(5 - w) > 8$

24. $5(x - 2) \leq 3(x + 1)$

25. $y + 3(y + 3) < 2(y + 3) + 3$

In 26–29, replace the question mark between each pair of rational numbers with $>$, $<$, or $=$ to make the sentence true.

26. $\frac{4}{5} \, ? \, \frac{7}{10}$

27. $\frac{11}{4} \, ? \, \frac{8}{3}$

28. $\frac{8}{12} \, ? \, \frac{12}{18}$

29. $2\frac{2}{3} \, ? \, \frac{16}{6}$

In 30–32, $\overline{AB}$ intersects $\overline{CD}$ at E, $\angle A \cong \angle D$, and $\angle C \cong \angle B$.

30. If $AC = 10$, $CE = 4$, and $EB = 6$, find DB.

31. If $CE = 4$, $AE = 12$, and $BE = 5$, find DE.

32. If $AE = 16$, $BE = 9$, and the ratio of $CE:ED$ is $1:4$, find CE and DE.

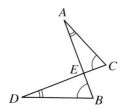

Ex. 30–32

In 33–38, in each case perform the indicated operations and simplify.

33. $(x + 2b) + (x - 3b)$

34. $(3x^2 - 2x + 7) - (x^2 - 2x - 7)$

35. $(x + 2b)(x - 3b)$

36. $(2y^2 - 7y - 15) \div (y - 5)$

37. $[3x - 2(x - 3) + 2]^2$

38. $(2k + 1)(2k - 1) - (2k - 1)^2$

In 39–46, factor each polynomial completely.

39. $x^2 + 14x + 49$

40. $6b^2 + 9b$

41. $4x^2 - 25$

42. $3y^2 + 7y - 6$

43. $4x^2 - 12x + 8$

44. $3y^3 - 48y$

45. $x^3 - 2x^2 - 9x + 18$

46. $ac + 2c - 3ab - 6b$

In 47–50, write each given sentence in words. Let $x \in$ {rational numbers}.

47. $\forall_x : x^2 \geq 0$

48. $\exists_x : x$ is prime.

49. $\exists_x : x$ is not even.

50. $\sim\exists_x : x + 1 = 1$

In 51–54, write the negation of each given sentence.

51. All rhombuses are squares.
52. There exists an integer that is divisible by 5.
53. Some integers do not have additive inverses.
54. No rational numbers are even.

In 55–69, $S = \{a, b, c\}$ and $*$ and # are operations defined by the tables.

55. Is S closed under $*$?
56. Is $*$ commutative?
57. Give two examples to show that $*$ is associative.
58. What is the identity element for $*$?
59. For each element of S, name the inverse under $*$.
60. Is $(S, *)$ a commutative group?

$*$	a	b	c
a	b	c	a
b	c	a	b
c	a	b	c

61. Is S closed under #?
62. Is # commutative?
63. Give two examples to show that # is associative.
64. What is the identity element for #?
65. For each element of S, name the inverse under #, if it exists.
66. Is $S/\{c\}$ closed under #?
67. Is $(S/\{c\}, \#)$ a commutative group?
68. Give two examples to show that # is distributive over $*$.
69. Is $(S, *, \#)$ a field?

#	a	b	c
a	a	b	c
b	b	a	c
c	c	c	c

70. Find the error in the following "proof" that $4 = 0$.

$$\text{Given: } a = 4$$
$$a^2 = 4a$$
$$a^2 - 16 = 4a - 16$$
$$(a + 4)(a - 4) = 4(a - 4)$$
$$a + 4 = 4$$
$$a = 0$$
$$\text{But } a = 4 \text{ is given.}$$
$$\text{Therefore, } 4 = 0.$$

CUMULATIVE REVIEW WITH OPEN-RESPONSE PROBLEMS

1. Write a statement that is logically equivalent to "If today is Saturday or Sunday, then I do not have to go to school."

2. In the diagram $\ell_1 \parallel \ell_2$ and $\ell_2 \parallel \ell_3$.

   a. What postulate can be used to prove that $\ell_1 \parallel \ell_3$?

   b. If m$\angle 1 = 65$, determine m$\angle 2$.

3. Solve for x: $7x - 5 > 10x + 7$

4. *Given:* $\triangle ABC$ with $\overline{AC} \cong \overline{BC}$ and m$\angle ACB < 90$.

   Prove: m$\angle A > 45$.

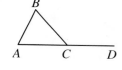

Ex. 4

5. Points $A(1, 0)$, $B(5, 0)$, and $C(8, 4)$ are the vertices of parallelogram $ABCD$. What are the coordinates of D?

6. Prove that the length of the line segment joining the midpoints of the two nonparallel sides of a trapezoid is equal to one-half the sum of the lengths of the parallel sides.

7. Prove that if the midpoint of one side of a triangle is equidistant from the three vertices of the triangle, the triangle is a right triangle.

Exploration

Let H be the set of numbers in the form $\frac{a}{2}$ where a is an integer. The set H is a subset of the rational numbers.

a. Show that (H, +) is a commutative group.

b. Show that (H, ∗) is not a group.

Chapter 9
Rational Expressions

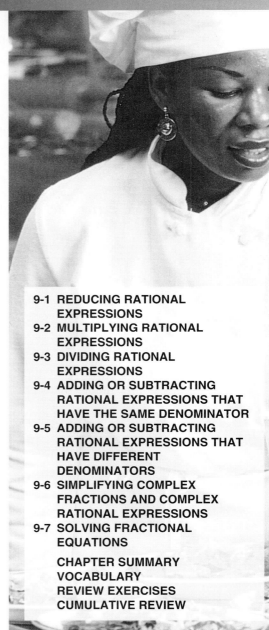

Jennifer is enrolled at a famous culinary institute, studying to become a chef. To prepare the dressing for a salad, she is combining these ingredients:

$\frac{2}{3}$ cup olive oil

$\frac{1}{3}$ cup white wine vinegar

$\frac{1}{2}$ teaspoon salt

$\frac{1}{4}$ teaspoon dried oregano

$\frac{1}{8}$ teaspoon pepper

Classical recipes, as shown here, involve *fractional* measures. Although calculators and computers lead to increased use of decimals, fractions continue to play an important role in our lives.

Incidentally, about three-fourths of the students enrolled at leading culinary schools are male.

In this chapter, we will study algebraic fractions, more commonly called *rational expressions*.

9-1 REDUCING RATIONAL EXPRESSIONS

When the numerator and the denominator of an algebraic fraction are polynomials, the fraction is called a *rational expression*.

● **DEFINITION.** A *rational expression* is the quotient of two polynomials. Examples of rational expressions include:

$$\frac{3}{5} \qquad \frac{-x}{8} \qquad \frac{2}{x} \qquad \frac{6}{x-7} \qquad \frac{3x-6}{x^2-2x-8}$$

Rational expressions follow the same rules and possess the same properties as rational numbers. Compare the two forms that follow:

In a *rational number* $\frac{a}{b}$:	In a *rational expression* $\frac{A}{B}$:
a and b are integers, and $b \neq 0$.	A and B are polynomials, and $B \neq 0$.

Since division by 0 is not possible, we know that $\frac{3}{0}$ has no meaning. In the same way, any rational expression whose denominator equals 0 is *meaningless* or is *not defined*. By setting each denominator equal to 0, we see that $\frac{2}{x}$, one of the examples above, has no meaning when $x = 0$, and $\frac{6}{x-7}$, another example, has no meaning when $x = 7$.

Reducing to Lowest Terms

A rational expression is **reduced to lowest terms**, or stated in **simplest form**, when its numerator and denominator have no common factors other than 1 and -1.

When a fraction is not in lowest terms, we learned to divide its numerator and denominator by the same nonzero number to find an equivalent fraction in lowest terms. This procedure, applied to rational numbers, is applied also to rational expressions.

Rational Numbers   *Rational Expressions*

$$\frac{5}{10} = \frac{5 \div 5}{10 \div 5} = \frac{1}{2} \qquad\qquad \frac{3x}{x^2+2x} = \frac{3x \div x}{(x^2+2x) \div x} = \frac{3}{x+2}$$

In general, if we *completely factor* the numerator and denominator of a rational expression, we can discover all common factors before reducing. This process, indicated as a **cancellation**, is simply an alternative way of dividing the numerator and denominator by the same nonzero number.

Note how we use cancellation in each of the following examples:

Rational Numbers	*Rational Expressions*

$$\frac{5}{10} = \frac{\overset{1}{\cancel{5}}}{\cancel{5} \cdot 2} = \frac{1}{2} \qquad \Bigg| \qquad \frac{3x}{x^2 + 2x} = \frac{3 \cdot \overset{1}{\cancel{x}}}{\cancel{x}(x + 2)} = \frac{3}{x + 2} \quad (x \neq 0, -2)$$

As the next rational expression is reduced, we note the importance of complete factorization and we use this example to make some observations.

$$\frac{4y^2 - 4y}{4y^2 - 12y + 8} = \frac{4y(y - 1)}{4(y^2 - 3y + 2)} = \frac{\overset{1}{\cancel{4}}y\overset{1}{\cancel{(y - 1)}}}{\cancel{4}(y - 2)\cancel{(y - 1)}} = \frac{y}{y - 2} \quad (y \neq 1, 2)$$

We observe:

1. The denominator in factored form is $4(y - 2)(y - 1)$. Let this equal 0 to see that $\dfrac{4y^2 - 4y}{4y^2 - 12y + 8}$ has no meaning when $y = 2$ or $y = 1$, indicated by writing $(y \neq 1, 2)$.

2. The rational expression $\dfrac{y}{y - 2}$ is reduced to simplest form because both numerator and denominator are prime polynomials. It is incorrect to cancel y from both numerator and denominator because y is *not a factor* in the denominator. Rather, y is a term in the binomial $(y - 2)$ in the denominator.

3. To give a numerical demonstration that $\dfrac{4y^2 - 4y}{4y^2 - 12y + 8} = \dfrac{y}{y - 2}$, substitute any number for y in both expressions except $y = 2$ and $y = 1$. This may serve as a check of your work.

For example, let $y = 3$:

$$\frac{4y^2 - 4y}{4y^2 - 12y + 8} = \frac{4(3)^2 - 4(3)}{4(3)^2 - 12(3) + 8} = \frac{4(9) - 4(3)}{4(9) - 12(3) + 8}$$

$$= \frac{36 - 12}{36 - 36 + 8} = \frac{24}{8} = 3$$

Also, $\dfrac{y}{y - 2} = \dfrac{(3)}{(3) - 2} = \dfrac{3}{1} = 3$.

Reducing to −1

In some rational expressions, the numerator and the denominator (or their factors) are *additive inverses*. In these cases, the rational expressions (or their factors) reduce to −1.

Rational Numbers	*Rational Expressions*

$$\frac{-9}{9} = \frac{-1 \cdot \overset{1}{\cancel{9}}}{\cancel{9}} = -1 \qquad \Bigg| \qquad \frac{3 - k}{k - 3} = \frac{-1(-3 + k)}{k - 3} = \frac{-1\overset{1}{\cancel{(k - 3)}}}{\cancel{(k - 3)}} = -1 \quad (k \neq 3)$$

As the rational expression above was reduced to lowest terms, -1 was used as a factor to obtain the common factor $(k - 3)$ in both numerator and denominator. Since this rational expression is undefined if $k = 3$, it is important to note $k \neq 3$ when writing the reduced form. In other words,

$$\frac{3 - k}{k - 3} = -1 \quad \text{if and only if} \quad k \neq 3$$

- In general, whenever a rational expression is reduced, it is understood that the equivalent form of the expression equals the original expression only for the values whereby the original fraction is defined, or the original fraction has meaning.

EXAMPLES

1. For what values of x does $\dfrac{4x + 8}{x^2 - 2x - 8}$ have no meaning?

How to Proceed:

(1) Set the denominator equal to 0.

(2) Factor the trinomial.

(3) Let each factor equal 0.

(4) Solve the resulting equations.

Solution:

Let $x^2 - 2x - 8 = 0$

$(x - 4)(x + 2) = 0$

$x - 4 = 0 \ \big| \ x + 2 = 0$

$x = 4 \ \big| \ \quad x = -2$

Answer: $\dfrac{4x + 8}{x^2 - 2x - 8}$ is meaningless, or is not defined, when $x = 4$ or $x = -2$.

---

2. Reduce the rational expression $\dfrac{4x + 8}{x^2 - 2x - 8}$ to lowest terms.

How to Proceed:

(1) Factor both numerator and denominator completely.

(2) Cancel, or divide numerator and denominator by all common factors.

(3) Exclude values for which the original fraction is undefined.

Solution:

$$\frac{4x + 8}{x^2 - 2x - 8} = \frac{4(x + 2)}{(x - 4)(x + 2)}$$

$$= \frac{4(x + 2)}{(x - 4)(x + 2)}$$

$$= \frac{4}{x - 4} \quad (x \neq 4, -2)$$

Answer: $\dfrac{4}{x - 4}$ $(x \neq 4, -2)$

3. Write the expression $\dfrac{12 - 6x}{x^2 - 4}$ in lowest terms.

Solution

$$\frac{12 - 6x}{x^2 - 4} = \frac{6(2 - x)}{(x + 2)(x - 2)} = \frac{6(-1)(-2 + x)}{(x + 2)(x - 2)} = \frac{6(-1)\overset{1}{\cancel{(x - 2)}}}{(x + 2)\underset{1}{\cancel{(x - 2)}}} = \frac{-6}{x + 2}$$

Answer: $\dfrac{-6}{x + 2}$ $(x \neq \pm 2)$

---

4. Reduce to simplest form: $\dfrac{a^2x - ax^2}{a^2x^2 - a^3x}$.

Solution

$$\frac{a^2x - ax^2}{a^2x^2 - a^3x} = \frac{ax(a - x)}{a^2x(x - a)} = \frac{\overset{1}{\cancel{ax}}(-1)\overset{1}{\cancel{(x - a)}}}{\underset{a}{\cancel{a^2x}}\underset{1}{\cancel{(x - a)}}} = \frac{-1}{a}$$

Answer: $\dfrac{-1}{a}$ $(a \neq 0, x \neq 0, x \neq a)$

EXERCISES WITH OPEN-RESPONSE PROBLEMS

In 1–8, for what value(s) of x does each expression have no meaning?

1. $\dfrac{5}{x}$

2. $\dfrac{5}{x^2}$

3. $\dfrac{8x}{x - 6}$

4. $\dfrac{x - 6}{8x}$

5. $\dfrac{14 - x}{7 + x}$

6. $\dfrac{6x}{3x - 1}$

7. $\dfrac{x + 2}{x^2 - 9}$

8. $\dfrac{2x - 5}{x^2 + x - 20}$

In 9–12, find the value(s) of the variable for which each rational expression is not defined.

9. $\dfrac{9y}{(y + 3)^2}$

10. $\dfrac{4b}{b^2 + 5b}$

11. $\dfrac{z^2 + 10z}{z^2 - 7z + 10}$

12. $\dfrac{2x - 8}{x^3 - 16x}$

In 13–36, reduce each rational expression to lowest terms.

13. $\dfrac{6x^3}{8x}$

14. $\dfrac{8a^2y^2}{4ay^6}$

15. $\dfrac{3bx^2}{(3bx)^2}$

16. $\dfrac{15(x - 4)}{20(x - 4)}$

17. $\dfrac{x - 25}{25 - x}$

18. $\dfrac{2y + 4}{3y + 6}$

19. $\dfrac{2z}{2z^2 + 6z}$

20. $\dfrac{16x^2}{2x^2 - 4x}$

21. $\dfrac{bx^3 - b^2x^2}{bx^3 - 2b^2x^2}$

22. $\dfrac{k^2 - 25}{k + 5}$

23. $\dfrac{y^2 - 81}{(y - 9)^2}$

24. $\dfrac{(x - 1)^2}{2 - 2x}$

25. $\dfrac{3a + 3}{a^2 - 1}$

26. $\dfrac{2p - 8}{(4 - p)^2}$

27. $\dfrac{(x - a)^2}{x^2 - a^2}$

28. $\dfrac{x^3y - x^2y^2}{xy^3 - x^2y^2}$

29. $\dfrac{1 - 9x^2}{3x^2 - x}$

30. $\dfrac{5a^2 - 45}{5a - 15}$

31. $\dfrac{x^2 - 81}{81 - x^2}$

32. $\dfrac{y^2 - 2y}{y^2 - y - 2}$

33. $\dfrac{2y^3 - 8y}{4y^2 - 8y}$

34. $\dfrac{x^2 + x - 2}{x^2 + 3x - 4}$

35. $\dfrac{3y^2 - 12y}{y^3 - 16y}$

36. $\dfrac{16 - 6x - x^2}{x^2 - 64}$

37. Find a fraction equivalent to $\dfrac{9}{x - 2}$ whose denominator is $2 - x$.

In 38–42, select the *numeral* preceding the expression that best completes the sentence or answers the question.

38. The expression $\dfrac{y}{y - 5}$ equals

(1) $\dfrac{y}{5 - y}$
(2) $\dfrac{-y}{y - 5}$
(3) $\dfrac{-y}{5 - y}$
(4) $\dfrac{y}{y + 5}$

39. Which rational expression is in simplest form?

(1) $\dfrac{x^2 + 2x}{x^2 + 2x}$
(2) $\dfrac{x^2 + 2x}{x^2 + 4x}$
(3) $\dfrac{x^2 + 2x}{x + 2}$
(4) $\dfrac{x^2 + 2x}{x^2 + 4}$

40. Which expression is defined for every rational number?

(1) $\dfrac{x^2 + 5}{x^2 + 4}$
(2) $\dfrac{x^2 + 5x}{x^2 + 4x}$
(3) $\dfrac{x^2 - 5}{x^2 - 4}$
(4) $\dfrac{4x^2 - 1}{4x - 1}$

41. If $x \neq a$, which is a true statement?

(1) $\dfrac{x - a}{a - x} = 1$
(2) $\dfrac{x - a}{a - x} = -1$
(3) $\dfrac{x^2 - a^2}{x - a} = 1$
(4) $\dfrac{x^2 - a^2}{x - a} = -1$

42. The expression $\dfrac{x - 3}{x^2 - 9} = \dfrac{1}{x + 3}$ for which of the following domains?

(1) Rational numbers
(2) Rational numbers/{9}
(3) Rational numbers/{3}
(4) Rational numbers/{3, −3}

43. a. Find the numerical value of $\dfrac{x^2 + 18x}{x + 18}$ when: (*1*) $x = 5$ (*2*) $x = 9$ (*3*) $x = 17$

b. What pattern, if any, do you observe for the answers to part **a**?

c. Find the numerical value of $\dfrac{x^2 + 18x}{x + 18}$ when $x = 372.1984$.

44. What is the value, in lowest terms, of $\dfrac{ay^2 - 3ay - 2b}{3ay - ay^2 + 2b}$ when the expression is defined?

9-2 MULTIPLYING RATIONAL EXPRESSIONS

The *product of two fractions* is a fraction whose numerator is the product of the given numerators and whose denominator is the product of the given denominators. In general, for $\dfrac{a}{b}$ and $\dfrac{x}{y}$, where $b \neq 0$ and $y \neq 0$:

$$\frac{a}{b} \cdot \frac{x}{y} = \frac{ax}{by}$$

In the following example, two procedures are used. In Method 1, we multiply terms and reduce the answer to simplest form. In Method 2, we divide the numerator and the denominator by all common factors before finding the final product. This second procedure, called *cancellation*, reduces the computation required.

METHOD 1. Multiply and Reduce

$$\frac{5}{12} \cdot \frac{8}{5} = \frac{5 \cdot 8}{12 \cdot 5} = \frac{40}{60} = \frac{2 \cdot \cancel{20}^{1}}{3 \cdot \cancel{20}_{1}} = \frac{2}{3}$$

METHOD 2. Cancellation

$$\frac{5}{12} \cdot \frac{8}{5} = \frac{\cancel{5}}{\cancel{12}_{3}} \cdot \frac{\cancel{8}^{2}}{\cancel{5}_{1}} = \frac{2}{3}$$

The *product of two rational expressions* is found by the same procedures as those used for fractions in arithmetic. For example:

METHOD 1. Multiply and Reduce

$$\frac{2x^2}{5y} \cdot \frac{10y^3}{5x^2} = \frac{2x^2 \cdot 10y^3}{5y \cdot 5x^2} = \frac{20x^2y^3}{25x^2y} = \frac{4y^2 \cdot \cancel{5x^2y}^{1}}{5 \cdot \cancel{5x^2y}_{1}} = \frac{4y^2}{5}$$

METHOD 2. Cancellation

$$\frac{2x^2}{5y} \cdot \frac{10y^3}{5x^2} = \frac{\cancel{2x^2}^{2}}{\cancel{5y}_{1}} \cdot \frac{\cancel{10y^3}^{2y^2}}{\cancel{5x^2}_{5}} = \frac{4y^2}{5}$$

Where possible, polynomials should be *factored* and the cancellation procedure used, as shown in the following example.

EXAMPLE

Multiply, and express the product in simplest form: $\dfrac{xy + 3y}{6x} \cdot \dfrac{2x^2 - 6x}{x^2 - 9}$.

How to Proceed:

(1) Write the problem.

(2) Factor all numerators and denominators.

(3) Cancel common factors in the numerators and denominators.

(4) Multiply remaining factors in the numerator; multiply remaining factors in the denominator.

Solution:

$$\frac{xy + 3y}{6x} \cdot \frac{2x^2 - 6x}{x^2 - 9}$$

$$= \frac{y(x + 3)}{6x} \cdot \frac{2x(x - 3)}{(x + 3)(x - 3)}$$

$$= \frac{y\cancel{(x + 3)}^{1}}{\cancel{6x}_{3}} \cdot \frac{\cancel{2x}^{1}\cancel{(x - 3)}^{1}}{\cancel{(x + 3)}_{1}\cancel{(x - 3)}_{1}}$$

$$= \frac{y}{3}$$

Answer: $\dfrac{y}{3}$ $(x \neq 0, 3, -3)$

EXERCISES WITH OPEN-RESPONSE PROBLEMS

In 1–21, in each case, multiply, and express the product in its simplest form.

1. $\frac{8}{x} \cdot \frac{x}{9}$

2. $\frac{3b}{4b} \cdot \frac{4x}{6}$

3. $\frac{18a^2x}{5b^3} \cdot \frac{3b}{27ax}$

4. $\frac{x+7}{2bc} \cdot \frac{4bc^2}{x+7}$

5. $\frac{x-a}{12a^3} \cdot \frac{8a^4}{x-a}$

6. $\frac{x-y}{5z} \cdot \frac{5z}{y-x}$

7. $\frac{y-2}{3m} \cdot \frac{m^3}{2-y}$

8. $\frac{4ax^2}{(3y)^3} \cdot \frac{3y^3}{(2ax)^2}$

9. $\frac{2x+6}{x^2} \cdot \frac{3x^2}{6x+18}$

10. $\frac{xy}{x^2-4x} \cdot \frac{x^2-16}{4y}$

11. $\frac{b+8}{5b^2} \cdot \frac{3b^2-24b}{b^2-64}$

12. $\frac{4x-20}{4x+20} \cdot \frac{3x^2+30x}{3x^2-15x}$

13. $\frac{a^3-a^2b}{a^2-b^2} \cdot \frac{ab^2+b^3}{a^2b^3}$

14. $\frac{y^2+y}{y+2} \cdot \frac{y^2-4}{y^2+3y}$

15. $\frac{(x+1)^2}{x^3-x} \cdot \frac{(x-1)^2}{x}$

16. $\frac{2x^2-10x}{x^2+2x} \cdot \frac{x^2+5x+6}{x^2-2x-15}$

17. $\frac{y^2+2y-8}{y^2+3y-4} \cdot \frac{3y^2+3y}{3y-6}$

18. $\frac{6a^2+2a}{9a^2+6a+1} \cdot \frac{9a^2-1}{6a^2}$

19. $\frac{2b^2+3b-2}{4b^2+8b} \cdot \frac{8b^3-8b^2}{2b^2-b}$

20. $\frac{2x-12}{3x-6} \cdot \frac{x^2-4}{x^2-36} \cdot \frac{3x+18}{4x+8}$

21. $\frac{x^2-12x+27}{x^2-81} \cdot \frac{x+9}{3-x}$

In 22–25, select the *numeral* preceding the expression that best completes the sentence.

22. The product of $\frac{5-y}{(3y)^2}$ and $\frac{9y^2}{y-5}$ is

(1) 1   (2) -1 (3) 3   (4) -3

23. If the side of a square measures $\frac{x+1}{x+2}$, the area of the square, in terms of x, is

(1) $\frac{x+1}{x+2}$ (2) $\frac{x^2+1}{x^2+4}$ (3) $\frac{x^2+2x+1}{x^2+4x+4}$ (4) $\frac{1}{4}$

24. The product $\frac{x^2-100}{x-2} \cdot \frac{x-2}{5x-50} = \frac{x+10}{5}$ for all rational values of x where

(1) $x \neq 2$ (2) $x \neq 10$ (3) $x \neq 2, 10$ (4) $x \neq 2, 5, 10$

25. If $x = 12$, the value of the product $\frac{3x^2+21x}{12x^2} \cdot \frac{4x^2-28x}{x^2-49}$ is

(1) 1   (2) 0   (3) 12   (4) $\frac{1}{12}$

26. Jack says that the product $\frac{k+2}{6k+18} \cdot \frac{3k^2+15k+18}{k^2+4k+4}$ is always equal to $\frac{1}{2}$. Jean maintains that the product is $\frac{1}{2}$ only when k is positive. Which person, if either, is correct? Explain your reasoning.

27. To evaluate the product $\dfrac{x^2 - 25}{x^2 - 5x} \cdot \dfrac{x}{3x + 15}$ when $x = 8$, Wylie made the following entry on his calculator:

Enter: ⬜ $($ ⬜ 8 ⬜ x^2 ⬜ $-$ ⬜ 25 ⬜ $)$ ⬜ $\div$ ⬜ $($ ⬜ 8 ⬜ x^2 ⬜ $-$ ⬜ 5 ⬜ $\times$ ⬜ 8 ⬜ $)$
⬜ $\times$ ⬜ 8 ⬜ $\div$ ⬜ $($ ⬜ 3 ⬜ $\times$ ⬜ 8 ⬜ $+$ ⬜ 15 ⬜ $)$ ⬜ $=$

a. What is the display on the calculator?
b. What is the value of the product when $x = 8$?
c. Explain an alternative method to evaluate the product.
d. Explain why the following calculator entry does *not* give the correct value of the product when $x = 8$.

Enter: ⬜ $($ ⬜ 8 ⬜ x^2 ⬜ $-$ ⬜ 25 ⬜ $)$ ⬜ $\times$ ⬜ 8 ⬜ $\div$ ⬜ $($ ⬜ 8 ⬜ x^2
⬜ $-$ ⬜ 5 ⬜ $\times$ ⬜ 8 ⬜ $)$ ⬜ $\times$ ⬜ $($ ⬜ 3 ⬜ $\times$ ⬜ 8 ⬜ $+$ ⬜ 15 ⬜ $)$ ⬜ $=$

9-3 DIVIDING RATIONAL EXPRESSIONS

There are many ways to indicate a division such as "10 divided by 2 equals 5." In each of the following formats, 10 is the *dividend*, 2 is the *divisor*, and 5 is the *quotient*:

$$\begin{array}{c}5 \\ 2\overline{)10}\end{array} \qquad 10 \div 2 = 5 \qquad \frac{10}{2} = 5$$

Since $10 \div 2 = \frac{10}{2} = 10 \cdot \frac{1}{2}$, it follows that a division problem can be answered by performing a related problem in multiplication. This is true also when dividing any fraction by a nonzero fraction.

Division:	$10 \div 2 = 5$
Multiplication:	$10 \cdot \frac{1}{2} = 5$

The **quotient of two fractions**, that is, the dividend divided by a nonzero divisor, is found by multiplying the dividend by the *reciprocal* (or multiplicative inverse) of the divisor. For example:

$$\frac{9}{8} \div \frac{3}{2} = \frac{9}{8} \cdot \frac{2}{3} = \frac{\overset{3}{\cancel{9}}}{\underset{4}{\cancel{8}}} \cdot \frac{\overset{1}{\cancel{2}}}{\underset{1}{\cancel{3}}} = \frac{3}{4}$$

In general, for $\frac{a}{b}$ and $\frac{x}{y}$, where $b \neq 0$, $x \neq 0$, and $y \neq 0$:

$$\frac{a}{b} \div \frac{x}{y} = \frac{a}{b} \cdot \frac{y}{x} = \frac{ay}{bx}$$

The *quotient of two rational expressions* is found by the same procedure as that used for fractions in arithmetic. Since the division of rational numbers is restated as a multiplication, polynomials of two or more terms should be *factored* before the cancellation method is used.

EXAMPLES

1. Divide, and express the quotient in simplest form: $\dfrac{x^2 - 9}{4x} \div \dfrac{3x + 9}{2x}$

<table>
<tr><td align="center">How to Proceed:</td><td align="center">Solution:</td></tr>
<tr><td>(1) Rewrite the problem, indicating that the dividend is to be multiplied by the reciprocal of the divisor.</td><td>$\dfrac{x^2 - 9}{4x} \div \dfrac{3x + 9}{2x}$

$= \dfrac{x^2 - 9}{4x} \cdot \dfrac{2x}{3x + 9}$</td></tr>
<tr><td>(2) Factor all numerators and denominators, and use cancellation.</td><td>$= \dfrac{\overset{1}{\cancel{(x + 3)}}(x - 3)}{\underset{2}{\cancel{4x}}} \cdot \dfrac{\overset{1}{\cancel{2x}}}{3\overset{1}{\cancel{(x + 3)}}}$</td></tr>
<tr><td>(3) Multiply remaining factors in numerator; multiply remaining factors in denominator.</td><td>$= \dfrac{x - 3}{6}$</td></tr>
</table>

Answer: $\dfrac{x - 3}{6}$ $(x \neq 0, -3)$

Note: If $x = 0$, both of the given fractions are meaningless or undefined. If $x = -3$, the divisor $\left(\dfrac{3x + 9}{2x}\right)$ equals 0 and its reciprocal is undefined.

---

2. Perform the division, and express the quotient in simplest form:
$$\frac{a^2 - ay - 2y^2}{3a^3} \div \frac{a^2 - 4y^2}{3a^3 + 6a^2y}.$$

Solution

$$\frac{a^2 - ay - 2y^2}{3a^3} \div \frac{a^2 - 4y^2}{3a^3 + 6a^2y} = \frac{a^2 - ay - 2y^2}{3a^3} \cdot \frac{3a^3 + 6a^2y}{a^2 - 4y^2}$$

$$= \frac{(a + y)\overset{1}{\cancel{(a - 2y)}}}{\underset{a}{\cancel{3a^3}}} \cdot \frac{3\overset{1}{\cancel{a^2}}\overset{1}{\cancel{(a + 2y)}}}{\underset{1}{\cancel{(a - 2y)}}\underset{1}{\cancel{(a + 2y)}}}$$

$$= \frac{a + y}{a}$$

Answer: $\dfrac{a + y}{a}$ $(a \neq 0, a \neq \pm 2y)$

EXERCISES WITH OPEN-RESPONSE PROBLEMS

In 1–21, in each case, divide, and express the quotient in its simplest form.

1. $\dfrac{y}{2} \div \dfrac{y}{3}$

2. $\dfrac{3k}{7} \div \dfrac{6k^2}{14}$

3. $\dfrac{1}{ab} \div \dfrac{1}{ab^2}$

4. $\dfrac{x+5}{3a^2} \div \dfrac{x+5}{2a}$

5. $\dfrac{y-b}{b^3y} \div \dfrac{y-b}{by^3}$

6. $\dfrac{x-2}{4m} \div \dfrac{2-x}{4m}$

7. $\dfrac{2y-3}{y^3} \div \dfrac{3-2y}{3y}$

8. $\dfrac{(2x)^2}{(3y)^3} \div \dfrac{2x^2}{3y^3}$

9. $\dfrac{3k-3}{k} \div \dfrac{12k-12}{4k^2}$

10. $\dfrac{6x}{x-3} \div 2x$

11. $\dfrac{c^2-d^2}{cd-d^2} \div (c^2+cd)$

12. $\dfrac{x^2-1}{3} \div (3x-3)$

13. $\dfrac{x^2-4}{2y} \div \dfrac{x^2-2x}{xy}$

14. $\dfrac{(y-3)^2}{y^2-9} \div \dfrac{3y-9}{y+3}$

15. $\dfrac{m+3}{3m} \div \dfrac{6m}{m+3}$

16. $\dfrac{2x^2-8x}{x^2-16} \div \dfrac{8x^2}{(x+4)^2}$

17. $\dfrac{c^3-c^2y}{c^2-y^2} \div \dfrac{c^3y}{cy^2+y^3}$

18. $\dfrac{x^2-25}{x^2+7x} \div \dfrac{x^2+7x+10}{x^2+9x+14}$

19. $\dfrac{3r^3t-3r^2t^2}{3r^2t+3rt^2} \div \dfrac{(r-t)^2}{r^2-t^2}$

20. $\dfrac{2y^2+11y+5}{4y^2+4y+1} \div \dfrac{2y^3+10y^2}{4y^3}$

21. $\dfrac{x^3-36x}{x^2+7x+6} \div \dfrac{6x^2-x^3}{x^2+x}$

In 22 and 23, select the *numeral* preceding the expression that best completes the sentence.

22. $\dfrac{x-2}{x-1} \div \dfrac{x-2}{x-1} = 1$ for all rational values of x where

(1) $x \neq 1$ (2) $x \neq 2$ (3) $x \neq 1, 2$ (4) $x \neq 1, 2, 0$

23. The quotient $\dfrac{x-3}{x} \div \dfrac{x-2}{x} = \dfrac{x-3}{x-2}$ for all rational values of x where

(1) $x \neq 0$ (2) $x \neq 0, 2$ (3) $x \neq 0, 3$ (4) $x \neq 0, 2, 3$

24. If $\dfrac{x^2-49}{2x+6}$ represents the area of a rectangle and $\dfrac{x+7}{x+3}$ represents the measure of its length, find the rational expression that represents the measure of its width.

25. Evaluate $\dfrac{9-2x}{x-7} \div \dfrac{2x^2-9x}{x^2-7x}$ when:

a. $x = 1$ **b.** $x = 10$ **c.** $x = 78$ **d.** $x = 0.1\overline{6}$ **e.** $x = 92.71$

26. Given: $a \div b = x^2 - 1$

$b \div c = \dfrac{x}{x+1}$

$c \div d = \dfrac{x}{x-1}$

Express the value of $a \div d$ in terms of x.

9-4   ADDING OR SUBTRACTING RATIONAL EXPRESSIONS THAT HAVE THE SAME DENOMINATOR

The *sum (or difference) of two fractions that have the same denominator* is a fraction whose numerator is the sum (or difference) of the given numerators and whose denominator is the common denominator of the given fractions. We can show that this is true by using the distributive property, as follows.

Addition: $\frac{3}{10} + \frac{1}{10} = 3 \cdot \frac{1}{10} + 1 \cdot \frac{1}{10} = (3 + 1) \cdot \frac{1}{10} = 4 \cdot \frac{1}{10} = \frac{4}{10} = \frac{2}{5}$

Subtraction: $\frac{7}{12} - \frac{5}{12} = 7 \cdot \frac{1}{12} - 5 \cdot \frac{1}{12} = (7 - 5) \cdot \frac{1}{12} = 2 \cdot \frac{1}{12} = \frac{2}{12} = \frac{1}{6}$

The *sum (or difference) of two rational expressions that have the same denominator* is found by the same procedure as that used for fractions in arithmetic.

In general, for $\frac{a}{b}$ and $\frac{c}{b}$, where $b \neq 0$:

$$\frac{a}{b} + \frac{c}{b} = \frac{a + c}{b} \qquad \text{and} \qquad \frac{a}{b} - \frac{c}{b} = \frac{a - c}{b}$$

Once we understand the mathematical principles upon which the addition (or subtraction) of fractions or rational expressions depends, we eliminate the middle steps. Final answers should always be reduced to lowest terms, as seen in the following examples:

$$\frac{3}{10} + \frac{1}{10} = \frac{4}{10} = \frac{2}{5}$$

$$\frac{7}{12} - \frac{5}{12} = \frac{2}{12} = \frac{1}{6}$$

$$\frac{3a^2}{8x} + \frac{7a^2}{8x} - \frac{6a^2}{8x} = \frac{3a^2 + 7a^2 - 6a^2}{8x} = \frac{4a^2}{8x} = \frac{\overset{1}{4} \cdot a^2}{\underset{1}{4} \cdot 2x} = \frac{a^2}{2x} \quad (x \neq 0)$$

PROCEDURE.   To add (or subtract) rational expressions that have the same denominator:

1. Write a rational expression whose numerator is the sum (or difference) of the given numerators and whose denominator is the common denominator. Since a fraction bar is a symbol of grouping, place all numerators of two or more terms in parentheses, as seen in the examples that follow.

2. In the resulting expression, factor the numerator and factor the denominator. Then, cancel all common factors.

EXAMPLES

1. Add, and express the sum in lowest terms: $\dfrac{x^2 - 5}{2x^2} + \dfrac{5 - 4x}{2x^2}$

Solution

$$\dfrac{x^2 - 5}{2x^2} + \dfrac{5 - 4x}{2x^2} = \dfrac{(x^2 - 5) + (5 - 4x)}{2x^2} = \dfrac{x^2 - 5 + 5 - 4x}{2x^2}$$

Factor the numerator of the sum and reduce to lowest terms.

$$= \dfrac{x^2 - 4x}{2x^2} = \dfrac{\overset{1}{\cancel{x}}(x - 4)}{\underset{2x}{\cancel{2x^2}}} = \dfrac{x - 4}{2x}$$

Answer: $\dfrac{x - 4}{2x}$ $(x \neq 0)$

2. Perform the indicated operation, and reduce to lowest terms: $\dfrac{7y - 3}{y^2 - 9} - \dfrac{y + 15}{y^2 - 9}$.

Solution

$$\dfrac{7y - 3}{y^2 - 9} - \dfrac{y + 15}{y^2 - 9} = \dfrac{(7y - 3) - (y + 15)}{y^2 - 9} = \dfrac{7y - 3 - y - 15}{y^2 - 9}$$

Factor the numerator and denominator of the difference and reduce to lowest terms.

$$= \dfrac{6y - 18}{y^2 - 9} = \dfrac{6(\overset{1}{\cancel{y - 3}})}{(y + 3)(\underset{1}{\cancel{y - 3}})} = \dfrac{6}{y + 3}$$

Answer: $\dfrac{6}{y + 3}$ $(y \neq 3, -3)$

EXERCISES WITH OPEN-RESPONSE PROBLEMS

In 1–21, in each case, perform the indicated operation(s) and express the result in lowest terms.

1. $\dfrac{3x}{5} + \dfrac{4x}{5} + \dfrac{3x}{5}$

2. $\dfrac{7}{4y} + \dfrac{3}{4y} - \dfrac{2}{4y}$

3. $\dfrac{9a}{7b} - \dfrac{a}{7b} + \dfrac{3a}{7b}$

4. $\dfrac{x}{2c} + \dfrac{y}{2c} + \dfrac{z}{2c}$

5. $\dfrac{2b}{2b + 3} + \dfrac{3}{2b + 3}$

6. $\dfrac{4}{x - 4} - \dfrac{x}{x - 4}$

7. $\dfrac{5x - 3}{4x - 4} - \dfrac{2x}{4x - 4}$

8. $\dfrac{y}{y^2 - 36} - \dfrac{6}{y^2 - 36}$

9. $\dfrac{5z + 9}{z^2 - 25} + \dfrac{16}{z^2 - 25}$

10. $\dfrac{3a}{(a - 2)^2} - \dfrac{6}{(a - 2)^2}$

11. $\dfrac{4b}{5b - 10} - \dfrac{b + 6}{5b - 10}$

12. $\dfrac{2k^2}{k^2 + 3k} - \dfrac{k^2 + 9}{k^2 + 3k}$

13. $\dfrac{c^2 d + 1}{c^2 - d^2} - \dfrac{cd^2 + 1}{c^2 - d^2}$

14. $\dfrac{x^2 y + 2}{2xy} - \dfrac{xy^2 + 2}{2xy}$

15. $\dfrac{3p + 8}{p^2 - 4} + \dfrac{2p + 7}{p^2 - 4}$

16. $\dfrac{x^2 + x}{4x^2 - 1} + \dfrac{x^2}{4x^2 - 1}$

17. $\dfrac{5y}{y^2 - 5y} - \dfrac{y^2}{y^2 - 5y}$

18. $\dfrac{x^2 + 1}{x^2 - 16} + \dfrac{5x + 3}{x^2 - 16}$

19. $\dfrac{y^2 + 6}{y^2 - 2y} - \dfrac{5y}{y^2 - 2y}$

20. $\dfrac{x^2 + 16}{4 - x} - \dfrac{8x}{4 - x}$

21. $\dfrac{d^2 + 8}{d^3 - d} - \dfrac{8 - d}{d^3 - d}$

In 22–26, copy and complete the table by adding, subtracting, multiplying, and dividing the expressions that represent A and B. Express each answer in simplest form in the appropriate column.

	A	B	$A + B$	$A - B$	AB	$A \div B$
22.	$\dfrac{x^2}{a}$	$\dfrac{x^2}{a}$				
23.	$\dfrac{12b}{y}$	$\dfrac{4b}{y}$				
24.	$\dfrac{5a}{2c}$	$\dfrac{3b}{2c}$				
25.	$\dfrac{2x}{x+3}$	$\dfrac{6}{x+3}$				
26.	$\dfrac{x}{x-y}$	$\dfrac{y}{x-y}$				

In 27 and 28, select the *numeral* preceding the expression that best completes the sentence.

27. The sum $\dfrac{x-4}{x-3} + \dfrac{1}{x-3} = 1$ for all rational values of x where

(1) $x \neq 3$ (2) $x \neq 3, 4$ (3) $x \neq 0, 3$ (4) $x \neq 0, 3, 4$

28. For $x \neq -1$, the difference $\dfrac{x^2 + 3x}{x+1} - \dfrac{3x-1}{x+1}$ is equal to

(1) $x - 1$ (2) $x + 1$ (3) $\dfrac{x^2-1}{x+1}$ (4) $\dfrac{x^2+1}{x+1}$

In 29–33, let $x = \dfrac{3c}{c+1}$ and $y = \dfrac{-2c}{c+1}$, where $c > 0$.

a. Perform the indicated operation, and express the result in lowest terms.
b. Indicate whether the result is positive or negative, and explain your answer.

29. xy **30.** $x - y$ **31.** $x \div y$ **32.** $x^2 - y^2$ **33.** $y^2 - x^2$

9-5   ADDING OR SUBTRACTING RATIONAL EXPRESSIONS THAT HAVE DIFFERENT DENOMINATORS

Finding Equivalent Fractions

Fractions that are equal in value are called ***equivalent fractions***.

For example, $\frac{3}{6}$, $\frac{4}{8}$, and $\frac{10}{20}$ are equivalent fractions because when simplified, we can see they are all equal in value to $\frac{1}{2}$.

The *sum (or difference) of two fractions that have different denominators* is found by transforming all values to equivalent fractions having the same denominator before adding or subtracting the fractions. To find equivalent fractions, we multiply by the identity element 1, written in the form of a fraction. For example:

$$\frac{3}{8} + \frac{2}{5} = \frac{3}{8} \cdot 1 + \frac{2}{5} \cdot 1$$
$$= \frac{3}{8} \cdot \frac{5}{5} + \frac{2}{5} \cdot \frac{8}{8}$$
$$= \frac{15}{40} + \frac{16}{40}$$
$$= \frac{31}{40}$$

$$\frac{4}{5} - \frac{1}{2} = \frac{4}{5} \cdot 1 - \frac{1}{2} \cdot 1$$
$$= \frac{4}{5} \cdot \frac{2}{2} - \frac{1}{2} \cdot \frac{5}{5}$$
$$= \frac{8}{10} - \frac{5}{10}$$
$$= \frac{3}{10}$$

It is always helpful to find the **lowest common denominator (L.C.D.)** for two or more fractions. The L.C.D. can be described in two ways:

1. The L.C.D. is the product of all factors of the first denominator times the factors of the second denominator that are not factors of the first.

$$12 = 2 \cdot 2 \cdot 3$$
$$18 = 2 \quad \cdot 3 \cdot 3$$
$$\overline{\text{L.C.D.} = 2 \cdot 2 \cdot 3 \cdot 3 = 36}$$

2. The L.C.D. is the product of the highest powers of all the prime factors of the given denominators.

$$12 = 2^2 \cdot 3^1$$
$$18 = 2^1 \cdot 3^2$$
$$\overline{\text{L.C.D.} = 2^2 \cdot 3^2 = 4 \cdot 9 = 36}$$

For example, the sum of $\frac{7}{12}$ and $\frac{5}{18}$ is found by changing these fractions to equivalent fractions with denominators of 36, the L.C.D. This addition is shown below in a numerical format and with geometric models.

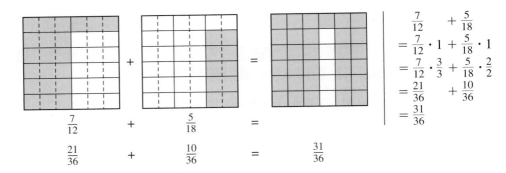

$$\frac{7}{12} + \frac{5}{18}$$
$$= \frac{7}{12} \cdot 1 + \frac{5}{18} \cdot 1$$
$$= \frac{7}{12} \cdot \frac{3}{3} + \frac{5}{18} \cdot \frac{2}{2}$$
$$= \frac{21}{36} + \frac{10}{36}$$
$$= \frac{31}{36}$$

$$\frac{7}{12} \quad + \quad \frac{5}{18} \quad = $$

$$\frac{21}{36} \quad + \quad \frac{10}{36} \quad = \quad \frac{31}{36}$$

Addition and Subtraction of Rational Expressions

The *sum (or difference) of two rational expressions that have different denominators* is found by the same procedures as those used for fractions in arithmetic.

For example, to add $\dfrac{x}{x^2 - 16} + \dfrac{x + 7}{2x^2 + 8x}$, we must first find the least common denominator of these expressions.

$$
\begin{aligned}
\text{Factors of } x^2 - 16 &= \quad (x + 4)(x - 4) \\
\text{Factors of } 2x^2 + 8x &= 2x(x + 4) \\
\hline
\text{L.C.D.} &= 2x(x + 4)(x - 4) \text{ or } 2x^3 - 32x
\end{aligned}
$$

Then, after changing the two rational expressions into equivalent expressions with the same denominator, we can add the derived expressions.

$$
\frac{x}{x^2 - 16} = \frac{x}{(x + 4)(x - 4)} \cdot \frac{2x}{2x} = \frac{2x^2}{2x(x + 4)(x - 4)}
$$

$$
+ \frac{x + 7}{2x^2 + 8x} = \frac{(x + 7)}{2x(x + 4)} \cdot \frac{(x - 4)}{(x - 4)} = + \frac{x^2 + 3x - 28}{2x(x + 4)(x - 4)}
$$

$$
\frac{3x^2 + 3x - 28}{2x(x + 4)(x - 4)} \quad (x \neq 0, \pm 4)
$$

PROCEDURE.   To add (or subtract) rational expressions that have *different* denominators:

1. Change the rational expressions into equivalent expressions that have the *same* denominator.

2. Add (or subtract) numerators; keep the common denominator.

3. Factor the resulting expression. Simplify by canceling common factors.

In general, for $\dfrac{a}{b}$ and $\dfrac{c}{d}$, where $b \neq 0$ and $d \neq 0$:

$$
\frac{a}{b} + \frac{c}{d} = \frac{a}{b}\left(\frac{d}{d}\right) + \frac{c}{d}\left(\frac{b}{b}\right) = \frac{ad}{bd} + \frac{bc}{bd} = \frac{ad + bc}{bd} \quad \text{and} \quad \frac{a}{b} - \frac{c}{d} = \frac{ad - bc}{bd}
$$

Although we can add or subtract rational expressions with any common denominator, the work is simplified when we use the lowest common denominator.

Mixed Expressions

A mixed number, such as $3\frac{1}{4}$, is the sum of an integer and a fraction, that is, $3 + \frac{1}{4}$. A mixed number can be transformed into a fraction by writing the integer as an equivalent fraction with the same denominator as the fraction. For example:

$$
3\frac{1}{4} = 3 + \frac{1}{4} = \frac{3}{1} \cdot \frac{4}{4} + \frac{1}{4} = \frac{12}{4} + \frac{1}{4} = \frac{12 + 1}{4} = \frac{13}{4}
$$

A **mixed expression** is the sum (or difference) of a polynomial and a rational expression. Again, the same procedures just learned can be used to transform a mixed expression into a rational expression. For example:

$$x + \frac{3}{x+5} = \frac{x}{1} \cdot \frac{(x+5)}{(x+5)} + \frac{3}{x+5} = \frac{x(x+5)}{x+5} + \frac{3}{x+5}$$

$$= \frac{x^2 + 5x}{x+5} + \frac{3}{x+5}$$

$$= \frac{x^2 + 5x + 3}{x+5} \quad (x \neq -5)$$

EXAMPLES

1. Subtract, and express the answer in simplest form: $\dfrac{x+2}{x^2-x} - \dfrac{6}{x^2-1}$.

How to Proceed:	*Solution:*

(1) Find the L.C.D. Notice that $(x-1)$ is a factor in both denominators.

$$x^2 - x = x(x-1)$$
$$x^2 - 1 = (x-1)(x+1)$$
$$\text{L.C.D.} = x(x-1)(x+1)$$

(2) Transform the rational expressions into equivalent expressions having an L.C.D. of $x(x-1)(x+1)$. To do this, multiply each rational expression by an appropriate form of the identity element 1.

$$\frac{x+2}{x^2-x} - \frac{6}{x^2-1}$$

$$= \frac{x+2}{x(x-1)} - \frac{6}{(x-1)(x+1)}$$

$$= \frac{x+2}{x(x-1)} \cdot \frac{(x+1)}{(x+1)} - \frac{(x)}{(x)} \cdot \frac{6}{(x-1)(x+1)}$$

$$= \frac{(x+2)(x+1)}{x(x-1)(x+1)} - \frac{6(x)}{x(x-1)(x+1)}$$

$$= \frac{x^2 + 3x + 2}{x(x-1)(x+1)} - \frac{6x}{x(x-1)(x+1)}$$

(3) Subtract numerators; maintain the L.C.D.

$$= \frac{x^2 + 3x + 2 - 6x}{x(x-1)(x+1)}$$

$$= \frac{x^2 - 3x + 2}{x(x-1)(x+1)}$$

(4) Factor numerator; simplify by cancellation.

$$= \frac{\overset{1}{\cancel{(x-1)}}(x-2)}{x\underset{1}{\cancel{(x-1)}}(x+1)}$$

$$= \frac{x-2}{x(x+1)} \quad \text{or} \quad \frac{x-2}{x^2+x}$$

Answer: $\dfrac{x-2}{x(x+1)}$ or $\dfrac{x-2}{x^2+x}$ $(x \neq 0, 1, -1)$

2. Add, and express the sum in simplest form: $\dfrac{3y}{2y-6} + \dfrac{9}{6-2y}$.

How to Proceed:

(1) Since one denominator is the additive inverse of the other, multiply one of the rational expressions by $\dfrac{(-1)}{(-1)}$ to form a common denominator.

(2) Add numerators; maintain the common denominator.

(3) Factor and reduce to simplest form.

Solution:

$$\dfrac{3y}{2y-6} + \dfrac{9}{6-2y}$$

$$= \dfrac{3y}{2y-6} + \dfrac{(-1)}{(-1)} \cdot \dfrac{9}{(6-2y)}$$

$$= \dfrac{3y}{2y-6} + \dfrac{-9}{2y-6}$$

$$= \dfrac{3y+(-9)}{2y-6}$$

$$= \dfrac{3y-9}{2y-6}$$

$$= \dfrac{3\overset{1}{\cancel{(y-3)}}}{2\underset{1}{\cancel{(y-3)}}} = \dfrac{3}{2}$$

Answer: $\dfrac{3}{2}$ $\quad (y \neq 3)$

---

3. Transform $y - 5 + \dfrac{3}{y+2}$ into a rational expression.

How to Proceed:

(1) Multiply all terms in the polynomial $y - 5$ by the identity $\dfrac{(y+2)}{(y+2)}$.

(2) Add numerators; maintain the common denominator.

Solution:

$$y - 5 + \dfrac{3}{y+2}$$

$$= \dfrac{(y-5)}{1} \cdot \dfrac{(y+2)}{(y+2)} + \dfrac{3}{y+2}$$

$$= \dfrac{y^2 - 3y - 10}{y+2} + \dfrac{3}{y+2}$$

$$= \dfrac{y^2 - 3y - 10 + 3}{y+2}$$

$$= \dfrac{y^2 - 3y - 7}{y+2}$$

Answer: $\dfrac{y^2 - 3y - 7}{y+2}$ $\quad (y \neq -2)$

4. Simplify: $\left(x - \frac{16}{x}\right)\left(1 + \frac{4}{x - 4}\right)$.

How to Proceed:

(1) Transform each mixed expression into a rational expression.

(2) Perform the indicated multiplication after factoring and canceling all common factors.

Solution:

$$\left(x - \frac{16}{x}\right)\left(1 + \frac{4}{x - 4}\right)$$

$$= \left(\frac{x}{1} \cdot \frac{x}{x} - \frac{16}{x}\right)\left(\frac{1}{1} \cdot \frac{x - 4}{x - 4} + \frac{4}{x - 4}\right)$$

$$= \left(\frac{x^2}{x} - \frac{16}{x}\right)\left(\frac{x - 4}{x - 4} + \frac{4}{x - 4}\right)$$

$$= \left(\frac{x^2 - 16}{x}\right)\left(\frac{x}{x - 4}\right)$$

$$= \frac{(x + 4)(\overset{1}{\cancel{x - 4}})}{\cancel{x}} \cdot \frac{\cancel{x}}{(\cancel{x - 4})}$$

$$= x + 4$$

Answer: $x + 4 \quad (x \neq 0, 4)$

EXERCISES WITH OPEN-RESPONSE PROBLEMS

In 1–32, in each case, perform the indicated operation(s), and express the answer in simplest form.

1. $\frac{3x}{8} + \frac{x}{4}$

2. $\frac{7b}{10} - \frac{2b}{5}$

3. $\frac{3}{4x} - \frac{3}{8x}$

4. $\frac{y}{2} + \frac{y}{3} - \frac{y}{6}$

5. $\frac{3}{4a} - \frac{2}{3a} + \frac{1}{6a}$

6. $\frac{c + 2}{2} + \frac{c - 3}{3}$

7. $\frac{1}{a} - \frac{1}{b}$

8. $\frac{4x + 3}{3x} + \frac{x - 1}{x}$

9. $\frac{4y + 3}{3y} - \frac{y + 2}{y}$

10. $\frac{x + 5}{x} - \frac{8}{x^2}$

11. $\frac{3a - 2}{5a} + \frac{2a - 3}{4a}$

12. $\frac{x - y}{xy^2} + \frac{x + y}{x^2 y}$

13. $\frac{2}{x} + \frac{3}{x - 5}$

14. $\frac{1}{y - 2} + \frac{5}{y - 3}$

15. $\frac{1}{c - d} - \frac{1}{c + d}$

16. $\frac{2y}{y - 5} + \frac{10}{5 - y}$

17. $\frac{2m}{6m - 3} + \frac{1}{3 - 6m}$

18. $\frac{a^2}{a - b} + \frac{b^2}{b - a}$

19. $\frac{x}{x + 2} - \frac{8}{x^2 - 4}$

20. $\frac{y}{y - 3} - \frac{18}{y^2 - 9}$

21. $\frac{z + 3}{z - 2} - \frac{10}{z^2 - 2z}$

22. $\frac{3y + 1}{y^2 - 16} + \frac{y - 2}{2y + 8}$

23. $\frac{b}{(b - 7)^3} - \frac{1}{(b - 7)^2}$

24. $\frac{x + y}{x - y} + \frac{x - y}{x + y}$

25. $\frac{2}{x^2 - 36} - \frac{1}{x^2 + 6x}$

26. $\frac{4}{y^2 - 9} - \frac{2}{y^2 - 3y}$

27. $\frac{10x}{x^2 - 25} + \frac{5}{5 - x}$

28. $\frac{1}{x^2 + 4x + 3} + \frac{1}{x^2 - 1}$

29. $\frac{7}{y^2 - 49} - \frac{6}{y^2 - 2y - 35}$

30. $\frac{9}{x^2 + 7x + 10} + \frac{3}{x + 5} - \frac{1}{x + 2}$

31. $\frac{2}{2y - 1} - \frac{1}{2y + 1} - \frac{2}{4y^2 - 1}$

32. $\frac{2}{x + 3} - \frac{1}{x - 3} - \frac{x - 9}{x^2 - 9}$

In 33–44, transform each mixed expression into a rational expression.

33. $a + \frac{b}{3}$

34. $x + \frac{1}{x}$

35. $1 - \frac{x}{x + y}$

36. $x - 3 + \frac{2}{x}$

37. $y - 1 + \frac{y - 1}{y}$

38. $z + \frac{z}{z - 1}$

39. $a - \frac{ab}{a + b}$

40. $2x + \frac{ax}{x - a}$

41. $x + 4 + \frac{12}{x - 4}$

42. $y - 1 + \frac{1}{y + 1}$

43. $k + 2 - \frac{4k}{k + 2}$

44. $y + 3 - \frac{y - 6}{y - 2}$

In 45–58, in each case, perform the indicated operation and express the answer in simplest form.

45. $\left(4 - \frac{1}{x}\right)\left(\frac{2x}{4x - 1}\right)$

46. $\left(1 - \frac{5}{y}\right)\left(\frac{y}{5 - y}\right)$

47. $\left(1 + \frac{y}{x}\right)\left(\frac{x}{x^2 - y^2}\right)$

48. $\left(\frac{3b}{b - 3}\right)\left(2 - \frac{6}{b}\right)$

49. $\left(y + \frac{4}{y - 4}\right)\left(\frac{y - 4}{2y - 4}\right)$

50. $\left(k + 2 + \frac{1}{k}\right)\left(\frac{1}{k + 1}\right)$

51. $\left(1 - \frac{8}{x}\right)\left(1 + \frac{8}{x - 8}\right)$

52. $\left(2 + \frac{6}{d}\right)\left(d - \frac{3d}{d + 3}\right)$

53. $\left(y - \frac{25}{y}\right) \div \left(1 + \frac{5}{y}\right)$

54. $\left(x - \frac{36}{x}\right) \div \left(x - 8 + \frac{12}{x}\right)$

55. $\left(x - 5 + \frac{6}{x}\right) \div \left(3 - \frac{6}{x}\right)$

56. $\left(y - 2 + \frac{1}{y}\right) + \left(1 - \frac{1}{y}\right)$

57. $\left(y - 2 + \frac{3}{y + 2}\right) \div \left(y + \frac{1}{y + 2}\right)$

58. $\left(y - 3 + \frac{5}{y + 3}\right) + \left(y - \frac{y}{y + 3}\right)$

In 59–62, copy and complete the table by adding, subtracting, multiplying, and dividing the expressions that represent A and B. Express each answer in simplest form in the appropriate column.

	A	B	$A + B$	$A - B$	AB	$A \div B$
59.	$\frac{1}{y}$	$\frac{1}{x}$				
60.	$\frac{c}{d}$	$\frac{d}{c}$				
61.	$\frac{x}{x - 2}$	$\frac{x}{2 - x}$				
62.	$4y$	$\frac{1}{y}$				

63. Find the value of $\frac{k + 2}{k - 5} - \frac{k + 16}{3k - 15}$ when: **a.** $k = 9$ **b.** $k = 0.3$ **c.** $k = 4.\overline{5}$

64. a. When a number is divided by 4, the quotient is 7 and the remainder is 3, written as $7\frac{3}{4}$. Find the number that is the dividend.

   b. When a polynomial is divided by $x + 3$, the quotient is $x - 4$ and the remainder is 2, written as $x - 4 + \frac{2}{x + 3}$. Find the polynomial that is the dividend.

9-6 SIMPLIFYING COMPLEX FRACTIONS AND COMPLEX RATIONAL EXPRESSIONS

A *complex fraction* contains one or more fractions in its numerator, its denominator, or both. There are two procedures by which a complex fraction is transformed into a simple fraction.

$$\boxed{\begin{array}{c} \textit{Complex Fractions} \\[6pt] \dfrac{\frac{1}{5}}{\frac{9}{10}} \qquad \dfrac{2\frac{1}{3}}{7} \qquad \dfrac{\frac{3}{8}}{3\frac{1}{4}} \end{array}}$$

METHOD 1:

Multiply the complex fraction by $\frac{k}{k}$, a form of the identity element 1, where k is the L.C.D. of all fractions that are part of the complex fraction.

For example, simplify $\dfrac{\frac{1}{5}}{\frac{9}{10}}$.

For $\frac{1}{5}$ and $\frac{9}{10}$, the L.C.D. = 10.

$$\frac{\frac{1}{5}}{\frac{9}{10}} = \frac{\frac{1}{5}}{\frac{9}{10}} \cdot \frac{10}{10} = \frac{\frac{1}{5} \cdot \overset{2}{\cancel{10}}}{\frac{9}{\cancel{10}} \cdot \cancel{10}} = \frac{2}{9}$$

METHOD 2:

Change the numerator to a single fraction; change the denominator to a single fraction; and then divide the numerator by the denominator.

For example, simplify $\dfrac{\frac{1}{5}}{\frac{9}{10}}$.

$$\frac{\frac{1}{5}}{\frac{9}{10}} = \frac{1}{5} \div \frac{9}{10} = \frac{1}{\cancel{5}} \cdot \frac{\overset{2}{\cancel{10}}}{9} = \frac{2}{9}$$

Let us consider another example, in which we simplify $\dfrac{2\frac{1}{3}}{7}$ using both methods.

METHOD 1:

Since $2\frac{1}{3} = \frac{7}{3}$ and $7 = \frac{7}{1}$, the L.C.D. = 3.

$$\frac{2\frac{1}{3}}{7} = \frac{\frac{7}{3}}{\frac{7}{1}} \cdot \frac{3}{3} = \frac{\frac{7}{\cancel{3}} \cdot \cancel{3}}{\frac{7}{1} \cdot 3} = \frac{7}{21} = \frac{1}{3}$$

METHOD 2:

$$\frac{2\frac{1}{3}}{7} = \frac{\frac{7}{3}}{\frac{7}{1}} = \frac{7}{3} \div \frac{7}{1} = \frac{\overset{1}{\cancel{7}}}{3} \cdot \frac{1}{\cancel{7}} = \frac{1}{3}$$

A *complex rational expression* contains one or more rational expressions in its numerator, its denominator, or both. Complex expressions are simplified by the same procedures used to simplify complex fractions, as seen in the examples that follow.

<table>
<tr><td colspan="2">*Complex Rational Expressions*</td></tr>
<tr><td>$\dfrac{\dfrac{3}{ax}}{\dfrac{6}{bx}}$</td><td>$\dfrac{\dfrac{x^2}{16}-1}{\dfrac{x}{8}-\dfrac{1}{2}}$</td></tr>
</table>

EXAMPLES

1. Express in simplest form: $\dfrac{\dfrac{x^2}{16}-1}{\dfrac{x}{8}-\dfrac{1}{2}}$

Solution

METHOD 1:

The L.C.D. of the expressions is 16. Multiply by $\frac{16}{16}$ and reduce.

$$\frac{\dfrac{x^2}{16}-1}{\dfrac{x}{8}-\dfrac{1}{2}}=\frac{16}{16}\cdot\frac{\left(\dfrac{x^2}{16}-1\right)}{\left(\dfrac{x}{8}-\dfrac{1}{2}\right)}$$

$$=\frac{\overset{1}{16}\cdot\dfrac{x^2}{16}-16\cdot1}{\overset{2}{16}\cdot\dfrac{x}{8}-\overset{8}{16}\cdot\dfrac{1}{2}}$$

$$=\frac{x^2-16}{2x-8}$$

$$=\frac{(x+4)(x-4)}{2(x-4)}$$

$$=\frac{x+4}{2}$$

METHOD 2:

Change both numerator and denominator to single fractions. Then divide and simplify.

$$\frac{\dfrac{x^2}{16}-1}{\dfrac{x}{8}-\dfrac{1}{2}}=\frac{\dfrac{x^2}{16}-1\left(\dfrac{16}{16}\right)}{\dfrac{x}{8}-\dfrac{1}{2}\left(\dfrac{4}{4}\right)}$$

$$=\frac{\dfrac{x^2}{16}-\dfrac{16}{16}}{\dfrac{x}{8}-\dfrac{4}{8}}=\frac{\dfrac{x^2-16}{16}}{\dfrac{x-4}{8}}$$

$$=\frac{x^2-16}{16}\div\frac{x-4}{8}$$

$$=\frac{x^2-16}{16}\cdot\frac{8}{x-4}$$

$$=\frac{(x+4)(x-4)}{16}\cdot\frac{8}{(x-4)}$$

$$=\frac{x+4}{2}$$

Answer: $\dfrac{x+4}{2}$ $(x\neq4)$

2. Express in simplest form: $\dfrac{\frac{3}{ax}}{\frac{6}{bx}}$

Solution

METHOD 1:

The L.C.D. of $\frac{3}{ax}$ and $\frac{6}{bx}$ is abx.

Multiply by $\frac{abx}{abx}$ and reduce.

$$\dfrac{\frac{3}{ax}}{\frac{6}{bx}} = \frac{abx}{abx} \cdot \dfrac{\frac{3}{ax}}{\frac{6}{bx}} = \dfrac{\overset{b}{\cancel{abx}} \cdot \frac{3}{\cancel{ax}}}{\underset{a}{\cancel{abx}} \cdot \frac{6}{\cancel{bx}}}$$

$$= \frac{3b}{6a} = \frac{b}{2a}$$

METHOD 2:

Divide the numerator by the denominator and simplify.

$$\dfrac{\frac{3}{ax}}{\frac{6}{bx}} = \frac{3}{ax} \div \frac{6}{bx}$$

$$= \dfrac{\overset{1}{\cancel{3}}}{\underset{a}{\cancel{ax}}} \cdot \dfrac{\overset{b}{\cancel{bx}}}{\underset{2}{\cancel{6}}} = \frac{b}{2a}$$

Answer: $\dfrac{b}{2a}$ $\quad (a \neq 0, b \neq 0, x \neq 0)$

EXERCISES WITH OPEN-RESPONSE PROBLEMS

In 1–45, express each complex fraction or rational expression in simplest form.

1. $\dfrac{\frac{3}{7}}{\frac{4}{7}}$

2. $\dfrac{\frac{x}{5}}{\frac{2x}{5}}$

3. $\dfrac{\frac{3}{8}}{\frac{3}{4}}$

4. $\dfrac{\frac{5}{3x}}{\frac{1}{2x}}$

5. $\dfrac{2\frac{1}{2}}{3}$

6. $\dfrac{x + \frac{1}{x}}{6}$

7. $\dfrac{7}{8\frac{3}{4}}$

8. $\dfrac{y - 1}{y - \frac{1}{y}}$

9. $\dfrac{\frac{a^2}{b}}{\frac{a}{b^2}}$

10. $\dfrac{\frac{2}{k}}{1 + \frac{2}{k}}$

11. $\dfrac{\frac{a + b}{2a}}{\frac{a + b}{3a}}$

12. $\dfrac{\frac{24}{x - 3}}{\frac{36}{x - 3}}$

13. $\dfrac{\frac{1}{d}}{\frac{1}{d} - 1}$

14. $\dfrac{y - \frac{1}{2}}{y + \frac{1}{2}}$

15. $\dfrac{1 - \frac{2}{x}}{1 - \frac{4}{x^2}}$

16. $\dfrac{z + \frac{1}{5}}{z^2 - \frac{1}{25}}$

17. $\dfrac{\frac{1}{7} + \frac{1}{b}}{\frac{1}{b}}$

18. $\dfrac{\frac{1}{r} + \frac{1}{m}}{\frac{1}{r} - \frac{1}{m}}$

19. $\dfrac{x - \frac{1}{x}}{\frac{1 - x^2}{x}}$

20. $\dfrac{\frac{a^2 - b^2}{a}}{1 - \frac{b}{a}}$

21. $\dfrac{\frac{x - 5}{x}}{\frac{x}{5} - 1}$

22. $\dfrac{\frac{b}{a} - 1}{\frac{1}{a} - \frac{1}{b}}$

23. $\dfrac{\frac{y}{3} + \frac{3}{y}}{\frac{1}{3} + \frac{1}{y}}$

24. $\dfrac{\frac{x + y}{x}}{\frac{1}{x} + \frac{1}{y}}$

25. $\dfrac{\frac{b^2}{4} - 1}{\frac{b}{4} - \frac{1}{2}}$

26. $\dfrac{\dfrac{2}{x^2}+\dfrac{2}{y^2}}{\dfrac{4}{xy}}$

27. $\dfrac{\dfrac{4}{x}-\dfrac{8}{x^2}}{1-\dfrac{2}{x}}$

28. $\dfrac{\dfrac{k}{2}-\dfrac{k}{6}}{\dfrac{k}{2}+\dfrac{k}{3}}$

29. $\dfrac{\dfrac{1}{7}-\dfrac{1}{x}}{\dfrac{x}{7}-\dfrac{7}{x}}$

30. $\dfrac{1-\dfrac{y}{8}}{\dfrac{1}{8}-\dfrac{1}{y}}$

31. $\dfrac{\dfrac{9}{2}+\dfrac{3}{2x}}{\dfrac{9x}{2}-\dfrac{1}{2x}}$

32. $\dfrac{\dfrac{a}{b}-\dfrac{b}{a}}{1-\dfrac{b}{a}}$

33. $\dfrac{6+\dfrac{12}{t}}{3t-\dfrac{12}{t}}$

34. $\dfrac{\dfrac{x}{2}-\dfrac{8}{x}}{\dfrac{1}{4}-\dfrac{1}{x}}$

35. $\dfrac{\dfrac{3}{a^2}+\dfrac{5}{a^3}}{\dfrac{10}{a}+6}$

36. $\dfrac{\dfrac{1}{n}-3}{3n-1}$

37. $\dfrac{1+\dfrac{4}{x}+\dfrac{3}{x^2}}{1-\dfrac{9}{x^2}}$

38. $\dfrac{1+\dfrac{2}{y}-\dfrac{24}{y^2}}{1+\dfrac{4}{y}-\dfrac{12}{y^2}}$

39. $\dfrac{\dfrac{1}{k}-\dfrac{3}{k^2}+\dfrac{2}{k^3}}{\dfrac{1}{k}-\dfrac{4}{k^2}+\dfrac{4}{k^3}}$

40. $\dfrac{1+\dfrac{7}{y-2}}{1+\dfrac{3}{y+2}}$

41. $\dfrac{1+\dfrac{4}{x+1}}{x-1-\dfrac{24}{x+1}}$

42. $\dfrac{\dfrac{3}{x-2}-\dfrac{3}{x+2}}{\dfrac{12}{x^2-4}}$

43. $\dfrac{\dfrac{3}{b}-1}{1-\dfrac{6}{b}+\dfrac{9}{b^2}}$

44. $\dfrac{\dfrac{5}{a+b}-\dfrac{5}{a-b}}{\dfrac{10}{a^2-b^2}}$

45. $1-\dfrac{1}{1+\dfrac{1}{x}}$

46. For what rational values of x will $\dfrac{\dfrac{x^2}{5}-5}{\dfrac{x}{5}-1}=x+5$?

(1) All rational numbers

(2) Rational numbers/$\{0, 5\}$

(3) Rational numbers/$\{5\}$

(4) Rational numbers/$\{5, -5\}$

47. a. Evaluate the rational expression $\dfrac{1+\dfrac{3}{k-1}}{2+\dfrac{6}{k-1}}$ when:

(1) $k=2$

(2) $k=0$

(3) $k=101$

(4) $k=-3.76$

b. Explain why the rational expression in part **a** is undefined when:

(1) $k=1$

(2) $k=-2$

48. a. Write the rational expression $\dfrac{1+\dfrac{1}{x}-\dfrac{12}{x^2}}{1-\dfrac{4}{x}-\dfrac{32}{x^2}}$ in simplest form.

b. Find the value of this rational expression when:

(1) $x=9$

(2) $x=3$

(3) $x=23$

(4) $x=508$

c. Find the value of x that makes this rational expression equal to:

(1) 0

(2) 2

(3) -4

(4) $\frac{1}{2}$

d. Is it possible for this rational expression to equal 1? Explain your answer.

9-7 SOLVING FRACTIONAL EQUATIONS

Equations with Fractional Coefficients

To solve an equation containing a numerical coefficient that is a fraction, we may use one of two procedures. In each method, the equation is transformed into a series of simpler equivalent equations. Consider the following three examples:

1. Solve for x: $\frac{1}{5}x + 2 = 6$.

METHOD 1:	METHOD 2:
Use the standard procedure to simplify a first-degree equation.	First, clear the equation of all fractions. To do this, multiply both sides by the L.C.D. of all fractions in the equation. Then use standard procedures.

METHOD 1:

Use the standard procedure to simplify a first-degree equation.

$$\frac{1}{5}x + 2 = 6$$

$$\frac{1}{5}x + 2 - 2 = 6 - 2$$

$$\frac{1}{5}x = 4$$

$$5 \cdot \frac{1}{5}x = 5 \cdot 4$$

$$x = 20 \quad \textit{Answer}$$

METHOD 2:

First, clear the equation of all fractions. To do this, multiply both sides by the L.C.D. of all fractions in the equation. Then use standard procedures.

$$\frac{1}{5}x + 2 = 6$$

$$5\left(\frac{1}{5}x + 2\right) = 5(6)$$

$$5 \cdot \frac{1}{5}x + 5 \cdot 2 = 5(6)$$

$$x + 10 = 30$$

$$x = 20 \quad \textit{Answer}$$

Fractional Equations

An equation is called a ***fractional equation*** when a variable appears in the *denominator* of one or more of its terms. Thus, $\frac{1}{5}x + 2 = 6$ is not a true fractional equation but is simply an equation with rational coefficients. Examples of fractional equations include:

$$\frac{1}{12} + \frac{1}{y} = \frac{1}{4} \qquad \text{and} \qquad \frac{x}{x-1} = \frac{2}{x} + \frac{1}{x-1}$$

To solve a fractional equation, we use the procedure stated in Method 2 above, namely:

- **Clear the equation of all fractions by multiplying both sides by the L.C.D. of all fractions and rational expressions in the equation.**

2. Solve for y and check: $\frac{1}{12} + \frac{1}{y} = \frac{1}{4}$.

Multiply both sides of the equation by the L.C.D., $12y$. Apply the distributive property, and simplify the equation.

Check:

$$\frac{1}{12} + \frac{1}{y} = \frac{1}{4}$$

$$12y\left(\frac{1}{12} + \frac{1}{y}\right) = 12y\left(\frac{1}{4}\right)$$

$$\overset{y}{\cancel{12y}} \cdot \frac{1}{\underset{1}{\cancel{12}}} + \overset{12}{\cancel{12y}} \cdot \frac{1}{\underset{1}{\cancel{y}}} = \overset{3y}{\cancel{12y}}\left(\frac{1}{\underset{1}{\cancel{4}}}\right)$$

$$y + 12 = 3y$$

$$12 = 2y$$

$$6 = y$$

$$\frac{1}{12} + \frac{1}{y} = \frac{1}{4}$$

$$\frac{1}{12} + \frac{1}{6} \overset{?}{=} \frac{1}{4}$$

$$\frac{1}{12} + \frac{2}{12} \overset{?}{=} \frac{1}{4}$$

$$\frac{3}{12} \overset{?}{=} \frac{1}{4}$$

$$\frac{1}{4} = \frac{1}{4} \quad ✔$$

Answer: $y = 6$, or solution set $= \{6\}$.

Fractional Equations with Extraneous Roots

If we multiply both sides of an equation by the L.C.D. of all denominators in the equation, we do *not necessarily* form an equivalent equation. Let us study a situation in which the derived equation is *not* equivalent to the original equation.

3. Solve for x and check: $\frac{x}{x-1} = \frac{2}{x} + \frac{1}{x-1}$.

Multiply both sides of the equation by the L.C.D., $x(x - 1)$.

$$\frac{x}{x-1} = \frac{2}{x} + \frac{1}{x-1}$$

$$x(x-1)\left(\frac{x}{x-1}\right) = x(x-1)\left(\frac{2}{x} + \frac{1}{x-1}\right)$$

$$x\overset{1}{\cancel{(x-1)}} \cdot \frac{x}{\underset{1}{\cancel{(x-1)}}} = \overset{1}{\cancel{x}}(x-1) \cdot \frac{2}{\underset{1}{\cancel{x}}} + x\overset{1}{\cancel{(x-1)}} \cdot \frac{1}{\underset{1}{\cancel{(x-1)}}}$$

$$x \cdot x = (x-1) \cdot 2 + x \cdot 1$$

$$x^2 = 2x - 2 + x$$

$$x^2 = 3x - 2$$

Since the equation contains x^2, write it in the standard form of a quadratic equation. Then solve the equation.

$$x^2 = 3x - 2$$
$$x^2 - 3x + 2 = 0$$
$$(x - 2)(x - 1) = 0$$

$x - 2 = 0$	$x - 1 = 0$
$x = 2$	$x = 1$

Check the roots of the quadratic equation, namely, $x = 2$ and $x = 1$, in the original fractional equation *before* writing an answer.

Check for $x = 2$:

$$\frac{x}{x - 1} = \frac{2}{x} + \frac{1}{x - 1}$$

$$\frac{2}{2 - 1} \overset{?}{=} \frac{2}{2} + \frac{1}{2 - 1}$$

$$\frac{2}{1} \overset{?}{=} \frac{2}{2} + \frac{1}{1}$$

$$2 \overset{?}{=} 1 + 1$$

$$2 = 2 \ ✔$$

Check for $x = 1$:

$$\frac{x}{x - 1} = \frac{2}{x} + \frac{1}{x - 1}$$

$$\frac{1}{1 - 1} \overset{?}{=} \frac{2}{1} + \frac{1}{1 - 1}$$

$$\frac{1}{0} = 2 + \frac{1}{0}$$

Division by 0 is not defined. Thus, the statement here is meaningless, and 1 is not a root of the original equation.

Answer: $x = 2$, or solution set $= \{2\}$.

In this example, $x = 1$ is called an ***extraneous root***, or an "extra" root, because it is a root of the *derived* equation, $x^2 = 3x - 2$, but it is *not* a root of the *original* equation, $\frac{x}{x - 1} = \frac{2}{x} + \frac{1}{x - 1}$. How is this possible? The derived equation was formed when we multiplied both sides of the original equation by the L.C.D., $x(x - 1)$.

But wait. If $x = 1$, then the L.C.D. $= x(x - 1) = 1(1 - 1) = 1(0) = 0$. Just as $x = 1$ is meaningless for the original equation, so is it meaningless to say that an L.C.D. equals 0, and to multiply both sides of the equation by 0.

We recall that the *multiplication property of zero* states that the product of 0 and any number is 0. In general terms:

For any number a: $a \cdot 0 = 0$ and $0 \cdot a = 0$

Although this statement is true for all numbers, multiplying the sides of an equation by 0 may pose problems, as we have just seen.

If the two sides of an equation are multiplied by a polynomial expression that might represent 0, we observe:

- **Since the derived equation is not necessarily equivalent to the original equation, each root of the derived equation should be checked only in the original equation to see whether it is a member of the solution set.**

EXAMPLES

1. Solve for x: $2 + \dfrac{4}{x-4} = \dfrac{x}{x-4}$.

Solution Multiply both sides of the equation by the L.C.D., $x - 4$.

$$2 + \frac{4}{x-4} = \frac{x}{x-4}$$

$$\left(2 + \frac{4}{x-4}\right) \cdot (x-4) = \left(\frac{x}{x-4}\right) \cdot (x-4)$$

$$2 \cdot (x-4) + \frac{4}{(x-4)} \cdot (x-4) = \left(\frac{x}{x-4}\right) \cdot (x-4)$$

$$2(x-4) + 4 = x$$

$$2x - 8 + 4 = x$$

$$2x - 4 = x$$

$$2x = x + 4$$

$$x = 4$$

Check the only possible root, $x = 4$, in the original equation. Since the statement formed is not defined, 4 is not a root of the equation. Thus, the solution set is empty, or no root exists.

Answer: $\varnothing$, or { }

Check for $x = 4$:

$$2 + \frac{4}{x-4} = \frac{x}{x-4}$$

$$2 + \frac{4}{4-4} \overset{?}{=} \frac{4}{4-4}$$

$$2 + \frac{4}{0} \overset{?}{=} \frac{4}{0} \quad \text{(Not defined)}$$

2. Solve for y: $\dfrac{y-2}{y} = \dfrac{4}{y^2 - 2y}$.

How to Proceed: *Solution:*

(1) Factor all denominators to find the L.C.D., $y(y-2)$.

$$y = y$$
$$y^2 - 2y = y(y-2)$$
$$\overline{\text{L.C.D.} = y(y-2)}$$
$$\frac{y-2}{y} = \frac{4}{y^2 - 2y}$$
$$\frac{y-2}{y} = \frac{4}{y(y-2)}$$

(2) Multiply both sides of the equation by the L.C.D., $y(y-2)$, and solve the resulting quadratic equation.

$$y(y-2) \cdot \frac{y-2}{y} = y(y-2) \cdot \frac{4}{y(y-2)}$$

$$\overset{1}{y}(y-2) \cdot \frac{y-2}{\underset{1}{y}} = \overset{1}{y}(\overset{1}{y-2}) \cdot \frac{4}{\underset{1}{y}(\underset{1}{y-2})}$$

$$(y-2)(y-2) = 4$$
$$y^2 - 4y + 4 = 4$$
$$y^2 - 4y = 0$$
$$y(y-4) = 0$$

$$y = 0 \quad \Big| \quad \begin{array}{c} y - 4 = 0 \\ y = 4 \end{array}$$

(3) *Check* the possible roots, $y = 0$ and $y = 4$, in the original equation.

Check for $y = 0$:

$$\frac{y-2}{y} = \frac{4}{y^2 - 2y}$$
$$\frac{0-2}{0} \overset{?}{=} \frac{4}{0-0}$$

With denominators of 0, the statement is meaningless. Thus, $y = 0$ is an extraneous root, and 0 is not part of the solution.

Check for $y = 4$:

$$\frac{y-2}{y} = \frac{4}{y^2 - 2y}$$
$$\frac{4-2}{4} \overset{?}{=} \frac{4}{16 - 8}$$
$$\frac{2}{4} \overset{?}{=} \frac{4}{8}$$
$$\frac{1}{2} = \frac{1}{2} \quad ✔$$

Answer: $y = 4$, or solution set $= \{4\}$.

3. Barbara would take 10 hours to wallpaper the kitchen, and Gayle 14 hours to wallpaper the same kitchen. How long would Barbara and Gayle, working together, take to wallpaper the kitchen?

How to Proceed:

(1) Identify the variable.

(2) Write an equation. In 1 hour, Barbara can complete $\frac{1}{10}$ of the job, Gayle can complete $\frac{1}{14}$ of the job, and, working together, they can complete $\frac{1}{x}$ of the job.

(3) Multiply by the L.C.D., $70x$, and solve the equation.

Solution:

Let x = time, in hours, to wallpaper when working together.

$$\frac{1}{10} + \frac{1}{14} = \frac{1}{x}$$

$$70x\left(\frac{1}{10} + \frac{1}{14}\right) = 70x\left(\frac{1}{x}\right)$$

$$70x\left(\frac{1}{10}\right) + 70x\left(\frac{1}{14}\right) = 70x\left(\frac{1}{x}\right)$$

$$7x + 5x = 70$$

$$12x = 70$$

$$x = 5\frac{10}{12} = 5\frac{5}{6}$$

Answer: $5\frac{5}{6}$ hours, or 5 hours 50 minutes

EXERCISES WITH OPEN-RESPONSE PROBLEMS

In 1–47, solve each equation and check.

1. $\frac{4}{3x} + \frac{1}{3} = 1$

2. $\frac{y+3}{2y} = \frac{2}{3}$

3. $\frac{3}{2z} + \frac{1}{z} = \frac{1}{2}$

4. $\frac{5a}{a+4} = \frac{5}{2}$

5. $\frac{9}{2b+7} = \frac{3}{b}$

6. $\frac{1}{c} + \frac{1}{3c} = \frac{2}{3}$

7. $\frac{3x+12}{x+4} = \frac{5}{3}$

8. $\frac{4y-1}{5y} = \frac{3}{y}$

9. $\frac{k}{6} = \frac{5}{6} - \frac{1}{k}$

10. $\frac{1}{6} + \frac{1}{12} = \frac{1}{m}$

11. $\frac{4}{3w+7} = \frac{1}{2}$

12. $\frac{t}{t-3} = \frac{3}{4}$

13. $\frac{x}{x+3} = \frac{8}{x+6}$

14. $\frac{12}{y} = \frac{9}{y-3}$

15. $\frac{2z}{z-4} = \frac{2z-4}{z-5}$

16. $\frac{b-2}{2} = \frac{5}{b-5}$

17. $\frac{c-5}{c-5} = \frac{1}{c}$

18. $\frac{3-2d}{3+2d} = \frac{1}{2}$

19. $\frac{x+3}{2x+5} = \frac{1}{x+3}$

20. $\frac{1}{15} + \frac{1}{y} = \frac{1}{6}$

21. $\frac{h+2}{h+6} = \frac{h}{h+2}$

22. $\frac{y+1}{y-1} = \frac{y+4}{y+5}$

23. $\frac{2p-1}{2p+5} = \frac{p-1}{p+3}$

24. $\frac{x}{3} = \frac{4}{x+4}$

25. $\frac{1}{k-2} = \frac{6}{k^2 - 2k}$

26. $\frac{3x-6}{2-x} = \frac{3}{2}$

27. $\frac{y^2 - 2}{y^2 - 16} = \frac{y-2}{y-4}$

28. $\frac{x+2}{x-2} - \frac{4}{3} = \frac{5}{x-2}$

29. $\frac{y+3}{y+2} = \frac{2}{y} + \frac{1}{y+2}$

30. $\frac{b}{b+4} - \frac{1}{b} = \frac{2}{b+4}$

31. $\frac{2}{w-3} + 4 = \frac{2}{w-3}$

32. $\frac{x}{x-3} - \frac{4}{x} = \frac{3}{x-3}$

33. $\frac{1}{m+10} + \frac{1}{5} = \frac{3}{m+10}$

34. $\frac{3y}{y-7} - \frac{3}{2} = \frac{21}{y-7}$

35. $\frac{x}{x-2} - \frac{5}{x} = \frac{2}{x-2}$

36. $\frac{1}{2} + \frac{1}{d-2} = \frac{d}{16}$

37. $\frac{1}{h+1} + \frac{1}{h-1} = \frac{6}{h^2 - 1}$

38. $\frac{x}{x+8} + \frac{16}{x^2 - 64} = \frac{1}{x-8}$

39. $\frac{t}{t+6} + \frac{16}{t^2 - 36} = \frac{1}{t-6}$

40. $\frac{4}{y+2} + \frac{1}{y^2 - 4} = \frac{1}{y-2}$

41. $\frac{x+2}{x+5} + \frac{x-1}{x^2 - 25} = 1$

42. $\frac{x-1}{x-5} - \frac{1}{x} = \frac{20}{x^2 - 5x}$

43. $\frac{2y+1}{3y-18} - \frac{5}{y-6} = \frac{1}{3}$

44. $\frac{1}{2b+6} + \frac{1}{2b-6} = \frac{4}{b^2 - 9}$

45. $\frac{x}{2x+8} + \frac{1}{x-4} = \frac{16}{x^2 - 16}$

46. $\frac{x+1}{x} + \frac{x-1}{x} = \frac{x+6}{x+1}$

47. $\frac{y}{y+3} + \frac{y}{y-3} = \frac{18}{y^2 - 9}$

48. Let $\frac{x}{x+4}$ represent a fraction. If 1 is subtracted from the numerator, then the new fraction formed, $\frac{x-1}{x+4}$, is equal to $\frac{1}{2}$. Find the original fraction.

49. In a fraction, the denominator is 3 more than the numerator. If 1 is added to the numerator and 1 is added to the denominator, the new fraction formed equals $\frac{3}{4}$. Find the original fraction.

50. Let $\frac{3k}{5k}$ represent a fraction that is equivalent to $\frac{3}{5}$. If 4 is subtracted from the numerator and 4 is subtracted from the denominator, the new fraction equals $\frac{1}{2}$. Find the original fraction.

51. A fraction is equivalent to $\frac{2}{3}$. If 5 is added to the numerator and 5 is added to the denominator, the new fraction is equal to $\frac{3}{4}$. Find the original fraction.

52. Pipe A can fill an industrial tank in 8 hours, and pipe B can fill the same tank in 4 hours. Let x represent the number of hours needed to fill the tank when both pipes are in operation. In 1 hour, pipe A fills $\frac{1}{8}$ of the tank, pipe B fills $\frac{1}{4}$ of the tank, and, with both pipes working, $\frac{1}{x}$ of the tank is filled. Use the equation $\frac{1}{8} + \frac{1}{4} = \frac{1}{x}$ to find the time needed to fill the tank when the two pipes are working together.

53. If Felix takes 12 hours, and Oscar takes 8 hours, to paint an average room, how long will it take them, working together, to paint an average room?

54. If one clerk takes 20 minutes to sort the mail and a second clerk takes 30 minutes to do the same job, how many minutes will both clerks, working together, take to sort the mail?

55. Laura and Charlie do yard work each week for Mrs. Macrina. When Laura works alone, she takes 3 hours for the yard work; when she and Charlie work together, they do the job in 2 hours. How long does Charlie take to do the yard work if he works alone?

56. Mary and Joanna are sisters who like to do things together.

    a. Mary takes 10 minutes, and Joanna takes 15 minutes, to fold laundry. What is the fewest number of minutes they take to fold laundry together?

    b. Mary takes 10 minutes, and Joanna takes 15 minutes, to read the morning paper. If they share different sections of the paper, what is the fewest number of minutes they take to read the morning paper together?

    c. Mary takes at least 10 minutes, and Joanna at least 15 minutes, to speak to someone on the telephone. What is the fewest number of minutes they take to speak to their brother if they are together when he calls? (*Hint:* This is not a three-way call.)

57. McGurn and Son are electricians. When they work together, Bob and Ted can install wiring in a new house in 15 hours. If Ted works alone, he needs 16 more hours to do this job than Bob needs when he works alone. Find the time required to install the wiring when:

    a. Bob works alone   **b.** Ted works alone

CHAPTER SUMMARY

    A ***rational expression*** is the quotient of two polynomials. A rational expression is defined only if values of the variable do not produce a denominator of 0.

    A rational expression is ***reduced to lowest terms***, or stated in ***simplest form***, when its numerator and denominator have no common factors other than 1 and -1.

    Operations with rational expressions follow the same rules as operations with arithmetic fractions.

$$\text{\textit{Multiplication:}} \quad \frac{a}{b} \cdot \frac{x}{y} = \frac{ax}{by} \quad (b \neq 0, \, y \neq 0)$$

$$\text{\textit{Division:}} \quad \frac{a}{b} \div \frac{x}{y} = \frac{a}{b} \cdot \frac{y}{x} = \frac{ay}{bx} \quad (b \neq 0, \, x \neq 0, \, y \neq 0)$$

Addition and subtraction with the same denominator:

$$\frac{a}{b} + \frac{c}{b} = \frac{a+c}{b} \quad (b \neq 0) \qquad \frac{a}{b} - \frac{c}{b} = \frac{a-c}{b} \quad (b \neq 0)$$

Addition and subtraction with different denominators (first, obtain a common denominator):

$$\frac{a}{b} + \frac{c}{d} = \frac{a}{b}\left(\frac{d}{d}\right) + \frac{c}{d}\left(\frac{b}{b}\right) = \frac{ad}{bd} + \frac{bc}{bd} = \frac{ad + bc}{bd} \quad (b \neq 0, \, d \neq 0)$$

$$\frac{a}{b} - \frac{c}{d} = \frac{ad - bc}{bd} \quad (b \neq 0, \, d \neq 0)$$

A *complex rational expression* contains one or more rational expressions (just as a *complex fraction* contains one or more fractions) in its numerator, its denominator, or both.

A *fractional equation* is an equation in which a variable appears in the denominator of one or more of the terms. To solve a fractional equation, multiply both sides of the equation by the *lowest common denominator (L.C.D.)* to clear fractions; then since the derived equation is not necessarily equivalent to the original equation, check every root of the derived equation in the original equation to disallow any *extraneous* (extra) *root*.

VOCABULARY

9-1	Rational expression	Reduced to lowest terms	Simplest form
	Cancellation		
9-5	Equivalent fractions	Lowest common denominator	
	Mixed expression		
9-6	Complex fraction	Complex rational expression	
9-7	Fractional equation	Extraneous root	

REVIEW EXERCISES WITH OPEN-RESPONSE PROBLEMS

In 1–3, find the value(s) of x for which each rational expression is *not* defined.

1. $\dfrac{x-2}{3x-12}$ **2.** $\dfrac{5x}{x^2+5x}$ **3.** $\dfrac{x-6}{x+5x-24}$

In 4–16, in each case, perform the indicated operation(s) and express the answer in simplest form.

4. $\dfrac{a-b}{16b^3} \cdot \dfrac{12b^4}{a-b}$ **5.** $\dfrac{y^2-4y}{y^2+3y} \cdot \dfrac{y^2-9}{y-4}$ **6.** $\dfrac{2x-9}{x+1} \div \dfrac{9-2x}{3x+3}$

7. $\dfrac{(y+1)^2}{y^2+y} \div \dfrac{y^2-1}{y^2}$ **8.** $\dfrac{9x}{3x+5} + \dfrac{15}{3x+5}$ **9.** $\dfrac{2y-5}{y^2-25} - \dfrac{5}{y^2-25}$

10. $\dfrac{x+1}{x} + \dfrac{x-3}{3x}$ **11.** $\dfrac{2y}{y-7} + \dfrac{14}{7-y}$ **12.** $\dfrac{k}{k-2} - \dfrac{8}{k^2-4}$

13. $\dfrac{1}{y+6} + \dfrac{2}{y-6} + \dfrac{12}{y^2-36}$ **14.** $\dfrac{x^2-4x-32}{x^2+12x+32} \div \dfrac{(x-8)^2}{x^2-64}$

15. $\left(2 + \dfrac{2}{x-4}\right) \div \left(1 + \dfrac{x-1}{2x-8}\right)$ **16.** $\left(x+1+\dfrac{1}{x-1}\right)\left(x-4+\dfrac{3}{x}\right)$

In 17–20, change each expression to its simplest form.

17. $\dfrac{1 - \frac{8}{x}}{\frac{8}{x}}$

18. $\dfrac{\frac{x - y}{x}}{\frac{x}{y} - 1}$

19. $\dfrac{\frac{a^2}{20} - 5}{\frac{a}{20} - \frac{1}{2}}$

20. $\dfrac{\frac{1 + 2t}{4t}}{t - \frac{1}{4t}}$

21. The product $\dfrac{x + 4}{x - 4} \cdot \dfrac{x + 12}{x + 4} = \dfrac{x + 12}{x - 4}$ for all rational values of x where

   (1) $x \neq 4$ (2) $x \neq -4$ (3) $x \neq 4, -4$ (4) $x \neq 4, -4, -12$

In 22–27, solve each equation and check.

22. $\dfrac{1}{k} + \dfrac{1}{4} = \dfrac{9}{4k}$

23. $\dfrac{x}{6} = \dfrac{1}{6} + \dfrac{2}{x}$

24. $\dfrac{2x}{x - 8} - \dfrac{5}{2} = \dfrac{x + 8}{x - 8}$

25. $\dfrac{2}{x + 6} = \dfrac{3x + 4}{x^2 + 6x}$

26. $\dfrac{w - 3}{w - 3} = \dfrac{1}{w}$

27. $\dfrac{y}{y + 7} + \dfrac{42}{y^2 - 49} = \dfrac{3}{y - 7}$

28. Given the rational expression: $\dfrac{1 - \frac{3}{y} + \frac{2}{y^2}}{1 - \frac{5}{y} + \frac{6}{y^2}}$

   a. Find the value of the rational expression when:

   (1) $y = 5$ (2) $y = -5$ (3) $y = 1{,}003$

   b. For what values of y is the rational expression undefined?

   c. Find the value of y that makes the expression equal to:

   (1) 0 (2) $\frac{2}{3}$ (3) 3

   d. Is it possible for the given rational expression to equal 1? Explain your answer.

29. The Sullivans went skiing for the weekend. They traveled for 70 miles at a constant rate of speed. Then they encountered snow-covered roads, and had to reduce their speed by 30 miles per hour for the last 12 miles. The trip took 2 hours. Find the rate of speed for each part of the trip.

   Hint: Express the time for each part of the trip as $\frac{\text{distance}}{\text{rate}}$.

CUMULATIVE REVIEW WITH OPEN-RESPONSE PROBLEMS

1. Express $\frac{7}{36}$ as a repeating decimal.

2. Express $0.6\overline{18}$ as the ratio of integers.

3. Write the negation of the statement "All trees lose their leaves in winter."

4. If p represents the sentence "$(x + 2)^2 = x^2 + 4$."
   a. Write $\forall_x : p$ in words.
   b. Is $\forall_x : p$ true or false?
   c. Write the negation of $\forall_x : p$ in symbols.
   d. Write the negation of $\forall_x : p$ in words.

5. Write the following rational numbers in order, starting with the least:

$$\frac{12}{29}, \qquad \frac{6}{13}, \qquad \frac{4}{9}, \qquad \frac{3}{7}$$

6. What is the solution set of $2 - \frac{x}{5} > x - 4$?

7. Let $S = \{p, q, r, s\}$ and let $*$ be an operation defined by the table.
   a. Does $(S, *)$ have an identity? If so, what is the identity?
   b. If $(S, *)$ has an identity element, find the inverse of each element, if the inverse exists.

$*$	p	q	r	s
p	r	s	p	q
q	s	r	q	p
r	p	q	r	s
s	q	p	s	r

Exploration

To solve the inequality $\frac{1}{k} + \frac{1}{5} \leq \frac{1}{2k}$, Aaron began by multiplying both sides of the inequality by $10k$ and then completed the proof as shown below. After finding the solution shown, he substituted -3 in the inequality but found that it did not check. Explain the error that Aaron made in solving the inequality.

Solution: $\quad \frac{1}{k} + \frac{1}{5} \leq \frac{1}{2k}$

$$10k\left(\frac{1}{k}\right) + 10k\left(\frac{1}{5}\right) \leq 10k\left(\frac{1}{2k}\right)$$

$$10 + 2k \leq 5$$

$$2k \leq -5$$

$$k \leq -\frac{5}{2}$$

Check: Let $k = -3$

$$\frac{1}{k} + \frac{1}{5} \leq \frac{1}{2k}$$

$$\frac{1}{-3} + \frac{1}{5} \overset{?}{\leq} \frac{1}{2(-3)}$$

$$-\frac{10}{30} + \frac{6}{30} \overset{?}{\leq} -\frac{5}{30}$$

$$-\frac{4}{30} \leq -\frac{5}{30} \quad \text{(False)}$$

Chapter 10
The Real Numbers

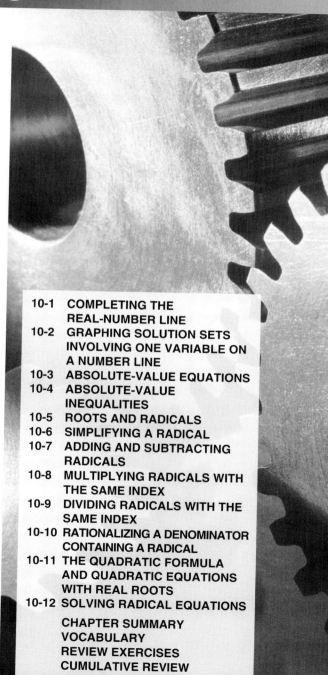

The irrational number that we designate as π has intrigued and challenged mathematicians of all cultures throughout the ages. The ratio of the circumference to the diameter of any circle is known to be a constant—but a constant that is not a rational number.

The early Greeks called this ratio π and used the perimeters of regular polygons to find a rational approximation of its value. Archimedes, using polygons with 96 sides, showed that the value of π is less than $3\frac{1}{7}$ and greater than $3\frac{10}{71}$. Other ancient estimates were given by the Babylonians $\left(\frac{25}{8}\right)$, the Egyptians $\left(\frac{256}{81}\right)$, the Chinese $\left(\frac{355}{113}\right)$, and the Indians $(\sqrt{10})$. In 1596, the German mathematician Ludolph van Ceulen calculated π to 35 decimal places. Computers have made it possible to write the approximate rational value of π to millions of decimal places.

Compare the decimal equivalents of the rational numbers found by ancient civilizations with the value given below to 35 decimal places:

$$\pi \approx 3.14159265358979323846264338327950288$$

10-1 COMPLETING THE REAL-NUMBER LINE

In Chapter 8, we learned that every rational number can be associated with a point on the number line. Although the set of rational numbers is a dense set and an infinite number of other rationals lie between every two rational numbers, the number line that contains only the graphs of all rational numbers is not complete. "Holes" in the line are reserved for numbers that are not rational. For example, $\sqrt{2}$, $\sqrt{3}$, and $\sqrt{5}$ are not rational numbers, but we can locate a point associated with each of these numbers on the number line.

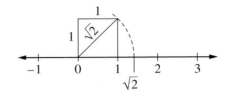

In the figure at the right, a square has been constructed on the number line with vertices at the graphs of 0 and 1 so that the length of each side of the square is 1 unit. A diagonal separates the square into two right triangles. We can use the Pythagorean Theorem to find the length of the diagonal, d, a positive number.

$$d^2 = 1^2 + 1^2 = 1 + 1 = 2$$
$$d = \sqrt{2}$$

By placing the point of a pair of compasses on 0 on the number line and opening the compasses to a length equal to that of the diagonal of the square, we can draw an arc that intersects the number line at the point that is the graph of $\sqrt{2}$.

Now that we have located the graph of $\sqrt{2}$ on the number line, we can construct a rectangle whose dimensions are 1 by $\sqrt{2}$, placing two of its vertices at 0 and at $\sqrt{2}$, as shown at the right. A diagonal separates the rectangle into two right triangles, and the Pythagorean Theorem can again be used to find the length of the diagonal, d.

$$d^2 = 1^2 + (\sqrt{2})^2 = 1 + 2 = 3$$
$$d = \sqrt{3}$$

With a pair of compasses we can draw an arc whose length is equal to the length of the diagonal. This arc will intersect the number line at the point that is the graph of $\sqrt{3}$.

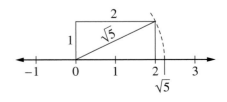

This process can be continued to find the graphs of other irrational numbers of the form $\sqrt{a}$, $a > 0$. In the figure at the right, a rectangle whose dimensions are 2 units by 1 unit is used to locate the position of $\sqrt{5}$ on the number line.

The Irrational Numbers

The numbers $\sqrt{2}$, $\sqrt{3}$, and $\sqrt{5}$ are irrational numbers. To define an irrational number, let us recall a discovery made in Chapter 8; namely, a number is *rational* if and only if the number can be expressed as a repeating decimal.

- **DEFINITION.** An *irrational number* is a nonrepeating decimal (one that does not terminate or end).

There are infinitely many irrational numbers. In each of these examples:

$$0.10110111011110111110\ldots \qquad \text{and} \qquad -0.1234567891011121314\ldots$$

the three dots indicate that the pattern continues without end. We note, however, that the same sequence of numbers does not repeat, as it does in the rational number $0.\overline{3} = 0.333\ldots = \frac{1}{3}$. Thus, there is no way to represent either number shown above in the form of a rational number, that is, $\frac{a}{b}$, where a and b are integers and $b \neq 0$.

If k is a positive number but not a perfect square, then $\sqrt{k}$ is irrational. Such irrational numbers include $\sqrt{2}$, $\sqrt{3}$, $\sqrt{5}$, $\sqrt{1.4}$, and $\sqrt{\frac{1}{2}}$. Pi, written symbolically as π, is also an irrational number.

$$\pi = 3.14159265358979323846264338327950288841971\ldots$$

Here, the three dots indicate that the number continues, but we are uncertain of the next digit or we do not wish to display any more digits. Although modern computers can calculate π to millions of decimal places, the exact value of π cannot be written as a finite decimal. For this reason we often use *approximate rational values* when evaluating expressions that contain π or other irrational numbers. For example, if we use the symbol $\approx$ for "is approximately equal to," we can write $\pi \approx 3.14$ or $\pi \approx 3.1416$.

A calculator can be used to find approximate rational values of many irrational numbers.

Enter:	2 $\boxed{\sqrt{x}}$	*Enter:*	3 $\boxed{\sqrt{x}}$	*Enter:*	5 $\boxed{\sqrt{x}}$
Display:	$\boxed{1.41421356}$	*Display:*	$\boxed{1.73205081}$	*Display:*	$\boxed{2.23606798}$

Therefore we can write:

$$\sqrt{2} \approx 1.41421356 \qquad \sqrt{3} \approx 1.73205081 \qquad \sqrt{5} \approx 2.23606798$$

The Real Numbers

- **DEFINITION.** The *set of real numbers* is the union of the set of rational numbers and the set of irrational numbers.

In other words, every number that can be expressed as a decimal, whether the decimal is repeating or nonrepeating, is a real number.

By identifying points that correspond to irrational numbers as well as points that correspond to rational numbers, we completely fill in the ***real-number line***.

There is a ***one-to-one correspondence*** between the set of real numbers and the set of points on the number line. In other words:

1. For every real number, there is one and only one point on the number line.

2. For every point on the number line, there is one and only one real number.

The Properties of the Real Numbers

The set of real numbers, symbolized here as R, is an ordered field under the operations of addition and multiplication. The properties for the set of rational numbers listed in Chapter 8 are now extended to the set of real numbers. Let us restate these properties for R, both in words and in symbols.

- **(Real numbers, +, ·, >) is an ordered field, satisfying the following properties:**

In Words	*In Symbols*
1. $(R, +)$ is *closed*.	1. $\forall_{a,b} \in R$: $a + b = c$, where $c \in R$.
2. $(R, +)$ is *associative*.	2. $\forall_{a,b,c} \in R$: $(a + b) + c = a + (b + c)$.
3. $(R, +)$ has a unique *identity* element (0).	3. $\exists_0 \in R, \forall_x \in R$: $x + 0 = x$, and $0 + x = x$.
4. Every element of $(R, +)$ has an *inverse* $(-x)$.	4. $\forall_x \in R, \exists_{(-x)} \in R$: $x + (-x) = 0$, and $(-x) + x = 0$.
5. $(R, +)$ is *commutative*.	5. $\forall_{a,b} \in R$: $a + b = b + a$.
6. $(R/\{0\}, \cdot)$ is *closed*.	6. $\forall_{a,b} \in R/\{0\}$: $ab = c$, where $c \in R/\{0\}$.
7. $(R/\{0\}, \cdot)$ is *associative*.	7. $\forall_{a,b,c} \in R/\{0\}$: $(ab)c = a(bc)$.
8. $(R/\{0\}, \cdot)$ has a unique *identity* element (1).	8. $\exists_1 \in R/\{0\}, \forall_x \in R/\{0\}$: $x \cdot 1 = x$, and $1 \cdot x = x$.
9. Every element of $(R/\{0\}, \cdot)$ has an *inverse* $\left(\frac{1}{x}\right)$.	9. $\forall_x \in R/\{0\}, \exists_{1/x} \in R/\{0\}$: $x \cdot \frac{1}{x} = 1$, and $\frac{1}{x} \cdot x = 1$.

In Words	*In Symbols*

10. $(R/\{0\}, \cdot)$ is *commutative*.

           10. $\forall_{a,b} \in R/\{0\}$: $ab = ba$.

11. Multiplication *distributes* over addition.

           11. $\forall_{a,b,c} \in R$: $a(b + c) = ab + ac$, and $ab + ac = a(b + c)$.

12. *Trichotomy property.*

           12. $\forall_{a,b} \in R$, one and only one is true: $a > b$, or $a = b$, or $a < b$.

13. *Transitive property of inequalities.*

           13. $\forall_{a,b,c} \in R$:
If $a > b$ and $b > c$, then $a > c$.
If $c < b$ and $b < a$, then $c < a$.

14. *Addition property of inequalities.*

           14. $\forall_{a,b,c} \in R$:
If $a > b$, then $a + c > b + c$.
If $a < b$, then $a + c < b + c$.

15. *Multiplication property of inequalities.*

           15. $\forall_{a,b,c} \in R$, where c is *positive*:
If $a > b$ and $c > 0$, then $ac > bc$.
If $a < b$ and $c > 0$, then $ac < bc$.
$\forall_{a,b,c} \in R$, where c is *negative*:
If $a > b$ and $c < 0$, then $ac < bc$.
If $a < b$ and $c < 0$, then $ac > bc$.

In addition to the properties of an ordered field, the set of real numbers obeys the postulates of equality and the zero property of multiplication:

1. *Reflexive property of equality.*

           1. $\forall_a \in R$: $a = a$.

2. *Symmetric property of equality.*

           2. $\forall_{a,b} \in R$:   If $a = b$, then $b = a$.

3. *Transitive property of equality.*

           3. $\forall_{a,b,c} \in R$:
If $a = b$ and $b = c$, then $a = c$.

4. *Substitution property of equality.*

           4. $\forall_{a,b} \in R$:
If $a = b$, then a or b may replace each other in any expression.

5. *Addition property of equality.*

           5. $\forall_{a,b,c} \in R$:
If $a = b$, then $a + c = b + c$.

6. *Multiplication property of equality.*

           6. $\forall_{a,b,c} \in R$:
If $a = b$, then $ac = bc$.

7. *Zero property of multiplication.*

           7. $\forall_x \in R$: $x \cdot 0 = 0$, and $0 \cdot x = 0$.

From this point on, unless otherwise stated, we will assume that all work is to be performed using the domain of real numbers.

EXAMPLE

Prove that, if a is irrational and b is rational, then $a + b$ is irrational.

Solution Use an indirect proof. Let $a + b = c$, and assume that c is rational. Since b is rational, there exists a rational number $-b$ such that $b + (-b) = 0$. Therefore:

$$a + b = c$$
$$a + b + (-b) = c + (-b)$$
$$a = c + (-b)$$

Then, a is the sum of two rational numbers. Therefore, a is rational because the rational numbers are closed under addition. Since this statement contradicts the given fact that a is irrational, the assumption is false and c is an irrational number.

EXERCISES WITH OPEN-RESPONSE PROBLEMS

In 1–15, tell whether each number is rational or irrational.

1. -2
2. 0
3. $\sqrt{2}$
4. $\sqrt{625}$
5. π
6. $\sqrt{90}$
7. $\frac{1}{2}$
8. 3.67
9. $\sqrt{\frac{1}{4}}$
10. $\sqrt{\frac{1}{3}}$
11. $\sqrt{3.6}$
12. $\sqrt{0.36}$
13. $0.20202020\ldots$
14. $0.2020020002\ldots$
15. $0.248163264\ldots$

16. Is the set of irrational numbers closed under addition? (*Hint:* Add $\sqrt{3}$ and $-\sqrt{3}$.)
17. Is the set of irrational numbers closed under multiplication?

18. **a.** Construct a rectangle whose sides measure 1 and 3 in such a way that one of its vertices is at 0 on a number line.
    b. Using this rectangle, locate the graph of $\sqrt{10}$ on the number line.
    c. Locate the graph of $-\sqrt{10}$ on the same number line.

In 19–26, identify the property of the real numbers that is illustrated by each given statement.

19. $\sqrt{19} + 0 = \sqrt{19}$
20. $\pi + (-\pi) = 0$
21. $\sqrt{10} \cdot 1 = \sqrt{10}$
22. $\sqrt{5} \cdot \frac{1}{4} = \frac{1}{4} \cdot \sqrt{5}$
23. $\frac{\sqrt{3}}{2} \cdot \frac{2}{\sqrt{3}} = 1$
24. $\pi + 4 = 4 + \pi$
25. $3(2 + \sqrt{7}) = 3 \cdot 2 + 3\sqrt{7}$
26. $3 + (2 + \sqrt{7}) = (3 + 2) + \sqrt{7}$

In 27–30, in each case, tell which of the three given relations is true.

27. $0.2 > 0.\overline{2}$ or $0.2 = 0.\overline{2}$ or $0.2 < 0.\overline{2}$
28. $\sqrt{2} > 1.4$ or $\sqrt{2} = 1.4$ or $\sqrt{2} < 1.4$
29. $\pi > \frac{22}{7}$ or $\pi = \frac{22}{7}$ or $\pi < \frac{22}{7}$
30. $0.\overline{5} > \frac{5}{9}$ or $0.\overline{5} = \frac{5}{9}$ or $0.\overline{5} < \frac{5}{9}$

31. Prove that, if a is irrational and b is a nonzero rational number, then ab is irrational. Use an indirect proof.

10-2 GRAPHING SOLUTION SETS INVOLVING ONE VARIABLE ON A NUMBER LINE

The ***graph of a solution set*** of an open sentence involving *one variable* is the set of points on the *real-number line* that are associated with elements of the solution set. In constructing or reading such graphs, we observe:

1. A darkened circle, •, is drawn as a point on the number line to represent a number in the solution set.

2. A darkened segment, ——— , or a darkened ray, ——→ , indicates that all real numbers associated with points on the segment or the ray are in the solution set.

3. A nondarkened circle, ○, shown as an endpoint of a segment or a ray indicates that the number associated with that point is not in the solution set.

For example, the solution set of $3x + 8 < 5$ is graphed as follows:

1. Simplify the given inequality. Since $3x + 8 < 5$ and $x < -1$ are equivalent, both sentences have the same solution set and, thus, the same graph.

$$3x + 8 < 5$$
$$3x + 8 - 8 < 5 - 8$$
$$3x < -3$$
$$x < -1$$

2. To show the solution set, graph all points to the left of -1, and place a nondarkened circle which shows that -1 is not included.

Answer:

Graphing Conjunctions and Disjunctions

The expression $1 < x < 5$ is read as "1 is less than x, and x is less than 5." In logic, we learned that a ***conjunction*** is a compound sentence that combines two simple sentences by using the word *and* (symbol: $\wedge$).

Thus, we observe:

$1 < x < 5$ is equivalent to the conjunction $(1 < x) \wedge (x < 5)$.

Also

$1 < x < 5$ is equivalent to the conjunction $(x > 1) \wedge (x < 5)$.

The solution set of a conjunction of two open sentences contains only the values of the variable that are true for *both* open sentences. Thus, the graph of the solution set of a conjunction is the ***intersection*** of the graphs of the simple open sentences.

For example, the solution set of $(x > 1) \wedge (x < 5)$ is graphed as follows:

Think:

1. Think of the graph of $x > 1$ and the graph of $x < 5$ as they would appear on the same number line.

Write:

2. To show the solution set of the conjunction, graph the intersection of the two sets of points seen in step 1. Thus, any point on the graph will be true for both conditions, $x > 1$ *and* $x < 5$.

Note: The graph of $(x > 1) \wedge (x < 5)$ is also the graph of $1 < x < 5$.

We can draw this graph on a graphing calculator that has logic capabilities (for example, the TI-83). We begin by placing the calculator in DOT mode for graphing and selecting a WINDOW that includes values of x from -2.7 to 6.7. The logic connectives are contained in a menu accessed by the [TEST] key.

Enter: Y= | (| X,T,θ,n | 2nd | TEST | 3 1 |)
2nd | TEST | ▶ | 1 | (| X,T,θ,n
2nd | TEST | 5 5 |) | GRAPH

Display:

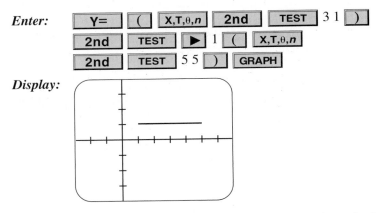

If a graphing calculator, for example the TI-81, does not have logic capabilities, we can draw the graph as the product of the two inequalities, since this product will be 1 when both inequalities are true and 0 when one or both inequalities are false. We begin by placing the calculator in DOT mode for graphing and selecting a RANGE that includes values of x from -2.7 to 6.7.

Enter: Y= | (| X|T | 2nd | TEST | 3 1 |)
(| X|T | 2nd | TEST | 5 5 |) | GRAPH

The display will be the same as that shown above.

A ***disjunction*** is a compound sentence that combines two simple sentences by using the word *or* (symbol: ∨). The solution set of a disjunction of two open sentences contains all values of the variable that are true for *either* one or the other open sentence, or both. Thus, the graph of the solution set of a disjunction is the ***union*** of the graphs of the simple open sentences.

For example, the solution set of $(x \geq 2) \vee (6 < x)$ is graphed as follows:

Think:

1. Think of the graph of $x \geq 2$ and the graph of $6 < x$ (equivalent to $x > 6$) as they would appear on the same number line.

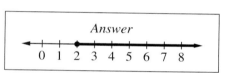

Write:

2. To show the solution set of the disjunction, graph the union of the two sets of points in step 1. Thus, any point on the graph will fit one or both of the conditions, $x \geq 2$ *or* $6 < x$.

On a graphing calculator with logic capabilities, we enter the compound inequality as [**Y=**], selecting "or" from the logic menu.

Enter: [**Y=**] [**(**] [**X,T,θ,n**] [**2nd**] [**TEST**] 4 2 [**)**]
[**2nd**] [**TEST**] [**▶**] 2 [**(**] 6
[**2nd**] [**TEST**] 5 [**X,T,θ,n**] [**)**] [**GRAPH**]

Display:

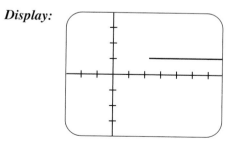

On a graphing calculator that does not have logic capabilities, we use the sum of the inequalities minus their product. If p and q represent inequalities, the chart on the next page shows how $p + q - pq$ yields 1 for all values of x for which the disjunction $p \vee q$ is true.

Truth Value			Calculator Value			
p	q	$p \vee q$	p	q	pq	$p + q - pq$
T	T	T	1	1	1	1
T	F	T	1	0	0	1
F	T	T	0	1	0	1
F	F	F	0	0	0	0

Enter:

Y=	(	X	T	2nd	TEST	4 2	)
+	(6	2nd	TEST	5 X	T	)
−	(	X	T	2nd	TEST	4 2	)
(6	2nd	TEST	5 X	T	)	GRAPH

The display is the same as that given on the preceding page.

EXAMPLE

Which of the following expressions is represented by the graph at the right?

$$-3\ -2\ -1\ \ 0\ \ 1\ \ 2\ \ 3\ \ 4\ \ 5$$

(1) $(x < -1) \wedge (x \geq 0)$ (2) $(x \leq -1) \wedge (x > 0)$

(3) $(x < -1) \vee (x \geq 0)$ (4) $(x \leq -1) \vee (x > 0)$

Solution   The graph shows the *union* of two sets of points having no elements in common. Since union indicates a *disjunction*, study only choices (3) and (4), which involve the word *or*, shown by the symbol $\vee$. The graph indicates that -1 is not an element of the set, while 0 is an element. Therefore, the correct choice is $(x < -1) \vee (x \geq 0)$.

Answer: (3)

EXERCISES WITH OPEN-RESPONSE PROBLEMS

In 1–20, graph the solution set of each given sentence on a number line.

1. $x + 7 < 8$ **2.** $3x \geq 18$ **3.** $2 \geq x$ **4.** $2y - 3 \geq 7$

5. $5 + 4y > 5$ **6.** $6y - 5 = 7$ **7.** $5k < 4k - 2$ **8.** $5 < 8 + w$

9. $3 \leq 2 - p$ **10.** $2x + 6 = 9$ **11.** $4y - 1 \geq 1$ **12.** $x + 4 > 4 + \pi$

13. $\frac{b}{2} < -2$ **14.** $\frac{x}{3} - 1 \geq \frac{x}{2}$ **15.** $-3 \leq x < 0$ **16.** $5 - x \geq 3$

17. $(x > -2) \wedge (x \leq 4)$

19. $(y \leq 1) \vee (y < 5)$

18. $(x > 2) \vee (x \leq -4)$

20. $(y \geq -2) \vee (y > -1)$

In 21–24, graph each given set on a real-number line.

21. $\{x | 3 \leq x \leq 8\}$

23. $\{k | (k < -5) \vee (k > -3)\}$

22. $\{y | -2\frac{1}{2} < y < 1\frac{1}{2}\}$

24. $\{x | (x \leq -3) \vee (x \leq -1.3)\}$

In 25–28, select the *numeral* preceding the expression that best answers the question.

25. Which of the following expressions is represented by the graph at the right?

   (1) $-2 < x \leq 1$ (2) $(x > -2) \vee (x \leq 1)$

   (3) $-2 \leq x < 1$ (4) $(x \geq -2) \vee (x < 1)$

26. Which of the following expressions is represented by the graph at the right?

   (1) $(x < -3) \wedge (x \geq -1)$ (2) $(x < -3) \vee (x \geq -1)$

   (3) $(x \leq -3) \wedge (x > -1)$ (4) $(x \leq -3) \vee (x > -1)$

27. Which of the following expressions is represented by the graph at the right?

   (1) $(y \geq 1) \vee (y > -2)$ (2) $(y > 1) \vee (y \geq -2)$

   (3) $(y \geq 1) \wedge (y > -2)$ (4) $(y > 1) \wedge (y \geq -2)$

28. Which expression has the entire real-number line as its graph?

   (1) $(x > 6) \wedge (x \leq 10)$ (2) $(x < 6) \wedge (x \geq 10)$

   (3) $(x > 6) \vee (x \leq 10)$ (4) $(x < 6) \vee (x \geq 10)$

10-3   ABSOLUTE-VALUE EQUATIONS

Absolute Value of a Real Number

The absolute value of a real number n, written in symbols as $|n|$, can be defined in various ways.

- **Arithmetic Definition.** The *absolute value* of a real number n is the maximum of the number n and its additive inverse $(-n)$. In symbols:

$$|n| = n \max (-n)$$

For example:

1. Since $|4| = 4 \max (-4) = 4$, we write: $|4| = 4.$
2. Since $|-3| = (-3) \max 3 = 3$, we write: $|-3| = 3.$
3. The absolute value of 0 is defined as 0: $|0| = 0.$
   We note that $|0| = 0 \max 0 = 0.$

● **Geometric Definition:** The **absolute value** of a real number n is the distance between the graphs of the numbers n and 0 on the real-number line.

Using the geometric definition, we again show the absolute values of 4, -3, and 0 in the diagrams below.

The distance between the graphs of 4 and 0 is 4. Thus:

$$|4| = 4$$

The distance between the graphs of -3 and 0 is 3. Thus:

$$|-3| = 3$$

The distance from 0 to itself is 0. Thus:

$$|0| = 0$$

The solution set of the absolute-value equation $|x| = 2$ is $\{2, -2\}$ because the graphs of 2 and -2 are each at a distance of 2 units from the graph of 0. Thus, $|-2| = 2$ and $|2| = 2$.

Some mathematicians write $|x| = 2$ as $|x - 0| = 2$ to show that the distance between the graphs of x and 0 is 2.

● **Algebraic Definition:** The **absolute value** of a real number n is defined as:

$$|n| = \begin{cases} n & \text{if } n \geq 0 \\ -n & \text{if } n < 0 \end{cases}$$

Using a geometric approach above, we saw that the solution set of $|x| = 2$ is $\{2, -2\}$. We can solve this same equation using the algebraic definition.

Solve $|x| = 2$.

If $x \geq 0$, then $|x| = x.$ If $x < 0$, then $|x| = -x.$
When $|x| = 2$,   When $|x| = 2$,
$x = 2$ $-x = 2$
                            $x = -2$

Answer: $x = 2$ or $x = -2$ or   solution set $= \{2, -2\}$

Derived Equations

When we used the algebraic definition of absolute value to solve the equation $|x| = 2$, we obtained the *derived equations*, $x = 2$ or $x = -2$.

In general, if $|x| = k$, where $k > 0$, we derive the equations

$$x = k \quad \text{or} \quad x = -k.$$

The procedure for solving an absolute-value equation involves the use of such derived equations. This procedure is outlined in Examples 1 and 2 below. As seen here, a **derived equation** is usually a simpler equation that is not always a true equivalent of a more complicated original equation. For this reason, the roots of all derived equations must be checked in the original equation so that **extraneous** (or *extra*) **roots** are not included in the solution set.

EXAMPLES

1. Solve $|x - 4| = 3$ and graph the solution set.

How to Proceed:

(1) Write the absolute-value equation.

(2) Using disjunction, write two derived equations.

(3) Solve the derived equations.

(4) Check the roots of the derived equations in the absolute-value equation.

(5) Write the answer or the solution set.

(6) Graph the solution set.

Solution:

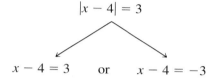

$$|x - 4| = 3$$

$$x - 4 = 3 \quad \text{or} \quad x - 4 = -3$$

$x - 4 + 4 = 3 + 4$	$x - 4 + 4 = -3 + 4$
$x = 7$	$x = 1$

Check for x = 7.	*Check for* x = 1.
$\lvert x - 4 \rvert = 3$	$\lvert x - 4 \rvert = 3$
$\lvert 7 - 4 \rvert \overset{?}{=} 3$	$\lvert 1 - 4 \rvert \overset{?}{=} 3$
$\lvert 3 \rvert \overset{?}{=} 3$	$\lvert -3 \rvert \overset{?}{=} 3$
$3 = 3$	$3 = 3$
(True)	(True)

Answer: $x = 7$ or $x = 1$ or solution set $= \{1, 7\}$

Note: In geometric terms, $|x - 4| = 3$ means that the distance between the graphs of x and 4 is 3 units. Given $|x - 4| = 3$, we know that $x = 1$ or $x = 7$.

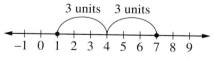

In the diagram, we see that the distance between the graphs of 1 and 4 is 3, and the distance between the graphs of 7 and 4 is also 3.

2. Solve $|x| + 3 = 2x$ and graph the solution set.

How to Proceed:	*Solution:*

(1) Write the given equation.

$$|x| + 3 = 2x$$

(2) Transform the equation into an equivalent sentence in which the absolute-value expression is isolated on one side of the equation.

$$|x| + 3 - 3 = 2x - 3$$
$$|x| = 2x - 3$$

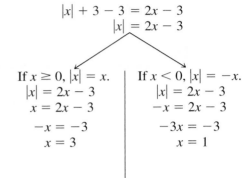

(3) Using the algebraic definition, write two equations.

If $x \geq 0$, $\|x\| = x$.	If $x < 0$, $\|x\| = -x$.
$\|x\| = 2x - 3$	$\|x\| = 2x - 3$
$x = 2x - 3$	$-x = 2x - 3$

(4) Solve the equations. (Notice the second equation. Since $x < 0$ and $x = 1$ are not both true, $x = 1$ cannot be a root. See the check.)

$-x = -3$	$-3x = -3$
$x = 3$	$x = 1$

(5) Check the roots of the derived equations in the original absolute-value equation. (Note that $x = 1$ is an *extraneous* root because 1 is not a root of the absolute-value equation.)

Check for x = 3.	*Check for* x = 1.
$\|x\| + 3 = 2x$	$\|x\| + 3 = 2x$
$\|3\| + 3 \overset{?}{=} 2(3)$	$\|1\| + 3 \overset{?}{=} 2(1)$
$3 + 3 \overset{?}{=} 6$	$1 + 3 \overset{?}{=} 2$
$6 = 6$	$4 = 2$
(True)	(False)

(6) Write the answer.

Answer: $x = 3$ or   solution set $= \{3\}$

(7) Graph the solution set.

Alternative Method: In step 3, write the two derived equations, $x = 2x - 3$ and $x = -(2x - 3)$. These equations have the roots $x = 3$ and $x = 1$, respectively.

---

3. Which is the solution set of $|n| = -5$?

(1) $\{5\}$ (2) $\{-5\}$ (3) $\{5, -5\}$ (4) $\{\ \ \}$

Solution   There is no number whose absolute value is a *negative* number. This can be demonstrated by checking 5 and -5 in the equation $|n| = -5$.

Check for n = 5.	*Check for* n = -5.
$\|5\| \overset{?}{=} -5$	$\|-5\| \overset{?}{=} -5$
$5 = -5$ (False)	$5 = -5$ (False)

Thus, the solution set is the empty set, $\{\ \ \}$.

Answer: (4)

EXERCISES WITH OPEN-RESPONSE PROBLEMS

In 1–32, solve each absolute-value equation.

1. $|x| = 4$

2. $|y| = \frac{1}{2}$

3. $|-w| = 2$

4. $|n| = -9$

5. $|p| = 0$

6. $|2k| = 7$

7. $|x| + 3 = 4$

8. $|y| - 4 = 2$

9. $5 + |m| = 1$

10. $|x + 3| = 4$

11. $|y - 4| = 2$

12. $|5 + m| = 1$

13. $|k + 4| = 6$

14. $|2 - k| = 3$

15. $|2b + 9| = 0$

16. $|y - 3| = 3$

17. $|y - 3| = -3$

18. $|2 - b| = 4$

19. $|4 - 3x| = x$

20. $|4 - x| = 3x$

21. $|x| - 4 = 3x$

22. $|3x| + 4 = x$

23. $|2k - 3| = k$

24. $|k - 3| = 2k$

25. $|k| - 3 = 2k$

26. $|2k| + 3 = k$

27. $|y - 1| = 3y$

28. $|2x + 5| = x + 4$

29. $|2x + 5| = x + 1$

30. $|y + 3| + 5 = 2y$

31. $|y - 4| - 3y = 6$

32. $|x| + x = 4 - 3x$

In 33–35, select the *numeral* preceding the expression that best answers the question.

33. Which equation has { } as its solution set?

   (1) $|x| = 7$ (2) $|-x| = 7$ (3) $|x| = -7$ (4) $|x - 7| = 0$

34. Which equation has a solution set consisting of one and only one real number?

   (1) $|y| = 1$ (2) $|y| = 2$ (3) $|y| = -3$ (4) $|y| = 0$

35. Which expression correctly states the derived equations for $|x| + 3 = 5$?

   (1) $(x + 3 = 5) \vee (x + 3 = -5)$ (2) $(x = 2) \vee (x = -2)$

   (3) $(x + 3 = 5) \wedge (x + 3 = -5)$ (4) $(x = 2) \wedge (x = -2)$

10-4   ABSOLUTE-VALUE INEQUALITIES

The three conditions that involve absolute value and their corresponding graphs are shown below.

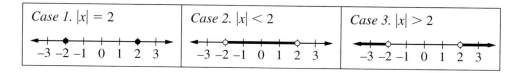

| Case 1. $|x| = 2$ | Case 2. $|x| < 2$ | Case 3. $|x| > 2$ |

Case 1. If $|x| = 2$, we learned that $x = -2$ or $x = 2$. We recall that the distance between the graphs of -2 and 0 is 2 units, and the distance between the graphs of 2 and 0 is also 2 units.

Case 2. If $|x| < 2$, then the distance between the graphs of x and 0 is *less than 2 units*. Thus, x may be any real number less than 2 and greater than -2. The solution set, written as $\{x | -2 < x < 2\}$, is equivalent to the *conjunction* $\{x | x > -2 \text{ and } x < 2\}$.

Let us apply the algebraic definition of absolute value to the general case: $|x| < k$, where k is positive.

1. If $x \geq 0$, $|x| = x$. When $|x| < k$,
$$x < k. \text{ Therefore, } 0 \leq x < k.$$

2. If $x < 0$, $|x| = -x$. When $|x| < k$,
$$-x < k, \text{ or}$$
$$x > -k. \text{ Therefore, } -k < x < 0.$$

3. The solution of $|x| < k$, when $k > 0$, is $(-k < x < 0) \vee (0 \leq x < k)$. The union of these disjoint sets can be written as $-k < x < k$.

We have therefore proved:

- **If $|x| < k$, where k is positive, its solution set is $\{x|-k < x < k\}$.**

The graph of $\{x|-k < x < k\}$, as shown at the left, is a segment that includes the graphs of all real numbers between $-k$ and k, but excludes the graphs of these endpoints.

From $|x| < k$, where k is positive, we can derive this expression:

$$-k < x < k \qquad \text{or} \qquad x > -k \text{ and } x < k$$
$$\text{or } (x > -k) \wedge (x < k)$$

Case 3. If $|x| > 2$, then the distance between the graphs of x and 0 is *greater than 2 units.* Thus, x may be any real number greater than 2 or less than -2. The solution set, written as $\{x|x < -2 \text{ or } x > 2\}$ or as $\{x|(x < -2) \vee (x > 2)\}$, is a *disjunction* of two sets of numbers with no elements in common.

Again, we will apply the algebraic definition of absolute value to the general case: $|x| > k$, where k is positive.

1. If $x \geq 0$, $|x| = x$. When $|x| > k$,
$$x > k. \text{ Therefore, } x > k.$$

2. If $x < 0$, $|x| = -x$. When $|x| > k$,
$$-x > k, \text{ or}$$
$$x < -k. \text{ Therefore, } x < -k.$$

3. The solution of $|x| > k$, when $k > 0$, is $(x < -k) \vee (x > k)$.

We have therefore proved:

- **If $|x| > k$, where k is positive, its solution set is $\{x|x < -k \text{ or } x > k\}$.**

The graph of $\{x|x < -k \text{ or } x > k\}$, as shown at the left, is the union of two rays, one to the right of k and one to the left of $-k$, excluding the graphs of the endpoints of these rays.

From $|x| > k$, where k is positive, we can derive this expression:

$$x < -k \text{ or } x > k \qquad \text{or} \qquad (x < -k) \vee (x > k)$$

EXAMPLES

1. Solve $|2x + 3| < 7$ and graph the solution set.

How to Proceed:	*Solution:*
(1) Write the given inequality.	$|2x + 3| < 7$
(2) Write a derived expression.	$-7 < 2x + 3 < 7$
(3) Simplify: add -3 to each side of the inequality, and divide each side by 2.	$-7 - 3 < 2x + 3 - 3 < 7 - 3$ $-10 < 2x \qquad\qquad < 4$ $-5 < x \qquad\qquad < 2$
(4) Write the solution set.	*Solution set:* $\{x \mid -5 < x < 2\}$
(5) Graph the solution set.	

Note: In step 2, it is possible to write ($2x + 3 > -7$ *and* $2x + 3 < 7$) as the derived expression. By simplifying this expression, we arrive at the solution set $\{x \mid x > -5 \text{ and } x < 2\}$, which is equivalent to the solution set $\{x \mid -5 < x < 2\}$.

---

2. Solve $|3 + y| - 2 \geq 0$ and graph the solution set.

How to Proceed:	*Solution:*
(1) Write the given inequality.	$|3 + y| - 2 \geq 0$
(2) Transform the inequality into an equivalent sentence in which the absolute value is isolated on one side of the inequality.	$|3 + y| - 2 + 2 \geq 0 + 2$ $|3 + y| \geq 2$
(3) Write a derived expression.	$3 + y \leq -2 \qquad \text{or} \qquad 3 + y \geq 2$
(4) Add -3 to each side of the inequality.	$3 + y - 3 \leq -2 - 3 \ \Big| \ 3 + y - 3 \geq 2 - 3$ $y \leq -5 \qquad \text{or} \qquad y \geq -1$
(5) Write the solution set.	*Solution set:* $\{y \mid y \leq -5 \text{ or } y \geq -1\}$
(6) Graph the solution set.	

EXERCISES WITH OPEN-RESPONSE PROBLEMS

In 1–20:   **a.** Solve each absolute-value inequality.   **b.** Graph the solution set.

1. $|x| < 3$ **2.** $|y| > 3$ **3.** $|w| \leq 4$ **4.** $\left|\frac{p}{2}\right| \geq 4$

5. $|2x| > 5$ **6.** $|-3y| < 18$ **7.** $|x| - 1 < 4$ **8.** $3 + |y| \leq 5$

9. $|x| - 2 \geq 1.5$ **10.** $|x - 1| < 4$ **11.** $|3 + y| \leq 5$ **12.** $|x - 2| \geq 1.5$

13. $\left|\frac{w}{5}\right| \geq 1.2$ **14.** $\left|\frac{x + 5}{3}\right| < 2$ **15.** $\left|\frac{k}{3} + 2\right| \leq 2$ **16.** $|2b + 3| > 5$

17. $|2 + 3d| \geq 4$ **18.** $|2m - 1| > 2$ **19.** $|5 - a| > 1$ **20.** $|6 - 2c| \leq 4$

In 21–26, select the *numeral* preceding the expression or the diagram that best completes the sentence or answers the question.

21. Which is the solution set of $|2x - 3| < 5$?

(1) $\{x | -4 < x < 1\}$ (2) $\{x | x < -4 \text{ or } x > 1\}$

(3) $\{x | -1 < x < 4\}$ (4) $\{x | x < -1 \text{ or } x > 4\}$

22. Which represents the solution set for y in $|8 + y| > 3$?

(1) $\{y | (y < -11) \vee (y > -5)\}$ (2) $\{y | -11 < y < -5\}$

(3) $\{y | (y < -5) \vee (y > 5)\}$ (4) $\{y | -5 < y < 5\}$

23. If $|2 - x| > 8$, the solution set is

(1) $\{x | -6 < x < 10\}$ (2) $\{x | x > -6 \text{ or } x < 10\}$

(3) $\{x | -10 < x < 6\}$ (4) $\{x | x < -6 \text{ or } x > 10\}$

24. Which of the given inequalities has $\emptyset$ as its solution set?

(1) $|x| > 2$ (2) $|x| < 2$ (3) $|x| > -2$ (4) $|x| < -2$

25. Which is the graph of the solution set of $|x - 3| > 4$?

(1)   (2)

(3)   (4)

26. Which of the following inequalities has a solution set represented by the graph at the right?

(1) $|x - 4| < 2$ (2) $|x - 2| < 4$ (3) $|x - 4| > 2$ (4) $|x - 2| > 4$

10-5 ROOTS AND RADICALS

Square Root

In Section 1 of this chapter, we located the graphs of numbers such as $\sqrt{2}$, $\sqrt{3}$, and $\sqrt{5}$ on the real-number line. These numbers, written using a *radical sign*, $\sqrt{}$, are used to solve equations such as the following:

Solve $x^2 = 25$.
$$x = \pm\sqrt{25}$$
$$x = \sqrt{25} \text{ or } -\sqrt{25}$$
$$x = 5 \text{ or } -5$$
Solution set $= \{5, -5\}$

Solve $y^2 = 3$.
$$y = \pm\sqrt{3}$$
$$y = \sqrt{3} \text{ or } -\sqrt{3}$$
Solution set $= \{\sqrt{3}, -\sqrt{3}\}$

The equation $x^2 = 25$ has two solutions, 5 and -5, because $(5)(5) = 25$ and $(-5)(-5) = 25$. Therefore 25 has two square roots, 5 and -5, written as $\pm\sqrt{25}$ or ±5. These square roots are rational numbers.

The equation $y^2 = 3$ also has two solutions, $\sqrt{3}$ and $-\sqrt{3}$, because $(\sqrt{3})(\sqrt{3}) = 3$ and $(-\sqrt{3})(-\sqrt{3}) = 3$. Therefore 3 has two square roots, $\sqrt{3}$ and $-\sqrt{3}$, written as $\pm\sqrt{3}$. These square roots are irrational numbers.

We say that the square root of a positive number k is x if and only if $x \cdot x = k$, or $x^2 = k$.

- **DEFINITION.** A *square root* of a number is one of the two equal factors whose product is that number.

In certain situations, such as a geometric problem in which a length must be a positive number, we restrict a solution to the positive square root. However, since for all x, $(x)(x) = (-x)(-x) = x^2$, we can make the following observation:

- **Every positive real number has two square roots.**

If $k > 0$, the square roots of k are $\pm\sqrt{k}$, that is, $\sqrt{k}$ or $-\sqrt{k}$. To indicate that both square roots are to be found, we place a plus sign and a minus sign together in front of the radical sign. For example:

$$\pm\sqrt{49} = \pm7 \qquad \pm\sqrt{\frac{4}{9}} = \pm\frac{2}{3} \qquad \pm\sqrt{0.16} = \pm0.4$$

- **DEFINITION.** The *principal square root* of a positive number k is its positive square root, $\sqrt{k}$.

Thus, a principal square root indicates only one root. For example:

$$\sqrt{49} = 7 \qquad \sqrt{\frac{4}{9}} = \frac{2}{3} \qquad \sqrt{0.16} = 0.4$$

To indicate that only the *negative square root* of a number is to be found, we place a minus sign in front of the radical sign. For example:

$$-\sqrt{49} = -7 \qquad -\sqrt{\frac{4}{9}} = -\frac{2}{3} \qquad -\sqrt{0.16} = -0.4$$

For numbers that are not positive real numbers, we observe:

1. The square root of 0 is 0, that is, $\sqrt{0} = 0$. This is true because 0 is the only number whose square is 0.

2. The square roots of a negative real number are not real numbers. If $k < 0$, then $\pm\sqrt{k}$ are not real numbers. For example, $\sqrt{-4}$ is not a real number because there is no real number that, when squared, is -4. We will study these square roots in Chapter 20, The Complex Numbers.

Cube Root

● **DEFINITION.** A *cube root* of a number is one of three equal factors whose product is that number.

The cube root of a number k is x, written $\sqrt[3]{k} = x$, if and only if $x \cdot x \cdot x = k$, or $x^3 = k$. Since $(2)(2)(2) = 8$, we can say that 2 is a cube root of 8.

Every nonzero real number has three cube roots, one of which is a *real number* called the *principal cube root* of the number. For example, when we write $\sqrt[3]{8} = 2$, we are indicating that 2 is the principal cube root of 8. The other two cube roots of 8 are not real numbers; these roots will be studied in Chapter 20, The Complex Numbers.

Since $(-5)(-5)(-5) = -125$, we know that $\sqrt[3]{-125} = -5$, a real number. By the definition stated earlier, -5 is the principal cube root of -125. Let us consider other examples:

$$\sqrt[3]{64} = 4 \qquad \sqrt[3]{-64} = -4 \qquad \sqrt[3]{\frac{1}{27}} = \frac{1}{3} \qquad \sqrt[3]{-\frac{1}{27}} = -\frac{1}{3}$$

We observe that the principal cube root of a positive real number is a positive real, and the principal cube root of a negative real number is a negative real. Because 0 is the only number whose cube is 0, we know that $\sqrt[3]{0} = 0$.

The *n*th Root of a Number

● **DEFINITION.** The *nth root* of a number (where n is any counting number) is one of n equal factors whose product is that number.

Since $(3)(3)(3)(3) = 81$, then 3 is a fourth root of 81, written as $\sqrt[4]{81} = 3$. Since $x \cdot x \cdot x \cdot x \cdot x = x^5$, then x is a fifth root of x^5, written as $\sqrt[5]{x^5} = x$.

The *principal nth root* of a number k is written as

$$\sqrt[n]{k}$$

where $k =$ the *radicand*,

$n =$ the *index*, a counting number that indicates the root to be taken,

$\sqrt[n]{k} =$ the *radical*, or principal *n*th root of k.

For example, $\sqrt[5]{32}$ is a radical whose radicand is 32 and whose index is 5. When the radical is a square root, as in $\sqrt{81}$, it is understood that the index is 2.

To determine the value of $\sqrt[n]{k}$, the principal nth root of k, we observe:

1. If n is an odd counting number, then $\sqrt[n]{k}$ = the one real number r such that $r^n = k$. For example:

$$\sqrt[3]{125} = 5 \qquad \sqrt[5]{-32} = -2 \qquad \sqrt[7]{1} = 1 \qquad \sqrt[9]{-1} = -1 \qquad \sqrt[9]{0} = 0$$

2. If n is an even counting number and k is a nonnegative number, then $\sqrt[n]{k}$ = the nonnegative real number r such that $r^n = k$. for example:

$$\sqrt{100} \ (\text{or } \sqrt[2]{100}) = 10 \qquad \sqrt[4]{625} = 5 \qquad \sqrt[6]{1} = 1 \qquad \sqrt[8]{0} = 0$$

(*Note:* If n is an even counting number and k is a negative number, as in $\sqrt{-9}$ and $\sqrt[4]{-1}$, then $\sqrt[n]{k}$ is not defined in the set of real numbers. These roots will be defined in Chapter 20, The Complex Numbers.)

In our daily lives, we often use *approximate rational values* for irrational numbers. For example, if we have determined mathematically that a piece of wood $\sqrt{2}$ meters long is needed for a project, we would probably ask the salesperson at the lumberyard for a piece of wood slightly longer than 1.4 meters. Although $\sqrt{2} \neq 1.4$ and $\sqrt{2} \neq 1.414$, the rational numbers are close enough to $\sqrt{2}$ so that we can state $\sqrt{2} \approx 1.414$; that is, the square root of 2 is approximately equal to 1.414.

The calculator is the usual method of finding approximate values of $\sqrt{k}$ when k is not a perfect square. Every scientific calculator has a square root key, $\boxed{\sqrt{x}}$ or $\boxed{\sqrt{}}$. Depending on the model of scientific calculator being used, one of the two methods shown below will find an approximate value for an irrational number such as $\sqrt{15}$:

Enter: METHOD 1:   15 $\boxed{\sqrt{x}}$

METHOD 2: $\boxed{\sqrt{x}}$ 15 $\boxed{=}$

Display: $\boxed{3.872983346}$

Many scientific calculators have a key, $\boxed{\sqrt[x]{y}}$, that will find a rational approximation for any root of a number. The order in which the index and radicand of the root are entered differs, however, and you must try different sequences of keys to find what is right for your calculator. In some cases, as shown in Methods 3 and 4 below, the $\boxed{\sqrt[x]{y}}$ key is accessed by first pressing the $\boxed{\text{2nd}}$, $\boxed{\text{SHIFT}}$, or $\boxed{\text{INV}}$ key. For example, to find an approximate value for $\sqrt[4]{24}$, most scientific calculators will use one of the following methods:

Enter: METHOD 1:   24 $\boxed{\sqrt[x]{y}}$ 4 $\boxed{=}$

METHOD 2:   4 $\boxed{\sqrt[x]{y}}$ 24 $\boxed{=}$

METHOD 3:   24 $\boxed{\text{2nd}}$ $\boxed{\sqrt[x]{y}}$ 4 $\boxed{=}$

METHOD 4:   4 $\boxed{\text{2nd}}$ $\boxed{\sqrt[x]{y}}$ 24 $\boxed{=}$

Display: $\boxed{2.21336383}$

On some graphing calculators, the cube root and the nth root functions are in the $\boxed{\text{MATH}}$ menu.

EXAMPLES

1. Find the square root of 144.

Solution   There are two square roots of 144, written as $\pm\sqrt{144}$. Since $(12)(12) = 144$, and $(-12)(-12) = 144$, then $\pm\sqrt{144} = \pm 12$.

Answer: $+12$ or -12 or ± 12

In 2–5, evaluate each given expression by finding the indicated root. Let each variable represent a positive number.

2. $\sqrt{144}$ **3.** $\sqrt{100x^4}$ **4.** $\sqrt[3]{-8y^3}$ **5.** $-\sqrt[5]{-1}$

<table>
<tr><td align="center">Solutions:</td><td align="center">Answers:</td></tr>
<tr><td>

2. Since $\sqrt{144}$ indicates the principal square root of 144, then $\sqrt{144} = 12$.
3. Since $(10x^2)(10x^2) = 100x^4$, then $\sqrt{100x^4} = 10x^2$.
4. Since $(-2y)(-2y)(-2y) = -8y^3$, then $\sqrt[3]{-8y^3} = -2y$.
5. Here, $-\sqrt[5]{-1} = -(\sqrt[5]{-1}) = -(-1) = 1$.

</td><td>

2. $\sqrt{144} = 12$

3. $\sqrt{100x^4} = 10x^2$

4. $\sqrt[3]{-8y^3} = -2y$
5. $-\sqrt[5]{-1} = 1$

</td></tr>
</table>

6. Find the *smallest integral* value of x for which $\sqrt{2x-9}$ represents a real number.

Solution   (1) A square-root radical is a real number if and only if the radicand is greater than or equal to 0. Thus, write the inequality: $2x - 9 \geq 0$

(2) Simplify the inequality. $2x \geq 9$

(3) Since $x \geq 4\frac{1}{2}$ is equivalent to $2x - 9 \geq 0$, select the smallest integer x so that $x \geq 4\frac{1}{2}$ is true. $x \geq 4\frac{1}{2}$

$x = 5$

(4) *Check* the answer ($x = 5$) and the next smallest integer ($x = 4$). If $x = 5$, then $\sqrt{2x-9} = \sqrt{2(5)-9} = \sqrt{10-9} = \sqrt{1}$, a real number. If $x = 4$, then $\sqrt{2x-9} = \sqrt{2(4)-9} = \sqrt{8-9} = \sqrt{-1}$, *not* a real number.

Answer: 5

EXERCISES WITH OPEN RESPONSE PROBLEMS

In 1–40, evaluate each given expression by finding the indicated root(s). Let each variable represent a positive number.

1. $\sqrt{9}$ **2.** $\pm\sqrt{9}$ **3.** $-\sqrt{9}$ **4.** $\sqrt{225}$

5. $-\sqrt{121}$ **6.** $\sqrt{n^2}$ **7.** $\sqrt{0.25}$ **8.** $\pm\sqrt{0.04}$

9. $\sqrt{64}$ **10.** $\sqrt[3]{64}$ **11.** $\sqrt[6]{64}$ **12.** $-\sqrt{400}$

13. $\sqrt{81x^2}$ **14.** $\sqrt{4y^4}$ **15.** $-\sqrt{b^6}$ **16.** $\sqrt{16x^{16}}$

17. $\pm\sqrt{\dfrac{4}{49}}$ **18.** $-\sqrt{\dfrac{25}{9}}$ **19.** $\pm\sqrt{\dfrac{a^2}{36}}$ **20.** $\sqrt{\dfrac{m^8}{100}}$

21. $\sqrt[3]{27}$ **22.** $\sqrt[3]{-27}$ **23.** $-\sqrt[3]{27}$ **24.** $-\sqrt[3]{-27}$

25. $\sqrt[3]{1000}$ **26.** $\sqrt[3]{k^3}$ **27.** $\sqrt[3]{-125}$ **28.** $\sqrt[3]{216}$

29. $\sqrt[3]{-8y^{12}}$ **30.** $\sqrt[4]{81}$ **31.** $-\sqrt[4]{625}$ **32.** $\sqrt[4]{0}$

33. $\sqrt[4]{16x^{16}}$ **34.** $\sqrt[5]{-243}$ **35.** $\sqrt[5]{32y^5}$ **36.** $-\sqrt[5]{x^{10}}$

37. $\sqrt[7]{-1}$ **38.** $-\sqrt[9]{-1}$ **39.** $-\sqrt[3]{0.008}$ **40.** $-\sqrt[7]{-x^7}$

In 41–52: **a.** State whether each number is rational or irrational. **b.** If the number is irrational, write a rational approximation to the *nearest thousandth*.

41. $\sqrt{25}$ **42.** $\sqrt{8}$ **43.** $\sqrt[3]{8}$ **44.** $\sqrt[3]{-1}$

45. $\sqrt{27}$ **46.** $-\sqrt{196}$ **47.** $\sqrt{1.44}$ **48.** $\sqrt{0.04}$

49. $\sqrt{0.4}$ **50.** $\sqrt[3]{4}$ **51.** $\sqrt[3]{-343}$ **52.** $\sqrt[3]{0.64}$

In 53–56, find, in each case, the *smallest* value of x for which the radical represents a real number.

53. $\sqrt{x-8}$ **54.** $\sqrt{x+3}$ **55.** $\sqrt{2x-5}$ **56.** $\sqrt{3x-10}$

In 57–64, find, in each case, the *smallest integral* value of x for which the radical represents a real number.

57. $\sqrt{2x-5}$ **58.** $\sqrt{3x-10}$ **59.** $\sqrt{5x}$ **60.** $\sqrt{4x-25}$

61. $\sqrt{2x+1}$ **62.** $\sqrt{4+3x}$ **63.** $\sqrt{\dfrac{2x-9}{9}}$ **64.** $\sqrt{\dfrac{2x+7}{5}}$

65. *True* or *False*: The principal square root of a positive number is positive.

66. *True* or *False*: The principal nth root of a nonzero number is positive.

67. *True* or *False*: If n is an even counting number, then $\sqrt[n]{k^n} = |k|$.

68. a. Solve for x: $5^2 + x^2 = 13^2$.

  b. In a right triangle whose hypotenuse measures 13, one leg has a measure of 5. Find the measure of the other leg.

  c. In what ways are parts **a** and **b** alike?   **d.** In what ways are parts **a** and **b** different?

69. a. Solve for n: $n^2 = 7$.
 b. If the area of a square is 7 square units, find the length of one of the sides.
 c. In what ways are parts **a** and **b** different?

70. a. Solve for x: $2x^2 = 4$.
 b. If the diagonal of a square has a length of 2, find the length of one side of the square.
 c. In what ways are parts **a** and **b** different?
 d. Find the area of the square described in part **b**.

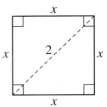

71. a. Find the one real number y such that $y^3 = 1000$.
 b. If the volume of a cube is 1000 cubic centimeters, find the length of one edge of the cube.
 c. In what ways are parts **a** and **b** alike?
 d. If a cube whose volume is 1000 cubic centimeters is filled with water, the cube will hold 1 liter (or 1000 milliliters) of the liquid. How many milliliters are contained in 1 cubic centimeter of water?

In 72–83, solve each equation for the variable when the replacement set is the set of real numbers.

72. $x^2 = 16$ **73.** $y^2 = 169$ **74.** $w^2 = 5$ **75.** $3y^2 = 75$

76. $k^2 = 75$ **77.** $n^2 - 4 = 0$ **78.** $x^2 - 10 = 0$ **79.** $x^2 + 1 = 0$

80. $y^3 + 1 = 0$ **81.** $8b^3 = 1$ **82.** $y^4 = 16$ **83.** $n^4 - 81 = 0$

In 84 and 85, select the *numeral* preceding the expression that best answers the question.

84. Which radical is *not* a real number?
 (1) $-\sqrt{1}$ (2) $\sqrt{-1}$ (3) $-\sqrt[3]{1}$ (4) $\sqrt[3]{-1}$

85. Which of the following statements is *false*?
 (1) $-\sqrt[3]{(4)^3} = -4$ (2) $\sqrt[3]{(-4)^3} = -4$ (3) $\sqrt[4]{(-3)^4} = -3$ (4) $\sqrt[4]{(-3)^4} = 3$

86. Let k represent any nonnegative real number.
 a. For what real numbers is the sentence $k = \sqrt{k}$ true?
 b. For what real numbers is the sentence $k > \sqrt{k}$ true?
 c. For what real numbers is the sentence $k < \sqrt{k}$ true?

87. a. Give a counterexample to prove the universally quantified statement $\forall_x : \sqrt{x^2} = x$ is false.
 b. Write a true universally quantified statement that expresses $\sqrt{x^2}$ in terms of x.

10-6 SIMPLIFYING A RADICAL

Square-Root Radicals with Integral Radicands

Since $\sqrt{9 \cdot 16} = \sqrt{144} = 12$ and $\sqrt{9} \cdot \sqrt{16} = 3 \cdot 4 = 12$, it can be said that $\sqrt{9 \cdot 16} = \sqrt{9} \cdot \sqrt{16}$. This example illustrates the following property:

● **The square root of a product of positive numbers is equal to the product of the square roots of the numbers.**

In general, if a and b are positive numbers:

$$\sqrt{a \cdot b} = \sqrt{a} \cdot \sqrt{b}$$

If the radicand of a square-root radical is a positive integer and if the radicand contains a factor that is a perfect square, we can use the given rule to find one or more equivalent radicals. For example:

$$\sqrt{200} = \sqrt{4 \cdot 50} = \sqrt{4} \cdot \sqrt{50} = 2\sqrt{50}$$
$$\sqrt{200} = \sqrt{25 \cdot 8} = \sqrt{25} \cdot \sqrt{8} = 5\sqrt{8}$$
$$\sqrt{200} = \sqrt{100 \cdot 2} = \sqrt{100} \cdot \sqrt{2} = 10\sqrt{2}$$

- **DEFINITION.** The *simplest form of a square-root radical* is a monomial of the form $k\sqrt{r}$, where k is a nonzero rational number and the radicand r is a positive integer containing no perfect-square factors other than 1.

In other words, the greatest perfect square has been factored out of the radicand. The greatest perfect-square factor of 200 is 100. Therefore, since $\sqrt{200} = \sqrt{100} \cdot \sqrt{2} = 10\sqrt{2}$ and since the radicand 2 contains no perfect-square factors other than 1, we can state:

$$\sqrt{200} \text{ in its simplest form is } 10\sqrt{2}$$

(*Note:* In $2\sqrt{50}$, the radicand 50 contains the perfect-square factor 25. In $5\sqrt{8}$, the radicand 8 contains the perfect-square factor 4. For these reasons, neither $2\sqrt{50}$ nor $5\sqrt{8}$ is the simplest form of $\sqrt{200}$.)

Square-Root Radicals with Fractional Radicands

Since $\sqrt{\frac{9}{16}} = \frac{3}{4}$ and $\frac{\sqrt{9}}{\sqrt{16}} = \frac{3}{4}$, then $\sqrt{\frac{9}{16}} = \frac{\sqrt{9}}{\sqrt{16}}$. This example illustrates the following property:

- **The square root of a quotient of positive numbers is equal to the quotient of the square roots of the numbers.**

In general, if a and b are positive numbers:

$$\sqrt{\frac{a}{b}} = \frac{\sqrt{a}}{\sqrt{b}}$$

This rule is used to simplify a square-root radical in which the radicand is a fraction. We have learned that the simplest form of a square-root radical is $k\sqrt{r}$, where k is rational and the radicand r is a positive *integer*. Let us consider two cases.

Case 1. If the denominator of the fractional radicand is a perfect square, we apply the rule directly. For example:

In simplest form: $\quad \sqrt{\frac{5}{16}} = \frac{\sqrt{5}}{\sqrt{16}} = \frac{\sqrt{5}}{4}$

Since $\frac{\sqrt{5}}{4} = \frac{1}{4} \cdot \sqrt{5} = \frac{1}{4}\sqrt{5}$, we can write the simplest form of $\sqrt{\frac{5}{16}}$ in either of two ways: $\frac{\sqrt{5}}{4}$ or $\frac{1}{4}\sqrt{5}$. If we compare each monomial to the general form $k\sqrt{r}$, we see that $k = \frac{1}{4}$, a rational number, and the radicand $r = 5$, a positive *integer*.

Case 2. If the denominator of the fractional radicand is *not* a perfect square, we multiply the fraction by some form of the identity element 1 to find an equivalent fraction whose denominator is a perfect square. Then, we apply the given rule. For example:

$$\textit{In simplest form:} \qquad \sqrt{\frac{2}{3}} = \sqrt{\frac{2}{3} \cdot \frac{3}{3}} = \sqrt{\frac{6}{9}} = \frac{\sqrt{6}}{\sqrt{9}} = \frac{\sqrt{6}}{3}$$

Here, we observe that $\frac{2}{3}$ is multiplied by $\frac{3}{3}$ (a form of the identity element 1) to transform $\frac{2}{3}$ to the equivalent fraction $\frac{6}{9}$. The rule is applied at this point, showing us that the simplest form of $\sqrt{\frac{2}{3}}$ is $\frac{\sqrt{6}}{3}$, or $\frac{1}{3}\sqrt{6}$. When this expression is compared to the general form $k\sqrt{r}$, we see that $k = \frac{1}{3}$, a rational number, and the radicand $r = 6$, a positive *integer*.

(*Note:* It is true that $\sqrt{\frac{2}{3}} = \frac{\sqrt{2}}{\sqrt{3}}$, but the fraction $\frac{\sqrt{2}}{\sqrt{3}}$ does not fit the general form of a radical in simplest form, namely, $k\sqrt{r}$. In Section 10-10, we will study a method for changing fractions such as $\frac{\sqrt{2}}{\sqrt{3}}$ to equivalent fractions with rational denominators. For now, let us follow the procedures outlined in Case 2.)

Radicals of Index *n*

The rules we have just learned for square-root radicals (or radicals of index 2) can be extended to other radicals.

In general, if a and b are positive numbers and the index n is a counting number, it can be shown that:

$$\sqrt[n]{a \cdot b} = \sqrt[n]{a} \cdot \sqrt[n]{b} \qquad \textbf{and} \qquad \sqrt[n]{\frac{a}{b}} = \frac{\sqrt[n]{a}}{\sqrt[n]{b}}$$

Just as we found perfect-square factors to simplify radicals of index 2, we will find perfect-cube factors to simplify radicals of index 3, and so on. The **simplest form of a radical** whose index is a counting number n is now written as $k\sqrt[n]{r}$. Here, k is a nonzero rational number and the radicand r is a positive integer containing no factor other than 1 that is a perfect nth power.

For example:

1. *In simplest form:* $\sqrt[3]{40} = \sqrt[3]{8 \cdot 5} = \sqrt[3]{8} \cdot \sqrt[3]{5} = 2\sqrt[3]{5}$

2. *In simplest form:* $\sqrt[4]{\dfrac{9}{16}} = \dfrac{\sqrt[4]{9}}{\sqrt[4]{16}} = \dfrac{\sqrt[4]{9}}{2}$ or $\dfrac{1}{2}\sqrt[4]{9}$

3. *In simplest form:* $\sqrt[3]{\dfrac{9}{16}} = \sqrt[3]{\dfrac{9}{16} \cdot \dfrac{4}{4}} = \sqrt[3]{\dfrac{36}{64}} = \dfrac{\sqrt[3]{36}}{\sqrt[3]{64}} = \dfrac{\sqrt[3]{36}}{4}$

EXAMPLES

In 1 and 2, simplify each radical.

| | **1.** $\sqrt{48}$ | | **2.** $\sqrt[3]{48}$ |

How to Proceed:	*Solution:*	*Solution:*
(1) Factor the radicand so that the perfect power is a factor.	**1.** $\sqrt{48} = \sqrt{16 \cdot 3}$	**2.** $\sqrt[3]{48} = \sqrt[3]{8 \cdot 6}$
(2) Express the radical as the product of the roots of the factors.	$\sqrt{48} = \sqrt{16} \cdot \sqrt{3}$	$\sqrt[3]{48} = \sqrt[3]{8} \cdot \sqrt[3]{6}$
(3) Simplify the radical containing the largest perfect power.	$\sqrt{48} = 4\sqrt{3}$ *Answer:* $4\sqrt{3}$	$\sqrt[3]{48} = 2\sqrt[3]{6}$ *Answer:* $2\sqrt[3]{6}$

In 3–6, simplify each radical expression. (All variables represent positive numbers.)

3. $2\sqrt{98}$ **4.** $\frac{1}{4}\sqrt{96x^2}$ **5.** $\sqrt{45a^4b^3}$ **6.** $\sqrt[3]{n^7}$

Solutions   Use the procedure outlined in Examples 1 and 2. If necessary, simplify terms outside the radical as the fourth step.

3. $2\sqrt{98} = 2\sqrt{49 \cdot 2} = 2\sqrt{49} \cdot \sqrt{2} = 2 \cdot 7\sqrt{2} = 14\sqrt{2}$ *Answer*

4. $\frac{1}{4}\sqrt{96x^2} = \frac{1}{4}\sqrt{16x^2 \cdot 6} = \frac{1}{4}\sqrt{16x^2} \cdot \sqrt{6} = \frac{1}{4} \cdot 4x\sqrt{6} = x\sqrt{6}$ *Answer*

5. $\sqrt{45a^4b^3} = \sqrt{9a^4b^2 \cdot 5b} = \sqrt{9a^4b^2} \cdot \sqrt{5b} = 3a^2b\sqrt{5b}$ *Answer*

6. $\sqrt[3]{n^7} = \sqrt[3]{n^6 \cdot n} = \sqrt[3]{n^6} \cdot \sqrt[3]{n} = n^2\sqrt[3]{n}$ *Answer*

In 7 and 8, express each radical in simplest form.

7. $\sqrt{\dfrac{1}{12}}$ **8.** $\sqrt[3]{\dfrac{3}{4}}$

| *How to Proceed:* | *Solution:* | *Solution:* |

(1) Change the radicand to an equivalent fraction whose denominator is a perfect power.

(2) Express the radical as the quotient of two roots.

(3) Simplify the radical in the denominator.

7. $\sqrt{\dfrac{1}{12}} = \sqrt{\dfrac{1}{12} \cdot \dfrac{3}{3}}$

$= \sqrt{\dfrac{3}{36}}$

$= \dfrac{\sqrt{3}}{\sqrt{36}}$

$= \dfrac{\sqrt{3}}{6}$

8. $\sqrt[3]{\dfrac{3}{4}} = \sqrt[3]{\dfrac{3}{4} \cdot \dfrac{2}{2}}$

$= \sqrt[3]{\dfrac{6}{8}}$

$= \dfrac{\sqrt[3]{6}}{\sqrt[3]{8}}$

$= \dfrac{\sqrt[3]{6}}{2}$

Answers: **7.** $\dfrac{\sqrt{3}}{6}$ or $\dfrac{1}{6}\sqrt{3}$ **8.** $\dfrac{\sqrt[3]{6}}{2}$ or $\dfrac{1}{2}\sqrt[3]{6}$

In 9 and 10, simplify each radical.

9. $\sqrt{\dfrac{8}{25}}$ **10.** $\sqrt[3]{\dfrac{8}{25}}$

Solutions   Use the procedure outlined in Examples 7 and 8. However, the radical remaining in the numerator may sometimes be simplified, as seen in these problems.

9. $\sqrt{\dfrac{8}{25}} = \dfrac{\sqrt{8}}{\sqrt{25}} = \dfrac{\sqrt{4 \cdot 2}}{\sqrt{25}} = \dfrac{\sqrt{4} \cdot \sqrt{2}}{\sqrt{25}} = \dfrac{2\sqrt{2}}{5}$ or $\dfrac{2}{5}\sqrt{2}$ *Answer*

10. $\sqrt[3]{\dfrac{8}{25}} = \sqrt[3]{\dfrac{8}{25} \cdot \dfrac{5}{5}} = \sqrt[3]{\dfrac{8 \cdot 5}{125}} = \dfrac{\sqrt[3]{8 \cdot 5}}{\sqrt[3]{125}} = \dfrac{\sqrt[3]{8} \cdot \sqrt[3]{5}}{\sqrt[3]{125}} = \dfrac{2\sqrt[3]{5}}{5}$ *Answer*

EXERCISES WITH OPEN-RESPONSE PROBLEMS

In 1–28, simplify each radical expression. (All variables represent positive numbers.)

1. $\sqrt{75}$ **2.** $\sqrt{32}$ **3.** $\sqrt{45}$ **4.** $-\sqrt{300}$

5. $\sqrt{24}$ **6.** $\sqrt[3]{24}$ **7.** $\sqrt{54}$ **8.** $\sqrt[3]{54}$

9. $2\sqrt{50}$ **10.** $-3\sqrt{28}$ **11.** $5\sqrt{12}$ **12.** $3\sqrt[3]{56}$

13. $\dfrac{1}{2}\sqrt{8}$ **14.** $\dfrac{2}{5}\sqrt{500}$ **15.** $-\dfrac{2}{3}\sqrt{27}$ **16.** $\dfrac{5}{8}\sqrt{80}$

17. $\sqrt{49x}$ **18.** $\sqrt{a^2 b}$ **19.** $\sqrt{n^3}$ **20.** $\sqrt{4cd^2}$

21. $\sqrt{9y^9}$ **22.** $7\sqrt{40x^2}$ **23.** $\sqrt{200w}$ **24.** $\sqrt{18a^3 b^5}$

25. $-2\sqrt{63k^4}$ **26.** $\dfrac{3}{2}\sqrt{20y}$ **27.** $\sqrt[3]{16x^6}$ **28.** $\dfrac{4}{5}\sqrt[3]{125y^5}$

In 29–48, write each expression in simplest form. (All variables represent positive numbers.)

29. $\sqrt{\dfrac{2}{9}}$

30. $12\sqrt{\dfrac{5}{36}}$

31. $4\sqrt{\dfrac{17}{64}}$

32. $\sqrt{\dfrac{18}{49}}$

33. $\sqrt{\dfrac{1}{5}}$

34. $6\sqrt{\dfrac{1}{2}}$

35. $-\sqrt{\dfrac{2}{3}}$

36. $\sqrt{\dfrac{3}{50}}$

37. $8\sqrt{\dfrac{5}{32}}$

38. $-\sqrt{\dfrac{7}{27}}$

39. $\sqrt{\dfrac{4}{5}}$

40. $4\sqrt{\dfrac{9}{8}}$

41. $\sqrt[3]{\dfrac{4}{27}}$

42. $4\sqrt[3]{\dfrac{7}{64}}$

43. $\sqrt[3]{\dfrac{4}{9}}$

44. $\sqrt[3]{\dfrac{8}{25}}$

45. $\sqrt{\dfrac{x}{y^2}}$

46. $\sqrt{\dfrac{a^4}{b}}$

47. $\sqrt{\dfrac{w^2}{7}}$

48. $\sqrt{\dfrac{p}{q}}$

In 49–60:   **a.** Write each expression in simplest form.   **b.** Find the approximate rational value of the expression to the *nearest tenth* by using $\sqrt{2} \approx 1.414$, $\sqrt{3} \approx 1.732$, or $\sqrt{5} \approx 2.236$.

49. $\sqrt{98}$

50. $\sqrt{20}$

51. $\sqrt{108}$

52. $\sqrt{180}$

53. $\sqrt{147}$

54. $\dfrac{1}{3}\sqrt{72}$

55. $2\sqrt{125}$

56. $\sqrt{\dfrac{2}{49}}$

57. $\sqrt{\dfrac{3}{4}}$

58. $\sqrt{\dfrac{1}{3}}$

59. $\sqrt{\dfrac{1}{2}}$

60. $\sqrt{\dfrac{4}{5}}$

In 61–63, select the *numeral* preceding the expression that best completes the sentence or answers the question.

61. Which radical expression is *not* equivalent to $\sqrt{800}$?
 (1) $10\sqrt{8}$
 (2) $4\sqrt{50}$
 (3) $5\sqrt{16}$
 (4) $20\sqrt{2}$

62. Which radical expression is *not* equivalent to $\sqrt[3]{1000}$?
 (1) 10
 (2) $5\sqrt[3]{8}$
 (3) $2\sqrt[3]{125}$
 (4) $4\sqrt[3]{25}$

63. If the sides of a triangle measure $6\sqrt{6}$, $3\sqrt{24}$, and $2\sqrt{54}$, then the triangle is *best* described as being
 (1) isosceles
 (2) scalene
 (3) equilateral
 (4) right

10-7 ADDING AND SUBTRACTING RADICALS

Like radicals are radicals that have the same index and the same radicand. For example, $3\sqrt{7}$ and $2\sqrt{7}$ are like radicals, as are $5\sqrt[3]{2}$ and $\sqrt[3]{2}$.

We recall that addition and subtraction of like monomial terms are based on the distributive property. For example, $3y + 2y = (3 + 2)y = 5y$. In the same way, we use the distributive property to add and subtract like radicals, as shown in the following examples.

Case 1. **Addition of Like Radicals**
Find the perimeter of a rectangle whose sides measure $3\sqrt{7}$ and $2\sqrt{7}$.

Solution $3\sqrt{7} + 2\sqrt{7} + 3\sqrt{7} + 2\sqrt{7}$
$= (3 + 2 + 3 + 2)\sqrt{7}$
$= 10\sqrt{7}$ *Answer*

$3\sqrt{7}$

$2\sqrt{7}$

Case 2. **Subtraction of Like Radicals**
Subtract $\sqrt[3]{2}$ from $5\sqrt[3]{2}$.

Solution $5\sqrt[3]{2} - \sqrt[3]{2} = 5\sqrt[3]{2} - 1\sqrt[3]{2}$
$= (5 - 1)\sqrt[3]{2}$
$= 4\sqrt[3]{2}$ *Answer*

Unlike radicals are radicals that do not have the same index or the same radicand, or have neither the same index nor the same radicand. In many cases, the sum or the difference of unlike radicals cannot be stated as a single term. For example:

1. $\sqrt{5}$ and $\sqrt{3}$ are unlike radicals whose sum is $\sqrt{5} + \sqrt{3}$.
2. $\sqrt[3]{7}$ and $\sqrt{7}$ are unlike radicals whose difference is $\sqrt[3]{7} - \sqrt{7}$, in the order given.

In some cases, however, unlike radicals can be written as like radicals that are equivalent to the given unlike radicals. When this can be done, the sum or difference of the radicals is a single term, as seen in the following example.

Case 3. **Simplification with Unlike Radicals**
Express $\sqrt{48} + \sqrt{12} - \sqrt{3}$ in simplest form.

Solution $\sqrt{48} + \sqrt{12} - \sqrt{3} = \sqrt{16 \cdot 3} + \sqrt{4 \cdot 3} - \sqrt{3}$
$= \sqrt{16} \cdot \sqrt{3} + \sqrt{4} \cdot \sqrt{3} - \sqrt{3}$
$= 4\sqrt{3} + 2\sqrt{3} - 1\sqrt{3}$
$= (4 + 2 - 1)\sqrt{3}$
$= 5\sqrt{3}$ *Answer*

PROCEDURE.   To add (or subtract) radicals:

1. If necessary, *simplify* the radicals to be added or subtracted.
2. *Combine like radicals* by using the distributive property.

Since a radical sometimes represents an irrational number, let us make two general observations regarding sums (or differences) involving irrational numbers.

1. *The sum (or difference) of two irrational numbers may be either an irrational number or a rational number.*

For example, the sum of $\sqrt{5}$ and $\sqrt{3}$ is $\sqrt{5} + \sqrt{3}$, an irrational number, and the difference of $\sqrt{7}$ and $\sqrt{2}$ is $\sqrt{7} - \sqrt{2}$, also an irrational number. However, the sum of $\sqrt{5}$ and $(-\sqrt{5})$ is 0, a rational number, while the difference of $\sqrt{7}$ and $\sqrt{7}$ is $\sqrt{7} - \sqrt{7}$ or 0, also a rational number.

2. *The sum (or difference) of an irrational number and a rational number is an irrational number.*

For example, the sum of $\sqrt{3}$ (irrational) and 8 (rational) is $\sqrt{3} + 8$, an irrational number. The difference is $\sqrt{3} - 8$, also an irrational number.

EXAMPLES

1. Express in simplest form: $\sqrt{27} + 6\sqrt{\frac{1}{3}} + \sqrt{50} - \sqrt{8}$.

How to Proceed: *Solution:*

(1) Simplify each radical.

$$\sqrt{27} \quad + 6\sqrt{\frac{1}{3}} \quad + \sqrt{50} \quad - \sqrt{8}$$

$$= \sqrt{9 \cdot 3} \quad + 6\sqrt{\frac{1}{3} \cdot \frac{3}{3}} + \sqrt{25 \cdot 2} \quad - \sqrt{4 \cdot 2}$$

$$= \sqrt{9} \cdot \sqrt{3} + 6 \cdot \frac{\sqrt{3}}{\sqrt{9}} \quad + \sqrt{25} \cdot \sqrt{2} - \sqrt{4} \cdot \sqrt{2}$$

$$= 3\sqrt{3} \quad + \overset{2}{\cancel{6}} \cdot \frac{\sqrt{3}}{\underset{1}{\cancel{3}}} \quad + 5\sqrt{2} \quad - 2\sqrt{2}$$

(2) Combine like radicals by using the distribution property.

$$= 3\sqrt{3} + 2\sqrt{3} + 5\sqrt{2} - 2\sqrt{2}$$
$$= (3 + 2)\sqrt{3} + (5 - 2)\sqrt{2}$$
$$= 5\sqrt{3} + 3\sqrt{2} \quad Answer$$

2. a. Find the sum of the irrational numbers $2\sqrt{5}$ and $(9 - \sqrt{20})$.
   b. State whether the sum is rational or irrational.

Solutions   **a.** $2\sqrt{5} + (9 - \sqrt{20}) = 2\sqrt{5} + 9 - \sqrt{4 \cdot 5} = 2\sqrt{5} + 9 - 2\sqrt{5} = 9$.
   b. The sum, 9, is a rational number.

Answers: **a.** 9   **b.** Rational

EXERCISES WITH OPEN-RESPONSE PROBLEMS

In 1–15, combine the radicals. (All variables represent positive numbers.)

1. $8\sqrt{3} + 9\sqrt{3}$

2. $6\sqrt{7} - 4\sqrt{7}$

3. $8\sqrt{6} - \sqrt{6}$

4. $\sqrt{72} + \sqrt{18}$

5. $\sqrt{48} + \sqrt{75}$

6. $\sqrt{63} - \sqrt{28}$

7. $\sqrt{180} - \sqrt{80}$

8. $2\sqrt{8} - \sqrt{32}$

9. $\sqrt{54} + 3\sqrt{24}$

10. $\sqrt{81x} + \sqrt{9x}$

11. $\sqrt{45y} - \sqrt{20y}$

12. $9\sqrt{x^3} - \sqrt{9x^3}$

13. $\frac{3\sqrt{7}}{7} - \sqrt{\frac{1}{7}}$

14. $2\sqrt{\frac{1}{8}} + \sqrt{\frac{1}{2}}$

15. $\sqrt{125} + \sqrt{\frac{1}{5}}$

In 16–25, write each expression in simplest form. (All variables represent positive numbers.)

16. $\sqrt{700} + 8\sqrt{7} - 3\sqrt{28}$

17. $\sqrt{160} - \sqrt{40} + \sqrt{90}$

18. $\sqrt{50} - \sqrt{98} + \sqrt{128}$

19. $\sqrt{192} - \sqrt{27} - \sqrt{108}$

20. $\sqrt{20} + \sqrt{5} + \sqrt{150} - \sqrt{96}$

21. $\sqrt{125} + \sqrt{12} - \sqrt{45} + \sqrt{75}$

22. $\sqrt[3]{64x} - \sqrt[3]{8x} + \sqrt[3]{27x}$

23. $\sqrt[3]{250y^3} - \sqrt[3]{16y^3}$

24. $\sqrt{\frac{1}{10}} + \sqrt{\frac{2}{5}} - \frac{1}{10}\sqrt{90}$

25. $\sqrt{\frac{4}{3}} + \sqrt{\frac{1}{3}} + \sqrt{44}$

In 26–35, in each case, two irrational numbers are given. **a.** Find the sum of the numbers in simplest form. **b.** State whether the sum is rational or irrational.

26. $\sqrt{14} + 3\sqrt{14}$

27. $3\sqrt{17} + (-\sqrt{17})$

28. $5\sqrt{7} + (-\sqrt{175})$

29. $12\sqrt{3} + (-3\sqrt{12})$

30. $(3 + \sqrt{2}) + (9 - \sqrt{2})$

31. $6\sqrt{15} + (2 - 3\sqrt{60})$

32. $(8 - \sqrt{5}) + (3 + \sqrt{20})$

33. $(10 - 8\sqrt{6}) + \sqrt{216}$

34. $2\sqrt{13} + (\sqrt{256} - \sqrt{52})$

35. $\left(\sqrt{\frac{4}{9}} - \sqrt{13}\right) + \frac{1}{3}\sqrt{117}$

In 36 and 37, select the *numeral* preceding the expression that best answers the question.

36. Which expression is equivalent to the sum of $\sqrt{600}$ and $\sqrt{400}$?

(1) $10\sqrt{10}$　　(2) $10\sqrt{6} + 20$　　(3) $12\sqrt{6}$　　(4) $30\sqrt{6}$

37. Which expression is equivalent to $\sqrt{\frac{3}{2}} + \sqrt{\frac{2}{3}} + \sqrt{\frac{1}{6}}$?

(1) $\sqrt{6}$　　(2) $\frac{\sqrt{3}}{2} + \frac{\sqrt{2}}{3} + \frac{\sqrt{6}}{6}$　　(3) $\frac{\sqrt{66}}{11}$　　(4) $\frac{\sqrt{21}}{3}$

In 38–41, express the perimeter of the figure: **a.** in simplest radical form   **b.** as a rational number correct to the *nearest tenth*

38.

$6\sqrt{5}$

$\sqrt{45}$

39.

$\sqrt{75}$ $\sqrt{48}$

$\sqrt{27}$

40.

$\sqrt{18}$

3

41.

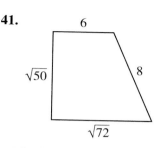

6

$\sqrt{50}$ 8

$\sqrt{72}$

10-8   MULTIPLYING RADICALS WITH THE SAME INDEX

Monomial Terms

We have learned that, if a and b are positive numbers and the index n is a counting number, then $\sqrt[n]{a \cdot b} = \sqrt[n]{a} \cdot \sqrt[n]{b}$. By applying the symmetric property of equality to the given statement, we form a rule to find the product of two radicals with the same index, namely:

If a and b are positive numbers and the index n is a counting number, then:

$$\sqrt[n]{a} \cdot \sqrt[n]{b} = \sqrt[n]{a \cdot b}$$

For example, $\sqrt{2} \cdot \sqrt{7} = \sqrt{14}$, and $\sqrt[3]{5} \cdot \sqrt[3]{4} = \sqrt[3]{20}$. Let us extend this concept to the multiplication of terms containing radicals with coefficients. For example:

If the sides of a rectangle measure $5\sqrt{3}$ and $2\sqrt{6}$, find the area of the rectangle.

$2\sqrt{6}$

$5\sqrt{3}$

Solution: For a rectangle, area $A = \ell w$. Notice how the associative and commutative properties of multiplication are used to find the area.

$$A = \ell w = (5\sqrt{3})(2\sqrt{6}) = 5 \cdot (\sqrt{3} \cdot 2) \cdot \sqrt{6} = 5 \cdot (2 \cdot \sqrt{3}) \cdot \sqrt{6}$$
$$= (5 \cdot 2)(\sqrt{3} \cdot \sqrt{6}) = 10\sqrt{18}$$

The area contains a radical that can be simplified:

$$A = 10\sqrt{18} = 10\sqrt{9 \cdot 2} = 10\sqrt{9} \cdot \sqrt{2} = 10 \cdot 3\sqrt{2} = 30\sqrt{2}$$

Answer: $30\sqrt{2}$ square units

From this example, we make the following generalization: If a and b are positive numbers and the index n is a counting number, then:

$$x\sqrt[n]{a} \cdot y\sqrt[n]{b} = xy\sqrt[n]{ab}$$

PROCEDURE.   To multiply monomial terms containing radicals with the same index:

1. Multiply the coefficients to find the coefficient of the product.

2. Multiply the radicands to find the radicand of the product.

3. If possible, simplify the radical in the resulting product.

Polynomial Terms

By using the distributive property and the procedure outlined above, we can multiply polynomial expressions containing radical terms.

*Case 1. **Multiplying a polynomial by a monomial.***

$$\sqrt{5}(3\sqrt{2} + \sqrt{7}) = \sqrt{5} \cdot 3\sqrt{2} + \sqrt{5} \cdot \sqrt{7}$$
$$= 3\sqrt{10} + \sqrt{35}$$

*Case 2. **Multiplying a polynomial by a polynomial.***

Three methods, similar to those learned in multiplying algebraic polynomials, are given here to find the product $(2 + \sqrt{3})(6 - \sqrt{3})$. We notice that the distributive property is used in each method.

METHOD 1

$$(2 + \sqrt{3})(6 - \sqrt{3})$$
$$= 2(6 - \sqrt{3}) + \sqrt{3}(6 - \sqrt{3})$$
$$= 2 \cdot 6 - 2 \cdot \sqrt{3} + \sqrt{3} \cdot 6 - \sqrt{3} \cdot \sqrt{3}$$
$$= 12 - 2\sqrt{3} + 6\sqrt{3} - 3$$
$$= 12 - 3 - 2\sqrt{3} + 6\sqrt{3}$$
$$= 9 + 4\sqrt{3}$$

METHOD 2

$$6 - \sqrt{3}$$
$$2 + \sqrt{3}$$

$$2(6 - \sqrt{3}) \rightarrow \overline{12 - 2\sqrt{3}}$$
$$\sqrt{3}(6 - \sqrt{3}) \rightarrow \underline{\quad + 6\sqrt{3} - 3}$$
$$12 + 4\sqrt{3} - 3 = 9 + 4\sqrt{3}$$

METHOD 3. Here, we use the procedure learned to multiply binomials mentally. To state the answer in simplest terms, we must combine 12 and -3, as well as like radicals $6\sqrt{3}$ and $-2\sqrt{3}$.

$$(2 + \sqrt{3})(6 - \sqrt{3})$$

$$= 12 + 4\sqrt{3} - 3$$

$$= 9 + 4\sqrt{3}$$

Since a radical sometimes represents an irrational number, let us make two general observations regarding products involving irrational numbers.

1. *The product of two irrational numbers may be either an irrational number or a rational number.*

   For example, $\sqrt{3} \cdot \sqrt{5} = \sqrt{15}$ (irrational),
   while $\sqrt{2} \cdot \sqrt{18} = \sqrt{36} = 6$ (rational).

2. *The product of an irrational number and any nonzero rational number is an irrational number.*

   For example, the product of $\sqrt{15}$ and 6 is $6\sqrt{15}$ (irrational).

EXAMPLES

In 1 and 2, in each case, multiply the radicals.

1. $8\sqrt{5} \cdot \frac{1}{4}\sqrt{15}$ **2.** $4\sqrt[3]{x^2} \cdot \sqrt[3]{16x^4}$

How to Proceed: *Solution:*   *Solution:*

(1) Multiply the coefficients, and multiply the radicands.

1. $8\sqrt{5} \cdot \frac{1}{4}\sqrt{15}$

$= \left(8 \cdot \frac{1}{4}\right)(\sqrt{5} \cdot \sqrt{15})$

$= 2\sqrt{75}$

2. $4\sqrt[3]{x^2} \cdot \sqrt[3]{16x^4}$

$= (4 \cdot 1)(\sqrt[3]{x^2} \cdot \sqrt[3]{16x^4})$

$= 4\sqrt[3]{16x^6}$

(2) Simplify the radical in the resulting product.

$= 2\sqrt{25 \cdot 3}$

$= 2\sqrt{25} \cdot \sqrt{3}$

$= 2 \cdot 5\sqrt{3}$

$= 10\sqrt{3}$ *Answer*

$= 4\sqrt[3]{8x^6 \cdot 2}$

$= 4\sqrt[3]{8x^6} \cdot \sqrt[3]{2}$

$= 4 \cdot 2x^2\sqrt[3]{2}$

$= 8x^2\sqrt[3]{2}$ *Answer*

3. Find the area of a square whose side measures $2\sqrt{5}$.

$2\sqrt{5}$

Solution

$$\begin{aligned}
\text{Area} &= (2\sqrt{5})^2 = 2\sqrt{5} \cdot 2\sqrt{5} \\
&= (2 \cdot 2)(\sqrt{5} \cdot \sqrt{5}) \\
&= 4\sqrt{25} \\
&= 4 \cdot 5 \\
&= 20 \quad \textit{Answer}
\end{aligned}$$

4. a. Multiply: $(4 + \sqrt{6})(4 - \sqrt{6})$.
   b. State whether the product is rational or irrational.

Solutions   **a.** $(4 + \sqrt{6})(4 - \sqrt{6})$
   $= 4(4 - \sqrt{6}) + \sqrt{6}(4 - \sqrt{6})$
   $= 4 \cdot 4 - 4 \cdot \sqrt{6} + \sqrt{6} \cdot 4 - \sqrt{6} \cdot \sqrt{6}$
   $= 16 - 4\sqrt{6} + 4\sqrt{6} - 6$
   $= 10$
   b. The product, 10, is a rational number.

   Answers: **a.** 10   **b.** Rational

EXERCISES WITH OPEN-RESPONSE PROBLEMS

In 1–24, multiply and express each product in simplest form. (All variables represent positive numbers.)

1. $\sqrt{5} \cdot \sqrt{20}$

2. $3\sqrt{32} \cdot \sqrt{2}$

3. $4\sqrt{5} \cdot \sqrt{10}$

4. $\frac{1}{3}\sqrt{18} \cdot \sqrt{6}$

5. $8\sqrt{3} \cdot \frac{1}{2}\sqrt{15}$

6. $2\sqrt{14} \cdot 6\sqrt{7}$

7. $\sqrt{\frac{1}{2}} \cdot \sqrt{72}$

8. $\sqrt{\frac{3}{4}} \cdot \sqrt{3}$

9. $5\sqrt{\frac{1}{3}} \cdot \sqrt{18}$

10. $\sqrt{x} \cdot \sqrt{x^5}$

11. $\sqrt{6y^3} \cdot \sqrt{2y}$

12. $\sqrt{ab^3} \cdot \sqrt{ab^5}$

13. $\sqrt[3]{5} \cdot \sqrt[3]{25}$

14. $2\sqrt[3]{2} \cdot 4\sqrt[3]{4}$

15. $\sqrt[3]{9x^2} \cdot \sqrt[3]{6x}$

16. $\sqrt{3}(4\sqrt{3} + \sqrt{12})$

17. $3\sqrt{2}(2\sqrt{8} - \sqrt{3})$

18. $2\sqrt{5}(3\sqrt{2} + \sqrt{45} - 4\sqrt{5})$

19. $\sqrt{\frac{2}{3}}(4\sqrt{6} - 2\sqrt{24} + 5\sqrt{3})$

20. $(2 + \sqrt{7})(3 + \sqrt{7})$

21. $(9 - \sqrt{2})(7 + \sqrt{2})$

22. $(5 + \sqrt{3})^2$

23. $(10 - \sqrt{5})(10 + \sqrt{5})$

24. $(3 + 2\sqrt{3})(3 - 2\sqrt{3})$

In 25–36, raise each expression to the indicated power, and simplify the result.

25. $(\sqrt{17})^2$ 　　　　　 **26.** $(2\sqrt{10})^2$ 　　　　　 **27.** $(3\sqrt{7})^2$ 　　　　　 **28.** $\left(\frac{1}{2}\sqrt{8}\right)^2$

29. $\left(8\sqrt{\frac{1}{2}}\right)^2$ 　　　 **30.** $(4\sqrt{2})^2$ 　　　　　 **31.** $(\sqrt[3]{2})^3$ 　　　　　 **32.** $(\sqrt[3]{9})^3$

33. $(2\sqrt[3]{6})^3$ 　　　　 **34.** $(4 + \sqrt{5})^2$ 　　　 **35.** $(3 - \sqrt{2})^2$ 　　 **36.** $(1 - \sqrt{8})^2$

In 37–48, two irrational numbers are given.　**a.** Find the product of the numbers in simplest form. **b.** State whether the product is rational or irrational.

37. $5\sqrt{5} \cdot 3\sqrt{3}$ 　　　　 **38.** $8\sqrt{8} \cdot 2\sqrt{2}$ 　　　　 **39.** $\frac{2}{5}\sqrt{3} \cdot 10\sqrt{12}$

40. $\frac{3}{8}\sqrt{10} \cdot 4\sqrt{\frac{2}{5}}$ 　 **41.** $\sqrt{5}(2\sqrt{20} + \sqrt{2})$ 　　 **42.** $3\sqrt{6}(2\sqrt{6} - \sqrt{24})$

43. $(2 + \sqrt{10})(5 + \sqrt{10})$ 　 **44.** $(2 + \sqrt{10})(5 - \sqrt{10})$ 　 **45.** $(5 + \sqrt{10})(5 - \sqrt{10})$

46. $(\sqrt{7} - 1)(\sqrt{7} + 1)$ 　 **47.** $(2 + \sqrt{8})(1 - \sqrt{2})$ 　 **48.** $(2 + \sqrt{2})(2 + \sqrt{2})$

In 49–52, express the area of each figure in simplest form.

49.
$3\sqrt{2}$

50.
$\sqrt{7}$
$\sqrt{28}$

51.
$5\sqrt{5}$
$\sqrt{45}$
$4\sqrt{5}$

52.
$2\sqrt{3}$
$\sqrt{12}$ 　 $\sqrt{15}$
$3\sqrt{3}$

53. The base and the height of a parallelogram measure $3\sqrt{7}$ centimeters and $2\sqrt{14}$ centimeters, respectively. Find the number of square centimeters in the area of the parallelogram, expressed: **a.** in simplest radical form 　**b.** as a rational number correct to the *nearest tenth*.

54. Find the value of $x^2 - 4$ when:
　　a. $x = 5$ 　　　　 **b.** $x = \sqrt{5}$ 　　　 **c.** $x = -2$
　　d. $x = \sqrt{3}$ 　　　 **e.** $x = \sqrt{3} - 1$ 　 **f.** $x = 3 + \sqrt{2}$

55. Find the value of $x^2 - 4x - 1$ when:
　　a. $x = 3$ 　　　　 **b.** $x = \sqrt{3}$ 　　　 **c.** $x = 2 + \sqrt{5}$

10-9   DIVIDING RADICALS WITH THE SAME INDEX

We have learned that, if a and b are positive numbers and the index n is a counting number, then $\sqrt[n]{\frac{a}{b}} = \frac{\sqrt[n]{a}}{\sqrt[n]{b}}$. By applying the symmetric property of equality to the given statement, we form a rule to find the quotient of two radicals with the same index, namely:

If a and b are positive numbers and the index n is a counting number, then:

$$\frac{\sqrt[n]{a}}{\sqrt[n]{b}} = \sqrt[n]{\frac{a}{b}}$$

For example, $\frac{\sqrt{30}}{\sqrt{6}} = \sqrt{\frac{30}{6}} = \sqrt{5}$ and $\frac{\sqrt[3]{48}}{\sqrt[3]{6}} = \sqrt[3]{\frac{48}{6}} = \sqrt[3]{8} = 2$. Let us extend this concept to the division of radical terms having coefficients. For example:

A parallelogram whose area is $10\sqrt{6}$ has a height $h = 2\sqrt{3}$. Find the length of the base b.

$h = 2\sqrt{3}$

b

Solution: In a parallelogram, area $A = bh$. Therefore, $b = \frac{A}{h}$. The necessary division is performed by using a property of fractions: $\frac{wx}{yz} = \frac{w}{y} \cdot \frac{x}{z}$.

$$b = \frac{A}{h} = \frac{10\sqrt{6}}{2\sqrt{3}} = \frac{10}{2} \cdot \frac{\sqrt{6}}{\sqrt{3}} = \frac{10}{2} \cdot \sqrt{\frac{6}{3}} = 5\sqrt{2} \quad \textit{Answer}$$

From this example, we make the following generalization: If a and b are positive numbers and the index n is a counting number, then:

$$x\sqrt[n]{a} \div y\sqrt[n]{b} = \frac{x\sqrt[n]{a}}{y\sqrt[n]{b}} = \frac{x}{y} \cdot \sqrt[n]{\frac{a}{b}}$$

PROCEDURE.   To divide monomial terms containing radicals with the same index:

1. Divide the coefficients to find the coefficient of the quotient.
2. Divide the radicands to find the radicand of the quotient.
3. If possible, simplify the radical in the resulting quotient.

Since a radical sometimes represents an irrational number, let us make two general observations regarding quotients involving irrational numbers.

1. *The quotient of two irrational numbers may be either an irrational number or a rational number.*
   For example, $\sqrt{40} \div \sqrt{8} = \sqrt{5}$ (irrational),
   while $\sqrt{40} \div \sqrt{10} = \sqrt{4} = 2$ (rational).

2. *The quotient of an irrational number and any nonzero rational number, in either order, is an irrational number.*
   For example, $\sqrt{5} \div 2 = \frac{\sqrt{5}}{2}$ (irrational).

   Also, $2 \div \sqrt{5} = \frac{2}{\sqrt{5}}$ (irrational).

EXAMPLES

In 1 and 2, in each case, divide the radicals.

1. $48\sqrt{54} \div 12\sqrt{3}$ **2.** $\sqrt[3]{32x^4} \div 2\sqrt[3]{x}$

How to Proceed:	*Solution:*	*Solution:*
(1) Divide the coefficients, and divide the radicands.	**1.** $\dfrac{48\sqrt{54}}{12\sqrt{3}}$	**2.** $\dfrac{\sqrt[3]{32x^4}}{2\sqrt[3]{x}}$
	$= \dfrac{48}{12} \cdot \dfrac{\sqrt{54}}{\sqrt{3}}$	$= \dfrac{1}{2} \cdot \dfrac{\sqrt[3]{32x^4}}{\sqrt[3]{x}}$
	$= 4\sqrt{18}$	$= \dfrac{1}{2}\sqrt[3]{32x^3}$
(2) Simplify the radical in the resulting quotient.	$= 4\sqrt{9} \cdot \sqrt{2}$	$= \dfrac{1}{2}\sqrt[3]{8x^3} \cdot \sqrt[3]{4}$
	$= 4 \cdot 3\sqrt{2}$	$= \dfrac{1}{2} \cdot 2x\sqrt[3]{4}$
	$= 12\sqrt{2}$ *Answer*	$= x\sqrt[3]{4}$ *Answer*

3. Simplify: $\dfrac{15\sqrt{8} - 5\sqrt{6}}{5\sqrt{2}}$.

Solution   Divide each term in the numerator by the denominator.

$$\frac{15\sqrt{8} - 5\sqrt{6}}{5\sqrt{2}} = \frac{15\sqrt{8}}{5\sqrt{2}} - \frac{5\sqrt{6}}{5\sqrt{2}} = \frac{15}{5} \cdot \frac{\sqrt{8}}{\sqrt{2}} - \frac{5}{5} \cdot \frac{\sqrt{6}}{\sqrt{2}}$$

$$= 3\sqrt{4} - 1\sqrt{3}$$

$$= 3 \cdot 2 - 1 \cdot \sqrt{3}$$

$$= 6 - \sqrt{3}   \textit{Answer}$$

EXERCISES WITH OPEN-RESPONSE PROBLEMS

In 1–20, divide and express each quotient in simplest form. (All variables represent positive numbers.)

1. $\sqrt{80} \div \sqrt{5}$ **2.** $12\sqrt{7} \div 2\sqrt{7}$ **3.** $\sqrt{170} \div \sqrt{17}$ **4.** $\sqrt{150} \div \sqrt{3}$

5. $10\sqrt{24} \div 2\sqrt{2}$ **6.** $9\sqrt{60} \div 3\sqrt{3}$ **7.** $\dfrac{28\sqrt{90}}{7\sqrt{2}}$ **8.** $\dfrac{24\sqrt{48}}{48\sqrt{6}}$

9. $\dfrac{45\sqrt{40}}{60\sqrt{10}}$

10. $\dfrac{30\sqrt[3]{128}}{6\sqrt[3]{2}}$

11. $\dfrac{6\sqrt[3]{60}}{15\sqrt[3]{10}}$

12. $\dfrac{3\sqrt[3]{96}}{12\sqrt[3]{4}}$

13. $\dfrac{\sqrt{98x^3}}{\sqrt{2x}}$

14. $\dfrac{2\sqrt{54y^5}}{6\sqrt{2y}}$

15. $\dfrac{\sqrt{20ab^5}}{2\sqrt{5ab^3}}$

16. $\dfrac{\sqrt{75}+\sqrt{48}}{\sqrt{3}}$

17. $\dfrac{2\sqrt{5}+6\sqrt{15}}{2\sqrt{5}}$

18. $\dfrac{\sqrt{108}-\sqrt{150}}{\sqrt{6}}$

19. $\dfrac{\sqrt{375}+\sqrt{540}}{\sqrt{3}}$

20. $\dfrac{\sqrt{180}-\sqrt{125}}{\sqrt{5}}$

In 21–26, in each case, two irrational numbers are given.   **a.** Find the quotient of the numbers in simplest form.   **b.** State whether the quotient is rational or irrational.

21. $\sqrt{54} \div \sqrt{6}$

22. $2\sqrt{90} \div \sqrt{18}$

23. $\sqrt{192} \div 3\sqrt{3}$

24. $\dfrac{\sqrt{72}+\sqrt{32}}{\sqrt{8}}$

25. $\dfrac{8\sqrt{24}+12\sqrt{2}}{4\sqrt{2}}$

26. $\dfrac{\sqrt{50}-\sqrt{8}}{4\sqrt{2}}$

In 27–29, express each quotient: **a.** in simplest radical form   **b.** as the approximate rational value to the *nearest tenth*.

27. $\dfrac{12\sqrt{70}}{24\sqrt{7}}$

28. $\dfrac{\sqrt{96}+\sqrt{27}}{\sqrt{3}}$

29. $\dfrac{3\sqrt{20}-\sqrt{15}}{\sqrt{5}}$

30. In a rectangle, if the area $A = 12\sqrt{30}$ and the base $b = 3\sqrt{5}$, find the measure of the height h.

31. In a triangle, if the area $A = 9\sqrt{6}$ and the base $b = 3\sqrt{3}$, find the measure of the height h.

Ex. 30

Ex. 31

32. **a.** If the perimeter of a square is $\sqrt{80}$, what is the length of one side of the square?
    b. What is the area of the square?

10-10   RATIONALIZING A DENOMINATOR CONTAINING A RADICAL

- **DEFINITION.** To *rationalize the denominator* of a fraction (where the denominator is not a rational number) means to find an equivalent fraction in which the denominator is a rational number.

Monomial Denominators

In Section 10-9, it was stated that $2 \div \sqrt{5} = \frac{2}{\sqrt{5}}$, an irrational number. Although the fraction $\frac{2}{\sqrt{5}}$ has an irrational number as its denominator, it is possible to multiply this fraction by some form of the identity element 1 to find an equivalent fraction with a rational denominator. For example:

$$\frac{2}{\sqrt{5}} = \frac{2}{\sqrt{5}} \cdot 1 = \frac{2}{\sqrt{5}} \cdot \frac{\sqrt{5}}{\sqrt{5}} = \frac{2\sqrt{5}}{5}$$

Thus, when we rationalize the denominator of $\frac{2}{\sqrt{5}}$, we find the equivalent fraction $\frac{2\sqrt{5}}{5}$, where the denominator, 5, is a rational number. The process of rationalizing a denominator allows us to simplify the computation needed when working with irrational numbers. For example:

$$\frac{2}{\sqrt{5}} + \frac{\sqrt{5}}{5} = \frac{2\sqrt{5}}{5} + \frac{\sqrt{5}}{5} = \frac{3\sqrt{5}}{5}$$

Binomial Denominators

Given the fraction $\frac{2}{4 + \sqrt{11}}$, how can we rationalize the denominator? First, let us recall that the product of two binomials of the form $(a + b)$ and $(a - b)$ is a binomial that is written as the difference of two squares:

$$(a + b)(a - b) = a^2 - b^2$$

Each of $(a + b)$ and $(a - b)$ is the **conjugate** of the other. If a or b or both are irrational square-root radicals or rational numbers, then their squares are rational and the difference of their squares, $a^2 - b^2$, is rational. For example:

$$(4 + \sqrt{11})(4 - \sqrt{11}) = (4)^2 - (\sqrt{11})^2 = 16 - 11 = 7$$
$$(\sqrt{7} + 5)(\sqrt{7} - 5) = (\sqrt{7})^2 - (5)^2 = 7 - 25 = -18$$
$$(\sqrt{8} - \sqrt{5})(\sqrt{8} + \sqrt{5}) = (\sqrt{8})^2 - (\sqrt{5})^2 = 8 - 5 = 3$$

We can express the fraction $\frac{2}{4 + \sqrt{11}}$ as an equivalent fraction with a rational denominator by multiplying by a fraction whose numerator and denominator are the conjugate of $4 + \sqrt{11}$ as follows:

$$\frac{2}{4 + \sqrt{11}} = \frac{2}{(4 + \sqrt{11})} \cdot \frac{(4 - \sqrt{11})}{(4 - \sqrt{11})} = \frac{8 - 2\sqrt{11}}{16 - 11} = \frac{8 - 2\sqrt{11}}{5}$$

EXAMPLES

1. Rationalize the denominator: $\dfrac{10}{\sqrt{8}}$

How to Proceed: *Solution:*

(1) Multiply the fraction by a form of the identity element 1 to find an equivalent fraction with a rational denominator. Let the numerator and denominator of the identity 1 equal the least radical to yield the rational denominator.

$$\frac{10}{\sqrt{8}} = \frac{10}{\sqrt{8}} \cdot 1 = \frac{10}{\sqrt{8}} \cdot \frac{\sqrt{2}}{\sqrt{2}}$$

$$= \frac{10\sqrt{2}}{\sqrt{16}} \;\; = \frac{10\sqrt{2}}{4}$$

(2) Simplify the result.

$$= \frac{5\sqrt{2}}{2} \quad Answer$$

Note: If the identity 1 does not involve the least radical, then the radical in the resulting fraction can be simplified.

$$\frac{10}{\sqrt{8}} = \frac{10}{\sqrt{8}} \cdot \frac{\sqrt{8}}{\sqrt{8}} = \frac{10\sqrt{8}}{8} = \frac{10\sqrt{4 \cdot 2}}{8} = \frac{10 \cdot 2\sqrt{2}}{8} = \frac{20\sqrt{2}}{8} = \frac{5\sqrt{2}}{2}$$

---

2. Rationalize the denominator: $\dfrac{\sqrt[3]{6}}{4\sqrt[3]{9}}$

Solution   Use the procedure outlined in Example 1. Here, the resulting fraction cannot be simplified.

$$\frac{\sqrt[3]{6}}{4\sqrt[3]{9}} = \frac{\sqrt[3]{6}}{4\sqrt[3]{9}} \cdot \frac{\sqrt[3]{3}}{\sqrt[3]{3}} = \frac{\sqrt[3]{18}}{4\sqrt[3]{27}} = \frac{\sqrt[3]{18}}{4 \cdot 3} = \frac{\sqrt[3]{18}}{12} \quad Answer$$

---

3. Express $\dfrac{6}{3 - \sqrt{5}}$ as an equivalent fraction with a rational denominator.

How to Proceed: *Solution:*

(1) Multiply the fraction by a form of the identity element 1, where both numerator and denominator of the identity 1 equal the conjugate of the denominator of the given fraction.

$$\frac{6}{3 - \sqrt{5}} = \frac{6}{(3 - \sqrt{5})} \cdot \frac{(3 + \sqrt{5})}{(3 + \sqrt{5})}$$

$$= \frac{6(3 + \sqrt{5})}{9 - 5}$$

$$= \frac{6(3 + \sqrt{5})}{4}$$

(2) Simplify the result.

$$= \frac{\overset{3}{\cancel{6}}(3 + \sqrt{5})}{\underset{2}{\cancel{4}}}$$

Answer: $\dfrac{3(3 + \sqrt{5})}{2}$ or $\dfrac{9 + 3\sqrt{5}}{2}$

4. The expression $\dfrac{\sqrt{7}+1}{\sqrt{7}-2}$ is equivalent to

(1) $\dfrac{9+3\sqrt{7}}{5}$ (2) $\dfrac{5-\sqrt{7}}{3}$ (3) $3+\sqrt{7}$ (4) $3+3\sqrt{7}$

Solution   Use the procedure outlined in Example 3. Notice that the numerator of the resulting fraction is factored to simplify the result.

$$\frac{\sqrt{7}+1}{\sqrt{7}-2} = \frac{\sqrt{7}+1}{\sqrt{7}-2} \cdot 1 = \frac{(\sqrt{7}+1)}{(\sqrt{7}-2)} \cdot \frac{(\sqrt{7}+2)}{(\sqrt{7}+2)} = \frac{7+3\sqrt{7}+2}{7-4}$$

$$= \frac{9+3\sqrt{7}}{3} = \frac{\overset{1}{\cancel{3}}(3+\sqrt{7})}{\underset{1}{\cancel{3}}} = \frac{3+\sqrt{7}}{1} = 3+\sqrt{7}$$

Answer: (3)

EXERCISES WITH OPEN-RESPONSE PROBLEMS

In 1–45, rationalize the denominator of each fraction. If possible, simplify the result.

1. $\dfrac{1}{\sqrt{7}}$ **2.** $\dfrac{9}{\sqrt{2}}$ **3.** $\dfrac{8}{\sqrt{5}}$ **4.** $\dfrac{15}{\sqrt{10}}$ **5.** $\dfrac{3}{\sqrt{6}}$

6. $\dfrac{6}{\sqrt{3}}$ **7.** $\dfrac{4}{\sqrt{18}}$ **8.** $\dfrac{6}{\sqrt{8}}$ **9.** $\dfrac{15}{\sqrt{50}}$ **10.** $\dfrac{6}{\sqrt{27}}$

11. $\dfrac{4}{\sqrt{48}}$ **12.** $\dfrac{3}{2\sqrt{2}}$ **13.** $\dfrac{3}{2\sqrt{3}}$ **14.** $\dfrac{9}{4\sqrt{6}}$ **15.** $\dfrac{10}{3\sqrt{20}}$

16. $\dfrac{5\sqrt{2}}{\sqrt{5}}$ **17.** $\dfrac{\sqrt{6}}{4\sqrt{2}}$ **18.** $\dfrac{3\sqrt{8}}{4\sqrt{18}}$ **19.** $\dfrac{2}{\sqrt[3]{16}}$ **20.** $\dfrac{4\sqrt[3]{3}}{3\sqrt[3]{2}}$

21. $\dfrac{5}{2-\sqrt{3}}$ **22.** $\dfrac{4}{3+\sqrt{2}}$ **23.** $\dfrac{1}{4+\sqrt{5}}$ **24.** $\dfrac{5}{4+\sqrt{6}}$ **25.** $\dfrac{6}{4-\sqrt{10}}$

26. $\dfrac{9}{5-\sqrt{13}}$ **27.** $\dfrac{6}{\sqrt{7}+2}$ **28.** $\dfrac{4}{\sqrt{15}-3}$ **29.** $\dfrac{4}{\sqrt{5}-3}$ **30.** $\dfrac{11}{\sqrt{3}-5}$

31. $\dfrac{12}{\sqrt{17}+5}$ **32.** $\dfrac{\sqrt{7}}{3-\sqrt{7}}$ **33.** $\dfrac{\sqrt{3}}{\sqrt{3}+1}$ **34.** $\dfrac{2\sqrt{5}}{\sqrt{5}-1}$ **35.** $\dfrac{\sqrt{2}}{2-\sqrt{2}}$

36. $\dfrac{2+\sqrt{3}}{4-\sqrt{3}}$ **37.** $\dfrac{6-\sqrt{7}}{5-\sqrt{7}}$ **38.** $\dfrac{1+\sqrt{11}}{4-\sqrt{11}}$ **39.** $\dfrac{1+\sqrt{5}}{3-\sqrt{5}}$ **40.** $\dfrac{1+\sqrt{3}}{3-\sqrt{3}}$

41. $\dfrac{1+\sqrt{5}}{5+\sqrt{5}}$ **42.** $\dfrac{\sqrt{10}-3}{\sqrt{10}-2}$ **43.** $\dfrac{\sqrt{7}+\sqrt{3}}{\sqrt{7}-\sqrt{3}}$ **44.** $\dfrac{5\sqrt{2}+1}{2\sqrt{2}-1}$ **45.** $\dfrac{\sqrt{12}-2}{\sqrt{3}-1}$

In 46–53, in each case: **a.** Use a calculator to find an approximate value of the given fraction to the *nearest ten-thousandth*.   **b.** Write the given fraction as an equivalent fraction with a rational denominator. **c.** Use a calculator to find the value of the fraction in part **b** to the *nearest ten-thousandth*.

46. $\dfrac{1}{\sqrt{2}}$ **47.** $\dfrac{1}{\sqrt{3}}$ **48.** $\dfrac{3}{2\sqrt{2}}$ **49.** $\dfrac{1+\sqrt{2}}{\sqrt{2}}$

50. $\dfrac{\sqrt{3}-1}{\sqrt{3}}$ **51.** $\dfrac{1}{3-\sqrt{2}}$ **52.** $\dfrac{13}{4+\sqrt{3}}$ **53.** $\dfrac{2-\sqrt{3}}{2+\sqrt{3}}$

In 54–57, change each given expression to an equivalent fraction that does not have a radical in its denominator. (All variables represent positive numbers.)

54. $\dfrac{1}{\sqrt{k}}$ **55.** $\dfrac{y}{\sqrt{y}}$ **56.** $\dfrac{\sqrt{a}}{\sqrt{b}}$ **57.** $\dfrac{6}{\sqrt{6x}}$

In 58–61, select the *numeral* preceding the expression that best completes the sentence.

58. The expression $\dfrac{6}{4-\sqrt{7}}$ is equivalent to

    (1) $\dfrac{4+\sqrt{7}}{3}$ (2) $\dfrac{2(4+\sqrt{7})}{3}$ (3) $4+\sqrt{7}$ (4) $6(4+\sqrt{7})$

59. An expression equivalent to $\dfrac{2}{\sqrt{15}-4}$ is

    (1) $2\sqrt{15}+4$ (2) $2\sqrt{15}+8$ (3) $-2\sqrt{15}-4$ (4) $-2\sqrt{15}-8$

60. The expression $\dfrac{\sqrt{2}+2}{\sqrt{2}+1}$ is equivalent to

    (1) $\sqrt{2}$ (2) 2 (3) $\dfrac{3}{2}$ (4) $4+\sqrt{2}$

61. The expression $\dfrac{2-\sqrt{6}}{3-\sqrt{6}}$ is equivalent to

    (1) $\dfrac{\sqrt{6}}{3}$ (2) $\dfrac{-\sqrt{6}}{3}$ (3) $\sqrt{2}$ (4) $-\sqrt{2}$

10-11   THE QUADRATIC FORMULA AND QUADRATIC EQUATIONS WITH REAL ROOTS

We have learned that a *quadratic equation* is an equation that can be written in the form $ax^2 + bx + c = 0$, where a, b, and c are real numbers and $a \neq 0$.

Solving a Quadratic Equation

If a quadratic equation has *rational roots*, it is possible to solve the equation by factoring $ax^2 + bx + c$, and setting each factor equal to 0. An example of a quadratic equation with rational roots is shown at the right; the check is left to the student.

$$\text{Solve: } x^2 + 3x - 10 = 0$$
$$(x - 2)(x + 5) = 0$$

$$x - 2 = 0 \quad | \quad x + 5 = 0$$
$$x = 2 \quad | \quad x = -5$$

Answer: $x = 2$ or $x = -5$

Not every quadratic equation has rational roots. Therefore, some quadratic equations cannot be solved by factoring. We learned another procedure to find the roots of a quadratic equation $ax^2 + bx + c = 0$, namely, the use of the ***quadratic formula***:

$$x = \frac{-b \pm \sqrt{b^2 - 4ac}}{2a}$$

One of the derivations of the quadratic formula uses the perfect-square trinomial $4a^2x^2 + 4abx + b^2 = (2ax + b)^2$.

Derivation of the Quadratic Formula

How to Proceed:	*Solution:*
Given the general quadratic equation, where a, b, and c are real numbers and $a \neq 0$:	$ax^2 + bx + c = 0 \quad (a \neq 0)$
(1) Multiply both sides of the equation by $4a$.	$4a(ax^2 + bx + c) = 4a \cdot 0$ $4a^2x^2 + 4abx + 4ac = 0$
(2) Transform the equation, keeping all terms containing x on the left side.	$4a^2x^2 + 4abx = -4ac$
(3) Form a perfect square by adding b^2 to both sides.	$4a^2x^2 + 4abx + b^2 = b^2 - 4ac$
(4) Show the square of a binomial on the left side.	$(2ax + b)^2 = b^2 - 4ac$
(5) Take the square root of each side. Show two roots on the right side by writing $\pm$ before the radical.	$2ax + b = \pm\sqrt{b^2 - 4ac}$
(6) Add $-b$ to both sides.	$2ax = -b \pm \sqrt{b^2 - 4ac}$
(7) Divide both sides by $2a$ to obtain the *quadratic formula*.	$x = \frac{-b \pm \sqrt{b^2 - 4ac}}{2a}$

Thus, by the quadratic formula, the two roots of the equation are:

$$x_1 = \frac{-b + \sqrt{b^2 - 4ac}}{2a} \quad \text{and} \quad x_2 = \frac{-b - \sqrt{b^2 - 4ac}}{2a}$$

We have learned that the ***discriminant*** $b^2 - 4ac$ (the expression under the radical sign) indicates the nature of the roots of a quadratic equation with rational coefficients. These indicators are summarized on the following page.

For example:

1. If the discriminant $b^2 - 4ac$ is a positive number that is a perfect square, the quadratic equation has two rational roots. (See Example 1 that follows.)

2. If the discriminant $b^2 - 4ac = 0$, the quadratic equation has two *equal* rational roots or, in effect, one rational root.

3. If the discriminant $b^2 - 4ac$ is a positive number that is not a perfect square, the quadratic equation has irrational roots. (See Example 2 that follows.)

4. If the discriminant $b^2 - 4ac$ is a negative number, the roots of the quadratic equation are not in the set of real numbers. We will study such equations in Chapter 20 of this book.

EXAMPLES

1. Using the quadratic formula, find the roots of $2x^2 + 5x = 12$.

How to Proceed:	*Solution:*
(1) Transform the equation so that one side is 0.	$2x^2 + 5x = 12$ $2x^2 + 5x - 12 = 0$
(2) Compare the equation to $ax^2 + bx + c = 0$ to determine a, b, and c.	$a = 2, b = 5, c = -12$
(3) Substitute the values of a, b, and c in the quadratic formula, and simplify.	$x = \dfrac{-b \pm \sqrt{b^2 - 4ac}}{2a}$ $= \dfrac{-(5) \pm \sqrt{(5)^2 - 4(2)(-12)}}{2(2)}$ $= \dfrac{-5 \pm \sqrt{25 + 96}}{4}$ $= \dfrac{-5 \pm \sqrt{121}}{4} = \dfrac{-5 \pm 11}{4}$

$$x_1 = \frac{-5 + 11}{4} \qquad x_2 = \frac{-5 - 11}{4}$$
$$= \frac{6}{4} = \frac{3}{2} \qquad = \frac{-16}{4} = -4$$

Answer: $x = \frac{3}{2}$ or $x = -4$

The check of each root in the original equation is left to the student.

Note: The discriminant $b^2 - 4ac = 121$, a positive number that is a perfect square. Since the roots of $2x^2 + 5x - 12 = 0$ are *rational*, it is possible to solve this equation by factoring: $(2x - 3)(x + 4) = 0$. When each factor is set equal to 0, the roots are $x = \frac{3}{2}$ and $x = -4$.

2. a. Solve $x^2 - 10x + 13 = 0$ for values of x expressed in simplest radical form.
b. Solve $x^2 - 10x + 13 = 0$ for values of x to the *nearest hundredth*.

Solution

a. (1) Compare $x^2 - 10x + 13 = 0$ with $ax^2 + bx + c = 0$ to determine that $a = 1$, $b = -10$, and $c = 13$.

(2) Substitute these values in the quadratic formula, and simplify.

$$x = \frac{-b \pm \sqrt{b^2 - 4ac}}{2a} = \frac{-(-10) \pm \sqrt{(-10)^2 - 4(1)(13)}}{2(1)}$$

$$= \frac{10 \pm \sqrt{100 - 52}}{2} = \frac{10 \pm \sqrt{48}}{2}$$

$$= \frac{10 \pm \sqrt{16 \cdot 3}}{2} \quad \text{(\textit{Note}: Simplify the radical.)}$$

$$= \frac{10 \pm 4\sqrt{3}}{2} = \frac{10}{2} \pm \frac{4\sqrt{3}}{2} = 5 \pm 2\sqrt{3}$$

b. Use a calculator to find a rational approximation for each root.

Enter: 5 $\boxed{+}$ 2 $\boxed{\times}$ 3 $\boxed{\sqrt{x}}$ $\boxed{=}$
Display: $\boxed{8.464101615}$

This root, to the *nearest hundredth*, equals 8.46.

Enter: 5 $\boxed{-}$ 2 $\boxed{\times}$ 3 $\boxed{\sqrt{x}}$ $\boxed{=}$
Display: $\boxed{1.535898385}$

This root, to the *nearest hundredth*, equals 1.54.

Answers: **a.** $x = 5 \pm 2\sqrt{3}$
or
$x_1 = 5 + 2\sqrt{3}$ and $x_2 = 5 - 2\sqrt{3}$
b. $x_1 = 8.46$ and $x_2 = 1.54$

Note: The discriminant $b^2 - 4ac = 48$, a positive number that is not a perfect square. Since the roots of $x^2 - 10x + 13 = 0$ are *irrational*, the equation cannot be solved by factoring. To check the roots of this equation, substitute the irrational values found in part **a**, as shown below.

Check for x $= 5 + 2\sqrt{3}$:

$$x^2 - 10x + 13 = 0$$

$$(5 + 2\sqrt{3})(5 + 2\sqrt{3}) - 10(5 + 2\sqrt{3}) + 13 \overset{?}{=} 0$$

$$25 + 20\sqrt{3} + 12 - 50 - 20\sqrt{3} + 13 \overset{?}{=} 0$$

$$25 + \cancel{20\sqrt{3}} + 12 - 50 - \cancel{20\sqrt{3}} + 13 \overset{?}{=} 0$$

$$50 - 50 \overset{?}{=} 0$$

$$0 = 0 \quad ✔$$

Check for x $= 5 - 2\sqrt{3}$:

$$x^2 - 10x + 13 = 0$$
$$(5 - 2\sqrt{3})(5 - 2\sqrt{3}) - 10(5 - 2\sqrt{3}) + 13 \overset{?}{=} 0$$
$$25 - 20\sqrt{3} + 12 - 50 + 20\sqrt{3} + 13 \overset{?}{=} 0$$
$$25 - \cancel{20\sqrt{3}} + 12 - 50 + \cancel{20\sqrt{3}} + 13 \overset{?}{=} 0$$
$$50 - 50 \overset{?}{=} 0$$
$$0 = 0 \quad ✔$$

The rational approximations for the roots, 8.46 and 1.54, found in part **b**, will not check exactly because of the rounding involved in finding these approximations.

EXERCISES WITH OPEN-RESPONSE PROBLEMS

In 1–9, find the roots of each equation by using the quadratic formula, and check. Express irrational roots in simplest radical form.

1. $x^2 + 2x - 24 = 0$ **2.** $3x^2 + 7x + 2 = 0$ **3.** $2x^2 + 5 = 11x$
4. $x^2 - 6x + 7 = 0$ **5.** $x^2 - 6x + 9 = 0$ **6.** $x^2 = 6x + 1$
7. $2x^2 - 9 = 0$ **8.** $x^2 = 6x + 31$ **9.** $x(x + 4) = 1$

In 10–15, solve each quadratic equation for values of x expressed in simplest radical form, and check.

10. $x^2 - 8x + 13 = 0$ **11.** $x^2 - 10x + 18 = 0$ **12.** $x^2 = 2x + 5$
13. $x^2 = 6x + 11$ **14.** $3x^2 - 5 = 0$ **15.** $x(x + 8) = 34$

In 16–21, solve each quadratic equation for values of x: **a.** expressed in simplest radical form **b.** to the *nearest hundredth*

16. $x^2 - 12x + 29 = 0$ **17.** $x^2 + 10x + 1 = 0$ **18.** $x^2 + 3 = 7x$
19. $2x^2 + 1 = 4x$ **20.** $3x^2 = 2(x + 2)$ **21.** $4x^2 = 4x + 39$

In 22–30, find the roots of each equation to the nearest tenth.

22. $x^2 - 3x - 5 = 0$ **23.** $2x^2 + x = 7$ **24.** $3x(x - 2) = 1$
25. $x^2 + 8 = 10x$ **26.** $5x^2 = 3 - x$ **27.** $x^2 = 4(3x - 2)$
28. $\frac{x + 2}{2} + \frac{3}{x} = 5$ **29.** $2 - \frac{3}{x} = \frac{4}{x^2}$ **30.** $\frac{x - 2}{x + 2} = \frac{1}{x - 3}$

31. The length of a rectangle is 4 more than its width.
   a. Find the dimensions of the rectangle if its area is 12. Check.
   b. Find the dimensions of the rectangle in radical form if its area is 8. Check.

10-12 SOLVING RADICAL EQUATIONS

A *radical equation* in one variable is an equation that contains at least one radical with a variable term in the radicand. For example, $\sqrt{x-2} = 5$ is a radical equation. To solve a radical equation, we find a derived equation that does not contain radicals, as outlined in the procedure and the examples that follow.

PROCEDURE. To solve a radical equation containing only one radical:

1. Isolate the radical so that it is the only term on one side of the equation.
2. If the radical is a square root, square each side of the equation. In general, raise each side to a power equal to the index of the root to obtain a derived equation.
3. Solve the derived equation.
4. Since the derived equation may not be equivalent to the original radical equation, check all roots in the given radical equation and reject any extraneous roots.

EXAMPLES

1. Solve and check: $\sqrt{x-2} = 5$

Solution:

		Check:
(1) Write the equation.	$\sqrt{x-2} = 5$	$\sqrt{x-2} = 5$
(2) Square each side.	$(\sqrt{x-2})^2 = (5)^2$	$\sqrt{27-2} \overset{?}{=} 5$
(3) Solve the derived equation.	$x - 2 = 25$	$\sqrt{25} \overset{?}{=} 5$
	$x = 27$	$5 = 5$ ✔

Answer: $x = 27$

2. Solve and check: $\sqrt{2y-1} + 7 = 4$

Solution:

		Check:
(1) Write the equation.	$\sqrt{2y-1} + 7 = 4$	$\sqrt{2y-1} + 7 = 4$
(2) Isolate the radical.	$\sqrt{2y-1} = -3$	$\sqrt{2(5)-1} + 7 \overset{?}{=} 4$
(3) Square each side.	$(\sqrt{2y-1})^2 = (-3)^2$	$\sqrt{9} + 7 \overset{?}{=} 4$
(4) Solve the derived equation.	$2y - 1 = 9$	$3 + 7 \overset{?}{=} 4$
	$2y = 10$	$10 \neq 4$
	$y = 5$	

Since $y = 5$ is an *extraneous root* of the radical equation, it is rejected. Therefore, the equation has no root, and the solution is empty.

Answer: { } or $\varnothing$

3. Solve and check: $x = 1 + \sqrt{x + 5}$

Solution:

(1) Write the equation.

$$x = 1 + \sqrt{x + 5}$$

(2) Isolate the radical.

$$x - 1 = \sqrt{x + 5}$$

(3) Square each side.

$$(x - 1)^2 = (\sqrt{x + 5})^2$$
$$x^2 - 2x + 1 = x + 5$$

(4) Solve the derived quadratic equation.

$$x^2 - 3x - 4 = 0$$
$$(x - 4)(x + 1) = 0$$

$$x - 4 = 0 \qquad x + 1 = 0$$
$$x = 4 \qquad\quad x = -1$$

(5) Check each root in the original equation.

Check for x = 4.

$$x = 1 + \sqrt{x + 5}$$
$$4 \stackrel{?}{=} 1 + \sqrt{4 + 5}$$
$$4 \stackrel{?}{=} 1 + \sqrt{9}$$
$$4 \stackrel{?}{=} 1 + 3$$
$$4 = 4 ✔$$

Check for x = −1.

$$x = 1 + \sqrt{x + 5}$$
$$-1 \stackrel{?}{=} 1 + \sqrt{-1 + 5}$$
$$-1 \stackrel{?}{=} 1 + \sqrt{4}$$
$$-1 \stackrel{?}{=} 1 + 2$$
$$-1 \neq 3$$

(Reject −1 as a root.)

Answer: $x = 4$ or   solution set = $\{4\}$

---

4. Solve and check: $3\sqrt{x - 2} - 2\sqrt{x + 8} = 0$

Note: If a radical equation contains *two radicals*, there is no definite procedure to use in eliminating the radicals. However, as shown in the solution that follows, it is often helpful to transform the equation so that one radical is isolated on one side. In this case, since there are no other terms except 0, both radicals are eliminated when we square each side of the equation.

Solution:

$$3\sqrt{x - 2} - 2\sqrt{x + 8} = 0$$
$$3\sqrt{x - 2} = 2\sqrt{x + 8}$$
$$(3\sqrt{x - 2})^2 = (2\sqrt{x + 8})^2$$
$$9(x - 2) = 4(x + 8)$$
$$9x - 18 = 4x + 32$$
$$5x = 50$$
$$x = 10$$

Check:

$$3\sqrt{x - 2} - 2\sqrt{x + 8} = 0$$
$$3\sqrt{10 - 2} - 2\sqrt{10 + 8} \stackrel{?}{=} 0$$
$$3\sqrt{8} - 2\sqrt{18} \stackrel{?}{=} 0$$
$$3\sqrt{4 \cdot 2} - 2\sqrt{9 \cdot 2} \stackrel{?}{=} 0$$
$$3 \cdot 2\sqrt{2} - 2 \cdot 3\sqrt{2} \stackrel{?}{=} 0$$
$$6\sqrt{2} - 6\sqrt{2} \stackrel{?}{=} 0$$
$$0 = 0 ✔$$

Answer: $x = 10$ or   solution set = $\{10\}$

EXERCISES

In 1–42, solve each radical equation and check.

1. $\sqrt{x} = 3$

2. $\sqrt{3x} = 6$

3. $3\sqrt{x} = 6$

4. $\sqrt{6x} = 3$

5. $\sqrt[3]{y} = 4$

6. $\sqrt[3]{2x} = -2$

7. $\sqrt{2x} = -2$

8. $7 + \sqrt{x} = 13$

9. $5 + \sqrt{y} = 3$

10. $\sqrt{y - 6} = 2$

11. $\sqrt{y + 8} = 4$

12. $\sqrt{5 + y} = 3$

13. $\sqrt{4 - x} = 3$

14. $\sqrt{2x + 3} = 7$

15. $\sqrt{9 - 2k} = 5$

16. $4 - \sqrt{x} = 7$

17. $\sqrt{2y + 5} = -3$

18. $x = \sqrt{6x + 7}$

19. $y = \sqrt{6y + 16}$

20. $x = \sqrt{x}$

21. $y = 2\sqrt{2y - 3}$

22. $x = 2\sqrt{3 - x}$

23. $y - 2 = \sqrt{y}$

24. $x - 3 = 2\sqrt{x}$

25. $\sqrt{x^2 + 13} = x + 1$

26. $\sqrt{x^2 - 12} = x - 2$

27. $y - 3 = \sqrt{y^2 + 3y}$

28. $5 + \sqrt{4y - 3} = 2$

29. $x - 1 = \sqrt{5x - 9}$

30. $x + 2 = \sqrt{3x + 16}$

31. $\sqrt{2 - 2y} = y + 3$

32. $y = 3 + \sqrt{30 - 2y}$

33. $x = 4 + \sqrt{2x - 8}$

34. $3x = 2\sqrt{3x - 1}$

35. $\sqrt{5k - 3} = \sqrt{k + 13}$

36. $\sqrt{k^2 - 1} = \sqrt{k + 5}$

37. $3\sqrt{y - 3} = \sqrt{3y + 3}$

38. $2\sqrt{y + 7} - \sqrt{y + 25} = 0$

39. $\sqrt{x^2 - 9} = \sqrt{x + 3}$

40. $\sqrt{x^2 + 4} = 2\sqrt{x + 4}$

41. $\sqrt{13 - x^2} = 5 - x$

42. $x - \sqrt{x + 4} = 2$

In 43–50, select the *numeral* preceding the expression that best completes the sentence or answers the question.

43. The solution set of the equation $x = \sqrt{5x + 14}$ is

(1) $\{7, -2\}$

(2) $\{-2\}$

(3) $\{7\}$

(4) $\{\ \}$

44. The equation $\sqrt{2 - x} = 2 - x$ has for its roots

(1) 1, only

(2) 2, only

(3) 1 and 2

(4) neither 1 nor 2

45. The equation $\sqrt{y - 2} = 2 - y$ has for its roots

(1) 2 and 3

(2) 2, only

(3) 3, only

(4) neither 2 nor 3

46. The solution set of $5 - \sqrt{2x} = 9$ is

(1) $\{8\}$

(2) $\{2\}$

(3) $\{2, -2\}$

(4) $\{\ \}$

47. The solution set of $\sqrt{x^2 + 8} = 2\sqrt{2x - 1}$ is

(1) $\{2, 6\}$

(2) $\{2\}$

(3) $\{6\}$

(4) $\varnothing$

48. Given the equation $y = 3\sqrt{y}$, is roots are

(1) 0, only

(2) 0 and 3

(3) 3, only

(4) 0 and 9

49. Which equation has 4 as a root?

(1) $x = \sqrt{20 - x}$

(2) $\sqrt{x} = 2 - x$

(3) $\sqrt{x + 5} = 1 - x$

(4) $\sqrt{2x - 7} = -1$

50. Which equation has roots of 1 and 3?

(1) $y = \sqrt{2y - 1}$

(2) $y = \sqrt{4y - 3}$

(3) $y = \sqrt{6y - 9}$

(4) $y - 3 = \sqrt{6 - 2y}$

CHAPTER SUMMARY

An *irrational number* is a nonrepeating infinite decimal. The set of *real numbers* is the union of the set of rational numbers and the set of irrational numbers. The set of real numbers under the operations of addition and multiplication is an ordered field; that is, $(R, +, \cdot, >)$ is an ordered field.

The *graph of the solution set* of an inequality in one variable is a segment or ray, or the union of segments or rays that are subsets of the real-number line.

The *absolute value* of a number is the larger of that number or its additive inverse and is always a nonnegative number. Therefore:

$$n = \begin{cases} n & \text{if } n \geq 0 \\ -n & \text{if } n < 0 \end{cases}$$

To solve the absolute-value equation $|x| = k$, $k > 0$, we use the derived equations $x = k$ and $x = -k$. The solution set of the absolute-value inequality $|x| < k$, $k > 0$, is the intersection of the solution sets of the derived inequalities $x < k$ and $x > -k$, which may be written as $-k < x < k$. The solution set of the absolute-value inequality $|x| > k$, $k > 0$, is the union of the solution sets of the derived inequalities, $x > k$ and $x < -k$.

The *principal nth root* of a number k is written as $\sqrt[n]{k}$, where k is the *radicand*, n is the *index*, and $\sqrt[n]{k}$ is the *radical*. The *simplest form of a radical* is a monomial of the form $k\sqrt[n]{r}$, where k is a nonzero rational number and r is a positive integer that has no factor other than 1 that is the nth power of an integer.

The following rules define the operations with radicals for $a > 0$ and $b > 0$:

Addition: $c\sqrt[n]{a} + d\sqrt[n]{a} = (c + d)\sqrt[n]{a}$

Subtraction: $c\sqrt[n]{a} - d\sqrt[n]{a} = (c - d)\sqrt[n]{a}$

Multiplication: $\sqrt[n]{a} \cdot \sqrt[n]{b} = \sqrt[n]{ab}$

Division: $\dfrac{\sqrt[n]{a}}{\sqrt[n]{b}} = \sqrt[n]{\dfrac{a}{b}}$

To *rationalize the denominator* of a fraction when the denominator is not a rational number, multiply the fraction by some form of the identity 1. If the denominator of the given fraction is $\sqrt{k}$, multiply by $\dfrac{\sqrt{k}}{\sqrt{k}}$; if the denominator of the given fraction is $a + b$, where either a or b or both are square-root radicals and $a \neq b$, multiply by $\dfrac{a - b}{a - b}$.

The *standard form* of a *quadratic equation* is $ax^2 + bx + c = 0$, where $a \neq 0$. The roots of a quadratic equation can be found by using the *quadratic formula*, $x = \dfrac{-b \pm \sqrt{b^2 - 4ac}}{2a}$.

If a, b, and c are rational numbers, the ***discriminant***, $b^2 - 4ac$, determines the nature of the roots.

Value of Discriminant	Nature of Roots
Positive, perfect square	Two rational roots
Positive, not a perfect square	Two irrational roots
Zero	One rational root
Negative	No real roots

A ***radical equation*** in one variable is an equation that contains at least one radical with a variable term in the radicand. To solve a radical equation containing square-root radicals, isolate the radical and square each side of the equation to obtain a derived equation that does not contain radicals. Check the roots of the derived equation in the radical equation to eliminate extraneous roots.

VOCABULARY

10-1 Irrational number   Set of real numbers   Real-number line
One-to-one correspondence

10-2 Graph of a solution set   Conjunction   Intersection   Disjunction
Union

10-3 Absolute value   Derived equation   Extraneous roots

10-5 Square root   Principal square root   Cube root   Principal cube root
nth root   Principal nth root   Radicand   Index   Radical

10-6 Simplest form of a square-root radical

10-7 Like radicals   Unlike radicals

10-10 Conjugate

10-11 Quadratic equation   Quadratic formula   Discriminant

10-12 Radical equation

REVIEW EXERCISES WITH OPEN-RESPONSE PROBLEMS

In 1–5, identify the property of the real numbers that is illustrated by each given statement.

1. $\sqrt{7} \cdot 1 = \sqrt{7}$

2. $\sqrt{5} + (-\sqrt{5}) = 0$

3. $\sqrt{2} + (\sqrt{2} + \sqrt{3}) = (\sqrt{2} + \sqrt{2}) + \sqrt{3}$

4. $\sqrt{2}(\sqrt{2} + \sqrt{3}) = \sqrt{2} \cdot \sqrt{2} + \sqrt{2} \cdot \sqrt{3}$
5. $\sqrt{3} > 2$ or $\sqrt{3} = 2$ or $\sqrt{3} < 2$

In 6–11, solve each absolute-value equation.

6. $|x| - 3 = 5$ **7.** $|x - 3| = 5$ **8.** $|2x - 3| = 5$
9. $|y - 2| = -2$ **10.** $|3y - 4| = y$ **11.** $|y| - 4 = 3y$

In 12–17, graph the solution set of each given sentence on a real-number line.

12. $4x - 3 \geq 7$ **13.** $1 < 3 + y$ **14.** $-2 \leq x < 3$
15. $(x < 2) \vee (x \geq 3)$ **16.** $|x - 3| > 4$ **17.** $4 + |y| \leq 6$

In 18–21, select the *numeral* preceding the expression or the diagram that best completes the sentence or answers the question.

18. The solution set of $|3x + 1| = 2$ is

     (1) $\left\{ \frac{1}{3} \right\}$ (2) $\left\{ \frac{1}{3}, -\frac{1}{3} \right\}$ (3) $\left\{ \frac{1}{3}, -1 \right\}$ (4) $\{-1, 1\}$

19. Which represents the solution set for x in the inequality $|3 - x| > 6$?
     (1) $\{x | x < -9 \text{ or } x > 3\}$ (2) $\{x | x < -3 \text{ or } x > 9\}$
     (3) $\{x | x < -9 \text{ or } x > -3\}$ (4) $\{x | -3 < x < 9\}$

20. Which is the graph of the solution set of $|x + 4| < 2$?
     (1) -6 -2 (2) -6 -2
     (3) -6 -2 (4) -6 -2

21. Which is the graph of the solution set of $|6 + y| \geq 1$?
     (1) -7 -5 (2) -7 -5
     (3) -7 -5 (4) -7 -5

In 22–24, find the smallest integral value of x for which each radical represents a real number.

22. $\sqrt{x + 9}$ **23.** $\sqrt{3x - 14}$ **24.** $\sqrt{7 + 2x}$

In 24–32, evaluate each expression by finding the indicated root(s).

25. $\sqrt{81}$ **26.** $-\sqrt{625}$ **27.** $\pm\sqrt{196}$ **28.** $\sqrt{0.64}$
29. $\sqrt[3]{0}$ **30.** $\sqrt[3]{-64}$ **31.** $-\sqrt[3]{-8}$ **32.** $\sqrt[5]{-1}$

In 33–36, write each expression in simplest radical form.

33. $\sqrt{28}$ **34.** $\sqrt{8b^2}$ **35.** $\sqrt{\frac{3}{5}}$ **36.** $6\sqrt{\frac{4}{3}}$

In 37–46, perform the indicated operation, and write each answer in simplest form.

37. $\sqrt{90} + \sqrt{40}$ **38.** $\sqrt{98} - 2\sqrt{18}$ **39.** $(3\sqrt{5})^2$

40. $\sqrt{\frac{8}{3}} + \sqrt{\frac{2}{3}}$ **41.** $2\sqrt{5} \cdot \sqrt{15}$ **42.** $\frac{6\sqrt{60}}{24\sqrt{3}}$

43. $\sqrt{300} + \sqrt{50} - \sqrt{72} + \sqrt{3}$ **44.** $\sqrt{3}(2\sqrt{27} - \sqrt{6})$

45. $(2 + \sqrt{5})(3 - \sqrt{5})$ **46.** $\frac{3\sqrt{7} - 12\sqrt{21}}{3\sqrt{7}}$

In 47–50, rationalize the denominator of each fraction. If possible, simplify the result.

47. $\frac{30}{\sqrt{20}}$ **48.** $\frac{4}{3 + \sqrt{5}}$ **49.** $\frac{3}{\sqrt{10} - 2}$ **50.** $\frac{4 + \sqrt{2}}{3 - \sqrt{2}}$

In 51–54, in each case, two irrational numbers are given.   **a.** Perform the indicated operation.   **b.** State whether the result is rational or irrational.

51. $(2 + 3\sqrt{6}) + (5 - \sqrt{54})$ **52.** $(8 + \sqrt{3})(5 - \sqrt{3})$

53. $3\sqrt{50} - 5\sqrt{18}$ **54.** $(7\sqrt{2} + 10)(7\sqrt{2} - 10)$

In 55–57, solve each quadratic equation for values of x: **a.** expressed in simplest radical form   **b.** to the *nearest tenth*.

55. $x^2 - 8x + 4 = 0$ **56.** $x^2 + 4x = 6$ **57.** $3x^2 = 2(x + 1)$

In 58–60, solve each radical equation and check.

58. $\sqrt{4x + 1} = 5$ **59.** $x = \sqrt{3x + 28}$ **60.** $2 - \sqrt{x} = 9$

In 61–63, select the *numeral* preceding the expression that best completes the sentence or answers the question.

61. The expression $\frac{7}{4 + \sqrt{2}}$ is equivalent to

(1) $\frac{4 - \sqrt{2}}{2}$ (2) $\frac{4 + \sqrt{2}}{2}$ (3) $2 - \sqrt{2}$ (4) $2 + \sqrt{2}$

62. The equation $x + 2 = \sqrt{34 - 3x}$ has for its roots

(1) -10 and 3   (2) -10, only   (3) 3, only   (4) neither -10 nor 3

63. Which of the following equations has a solution set that is empty?
   (1) $\sqrt{x} + 1 = 2$ (2) $\sqrt{x + 1} = 2$ (3) $\sqrt{x} + 2 = 1$ (4) $\sqrt{x + 2} = 1$

64. The park department wants to place a distance marker at F, the beginning of two straight paths through a rectangular park, $ABCD$. One path extends to an adjacent side and the other to an opposite corner of the park, as shown in the diagram. The length of the park, CD, is 12 kilometers and the total length of the two paths, $FE + FD$, is 18 kilometers. If F is equidistant from E and C, what are the distances, FE and FD, to be listed on the marker?

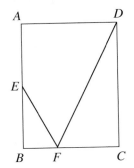

CUMULATIVE REVIEW WITH OPEN-RESPONSE PROBLEMS

1. Express $\frac{13}{44}$ as a repeating decimal.
2. Simplify: $x(x^2 - 2x - 1) - (x^3 - x)$.
3. Write the negation of "All primes are odd."
4. Factor completely: $10x^4 - 40x^3 + 5x^2 - 20x$.
5. Solve and check: $x - \dfrac{2}{2 - x} = \dfrac{x}{x - 2}$.

6. a. Simplify the complex fraction: $\dfrac{\dfrac{1}{x} - \dfrac{1}{a}}{\dfrac{1}{x^2} - \dfrac{1}{a^2}}$.

   b. For what values of a and x is the complex fraction in part **a** undefined?

Exploration

   The set of real numbers, the set of rational numbers, and the set of irrational numbers are all dense sets, that is, between any two numbers of these sets, there is another number from the set. Find five irrational numbers between 1 and 2.

Chapter **11**

Geometry of the Circle

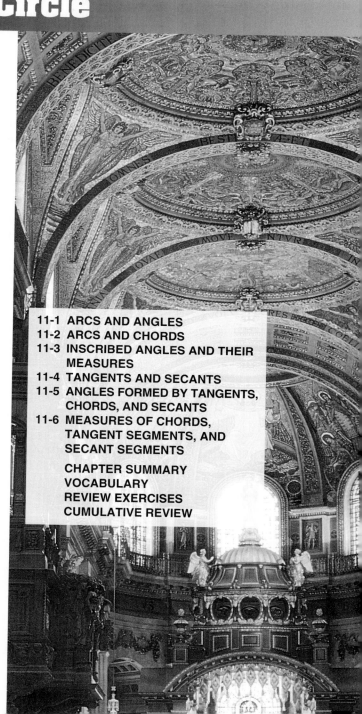

Ever since the invention of the wheel, the circle has had a major impact on civilization.

Many ancient customs and objects based on the use of the circle still exist today. Examples are the circular shape of astrological charts, rings, cups and plates, and most coins.

ARCH   DOME

Architecture showed advancement, first with the introduction of the arch, based on a semicircle, and later with the dome, based on a hemisphere. Some great buildings, including St. Paul's Cathedral in London and the Capitol in Washington, D.C., contain whispering domes. Because of the circular shape of the base of the dome, if a person speaks very softly, in a whisper, into the wall, his or her words can be heard clearly at any point along the circular base, even hundreds of feet away.

In this chapter, we will study how circles interact with lines and angles to produce many interesting mathematical relationships.

11-1 ARCS AND ANGLES

In our work in geometry in Math A, we showed that the locus of points equidistant from a given point is a circle. In this chapter, we will prove some important relationships involving the measures of angles, arcs, and line segments of circles.

- **DEFINITION.** A *circle* is the set of all points in a plane that are equidistant from a fixed point called the center of the circle.

If the center of a circle is point O, the circle is called circle O, written in symbols as $\odot O$.

A *radius* of a circle (plural, *radii*) is a line segment from the center of the circle to any point of the circle. If A, B, and C are points of circle O, then $\overline{OA}$, $\overline{OB}$, and $\overline{OC}$ are radii of the circle. Also, since every point of the circle is equidistant from its center, $OA = OB = OC$. Thus, $\overline{OA} \cong \overline{OB} \cong \overline{OC}$, illustrating the truth of the following statement:

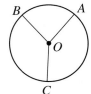

- **All radii of the same circle are congruent.**

A circle separates a plane into three sets of points. If we let the length of the radius of circle O be r, then:

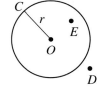

Point C is on the circle if $OC = r$.
Point D is outside the circle if $OD > r$.
Point E is inside the circle if $OE < r$.

The *interior of a circle* is the set of all points whose distance from the center of the circle is less than the length of the radius of the circle.

The *exterior of a circle* is the set of all points whose distance from the center of the circle is greater than the length of the radius of the circle.

Central Angles

Recall that an *angle* is the union of two rays having a common endpoint. The common endpoint is called the *vertex* of the angle.

- **DEFINITION.** A *central angle* of a circle is an angle whose vertex is the center of the circle.

In the accompanying diagram, $\angle LOM$ and $\angle MOR$ are central angles because the vertex of each angle is point O, the center of the circle.

Types of Arcs

An *arc* of a circle is any part of the circle. In the diagram at the left below, A, B, C, and D are points on circle O; and ∠AOB intersects the circle at two distinct points, A and B, separating the circle into two arcs.

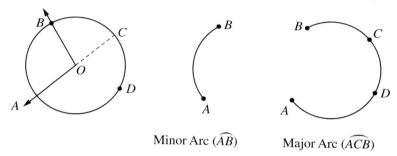

Minor Arc (⌢AB)   Major Arc (⌢ACB)

1. If m∠AOB < 180, points A and B and the points of the circle in the interior of ∠AOB make up *minor arc AB*, written as ⌢AB.

2. Points A and B and the points of the circle not in the interior of ∠AOB make up *major arc AB*. A major arc is usually named by three points: the two endpoints and any other point on the major arc. Thus, the major arc with endpoints A and B is written as ⌢ACB or ⌢ADB.

Note: If m∠AOC = 180, points A and C separate circle O into two equal parts, each of which is called a *semicircle*. In the diagram at the left above, ⌢ADC and ⌢ABC clearly identify two different semicircles.

An arc of a circle is called an *intercepted arc*, or an arc intercepted by an angle, if each endpoint of the arc is on a different ray of the angle and the other points of the arc are in the interior of the angle.

A *quadrant* is an arc that is one-fourth of a circle.

Degree Measure of an Arc

- **DEFINITION.** The *degree measure of an arc* is equal to the measure of the central angle that intercepts the arc.

In circle O, if m∠FOG = 80, the degree measure of arc FG is also 80, written as m⌢FG = 80. Using this same figure, let us make two additional observations:

1. The *degree measure of a major arc* is equal to 360 minus the degree of the minor arc having the same endpoints. Thus:

$$m\overset{\frown}{FEG} = 360 - m\overset{\frown}{FG} = 360 - 80 = 280.$$

2. The *degree measure of a semicircle* is 180. Here, m⌢EFG = 180.

$m\widehat{FG} = 80°$
$\widehat{FG} = 2$ cm

Caution: Do not confuse the degree measure of an arc with the length of an arc, which is discussed in Chapter 14. For example, the circumference of circle O may be 9 centimeters. In the diagram at the left, the degree measure of arc FG is 80, but the length of arc FG is $\frac{80}{360}$ (9 cm) $= \frac{2}{9}$ (9 cm) $= 2$ centimeters.

Congruent Circles, Congruent Arcs, and Arc Addition

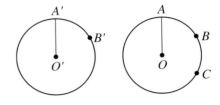

Congruent circles are circles with congruent radii. If $\overline{O'A'} \cong \overline{OA}$, then circles O' and O are congruent.

Congruent arcs are arcs of the same circle or of congruent circles that are equal in measure. If $m\widehat{AB} = m\widehat{BC}$, then $\widehat{AB} \cong \widehat{BC}$. Also, if $\overline{OA} \cong \overline{O'A'}$ and $m\widehat{AB} = m\widehat{A'B'}$, then $\widehat{AB} \cong \widehat{A'B'}$.

- **Arc Addition Postulate. If $\widehat{AB}$ and $\widehat{BC}$ are two arcs of the same circle having a common endpoint and no other points in common, then $\widehat{AB} + \widehat{BC} = \widehat{ABC}$ and $m\widehat{AB} + m\widehat{BC} = m\widehat{ABC}$.**

The arc that is the sum of two arcs may be a minor arc, a major arc, or semi-circle.

For example, A, B, C, and D are points of circle O, $m\widehat{AB} = 90$, $m\widehat{BC} = 40$, and $\overrightarrow{OB}$ and $\overrightarrow{OD}$ are opposite rays.

1. *Minor arc:* $\widehat{AB} + \widehat{BC} = \widehat{AC}$.
   Also, $m\widehat{AC} = m\widehat{AB} + m\widehat{BC} = 90 + 40 = 130$.

2. *Major arc:* $\widehat{AB} + \widehat{BCD} = \widehat{ABD}$.
   Also, $m\widehat{ABD} = m\widehat{AB} + m\widehat{BCD} = 90 + 180 = 270$.

3. *Semicircle:* Since $\overrightarrow{OB}$ and $\overrightarrow{OD}$ are opposite rays, $\angle BOD$ is a straight angle. Thus, $\widehat{BC} + \widehat{CD} = \widehat{BCD}$, a semicircle.
   Also, $m\widehat{BC} + m\widehat{CD} = m\widehat{BCD} = 180$.

- **Theorem 52. In a circle or in congruent circles, congruent central angles intercept congruent arcs.**

Given: Circle $O \cong$ circle O'.
   $\angle AOB \cong \angle COD$.
   $\angle AOB \cong \angle A'O'B'$.

To prove: $\widehat{AB} \cong \widehat{CD}$.
   $\widehat{AB} \cong \widehat{A'B'}$.

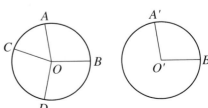

Plan: We will use the definition of the degree measure of an arc to prove that the arcs are congruent.

Proof: Statements   *Reasons*

1. Circle $O \cong$ circle O'.

                                   1. Given.

2. $\angle AOB \cong \angle COD$.
   $\angle AOB \cong \angle A'O'B'$.

                                   2. Given.

3. $m\angle AOB = m\angle COD$.
   $m\angle AOB = m\angle A'O'B'$.

                                   3. Congruent angles are angles that have the same measure.

4. $m\angle AOB = m\overset{\frown}{AB}$.
   $m\angle COD = m\overset{\frown}{CD}$.
   $m\angle A'O'B' = m\overset{\frown}{A'B'}$.

                                   4. The degree measure of an arc is equal to the measure of the central angle that intercepts the arc.

5. $m\overset{\frown}{AB} = m\overset{\frown}{CD}$.
   $m\overset{\frown}{AB} = m\overset{\frown}{A'B'}$.

                                   5. Transitive property of equality.

6. $\overset{\frown}{AB} \cong \overset{\frown}{CD}$.
   $\overset{\frown}{AB} \cong \overset{\frown}{A'B'}$.

                                   6. Congruent arcs are arcs of the same circle or of congruent circles that are equal in measure.

The converse of this theorem can be proved using the same definitions and postulate.

- **Theorem 53. In a circle or in congruent circles, congruent arcs are intercepted by congruent central angles.**

Use the diagram from Theorem 52. Given that circle $O \cong$ circle O', $\overset{\frown}{AB} \cong \overset{\frown}{CD}$, and $\overset{\frown}{AB} \cong \overset{\frown}{A'B'}$, it can be proved that $\angle AOB \cong \angle COD$ and $\angle AOB \cong \angle A'O'B'$. The proof is left to the student.

In Theorems 52 and 53, the condition that the angles and arcs be in the same circle or in congruent circles is important. For example, let us consider three circles, only two of which are congruent.

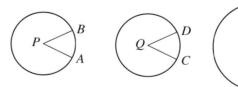

We let circle $P \cong$ circle Q, and circle $Q \not\cong$ circle R.

We also let the three central angles be congruent:
                                   $\angle APB \cong \angle CQD \cong \angle ERF$.

Then these angles are equal in measure: $m\angle APB = m\angle CQD = m\angle ERF$.

Their intercepted arcs are equal in measure:
                                     $m\overset{\frown}{AB} = m\overset{\frown}{CD} = m\overset{\frown}{EF}$.

But all three intercepted arcs are *not* congruent:
                                     $\overset{\frown}{AB} \cong \overset{\frown}{CD}$, but $\overset{\frown}{CD} \not\cong \overset{\frown}{EF}$.

EXAMPLE

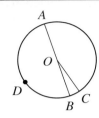

Let $\overrightarrow{OA}$ and $\overrightarrow{OB}$ be opposite rays of circle O, and m∠BOC = 15.
Find each indicated measure.

Solutions

a. m∠AOC
b. m$\widehat{AC}$
c. m$\widehat{BC}$
d. m$\widehat{AB}$
e. m$\widehat{ABC}$

a. m∠AOC = m∠AOB − m∠BOC
          = 180   −   15   = 165   *Answer*

b. m$\widehat{AC}$ = m∠AOC = 165   *Answer*

c. m$\widehat{BC}$ = m∠BOC = 15   *Answer*

d. Since $\widehat{AB}$ is a semicircle,
      m$\widehat{ADB}$ = 180   or   m$\widehat{ACB}$ = 180.   *Answer*

e. m$\widehat{ABC}$ = m$\widehat{AB}$ + m$\widehat{BC}$
          = 180 +   15   = 195   *Answer*

EXERCISES WITH OPEN-RESPONSE PROBLEMS

1. Find the measure of a central angle that intercepts an arc whose degree measure is:
   a. 70   **b.** 140   **c.** 23   **d.** 178   **e.** *r*

2. Find the degree measure of the arc intercepted by a central angle whose measure is:
   a. 30   **b.** 65   **c.** 117   **d.** 145   **e.** *r*

3. In circle O, m∠AOB = 87, m∠BOC = 93, and
m∠COD = 35. Find the degree measure of each of the
following:
   a. ∠DOA **b.** $\widehat{AB}$ **c.** $\widehat{BC}$ **d.** $\widehat{ABC}$
   e. $\widehat{DC}$ **f.** $\widehat{AD}$ **g.** $\widehat{BCD}$ **h.** $\widehat{CDB}$
   i. $\widehat{DBC}$ **j.** $\widehat{BCA}$ **k.** $\widehat{BAD}$ **l.** $\widehat{ABD}$

Ex. 3

4. In circle O, $\overleftrightarrow{AB}$ and $\overleftrightarrow{CD}$ intersect at O, the center of the
circle, and m∠AOC = 25. Find the degree measure of
each of the following:
   a. ∠COB **b.** ∠BOD **c.** ∠DOA
   d. $\widehat{AC}$ **e.** $\widehat{BC}$ **f.** $\widehat{BD}$
   g. $\widehat{AB}$ **h.** $\widehat{ACD}$ **i.** $\widehat{CBA}$

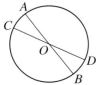

Ex. 4

5. In circle O, m$\angle POQ = 100$, m$\angle ROS = 40$, and $\angle POR \cong \angle QOS$.
Find the degree measure of each of the following:

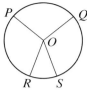

Ex. 5

   a. $\overarc{PQ}$ **b.** $\overarc{RS}$ **c.** $\angle QOS$ **d.** $\overarc{SQ}$
   e. $\angle ROP$ **f.** $\overarc{PR}$ **g.** $\angle QOR$ **h.** $\overarc{QR}$
   i. $\overarc{QPR}$ **j.** $\overarc{QRP}$ **k.** $\overarc{QPS}$ **l.** $\overarc{SQR}$

6. In circle O, $\angle AOC$ and $\angle COB$ are supplementary. If m$\angle AOC = 2x$,
m$\angle COB = x + 90$, and m$\angle AOD = 3x + 10$, find:

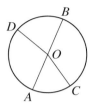

Ex. 6

   a. x **b.** m$\angle AOC$ **c.** m$\angle COB$ **d.** m$\angle AOD$
   e. m$\angle DOB$ **f.** m$\overarc{AC}$ **g.** m$\overarc{BC}$ **h.** m$\overarc{AB}$
   i. m$\overarc{AD}$ **j.** m$\overarc{DB}$ **k.** m$\overarc{ADC}$ **l.** m$\overarc{BCD}$
   m. m$\overarc{ACD}$ **n.** m$\overarc{BAC}$ **o.** m$\overarc{DAC}$ **p.** m$\overarc{DBC}$

Ex. 7

Ex. 8

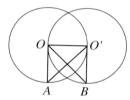

Ex. 9

7. *Given:* Circle O with $\overarc{AB} \cong \overarc{CD}$.
       To prove: $\triangle ABO \cong \triangle CDO$.

8. *Given:* $\overleftrightarrow{AB}$ intersects $\overleftrightarrow{CD}$ at O, the center of the circle.
       To prove: $\overline{AC} \cong \overline{BD}$.

9. *Given:* O' on circle O and O on circle O', $\overrightarrow{OA} \perp \overline{OO'}$ and $\overrightarrow{O'B} \perp \overline{OO'}$.
       To prove: $\overline{AO'} \cong \overline{BO}$.

11-2   ARCS AND CHORDS

- **DEFINITION.** A *chord* of a circle is a line segment whose endpoints are points of the circle.

- **DEFINITION.** A *diameter* of a circle is a chord that has as one of its points the center of the circle.

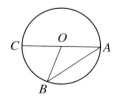

    In the diagram, $\overline{AB}$ and $\overline{AC}$ are chords of circle O, and $\overline{AC}$ is a diameter of circle O. Since the midpoint of a line segment is the point that separates the segment into two congruent parts, and radii $\overline{OA}$ and $\overline{OC}$ are two congruent parts of $\overline{AC}$, O is the midpoint of diameter $\overline{AC}$.

    If the length of a radius of a circle is r and the length of a diameter of that circle is d, then

$$d = 2r$$

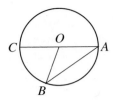

A chord, like a central angle, determines two points on the circle and, therefore, a major arc and a minor arc.

In the diagram, chord $\overline{AB}$, central $\angle AOB$, minor arc $\widehat{AB}$, and major arc $\widehat{ACB}$ are determined by points A and B of circle O. When we refer to the arc of a chord that is not a diameter, we mean the minor arc that has the same endpoints as the chord.

● **Theorem 54. In a circle or in congruent circles, congruent central angles have congruent chords.**

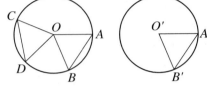

Given: $\odot O \cong \odot O'$.
        $\angle AOB \cong \angle COD$.
        $\angle AOB \cong \angle A'O'B'$.

To prove: $\overline{AB} \cong \overline{CD}$.
        $\overline{AB} \cong \overline{A'B'}$.

Plan: Prove triangles AOB, COD, and $A'O'B'$ congruent using s.a.s. $\cong$ s.a.s.

● **Theorem 55. In a circle or in congruent circles, congruent arcs have congruent chords.**

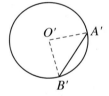

Given: $\odot O \cong \odot O'$.
        $\widehat{AB} \cong \widehat{CD}$.
        $\widehat{AB} \cong \widehat{A'B'}$.

To prove: $\overline{AB} \cong \overline{CD}$.
        $\overline{AB} \cong \overline{A'B'}$.

Plan: Draw $\overline{OA}$, $\overline{OB}$, $\overline{OC}$, $\overline{OD}$, $\overline{O'A'}$, $\overline{O'B'}$. Use Theorem 53 to show that the central angles are congruent. Then use Theorem 54.

The converse of Theorem 54 and the converse of Theorem 55 can be proved in a similar way.

● **Theorem 56. In a circle or in congruent circles, congruent chords have congruent central angles.**

Use circles O and O' in the diagram for Theorem 55. If $\overline{AB} \cong \overline{CD}$ and $\overline{AB} \cong \overline{A'B'}$, then $\angle AOB \cong \angle COD$ and $\angle AOB \cong A'O'B'$.

● **Theorem 57. In a circle or in congruent circles, congruent chords have congruent arcs.**

Use circles O and O' in the diagram for Theorem 55. If $\overline{AB} \cong \overline{CD}$ and $\overline{AB} \cong \overline{A'B'}$, then $\widehat{AB} \cong \widehat{CD}$ and $\widehat{AB} \cong \widehat{A'B'}$.

Chords Equidistant from the Center of a Circle

In Chapter 1, we defined the distance from a point to a line as the length of the perpendicular from the point to the line. The perpendicular is the shortest line segment that can be drawn from a point to a line.

● **Theorem 58. A diameter perpendicular to a chord bisects the chord and its arcs.**

Given: Circle O, diameter $\overline{CD}$, chord $\overline{AB}$,
$\overleftrightarrow{CD} \perp \overline{AB}$.

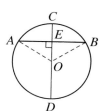

To prove: $\overline{AE} \cong \overline{BE}$, $\overarc{AC} \cong \overarc{BC}$, $\overarc{AD} \cong \overarc{BD}$.

Plan: Draw radii $\overline{OA}$ and $\overline{OB}$. Prove
right triangles AEO and BEO
are congruent by hy. leg $\cong$ hy. leg.

Proof: *Statements*

1. Draw radii $\overline{OA}$ and $\overline{OB}$.
2. $\overleftrightarrow{CD} \perp \overline{AB}$.
3. $\angle AEO$ and $\angle BEO$ are right angles.
4. $\overline{OA} \cong \overline{OB}$. (hy. $\cong$ hy.)
5. $\overline{OE} \cong \overline{OE}$. (leg $\cong$ leg)
6. Rt. $\triangle AEO \cong$ rt. $\triangle BEO$.
7. $\overline{AE} \cong \overline{BE}$.

8. $\angle AOE \cong \angle BOE$.
9. $\overarc{AC} \cong \overarc{BC}$.

10. $\angle AOD$ is supplementary to $\angle AOE$. $\angle BOD$ is supplementary to $\angle BOE$.
11. $\angle AOD \cong \angle BOD$.

12. $\overarc{AD} \cong \overarc{BD}$.

Reasons

1. Two points determine a line.
2. Given.
3. Perpendicular lines intersect to form right angles.
4. All radii of the same circle are congruent.
5. Reflexive property of congruence.
6. Hy. leg $\cong$ hy. leg.
7. Corresponding parts of congruent triangles are congruent.

8. Reason 7.
9. In a circle, congruent central angles have congruent chords.

10. If two angles form a linear pair, then they are supplementary.
11. Supplements of congruent angles are congruent.

12. Reason 9.

● **Corollary 58-1. The perpendicular bisector of a chord of a circle passes through the center of the circle.**

In the diagram, $\overleftrightarrow{CD}$ is the perpendicular bisector of chord $\overline{AB}$ in circle O. In Math A, it was shown that the perpendicular bisector of a line segment is the locus of points, or set of all points, equidistant from the endpoints of the segment. Therefore, a point is on $\overleftrightarrow{CD}$ if and only if it is equidistant from A and B. Since $OA = OB$, point O, the center of the circle, is on $\overleftrightarrow{CD}$.

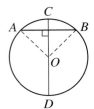

● **Theorem 59. If two chords of a circle are congruent, they are equidistant from the center of the circle.**

Given: Circle O with $\overline{AB} \cong \overline{CD}$.
$\overline{OE} \perp \overline{AB}$.
$\overline{OF} \perp \overline{CD}$.

To prove: $\overline{OE} \cong \overline{OF}$.

Plan: Draw $\overline{OB}$ and $\overline{OD}$. Show that right triangles *BOE* and *DOF* are congruent by hy. leg $\cong$ hy. leg.

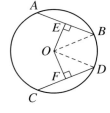

Proof: *Statements*

Statements	Reasons
1. Draw radii $\overline{OB}$ and $\overline{OD}$.	1. Two points determine a line.
2. $\overline{OE} \perp \overline{AB}$; $\overline{OF} \perp \overline{CD}$.	2. Given.
3. $\angle OEB$ and $\angle OFD$ are right angles.	3. Perpendicular lines intersect to form right angles.
4. $\overline{OE}$ bisects $\overline{AB}$; $\overline{OF}$ bisects $\overline{CD}$.	4. A diameter perpendicular to a chord bisects the chord.
5. $\overline{AB} \cong \overline{CD}$.	5. Given.
6. $\overline{BE} \cong \overline{DF}$. (leg $\cong$ leg)	6. Halves of congruent segments are congruent.
7. $\overline{OB} \cong \overline{OD}$. (hy. $\cong$ hy.)	7. All radii of the same circle are congruent.
8. Rt. $\triangle BOE \cong$ rt. $\triangle DOF$.	8. Hy. leg $\cong$ hy. leg.
9. $\overline{OE} \cong \overline{OF}$.	9. Corresponding parts of congruent triangles are congruent.

- **Theorem 60. If two chords of a circle are equidistant from its center, the chords are congruent.**

Use Theorem 59 diagram. If $\overline{OE} \perp \overline{AB}$, $\overline{OF} \perp \overline{CD}$, and $OE = OF$ in circle O, then $\overline{AB} \cong \overline{CD}$. Notice that Theorem 60 is the converse of Theorem 59. Theorem 60 is proved by a procedure similar to that used for Theorem 59; this proof is left to the student as an exercise.

A Polygon Inscribed in a Circle

If a polygon is inscribed in a circle, the vertices of the polygon are points of the circle and the sides of the polygon are chords of the circle. We can also say that the circle is circumscribed about the polygon. For example, in the accompanying diagram, A, B, C, and D are points of circle O. Therefore:

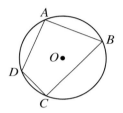

1. Polygon $ABCD$ is *inscribed* in circle O.
2. Circle O is *circumscribed* about polygon $ABCD$.

To circumscribe a circle about $\triangle ABC$:

(1) Construct $\overleftrightarrow{PQ}$, the perpendicular bisector of $\overline{AB}$.
(2) Construct $\overleftrightarrow{RS}$, the perpendicular bisector of $\overline{BC}$.
(3) Lines $\overleftrightarrow{PQ}$ and $\overleftrightarrow{RS}$ intersect at O.
Since O is on $\overleftrightarrow{PQ}$, $\overline{OA} \cong \overline{OB}$.
Since O is on $\overleftrightarrow{RS}$, $\overline{OB} \cong \overline{OC}$.
By the transitive property, $\overline{OA} \cong \overline{OC}$.

Therefore, O is on the perpendicular bisector of $\overline{AC}$.
(4) Using $\overline{OA}$ as a radius, draw circle O. Triangle ABC is inscribed in $\odot O$.

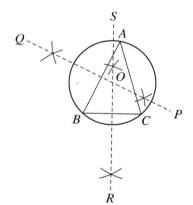

The construction to circumscribe a circle about a triangle, or to inscribe a triangle in a circle, indicates that the following statements can be proved:

- **Any three noncollinear points determine a circle.**
- **The perpendicular bisectors of the sides of a triangle are concurrent; that is, the three perpendicular bisectors meet at one point.**

EXAMPLES

1. Find the length of a chord 3 inches from the center of a circle whose radius measures 5 inches.

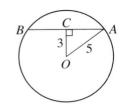

Solution   Since $\overline{OC} \perp \overline{BA}$, $\triangle AOC$ is a right triangle. By the Pythagorean Theorem:

$$(CA)^2 + 3^2 = 5^2$$
$$(CA)^2 + 9 = 25$$
$$(CA)^2 = 16$$
$$CA = 4 \quad \text{(A length is positive.)}$$

Since $\overline{OC}$ bisects $\overline{BA}$, $BC = CA$.
Thus, $BA = BC + CA = 4 + 4 = 8$.

Answer: The length of the chord is 8 inches.

---

2. In a circle of radius 10, $m\overset{\frown}{AB} = 90$.
   a. Find the length of chord $\overline{AB}$ in radical form.
   b. Find the distance of $\overline{AB}$ from the center of the circle in radical form.
   c. Express each length from parts **a** and **b** to the *nearest hundredth*.

Solutions   **a.** Since $m\overset{\frown}{AB} = 90$, then $m\angle AOB = 90$ and $\triangle AOB$ is a right triangle. Let $x = AB$. Then:

$$(AB)^2 = (OB)^2 + (OA)^2$$
$$x^2 = 10^2 + 10^2$$
$$= 100 + 100$$
$$= 200$$
$$x = \pm\sqrt{200} = \pm 10\sqrt{2}$$

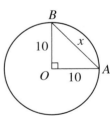

Since a length is positive, $AB = 10\sqrt{2}$ *Answer*

b. The distance OC is the length of the perpendicular to $\overline{AB}$. Therefore, C is the midpoint of $\overline{AB}$, and $\triangle AOC$ is a right triangle.

$$AC = \tfrac{1}{2}(10\sqrt{2}) = 5\sqrt{2}$$

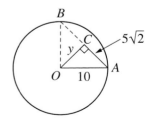

Let $y = OC$. Then:

$$(OC)^2 + (AC)^2 = (OA)^2$$
$$y^2 + (5\sqrt{2})^2 = 10^2$$
$$y^2 + 50 = 100$$
$$y^2 = 50$$
$$y = \pm\sqrt{50} = \pm 5\sqrt{2}$$

Since a length is positive, $OC = 5\sqrt{2}$ *Answer*

c. Enter each irrational number on a calculator, and round each display to two decimal places.

To evaluate $AB = 10\sqrt{2}$:

Enter: 10 ⊠ **2nd** $\boxed{\sqrt{x}}$ 2
   ENTER

Display: $\boxed{14.14213562}$

$AB \approx 14.14$ *Answer*

To evaluate $OC = 5\sqrt{2}$:

Enter: 5 ⊠ **2nd** $\boxed{\sqrt{x}}$ 2
   ENTER

Display: $\boxed{7.071067812}$

$OC \approx 7.07$ *Answer*

Note: Unless otherwise specified, leave each irrational measure (such as chord $AB = 10\sqrt{2}$) in irrational form to be *exact*. Although a rational approximation (such as chord $AB \approx 14.14$) is *not* exact, the approximation does provide a sense of the relative size of the measure.

EXERCISES WITH OPEN-RESPONSE PROBLEMS

1. Find the length of the radius of a circle whose diameter measures:
   a. 10 inches   **b.** 12 meters   **c.** 9 feet   **d.** 2.3 centimeters   **e.** d

2. Find the length of the diameter of a circle whose radius measures:
   a. $\sqrt{3}$ yards   **b.** 12 meters   **c.** $\frac{1}{4}$ foot   **d.** 0.05 millimeter   **e.** r

3. In the diagram, O is the center of the circle, and A, B, C, and D are points of the circle. Name:
   a. 4 radii   **b.** 2 diameters
   c. 4 chords   **d.** 4 central angles

4. In circle O, $\overline{AB}$ is a diameter, $AO = 3x - 1$, and $AB = 5x$. Find the length of a radius of the circle.

5. Points A, C, and D are points of circle O such that $\angle DAC$ is a right angle, $DA = 6$, and $AC = 8$. Find:
   a. the length of $\overline{CD}$, a diameter of the circle   **b.** OA

Ex. 3–5

In 6–19, $\overline{DE}$ is a diameter of circle O, and $\overline{DE} \perp$ chord $\overline{AB}$ at point C.

6. If $AB = 6$ and $OC = 4$, find OB.
7. If $AB = 14$ and $OC = 24$, find OB.
8. If $AB = 30$ and $OB = 17$, find OC.
9. If $AB = 32$ and $OB = 20$, find OC.
10. If $OB = 13$ and $OC = 5$, find AB.
11. If $OB = 15$ and $OC = 12$, find AB.
12. If $m\angle AOB = 90$, find: **a.** $m\widehat{AB}$ **b.** $m\widehat{AD}$ **c.** $m\widehat{AEB}$ **d.** $m\widehat{AE}$
13. If $m\angle AOE = 140$, find: **a.** $m\angle AOC$ **b.** $m\angle AOB$ **c.** $m\widehat{AB}$ **d.** $m\widehat{BD}$ **e.** $m\widehat{AEB}$
14. If $m\angle AOB = 90$ and $OC = 3$, find AB.

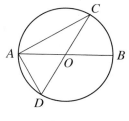

Ex. 6–19

15. If m∠*AOB* = 90 and *OA* = √8, find:

  a. *OB* **b.** *AB* **c.** *AC* **d.** *OC*

16. If m∠*AOB* = 60 and *OA* = 12, find:

  a. m∠*OAB* **b.** m∠*OBA* **c.** *AB* **d.** *AC* **e.** *OC*

17. If m∠*AOB* = 60 and *BC* = 2, find:

  a. *AC* **b.** *AB* **c.** *OB* **d.** *OA* **e.** *OC*

18. If *OD* = 41 and *CD* = 32, find:

  a. *OA* **b.** *OC* **c.** *AC* **d.** *AB*

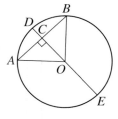

Ex. 6–19

19. Let *AB* = 24, *CD* = 8, and *OC* = *x*.

  a. Represent the length of $\overline{OB}$ in terms of *x*.

  b. Using *OB*, *OC*, and *CB*, write an equation that can be used to find *x*.

  c. Find *OC*. **d.** Find *OB*.

In 20–23, $\overline{AC}$ is a diameter and $\overline{AB}$ is a chord of circle *O*.

20. If *AC* = 12 and the distance from *O* to chord $\overline{AB}$ is 4, find the length of $\overline{AB}$:

  a. in exact radical form **b.** to the *nearest hundredth*

21. If *AC* = 16 and *AB* = 8, find the distance from *O* to $\overline{AB}$:

  a. in radical form **b.** to the *nearest hundredth*

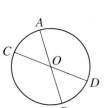

22. Chord $\overline{AB}$ is 14 meters, and the distance from *O* to $\overline{AB}$ is 5 meters. Find:

  a. the exact number of meters in $\overline{AC}$

  b. *AC* to the *nearest hundredth* of a meter

  c. *AC* to the *nearest centimeter*

Ex. 20–23

23. If $\overline{AC}$ is twice the length of $\overline{AB}$, and the distance from *O* to $\overline{AB}$ is 9 inches, find:

  a. the exact length of $\overline{AB}$

  b. the exact length of $\overline{AC}$

  c. *AB* to the *nearest tenth* of an inch

  d. *AC* to the *nearest tenth* of an inch

24. a. Are angles that have the same measure always congruent?

  b. Are arcs that have the same degree measure always congruent?

25. Draw an obtuse triangle. Construct circle *O* so that the triangle is inscribed in the circle.

26. Tell which two of the given quadrilaterals can *always* be inscribed in a circle: square, parallelogram, rhombus, rectangle, trapezoid.

27. *Given:*   In circle *O*, chords $\overline{AB}$ and $\overline{CD}$ intersect at *O*.

  To prove: m$\widehat{AC}$ = m$\widehat{BD}$.

28. *Given:*   In circle *O*, $\overline{DE} \cong \overline{FE}$.

  To prove: △*DOE* ≅ △*FOE*.

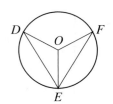

Ex. 27   **Ex. 28**

29. *Given:* $\triangle PQR$ is inscribed in circle O, $\overline{PQ} \cong \overline{PR}$.
  To prove: **a.** $\overparen{PQ} \cong \overparen{PR}$.
  b. $\overparen{PQR} \cong \overparen{PRQ}$.

30. *Given:* In circle O, $\overleftrightarrow{DOC} \perp$ chord $\overline{AB}$.
  To prove: **a.** $\triangle CDB \cong \triangle CDA$.
  b. $\triangle ABC$ is isosceles.

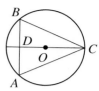

Ex. 29   **Ex. 30**

11-3 INSCRIBED ANGLES AND THEIR MEASURES

• **DEFINITION.** An *inscribed angle* of a circle is an angle whose vertex is on the circle and whose sides contain chords of the circle.

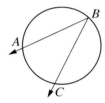

In the diagram, $\angle ABC$ is an inscribed angle that intercepts $\overparen{AC}$. We note that $\overrightarrow{BA}$ and $\overrightarrow{BC}$, the rays that form the angle, contain two chords of the circle, namely, $\overline{BA}$ and $\overline{BC}$.

In order to determine how the measure of an inscribed angle is related to the measure of its intercepted arc, we must consider three cases:

      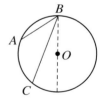

Case 1. The center of the circle is contained on one ray of $\angle ABC$.

Case 2. The center of the circle is in the interior of $\angle ABC$.

Case 3. The center of the circle is in the exterior of $\angle ABC$.

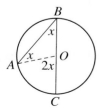

Case 1

In Case 1, we draw $\overline{OA}$ to form isosceles triangle AOB, in which $m\angle OAB = m\angle OBA = x$. Since the measure of an exterior angle of a triangle is equal to the sum of the measures of the two remote interior angles, $m\angle AOC = x + x = 2x$. Thus, $m\overparen{AC} = 2x$, since the measure of the central angle, $\angle AOC$, is equal to the measure of its intercepted arc, $\overparen{AC}$. Therefore:

$$m\angle ABC = x = \tfrac{1}{2}(2x) = \tfrac{1}{2}\,m\overparen{AC}$$

The measure of the inscribed angle is one-half the measure of its intercepted arc.

Let us now present a formal proof of the theorem for all cases.

- **Theorem 61. The measure of an inscribed angle of a circle is equal to one-half the measure of its intercepted arc.**

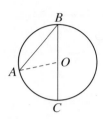

Case 1

Case 1. **The center of the circle is a point on one ray of the inscribed angle.**

Given: $\angle ABC$ inscribed in circle O, with O on $\overrightarrow{BC}$.

To prove: $m\angle ABC = \frac{1}{2} m\widehat{AC}$.

Plan: Draw $\overline{AO}$, and show that the measure of exterior angle AOC is twice the measure of $\angle ABC$.

Proof: *Statements*

Statements	Reasons
1. $\angle ABC$ inscribed in circle O; O is a point on $\overrightarrow{BC}$.	1. Given
2. Draw $\overline{AO}$.	2. Two points determine a line.
3. $\overline{AO} \cong \overline{OB}$.	3. All radii of the same circle are congruent.
4. $\angle A \cong \angle B$.	4. If two sides of a triangle are congruent, the angles opposite these sides are congruent.
5. $m\angle A = m\angle B$.	5. Congruent angles are equal in measure.
6. $m\angle AOC = m\angle A + m\angle B$.	6. The measure of an exterior angle of a triangle is equal to the sum of the measures of the two remote interior angles.
7. $m\angle AOC = m\angle B + m\angle B$ $= 2m\angle B$.	7. Substitution.
8. $m\angle AOC = m\widehat{AC}$.	8. The measure of an arc of a circle is equal to the measure of the central angle that intercepts the arc.
9. $2m\angle B = m\widehat{AC}$.	9. Transitive property of equality.
10. $m\angle B = \frac{1}{2} m\widehat{AC}$.	10. Multiplication property of equality.

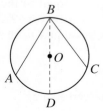

Case 2

Case 2. **The center of the circle is a point in the interior of the inscribed angle.**

Given: $\angle ABC$ is inscribed in circle O, with O in the interior of $\angle ABC$.

To prove: $m\angle ABC = \frac{1}{2} m\widehat{AC}$.

Plan: Draw $\overleftrightarrow{BO}$ and use Case 1.

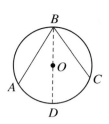

Case 2

Proof: *Statements*

1. $\angle ABC$ is inscribed in circle O; O is a point in the interior of $\angle ABC$.

2. Draw $\overleftrightarrow{BO}$ intersecting the circle at D.

3. $m\angle ABC = m\angle ABD + m\angle DBC$.

4. $m\angle ABD = \frac{1}{2} \, m\widehat{AD}$.

   $m\angle DBC = \frac{1}{2} \, m\widehat{DC}$.

5. $m\angle ABC = \frac{1}{2} \, m\widehat{AD} + \frac{1}{2} \, m\widehat{DC}$.

6. $m\angle ABC = \frac{1}{2} (m\widehat{AD} + m\widehat{DC})$.

7. $m\angle ABC = \frac{1}{2} \, m\widehat{AC}$.

Reasons

1. Given.

2. Two points determine a line.

3. The whole is equal to the sum of its parts.

4. Case 1.

5. Substitution.

6. Distributive property.

7. Arc addition postulate.

Case 3. **The center of the circle is a point in the exterior of the inscribed angle.**

Given: $\angle ABC$ inscribed in circle O, with O in the exterior of $\angle ABC$.

To prove: $m\angle ABC = \frac{1}{2} \, m\widehat{AC}$.

Plan: Draw $\overleftrightarrow{BO}$ and use Case 1.

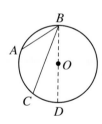

Case 3

Proof: *Statements*

1. $\angle ABC$ is inscribed in circle O; O is a point in the exterior of $\angle ABC$.

2. Draw $\overleftrightarrow{BO}$ intersecting the circle at D.

3. $m\angle ABC + m\angle CBD = m\angle ABD$.

4. $m\angle ABC = m\angle ABD - m\angle CBD$.

5. $m\angle ABD = \frac{1}{2} \, m\widehat{AD}$.

   $m\angle CBD = \frac{1}{2} \, m\widehat{CD}$.

6. $m\angle ABC = \frac{1}{2} \, m\widehat{AD} - \frac{1}{2} \, m\widehat{CD}$.

7. $m\angle ABC = \frac{1}{2} (m\widehat{AD} - m\widehat{CD})$.

8. $m\angle ABC = \frac{1}{2} \, m\widehat{AC}$.

Reasons

1. Given.

2. Two points determine a line.

3. The whole is equal to the sum of its parts.

4. Addition property of equality.

5. Case 1.

6. Substitution.

7. Distributive property.

8. Substitution.

● **Corollary 61-1. An angle inscribed in a semicircle is a right angle.**

In the diagram, $\angle ABC$ is inscribed in $\overset{\frown}{ABC}$, a semicircle of circle O. The arc intercepted by $\angle ABC$ is $\overset{\frown}{ADC}$, another semicircle whose degree measure is 180. Thus:

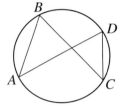

$$m\angle ABC = \tfrac{1}{2} m\overset{\frown}{ADC} = \tfrac{1}{2}(180) = 90.$$

● **Corollary 61-2. Two inscribed angles of a circle that intercept the same arc are congruent.**

In the diagram, $\angle ABC$ and $\angle ADC$ are inscribed angles, each of which intercepts arc $\overset{\frown}{AC}$. Since $m\angle ABC = \tfrac{1}{2} m\overset{\frown}{AC}$, and $m\angle ADC = \tfrac{1}{2} m\overset{\frown}{AC}$:

$m\angle ABC = m\angle ADC$ and $\angle ABC \cong \angle ADC$.

EXAMPLE

Given: $\triangle ABC$ is inscribed in a circle, $m\overset{\frown}{BC} = 100$, and $m\angle B = 70$.

Find: **a.** $m\angle A$ **b.** $m\overset{\frown}{AC}$

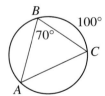

Solutions   The measure of an inscribed angle of a circle equals one-half the degree measure of its intercepted arc. Therefore:

a. $m\angle A = \tfrac{1}{2} m\overset{\frown}{BC}$

$m\angle A = \tfrac{1}{2}(100)$

$m\angle A = 50$

b. $m\angle B = \tfrac{1}{2} m\overset{\frown}{AC}$

$70 = \tfrac{1}{2} m\overset{\frown}{AC}$

$140 = m\overset{\frown}{AC}$

Answers: **a.** $m\angle A = 50$ **b.** $m\overset{\frown}{AC} = 140$

EXERCISES WITH OPEN-RESPONSE PROBLEMS

1. Find the measure of an inscribed angle that intercepts an arc whose degree measure is:
    a. 60   **b.** 140   **c.** 200   **d.** 75   **e.** r

2. Find the degree measure of an arc intercepted by an inscribed angle whose measure is:
    a. 60   **b.** 120   **c.** 15   **d.** 90   **e.** r

Ex. 3

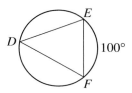

Ex. 4

3. Triangle ABC is inscribed in a circle, $m\angle A = 80$, and $m\widehat{AC} = 88$.
    Find: **a.** $m\widehat{BC}$ **b.** $m\angle B$ **c.** $m\angle C$ **d.** $m\widehat{AB}$

4. Triangle DEF is inscribed in a circle, $\overline{DE} \cong \overline{EF}$, and $m\widehat{EF} = 100$.
    Find: **a.** $m\angle D$ **b.** $m\widehat{DE}$ **c.** $m\angle F$ **d.** $m\angle E$ **e.** $m\widehat{DF}$

In 5–7, chords $\overline{AC}$ and $\overline{BD}$ of a circle intersect at E.

5. If $m\angle B = 40$ and $m\angle AEB = 102$, find:
    a. $m\angle A$ **b.** $m\widehat{BC}$ **c.** $m\widehat{AD}$ **d.** $m\angle D$ **e.** $m\angle C$

6. If $\overleftrightarrow{AB} \parallel \overleftrightarrow{DC}$ and $m\angle B = 36$, find:
    a. $m\angle D$ **b.** $m\widehat{AD}$ **c.** $m\widehat{BC}$ **d.** $m\angle A$ **e.** $m\angle C$

7. If $m\widehat{AD} = 100$, $m\widehat{AB} = 110$, and $m\widehat{BC} = 90$, find:
    a. $m\widehat{DC}$ **b.** $m\angle A$ **c.** $m\angle B$ **d.** $m\angle C$ **e.** $m\angle D$

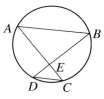

Ex. 5–7

In 8 and 9, diameter $\overline{DOE} \perp$ chord $\overline{AB}$ at F, $\overline{AOC}$ is a diameter, and $\overline{BC}$ is a chord of circle O.

8. If $m\widehat{BC} = 60$, find:
    a. $m\widehat{AB}$ **b.** $m\angle A$ **c.** $m\angle C$ **d.** $m\widehat{AD}$
    e. $m\angle AOD$ **f.** $m\widehat{CE}$ **g.** $m\widehat{ABE}$ **h.** $m\angle AOE$

9. If $m\angle AOD = 35$, find:
    a. $m\widehat{AD}$ **b.** $m\widehat{DB}$ **c.** $m\widehat{BC}$ **d.** $m\angle A$
    e. $m\angle C$ **f.** $m\angle B$ **g.** $m\widehat{CE}$ **h.** $m\widehat{AE}$

Ex. 8 and 9

10. If $\triangle ABC$ is inscribed in a circle so that $m\widehat{AB} : m\widehat{BC} : m\widehat{CA} = 2:3:4$, find:
    a. $m\widehat{AB}$ **b.** $m\widehat{BC}$ **c.** $m\widehat{CA}$ **d.** $m\angle A$ **e.** $m\angle B$ **f.** $m\angle C$

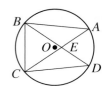

| **Ex. 11** | **Ex. 12** | **Ex. 13** | **Ex. 14** |

11. Quadrilateral $PQRS$ is inscribed in a circle, and $m\widehat{PQ} : m\widehat{QR} : m\widehat{RS} : m\widehat{SP} = 1:2:4:5$.
    Find: **a.** $m\widehat{PQ}$ **b.** $m\widehat{QR}$ **c.** $m\widehat{RS}$ **d.** $m\widehat{SP}$
    e. $m\angle S$ **f.** $m\angle Q$ **g.** $m\angle R$ **h.** $m\angle P$

12. *Given:* Chords $\overline{AD}$ and $\overline{BC}$ of circle O intersect at E, $\overline{AB} \cong \overline{CD}$.
    To prove: $\triangle ABE \cong \triangle CDE$.

13. *Given:* Diameters $\overline{BOD}$ and $\overline{COA}$ intersect at the center of circle O.
    To prove: $\triangle ABC \cong \triangle DCB$.

14. *Given:* Chords $\overline{AC}$ and $\overline{BD}$ of circle O intersect at E, $\widehat{AB} \cong \widehat{CD}$.
    To prove: $\triangle ABC \cong \triangle DCB$.

11-4 TANGENTS AND SECANTS

A line may have two points, one point, or no points in common with a circle, as shown in the diagram.

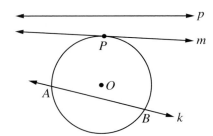

- **DEFINITION.** A *tangent* to a circle is a line in the plane of the circle that intersects the circle in exactly one point.

In the diagram, line *m* is tangent to circle *O* because the line intersects the circle at only one point, *P*.

- **DEFINITION.** A *secant* of a circle is a line that intersects the circle in two points.

In the diagram, line *k* is a secant of circle *O* because the line intersects the circle at two points, *A* and *B*.

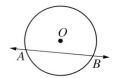

● **Postulate. At a given point on a circle, there is one and only one tangent to the circle.**

Let P be any point on circle O, and $\overline{OP}$ be a radius to that point. If line m containing points P and Q is perpendicular to $\overleftrightarrow{OP}$, it follows that $OQ > OP$ because the perpendicular is the shortest distance from a point to a line. Therefore, every point on line m except P is outside circle O, and line m must be tangent to circle O. From this discussion we may prove the following theorem.

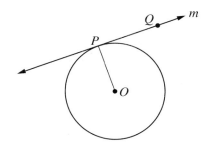

● **Theorem 62. If a line is perpendicular to a radius at its point of intersection with the circle, the line is tangent to the circle.**

The proof of this theorem is left to the student. Our next theorem is the converse of Theorem 62.

● **Theorem 63. If a line is tangent to a circle, the line is perpendicular to the radius drawn to the point of tangency.**

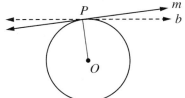

Given: Line m is tangent to circle O at point P.

To prove: Line m is perpendicular to $\overline{OP}$.

Plan: Use an indirect proof.

Paragraph proof: Either line m is perpendicular to $\overline{OP}$, or m is not perpendicular to $\overline{OP}$. Assume that m is not perpendicular to $\overline{OP}$; then there is some line, b, perpendicular to $\overline{OP}$ at point P. By Theorem 62, if line b is perpendicular to $\overline{OP}$, then b is tangent to circle O at P. But two lines, m and b, cannot both be tangent to circle O at point P (a contradiction of the postulate that, at any given point on the circle, there is one and only one tangent to the circle). Therefore, the assumption that m is not perpendicular to $\overline{OP}$ is false, and it is true that line m is perpendicular to $\overline{OP}$.

Common Tangents

● **DEFINITION. A *common tangent* is a line that is tangent to each of two circles.**

Since $\overleftrightarrow{AB}$ is tangent to circle O at A and to circle O' at B, $\overleftrightarrow{AB}$ is a common tangent.

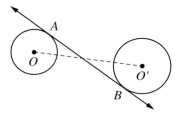

Line $\overleftrightarrow{AB}$ is called a **common internal tangent** because the tangent intersects the line segment joining the centers of the circles, here $\overline{OO'}$.

Since $\overleftrightarrow{CD}$ is tangent to circle P at C and to circle P' at D, $\overleftrightarrow{CD}$ is a common tangent.

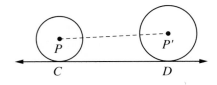

Line $\overleftrightarrow{CD}$ is called a **common external tangent** because the tangent does *not* intersect the line segment joining the centers of the circles, here $\overline{PP'}$.

Two circles in the same plane are said to be tangent to each other if they are tangent to the same line at the same point.

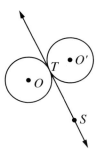

Externally Tangent Circles
$\overleftrightarrow{ST}$ is a common internal tangent.

Here, $\overleftrightarrow{ST}$ is tangent to circle O and to circle O' at T. Also, circle O is tangent to circle O'. Since all of the points of each circle, except the point of tangency, are exterior points of the other circle, the circles are externally tangent. Since $\overleftrightarrow{ST}$ intersects $\overline{OO'}$, $\overleftrightarrow{ST}$ is a common internal tangent.

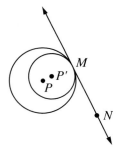

Internally Tangent Circles
$\overleftrightarrow{MN}$ is a common external tangent.

Here, $\overleftrightarrow{MN}$ is tangent to circle P and to circle P' at M. Also, circle P is tangent to circle P'. Since all of the points of one circle, except the point of tangency, are in the interior of the other circle, the circles are internally tangent. Since $\overleftrightarrow{MN}$ does not intersect $\overline{PP'}$, $\overleftrightarrow{MN}$ is a common external tangent to circles P and P'.

As shown in the diagrams, two circles can have four, three, two, one, or no common tangents.

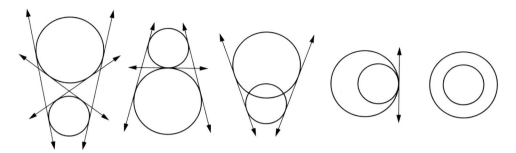

Tangent Segments

● **DEFINITION.** A *tangent segment* is a segment of a tangent line, one of whose endpoints is the point of tangency.

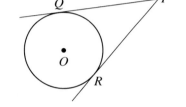

In the diagram, $\overline{PQ}$ and $\overline{PR}$ are tangent segments of the tangents $\overleftrightarrow{PQ}$ and $\overleftrightarrow{PR}$ to circle O from P.

● **Theorem 64. Tangent segments drawn to a circle from an external point are congruent.**

Given: $\overleftrightarrow{PQ}$ tangent to circle O at Q.
$\overleftrightarrow{PR}$ tangent to circle O at R.

To prove: $\overline{PQ} \cong \overline{PR}$.

Plan: Draw $\overline{OQ}$, $\overline{OR}$, and $\overline{OP}$. Prove right triangles PQO and PRO congruent by hy. leg $\cong$ hy. leg.

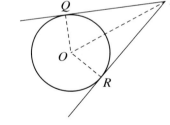

Proof: Statements

1. $\overleftrightarrow{PQ}$ is tangent to circle O at Q.
$\overleftrightarrow{PR}$ is tangent to circle O at R.

2. $\overleftrightarrow{PQ} \perp \overline{OQ}$.
$\overleftrightarrow{PR} \perp \overline{OR}$.

3. $\angle PQO$ and $\angle PRO$ are right angles.

4. $\overline{QO} \cong \overline{RO}$. (leg $\cong$ leg)

Reasons

1. Given.

2. If a line is tangent to a circle, it is perpendicular to the radius drawn to the point of tangency.

3. Perpendicular lines intersect and form right angles.

4. All radii of the same circle are congruent.

Proof: Statements	*Reasons*
5. $\overline{OP} \cong \overline{OP}$. (hy. $\cong$ hy.)	5. Reflexive property of equality.
6. Rt. $\triangle PQO \cong$ rt. $\triangle PRO$.	6. Hy. leg $\cong$ hy. leg.
7. $\overline{PQ} \cong \overline{PR}$.	7. Corresponding parts of congruent triangles are congruent.

- **Corollary 64-1. If two tangents are drawn to a circle from an external point, the line determined by that point and the center of the circle bisects the angle formed by the tangents.**

In the proof of Theorem 64, $\triangle PQO$ and $\triangle PRO$ were shown to be congruent. Therefore, $\angle QPO$ and $\angle RPO$ are congruent, and $\overleftrightarrow{PO}$ bisects $\angle QPR$.

A Polygon Circumscribed About a Circle

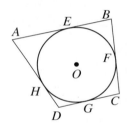

A polygon is circumscribed about a circle if each side of the polygon is tangent to the circle. When a polygon is circumscribed about a circle, the circle is inscribed in the polygon.

For example, in the accompanying diagram, $\overline{AB}$ is tangent to circle O at E, $\overline{BC}$ is tangent to circle O at F, $\overline{CD}$ is tangent to circle O at G, and $\overline{DA}$ is tangent to circle O at H. Therefore:

1. Polygon $ABCD$ is circumscribed about circle O.

2. Circle O is inscribed in polygon $ABCD$.

EXAMPLES

1. Triangle ABC is circumscribed about circle O, with D, E, and F as points of tangency for $\overleftrightarrow{AB}$, $\overleftrightarrow{BC}$, and $\overleftrightarrow{CA}$, respectively. If $AF = 6$ and $EB = 7$, find the length of $\overline{AB}$.

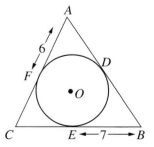

Solution   Since tangent segments drawn to a circle from an external point are congruent, then $AF = AD = 6$ and $EB = DB = 7$.

Therefore: $AB = AD + DB = 6 + 7 = 13$.

Answer: $AB = 13$

2. Point P is 9 inches from the center of a circle whose radius measures 6 inches.
    a. Find the exact length of a tangent segment from P to the circle.
    b. Express this length to the *nearest tenth* of an inch.

Solutions   Let R be a point at which a line from P is tangent to circle O. Since $\angle ORP$ is a right angle, $\triangle ORP$ is a right triangle in which $OR = 6$ and $OP = 9$.

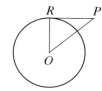

    a. Let PR = length of tangent segment from P to circle.
    By the Pythagorean Theorem:

$$(OR)^2 + (PR)^2 = (OP)^2$$
$$6^2 + (PR)^2 = 9^2$$
$$36 + (PR)^2 = 81$$
$$(PR)^2 = 45$$

Since a length is positive, $PR = \sqrt{45} = \sqrt{9 \cdot 5} = 3\sqrt{5}$.

    b. Approximate either $\sqrt{45}$ or $3\sqrt{5}$ by using a calculator. Round the display to one decimal place.

Enter: METHOD 1: | **2nd** | | $\sqrt{}$ | 45 | **ENTER** |

              METHOD 2:   3 | $\times$ | | **2nd** | | $\sqrt{}$ | 5 | **ENTER** |

Display: | 6.708203933 |

To the *nearest tenth*, this length is 6.7.

Answers: **a.** $\sqrt{45}$ inches or $3\sqrt{5}$ inches   **b.** 6.7 inches

EXERCISES WITH OPEN-RESPONSE PROBLEMS

In 1 and 2, $\triangle ABC$ is circumscribed about a circle, and D, E, and F are points of tangency.

1.

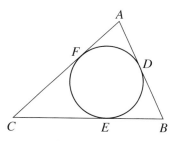

Let $AD = 5$, $EB = 5$, and $CF = 10$.
a. find lengths AB, BC, and CA.
b. Show that $\triangle ABC$ is isosceles.

2.

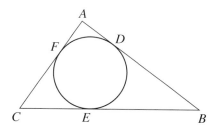

Let $AF = 10$, $CE = 20$, and $BD = 30$.
a. Find lengths AB, BC, and CA.
b. Show that $\triangle ABC$ is a right triangle.

In 3–9, $\overrightarrow{PQ}$ is tangent to circle O at P, $\overleftrightarrow{SQ}$ is tangent to circle O at S, and $\overleftrightarrow{OQ}$ intersects circle O at T and R.

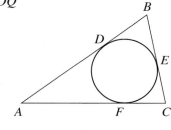

3. If $OP = 15$ and $PQ = 20$, find: **a.** OQ **b.** QS

4. If $OQ = 25$ and $PQ = 24$, find PO.

5. If $OP = 10$ and $PQ = 10$, find: **a.** QS **b.** OQ

6. If $OP = 9$ and $RQ = 6$, find: **a.** OQ **b.** PQ **c.** QS

7. If $RT = 12$ and $RQ = 4$, find: **a.** PO **b.** OQ **c.** PQ **d.** QS

Ex. 3–9

8. If $PQ = 2x - 4$, $SQ = x + 4$, and $OP = \frac{1}{2}x + 1$, find:
  a. x **b.** PQ **c.** OP **d.** OQ

9. If $PQ = 4x - 1$, $SQ = x + 11$, and $OP = 2x$, find:
  a. x **b.** PQ **c.** OP **d.** OQ

10. Triangle ABC is circumscribed about a circle, with D, E, and F as points of tangency. The perimeter of $\triangle ABC = 30$, $DB = 4$, and side $\overline{BC}$ has a length of 7.
  a. Find FC.   **b.** Find AF.   **c.** Find AD.
  d. Which best describes $\triangle ABC$?
    (1) isosceles   (2) right   (3) scalene   (4) obtuse

Ex. 10

11. Draw two *congruent* circles and the appropriate tangent lines showing a situation where the two circles have *exactly*:
  a. three common tangents
  b. four common tangents, with two internal and two external tangents
  c. two common tangents, with both tangents external

12. Line $\overleftrightarrow{RP}$ is tangent to circle O at P, and the circle bisects $\overline{OR}$ at point M. If tangent segment $\overline{RP}$ has a length of 3, find the length of a radius of circle O:
  a. in radical form
  b. to the *nearest hundredth*

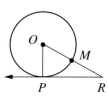

Ex. 12

13. Quadrilateral $ABCD$ is circumscribed about a circle with points of tangency E on $\overline{AB}$, F on $\overline{BC}$, G on $\overline{CD}$, and H on $\overline{DA}$. If $AE:EB = 3:1$, $AH:HD = 3:2$, F is the midpoint of $\overline{BC}$, and the perimeter of $ABCD$ is 70 millimeters, find the length of each side of the quadrilateral: AB, BC, CD, and DA.

Ex. 13

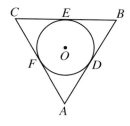

Ex. 14	Ex. 15	Ex. 16

14. *Given:* $\overleftrightarrow{PQ}$ and $\overleftrightarrow{PR}$ tangent to circle O at Q and R.
To prove: $\angle PQR \cong \angle PRQ$.

15. *Given:* $\overleftrightarrow{AC}$ and $\overleftrightarrow{BC}$ tangent to circle O at A and B.
To prove: $\overleftrightarrow{OC}$ bisects $\angle AOB$.
$\overset{\frown}{AD} \cong \overset{\frown}{BD}$.

16. *Given:* $\triangle ABC$ circumscribed about circle O with points of tangency D, E, and F; $\overline{AB} \cong \overline{AC}$.
To prove: E is the midpoint of $\overline{BC}$.

11-5 ANGLES FORMED BY TANGENTS, CHORDS, AND SECANTS

● **Theorem 65. The measure of an angle formed by a tangent and a chord intersecting at the point of tangency is equal to one-half the measure of the intercepted arc.**

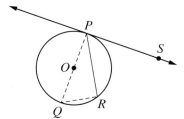

Given: Tangent $\overleftrightarrow{PS}$ intersects $\overline{PR}$ at point P on circle O.

To prove: $m\angle SPR = \frac{1}{2} m\overset{\frown}{PR}$.

Plan: The following steps outline a proof of the theorem.

1. Draw diameter $\overline{POQ}$ and chord $\overline{QR}$, forming $\triangle PQR$ with $\angle R$ a right angle.

2. Angle RQP and angle RPQ are complementary because they are the acute angles of a right triangle.

3. Since radius $\overline{OP} \perp$ tangent $\overleftrightarrow{PS}$, $\angle SPR$ and $\angle RPQ$ are complementary.

4. Because complements of the same angle are congruent, $\angle SPR \cong \angle RQP$.

5. Since $\angle RQP$ is an inscribed angle, $m\angle RQP = \frac{1}{2} m\overset{\frown}{PR}$.

6. By substitution: $m\angle SPR = \frac{1}{2} m\overset{\frown}{PR}$.

The formal proof is left to the student.

- **Theorem 66. The measure of an angle formed by two chords intersecting within a circle is equal to one-half the sum of the measures of the arcs intercepted by the angle and by its vertical angle.**

Given: Chords $\overline{AB}$ and $\overline{CD}$ intersect at E within the circle.

To prove: $m\angle AED = \frac{1}{2}(m\widehat{AD} + m\widehat{BC})$.

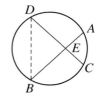

$\qquad\qquad m\angle CEB = \frac{1}{2}(m\widehat{AD} + m\widehat{BC})$.

Plan: Draw chord $\overline{BD}$, forming inscribed angles B and D.

Thus, $m\angle B = \frac{1}{2}m\widehat{AD}$, and $m\angle D = \frac{1}{2}m\widehat{BC}$.

Note that $\angle AED$ is an exterior angle of $\triangle BED$.
Therefore, $m\angle AED = m\angle B + m\angle D$

$$= \frac{1}{2}m\widehat{AD} + \frac{1}{2}m\widehat{BC}$$

$$= \frac{1}{2}(m\widehat{AD} + m\widehat{BC}).$$

Since vertical angles are congruent, $m\angle CEB = m\angle AED$.

Therefore, $m\angle CEB = \frac{1}{2}(m\widehat{AD} + m\widehat{BC})$.

Note: To prove that $m\angle CEA = m\angle BED = \frac{1}{2}(m\widehat{AC} + m\widehat{BD})$, draw $\overline{AD}$.

- **Theorem 67. The measure of an angle formed by a tangent and a secant, or two secants, or two tangents intersecting outside a circle is equal to one-half the difference of the measures of the intercepted arcs.**

(Three separate cases are involved in this theorem.)

Case 1. **An angle formed by a tangent and a secant intersecting outside the circle.**

Given: Tangent $\overleftrightarrow{PRS}$ and secant $\overleftrightarrow{PTQ}$ intersect at P outside circle O.

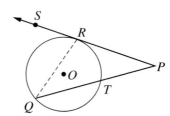

To prove: $m\angle P = \frac{1}{2}(m\widehat{RQ} - m\widehat{RT})$.

Proof:
1. Draw chord $\overline{RQ}$.
2. $m\angle P + m\angle Q = m\angle SRQ$.
3. $\qquad m\angle P = m\angle SRQ - m\angle Q$.
4. $\qquad m\angle SRQ = \frac{1}{2}m\widehat{RQ}$.
5. $\qquad m\angle Q = \frac{1}{2}m\widehat{RT}$.
6. $\qquad m\angle P = \frac{1}{2}m\widehat{RQ} - \frac{1}{2}m\widehat{RT}$.
7. $\qquad m\angle P = \frac{1}{2}(m\widehat{RQ} - m\widehat{RT})$.

Case 2. **An angle formed by two secants intersecting outside the circle.**

Given: Secants $\overline{PTR}$ and $\overline{PQS}$ intersect at P outside circle O.

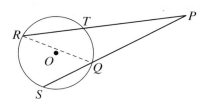

To prove: $m\angle P = \frac{1}{2}(m\widehat{RS} - m\widehat{TQ})$.

Proof:
1. Draw chord $\overline{RQ}$.
2. $m\angle P + m\angle R = m\angle RQS$.
3. $\qquad m\angle P = m\angle RQS - m\angle R$.
4. $\qquad m\angle RQS = \frac{1}{2} m\widehat{RS}$.
5. $\qquad m\angle R = \frac{1}{2} m\widehat{TQ}$.
6. $\qquad m\angle P = \frac{1}{2} m\widehat{RS} - \frac{1}{2} m\widehat{TQ}$.
7. $\qquad m\angle P = \frac{1}{2}(m\widehat{RS} - m\widehat{TQ})$.

Case 3. **An angle formed by two tangents intersecting outside the circle.** (Note that the intercepted arcs are a major arc and a minor arc having common endpoints.)

Given: Tangents $\overleftrightarrow{PRS}$ and $\overleftrightarrow{PQ}$ intersect at P outside circle O.

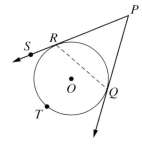

To prove: $m\angle P = \frac{1}{2}(m\widehat{RTQ} - m\widehat{RQ})$.

Proof:
1. Draw chord $\overline{RQ}$.
2. $m\angle P + m\angle PQR = m\angle SRQ$.
3. $\qquad m\angle P = m\angle SRQ - m\angle PQR$.
4. $\qquad m\angle SRQ = \frac{1}{2} m\widehat{RTQ}$.
5. $\qquad m\angle PQR = \frac{1}{2} m\widehat{RQ}$.
6. $\qquad m\angle P = \frac{1}{2} m\widehat{RTQ} - \frac{1}{2} m\widehat{RQ}$.
7. $\qquad m\angle P = \frac{1}{2}(m\widehat{RTQ} - m\widehat{RQ})$.

In each of the three cases shown above, the steps of a proof are given. A full and complete formal proof of Theorem 67 is shown when each of these steps is accompanied by the appropriate reason.

A formal proof may also be written in paragraph form provided that appropriate reasons accompany the logical presentation of the proof.

EXAMPLES

1. A tangent and a secant are drawn to circle O from an external point P. The tangent intersects the circle at Q, and the secant at R and S.
If $\text{m}\widehat{QR}:\text{m}\widehat{RS}:\text{m}\widehat{SQ} = 2:3:4$, find:
a. $\text{m}\widehat{QR}$ **b.** $\text{m}\widehat{RS}$ **c.** $\text{m}\widehat{SQ}$ **d.** $\text{m}\angle P$ **e.** $\text{m}\angle PQR$ **f.** $\text{m}\angle PRQ$

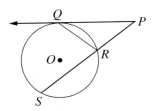

Solutions **a.** Let $\text{m}\widehat{QR} = 2x$, $\text{m}\widehat{RS} = 3x$, $\text{m}\widehat{SQ} = 4x$.

$$2x + 3x + 4x = 360$$
$$9x = 360$$
$$x = 40$$

Then $\text{m}\widehat{QR} = 2x = 80$

b. $\text{m}\widehat{RS} = 3x = 120$

c. $\text{m}\widehat{SQ} = 4x = 160$

d. $\text{m}\angle P = \frac{1}{2}(\text{m}\widehat{SQ} - \text{m}\widehat{QR})$ | **e.** $\text{m}\angle PQR = \frac{1}{2}\text{m}\widehat{QR}$

$\qquad = \frac{1}{2}(160 - 80)$ | $\qquad = \frac{1}{2}(80)$

$\qquad = \frac{1}{2}(80) = 40$ | $\qquad = 40$

f. Two approaches are shown below to find $\text{m}\angle PRQ$.

$\text{m}\angle PRQ = 180 - (\text{m}\angle P + \text{m}\angle PQR)$ | $\text{m}\angle PRQ = 180 - \text{m}\angle QRS$
$\qquad = 180 - (40 + 40)$ | $\qquad = 180 - \frac{1}{2}\text{m}\widehat{SQ}$
$\qquad = 180 - 80$ | $\qquad = 180 - \frac{1}{2}(160)$
$\qquad = 100$ | $\qquad = 180 - 80$
     | $\qquad = 100$

Note: In part **f**, the measure of $\angle PRQ$, an angle formed by a secant and a chord, is *not* equal to one-half the intercepted arc.

Answers: **a.** $\text{m}\widehat{QR} = 80$ **b.** $\text{m}\widehat{RS} = 120$ **c.** $\text{m}\widehat{SQ} = 160$
$\qquad$ **d.** $\text{m}\angle P = 40$ **e.** $\text{m}\angle PQR = 40$ **f.** $\text{m}\angle PRQ = 100$

2. Two tangents are drawn to a circle from an external point R such that $m\angle R = 70$. Find the degree measures of the major arc and the minor arc into which the circle is divided by the points of tangency.

Solution   If P and Q are the points of tangency, and S is any point on the major arc, then

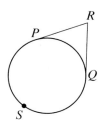

$$\text{Let } x = m\widehat{PQ}$$

$$360 - x = m\widehat{PSQ}$$

Solve: $m\angle R = \frac{1}{2}(m\widehat{PSQ} - m\widehat{PQ})$

$$70 = \frac{1}{2}(360 - x - x)$$

$$70 = \frac{1}{2}(360 - 2x)$$

$$70 = 180 - x$$

$$x = 110$$

Then $360 - x = 360 - 110 = 250$

Answer: Degree measure of minor arc is 110.
Degree measure of major arc is 250.

EXERCISES WITH OPEN-RESPONSE PROBLEMS

In 1–6, secants $\overleftrightarrow{SQP}$ and $\overleftrightarrow{TRP}$ intersect at P.

1. If $m\widehat{ST} = 200$ and $m\widehat{QR} = 100$, find $m\angle P$.
2. If $m\widehat{ST} = 150$ and $m\widehat{QR} = 70$, find $m\angle P$.
3. If $m\widehat{ST} = 100$ and $m\widehat{QR} = 10$, find $m\angle P$.
4. If $m\widehat{ST} = 210$ and $m\angle P = 50$, find $m\widehat{QR}$.
5. If $m\widehat{ST} = 185$ and $m\angle P = 80$, find $m\widehat{QR}$.
6. If $m\angle P = 10$ and $m\widehat{QR} = 10$, find $m\widehat{ST}$.

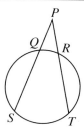

Ex. 1–6

In 7–12, tangent $\overleftrightarrow{PQ}$ and secant $\overleftrightarrow{PRT}$ intersect at P.

7. If $m\widehat{QT} = 90$ and $m\widehat{QR} = 30$, find $m\angle P$.
8. If $m\widehat{QT} = 112$ and $m\widehat{QR} = 75$, find $m\angle P$.
9. If $m\widehat{QT} = 88$ and $m\widehat{QR} = 10$, find $m\angle P$.
10. If $m\widehat{QT} = 200$ and $m\angle P = 80$, find $m\widehat{QR}$.
11. If $m\widehat{QT} = 150$ and $m\angle P = 25$, find $m\widehat{QR}$.
12. If $m\angle P = 45$ and $m\widehat{QR} = 90$, find $m\widehat{QT}$.

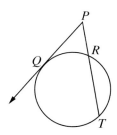

Ex. 7–12

In 13–18, tangents $\overleftrightarrow{PQ}$ and $\overleftrightarrow{PR}$ intersect at P; point S is on major arc $\overarc{QR}$.

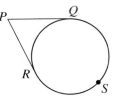

13. If $m\overarc{QSR} = 200$, find $m\angle P$.
14. If $m\overarc{QSR} = 300$, find $m\angle P$.
15. If $m\overarc{QR} = 110$, find $m\angle P$.
16. If $m\overarc{QR} = 150$, find $m\angle P$.
17. If $m\angle P = 90$, find $m\overarc{QR}$.
18. If $m\angle P = 75$, find $m\overarc{QSR}$.

Ex. 13–18

In 19–24, chords $\overline{AB}$ and $\overline{CD}$ of the circle intersect at E.

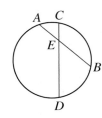

19. If $m\overarc{AC} = 20$ and $m\overarc{BD} = 100$, find $m\angle AEC$.
20. If $m\overarc{CB} = 120$ and $m\overarc{AD} = 180$, find $m\angle AED$.
21. If $m\overarc{AC} = 27$ and $m\overarc{DB} = 81$, find $m\angle DEB$.
22. If $m\overarc{AC} = 30$ and $m\angle AEC = 55$, find $m\overarc{BD}$.
23. If $m\overarc{BD} = 75$ and $m\angle DEB = 60$, find $m\overarc{AC}$.
24. If $m\angle AED = 100$ and $m\overarc{CB}:m\overarc{DA} = 3:5$, find:
    a. $m\overarc{CB}$ **b.** $m\overarc{DA}$

Ex. 19–24

25. Two tangent segments $\overline{PA}$ and $\overline{PB}$ are drawn to circle O from an external point P. If the degree measure of major arc $\overarc{AB}$ is 220, find $m\angle APB$.
26. Two tangent segments $\overline{PA}$ and $\overline{PB}$ are drawn to circle O from external point P. If the degree measure of major arc $\overarc{AB}$ is twice the degree measure of minor arc $\overarc{AB}$, find $m\angle APB$.

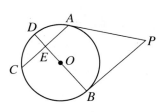

Ex. 27   **Ex. 28**   **Ex. 29**

27. In the diagram, $\overleftrightarrow{PA}$ is tangent to circle O at A, and secant $\overleftrightarrow{PBC}$ intersects circle O at B and C. Chord $\overline{AD}$ intersects chord $\overline{BC}$ at E, $\overline{AB}$ and $\overline{CD}$ are chords, $m\overarc{AC} = 70$, $m\angle P = 15$, and $m\overarc{CD}:m\overarc{BD} = 3:2$. Find:
    a. $m\overarc{AB}$ **b.** $m\overarc{BD}$ **c.** $m\overarc{CD}$ **d.** $m\angle PAB$
    e. $m\angle BCD$ **f.** $m\angle CED$ **g.** $m\angle ABP$ **h.** $m\angle PAD$

28. In the diagram, $\overline{AOB}$ is a diameter of circle O, $\overleftrightarrow{CB}$ is tangent to the circle at B, $\overleftrightarrow{EADC}$ and $\overleftrightarrow{EFB}$ are secants, $\overline{OD}$ is a radius, $m\overarc{AD} = 100$, and $m\angle ABF = 20$. Find:
    a. $m\angle AOD$ **b.** $m\angle CAB$ **c.** $m\overarc{AF}$ **d.** $m\angle E$
    e. $m\angle EAB$ **f.** $m\angle C$ **g.** $m\angle ABC$ **h.** $m\angle CDO$

29. In the diagram, $\overleftrightarrow{PA}$ and $\overleftrightarrow{PB}$ are tangent to circle O at A and B. Diameter $\overline{BD}$ and chord $\overline{AC}$ intersect at E, $m\overarc{CB} = 120$, and $m\angle P = 50$. Find:
    a. $m\overarc{AB}$ **b.** $m\overarc{AD}$ **c.** $m\overarc{CD}$ **d.** $m\angle DEC$ **e.** $m\angle PBD$ **f.** $m\angle PAC$

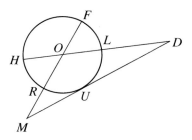

| **Ex. 30** | **Ex. 31** | **Ex. 32** |

30. In the diagram $\overleftrightarrow{PA}$ is tangent to circle O at A and $\overleftrightarrow{PC}$ intersects circle O at D and C. Chord $\overline{CA}$ is drawn, chords $\overline{BA}$ and $\overline{CD}$ intersect at E, m$\widehat{BC}$ = 45, m$\angle BEC$ = 65, m$\widehat{BD}$ = x, and m$\widehat{CA}$ = $2x + 20$. Find:

a. m$\widehat{DA}$ **b.** m$\widehat{BD}$ **c.** m$\angle CPA$ **d.** m$\angle BAC$ **e.** m$\angle BAP$ **f.** m$\angle PCA$

31. In the diagram, $\overleftrightarrow{PA}$ is tangent to circle O at A, $\overleftrightarrow{PBC}$ is a secant, $\overline{AB}$ and $\overline{CA}$ are chords, m$\angle P$ = 40, and m$\widehat{AC}$:m$\widehat{AB}$ = 7:3. Find:

a. m$\widehat{AC}$ **b.** m$\widehat{BC}$ **c.** m$\angle ACB$ **d.** m$\angle ABC$ **e.** m$\angle PAB$ **f.** m$\angle ABP$

32. In the diagram, $\overleftrightarrow{MUD}$ is tangent to circle O at U, secants $\overleftrightarrow{HOLD}$ and $\overleftrightarrow{FORM}$ intersect at O, and m$\widehat{RU}$ = m$\widehat{UL}$ = 65. Find:

a. m$\widehat{HR}$ **b.** m$\widehat{FL}$ **c.** m$\angle FOL$ **d.** m$\angle LOR$ **e.** m$\angle FMD$ **f.** m$\angle HDM$

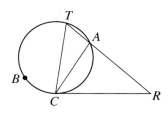

| **Ex. 33** | **Ex. 34** | **Ex. 35** |

33. In the diagram, $\overleftrightarrow{BUS}$ is tangent to circle O at U, secant $\overleftrightarrow{BAN}$ intersects diameter $\overline{TOE}$ at R, $\overleftrightarrow{ET}$ intersects $\overleftrightarrow{BUS}$ at S, m$\widehat{EN}$ = 60, m$\widehat{EA}$ = 40, and m$\widehat{AU}$:m$\widehat{UT}$ = 4:3. Find:

a. m$\widehat{NT}$ **b.** m$\angle ERA$ **c.** m$\widehat{AU}$ **d.** m$\widehat{UT}$

e. m$\angle ERN$ **f.** m$\angle BSE$ **g.** m$\angle NBS$ **h.** m$\angle SRB$

34. In the diagram, $\overrightarrow{PRY}$ and $\overrightarrow{PCB}$ are tangents to circle O at R and C, respectively. Diameter $\overline{COIN}$ and chord $\overline{RIM}$ intersect at point I, m$\widehat{NM}$ = 50, and m$\angle P$ = 40. Find:

a. m$\widehat{MC}$ **b.** m$\widehat{RC}$ **c.** m$\widehat{NR}$ **d.** m$\angle RIC$

e. m$\angle RIN$ **f.** m$\angle OCB$ **g.** m$\angle MRY$ **h.** m$\angle MRP$

35. In the diagram, tangent $\overleftrightarrow{RC}$ intersects the circle at C, secant $\overleftrightarrow{RAT}$ intersects the circle at A and T, $\overline{AC}$ and $\overline{TC}$ are chords, $\widehat{CBT}$ is a major arc, and m$\widehat{TA}$:m$\widehat{AC}$:m$\widehat{CBT}$ = 1:3:5. Find:

a. m$\widehat{TA}$ **b.** m$\widehat{AC}$ **c.** m$\widehat{CBT}$ **d.** m$\angle CTA$

e. m$\angle ACR$ **f.** m$\angle CRT$ **g.** m$\angle ACT$ **h.** m$\angle CAR$

In 36–41, secants $\overleftrightarrow{PAB}$ and $\overleftrightarrow{PCD}$ are drawn to circle O from P. Chords $\overline{BC}$ and $\overline{AD}$ intersect at E. Line $\overleftrightarrow{GF}$ is tangent to the circle at D, $\overline{BOC}$ is a diameter, $\overline{OD}$ is a radius, and $\overline{BD}$ is a chord.

36. Express each of the following in terms of the degree measures of intercepted arcs:
   a. m∠COD   **b.** m∠ABC   **c.** m∠BEA
   d. m∠P   **e.** m∠CDF

37. Name an angle congruent to each of the following:
   a. ∠ABC   **b.** ∠BAD   **c.** ∠CED
   d. ∠CDB   **e.** ∠PAD

38. If m$\widehat{AB}$ = 140, find m∠ABC.

39. If m$\widehat{BD}$ = 80 and m$\widehat{AC}$ = 30, find:
   a. m∠P   **b.** m∠AEC   **c.** m∠COD   **d.** m∠CDF   **e.** m∠BOD

40. If m$\widehat{BD}$ = m$\widehat{CD}$ and m$\widehat{BA}$:m$\widehat{AC}$ = 4:1, find:
   a. m$\widehat{BD}$ **b.** m$\widehat{AC}$ **c.** m$\widehat{AB}$ **d.** m∠P   **e.** m∠ADF
   f. m∠AEB   **g.** m∠ADC   **h.** m∠PAD   **i.** m∠ADO   **j.** m∠ODB

41. If m∠AEB = 130 and m$\widehat{AB}$ = 150, find:
   a. m$\widehat{CD}$ **b.** m$\widehat{AC}$ **c.** m$\widehat{BD}$ **d.** m∠COD   **e.** m∠BCD
   f. m∠P   **g.** m∠CDA   **h.** m∠PAD   **i.** m∠CDF   **j.** m∠BDC

Ex. 36–41

11-6 MEASURES OF CHORDS, TANGENT SEGMENTS, AND SECANT SEGMENTS

We have been using theorems to establish the relationships between the measures of angles of a circle and the measures of the intercepted arcs. Now we will study the measures of line segments related to the circle. To do this, we will need to use similar triangles. We have learned that two polygons are similar if there is a one-to-one correspondence between vertices such that:

1. all pairs of corresponding angles are congruent; and

2. the ratios of the lengths of all pairs of corresponding sides are equal.

As a result of this definition, we know that the following statement is true:

● **Corresponding sides of similar triangles are in proportion.**

The most commonly used method of proving that two triangles are similar is the following theorem:

● **Two triangles are similar if two angles of one triangle are congruent to two angles of the other.**

We use statements about similar triangles to prove the following theorem:

- **Theorem 68. If two chords intersect within a circle, the product of the measures of the segments of one chord equals the product of the measures of the segments of the other.**

Given: Chords $\overline{AB}$ and $\overline{CD}$ intersect at E, an interior point of circle O.

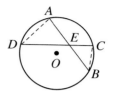

To prove: $(AE)(EB) = (CE)(ED)$.

Plan: Draw $\overline{AD}$ and $\overline{BC}$.
Prove $\triangle AED \sim \triangle CEB$ by a.a. $\cong$ a.a.

Proof:

Statements	Reasons
1. Draw $\overline{AD}$ and $\overline{BC}$.	1. Two points determine a line.
2. $\angle A \cong \angle C$. (a. $\cong$ a.)	2. Inscribed angles of a circle that intercept the same arc are congruent.
3. $\angle D \cong \angle B$. (a. $\cong$ a.)	3. Reason 2.
4. $\triangle AED \sim \triangle CEB$.	4. a.a. $\cong$ a.a.
5. $\frac{AE}{ED} = \frac{CE}{EB}$.	5. Corresponding sides of similar triangles are in proportion.
6. $(AE)(EB) = (CE)(ED)$.	6. In a proportion, the product of the means is equal to the product of the extremes.

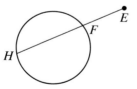

Does a similar relationship exist for two secants intersecting outside the circle? First let us identify the segments formed when a secant line intersects a circle. In the diagram, $\overleftrightarrow{EH}$ intersects the circle in points F and H, forming three segments:

1. $\overline{FH}$ is a *chord* of the circle because its endpoints are points on the circle.
2. $\overline{EF}$ is called an ***external segment of the secant*** because it is a line segment whose endpoints are an external point, E, and a point on the circle, F, *nearer* to the external point than any other point of chord $\overline{FH}$.
3. $\overline{EH}$ is called a ***secant segment*** because it is a line segment whose endpoints are an external point, E, and a point on the circle, H, *farther* from the external point than any other point of chord $\overline{FH}$. The secant segment is the sum of the chord, $\overline{FH}$, and the external segment, EF, of the secant.

Secant segments are involved in the next two theorems. In Theorem 69, a secant and a tangent intersect outside the circle and, in Theorem 70, two secants intersect outside the circle.

- **Theorem 69. If a tangent and a secant are drawn to a circle from an external point, then the square of the measure of the tangent segment is equal to the product of the measures of the secant segment and its external segment.**

Given: Tangent $\overline{PA}$ and secant $\overline{PBC}$ intersect at P, outside a circle.

To prove: $(PA)^2 = (PC)(PB)$.

Plan: Draw $\overline{AC}$ and $\overline{AB}$.
Prove $\triangle PAB \sim \triangle PCA$ by a.a. $\cong$ a.a.

Proof: Statements

1. Draw $\overline{AC}$ and $\overline{AB}$.	1. Two points determine a line.
2. $m\angle PAB = \frac{1}{2} m\overset{\frown}{AB}$.	2. The measure of an angle formed by a tangent and a chord intersecting at the point of tangency is equal to one-half the measure of the intercepted arc.
3. $m\angle C = \frac{1}{2} m\overset{\frown}{AB}$.	3. The measure of an inscribed angle of a circle is equal to one-half the measure of its intercepted arc.
4. $m\angle PAB = m\angle C$.	4. Transitive property of equality.
5. $\angle PAB \cong \angle C$.	5. Two angles are congruent if they have the same measure.
6. $\angle P \cong \angle P$.	6. Reflexive property of congruence.
7. $\triangle PAB \sim \triangle PCA$.	7. a.a. $\cong$ a.a.
8. $\frac{PB}{PA} = \frac{PA}{PC}$.	8. Corresponding sides of similar triangles are in proportion.
9. $(PA)^2 = (PC)(PB)$.	9. In a proportion, the product of the means equals the product of the extremes.

Reasons (column header)

Note: If two means of a proportion are equal, then either mean is called the *mean proportional* between the remaining two terms of the proportion. For example, in $\frac{2}{6} = \frac{6}{18}$, and in $(6)^2 = (2)(18)$, 6 is the mean proportional between 2 and 18. Therefore, Theorem 69 may be restated as follows:

- **If a tangent and a secant are drawn to a circle from an external point, then the measure of the tangent segment is the mean proportional between the measures of the secant segment and its external segment.**

● **Theorem 70. If two secants intersect outside a circle, then the product of the measures of one secant segment and its external segment is equal to the product of the measures of the other secant segment and its external segment.**

Given: Secants $\overline{ABC}$ and $\overline{ADE}$ intersect at A, outside a circle.

To prove: $(AC)(AB) = (AE)(AD)$.

Plan: Draw $\overline{BE}$ and $\overline{CD}$. Since $\angle C \cong \angle E$, and $\angle A \cong \angle A$, it follows by a.a. $\cong$ a.a. that $\triangle ACD \sim \triangle AEB$.

Thus, $\frac{AC}{AD} = \frac{AE}{AB}$, or

$(AC)(AB) = (AE)(AD)$.

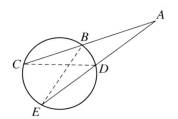

The formal proof is left to the student.

EXAMPLES

1. In the accompanying diagram, $\overleftrightarrow{PC}$ is tangent to the circle at C, and $\overleftrightarrow{PAB}$ is a secant with $PA = 2$ and $AB = 3$.
  a. Find the exact length of $\overline{PC}$.
  b. Find PC to the *nearest hundredth*.

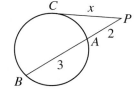

Solutions   **a.** (1) Identify the needed measures.
      For the secant, its external segment $PA = 2$.
      The secant segment $PB = PA + AB = 2 + 3 = 5$.
      Let the tangent segment $PC = x$.
    (2) Since a tangent and a secant are drawn to a circle
      from an external point, it follows that: $(PC)^2 = (PA)(PB)$
    (3) Substitute values and solve the equation: $(x)^2 = (2)(5)$
                              $x^2 = 10$
                              $x = \pm\sqrt{10}$
      Since a length is positive: $PC = \sqrt{10}$

  b. Use a calculator to find a rational approximation for $\sqrt{10}$.

    Enter: [**2nd**] [$\sqrt{}$] 10 [**ENTER**]

    Display: [3.16227766]

    Round the display value to two decimal places: 3.16.

  Answers: **a.** $PC = \sqrt{10}$ **b.** $PC \approx 3.16$

2. Chords $\overline{AB}$ and $\overline{CD}$ intersect in a circle at point E. If $AE = 6$, $EB = 10$, and $ED = 12$, find CE.

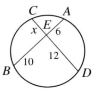

Solution (1) As an aid, draw and label the chords in a circle, as shown at the right.

Let $CE = x$.

(2) The product of the measures of the segments of one chord equals the product of the measures of the segments of the other:

$(CE)(ED) = (AE)(EB)$

(3) Substitute values and solve the equation:

$(x)(12) = (6)(10)$

$12x = 60$

$x = 5$

Answer: $CE = 5$

---

3. Find the length of a chord 3 centimeters from the center of a circle whose radius measures 5 centimeters.

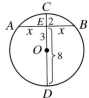

Solution (1) Draw and label chords in the circle, and identify the needed measures. Since the distance from the center of the circle to chord $\overline{AB}$ is shown by $OE = 3$, then:

$CE = OC - OE = 5 - 3 = 2$

$ED = EO + OD = 3 + 5 = 8$

Also, since a diameter that is perpendicular to a chord bisects the chord, let:

$AE = x$ and $EB = x$

(2) For two chords that intersect within a circle, the product of the measures of the segments of one chord equals the product of the measures of the segments of the other:

$(AE)(EB) = (CE)(ED)$

(3) Substitute values and solve the equation:

$(x)(x) = (2)(8)$

$x^2 = 16$

$x = \pm 4$

Since a length is positive:

$AB = AE + EB = 4 + 4 = 8$

Answer: The length of the chord is 8 centimeters.

Note: An alternative solution to this problem is found in Section 11-2; see Example 1.

4. From point P, secants $\overleftrightarrow{PAB}$ and $\overleftrightarrow{PCD}$ are drawn to a circle. If $PA = 2$, $AB = 4$, and $CD = 3$, find the length of secant segment PD to the *nearest tenth*.

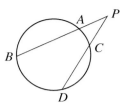

Solution   (1) Identify the needed measures.

For $\overleftrightarrow{PAB}$:   external segment $PA = 2$
   secant segment $PB = PA + AB = 2 + 4 = 6$

For $\overleftrightarrow{PCD}$:   external segment $PC = x$
   secant segment $PD = PC + CD = x + 3$

(2) The product of the measures of one secant segment and its external segment equals the product of the measures of the other secant segment and its external segment:

$$(PD)(PC) = (PB)(PA)$$

(3) Substitute values and simplify:

$$(x + 3)(x) = (6)(2)$$
$$x^2 + 3x = 12$$
$$x^2 + 3x - 12 = 0$$

(4) Solve the second-degree equation by using the quadratic formula:

$$x = \frac{-b \pm \sqrt{b^2 - 4ac}}{2a} \quad [a = 1, b = 3, c = -12]$$

$$= \frac{-(3) \pm \sqrt{(3)^2 - 4(1)(-12)}}{2(1)}$$

$$= \frac{-3 \pm \sqrt{9 + 48}}{2} = \frac{-3 \pm \sqrt{57}}{2}$$

(5) Since a length is positive, reject the negative root, $\dfrac{-3 - \sqrt{57}}{2}$. Approximate the value of $\dfrac{-3 + \sqrt{57}}{2}$ using a calculator.

Enter: $\boxed{(}$ $\boxed{(-)}$ 3 $\boxed{+}$ $\boxed{\text{2nd}}$ $\boxed{\sqrt{}}$ 57 $\boxed{)}$ $\boxed{)}$ $\boxed{\div}$ 2 $\boxed{\text{ENTER}}$

Display: $\boxed{2.274917218}$

(6) Substitute to find the length of $\overline{PD}$:

$$PD = x + 3$$
$$= 2.274917218 + 3$$
$$= 5.274917218$$

(7) Round to the nearest tenth:

$$\approx 5.3$$

Answer: The length of secant segment PD, to the *nearest tenth*, is 5.3.

EXERCISES WITH OPEN-RESPONSE PROBLEMS

(Unless otherwise noted, lengths that are irrational should be left in simplest radical form.)

In 1–15, chords $\overline{AB}$ and $\overline{CD}$ intersect at E.

1. If $CE = 12$, $ED = 2$, and $AE = 3$, find EB.
2. If $CE = 18$, $ED = 2$, and $BE = 6$, find AE.
3. If $AE = 5$, $EB = 7$, and $CE = 10$, find ED.
4. If $CE = 18$, $ED = 6$, and $AE = 4$, find EB.
5. If $AB = 9$, $EA = 4$, and $CE = 2$, find ED.
6. If $AB = 16$, $BE = 3$, and $CE = 9$, find ED.
7. If $AE = 9$, $EB = 16$, and $CE = ED$, find CE.
8. If $CE = 5$, $ED = 10$, and $AE = EB$, find AE.
9. If $EB = 8$, $ED = 10$, and AE is 1 more than CE, find CE.
10. If $AE = 3$, $CE = 5$, and ED is 4 less than EB, find EB.
11. If $CE = 7$, $ED = 8$, and EB is 1 more than AE, find AE.
12. If $AE = 1$, $EB = 7$, and $CE = ED$, find ED.
13. If $AB = 12$, $AE = 5$, and $CE = ED$, find CE.
14. If $CD = 10$, $CE = 4$, and EB is 5 more than AE, find AE.
15. If $AE = 6.4$, $EB = 2.5$, and CE is 8 times ED, find ED.

Ex. 1–15

16. Chords $\overline{CD}$ and $\overline{JK}$ intersect at point E within a circle. If $CE = 10$, $ED = 6$, and $JE = 4$, find EK.

17. Chords $\overline{AB}$ and $\overline{CD}$ intersect at point E within a circle; $AE = 9$ and $EB = 1$.
   a. If $CD = 6$ and $CE = x$, what expression represents ED in terms of x?
   b. Find CE.   c. Find ED.

18. If chords $\overline{AB}$ and $\overline{RS}$ intersect at point E within a circle so that $AE = 4$, $EB = 9$, and $RE:ES = 3:4$, find: a. RE b. ES c. RS

In 19–28, $\overleftrightarrow{AF}$ is tangent to the circle at F, and secant $\overleftrightarrow{ABC}$ intersects the circle at B and C.

19. If $AF = 8$ and $AB = 4$, find AC.   20. If $AC = 12$ and $AB = 3$, find AF.
21. If $AB = 3$ and $AC = 10$, find AF.   22. If $AF = 6$ and $AC = 8$, find AB.
23. If $AB = 2$ and $BC = 6$, find AF.   24. If $AB = 4$ and $BC = 21$, find AF.
25. If $AC:AB = 4:1$ and $AF = 12$, find AB.
26. If $AB:BC = 1:3$ and $AF = 7$, find AB.
27. If $AF = 10$ and $BC = 15$, find AB.
28. If $AC = 3$ and $BC = 1$, find AF.

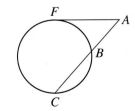

Ex. 19–28

29. From an external point P, $\overleftrightarrow{PT}$ is tangent to a circle at T, and secant $\overleftrightarrow{PDE}$ intersects the circle at D and E. If PD is 2 more than DE, and $PT = 12$, find: a. DE b. PD c. PE

In 30–39, secants $\overleftrightarrow{ABC}$ and $\overleftrightarrow{ADE}$ intersect at point A outside the circle.

30. If $AC = 15$, $AB = 6$, and $AE = 10$, find AD.
31. If $AC = 20$, $AB = 5$, and $AD = 4$, find AE.
32. If $AB = 9$, $BC = 11$, and $AD = 10$, find AE.
33. If $AB = 3$, $BC = 7$, and $AD = 5$, find DE.
34. If $AB = 2$, $AD = 3$, and $DE = 6$, find BC.
35. If $AB = BC = 4$, and $AD = 5$, find AE.
36. If $AC = 18$, $AB = 4$, and $ED = 1$, find AD.
37. If $AD = 6$, $AE = 16$, and $AC = 12$, find: **a.** AB **b.** BC
38. If $AD = 3$, $AE = 8$, and $AB = BC$, find: **a.** AB **b.** AC
39. If $AD = 6$, $DE = 4$, and BC is 2 more than AB, find: **a.** AB **b.** BC

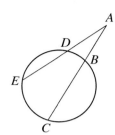

Ex. 30–39

40. In a circle, diameter $\overline{AB}$ is extended through B to an external point P, and tangent segment $\overline{PC}$ is drawn to point C on the circle. If $BP = 4$ and $PC = 6$, find the length of $\overline{AB}$.

41. Secant $\overleftrightarrow{ABC}$ and tangent $\overleftrightarrow{AD}$ intersect at A outside the circle, while B, C, and D are points on the circle. If $AB = 6$ and $BC = 9$, find:
   a. the exact length of the tangent segment, $\overline{AD}$
   b. AD to the *nearest hundredth*

42. In the diagram, tangent $\overleftrightarrow{PA}$ and secant $\overleftrightarrow{PBC}$ are drawn to circle O from point P. Chord $\overline{DE}$ bisects chord $\overline{BC}$ at M, $PA = 4$, $PB = 2$, and $DE = 10$. Find:
   a. PC **b.** BC **c.** CM **d.** DM, where $DM > ME$

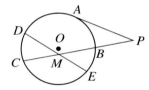

Ex. 42

43. From point P, secants $\overleftrightarrow{PAB}$ and $\overleftrightarrow{PCD}$ are drawn to a circle so that A, B, C, and D are points on the circle. If $PA = 1$, $AB = 3$, and $CD = 2$, find the length of $\overline{PD}$ to the *nearest thousandth*.

44. From point P outside a circle, tangent $\overleftrightarrow{PT}$ and secant $\overleftrightarrow{PRS}$ are drawn so that R, S, and T are on the circle. If chord $RS = 5$ and $PT = 3$, find the length of $\overline{PS}$ to the *nearest hundredth*.

45. In the diagram, secants $\overleftrightarrow{PAB}$ and $\overleftrightarrow{PCD}$ are drawn to a circle from P. Chords $\overline{AD}$ and $\overline{BC}$ intersect at E, with $BE > EC$. If $PA = 14$, $AB = 10$, $PC = 16$, $AE = 4$, $ED = 4$, and $BC = 10$, find:
   a. CD **b.** PD **c.** CE **d.** EB

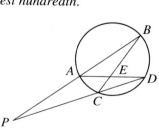

Ex. 45

46. From point P outside a circle, tangent $\overleftrightarrow{PC}$ and secant $\overleftrightarrow{PAB}$ are drawn so that A, B, and C are points on the circle. Chord $\overline{CD}$ is drawn to intersect chord $\overline{AB}$ at E. If $PA = 2$, $AE = 3$, $EB = 4$, and $CE:ED = 2:1$, find:
   a. the exact length of   *(1)* PC *(2)* ED *(3)* CE
   b. the length, to the *nearest tenth*, of   *(1)* PC *(2)* ED *(3)* CE

47. Chord $\overline{AB}$ is 2 inches from the center of circle O. If the radius of circle O is 6 inches, find:
   a. the exact length of $\overline{AB}$ **b.** AB to the *nearest thousandth* of an inch

CHAPTER SUMMARY

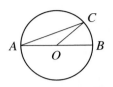

Radii: $\overline{OA}, \overline{OB}, \overline{OC}$
Diameter: $\overline{AB}$
Chords: $\overline{AC}, \overline{AB}$

A *circle* is a set of points in a plane such that the points are equidistant from a fixed point called the center.

A *radius* (plural, *radii*) is a line segment from the center of the circle to any point on the circle. A *chord* of a circle is a line segment whose endpoints are points of the circle. A *diameter* of a circle is a chord that has the center of the circle as one of its points. In a circle, the length of a diameter, d, is twice the length of a radius, r, or $d = 2r$.

A *tangent* is a line in the plane that intersects the circle in exactly one point. A *tangent segment* is a segment of the tangent, one of whose endpoints is the point of tangency.

A *secant* is a line that intersects the circle in two points. A *secant segment* has as endpoints a point external to the circle and the point *farthest* from the external point at which the secant intersects the circle. An *external segment* of a secant has as endpoints the point external to the circle and the point *nearest* the external point at which the secant intersects the circle.

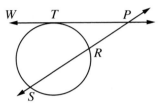

Tangent: $\overleftrightarrow{PTW}$
Tangent segment: $\overline{PT}$
Secant: $\overleftrightarrow{PRS}$
Secant segment: $\overline{PS}$
External segment of secant: $\overline{PR}$

In a circle, the measures of angles are related to the measures of intercepted arcs.

1. A *central angle* has its vertex at the center of the circle. The measure of a central angle equals the degree measure of its intercepted arc.

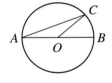

$$m\angle COB = m\widehat{CB}$$

2. An *inscribed angle* is an angle whose vertex is on the circle and whose sides contain chords of the circle; its measure is equal to one-half the degree measure of its intercepted arc.

$$m\angle CAB = \tfrac{1}{2}\, m\widehat{CB}$$

3. An angle formed by two chords intersecting within a circle is equal in measure to one-half the sum of the degree measures of their intercepted arcs.

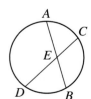

$$m\angle AEC = \tfrac{1}{2}\,(m\widehat{AC} + m\widehat{DB})$$

$$m\angle AED = \tfrac{1}{2}\,(m\widehat{AD} + m\widehat{CB})$$

4. An angle formed by a tangent and a chord is equal in measure to one-half the degree measure of its intercepted arc.

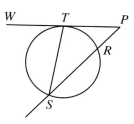

$$m\angle WTS = \tfrac{1}{2}\,m\widehat{ST}$$

5. An angle formed by a tangent and a secant (or by any two tangents or by two secants) intersecting outside the circle is equal in measure to one-half the difference of the degree measures of their intercepted arcs.

$$m\angle P = \tfrac{1}{2}\,(m\widehat{ST} - m\widehat{RT})$$

Relationships also exist between the measures of line segments associated with a circle.

1. Chords intersecting within a circle	2. Secants intersecting outside a circle	3. Tangent and secant intersecting outside a circle
		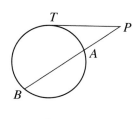
$(AE)(EB) = (CE)(ED)$	$(PD)(PC) = (PB)(PA)$	$(PT)^2 = (PB)(PA)$

VOCABULARY

11-1	Circle Radius Angle Vertex Central angle Arc	
	Minor arc Major arc Semicircle Intercepted arc Quadrant	
	Degree measure of an arc Congruent circles Congruent arcs	
11-2	Chord Diameter	
11-3	Inscribed angle	
11-4	Tangent Secant Common tangent Common internal tangent	
	Common external tangent Tangent segment	
11-6	External segment of the secant Secant segment	

REVIEW EXERCISES WITH OPEN-RESPONSE PROBLEMS

1. In circle O, $\overline{AOB}$ is a diameter, $\overline{OC}$ is a radius, and m$\angle AOC = 140$.
   Find: **a.** m$\widehat{AC}$ **b.** m$\widehat{BC}$ **c.** m$\widehat{BAC}$

2. In circle O, $\overline{AOB}$ is a diameter, $\overline{OC}$ is a radius, $AB = 3x - 1$, and $OC = 2x - 3$.
   Find: **a.** x **b.** OC **c.** AB **d.** m$\widehat{ACB}$

Ex. 1 and 2

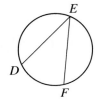

Ex. 3

3. In a circle, chord $\overline{DE} \cong$ chord $\overline{FE}$, and m$\widehat{DF} = 80$.
   Find: **a.** m$\angle DEF$
   b. m$\widehat{DE}$
   c. m$\widehat{DFE}$

In 4–8, chords $\overline{AB}$ and $\overline{CD}$ of a circle intersect at E.

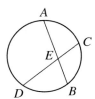

Ex. 4–8

4. If m$\widehat{AC} = 50$ and m$\widehat{DB} = 110$, find m$\angle AEC$.
5. If m$\angle DEB = 60$ and m$\widehat{AC} = 45$, find m$\widehat{DB}$.
6. If $DE = 9$, $EC = 2$, and $AE = 3$, find EB.
7. If $DE = 6$, $EC = 2$, and $AE = EB$, find AE:
   a. in simplest radical form
   b. to the *nearest tenth*

8. If $\overline{DC}$ is a diameter, m$\widehat{AC} = 30$, and m$\widehat{CB} = 80$, find:
   a. m$\widehat{AD}$ **b.** m$\angle AED$ **c.** m$\widehat{ADB}$ **d.** m$\widehat{BAD}$

In 9–14, $\overleftrightarrow{PA}$ is tangent to circle O at A, and secant $\overleftrightarrow{PBC}$ intersects circle O at B and C.

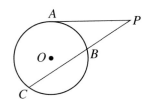

Ex. 9–14

9. If m$\widehat{AC} = 150$ and m$\widehat{AB} = 110$, find m$\angle P$.
10. If m$\widehat{AC} = 160$ and m$\widehat{AB} = $ m$\widehat{BC}$, find m$\angle P$.
11. If $PB = 15$ and $PC = 60$, find PA.
12. If $PB = 4$ and $BC = 5$, find PA.
13. If $PA = 5$ and $PB = 2$, find PC.
14. If $PA = 8$ and $BC = 12$, find   **a.** PB **b.** PC

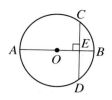

Ex. 15–19

In 15–19, diameter $\overline{AB}$ of circle O is perpendicular to chord $\overline{CD}$ at E.

15. If $CD = 10$, find ED.

16. If $OE = 6$ and $OB = 10$, find: **a.** EB **b.** AE **c.** CE **d.** CD

17. If $EB = 4$ and $CE = 6$, find: **a.** AE **b.** AB **c.** OA

18. If $AE = 5$ and $EB = 3$, find:
   a. CE in radical form   **b.** CD in radical form
   c. CD to the *nearest hundredth*

19. If $CE = 8$ and $AB = 20$, find OE, the distance of the chord from the center of circle O.

In 20–25, secants $\overleftrightarrow{PAB}$ and $\overleftrightarrow{PCD}$ meet at an external point P, and intersect the circle at points A, B, C, and D.

20. If $\overset{\frown}{BD} = 130$ and $m\overset{\frown}{AC} = 40$, find $m\angle P$.

21. If $m\angle P = 40$ and $m\overset{\frown}{BD} = 150$, find $m\overset{\frown}{AC}$.

22. If $PA = 4$, $PB = 15$, and $PC = 6$, find PD.

23. If $PC = 2$, $CD = 4$, and $AB = 1$, find:
   a. PA **b.** PB

24. If $PA = 4$, $AB = 10$, and $PC = 5$, find:
   a. PD **b.** CD

25. If $PA = 2$, $AB = 5$, and $PC = CD$, find:
   a. the exact length of $\overline{PC}$ **b.** the exact length of $\overline{PD}$
   c. PD to the *nearest thousandth*

Ex. 20–25

26. Two tangents to circle O from point P meet the circle at points A and B. If the degree measure of major arc $\overset{\frown}{AB}$ is 200, find $m\angle P$.

27. From point P, tangents $\overleftrightarrow{PA}$ and $\overleftrightarrow{PB}$ are drawn to circle O. If $m\angle P = 36$, find:
   a. the degree measure of minor arc $\overset{\frown}{AB}$
   b. the degree measure of major arc $\overset{\frown}{AB}$

28. In a circle whose radius measures 13 centimeters, chord $\overline{AX}$ is 5 centimeters from the center of the circle. Find the length of $\overline{AX}$.

29. In a circle, a chord 10 inches long is 2 inches from the center of the circle. For this circle, find the length of:
   a. the radius   **b.** the diameter
   c. the diameter to the *nearest thousandth* of an inch

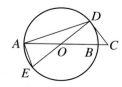

Ex. 30

30. In the diagram, diameter $\overline{AOB}$ is extended to point C, $\overleftrightarrow{CD}$ is tangent to circle O at D, $\overline{DOE}$ is a diameter, and $m\overset{\frown}{BD}:m\overset{\frown}{AD} = 2:7$. Find:
   a. $m\overset{\frown}{BD}$ **b.** $m\overset{\frown}{AD}$ **c.** $m\angle E$ **d.** $m\angle C$
   e. $m\overset{\frown}{AE}$ **f.** $m\overset{\frown}{EB}$ **g.** $m\angle CDE$ **h.** $m\angle ADC$

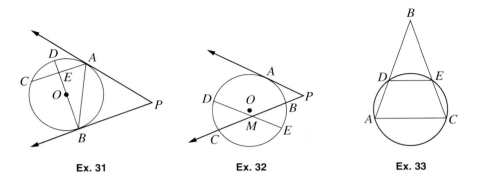

| Ex. 31 | Ex. 32 | Ex. 33 |

31. In the diagram, $\overrightarrow{PA}$ and $\overleftrightarrow{PB}$ are tangent to circle O at A and B, and $\overline{AB}$ is a chord. Diameter $\overleftrightarrow{BOD}$ and chord $\overline{AC}$ intersect at E, m$\widehat{CB} = 160$, and m$\angle APB = 40$. Find: **a.** m$\widehat{ADCB}$ **b.** m$\widehat{AB}$ **c.** m$\widehat{CD}$ **d.** m$\widehat{DA}$ **e.** m$\angle DEC$ **f.** m$\angle PAC$ **g.** m$\angle PBD$ **h.** m$\angle PBA$ **i.** m$\angle BEC$

32. In the diagram, $\overrightarrow{PA}$ is tangent to circle O at A, $\overleftrightarrow{PBC}$ intersects the circle at B and C, chord $\overline{DE}$ bisects chord $\overline{BC}$ at M, $PA = 9$, $PB = 3$, $DE = 30$, and $EM < DM$. Find: **a.** PC **b.** BC **c.** CM **d.** EM **e.** DM

33. *Given:* Secants $\overleftrightarrow{ADB}$ and $\overleftrightarrow{CEB}$ intersect at B.
$\overline{AD} \cong \overline{CE}$.

   To prove: $\triangle ABC$ is isosceles.

34. *Given:* Tangent $\overleftrightarrow{AB}$ and secant $\overleftrightarrow{BDC}$ intersect at B outside circle O. $\overline{AOC}$ is a diameter, and $\overline{AD}$ is a chord.

   To prove: $\triangle ABC \sim \triangle DAC$.

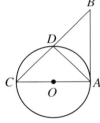

Ex. 34

CUMULATIVE REVIEW WITH OPEN-RESPONSE PROBLEMS

1. Express $0.3\overline{45}$ as the ratio of integers in simplest form.
2. Simplify: $\dfrac{x^2 - 9}{3} + \dfrac{x^2 - 6x + 9}{3x - 9}$
3. Solve and check: $3 - \sqrt{x - 1} = 0$
4. Graph the solution set of $|2x - 1| - 1 > 2$.
5. Simplify: $\sqrt{72} + 2\sqrt{8} - \sqrt{27}$

Exploration

   A quadrilateral that has at least one pair of parallel sides is inscribed in a circle. Show that this quadrilateral must be a rectangle or an isosceles trapezoid.

Chapter *12*
Relations and Functions

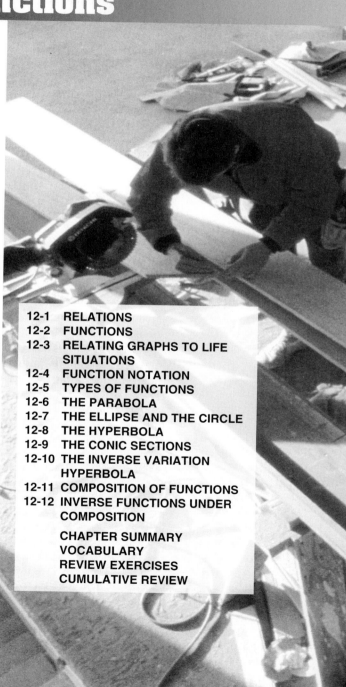

A carpenter who specializes in custom-made furniture was asked to build an oval table 10 feet long and 6 feet wide. In order to draw a pattern from which to cut the tabletop, the carpenter placed two tacks in the underside of the wood and attached to them the opposite ends of a string that was longer than the distance between the two tacks. The carpenter then placed the point of a pencil in the loop of string and, keeping the string taut, traced the shape of the tabletop as shown below.

The carpenter was using one of the definitions of a relation called an *ellipse* to draw the pattern for the table. Relations, functions, and their graphs are used in solving many of the problems encountered in science, in business, in technology, and in our personal lives.

12-1 RELATIONS

In our daily lives, we often "relate" one set of information to another. For example, the table at the right lists the heights of the first-string players on a school's basketball team. This relation between a set of heights and a set of players can also be stated as a *set of ordered pairs*:

Height (cm)	Player
183	Florio
185	Laube
186	Richko
186	Andrews
188	Jones

{(183, Florio), (185, Laube), (186, Richko), (186, Andrews), (188, Jones)}

● **DEFINITION.** A *relation* is a set of ordered pairs.

The *domain* of a relation is the set consisting of all first elements of the ordered pairs. In the example above, the domain is the set of heights, {183, 185, 186, 188}.

The *range* of a relation is the set consisting of all second elements of the ordered pairs. In the given example, the range is the set of players, namely, {Florio, Laube, Richko, Andrews, Jones}.

As shown at the right, the relation can also be displayed by means of an *arrow diagram*. Arrows are drawn from the elements in the domain to their corresponding elements in the range.

In a relation, an element in the domain may correspond to more than one element in the range. Here, for example, 186 → Richko and 186 → Andrews. Note, however, element 186 is listed only once in the domain.

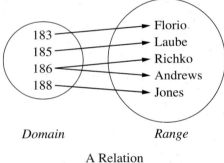

Domain   *Range*

A Relation

Relations and Finite Sets

When the number of ordered pairs in a relation is finite, there are many ways to display the relation. For example, consider the relation "is less than," using the set of numbers {1, 2, 3}.

1. *Set of Ordered Pairs*

Let x and y be elements of the set {1, 2, 3}. List all ordered pairs (x, y), where x is less than y. Since $1 < 2$, $1 < 3$, and $2 < 3$, and there are no other ordered pairs that fit the given conditions, the relation is the set of ordered pairs:

$$\{(1, 2), (1, 3), (2, 3)\}$$

2. *Table of Values*

   The ordered pairs that define the relation may also be listed as a table of values. Whether using ordered pairs or a table, we notice that:

x	*y*
1	2
1	3
2	3

the domain (or set of *x*-coordinates) = {1, 2}

the range (or set of *y*-coordinates) = {2, 3}

3. *Graph*

   In a coordinate graph, the domain is a subset of the numbers on the *x*-axis, and the range is a subset of the numbers on the *y*-axis. Only elements 1, 2, and 3 are listed on each axis so that they will correspond to the finite set {1, 2, 3}.

   There are two ways to display this relation as a coordinate graph.

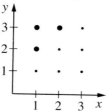

Here, heavy dots are placed on points (1, 2), (1, 3), and (2, 3) to show the relation *x* < *y*.

or

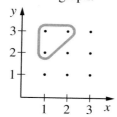

Here, points (1, 2), (1, 3), and (2, 3) are encircled to show the relation *x* < *y*.

4. *Arrow Diagram*

   After indicating two sets, draw arrows from the elements in the domain to their corresponding elements in the range. Notice again that the domain is {1, 2} and the range is {2, 3}.

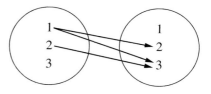

Domain = {1, 2}   Range = {2, 3}

5. *Number Lines*

   Whether one number line (Figure 1) or two number lines (Figure 2) are used, arrows are again drawn from the elements in the domain to their corresponding elements in the range to display the relation.

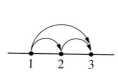

Figure 1

Figure 2

Note: A relation is sometimes identified by means of a single letter. For example, to name the relation we have just studied, we could write

$$R = \{(1, 2), (1, 3), (2, 3)\} \qquad \text{or} \qquad r = \{(1, 2), (1, 3), (2, 3)\}.$$

Relations and Infinite Sets

When the number of ordered pairs in a relation is infinite, we usually rely on one of two methods to indicate the relation.

1. *A Rule*

In some cases, a relation can be specified by a rule that makes it possible for us to determine the ordered pairs in the relation. Two such relations, one involving an equation and one involving an inequality, are stated here.

$$\text{Relation } A = \left\{ (x, y) \middle| y = \tfrac{1}{2}x + 1 \text{ and } x \in \text{ real numbers} \right\}$$

$$\text{Relation } B = \{ (x, y) | x < y \text{ and } x \in \text{ real numbers} \}$$

In each of these relations, the domain is the set of real numbers. Let us make an agreement that allows us to abbreviate the set notation for each of these relations:

● If no set is specified, the domain will be the set of real numbers.

We can now rewrite each of these relations as follows:

$$\text{Relation } A = \left\{ (x, y) \middle| y = \tfrac{1}{2}x + 1 \right\}$$

$$\text{Relation } B = \{ (x, y) | x < y \}$$

2. *A Graph*

Since a coordinate graph is a picture of a set of ordered pairs, a relation can be shown as a graph. Elements of the domain are values on the *x*-axis; elements of the range are values on the *y*-axis. The graphs of relations *A* and *B* stated above are presented here.

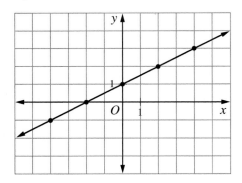

Relation *A*
$\{ (x, y) | y = \tfrac{1}{2}x + 1 \}$

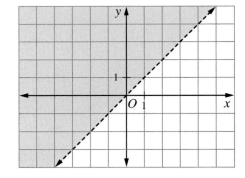

Relation *B*
$\{ (x, y) | x < y \}$

Every graph of a set of ordered pairs of real numbers displays a relation, even if it is not possible to describe that relation by a rule, that is, an equation or inequality.

KEEP IN MIND ——————————————

A relation is a set of ordered pairs.

EXAMPLES

1. The accompanying arrow diagram shows the relation "is a divisor of" between the set of numbers {2, 4, 5} and the set {1, 2, 3, 4, 5, 6}.

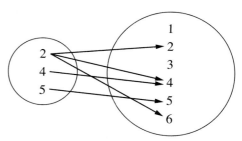

    a. Write the indicated relation as a set of ordered pairs.

    b. State the domain of the relation.

    c. State the range of the relation.

Solutions **a.** Every arrow points from an x-coordinate to its corresponding y-coordinate(s).

    b. The domain is the set of x-coordinates in the relation.

    c. The range is the set of y-coordinates in the relation. Notice that 1 and 3 are not in the relation.

Answers

  a. {(2, 2), (2, 4), (2, 6), (4, 4), (5, 5)}

  b. Domain = {2, 4, 5}

  c. Range = {2, 4, 5, 6}

---

2. For the relation shown in the accompanying diagram, state:

    a. the domain   **b.** the range

Solutions **a.** The domain is the set of x-coordinates. The point farthest to the left has an x-coordinate of -2. At the right, the graph approaches but *does not include* the point whose x-coordinate is 4. Since every real number between -2 and 4 is an x-coordinate for one or more points on the graph, the domain is $\{x\mid -2 \le x < 4\}$.

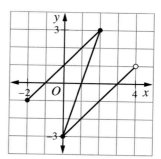

  b. The range is the set of y-coordinates. The highest point on the graph has a y-coordinate of 3, and the lowest point has a y-coordinate of -3. Since every real number between -3 and 3 inclusive is a y-coordinate for one or more points on the graph, the range is $\{y\mid -3 \le y \le 3\}$.

Answers:

  a. Domain = $\{x\mid -2 \le x < 4\}$

  b. Range = $\{y\mid -3 \le y \le 3\}$

EXERCISES WITH OPEN-RESPONSE PROBLEMS

In 1–4:   **a.** State the domain of each relation.   **b.** State the range of each relation.

1. {(3, 5), (4, 6), (5, 5), (6, 6)}

2. {(1, 2), (1, 1), (1, 0), (1, −1)}

3. {(2, 7), (3, 1), (2, 1), (3, 9)}

4. {(0, 2), (0, 4), (1, 2), (3, 4)}

In 5–17, in each case a relation is represented.   **a.** Write each relation as a set of ordered pairs.
b. State the domain of the relation.   **c.** State the range of the relation.

5.

6.

7.

8.

9.

10.

11.

12.

13.

14.

15.

16.

17.

In 18–23, in each case the *x*-coordinates and *y*-coordinates of the ordered pairs in the given relation are real numbers. **a.** State the domain of each relation. **b.** State the range of each relation.

18.

19.

20.

21.

22.

23.

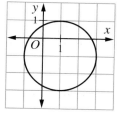

24. Relation *R* contains the following ordered pairs: $(-1, 3)$, $(0, 4)$, $(1, 5)$, $(2, 0)$, $(2, 1)$, $(2, 2)$, $(2, 3)$, $(2, 4)$, $(2, 6)$, $(3, 3)$, $(3, 7)$, $(4, 3)$, $(4, 6)$, $(5, 4)$, and $(5, 5)$.
 a. Draw a coordinate graph of relation *R*.
 b. Which elements of the domain correspond to more than one *y*-coordinate?
 c. What is the largest number in the range?
 d. State the range of the relation.

25. Relation $M = \{(x, y) | y < x - 5\}$, and its domain is the set of real numbers. **a.** Name two ordered pairs in relation *M* each of which has an *x*-coordinate of 6. **b.** Name two ordered pairs in relation *M* each of which has a *y*-coordinate of -5.

12-2 FUNCTIONS

Let us look carefully at the two relations shown below. While each relation matches fathers with their children, there is a very important difference between the two relations.

A father may have more than one child, but a child has one and only one father.

Relation C   Relation F

In relation C, Mr. Shaper has 2 children, Mr. Campbell has 3 children, and Mr. Miller has 1 child. Thus, every father listed in the domain corresponds to 1, 2, or 3 children listed in the range.

In relation F, however, every child listed in the domain corresponds to *one and only one* father listed in the range. Although both C and F are relations, only relation F is called a *function*.

● **DEFINITION.** A *function* is a relation in which each element of the domain corresponds to one and only one element in the range.

Case 1. A relation that is a function.

At the right, every element in the domain is matched to an element in the range by the rule $x \rightarrow x^2$. Since every number has one and only one square, this relation is a function. This function may be listed as a set of ordered pairs:

$\{(0, 0), (1, 1), (-1, 1), (2, 4), (-2, 4)\}$

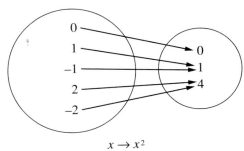

$x \rightarrow x^2$

A function

Case 2. A relation that is not a function.

At the right, every element in the domain is matched to its square root(s) in the range by the rule $x \rightarrow \pm\sqrt{x}$. Since every nonzero number has two square roots, this is not a function. This relation may be listed as a set of ordered pairs:

$\{(0, 0), (1, 1), (1, -1), (4, 2), (4, -2)\}$

In terms of ordered pairs, how do the two examples differ?

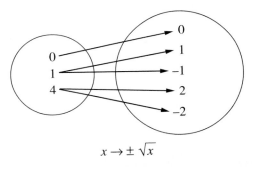

$x \rightarrow \pm\sqrt{x}$

Not a function

1. A function: $\{(0, 0), (1, 1), (-1, 1), (2, 4), (-2, 4)\}$

2. Not a function: $\{(0, 0), (1, 1), (1, -1), (4, 2), (4, -2)\}$

Same first element   Same first element

If two or more ordered pairs in a relation have the same first element, then some element in the domain corresponds to more than one element in the range. Thus, the relation is not a function, as seen in case 2. This leads to an alternative definition of function.

● **DEFINITION.** A *function* is a relation in which no two ordered pairs have the same first element.

Functions and Graphs

We have learned that a relation whose domain and range are subsets of the real numbers can be displayed as a coordinate graph. We will now study a method that enables us to tell very quickly when a relation presented as a graph is a function.

The set of ordered pairs of the function previously described in case 1 is shown on the graph in Figure 1. Each ordered pair (x, y) is determined by the rule $x \to x^2$. Since the second element, y, of each ordered pair is equal to x^2, it follows that

$y = x^2$ is equivalent to the rule $x \to x^2$.

Figure 1

In a function, every element x of the domain corresponds to one and only one element y in the range. We need to keep this in mind to understand the vertical-line test for a function.

- *Vertical-line Test for a Function:* If each vertical line drawn through the graph of a relation intersects the graph at one and only one point, then the relation is a function.

When the domain is $\{-2, -1, 0, 1, 2\}$, the five points whose coordinates satisfy the equation $y = x^2$ are graphed in Figure 2. We know that this relation is a function.

The vertical line whose equation is $x = -1$ intersects the graph of the relation at one and only one point, $(-1, 1)$. Thus, if $x = -1$, then $y = 1$. Similarly, each vertical line that passes through a point in the relation will intersect one and only one point of the relation.

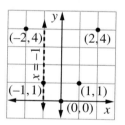

Figure 2

Note: If a domain had not been specified, the relation $y = x^2$ would have as its domain the set of all real numbers, as graphed in Figure 3. The vertical-line test demonstrates geometrically that every real number has one and only one square. Thus, we can claim that

$y = x^2$ is a function

or

$y = x^2$ is a function of x.

Figure 3

The set of ordered pairs described in case 2 is shown in Figure 4. These are the points that fit the rule $x \rightarrow \pm\sqrt{x}$ when the domain is $\{0, 1, 4\}$. Let us apply the vertical-line test to show that this relation is not a function.

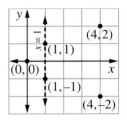

Figure 4

The vertical line whose equation is $x = 1$ intersects the graph of the relation at two points: $(1, 1)$ and $(1, -1)$. Thus, if $x = 1$, then $y = 1$ or $y = -1$. This vertical-line test demonstrates that there is at least one element x of the domain that corresponds to more than one element y of the range.

Note: The rule $x \rightarrow \pm\sqrt{x}$ determines a set of ordered pairs (x, y) that satisfy the equation $y = \pm\sqrt{x}$. By squaring both sides of this equation, we obtain the equation $y^2 = x$. Since, in the set of real numbers, $\sqrt{x}$ is defined only for positive numbers and 0, the largest subset of the real numbers that can be the domain of $y = \pm\sqrt{x}$ or $y^2 = x$ is the set of nonnegative real numbers. The relation is graphed using this domain in Figure 5.

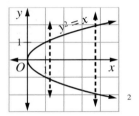

Figure 5

The vertical-line test demonstrates in Figure 5 that every positive real number has two square roots. Thus, for the equation $y = \pm\sqrt{x}$ or $y^2 = x$, y is not a function of x. However, it is correct to state that x is a function of y. This fact can be demonstrated geometrically by rotating the graph $90°$ (that is, by turning the book sideways) so that the y-axis is a horizontal line.

Nevertheless, to avoid confusion, we will agree that

1. When testing for a function, unless otherwise stated, we will test to see whether the relation is a function of x only.

2. If a relation is not a function of x, we will simply state that the relation is not a function.

Therefore, using the graph in Figure 5, we state that $y^2 = x$ is *not* a function.

Restricted Domains and Functions

For a relation to be a function, each element of the domain must correspond to one and only one element of the range. For example, $y = \frac{1}{x}$ is not a function for the set of real numbers because no y-value corresponds to x-value 0. But for the set of nonzero real numbers, written in symbols as $R/\{0\}$, $y = \frac{1}{x}$ is a function. Therefore, the relation $y = \frac{1}{x}$ is a function for a *restricted domain*.

● **If no set is specified as the domain of a relation, it is often possible to form a function that is a subset of the given relation by letting the domain be the largest possible subset of the real numbers for which a function exists, that is, for which every element of the domain corresponds to one and only one real number in the range.**

For example, $y = \frac{1}{x-3}$ and $y = \sqrt{x}$ are not functions if the domain is the set of all real numbers; but $y = \frac{1}{x-3}$ is a function whose domain is $R/\{3\}$, and $y = \sqrt{x}$ is a function whose domain is $\{x | x \geq 0\}$. We will study restricted domains in greater detail in Section 12-5.

KEEP IN MIND _____

A function is a relation in which:

1. each element of the domain corresponds to one and only one element in the range

or

2. no two ordered pairs have the same first element.

EXAMPLES

In 1–4, in each case, let the domain = $\{1, 2, 3\}$. State whether or not each indicated relation is a function.

1.

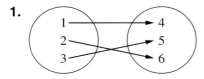

Solution   Every element in the domain corresponds to *one and only one* element in the range.

Answer: This relation *is* a function with range $\{4, 5, 6\}$.

_____

2.

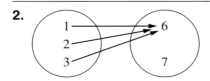

Solution   Every element in the domain corresponds to *one and only one* element in the range.

Answer: This relation *is* a function with range $\{6\}$.

_____

3.

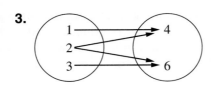

Solution   Element 2 in the domain corresponds to *more than one* element in the range.

Answer: This relation *is not* a function.

4.

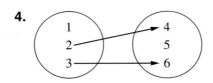

Solution   Element 1 in the domain corresponds to *no* element in the range.

Answer: For the domain {1, 2, 3}, this relation *is not* a function.

---

5. Find the largest possible *restricted domain* that allows the relation in Example 4 to be a function.

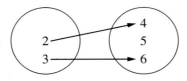

Solution   Exclude element 1 from the domain because this element corresponds to no element in the range. Thus, the domain is restricted to elements 2 and 3, each of which corresponds to one and only one element in the range, {4, 6}.

Answer: A function exists for the restricted domain {2, 3}.

---

6. Which relation, if either, is a function?

$$A = \{(0, 3), (1, 8), (1, 5)\} \qquad B = \{(0, 2), (1, 2), (3, 2)\}$$

Solution   Relation A contains pairs (1, 8) and (1, 5). Since 1 corresponds to both 8 and 5, A is not a function. In relation B, however, no two ordered pairs have the same first element.

Answer: B is a function.

---

7. Which graph represents a relation that is a function?

  (1)   (2)   (3)   (4)

Solution By the vertical-line test, only in (2) will every vertical line intersect the graph of the relation at one and only one point. For example, consider the vertical line whose equation is $x = 2$:

In (1), when $x = 2$, then $y = 1$, or $y = -1$. (*Not* a function.)

In (3), when $x = 2$, then $y = 1$, $y = 0$, or $y = -1$. (*Not* a function.)

In (4), when $x = 2$, then y may be any real number. (*Not* a function.)

Answer: (2)

EXERCISES WITH OPEN-RESPONSE PROBLEMS

In 1–8, in each case let the domain = {0, 1, 2}. **a.** State whether or not each indicated relation is a function. **b.** If the relation is not a function, explain why.

1.

2.

3.

4.

5.

6.

7.

8.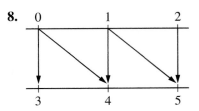

9. For the relations in Exercises 1–8 that are *not* functions, state the exercise number and the largest possible *restricted domain* that allows the relation to be a function.

In 10–13:   **a.** State the domain of each relation.   **b.** State the range of each relation.   **c.** Tell whether or not the relation is a function.

10. {(2, 3), (3, 5), (4, 7), (5, 9)}

11. {(3, 1), (2, 3), (1, 2), (3, 2)}

12. {(6, 6), (6, 3), (6, 2), (6, 1)}

13. {(5, 2), (6, 1), (7, 2), (8, 1)}

In 14–19, let the domain = {−1, 0, 1}.

a. Copy the encircled sets at the right, and draw an arrow diagram to indicate the ordered pairs in the relation whose rule is given.

b. State the range of the relation.

c. For the domain {−1, 0, 1}, state whether or not the relation is a function.

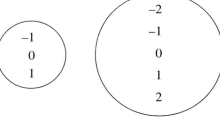

14. $x \rightarrow x$

15. $x \rightarrow x^2$

16. $x \rightarrow x - 1$

17. $x \rightarrow 2x + 1$

18. $x \rightarrow 1 - x$

19. $x \rightarrow y$, where $y < x$

Ex. 14–19

20. Let $A = \{(10, 3), (7, 2), (-2, 5), (x, 1)\}$. Name all possible values that x may *not* represent if relation A is to be a function.

21. The domain of function F is $\{-2, \sqrt{2}, \sqrt{3}, 2\}$, and the rule of the function is $x \rightarrow x^2 + 3$. List all ordered pairs in this function.

22. The domain of function B is $\{1, \sqrt{2}, \sqrt{3}, 2\}$, and the rule of the function is $x \rightarrow 3x - 2$. What is the range of function B?

In 23–34, determine whether or not each graph represents a function. (*Hint:* Use the vertical-line test.)

23.

24.

25.

26.

27.

28.

29.

30.

31.

32.

33.

34.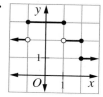

35. a. What is the domain of the relation whose graph is given in Exercise 23?
  b. What is its range?
36. a. What is the domain of the relation whose graph is given in Exercise 28?
  b. What is its range?
37. a. What is the domain of the relation whose graph is given in Exercise 34?
  b. What is its range?

In 38–50, in each case, let $D \rightarrow R$ represent a domain D corresponding to a range R.
  a. Is the relation a function?
  b. If not, explain why.

38. Cost of item in store $\rightarrow$ sales tax
39. Sisters $\rightarrow$ brothers
40. People $\rightarrow$ ages
41. Heights $\rightarrow$ students
42. Students $\rightarrow$ teachers
43. States $\rightarrow$ capitals
44. Homes in the United States $\rightarrow$ zip codes
45. Cities in the United States $\rightarrow$ zip codes
46. Birthdays $\rightarrow$ people
47. School lockers $\rightarrow$ students
48. Letters sent first class $\rightarrow$ cost of postage
49. Cars being driven $\rightarrow$ drivers at the wheel
50. Drivers' license registration numbers $\rightarrow$ licensed drivers

51. Describe three functions, similar to those listed in Exercises 38–50, that exist in the world about us.

12-3 RELATING GRAPHS TO LIFE SITUATIONS

In many real-world situations, it is not possible to write an algebraic equation to describe a relation or function. It is possible, however, to draw a graph of the relation or function that is easily understood. Let us consider the following situation.

Evander walks to school at a steady rate for 5 minutes. Then, seeing his friends up ahead, he runs to meet them. He catches up to his friends in 2 minutes, and they all walk together to school at a steady rate.

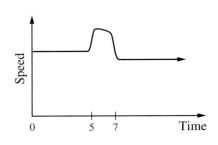

The graph shown here compares the time elapsed to Evander's speed, or the rate at which he walks and runs. We observe the following:

1. The horizontal axis represents time (given here in minutes), and the vertical axis represents speed (although no specific rate is given).

2. From 0 to 5 minutes, as Evander walks, his speed is steady or constant.

3. After 5 minutes, as Evander starts to run, his speed first increases and then decreases as he catches up with his friends.

4. Evander meets his friends at the 7-minute mark.

5. After 7 minutes, Evander walks with his friends at a steady rate of speed.

Note: When speed is a function of time, a steady or uniform speed is represented on a graph by a horizontal line segment.

In the examples and exercises that follow, we will draw or identify graphs that relate to life situations.

EXAMPLES

1. A driver stopped her car for a traffic light. After waiting for the light to turn green, the driver continued on her way.
   Which of the following graphs best represents the situation described?

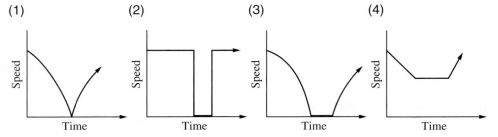

Solution   In graph (1), the driver decelerated to a speed of 0 but then accelerated without waiting for the light to change. In graph (2), although the driver stopped for the light, the
graph does not show the time needed to decelerate to a speed to 0 and then to accel-
erate. In graph (4), the driver never stopped because the speed did not decrease to 0.

Answer: Graph (3) correctly shows the driver decelerating to 0, waiting for the light
to change, and then accelerating.

---

2. A driver traveled at a uniform rate of speed and then stopped for a traffic light. After
waiting for the light to turn green, the driver accelerated to the same rate of speed.
Sketch a graph to compare the distance the car traveled to the time that elapsed.

Solution   The following step-by-step procedure shows how the graph is constructed.

(1) As the car moved forward, its distance increased.
The distance traveled at a uniform rate of speed
can be represented by a straight line with a positive (upward) slope:

$$\text{speed} = \frac{\text{change in distance}}{\text{change in time}}.$$

(2) As the car slowed to a stop, the distance traveled
is shown by a curved line that rises more and
more slowly.

(3) When the car was stopped, the distance traveled
remained unchanged, as shown by a horizontal
line whose slope = 0.

(4) As the car accelerated, the distance traveled is
shown by a curved line that rises more and more
quickly.

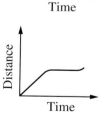

(5) When the car resumed its uniform rate of speed,
the distance traveled is again represented by a
straight line with a positive slope.

Answer: The graph shown in step (5).

EXERCISES WITH OPEN-RESPONSE PROBLEMS

In 1–13, for each situation described, select the *numeral* preceding the graph that best represents the situation.

1. A child is on a seesaw. Compare the height above ground to the time elapsed.

2. A child is on a swing. Compare the height above ground to the time elapsed.

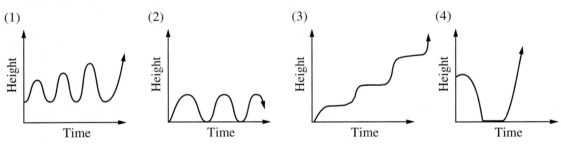

3. A boy climbs a hill, slowing down as he reaches the top, and then runs down the hill. Compare the boy's speed to the time elapsed.

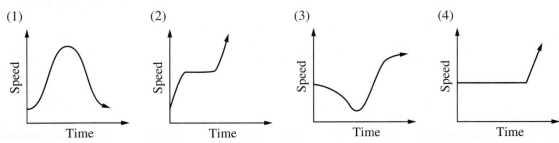

4. A shopper pushed a cart down the aisle, stopping twice to pick up items from the shelf. Compare the shopper's speed to the time elapsed.

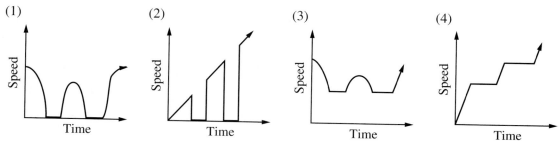

(1)   (2)   (3)   (4)

5. A shopper pushed a cart down the aisle, stopping twice to pick up items from the shelf. Compare the distance traveled to the time elapsed.

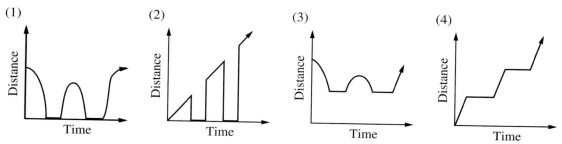

(1)   (2)   (3)   (4)

6. A shopping cart starts to roll down an incline, picking up speed until it hits a wall and stops. Compare the speed of the cart to the time that passes.

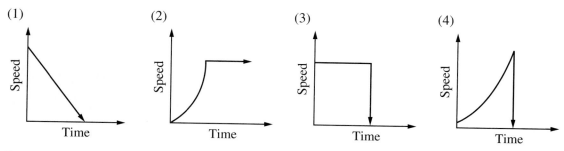

(1)   (2)   (3)   (4)

7. Dave runs for 5 minutes, slows down to walk for 2 minutes, and then starts to run again. Compare Dave's speed to the time elapsed.

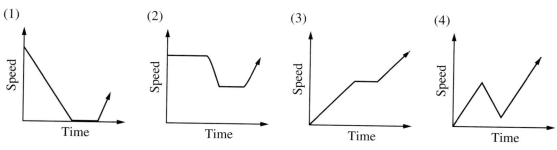

(1)   (2)   (3)   (4)

8. Faith parachutes from an airplane, free-falls for a while, opens her chute, slows down, and lands on the ground. Compare Faith's speed to the time elapsed.

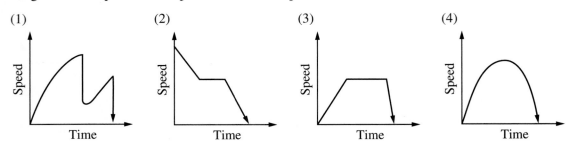

9. Faith parachutes from an airplane, free-falls for a while, opens her chute, slows down, and lands on the ground. Compare Faith's height above ground to the time elapsed.

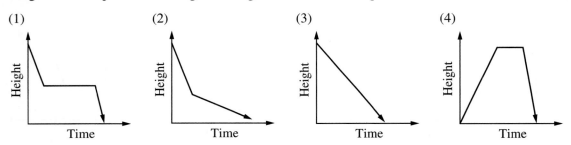

10. Barbara Kandybowicz took a ride on a Ferris wheel. Compare her height above ground to the time elapsed.

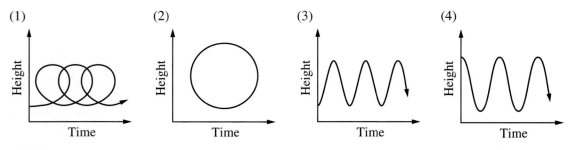

11. A unit of soldiers marched for 50 minutes, stopped for a 10-minute rest, and began to march again. Compare the soldiers' speed to the time elapsed.

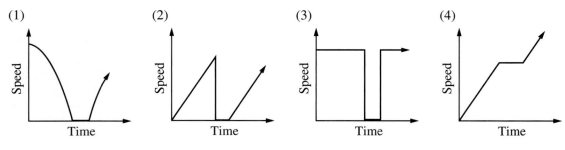

12. A unit of soldiers marched for 50 minutes, stopped for a 10-minute rest, and began to march again. Compare the distance the soldiers traveled to the time elapsed.

13. Chris Alexiou ran to catch a baseball. She caught the ball, threw it to first base, and walked back to her position. Compare Chris's speed to the time elapsed.

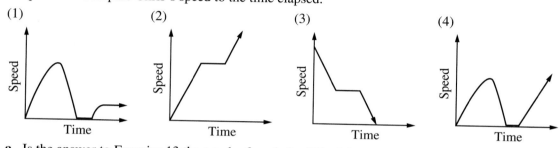

14. a. Is the answer to Exercise 13 the graph of a relation? Explain your answer.
   b. Is the answer to Exercise 13 the graph of a function? Explain your answer.

In 15–18, for each situation presented, draw a graph and label the axes to represent the situation described.

15. Fred Baumann jumps on a trampoline. Compare his height above ground to the time elapsed.

16. Rose Ambrosino takes a ride on a roller coaster. Compare her height above ground to the time that elapses during the ride.

17. A child climbs up the steps of a slide in a playground, sits down, and then slides down the device. Compare the child's height above ground to the time that elapses.

18. A child climbs up the steps of a slide in a playground, sits down, and then slides down the device. Compare the child's speed to the time that elapses.

19. a. Describe, in words, at least two real-life situations such as those described in the exercises in this section.   **b.** For each situation, draw a graph and label the axes.

In 20–22, for each graph the axes are not labeled. Describe a real-life situation for which each graph could be a model, and identify the labels that belong on each axis.

20.   **21.**   **22.**

12-4 FUNCTION NOTATION

If a function is defined by a rule or an equation, the rule may be expressed in a variety of ways. For example, let us consider function f in which every element in the range is 3 more than its corresponding element in the domain. This rule is indicated by any of the following expressions:

In Symbols	In Words
1. $f: x \rightarrow x + 3$	**1.** Under function f, x maps to $x + 3$. or Function f pairs x with $x + 3$. or The image of x under function f is $x + 3$.
2. $x \xrightarrow{\ \ f\ \ } x + 3$	**2.** Same as 1.
3. $f(x) = x + 3$	**3.** f of x equals $x + 3$.
4. $f = \{(x, y) \mid y = x + 3\}$	**4.** Function f is the set of ordered pairs (x, y) such that y equals $x + 3$.
5. $y = x + 3$	**5.** y equals $x + 3$.

The last expression, $y = x + 3$, is simply an abbreviated form of the function notation given in expression 4.

When we compare expressions 3 and 5, namely, $f(x) = x + 3$ and $y = x + 3$, it becomes clear by substitution that

$$f(x) = y$$

In other words, $f(x)$, read as f of x, is equal to the y-coordinate in an ordered pair. The symbol $f(x)$ does *not* indicate multiplication; rather, $f(x)$ indicates the substitution of an x-value to find its corresponding y-value, called $f(x)$. Let us compare the two expressions that follow:

$y = x + 3$	$f(x) = x + 3$
If $x = 2$, then $y = 2 + 3$	If $x = 2$, then $f(2) = 2 + 3$
and $y = 5$.	and $f(2) = 5$.

The ordered pair $(x, y) = (2, 5)$ is a member of the function $y = x + 3$.

The ordered pair $(x, f(x)) = (2, 5)$ is a member of the function $f(x) = x + 3$.

EXAMPLES

1. If function g is defined by $g(x) = 2x + 15$, find the value of $g(-3)$.

<table>
<tr><td>How to Proceed:</td><td>Solution:</td></tr>
</table>

How to Proceed:	*Solution:*
(1) Write the rule of the function.	$g(x) = 2x + 15$
(2) Substitute -3 for x, and simplify.	$g(-3) = 2(-3) + 15$
	$= -6 + 15$
	$= 9$

Answer: $g(-3) = 9$

---

2. The graph of function f is shown at the right.
   a. Find $f(-1)$.   **b.** Find $f(0)$.
   c. Find $f(1)$.   **d.** Find $f(3)$.

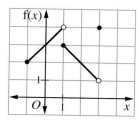

Solutions   **a.** Since $f(x) = y$, the ordered pair $(-1, 2)$ indicates that $f(-1) = 2$.
   b. Using the ordered pair $(0, 3)$, we see that $f(0) = 3$.
   c. Using the ordered pair $(1, 3)$, we see that $f(1) = 3$.
   d. Using the ordered pair $(3, 4)$, we see that $f(3) = 4$.

Answers: **a.** 2   **b.** 3   **c.** 3   **d.** 4

Note: While the domain of function f is $\{x | -1 \leq x \leq 3\}$, the range may be expressed in either of two ways:

$$\{y | 1 < y \leq 4\} \qquad \text{or} \qquad \{f(x) | 1 < f(x) \leq 4\}$$

EXERCISES WITH OPEN-RESPONSE PROBLEMS

In 1–6, in each case the rule that defines function f is given.
a. Find $f(1)$.   **b.** Find $f(2)$.

1. $f(x) = 4x$

2. $f(x) = x - 5$

3. $f(x) = x^2 - 1$

4. $f(x) = \frac{1}{x}$

5. $f(x) = 3x - 4$

6. $f(x) = \frac{x - 1}{x + 1}$

In 7–12, in each case the rule that defines function g is given.
a. Find g(3).   **b.** Find g(−1).

7. $g(x) = \frac{2x}{3}$

8. $g(x) = 8 - x$

9. $g(x) = \frac{x + 7}{x + 2}$

10. $g(x) = x^2 + x$

11. $g(x) = -x^2$

12. $g(x) = x^2 - 2x - 3$

In 13–17, function h is defined by $h(x) = \frac{x^2 - x}{4}$. Find each value.

13. h(4)   **14.** h(−4)   **15.** h(2)   **16.** h(1)   **17.** h(1.2)

In 18–22, function k is defined by $k(x) = \frac{6 - x}{x - 3}$. Find each value.

18. k(2)   **19.** k(9)   **20.** k(0)   **21.** k(6)   **22.** k(−3)

In 23–28, use the following functions m, p, and r:

$$x \xrightarrow{\ m\ } 2x \qquad x \xrightarrow{\ p\ } x^2 \qquad x \xrightarrow{\ r\ } x + 2$$

23. Find m(3).   **24.** Find p(3).   **25.** Find r(3).

26. Under which function (m, p, or r) will 5 map to 7?

27. Under which function (m, p, or r) will the image of $\frac{1}{2}$ be 1?

28. Of functions m, p, and r, which ones assign 2 in the domain to 4 in the range?

29. The graph of function f consists of the union of four line segments, as shown at the right.
   a. Find f(−1).   **b.** Find f(0).
   c. Find f(1).   **d.** Find f(2).
   e. Find $f\left(\frac{1}{2}\right)$.   **f.** Find $f\left(2\frac{2}{3}\right)$.
   g. State the domain of function f.
   h. State the range of function f.

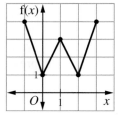

Ex. 29

30. The graph of function g is shown at the right.
   a. Find g(−1).   **b.** Find g(1).
   c. Find g(2).   **d.** Find g(0).
   e. Find $g\left(1\frac{1}{2}\right)$.   **f.** Find $g\left(-1\frac{1}{2}\right)$.
   g. For what value(s) of x will $g(x) = 2\frac{1}{2}$?
   h. State the domain of function g.
   i. State the range of function g.

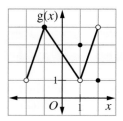

Ex. 30

In 31–34, in each case, select the *numeral* preceding the expression that best answers the question.

31. Which of the following functions contains the ordered pair (3, 1)?
  (1) $y = 3x$ (2) $y = x + 2$ (3) $y = x - 2$ (4) $y = 2x + 1$

32. In which of the following functions is 7 from the domain mapped to 10 in the range?
  (1) $\{(x, y)|y = x - 3\}$ (2) $\{(x, y)|y = x + 3\}$
  (3) $\{(x, y)|y = 7\}$ (4) $\{(x, y)|y = x + 7\}$

33. Which of the following is *not* a function?
  (1) $y = 2x$ (2) $x = 2y$ (3) $y = 2$ (4) $x = 2$

34. The domain of function F is $\{1, 0, -1\}$ and F: $x \to x^3 - x$. What is the range of F?
  (1) $\{0\}$ (2) $\{0, 2\}$ (3) $\{0, -2\}$ (4) $\{1, 0, -2\}$

35. Relation R $= \left\{(x, y)|y < \frac{1}{3}x - 2\right\}$.

  a. Name two ordered pairs in R each having an x-coordinate of 3.
  b. Name two ordered pairs in R each having a y-coordinate of -2.
  c. Is relation R a function? Explain your answer.

36. A car travels on a highway at an average rate of 55 miles per hour. For this particular car, the formula
$$\text{Distance} = \text{rate} \times \text{time}, \quad \text{or} \quad D = rt$$
can be stated as $D = 55t$.

  a. Does the rule $D = 55t$ describe a function? Explain why.
  b. *True* or *False*: Since $D = 55t$ and $f(t) = 55t$ each describe the same rule, it can be said that $D = f(t)$, or distance is a function of time.
  c. Find the distance traveled by the car:
    (1) in 1 hour   *(2)* in 2 hours   *(3)* in 3 hours 12 minutes

12-5 TYPES OF FUNCTIONS

In this section, some types of functions will be listed. Many of these functions should be familiar from earlier studies in mathematics.

1. *Linear Functions*

$$y = mx + b \qquad \text{OR} \qquad f(x) = mx + b$$

Any equation of the form $y = mx + b$ or $f(x) = mx + b$, where m and b are constants, is a function whose graph is a straight line. Recall that m is the slope of the line, and b is the y-intercept.

For example, $y = -4x + 3$ or $f(x) = -4x + 3$ defines a *linear function*. If $x = 2$, $y = -5$, or $f(2) = -5$. Since for every x-value there is one and only one y-value, this relation is a function.

2. *Constant Functions*

$$y = b \qquad \text{OR} \qquad f(x) = b$$

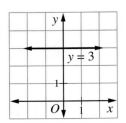

If the slope of a linear function is 0, or $m = 0$, then the linear function becomes $y = b$ or $f(x) = b$. This relation is called a **constant function** because every x corresponds to the same constant value, b.

For example, the graph of the constant function $y = 3$, or $f(x) = 3$, is shown at the left. Here, $f(1) = 3$, $f(2) = 3$, $f(-1) = 3$, and so forth. Although the domain consists of all real numbers, the range consists of a single element, $\{3\}$.

Note: The equation $x = b$ is *not* a constant function because its graph is a vertical line, indicating that x corresponds to more than one value of y.

3. *Quadratic Functions*

$$y = ax^2 + bx + c, (a \neq 0) \qquad \text{OR} \qquad f(x) = ax^2 + bx + c, (a \neq 0)$$

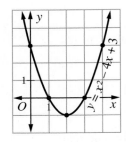

Any equation of the form $y = ax^2 + bx + c$, where $a \neq 0$, is a **quadratic function** whose graph is a parabola that has a vertical line of symmetry.

The quadratic equation whose graph appears at the left is $y = x^2 - 4x + 3$, or $f(x) = x^2 - 4x + 3$. Here, $f(0) = 3$, $f(1) = 0$, $f(2) = -1$, $f(3) = 0$, $f(4) = 3$, and so forth. Since every x-value corresponds to one and only one y-value, this relation is a function.

The vertical-line test can be used to demonstrate that quadratics of the form $y = ax^2 + bx + c$, where $a \neq 0$, or $f(x) = ax^2 + bx + c$, where $a \neq 0$, are functions.

Note: Quadratics of the form $x = ay^2 + by + c$, where $a \neq 0$, are *not* functions. For example, the quadratic $x = y^2$ contains two points whose coordinates are $(4, 2)$ and $(4, -2)$. Therefore there are at least two ordered pairs that have the same first element.

4. *Polynomial Functions*

$$y = a_n x^n + a_{n-1} x^{n-1} + a_{n-2} x^{n-2} + \cdots + a_0$$

or

$$f(x) = a_n x^n + a_{n-1} x^{n-1} + a_{n-2} x^{n-2} + \cdots + a_0$$

For example, consider $f(x) = x^4 - 2x^3 + x^2 - 4x + 3$. If $x = 2$, then $f(x) = f(2) = 16 - 16 + 4 - 8 + 3 = -1$. In the same way, for each value of x, there is one and only one corresponding $f(x)$. Thus, the given expression is a **polynomial function**.

Quadratic functions, linear functions, and constant functions are all polynomial functions. For example, the quadratic function $f(x) = x^2 - 4x + 3$ is a polynomial function for $n = 2$; the linear function $y = -4x + 3$ is a polynomial function for $n = 1$; the constant function $f(x) = 3$ is a polynomial function for $n = 0$.

5. *Absolute-Value Functions*

$$y = |ax + b|$$

$$f(x) = |ax + b|$$

Figure 1

Figure 2

The graph of the absolute-value equation $y = |x|$, or $f(x) = |x|$, is shown in Figure 1. The graph of the absolute-value equation $y = |2x - 4|$, or $f(x) = |2x - 4|$, is shown in Figure 2. In each equation, every value of x corresponds to one and only one $f(x)$, that is, one and only one value of y. Therefore, both $f(x) = |x|$ and $f(x) = |2x - 4|$ are ***absolute-value functions***.

Note: Absolute-value equations of the form $x = |ay + b|$ are *not* functions. For example, the equation $x = |y|$ contains two points whose coordinates are $(3, 3)$ and $(3, -3)$, indicating that an x-value corresponds to more than one y-value.

Absolute-value functions are easily graphed on a calculator. First set the graphing calculator in DOT mode.

To graph the absolute-value function:

Enter: | Y= | | MATH | | ▶NUM | | ENTER | 2
| X,T,θ,*n* | | — | 4 |) | | ENTER | | GRAPH |

Display:

The sequence of keys shown here and in the remainder of this book are for the TI-82 and the TI-83. Your graphing calculator may use a different sequence of keys.

6. *Step Functions*

The graph of a ***step function*** resembles a series of steps. There are many different step functions; let us consider one example, the ***greatest-integer function***:

$$y = [x] \qquad \text{or} \qquad f(x) = [x]$$

The symbol $[x]$ means the greatest integer equal to or less than x. Therefore, the greatest-integer function is indicated by the rule $y = [x]$, or $f(x) = [x]$. A partial graph of this step function is shown at the right.

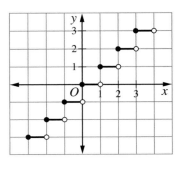

$$y = [x]$$

If $x = 2$, $f(x) = f(2) = [2] = 2$.

If $x = 2\frac{2}{3}$, $f(x) = f\left(2\frac{2}{3}\right) = \left[2\frac{2}{3}\right] = 2$.

If $x = 2.98$, $f(x) = f(2.98) = [2.98] = 2$.

However:

If $x = 3$, $f(x) = f(3) = [3] = 3$.

Therefore, if x is equal to or greater than 2 but less than 3, the greatest integer in x is 2. In symbols, we write: If $2 \leq x < 3$, then $[x] = 2$. This set of values is graphed on the line $y = 2$ as •——○, a segment with one missing endpoint.

Similar reasoning is used to complete the graph of this function. If x is an integer, then $[x] = x$. If x is not an integer, then $[x]$ is *less than* x. For example:

$$1 \leq 1.7 < 2 \text{ and } [1.7] = 1 \qquad\qquad -3 \leq -2.4 < -2 \text{ and } [-2.4] = -3$$

$$0 \leq 0.6 < 1 \text{ and } [0.6] = 0 \qquad\qquad -4 \leq -3\frac{1}{5} < -3 \text{ and } \left[-3\frac{1}{5}\right] = -4$$

The domain of the greatest-integer function $y = [x]$ is the set of real numbers, and the range is the set of integers. Other applications of step functions are given in the exercises under the heading "Applications with Functions."

To graph the greatest-integer function, first set the graphing calculator in DOT mode.

Enter: [Y=] [MATH] [▶NUM] 5 [X,T,θ,*n*] [ENTER] [GRAPH]

Display:

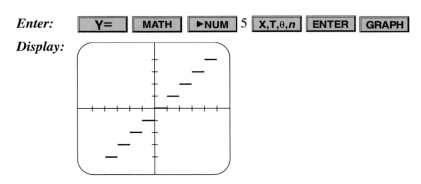

7. *Other Functions*

A great number of other functions exist in mathematics. Many transformations are functions, as we will see in Chapter 13. In later chapters of this book, we will study trigonometric functions, exponential functions, and logarithmic functions. Also, as we will see in the exercises that follow, there are many functions in the world about us.

It is important to remember that a relation is sometimes a function under a restricted domain. If no domain is specified, we have agreed to let the domain be the largest possible subset of the real numbers for which a function exists.

For example, $f(x) = \dfrac{1}{x^2 - 9}$ is a function whose domain is the set of real numbers/$\{3, -3\}$, and $g(x) = \sqrt{x - 4}$ is a function whose domain is $\{x \mid x \geq 4\}$. Other instances can be found in Examples 3 and 4, which follow.

EXAMPLES

1. In the function $\{(x, y) \mid y = 2x - 5\}$, the domain is $\{x \mid 0 \leq x \leq 4\}$. Find the range of the function.

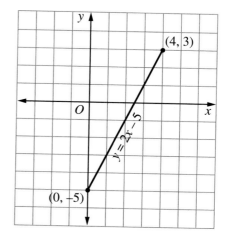

Solution   Since $y = 2x - 5$ is a linear function, consider the extreme values of x in the domain.

$$y = 2x - 5$$
When $x = 0$, $y = 2(0) - 5 = -5$.
When $x = 4$, $y = 2(4) - 5 = 3$.

For a linear function, the range consists of all real numbers between the extreme values of y. Here the range is $-5 \leq y \leq 3$. (Although it is not necessary to graph the function, the graph at the right is an aid in visualizing the solution.)

Answer: The range is $\{y \mid -5 \leq y \leq 3\}$.

2. The domain of $f(x) = 10 - x$ is $7 \leq x \leq 12$. What is the greatest value in the range of f?

Solution   Since $f(x) = 10 - x$ is a linear function, test the extreme values of x in the domain to find the extreme values of $f(x)$ in the range.

$$f(x) = 10 - x$$
$$\text{When } x = 7, f(7) = 10 - 7 = 3.$$
$$\text{When } x = 12, f(12) = 10 - 12 = -2.$$

The greatest value in the range of this linear function is 3.

Answer: 3

---

3. What is the domain of the function $k(x) = \frac{x-3}{x-6}$?

Solution   Every real number x corresponds to one and only one value $k(x)$, except when the denominator $x - 6$ is equal to 0.

$$\text{If } x - 6 = 0, \text{ then } x = 6.$$

Thus, the domain of the function is the set of real numbers less 6.

Answer: Real numbers/{6}.

---

4. What is the domain of the function $f(x) = \frac{1}{\sqrt{x-2}}$?

Solution   If $x = 2$, then $f(x) = \frac{1}{\sqrt{x-2}} = \frac{1}{\sqrt{2-2}} = \frac{1}{\sqrt{0}} = \frac{1}{0}$ (undefined). Also, if x is less than 2, then $f(x)$ contains the square root of a negative number; that is, $f(x)$ is not a real number. Since the range, as well as the domain, is to contain only real numbers, the domain of the function is restricted to real numbers greater than 2.

Answer: $\{x | x > 2\}$.

EXERCISES WITH OPEN-RESPONSE PROBLEMS

In 1–9, for each function: **a.** Identify the function as being a linear, constant, quadratic, absolute-value, or step function.   **b.** Find $f(3)$.   **c.** Find $f\left(\frac{1}{2}\right)$.

1. $f(x) = 2$

2. $f(x) = x$

3. $f(x) = [x]$

4. $f(x) = 2x^2$

5. $f(x) = 2 - x$

6. $f(x) = |2 - x|$

7. $f(x) = [2 - x]$

8. $f(x) = x^2 - x$

9. $f(x) = \pi$

In 10–12, for each given function and its domain, find the range.

10. $\{(x, y)|y = 3x - 2\}$; domain $= \{x|-2 \le x \le 2\}$

11. $f(x) = 5 - \frac{1}{2}x$; domain $= \{x|0 \le x \le 16\}$

12. $g:x \to 6 - x$; domain $= \{x|x \ge 0\}$

13. If the domain of $y = 4x - 3$ is $\{x|2 \le x \le 5\}$, what is the greatest value in its range?
14. The domain of $f(x) = 9 - 2x$ is $4 \le x \le 10$. What is the greatest value in the range of f?
15. Let the domain of the quadratic function $y = 1 + 4x - x^2$ be $0 \le x \le 4$.
 a. Graph the function, including all points whose x-coordinates are 0, 1, 2, 3, 4.
 b. What is the greatest value in the range of this function?

In 16–24, in each case, state the largest possible domain such that the given relation is a function.

16. $f(x) = \frac{2}{x - 2}$
17. $g(x) = \frac{x - 3}{x - 9}$
18. $h(x) = \frac{x}{x + 7}$

19. $m(x) = \frac{6}{x^2 - 16}$
20. $k:x \to \frac{1}{x^2 - 5x}$
21. $r:x \to 3x - 6$

22. $x \xrightarrow{f} \sqrt{x - 1}$
23. $x \xrightarrow{g} \frac{1}{\sqrt{x - 1}}$
24. $y = \frac{1}{x^2 + 1}$

In 25–30, for each given function: **a.** State the domain.   **b.** State the range.

25. $y = 2x$
26. $y = x^2$
27. $y = \sqrt{x}$

28. $h(x) = |x - 5|$
29. $f(x) = 10$
30. $x \xrightarrow{g} x + 10$

31. Given the function $f(x) = \frac{2x - 6}{x - 3}$:
 a. State the domain of the function.   **b.** Find f(5).
 c. Find f(38).   **d.** Find f(0).   **e.** Find f(−2).
 f. *True* or *False*: For every x in the domain stated in part **a**, $f(x) = 2$. Explain your answer.
 g. State the range of the function.

In 32–39, evaluate each expression, finding the greatest integer.

32. $[17]$
33. $\left[27\frac{1}{2}\right]$
34. $[1.23]$
35. $[0.8]$

36. $\left[-5\frac{1}{2}\right]$
37. $[-0.1]$
38. $\left[\frac{15}{4}\right]$
39. $\left[-\frac{15}{4}\right]$

In 40–42, in each case, select the *numeral* preceding the expression that best answers the question.

40. If $k(x) = \frac{x - 2}{x - 1}$, for what value of x will $k(x) = 0$?

 (1) 1
 (2) 2
 (3) both 1 and 2
 (4) neither 1 nor 2

41. Which of the following ordered pairs is *not* an element of the greatest-integer function $y = [x]$?
    (1) $(8, 8)$ (2) $(2.76, 2)$ (3) $(-3.6, -3)$ (4) $(-4.6, -5)$

42. Which of the following is *not* a function?
    (1) the line $y = 5x - 4$ (2) the parabola $y = x^2 - 3x$
    (3) the line $y = 2$ (4) the circle $x^2 + y^2 = 16$

    In 43–48:   **a.** Graph each given function for the domain $-3 \le x \le 3$.   **b.** Using this domain, state the range of the function.

43. $y = |x|$ **44.** $f(x) = |3x|$ **45.** $y = |x| + 2$
46. $f(x) = |x + 2|$ **47.** $y = 3 - |x|$ **48.** $f(x) = x + |x|$

    In 49–54, in each case: **a.** Graph the given function for the domain $0 \le x < 6$.   **b.** Using this domain, state the range of the function.

49. $f(x) = [x]$ **50.** $y = [x - 2]$ **51.** $g(x) = [3 - x]$
52. $y = \left[\frac{1}{2}x\right]$ **53.** $h(x) = \left[\frac{1}{3}x\right]$ **54.** $y = x - [x]$

Applications with Functions

55. A newspaper deliverer earns $0.07 for each paper delivered. Thus, the earnings E is a function of the number n of newspapers delivered, or $E = f(n)$. The formula to determine the deliverer's earnings is $E = 0.07n$, or $f(n) = 0.07n$.
    a. How much is earned when 20 papers are delivered? In other words, find $f(20)$.
    b. Find $f(15)$.   **c.** Find $f(32)$.   **d.** Find $f(57)$.
    e. If Jennifer earns $2.66 for a daily delivery, how many newspapers does she deliver each day?

56. The accompanying table shows the 8% sales taxes to be collected on amounts from $0.01 to $1.06. On sales over $1.06, the tax is computed by multiplying the amount of sale by 0.08, and rounding to the nearest whole cent.
    The sales tax t is a function of the amount A of the sale, that is, $t = f(A)$.
    a. Find the sales tax on an item costing $0.52; that is, find $f(\$0.52)$.
    b. Find $f(\$0.89)$.   **c.** Find $f(\$0.39)$.
    d. Find $f(\$0.08)$.   **e.** Find $f(\$9.95)$.
    f. *True* or *False*: Sales tax is an example of a step function.
    g. *True* or *False*: For amounts less than $1.00, the tax in the chart is equal to 8% of the amount, rounded to the nearest whole cent.

Amount of Sale	8% Sales Tax
$0.01 to $0.10	NONE
0.11 to 0.17	$0.01
0.18 to 0.29	0.02
0.30 to 0.42	0.03
0.43 to 0.54	0.04
0.55 to 0.67	0.05
0.68 to 0.79	0.06
0.80 to 0.92	0.07
0.93 to 1.06	0.08

57. If an object is dropped from a height, the distance d that it travels is a function of the time t for its fall, or $d = f(t)$. In Earth's gravity, this distance is found by the formula $d = 16t^2$, or $f(t) = 16t^2$, where d is distance, in feet, and t is time, in seconds. Assume that an object is dropped from the top of a tall building.

   a. How many feet will the object travel in 1 second? In other words, find f(1).

   b. Find f(2).   **c.** Find f(3).   **d.** Find f(4).

   e. If the object hits the ground in 7 seconds, how tall is the building?

58. A car-rental agency charges $50 for a rental of 3 days or less and $20 for each additional day or part thereof. A weekly rental costs $100. The graph at the right represents the charges for rentals of 1 week or less.

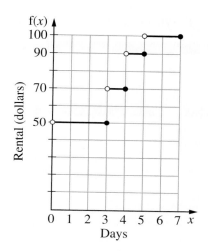

   a. *True* or *False*: The rental fee r is a function of the number of days d of rental, or $r = f(d)$.

   b. Find the rental fee for 4 days; that is, find f(4).

   c. Explain why f(6) ≠ $110.

   d. State the range of the function.

59. The rates charged to park a car in a city lot are shown in the accompanying table. The rate r is a function of the number of hours h that the car is parked, or $r = f(h)$.

   a. Graph the function for a 24-hour period.

   b. Find the rate to park a car for $2\frac{1}{2}$ hours; that is, find $f\left(2\frac{1}{2}\right)$.

   c. Find $f\left(4\frac{1}{4}\right)$.   **d.** Find f(7).   **e.** Find $f\left(10\frac{1}{2}\right)$.

Hours	Rate
First 2 hours or less	$3.00
Each additional 1 hour or part	$1.00
Maximum for 24 hours	$7.00

60. A local telephone call from a home phone, under timed service, costs $0.08 for the first 5 minutes or less and $0.01 for each additional minute or any part thereof.

   a. Graph this step function for costs of telephone calls lasting 12 minutes or less.

   b. *True* or *False*: The cost is a function of the time of the call.

   c. Using these rates, find the cost of a call lasting:

     (1) $6\frac{1}{2}$ minutes   *(2)* 10 minutes 45 seconds   *(3)* 1 hour

61. The table at the right shows the rates for a taxicab ride in a large city. The rate r is a function of the mileage m, or $r = f(m)$.

  a. Graph the function for all rates on rides of 1 mile or less.

  b. Find $f\left(\frac{1}{2} \text{ mile}\right)$.   **c.** Find $f(0.7 \text{ mile})$.

  d. Find $f\left(\frac{1}{4} \text{ mile}\right)$.   **e.** Find $f\left(\frac{7}{8} \text{ mile}\right)$.

  f. What is the rate for a cab ride of 6 miles?

Mileage	Rate
First $\frac{1}{10}$ mile or less	$1.20
Each additional $\frac{1}{10}$ mile or part	$0.10

12-6 THE PARABOLA

In Section 12-4, we described the second-degree polynomial function or quadratic function $f(x) = ax^2 + bx + c$ $(a \neq 0)$ as a function whose graph is a parabola. This function can be defined as a locus of points.

● **DEFINITION.** A *parabola* is the locus of points equidistant from a fixed point and a fixed line. The fixed point is called the *focus*, and the fixed line is the *directrix*.

Finding the Equation of a Parabola

The simplest equation for a parabola can be derived by placing the focus on the y-axis and the directrix perpendicular to the y-axis so that the origin is equidistant from the focus and directrix.

We will let the focus be point $F(0, d)$, the directrix be the line $y = -d$, and $P(x, y)$ be any point on the locus. The distance from any point on the locus to the focus is PF. The distance from any point on the locus to the directrix is the length of the perpendicular segment from P to the directrix. If M is the projection of P on the directrix, the distance from P to the directrix is PM.

Therefore:

$$PF = PM$$
$$\sqrt{(x - 0)^2 + (y - d)^2} = |y - (-d)|$$
$$(x - 0)^2 + (y - d)^2 = (y + d)^2$$
$$x^2 + y^2 - 2dy + d^2 = y^2 + 2dy + d^2$$
$$x^2 = 4dy$$
$$\frac{1}{4d} x^2 = y$$

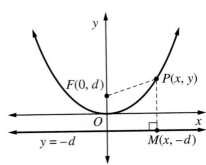

Every parabola is symmetric with respect to a line through the focus, perpendicular to the directrix. The axis of symmetry of the parabola $y = \frac{1}{4d} x^2$ is the y-axis. The turning point or *vertex* of this parabola is the origin, a point on the axis of symmetry that is equidistant from the focus and the directrix. When we compare the equation of this parabola with the general quadratic function $y = ax^2 + bx + c$, we see that $a = \frac{1}{4d}$, $b = 0$, and $c = 0$. The value of a is determined by the distance between the focus and the directrix. The values of b and c depend on the coordinates of the focus.

For example, to find an equation of the parabola whose focus is $(4, 1)$ and whose directrix is $y = -3$, we will let $P(x, y)$ be any point on the locus. The focus is point $F(4, 1)$, and the projection of P on the directrix $y = -3$ is $M(x, -3)$. Therefore:

$$PF = PM$$
$$\sqrt{(x - 4)^2 + (y - 1)^2} = |y - (-3)|$$
$$(x - 4)^2 + (y - 1)^2 = (y + 3)^2$$
$$x^2 - 8x + 16 + y^2 - 2y + 1 = y^2 + 6y + 9$$
$$x^2 - 8x + 8 = 8y$$
$$\frac{1}{8} x^2 - x + 1 = y$$

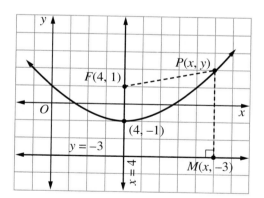

Graphing a Parabola

When we draw the graph of a parabola, whether by plotting points or by using a graphing calculator, it is helpful to know the equation of the axis of symmetry in order to choose a domain that includes the turning point.

For any parabola of the form $y = ax^2 + bx + c$, the axis of symmetry is a vertical line whose equation is $x = k$, where k is some constant.

Let us imagine that the parabola $y = ax^2 + bx + c$ crosses the x-axis at two points, as shown in the diagram below. Then $y = 0$ at both points, and, therefore, $ax^2 + bx + c = 0$. Since the roots of this quadratic equation are $\dfrac{-b \pm \sqrt{b^2 - 4ac}}{2a}$, it follows that the parabola crosses the x-axis at points $\left(\dfrac{-b - \sqrt{b^2 - 4ac}}{2a}, 0\right)$ and $\left(\dfrac{-b + \sqrt{b^2 - 4ac}}{2a}, 0\right)$.

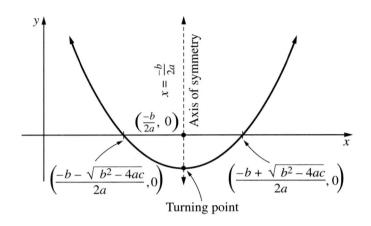

By definition, the axis of symmetry must pass through the midpoint of the two points of the parabola on the x-axis. By using the midpoint formula, or the average, we can find the x-value of this midpoint:

$$x = \frac{x_1 + x_2}{2} = \frac{1}{2}(x_1 + x_2) = \frac{1}{2}\left(\frac{-b - \sqrt{b^2 - 4ac}}{2a} + \frac{-b + \sqrt{b^2 - 4ac}}{2a}\right)$$

$$= \frac{1}{2}\left(\frac{-2b}{2a}\right) = \frac{1}{2}\left(\frac{-b}{a}\right) \qquad = \frac{-b}{2a}$$

The midpoint has the coordinates $\left(\frac{-b}{2a}, 0\right)$, and it follows that:

- **The equation of the axis of symmetry of the parabola $y = ax^2 + bx + c$ ($a \neq 0$) is $x = \frac{-b}{2a}$.**

It can also be seen in the diagram that the x-coordinate of the turning point is $\frac{-b}{2a}$. The y-coordinate of the turning point is found by substituting $\frac{-b}{2a}$ for x in the equation for the parabola; that is, $f\left(-\frac{b}{2a}\right)$. By completing the square on the first two terms of $y = ax^2 + bx + c$, it can be shown that the y-coordinate of the turning point may be represented as $\frac{4ac - b^2}{4a}$.

In a similar way, a parabola of the form $x = ay^2 + by + c$ has a horizontal line whose equation is $y = \frac{-b}{2a}$ as its axis of symmetry. The turning point of this parabola has a y-coordinate equal to $\frac{-b}{2a}$, and its x-coordinate is found by substituting $\frac{-b}{2a}$ for y in the equation of the parabola. The relation $x = ay^2 + by + c$ is not a function.

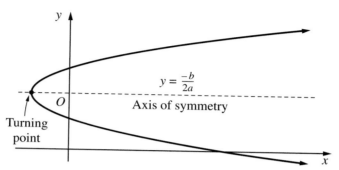

$$y = \frac{-b}{2a}$$
Axis of symmetry

Turning point

To see how these discoveries help us to graph a parabola, we will graph the function $f(x) = x^2 - 6x + 4$.

1. Find the *axis of symmetry* of the parabola.

$$x = \frac{-b}{2a} \qquad \text{or} \qquad x = \frac{-(-6)}{2(1)} = \frac{6}{2} = 3$$

Axis of symmetry

$$x = 3$$

2. Find the *turning point* of the parabola. The x-coordinate of the turning point is 3. The y-coordinate, or $f(x)$, is found by substituting $x = 3$ in the equation of the parabola.

$$y = x^2 - 6x + 4$$
$$y = (3)^2 - 6(3) + 4 = 9 - 18 + 4 = -5$$

Turning point

$$(3, -5)$$

3. Select values of x close to the axis of symmetry such as 0 to 6. After finding the corresponding y values, plot the coordinates and graph the parabola.

x	$x^2 - 6x + 4$	y
0	$0 - 0 + 4$	4
1	$1 - 6 + 4$	-1
2	$4 - 12 + 4$	-4
3	$9 - 18 + 4$	-5
4	$16 - 24 + 4$	-4
5	$25 - 30 + 4$	-1
6	$36 - 36 + 4$	4

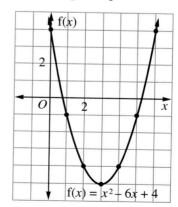

$$f(x) = x^2 - 6x + 4$$

To use a graphing calculator to sketch the graph, we choose a $\boxed{\textbf{WINDOW}}$ with Xmin $= -1$, Xmax $= 6$, Xscl $= 1$, Ymin $= -6$, Ymax $= 5$, and Yscl $= 1$.

Enter: $\boxed{\textbf{Y=}}$ $\boxed{\textbf{X,T,θ,}n}$ $\boxed{\textbf{x}^2}$ $\boxed{\textbf{–}}$ 6 $\boxed{\textbf{X,T,θ,}n}$

$\boxed{\textbf{+}}$ 4 $\boxed{\textbf{GRAPH}}$

Display:

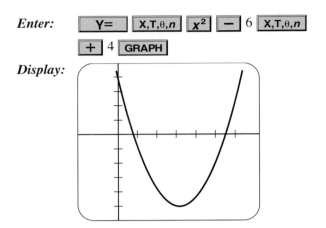

The equation of a parabola is a function if the directrix is perpendicular to the y-axis. If the directrix is parallel to the y-axis or is an oblique line, the equation of the parabola is a relation that is not a function. (See Example 2 on page 521.)

It is interesting to compare the graphs of some parabolas. Graph the following parabolas on the same screen in the standard viewing window: $y = x^2$, $y = x^2 + 3$, and $y = x^2 - 4$.

Enter: $\boxed{\textbf{Y=}}$ $\boxed{\textbf{X,T,θ,}n}$ $\boxed{\textbf{x}^2}$ $\boxed{\textbf{ENTER}}$

$\boxed{\textbf{X,T,θ,}n}$ $\boxed{\textbf{x}^2}$ $\boxed{\textbf{+}}$ 3 $\boxed{\textbf{ENTER}}$

$\boxed{\textbf{X,T,θ,}n}$ $\boxed{\textbf{x}^2}$ $-$ 4 $\boxed{\textbf{ENTER}}$ $\boxed{\textbf{GRAPH}}$

Display:

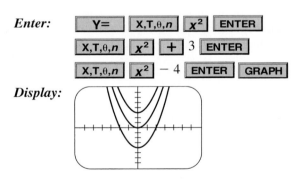

The graphs have the same shape and all open upward. The vertex of each graph is on the y-axis, but the graph is shifted up 3 units for $y = x^2 + 3$ and down 4 units for $y = x^2 - 4$.

Next graph $y = x^2$, $y = 2x^2$, and $y = 0.5x^2$.

Enter: $\boxed{\textbf{Y=}}$ $\boxed{\textbf{X,T,θ,}n}$ $\boxed{\textbf{x}^2}$ $\boxed{\textbf{ENTER}}$

2 $\boxed{\textbf{X,T,θ,}n}$ $\boxed{\textbf{x}^2}$ $\boxed{\textbf{ENTER}}$

.5 $\boxed{\textbf{X,T,θ,}n}$ $\boxed{\textbf{x}^2}$ $\boxed{\textbf{ENTER}}$ $\boxed{\textbf{GRAPH}}$

Display:

$$y = 2x^2$$
$$y = x^2$$
$$y = 0.5x^2$$

The graphs open upward, but the graph of $y = 2x^2$ is narrower than the graph of $y = x^2$ and the graph of $y = 0.5x^2$ is wider than the graph of $y = x^2$. As $|a|$ increases, the graph of $y = x^2$ narrows.

Finally, graph $y = x^2$, $y = -x^2$, $y = 2x^2$, and $y = -2x^2$.

Enter:

The graphs of $y = x^2$ and $y = 2x^2$ open upward, while the graphs of $y = -x^2$ and $y = -2x^2$ open downward.

The table below summarizes the characteristics of the graph of $y = ax^2 + bx + c$.

$$y = f(x) = ax^2 + bx + c$$

Axis of symmetry	$x = \dfrac{-b}{2a}$
Vertex (turning point)	$\left(\dfrac{-b}{2a}, f\left(\dfrac{-b}{2a}\right)\right)$
Direction of opening	Upward if $a > 0$, downward if $a < 0$
As the value of $|a|$ increases, the graph becomes narrower.	

The equation of any parabola $y = ax^2 + bx + c$ can also be expressed in the form $y = x^2 + (x - h^2) + k$ by completing the square. For example, if $y = x^2 - 6x + 4$, then

$$y = x^2 - 6x + 9 + 4 - 9 \qquad$$ Add and subtract $\left(\dfrac{-6}{2}\right)^2$ or 9 to obtain an
$$= (x - 3)^2 - 5 \qquad$$ equivalent equation.

When the equation for a parabola is expressed as $y = x^2 + (x - h^2) + k$, then the vertex is (h, k) and the equation of the axis of symmetry is $x = h$. The basic graph $y = x^2$ is shifted depending on the values of h and k: up $|k|$ units if k is positive, down $|k|$ units if k is negative, right $|h|$ units if h is positive, and left $|h|$ units if h is negative.

EXAMPLES

1. The focus of a parabola is point $F(4, -2)$, and the directrix is $y = 6$.
   a. Find the equation of the axis of symmetry.
   b. Find the coordinates of the turning point.
   c. Write an equation of the parabola.

Solutions

   a. The axis of symmetry is perpendicular to the directrix and passes through the focus. Since the directrix $y = 6$ is a horizontal line, the axis of symmetry is a vertical line through the focus $(4, -2)$. Therefore, the equation of the axis of symmetry is $x = 4$.

   b. The turning point is on the axis of symmetry, equidistant from the focus and the directrix. Here, the x-coordinate is 4 and its y-coordinate is the average of the y-coordinates of the focus $(4, -2)$ and the directrix $(y = 6)$. Therefore $y = \frac{-2 + 6}{2} = 2$, and the turning point is $(4, 2)$.

   c. Use the definition of a parabola:

$$PF = PM$$
$$\sqrt{(x - 4)^2 + (y - (-2))^2} = |y - 6|$$
$$(x - 4)^2 + (y + 2)^2 = (y - 6)^2$$
$$x^2 - 8x + 16 + y^2 + 4y + 4 = y^2 - 12y + 36$$
$$x^2 - 8x - 16 = -16y$$
$$-\frac{1}{16}x^2 + \frac{1}{2}x + 1 = y$$

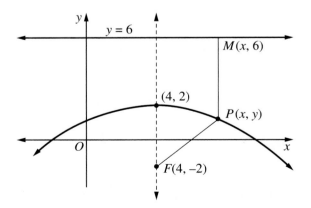

Answers: **a.** $x = 4$ **b.** $(4, 2)$ **c.** $y = -\frac{1}{16}x^2 + \frac{1}{2}x + 1$

2. Derive the equation of the locus of points equidistant from point $(1, 0)$ and the line $x = -1$.

Solution   The locus is a parabola with focus $F(1, 0)$ and directrix $x = -1$. Let $P(x, y)$ be any point of the locus.

$$PF = PM$$

$$\sqrt{(x - 1)^2 + (y - 0)^2} = |x - (-1)|$$

$$(x - 1)^2 + y^2 = (x + 1)^2$$

$$x^2 - 2x + 1 + y^2 = x^2 + 2x + 1$$

$$y^2 = 4x$$

$$\tfrac{1}{4} y^2 = x$$

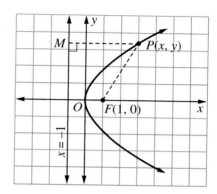

Answer: $x = \tfrac{1}{4} y^2$

---

3. Alan is standing on a hill 80 feet high. He throws a baseball upward with an initial velocity of 64 feet per second. The height of the ball h(t) in terms of the time t since the ball was thrown is $h(t) = -16t^2 + 64t + 80$.
   a. Find the time that the ball reaches its maximum height.
   b. Find the maximum height.

Solutions   **a.** Since $a = -16$, the parabola opens downward and has a maximum at the vertex. The maximum value occurs at

$$t = \frac{-b}{2a}$$

$$= \frac{-64}{-32} = 2$$

The ball reaches its maximum height at $t = 2$ seconds.

   b. The maximum height of the ball is the value of the function $h(t) = -16t^2 + 64t + 80$ at $t = 2$ seconds.

$$h(2) = -16(2^2) + 64(2) + 80$$

$$= -64 + 128 + 80$$

$$= 144$$

Answer: The ball reaches a maximum height of 144 feet.

EXERCISES

In 1–6, in each case derive an equation of the parabola with the given point as focus and the given line as directrix.

1. $(0, -3), y = 3$

2. $(0, 2), y = -2$

3. $(1, 1), y = 5$

4. $(1, 1), y = -3$

5. $(1, 0), x = -1$

6. $(1, 1), x = 5$

7. Write an equation of the axis of symmetry of a parabola whose focus is $(3, 4)$ and whose directrix is $y = -1$.

8. Write an equation of the axis of symmetry of a parabola whose focus is $(3, 4)$ and whose directrix is $x = -1$.

9. Write the coordinates of the turning point of a parabola whose focus is $(-2, 1)$ and whose directrix is $y = -3$.

10. Write the coordinates of the focus of a parabola if the turning point is $(2, -1)$ and the directrix is $y = 5$.

11. a. Sketch the graph of the function $y = \frac{1}{4}x^2$.
　　b. What is the turning point of the parabola?
　　c. What are the coordinates of the focus?
　　d. What is the equation of the directrix?

12. a. Sketch the graph of the function $y = -\frac{1}{4}x^2 + 2$.
　　b. What is the turning point of the parabola?
　　c. What are the coordinates of the focus?
　　d. What is the equation of the directrix?

13. Use a graphing calculator.
　　a. Graph $y = x^2$, $y = (x + 3)^2$, and $y = (x - 2)^2$.
　　b. Describe any similarities or differences among the graphs.
　　c. Write $y = (x + 3)^2$ and $y = (x - 2)^2$ in the form $y = ax^2 + bx + c$.

14. Examine each pair of equations and predict the graphs. Then use a graphing calculator to see if your prediction was correct. Describe the graphs.
　　a. $y = x^2$ and $y = x^2 + 5$
　　b. $y = x^2$ and $y = -0.3x^2$
　　c. $y = x^2$ and $y = 3x^2 - 2$

15. The weekly profit function in dollars of a small business that produces fruit jams is $P(x) = -0.4x^2 + 40x - 360$ where x is the number of jars of jam produced and sold.
　　a. Find the number of jars of jam that should be produced to maximize the weekly profit.
　　b. Find the maximum profit.

16. During archery practice, Paula shoots an arrow into the air such that its height at any time t, is given by the function $h(t) = -16t^2 + kt + 5$. If the maximum height of the arrow occurs at time $t = 3.5$ seconds, what is the value of k?

12-7   THE ELLIPSE AND THE CIRCLE

A second-degree equation in two variables in which both variables are squared can be written in the form $px^2 + qy^2 = r$. The equation defines a relation that is not a function. If p, q, and r are all positive or all negative, the graph is a circle or an ellipse, that is, a closed curve that has two axes of symmetry perpendicular to each other. If $p = q$, the graph is a circle; if $p \neq q$, the graph is an ellipse.

● **DEFINITION.** An *ellipse* is the locus of points such that the sum of the distances of any point on the locus from two fixed points is a constant. Each of the fixed points is a *focus* of the ellipse.

For example, if F_1 and F_2 are the foci, and P_1, P_2, and P_3 are points on the ellipse, then

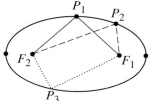

$$F_1P_1 + F_2P_1 = F_1P_2 + F_2P_2$$
$$= F_1P_3 + F_2P_3$$

The Equation of an Ellipse

An ellipse whose equation has the form $px^2 + qy^2 = r$, and that has its foci on an axis, with each focus equidistant from the origin, is symmetric with respect to each axis. If the ellipse intersects the x-axis at $(a, 0)$ and $(-a, 0)$ and the y-axis at $(0, b)$ and $(0, -b)$, the equation of the ellipse can be written in the form $\dfrac{x^2}{a^2} + \dfrac{y^2}{b^2} = 1$. If $a^2 > b^2$, the foci are on the x-axis.

If $y = 0$:

$$\frac{x^2}{a^2} + \frac{0^2}{b^2} = 1$$

$$\frac{x^2}{a^2} = 1$$

$$x^2 = a^2$$

$$x = \pm a$$

The x-intercepts are $\pm a$; $(a, 0)$ and $(-a, 0)$ are points of the ellipse.

If $x = 0$:

$$\frac{0^2}{a^2} + \frac{y^2}{b^2} = 1$$

$$\frac{y^2}{b^2} = 1$$

$$y^2 = b^2$$

$$y = \pm b$$

The y-intercepts are $\pm b$; $(0, b)$ and $(0, -b)$ are points of the ellipse.

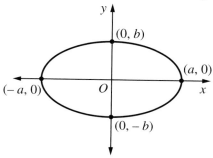

For example, the graph of the equation $4x^2 + 9y^2 = 36$ is an ellipse. To put the equation into intercept form, we divide each term by the constant term, 36, and then compare the resulting equation to the general intercept form.

$$4x^2 + 9y^2 = 36$$

$$\frac{4x^2}{36} + \frac{9y^2}{36} = \frac{36}{36}$$

$$\frac{x^2}{9} + \frac{y^2}{4} = 1 \longleftrightarrow \frac{x^2}{a^2} + \frac{y^2}{b^2} = 1$$

$$a^2 = 9 \qquad b^2 = 4$$

The intercepts are $\qquad a = \pm 3 \qquad b = \pm 2$

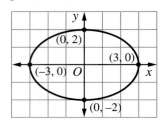

Therefore, the x-intercepts are 3 and -3 and the y-intercepts are 2 and -2. We graph the vertices, $(3, 0)$, $(-3, 0)$, $(0, 2)$, and $(0, -2)$, and draw an ellipse through these points.

The vertical-line test is applied to verify that the equation is a relation that is not a function. For example, $(0, 2)$ and $(0, -2)$ are two pairs of the relation that have the same first element.

To graph this relation on a graphing calculator, we must first solve for y in terms of x.

$$4x^2 + 9y^2 = 36$$

$$9y^2 = 36 - 4x^2$$

$$y^2 = \frac{36 - 4x^2}{9}$$

$$y = \pm\frac{\sqrt{36 - 4x^2}}{3}$$

Since for each y there are two values of x, one positive and one negative, we must enter the equation of the ellipse in two parts.

Enter: | Y= | | 2nd | | √ | 36 | − | 4

| X,T,θ,*n* | | x² | |) | | ÷ | 3 | ENTER |

| (−) | | 2nd | | √ | 36 | − | 4

| X,T,θ,*n* | | x² | |) | | ÷ | 3 | ENTER |

| GRAPH |

Display:

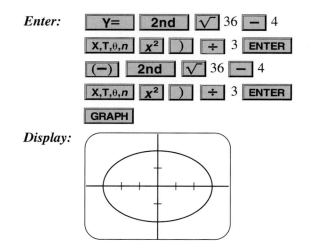

There are two lines of symmetry for an ellipse. The intersection of the two lines of symmetry is called the *center* of the ellipse. The segments of the lines of symmetry in the interior of the ellipse are called the **major axis** and the **minor axis** of the ellipse. The foci are always points of the major axis, which is the longer axis.

For $a^2 > b^2$:

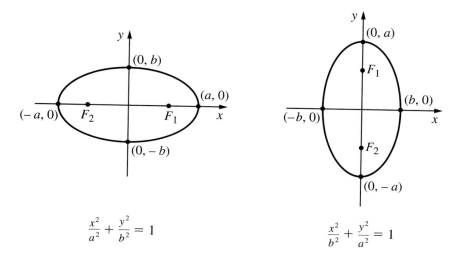

$$\frac{x^2}{a^2} + \frac{y^2}{b^2} = 1 \qquad\qquad \frac{x^2}{b^2} + \frac{y^2}{a^2} = 1$$

If the foci are points on the y-axis equidistant from the origin, that is, $F_1(0, c)$ and $F_2(0, -c)$, the equation of the ellipse is $\frac{x^2}{b^2} + \frac{y^2}{a^2} = 1$, where $a^2 > b^2$. For this ellipse, the major axis is the segment of the y-axis from $(0, a)$ to $(0, -a)$ and the minor axis is a segment of the x-axis from $(b, 0)$ to $(-b, 0)$.

The equation of an ellipse with center at (h, k) and a horizontal major axis is

$$\frac{(x - h)^2}{a^2} + \frac{(y - k)^2}{b^2} = 1$$

Geometrically, this equation represents the ellipse $\frac{x^2}{a^2} + \frac{y^2}{b^2} = 1$ translated h units left or right and k units up or down. Similarly, the equation of an ellipse with center at (h, k) and a vertical major axis is

$$\frac{(x - h)^2}{b^2} + \frac{(y - k)^2}{a^2} = 1$$

The Equation of a Circle

We can think of the circle as a special case of an ellipse in which the two foci are the same point. The definition of a circle can also be restated as given in Chapter 11. We will use this definition to derive the equation of a circle with any point as center.

- **DEFINITION.** A *circle* is the locus of points in a plane equidistant from a fixed point.

Recall that when the center of the circle is at the origin $(0, 0)$ and the radius is length r, the equation of the circle is $x^2 + y^2 = r^2$. For example, circle $x^2 + y^2 = 25$ has its center at the origin and has a radius of 5.

To write the equation of a circle whose center is at (h, k) and the length of whose radius is r, we let $P(x, y)$ represent any point on the circle and use the distance formula:

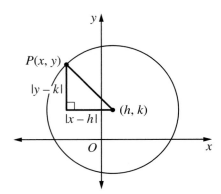

$$\sqrt{(x_1 - x_2)^2 + (y_1 - y_2)^2} = d$$

$$\sqrt{(x - h)^2 + (y - k)^2} = r$$

or $(x - h)^2 + (y - k)^2 = r^2$

EXAMPLES

1. The equation of an ellipse is $3x^2 + 12y^2 = 12$.
   a. Find the x- and y-intercepts of the graph.
   b. Sketch the graph.

Solutions   **a.** Write the equation in intercept form by dividing by the constant term.

$$3x^2 + 12y^2 = 12$$

$$\frac{3x^2}{12} + \frac{12y^2}{12} = \frac{12}{12}$$

$$\frac{x^2}{4} + \frac{y^2}{1} = 1$$

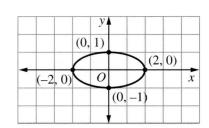

$$a^2 = 4 \qquad b^2 = 1$$
$$a = \pm 2 \qquad b = \pm 1$$

b. Plot points $(2, 0)$, $(-2, 0)$, $(0, 1)$, and $(0, -1)$, and draw the ellipse through these points.

Answers: **a.** The x-intercepts are ± 2, and the y-intercepts are ± 1.
   b. See graph.

2. Sketch a graph of $\frac{(x-2)^2}{16} + \frac{(y+3)^2}{9} = 1$.

Solution

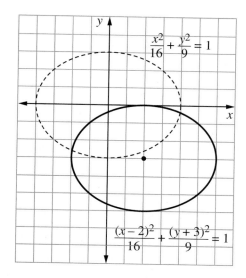

The graph has the same shape as the graph of $\frac{x^2}{16} + \frac{y^2}{9} = 1$. The center, however, is at $(2, -3)$. The graph of $\frac{x^2}{16} + \frac{y^2}{9} = 1$ must be translated 2 units right and 3 units down.

---

3. Write the equation of the locus of points 3 units from $(2, -1)$.

Solution   Use the formula $(x - h)^2 + (y - k)^2 = r^2$.

Substitute the given values: $h = 2, k = -1, r = 3$:

$$(x - 2)^2 + (y - (-1))^2 = 3^2$$

Answer: $(x - 2)^2 + (y + 1)^2 = 9$

EXERCISES WITH OPEN-RESPONSE PROBLEMS

In 1–6, for each equation: **a.** Find the x- and y-intercepts.   **b.** Sketch the graph.   **c.** State the domain and the range of the relation.

1. $x^2 + 4y^2 = 4$

2. $25x^2 + 4y^2 = 100$

3. $x^2 + 9y^2 = 9$

4. $x^2 + 9y^2 = 36$

5. $16x^2 + 4y^2 = 64$

6. $4x^2 + 3y^2 = 12$

7. Write an equation of the ellipse whose center is at the origin, whose major axis is a segment of the x-axis of length 12, and whose minor axis is of length 8.

8. a. Write the equation of the ellipse whose center is at (2, 1), whose major axis is a segment of the x-axis of length 20, and whose minor axis is of length 10.
   b. Sketch the graph of the ellipse.

In 9–14, in each case write an equation of the circle with the given length of the radius and the given point as the center.

9. $r = 2, (0, 0)$

10. $r = 5, (1, 3)$

11. $r = 1, (-1, 5)$

12. $r = 3, (0, -3)$

13. $r = 12, (-4, 0)$

14. $r = \sqrt{6}, (-2, -2)$

In 15–18, in each case find the coordinates of the center and the length of the radius for the circle whose equation is given.

15. $x^2 + y^2 = 16$

16. $(x - 3)^2 + (y - 1)^2 = 49$

17. $(x - 2)^2 + (y + 1)^2 = 4$

18. $(x + 6)^2 + (y + 5)^2 = 8$

19. Write an equation of the circle with center at (2, −3) that is tangent to the x-axis.
20. A circle whose center is in the second quadrant is tangent to both axes. Write an equation of the circle if the length of its radius is 6.
21. Find the equation of a circle that contains points (1, −2), (1, 4), and (5, 6).
22. A running track is shaped like an ellipse. The track is 240 feet long and 160 feet wide. Write an equation to describe the track. Assume that it is centered at the origin and the major axis is horizontal.
23. The transmitting tower for a local radio station is located on the town map at (3, 7). The station's signal can be picked up for a range of almost 15 miles. Write an equation for the boundary of the region in which the signal can be picked up.

12-8 THE HYPERBOLA

A second-degree equation of the form $px^2 + qy^2 = r$ that defines an ellipse and a circle also defines a hyperbola. If p and q have opposite signs, the graph of this relation is a hyperbola. Like the ellipse, the hyperbola has two axes of symmetry that are perpendicular to each other. A hyperbola can be defined as a locus.

● **DEFINITION.** A *hyperbola* is the locus of points such that the absolute value of the difference of the distances of any point on the locus from two fixed points is a constant. Each of the fixed points is a *focus* of the hyperbola.

For example, if in the diagram at the right F_1 and F_2 are the foci, and P_1, P_2, and P_3 are points on the hyperbola, then

$$|F_1P_1 - F_2P_1| = |F_1P_2 - F_2P_2|$$
$$= |F_1P_3 - F_2P_3|$$

A hyperbola whose equation is of the form $px^2 + qy^2 = r$ has its foci on an axis, equidistant from the center of the hyperbola, which in this case is the origin, so that the hyperbola is symmetric with respect to the x-axis and the y-axis. If the hyperbola intersects the x-axis at vertices $(a, 0)$ and $(-a, 0)$ and has no point of intersection with the y-axis, the equation of the hyperbola can be written in the form $\frac{x^2}{a^2} - \frac{y^2}{b^2} = 1.$

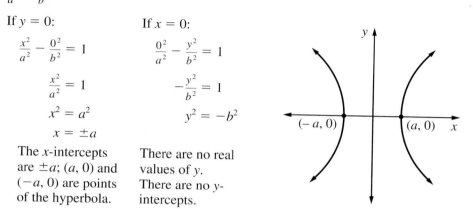

If $y = 0$:

$$\frac{x^2}{a^2} - \frac{0^2}{b^2} = 1$$

$$\frac{x^2}{a^2} = 1$$

$$x^2 = a^2$$

$$x = \pm a$$

The x-intercepts are $\pm a$; $(a, 0)$ and $(-a, 0)$ are points of the hyperbola.

If $x = 0$:

$$\frac{0^2}{a^2} - \frac{y^2}{b^2} = 1$$

$$-\frac{y^2}{b^2} = 1$$

$$y^2 = -b^2$$

There are no real values of y. There are no y-intercepts.

We know that the graph of the equation $3x^2 - y^2 = 12$ is a hyperbola because the coefficients of x^2 and y^2 have opposite signs. Because the coefficient of x^2 and the constant term are both positive, the graph has x-intercepts but no y-intercepts, as shown on page 530. We solve the equation for y in terms of x, choose values of x, and find the corresponding values of y.

$$3x^2 - y^2 = 12$$

$$-y^2 = -3x^2 + 12$$

$$y^2 = 3x^2 - 12$$

$$y = \pm\sqrt{3x^2 - 12}$$

x	$\pm\sqrt{3x^2 - 12}$	$=$	y
± 2	$\pm\sqrt{3(\pm 2)^2 - 12} = \pm\sqrt{0}$		0
± 3	$\pm\sqrt{3(\pm 3)^2 - 12} = \pm\sqrt{15}$	$=$	$\pm\sqrt{15}$
± 4	$\pm\sqrt{3(\pm 4)^2 - 12} = \pm\sqrt{36}$	$=$	± 6

The x-intercepts of the graph shown on page 530 are 2 and -2. For a value of x between 2 and -2, the value of y is the square root of a negative number, not a real number. Therefore, there is no real number that is the value of y when x is 0; that is, there are no y-intercepts. For each value of x that has an absolute value greater than 2, there are two values of y, a positive value and a negative value. Thus the equation $3x^2 - y^2 = 12$ is a relation that is not a function. The domain is $\{x \mid |x| \geq 2\}$, and the range is the set of real numbers.

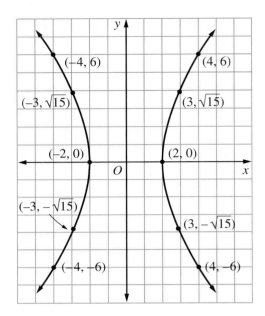

There are two lines of symmetry for the graph of $3x^2 - y^2 = 12$, the x-axis and the y-axis, and one point of symmetry, the origin. The ***transverse axis*** of a hyperbola is a segment of the line of symmetry that intersects the graph. The endpoints of the transverse axis are points on the hyperbola. For the hyperbola $3x^2 - y^2 = 12$, the endpoints of the transverse axis are $(-2, 0)$ and $(2, 0)$.

To graph the relation $3x^2 - y^2 = 12$ or $y = \pm\sqrt{3x^2 - 12}$ on a graphing calculator, we must enter the equation in two parts.

Enter: | Y= | | 2nd | | √ | 3 | X,T,θ,n | | x² |
−	12	)		ENTER
(−)		2nd		√	3	X,T,θ,n		x²
−	12	)		ENTER		GRAPH

Display:

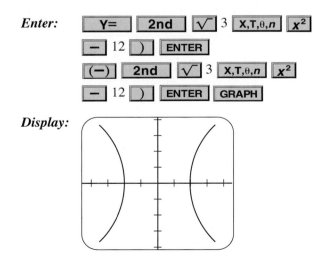

Asymptotes can be used as an aid in graphing hyperbolas. The asymptotes are two straight lines that go through the center of the hyperbola. As the values of x and y get larger, the graph of the hyperbola will approach the asymptotes. The equations of the asymptotes of a hyperbola whose center is the origin with a horizontal transverse axis are

$$y = \frac{b}{a}x \text{ and } y = \frac{-b}{a}x$$

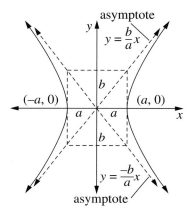

A hyperbola whose foci are on the y-axis has an equation that can be written in the form

$$\frac{y^2}{a^2} - \frac{x^2}{b^2} = 1 \qquad \text{or} \qquad -\frac{x^2}{b^2} + \frac{y^2}{a^2} = 1.$$

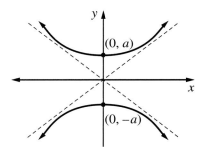

This curve intersects the y-axis at $(0, a)$ and $(0, -a)$ and has no x-intercepts. The domain is the set of real numbers, and the range is $\{y \mid y \geq a \text{ or } y \leq -a, a > 0\}$. The example that follows gives the equation of this type of hyperbola.

For a hyperbola with a vertical transverse axis, the equations of the asymptotes are

$$y = \frac{a}{b}x \text{ and } y = -\frac{a}{b}x$$

The equations of hyperbolas with center at (h, k) are

$$\frac{(x - h)^2}{a^2} - \frac{(y - k)^2}{b^2} = 1 \qquad\qquad \frac{(x - k)^2}{a^2} - \frac{(y - h)^2}{b^2} = 1$$

asymptotes $(y - k) = \pm\frac{b}{a}(x - h)$ asymptotes $(y - k) = \pm\frac{a}{b}(x - h)$
horizontal transverse axis   vertical transverse axis

EXAMPLES

1. a. Write the equation of the hyperbola $25x^2 - 4y^2 = 100$ in standard form.
  b. Determine the equations of the asymptotes.
  c. Sketch the graph of the hyperbola and its asymptotes.

Solutions **a.** Divide both sides of the equation by 100 to obtain a 1 on the right side of the equation.

$$\frac{25x^2}{100} - \frac{4y^2}{100} = \frac{100}{100}$$

$$\frac{x^2}{4} - \frac{y^2}{25} = 1$$

b. The equations of the asymptotes are $y = \frac{b}{a}x$ and $y = \frac{-b}{a}x$.
Since $a = 2$ and $b = 5$,

$$y = \frac{5}{2}x \text{ and } y = -\frac{5}{2}x$$

c. The graph is sketched at the right.

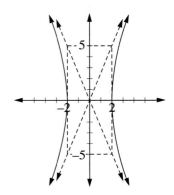

2. Find the length of the transverse axis of the hyperbola $2x^2 - 8y^2 = -16$.

Solution Write the equation in intercept form. Since the coefficient of x^2 is negative, there are no points of intersection with the x-axis. If $x = 0$, $y = \pm\sqrt{2}$. The transverse axis is a segment of the y-axis from $(0, \sqrt{2})$ to $(0, -\sqrt{2})$. The length of the transverse axis is $|\sqrt{2} - (-\sqrt{2})| = 2\sqrt{2}$.

$$\frac{2x^2}{-16} - \frac{8y^2}{-16} = \frac{-16}{-16}$$

$$-\frac{x^2}{8} + \frac{y^2}{2} = 1$$

$$0 + \frac{y^2}{2} = 1$$

$$y^2 = 2$$

$$y = \pm\sqrt{2}$$

Answer: $2\sqrt{2}$

EXERCISES WITH OPEN-RESPONSE PROBLEMS

In 1–6, answer the following questions for each equation:

a. The transverse axis is a segment of which axis?
b. What is the length of the transverse axis?
c. What are the domain and range of the relation?
d. What are the equations of the asymptotes?

1. $4x^2 - y^2 = 16$
4. $x^2 - 3y^2 = -9$

2. $3x^2 - 12y^2 = 24$
5. $x^2 - y^2 = 1$

3. $y^2 - x^2 = 9$
6. $-8x^2 + y^2 = 64$

7. **a.** Sketch the graph of $4x^2 - 9y^2 = 36$.
   b. Sketch the reflection in the line $x = y$ of the graph drawn in part **a.**
   c. Write an equation of the reflection drawn in part **b.**

8. **a.** Determine the center of the hyperbola $\dfrac{(x-3)^2}{9} - \dfrac{(y+2)^2}{4} = 1$.
   b. Write the equations of the asymptotes.
   c. Sketch the graph.

9. The hyperbola $\dfrac{(y-1)^2}{16} - \dfrac{(x+4)^2}{9} = 1$ is translated 4 units left and 1 unit up. Write the equation of the hyperbola in its new position.

12-9   THE CONIC SECTIONS

The curves that we studied in Sections 12-6 through 12-8 are called *conic sections* and have a common locus definition.

● **DEFINITION.** A **conic** is the locus of points such that the ratio of the distances of any point on the locus to a fixed point and to a fixed line is a constant. The constant ratio is a positive number called the **eccentricity** of the conic.

In the diagram at the right, F is the fixed point (the focus), m is the fixed line (the directrix), P is any point on the locus, and M is the projection of P on m. If the eccentricity of the conic is a positive number e:

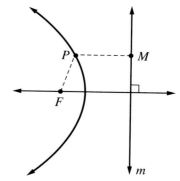

$$\frac{|PF|}{|PM|} = e$$

If $e < 1$, the conic is an ellipse.
If $e = 1$, the conic is a parabola.
If $e > 1$, the conic is a hyperbola.

For the parabola, $\dfrac{|PF|}{|PM|} = e$ or $|PF| = |PM|$. We derived the equation of the parabola using this definition in Section 12-6. For the ellipse and the hyperbola, we used definitions different from those given here in Sections 12-7 and 12-8.

Later in this section we will see how the definitions given earlier derive from those given here. In the derivations that follow, it can be seen that the difference in the equations of the hyperbola and the ellipse is the result of the different values of the eccentricity.

In order to have a curve that is symmetric with respect to the x-axis and the y-axis, we will let the focus point be point $F(ae, 0)$ and the directrix be the vertical line $x = \frac{a}{e}$, where a is an arbitrary positive constant. The eccentricity e of the conic is a positive constant.

Ellipse	*Hyperbola*
$e < 1 < \frac{1}{e}$	$e > 1 > \frac{1}{e}$
$ae < a < \frac{a}{e}$	$ae > a > \frac{a}{e}$

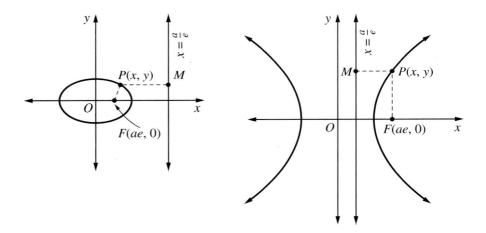

$$\frac{|PF|}{|PM|} = e$$

$$|PF| = e|PM|$$

$$\sqrt{(x - ae)^2 + (y - 0)^2} = e\left|x - \frac{a}{e}\right|$$

$$(x - ae)^2 + (y - 0)^2 = e^2\left(x - \frac{a}{e}\right)^2$$

$$x^2 - 2aex + a^2e^2 + y^2 = e^2\left(x^2 - 2\frac{a}{e}x + \frac{a^2}{e^2}\right)$$

$$x^2 - 2aex + a^2e^2 + y^2 = e^2x^2 - 2aex + a^2$$

$$x^2 - e^2x^2 + y^2 = a^2 - a^2e^2 \quad \text{Collect variable terms on the left side.}$$

$$x^2(1 - e^2) + y^2 = a^2(1 - e^2)$$

The equation $x^2(1 - e^2) + y^2 = a^2(1 - e^2)$ applies to both the ellipse and the hyperbola. The difference between the two curves depends on whether the constant $(1 - e^2)$ is positive or negative, as seen in the following:

<table>
<tr><td align="center">Ellipse</td><td align="center">Hyperbola</td></tr>
<tr><td align="center">$0 < e < 1$</td><td align="center">$e > 1$</td></tr>
<tr><td align="center">$0 < e^2 < 1$</td><td align="center">$e^2 > 1$</td></tr>
<tr><td align="center">$0 > -e^2 > -1$</td><td align="center">$-e^2 < -1$</td></tr>
<tr><td align="center">$1 > 1 - e^2 > 0$</td><td align="center">$1 - e^2 < 0$</td></tr>
<tr><td>The coefficients of x^2 and y^2 and the constant term are all positive.</td><td>The coefficients of x^2 and y^2 have opposite signs.</td></tr>
</table>

The intercept form of the equation of the curve is found by dividing each term by the constant term, $a^2(1 - e^2)$.

$$\frac{x^2(1 - e^2)}{a^2(1 - e^2)} + \frac{y^2}{a^2(1 - e^2)} = \frac{a^2(1 - e^2)}{a^2(1 - e^2)}$$

$$\frac{x^2}{a^2} + \frac{y^2}{a^2(1 - e^2)} = 1$$

<table>
<tr><td align="center">For the ellipse</td><td align="center">For the hyperbola</td></tr>
<tr><td>$1 - e^2 > 0$
Let $a^2(1 - e^2) = b^2$.</td><td>$1 - e^2 < 0$
Let $a^2(1 - e^2) = -b^2$.</td></tr>
<tr><td>$\dfrac{x^2}{a^2} + \dfrac{y^2}{b^2} = 1 \quad (0 < b < a)$</td><td>$\dfrac{x^2}{a^2} - \dfrac{y^2}{b^2} = 1$</td></tr>
<tr><td>Focus: $(ae, 0)$</td><td>Focus: $(ae, 0)$</td></tr>
<tr><td>Directrix: $x = \dfrac{a}{e}$</td><td>Directrix: $x = \dfrac{a}{e}$</td></tr>
<tr><td>The x-intercepts are a and $-a$.
The y-intercepts are b and $-b$.
Length of the major axis: $2a$
Length of the minor axis: $2b$</td><td>The x-intercepts are a and $-a$.
There are no y-intercepts.
Length of the transverse axis: $2a$</td></tr>
</table>

If the focus is on the y-axis and the directrix is perpendicular to the y-axis, similar equations result.

<table>
<tr><td align="center">For the ellipse</td><td align="center">For the hyperbola</td></tr>
<tr><td align="center">$\dfrac{x^2}{b^2} + \dfrac{y^2}{a^2} = 1$</td><td align="center">$-\dfrac{x^2}{b^2} - \dfrac{y^2}{a^2} = 1$</td></tr>
</table>

If we reflect the ellipse or the hyperbola, with its focus and directrix, over the y-axis, the image of $F(ae, 0)$ is $F'(-ae, 0)$ and the image of the directrix, $x = \frac{a}{e}$, is $x = -\frac{a}{e}$. F' and $x = -\frac{a}{e}$ are a new focus and directrix for the curve.

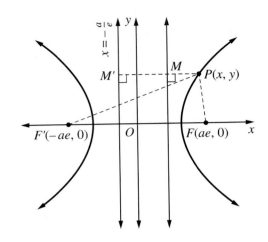

For the ellipse	For the hyperbola
$PF = ePM$	$PF = ePM$
$PF' = ePM'$	$PF' = ePM'$
$PF + PF' = ePM + ePM'$	$\lvert PF - PF' \rvert = \lvert ePM - ePM' \rvert$
$PF + PF' = e(PM + PM')$	$\lvert PF - PF' \rvert = e\lvert PM - PM' \rvert$

As seen in the diagram for the ellipse, $PM + PM'$ is the distance between the directrixes; that is, $\frac{a}{e} - \left(-\frac{a}{e}\right) = 2\frac{a}{e}$. Similarly, for the hyperbola, the distance $\lvert PM - PM' \rvert = 2\frac{a}{e}$. Thus:

$$PF + PF' = e\left(\frac{2a}{e}\right) = 2a \qquad \lvert PF - PF' \rvert = e\left(\frac{2a}{e}\right) = 2a$$

This result allows us to give the definitions of the ellipse, the circle, and the hyperbola from Sections 12-7 and 12-8.

An *ellipse* is the locus of points such that the sum of the distances from any point on the locus to two fixed points is a constant.

This definition of an ellipse makes it possible to define the circle as a special case of an ellipse in which the two focal points are the same point.

A *circle* is the locus of points such that the distance from any point on the locus to a fixed point is a constant.

A *hyperbola* is the locus of points such that the absolute value of the difference of the distances from any point on the locus to two fixed points is a constant.

The parabola, the ellipse, the circle, and the hyperbola are called *conic sections* because each of these curves is the intersection of a right circular cone with a plane as shown in the diagrams.

Circle

Ellipse

Parabola

Hyperbola

EXAMPLES

In 1–3, in each case, name the curve that is the graph of the equation.

1. $x^2 - 8y^2 = 16$ **2.** $x^2 = 1 - y^2$ **3.** $y = x^2 - 5x$

Solutions   **1.** Since both x and y are squared, compare the equation to $ax^2 + by^2 = c$. $a = 1, b = -8$, a and b have opposite signs.

Answer: hyperbola

2. Since both x and y are squared, compare the equation to $ax^2 + by^2 = c$. Write the equation as $x^2 + y^2 = 1$. $a = 1, b = 1, a = b$.

Answer: circle

3. Only one variable is squared.

Answer: parabola

---

4. Find the coordinates of the focus and the equation of the directrix of the hyperbola whose equation is $x^2 - y^2 = 2$.

How to Proceed:

(1) Write the equation in intercept form by dividing by the constant term.

(2) Compare with the equation $\frac{x^2}{a^2} - \frac{y^2}{b^2} = 1$. For the hyperbola: $a^2(1 - e^2) = -b^2$

(3) Solve for e, $e > 1$.

The focus is point $(ae, 0)$.

Solution:

$$x^2 - y^2 = 2$$

$$\frac{x^2}{2} - \frac{y^2}{2} = 1$$

$$a^2 = 2, b^2 = 2$$

$$2(1 - e^2) = -2$$

$$2 - 2e^2 = -2$$

$$-2e^2 = -4$$

$$e^2 = 2$$

$$e = \sqrt{2}$$

$$a = \sqrt{2}, e = \sqrt{2}$$

(4) The directrix is the line $x = \frac{a}{e}$.

$$\frac{a}{e} = \frac{\sqrt{2}}{\sqrt{2}} = 1$$

Answer: Focus: (2, 0)   Directrix: $x = 1$

Note: This hyperbola is its own image under a reflection in the y-axis. The image of the focus, (2, 0), is another focus, $(-2, 0)$, and the image of the directrix, $x = 1$, is another directrix, $x = -1$.

EXERCISES WITH OPEN-RESPONSE PROBLEMS

In 1–9, in each case:
a. Name the curve that is the graph of the equation.
b. Find the x- and y-intercept, if they exist.
c. Sketch the graph.
d. State whether or not the relation is a function.

1. $x^2 + y^2 = 1$

2. $3x^2 - 2y^2 = 6$

3. $y = -x^2 - 4$

4. $x^2 = 9 - 3y^2$

5. $x = y^2 - 3y + 1$

6. $x^2 = y^2 + 4$

7. $8y = x^2 + 2x$

8. $3x^2 + 3y^2 = 27$

9. $x^2 + 5y^2 = 20$

10. Write an equation of an ellipse that intersects the x-axis at $(+5, 0)$ and $(-5, 0)$ and the y-axis at $(0, +3)$ and $(0, -3)$.

11. An ellipse is symmetric with respect to the x- and y-axes. The major axis is a segment of the x-axis with length 12, and the length of the minor axis is 4. Write an equation of the ellipse.

12. a. Derive the equation of the parabola whose focus is (1, 1) and whose directrix is the x-axis.
b. Point $A(4, d)$ is on the parabola described in part **a**. Find d.
c. Find the distance from A to the focus.
d. Find the distance from A to the directrix.
e. Is A equidistant from the focus and the directrix?

13. The equation of an ellipse is $9x^2 + 25y^2 = 225$.
a. Find the x-intercepts.   **b.** Find the y-intercepts.
c. What is the length of the major axis?
d. What is the length of the minor axis?
e. What are the coordinates of the focal points?
f. Write the equations of the directrixes.

14. a. Derive the equation of the ellipse with focus at (4, 0), directrix at $x = 9$, and eccentricity $\frac{2}{3}$.
b. Find the x-intercepts.   **c.** Find the y-intercepts.
d. What is the length of the major axis?
e. What is the length of the minor axis?

15. a. Derive the equation of the ellipse with focus at (0, 4), directrix at $y = 9$, and eccentricity $\frac{2}{3}$.
b. Find the x-intercepts.   **c.** Find the y-intercepts.
d. What is the length of the major axis?
e. What is the length of the minor axis?

16. The ellipse whose equation is $5x^2 + 9y^2 = 180$ is reflected over the line $y = x$. Find the equation of the ellipse formed by this reflection.

17. a. Derive the equation of the hyperbola with focus at $(9, 0)$, directrix at $x = 1$, and eccentricity 3.
    b. Find the x-intercepts, if they exist.
    c. Find the y-intercepts, if they exist.
    d. What is the length of the transverse axis?

18. a. Derive the equation of the hyperbola with focus at $(0, 9)$, directrix at $y = 1$, and eccentricity 3.
    b. Find the x-intercepts, if they exist.
    c. Find the y-intercepts, if they exist.
    d. What is the length of the transverse axis?

19. The equation of a hyperbola is $3x^2 - y^2 = 12$.
    a. Find the x-intercepts, if they exist.
    b. Find the y-intercepts, if they exist.
    c. Find the length of the transverse axis.
    d. Find the coordinates of the focal points.
    e. Write the equations of the directrixes.

20. The points at which the carpenter placed the tacks to draw a pattern for the oval table described in the chapter opener are the focal points of the ellipse. The table is to be 10 feet long and 6 feet wide.
    a. How far apart should the tacks be placed?
    b. How long should the carpenter make the string?

12-10   THE INVERSE VARIATION HYPERBOLA

The distance from the Hamlin Park entrance to the farthest picnic area is 8 miles. To walk that distance at 4 miles per hour takes 2 hours. Traveling that distance by bicycle at a rate of 8 miles per hour takes 1 hour. To drive 8 miles at a rate of 20 miles per hour takes $\frac{2}{5}$ hour. As the rate at which we travel increases, the time required to travel a constant distance decreases. We say that, for a constant distance, rate and time *vary inversely*.

Rate	*Time*
4	2
8	1
20	$\frac{2}{5}$

We will let x represent rate in miles per hour and y represent time in hours. Then, using the formula (rate)(time) = distance, we can write the equation $xy = 8$ to express the relationship between the rate and the time needed to travel 8 miles. This is an example of ***inverse variation*** that illustrates the following principle:

●   If x and y *vary inversely*, then $xy = $ a nonzero constant. The value xy is the ***constant of variation***.

An Example of Inverse Variation

The number of days (x) needed to complete a job varies inversely as the number of workers (y) assigned to the job. If the job can be completed by 2 workers in 10 days, then the constant of variation is the product 2(10) or 20. To find the number of workers needed to complete the job in 5 days, we let $x = 5$ and solve for y in the equation $xy = 20$.

$$xy = 20$$
$$5y = 20$$
$$y = 4$$

Therefore, 4 workers can complete the job in 5 days. We note that, when the number of workers is increased by the factor 2, the number of days needed to complete the job is decreased by the reciprocal factor $\frac{1}{2}$.

x	y
10	2
5	4

Graphing Inverse Variation

To draw the graph of $xy = 20$, we find ordered pairs that are elements of the solution set. For the positive product 20, values of x and y can be either both positive or both negative.

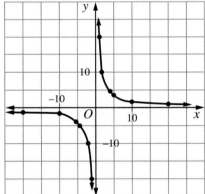

x	y
1	20
2	10
4	5
5	4
10	2
20	1

x	y
-1	-20
-2	-10
-4	-5
-5	-4
-10	-2
-20	-1

Hyperbola $xy = 20$

The graph, a hyperbola, consists of two parts. One part is in Quadrant I, where both x and y are positive, and the other part is in Quadrant III, where both x and y are negative. We notice that there is no value of x for which y is 0 and no value of y for which x is 0. Therefore the graph has no x-intercept and no y-intercept. Since for every nonzero value of x there is exactly one value of y, the equation $xy = 20$ defines a function whose domain and range are the set of nonzero real numbers.

EXAMPLES

1. The cost of hiring a bus for a trip to Niagara Falls is $400. The cost per person (x) varies inversely as the number of persons (y) who will go on the trip.
  a. Find the cost per person if 25 persons go on the trip.
  b. Find the number of persons who are going if the cost per person is $12.50.

Solutions   Since x and y vary inversely, write the equation $xy = 400$.

a.
$$xy = 400$$
$$x(25) = 400$$
$$x = \frac{400}{25}$$
$$x = 16$$

b.
$$xy = 400$$
$$12.50y = 400$$
$$y = \frac{400}{12.50}$$
$$y = 32$$

Answers: **a.** $16 per person   **b.** 32 persons

---

2. Draw the graph of $xy = -12$.

Solution   Since the product of x and y is negative, when x is positive, y will be negative; when x is negative, y will be positive.

x	y
1	−12
2	−6
3	−4
4	−3
6	−2
8	−1.5
12	−1

x	y
−1	12
−2	6
−3	4
−4	3
−6	2
−8	1.5
−12	1

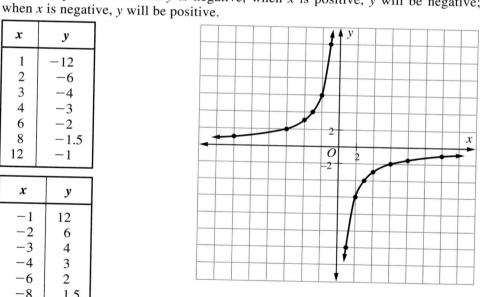

$$xy = -12$$

The graph has both line symmetry and point symmetry. The lines $y = x$ and $y = -x$ are lines of symmetry. The origin $(0, 0)$ is the point of symmetry.

EXERCISES WITH OPEN-RESPONSE PROBLEMS

In 1–8, draw the graph of each equation.

1. $xy = 6$ **2.** $xy = 15$ **3.** $xy = -4$ **4.** $xy = -2$

5. $y = \frac{10}{x}$ **6.** $y = -\frac{8}{x}$ **7.** $y = \frac{1}{x}$ **8.** $y = -\frac{1}{x}$

9. If 4 typists can complete the typing of a manuscript in 9 days, how long will 12 typists take to complete the manuscript?

10. If 4 typists can complete the typing of a manuscript in 9 days, how many typists are needed to complete the typing in 6 days?

11. If a man can drive from his home to Albany in 6 hours at 45 miles per hour, how long will the trip take if he drives at 60 miles per hour?

12. If a man can drive from his home to Albany in 6 hours at 45 miles per hour, at what speed did he drive if he made the trip in 5 hours?

13. Let S be the set of all rectangles that have an area of 600 square centimeters. The length varies inversely as the width.

     a. What is the length of a rectangle from set S whose width is 20 centimeters?

     b. What is the width of a rectangle from set S whose length is 100 centimeters?

12-11 COMPOSITION OF FUNCTIONS

We are familiar with operations in mathematics, such as addition and multiplication, and have used these operations to write polynomial functions. For example, $f(x) = x + 4$ and $g(x) = 2x$ are polynomial functions. When we add two polynomials, we are forming a new polynomial function called the *sum function*; and when we multiply two polynomials, we are forming a new function called the *product function*.

$$f(x) = 2x \qquad\qquad f(x) = 2x$$
$$g(x) = x + 4 \qquad\qquad g(x) = x + 4$$
$$f(x) + g(x) = 2x + (x + 4) \qquad f(x) \cdot g(x) = 2x(x + 4)$$
$$(f + g)(x) = 3x + 4 \qquad\qquad (f \cdot g)(x) = 2x^2 + 8x$$

The domain of $(f + g)(x)$ and $(f \cdot g)(x)$ is the intersection of the domains of f and of g—here, the set of real numbers.

Composition of functions is a binary operation in which the application of one function follows that of another. In other words, the function rule for one function is applied to the result of applying the function rule for another function.

Composition of Functions: Method 1

The composition of $f(x)$ following $g(x)$ can be written in the form $f(g(x))$. To evaluate this function, we treat the innermost function first. If $g(x) = x + 4$, then, for any real number x, $g(x)$ is the real number that is the sum of x and 4. If $f(x) = 2x$, then, for any real number x, $f(x)$ is the real number that is twice x. For example, to find $f(g(3))$:

1. First find $g(3)$. $g(3) = 3 + 4 = 7$
2. Then, using this result, 7, for x, find $f(7)$. $f(g(3)) = f(7) = 2(7) = 14$

Similarly, to find $f\left(g\left(\frac{1}{2}\right)\right)$, we first apply the rule for g to find $g\left(\frac{1}{2}\right)$ and then apply the rule for f to that number:

$$f\left(g\left(\tfrac{1}{2}\right)\right) = f\left(\tfrac{1}{2} + 4\right) = f\left(4\tfrac{1}{2}\right) = 2\left(4\tfrac{1}{2}\right) = 9$$

In general, for any number x under the given functions: $f(g(x))$

1. Function g adds 4 to each value in its domain. $= f(x + 4)$
2. Function f doubles each value in its domain. $= 2(x + 4)$
                                                                                                $= 2x + 8$

Therefore, the function $f(g(x)) = 2x + 8$ states the rule for the composition where g is applied first, or where f *follows* g.

Composition of Functions: Method 2

The expression $(f \circ g)(x)$ is read as f composition g of x, or as f *following* g of x. The symbol $\circ$, indicating composition, is an open circle, placed in a raised position between f and g. As in method 1, g must be applied first. Let us examine the procedure for the same functions, expressed in a different format.

$$x \xrightarrow{\ g\ } x + 4 \qquad x \xrightarrow{\ f\ } 2x$$

	Find $(f \circ g)(3)$.	Find $(f \circ g)\left(\frac{1}{2}\right)$.

1. Using g first, find the element in the range of g that corresponds to the given number from the domain of g.

$$3 \xrightarrow{\ g\ } 7 \qquad\qquad \tfrac{1}{2} \xrightarrow{\ g\ } 4\tfrac{1}{2}$$

2. Use the element from the range of g found in step 1 as an element of the domain of f, and apply the rule for f to this number.

$$3 \xrightarrow{\ g\ } 7 \xrightarrow{\ f\ } 14 \qquad \tfrac{1}{2} \xrightarrow{\ g\ } 4\tfrac{1}{2} \xrightarrow{\ f\ } 9$$
$$\underbrace{\qquad\qquad}_{f\,\circ\,g} \qquad\qquad \underbrace{\qquad\qquad}_{f\,\circ\,g}$$

3. Write the composition in terms of the given number from the domain of g and the final number from the range of f.

$$(f \circ g)(3) = 14 \qquad (f \circ g)\left(\tfrac{1}{2}\right) = 9$$

This same procedure can be applied to the general case to find the rule for the single function that represents $(f \circ g)(x)$.

$$x \xrightarrow{\;g\;} (x + 4) \xrightarrow{\;f\;} 2(x + 4) = 2x + 8$$

$$\underbrace{}_{f \circ g}$$

Thus, $(f \circ g)(x) = 2x + 8$ states the rule for the composition where g is applied first, or where f *follows* g.

These examples illustrate the fact that there are two equivalent forms of the composition f *following* g, namely:

$$f(g(x)) = (f \circ g)(x)$$

Note: For the composition f *following* g to be meaningful, each element in the range of g must be an element in the domain of f.

Group Properties Under Composition

With certain restrictions (explained in Section 12-12), it is true that a set of functions, under the operation of composition, is a *group*. Thus, four properties are satisfied:

1. *Closure.* The composition of two functions is a single function.

2. *Associativity.* For all functions f, g, and h:

$$(f \circ (g \circ h))(x) = ((f \circ g) \circ h)(x)$$

3. *Identity.* There is an identity function i under composition such that, for every function f:

$$(f \circ i)(x) = f(x) \qquad \text{and} \qquad (i \circ f)(x) = f(x)$$

For example:

$$\left.\begin{array}{l}\text{Let } f(x) = 3x + 7 \\ \text{Let } i(x) = x\end{array}\right\} \qquad x \xrightarrow{\;i\;} x \xrightarrow{\;f\;} 3x + 7 \quad\Big|\quad x \xrightarrow{\;f\;} 3x + 7 \xrightarrow{\;i\;} 3x + 7$$
$$(f \circ i)(x) = f(x) \qquad\quad (i \circ f)(x) = f(x)$$

● The ***identity function*** for the operation of composition may be written in one of three forms:

$$x \xrightarrow{\;i\;} x \qquad i(x) = x \qquad y = x$$

4. *Inverses.* For every function f (in a restricted set to be explained), for which there is an inverse function f^{-1} under composition:

$$(f \circ f^{-1})(x) = i(x) \qquad \text{and} \qquad (f^{-1} \circ f)(x) = i(x)$$

We will study the restriction, as well as ways to find the inverse f^{-1}, in the next section.

KEEP IN MIND _____

In the composition f *following* g, written as

$$f(g(x)) \qquad \text{or} \qquad (f \circ g)(x)$$

function g is applied before function f.

EXAMPLES

1. Using the function $f(x) = 3x$ and $g(x) = x - 4$, demonstrate that composition of functions is *not* commutative.

Solution   Use METHOD 1.

$f(g(x))$	$g(f(x))$
$= f(x - 4)$	$= g(3x)$
$= 3(x - 4)$	$= 3x - 4$
$= 3x - 12$	

Since $f(g(x)) = 3x - 12$ and $g(f(x)) = 3x - 4$, then $f(g(x)) \neq g(f(x))$. Thus, composition of functions is *not* commutative.

Alternative Solution   Use METHOD 2.

$$x \xrightarrow{g} x - 4 \xrightarrow{f} 3(x - 4) = 3x - 12 \qquad \qquad x \xrightarrow{f} 3x \xrightarrow{g} 3x - 4$$

$$(f \circ g)(x) = 3x - 12 \qquad \qquad \qquad (g \circ f)(x) = 3x - 4$$

Since $(f \circ g)(x) \neq (g \circ f)(x)$, composition of functions is *not* commutative.

Note: The commutative property is *not* required in a group.

2. Let $h(x) = x^2$ and $r(x) = x + 3$. **a.** Evaluate $(h \circ r)(5)$. **b.** Find the rule of the function $(h \circ r)(x)$.

Solutions **a.** To evaluate $(h \circ r)(5)$, apply r first. Under r, $5 \to 8$. Under h, 8 is squared.

$$5 \xrightarrow{\text{r}} 8 \xrightarrow{\text{h}} 64$$

$(h \circ r)(5) = 64$ *Answer*

b. Use the same process with $(h \circ r)(x)$. Under r, $x \to x + 3$. Under h, $x + 3$ is squared.

$$x \xrightarrow{\text{r}} x + 3 \xrightarrow{\text{h}} (x + 3)^2 = x^2 + 6x + 9$$

$(h \circ r)(x) = x^2 + 6x + 9$ *Answer*

Note: By substituting $x = 5$ in the rule $(h \circ r)(x) = x^2 + 6x + 9$, we can show again that $(h \circ r)(5) = (5)^2 + 6(5) + 9 = 25 + 30 + 9 = 64$.

EXERCISES WITH OPEN-RESPONSE PROBLEMS

In 1–8, using $f(x) = x + 5$ and $g(x) = 4x$, evaluate each composition.

1. $f(g(2))$ **2.** $g(f(2))$ **3.** $f(g(-1))$ **4.** $g(f(-1))$

5. $f(g(0))$ **6.** $g(f(0))$ **7.** $g\left(f\left(\frac{1}{2}\right)\right)$ **8.** $f\left(g\left(\frac{1}{2}\right)\right)$

In 9–16, using $f(x) = 3x$ and $g(x) = x - 2$, evaluate each composition.

9. $(f \circ g)(4)$ **10.** $(g \circ f)(4)$ **11.** $(f \circ g)(-2)$ **12.** $(g \circ f)(-2)$

13. $(g \circ f)(0)$ **14.** $(f \circ g)(0)$ **15.** $(g \circ f)\left(\frac{2}{3}\right)$ **16.** $(f \circ g)\left(\frac{2}{3}\right)$

In 17–24, using $h(x) = x^2$ and $p(x) = 2x - 3$, evaluate each composition.

17. $(h \circ p)(2)$ **18.** $(p \circ h)(2)$ **19.** $(p \circ h)(1)$ **20.** $(h \circ p)(1)$

21. $(p \circ h)(-3)$ **22.** $(h \circ p)(-3)$ **23.** $(h \circ p)(1.5)$ **24.** $(p \circ h)(1.5)$

25. Let $f(x) = x + 6$ and $g(x) = 3x$. **a.** Find the rule of the function $(f \circ g)(x)$. **b.** Find the rule of the function $(g \circ f)(x)$. **c.** Does $(f \circ g)(x) = (g \circ f)(x)$?

26. Let $r(x) = x - 8$ and $t(x) = x^2$. **a.** Find the rule of the function $(r \circ t)(x)$. **b.** Find the rule of the function $(t \circ r)(x)$. **c.** Does $(r \circ t)(x) = (t \circ r)(x)$?

27. Let $d(x) = 2x + 3$ and $c(x) = x - 3$.
  a. Evaluate $(d \circ c)(2)$. **b.** Find the rule of the function $(d \circ c)(x)$.
  c. Use the rule from part **b** to find the value of $(d \circ c)(2)$.
  d. Do the answers from parts **a** and **c** agree?

In 28–37, for the given functions f(x) and g(x), find, in each case, the rule of the composition (f ∘ g)(x).

28. $f(x) = 6x$; $g(x) = x - 2$

30. $f(x) = x$; $g(x) = 2x + 5$

32. $f(x) = 2x$; $g(x) = 5x$

29. $f(x) = x - 10$; $g(x) = 4x$

31. $f(x) = x - 3$; $g(x) = x - 5$

33. $f(x) = 3x + 2$; $g(x) = x - 3$

34. $f(x) = \frac{1}{2}x - 3$; $g(x) = 4x + 6$

36. $f(x) = x^2$; $g(x) = x - 5$

35. $f(x) = 5 - x$; $g(x) = x + 2$

37. $f(x) = 4 - x^2$; $g(x) = x - 2$

38. If $f(x) = x + 8$, then the rule of the composition $(f \circ f)(x)$ is

   (1) $x + 8$ (2) $x + 16$ (3) $2x + 8$ (4) $2x + 16$

39. If $g(x) = 2x + 5$, what is the rule of the composition $(g \circ g)(x)$?

In 40–45, let $h(x) = x^2 + 2x$, and $g(x) = x - 3$. In 40–44, evaluate each composition.

40. $(h \circ g)(4)$ **41.** $(h \circ g)(3)$ **42.** $(h \circ g)(2)$ **43.** $(h \circ g)(1)$

44. $(h \circ g)(-2)$ **45.** Find the rule of the function $(h \circ g)(x)$.

46. Let $f(x) = x + 5$, $g(x) = 2x$, and $h(x) = x - 2$.

   a. If $k(x) = (f \circ g)(x)$, find the rule of the function $k(x)$.

   b. Find the rule of $((f \circ g) \circ h)(x)$, that is, the rule of $((k) \circ h)(x)$.

   c. If $r(x) = (g \circ h)(x)$, find the rule of the function $r(x)$.

   d. Find the rule of $(f \circ (g \circ h))(x)$, that is, the rule of $(f \circ (r))(x)$.

   e. Using parts **b** and **d**, state whether or not $((f \circ g) \circ h)(x) = (f \circ (g \circ h))(x)$. If yes, tell what group property is demonstrated. If no, explain why.

In 47–58, let $b(x) = |x|$, $d(x) = [x]$, $f(x) = \frac{1}{x}$, $g(x) = x - 3$, and $h(x) = 2x$. Find the rule of each composition.

47. $(f \circ b)(x)$ **48.** $(d \circ g)(x)$ **49.** $(b \circ g)(x)$ **50.** $(g \circ d)(x)$

51. $(g \circ f)(x)$ **52.** $(h \circ g)(x)$ **53.** $(f \circ (g \circ h))(x)$ **54.** $(d \circ (h \circ f))(x)$

55. $(g \circ (h \circ b))(x)$ **56.** $(b \circ (f \circ h))(x)$ **57.** $(f \circ f \circ h)(x)$ **58.** $(f \circ h \circ f)(x)$

59. To find the 6% sales tax on any item sold in her store, Ms. Reres programmed her cash register to perform two functions. The first function, $s(x)$, multiplies the total price of the purchases, x, by 0.06, that is, $s(x) = 0.06x$. The second function, $r(x)$, rounds the tax to the nearest cent, that is, $r(x) = \frac{[100x + 0.5]}{100}$.

   a. Evaluate $(r \circ s)(\$1.39)$.   **b.** Evaluate $(r \circ s)(\$16.79)$.

   c. Can the 6% sales tax to be paid on a purchase of x dollars be found using $(r \circ s)(x)$?

   d. If $i(x) = x$, evaluate $i(\$1.39) + (r \circ s)(\$1.39)$.

   e. Evaluate $i(\$16.79) + (r \circ s)(\$16.79)$.

   f. If $c(x)$ is the total amount paid by a customer for an item priced at x dollars, does $c(x) = i(x) + (r \circ s)(x)$?

12-12 INVERSE FUNCTIONS UNDER COMPOSITION

Relation f, shown as a set of ordered pairs and illustrated in an arrow diagram, is a function because every x corresponds to one and only one y.

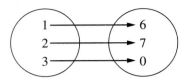

Function f

Function f = {(1, 6), (2, 7), (3, 0)}

Under function f, $x \rightarrow y$. There is another relation, called f^{-1}, in which $y \rightarrow x$. In this example, relation f^{-1} is a function because every element of the domain corresponds to one and only one element in the range. Function f^{-1}, called the inverse of f under composition, is an example of an ***inverse function***.

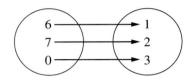

Inverse function f^{-1}

Inverse function f^{-1} = {(6, 1), (7, 2), (0, 3)}

We have stated that the identity function under composition is $x \rightarrow x$ or $i(x) = x$ or $y = x$. We note here that $(f^{-1} \circ f)(x) = i(x)$, and $(f \circ f^{-1})(x) = i(x)$.

$$
\begin{array}{ccc}
\xrightarrow{\ f\ } & \xrightarrow{\ f^{-1}\ } & \\
1 \longrightarrow 6 \longrightarrow 1 \\
2 \longrightarrow 7 \longrightarrow 2 \\
3 \longrightarrow 0 \longrightarrow 3
\end{array}
$$

$(f^{-1} \circ f)(x) = i(x)$

$$
\begin{array}{ccc}
\xrightarrow{\ f^{-1}\ } & \xrightarrow{\ f\ } & \\
6 \longrightarrow 1 \longrightarrow 6 \\
7 \longrightarrow 2 \longrightarrow 7 \\
0 \longrightarrow 3 \longrightarrow 0
\end{array}
$$

$(f \circ f^{-1})(x) = i(x)$

Relation g, shown as a set of ordered pairs and illustrated in an arrow diagram, is a function because every x corresponds to one and only one y.

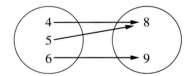

Function g

Function g = {(4, 8), (5, 8), (6, 9)}

Relation g^{-1}, however, in which the x and y elements are interchanged, is *not* a function.

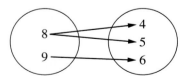

Relation g^{-1} is *not* a function.

Relation g^{-1} = {(8, 4), (8, 5), (9, 6)}

In g^{-1}, $8 \rightarrow 4$ and $8 \rightarrow 5$. Since one element, 8, corresponds to more than one element in the range, g^{-1} is called a one-to-many relation.

Conversely, in function g, $4 \rightarrow 8$ and $5 \rightarrow 8$. Since more than one element corresponds to the same one element, g is called a many-to-one function.

As illustrated by this example, a many-to-one function does *not* have an inverse function under composition.

Now let us consider function f, for which an inverse function exists. For every x, there is one and only one y. Also, for every second element y, there is one and only one first element x. Function f is called a one-to-one function.

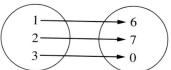

Function f is *one-to-one*.

By definition, a function is a **one-to-one function** if and only if each second element corresponds to one and only one first element.

As illustrated in the first example involving f and f^{-1}, a one-to-one function *does* have an inverse function under composition.

- **For every one-to-one function f, the set of ordered pairs obtained by interchanging the first and second elements of each pair in f is f^{-1}, the inverse function under composition.**

We have learned that the set of real numbers less 0 is a group under the operation of multiplication. Since 0 has no inverse under multiplication, it is necessary to restrict the set of real numbers to elements having inverses so that a group exists. In the same way, by restricting the set of functions to those having inverses, namely, one-to-one functions, we can now say:

- **The set of one-to-one functions, under the operation of composition, is a group.**

Ways to Find the Inverse Function

We will study the function whose rule is $f(x) = \frac{1}{2}x + 2$, or $y = \frac{1}{2}x + 2$, in the examples that follow. Whether stated as a rule or drawn on a coordinate graph, the function contains an infinite number of ordered pairs. Let us first examine a function with a finite number of ordered pairs by selecting three pairs of function f: (0, 2), (4, 4), and (6, 5).

1. *Ordered Pairs*

    The inverse under composition of a one-to-one function is formed by interchanging the x-coordinate and y-coordinate of each pair in the function.

    For example, if function f = {(0, 2), (4, 4), (6, 5)},
    then inverse function f^{-1} = {(2, 0), (4, 4), (5, 6)}.

2. *Coordinate Graph*

    In transformation geometry, we learned that $(x, y) \rightarrow (y, x)$ by a reflection in the line $y = x$. The inverse under composition of a one-to-one function f is graphed by reflecting function f in the line $y = x$, that is, the line whose equation is the identity function i.

In the figure at the right, the identity $i(x) = x$, or $y = x$, is graphed as a broken line along the diagonal.

The function $f(x) = \frac{1}{2}x + 2$, or $y = \frac{1}{2}x + 2$, is graphed. We note that f contains the points whose coordinates are $(0, 2)$, $(4, 4)$, and $(6, 5)$.

By reflecting f in the line $y = x$, we graph the inverse function f^{-1}. We see that f^{-1} contains the points whose coordinates are $(2, 0)$, $(4, 4)$, and $(5, 6)$. The equation of this inverse function is $f^{-1}(x) = 2x - 4$, or $y = 2x - 4$.

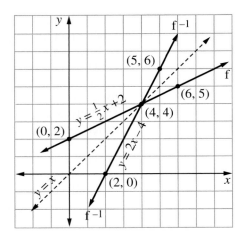

3. *Rule of the Inverse*

The rule of inverse function f^{-1} can be found by interchanging x and y in the rule of the given function f. For example:

1. Express $f(x) = \frac{1}{2}x + 2$ in terms of x and y.	f: $y = \frac{1}{2}x + 2$
2. Interchange x and y to form the inverse under composition.	$f^{-1}: x = \frac{1}{2}y + 2$
3. Solve for y.	$x - 2 = \frac{1}{2}y$
	$2(x - 2) = 2\left(\frac{1}{2}y\right)$
	$2x - 4 = y$

Note: The rule of inverse function f^{-1} may be written in one of two forms: $y = 2x - 4$, or $f^{-1}(x) = 2x - 4$.

To show that $y = 2x - 4$ is the inverse function of $y = \frac{1}{2}x + 2$, we demonstrate that the composition of these functions is the identity function.

$$y = \frac{1}{2}x + 2 \quad \text{or} \quad f(x) = \frac{1}{2}x + 2$$

$$y = 2x - 4 \quad \text{or} \quad f^{-1}(x) = 2x - 4$$

$$x \xrightarrow{f} \frac{1}{2}x + 2 \xrightarrow{f^{-1}} 2\left(\frac{1}{2}x + 2\right) - 4 = x + 4 - 4 = x$$

$$x \xrightarrow{f^{-1}} 2x - 4 \xrightarrow{f} \frac{1}{2}(2x - 4) + 2 = x - 2 + 2 = x$$

$$(f \circ f^{-1})(x) = (f^{-1} \circ f)(x) = x$$

Restricted Domains and Inverse Functions

The domain of the function $g(x) = x^2$, or $y = x^2$, is the set of real numbers. If x and y are interchanged, the rule for this new relation is $x = y^2$, or $y = \pm\sqrt{x}$. Since function g is not one-to-one, the relation $x = y^2$ is not a function. (See Figure 1.)

If the domain of g is restricted, however, so that g is a one-to-one function, then inverse g^{-1} under composition is a function. When the domain is restricted to the set of positive real numbers and 0, the inverse of the function $y = x^2$ is the function $x = y^2$. Since the range is restricted to the set of positive real numbers and 0, g^{-1} is one-to-one, and can be written as $y = \sqrt{x}$. (See Figure 2.)

Domain of g = {Real numbers} *Function* g: $y = x^2$ Relation formed by interchanging x and y: $y = \pm\sqrt{x}$ (*not* a function)	Restricted Domain of g = {Positive reals and 0} *Function* g: $y = x^2$ *Inverse Function* g^{-1}: $y = \sqrt{x}$ Range of g^{-1} = {Positive reals and 0}

Figure 1

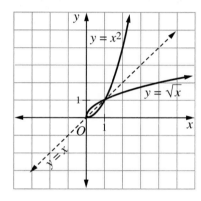

Figure 2

KEEP IN MIND ───────────────────────────────

1. Only a function f that is one-to-one has an inverse under composition. The domain of the inverse is the range of the original function.

2. This inverse f^{-1} is formed by interchanging x and y in the given function.

EXAMPLES

1. What is the inverse of the function $\{(3, 7), (2, 1), (5, -4)\}$?

Solution   Interchange the x-coordinate and y-coordinate of each pair in the given function to find its inverse under composition.

Answer: $\{(7, 3), (1, 2), (-4, 5)\}$

2. What is the inverse of the function $y = 3x + 5$?

Solution If the inverse of a function is being sought and no operation is named, the inverse is assumed to be the *inverse under composition*.

(1) Write the given function, f.

(2) To form f^{-1}, the inverse under composition, interchange x and y.

(3) Solve for y, so that the answer can be written in the form $y = mx + b$.

$$y = 3x + 5$$
$$x = 3y + 5$$
$$x - 5 = 3y$$
$$\frac{x - 5}{3} = y$$

Answer: $y = \frac{x-5}{3}$ or $y = \frac{1}{3}x - \frac{5}{3}$

Note: If the original function is written as $f(x) = 3x + 5$, then the inverse can be written as $f^{-1}(x) = \frac{x-5}{3}$ or as $f^{-1}(x) = \frac{1}{3}x - \frac{5}{3}$.

EXERCISES WITH OPEN-RESPONSE PROBLEMS

In 1–4, write the inverse of each given function.

1. $\{(1, 5), (2, 7), (3, -2), (4, -3)\}$

2. $\{(0, 6), (4, 2), (-1, 7), (-2, 8)\}$

3. $\{(1, 1), (2, 2), (3, 3), (4, 4)\}$

4. $\{(1, k), (2, k + 1), (3, k + 2)\}$

5. Let $f = \{(3, -2), (4, -2), (5, -1)\}$. **a.** Write the relation formed by interchanging the x-coordinate and y-coordinate of f. **b.** Is this new relation a function? If not, explain why.

6. *True* or *False*: The relation formed by interchanging x and y in each pair of a function is also a function. Explain your answer.

7. *True* or *False*: The relation formed by interchanging x and y in each pair of a one-to-one function is also a one-to-one function. Explain your answer.

In 8–16, write the equation of the inverse of each given function, solved for y.

8. $y = 3x$

9. $y = x - 6$

10. $y = \frac{1}{4}x$

11. $y = \frac{1}{3}x + 1$

12. $y = 4x - 8$

13. $y = 5 - x$

14. $y = \sqrt{x}$

15. $y - 12 = 3x$

16. $y + 7 = x^3$

In 17–20, in each case, select the *numeral* preceding the expression that best completes the sentence or answers the question.

17. If $f(x) = 6x - 2$, then the inverse function $f^{-1}(x)$ is

(1) $\frac{x + 2}{6}$
(2) $\frac{x}{6} + 2$
(3) $\frac{x + 1}{3}$
(4) $\frac{x}{3} + 1$

18. If $m(x) = 2x - 1$, then $m^{-1}(x)$ is

(1) $\frac{1}{2}x + 1$
(2) $\frac{1}{2}x + \frac{1}{2}$
(3) $2x + 1$
(4) $-2x + 1$

19. The inverse of the function $y = -2x$ is

(1) $y = 2x$
(2) $x = 2y$
(3) $x = -2y$
(4) $y = x - 2$

20. What is the inverse of the function $\{(3, 1), (4, -1), (-2, 6)\}$?

(1) $\{(3, -1), (4, 1), (-2, -6)\}$
(2) $\{(-1, 3), (1, 4), (-6, -2)\}$
(3) $\{(-3, -1), (-4, 1), (2, -6)\}$
(4) $\{(1, 3), (-1, 4), (6, -2)\}$

21. If $f(x) = 3x - 7$, evaluate: **a.** $f(2)$ **b.** $f^{-1}(-1)$

22. If $g(x) = \frac{2}{3}x + 4$, evaluate: **a.** $g(-3)$ **b.** $g^{-1}(2)$

23. If $h(x) = 5x - 2$, find the value of $(h^{-1} \circ h)(123)$.

In 24–26, in each case: **a.** Copy function f on graph paper.   **b.** Using the same axes, sketch the graph of f^{-1}, the inverse of f under composition.   **c.** State the domain and range of f.   **d.** State the domain and range of f^{-1}.

24.

25.

26.
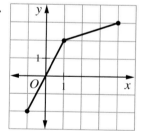

27. Demonstrate that the identity function $i(x) = x$ is its own inverse under composition.

In 28–30:   **a.** On graph paper, draw the graph of each function, including points whose x-coordinates are $-2, -1, 0, 1$, and 2.   **b.** On the same axes, draw the graph of the relation that is the reflection of the given function in the line $y = x$.   **c.** State whether or not the relation in part **b** is a function.   **d.** State the equation of the relation drawn in part **b**.

28. $y = x^3$
29. $y = |x|$
30. $y = 3$

31. Under composition, the identity function $y = x$ is its own inverse. Name another function in the form $y = mx + b$ that is its own inverse.

32. **a.** Graph $f(x) = 2x^2$ for $0 \leq x \leq 2$.
  b. What is the inverse of $f(x)$? Is the inverse a function? Explain.
  c. Graph $f^{-1}(x)$ on the same set of axes.
  d. Are there any points where $f(x)$ and $f^{-1}(x)$ intersect? If so, state the coordinates of these points.

33. On a certain day, the function $f(x) = 7.40x$ was used to convert U.S. dollars, x, to French francs.
  a. Find the inverse function and explain its meaning.
  b. On the same day, the function $p(x) = 24.2x$ was used to convert French francs to Spanish pesetas. Determine the function that could be used to convert U.S. dollars to Spanish pesetas.

34. The formula $K = \frac{F - 32}{1.8} + 273$ is used to convert Fahrenheit temperatures to Kelvin temperatures. Determine the formula that can be used to convert Kelvin temperatures to Fahrenheit temperatures.

CHAPTER SUMMARY

A *relation* is a set of ordered pairs. The *domain* of a relation is the set of all first elements of the ordered pairs, and the *range* of a relation is the set of all second elements. A *function* is a relation in which each element of the domain corresponds to one and only one element of the range. If each vertical line drawn through the graph of a relation intersects the graph in one and only one point, then the relation is a function.

If f is a set of ordered pairs (x, y), then $y = f(x)$. The following are frequently used functions.

1. *Linear functions:* $f(x) = mx + b$
2. *Constant functions:* $f(x) = b$
3. *Quadratic functions:* $f(x) = ax^2 + bx + c \quad (a \neq 0)$
4. *Polynomial functions:* $f(x) = a_n x^n + a_{n-1} x^{n-1} + a_{n-2} x^{n-2} + \cdots + a_1 x + a_0$
5. *Absolute-value functions:* $f(x) = |ax + b|$
6. *Step functions*, such as the greatest-integer function: $f(x) = [x]$

When a cone is intersected by a plane, the intersection is called a conic section or a conic. A *conic* is the locus of points such that the ratio of the distances of any point on the locus to a fixed point and to a fixed line is a constant. The fixed point is the *focus*, the fixed line is the *directrix*, and the constant is the *eccentricity*, e.

If $0 < e < 1$, the conic is an *ellipse*.

If $e = 1$, the conic is a *parabola*.

If $e > 1$, the conic is a *hyperbola*.

An ellipse can also be defined as the locus of points such that the sum of the distances of any point on the locus from two fixed points is a constant. A hyperbola can also be defined as the locus of points such that the absolute values of the difference of the distances of any point on the locus from two fixed points is a constant.

If *x* and *y vary inversely*, then $xy =$ a nonzero constant. The value of *xy* is called the **constant of variation**. The equation $xy = c$ defines a function whose domain and range are the set of nonzero real numbers and whose graph is a hyperbola.

Composition of functions is a binary operation in which the application of one function follows that of another. The composition of f(x) following g(x) is written in the form f(x) ∘ g(x) or f(g(x)). Composition of functions is not commutative.

The **identity function** is the function i(x) = x. If f(x) is a **one-to-one function**, then there exists an **inverse function** $f^{-1}(x)$ such that:

$$f(x) \circ f^{-1}(x) = f^{-1} \circ f(x) = i(x)$$

VOCABULARY

12-1	Relation Domain Range
12-2	Function Vertical-line test
12-5	Linear function Constant function Quadratic function Polynomial function Absolute-value function Step functions Greatest-integer function
12-6	Parabola Focus Directrix
12-7	Ellipse Circle Major axis Minor axis
12-8	Hyperbola Transverse axis
12-9	Conic Eccentricity
12-10	Inverse variation Constant of variation
12-11	Composition of functions Identity function
12-12	Inverse function One-to-one function

REVIEW EXERCISES WITH OPEN-RESPONSE PROBLEMS

In 1–9, in each case: **a.** State the domain of the relation.   **b.** State the range of the relation.   **c.** State whether the relation is a function. If not, explain why.

1.

2.

3.

4.

5.   **6.**   **7.**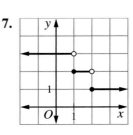

8. $\{(2, 2), (3, 1), (1, 3)\}$ **9.** $\{(2, 4), (3, 1), (2, 3), (3, 2)\}$

10. Draw a graph and label the axes to represent the following situation. Flight 101 took off and climbed quickly at a constant rate to its cruising altitude. It flew at this altitude for some time, then descended slowly to land at the next airport on its schedule. Compare the plane's altitude to time that elapsed.

11. If the function $f(x) = x^2 - 4x$, find the value of $f(-3)$.

12. If $g(x) = \sqrt[3]{x}$, find $g(-8)$.

In 13–15, in each case, select the *numeral* preceding the expression that best completes the sentence or answers the question.

13. Which of the following is *not* a function?

(1) $y = |5x|$ (2) $y = 5x^2$ (3) $y = 5$ (4) $x = 5$

14. The domain for $h(x) = 2x - 7$ is $-2 \le x \le 2$. The range is

(1) $-3 \le y \le 3$ (2) $-11 \le y \le -3$
(3) $-11 \le y \le 3$ (4) $-11 \le y \le 11$

15. The domain for $p(x) = 6 - 2x$ is $\{x | -5 \le x \le 1\}$. The greatest value in the range is

(1) 16   (2) 8   (3) -4 (4) 4

In 16–18, in each case, state the largest possible domain such that each given relation is a function.

16. $f(x) = \dfrac{x - 2}{x - 8}$ **17.** $x \xrightarrow{g} \dfrac{4}{x^2 + 4x}$ **18.** $y = \dfrac{1}{\sqrt{x - 8}}$

In 19–21, for each given function: **a.** State the domain.   **b.** State the range.

19. $f(x) = 4x - 12$ **20.** $x \xrightarrow{g} [x]$ **21.** $y = \sqrt{x - 8}$

22. Let $m(x) = 5x$ and $d(x) = x - 4$.
   a. Find $(m \circ d)(6)$.   **b.** Find $(d \circ m)(6)$.
   c. Write the rule for $(m \circ d)(x)$.   **d.** Write the rule for $(d \circ m)(x)$.

In 23–26:   **a.** Identify the graph of each of the following as a circle, an ellipse, a hyperbola, or a parabola.   **b.** Sketch the graph.

23. $4x^2 + y^2 = 4$ **24.** $y = x^2 - 4$
25. $y^2 = x^2 - 4$ **26.** $y^2 = 4 - x^2$

27. An ellipse for which the x- and y-axes are lines of symmetry intersects the x-axis at $(6, 0)$ and the y-axis at $(0, 2)$. Write an equation of the ellipse.

28. Which of the following is the equation of the graph shown at the right?

(1) $4x^2 + y^2 = 16$
(2) $x^2 + 4y^2 = 16$
(3) $x^2 + 2y^2 = 4$
(4) $2x^2 + y^2 = 4$

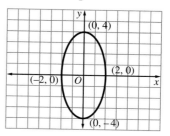

29. Which of the following is both a function and a hyperbola?

(1) $y^2 = 9 - x^2$ (2) $y^2 = x^2 - 9$ (3) $y = 9 - x^2$ (4) $y = \frac{9}{x}$

In 30–33, in each case, given functions f and g, find the rule of the composition $(f \circ g)(x)$.

30. $f(x) = x + 2;\ g(x) = x - 9$ **31.** $f(x) = 2x + 1;\ g(x) = x - 3$
32. $f(x) = x^2;\ g(x) = 2x + 1$ **33.** $f(x) = 3x + 6;\ g(x) = \frac{1}{3}x - 2$

34. Write the inverse of the function $\{(3, -8), (4, 1), (0, -5), (-2, 6)\}$.

In 35–37, write, in the form $y = mx + b$, the equation of the inverse of each given function.

35. $y = 6x$ **36.** $y = 2x - 14$ **37.** $y = 3 - \frac{1}{3}x$

38. What is the inverse of the function $y = \frac{3x - 2}{5}$?

(1) $y = \frac{3x + 2}{5}$ (2) $y = \frac{5x - 2}{3}$ (3) $y = \frac{5x + 2}{3}$ (4) $y = \frac{3x - 2}{5}$

39. Let $f(x) = 5x - 4$.
 a. Write the rule for f^{-1}, the inverse under composition.
 b. Find $f(2)$.   **c.** Find $f^{-1}(6)$.   **d.** Find $f^{-1}(0)$.
 e. Find $(f^{-1} \circ f)(17)$.   **f.** Explain why f is a one-to-one function.

40. The identity function under composition is:
(1) $y = 0$ (2) $y = x$ (3) $y = 1$ (4) $y = \frac{1}{x}$

41. The charges for a telephone call from New York City to Philadelphia, dialed directly on a home phone, are $0.52 for the first minute or less and $0.35 for each additional minute or portion thereof.
 a. Graph this step function for charges on calls lasting 6 minutes or less. Let x represent the time, and $f(x)$ the charge.
 b. For the domain $0 < x \le 6$, what is the range?
 c. What is the charge for a 1-hour phone call from New York City to Philadelphia?
 d. If the charge for a New York City–Philadelphia call is $6.12, what was the maximum time, in minutes, for this call?
 e. Is the relation formed by interchanging x and $f(x)$ from part **a** also a function? Explain your answer.

42. A model rocket launched vertically into the air has its height above ground given by $h(t) = -16t^2 + 160t + 6$ where t is in seconds and h is in feet.
 a. At what time does the rocket reach its maximum height?
 b. What is the maximum height?

CUMULATIVE REVIEW

1. Factor completely: $2x^3 + 5x^2 - 8x - 20$.

2. Write $\dfrac{2}{3 - \sqrt{5}}$ as an equivalent fraction with an integral denominator.

3. a. Express the roots of $3x^2 - 4x - 1 = 0$ in simplest radical form.
 b. Express the roots found in part **a** to the *nearest hundredth*.

4. The diameter of circle O is $\overline{AB}$, $\overleftrightarrow{PB}$ is tangent to circle O at B and $\overline{PCOD}$ intersects the circle at C and D. Chord $\overline{DB}$ is drawn. If $m\angle AOD = 42$, find the measure of each of the following:

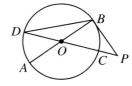

 a. $\overset{\frown}{AD}$ **b.** $\overset{\frown}{AC}$ **c.** $\angle CDB$ **d.** $\angle DPB$ **e.** $\angle DBP$

5. Solve and check: $\sqrt{2x^2 - 2} = x + 1$.

6. Add and reduce to lowest terms: $\dfrac{2}{x^2 - 9} + \dfrac{1}{3x + 9}$.

7. Solve the inequality $|1 - 2x| > 3$, and graph the solution set.

8. A formula used in optics is $\frac{1}{p} + \frac{1}{q} = \frac{1}{f}$ where p represents the distance of the object from a mirror or lens, q represents the distance of the image from the mirror, and f represents the focal length of the mirror. If a mirror has a focal length of 6 inches, how far from the mirror will the image appear if a vase is 12 inches from the mirror?

9. The period (or length of time for one complete swing back and forth) of a pendulum is given by $T = 2\pi\sqrt{\dfrac{L}{32}}$ where L is the length of the pendulum in feet.

 Find, to the nearest tenth of a second, the period of a grandfather clock with a 4-foot pendulum.

10. a. Graph the relation $(3, 2)$, $(7, 2)$, $(7, -2)$, and $(3, -2)$. Identify the figure determined by these vertices.
 b. Find the inverse of the relation given above. Then graph the inverse relation and explain if the ordered pairs determine a congruent figure.

Exploration

The cost of first-class mail is $0.34 for the first ounce or part of an ounce and $0.21 for each additional ounce or part of an ounce, up to 13 ounces. For letters or packages weighing from 13 ounces to 32 ounces the cost is $3.95. Use the greatest-integer function or the ceiling function to write a function that gives the cost of first-class mail in terms of its weight for the domain $0 < x \le 32$.

Chapter 13

Transformation Geometry and Functions

Early civilizations used tiles called *tessalae* to adorn palaces and areas of worship.

A standard or regular *tessellation* consists of a single shape repeated in a pattern to fill a plane completely, with no wasted space and no overlapping. A tessellation may be formed using a basic shape such as a square or a rectangle; think of ceiling tiles, floor tiles, and brick sidewalks. As congruent pieces are removed and then added back to the remaining shape in some other position, new tessellations are created.

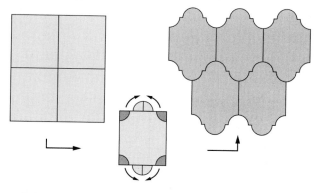

Many works by the artist M. C. Escher are based on tessellations of birds, fish, and lizards. Study his art, and then create a tessellation of your own design.

Every tessellation illustrates a *transformation* or change of position of the points in a plane. Transformations are functions, as we will learn in this chapter.

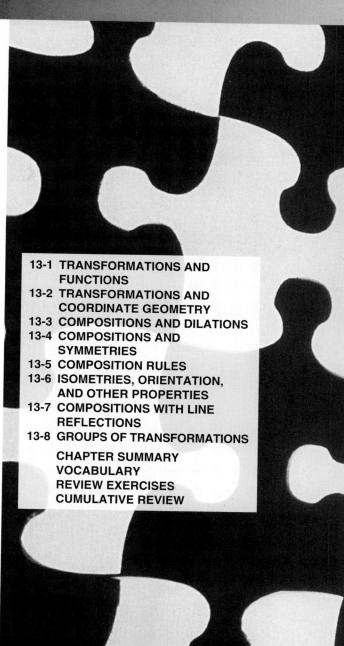

13-1 TRANSFORMATIONS AND FUNCTIONS

Let us imagine that a string holding 30 identical beads breaks. If all the beads are recovered and restrung, most or all of them will be in new positions, although a few may occupy their original places. In any case, when completed, the new string of beads will look exactly like the old one.

Now let us think of any plane or flat surface. The points on the plane are like beads. Under a *transformation of the plane*, points will move about: some points may remain fixed, and other points will change position. After the transformation, however, the plane again appears full and complete, with no missing points.

Plane

● **DEFINITION. A *transformation of the plane*** is a one-to-one correspondence between the points in a plane that demonstrates a change in position or a fixed position for each point in the plane.

An infinite number of transformations can take place in a plane. In this section, we will review four basic transformations studied in Math A.

Line Reflections

At the right, $\triangle ABC \cong \triangle A'B'C$. One triangle will coincide with the other if we fold this page along like k, the ***line of reflection***. Thus, points A and A' correspond to each other, and points B and B' correspond to each other. Point C is called a ***fixed point*** because C is found on the line of reflection.

The term ***image*** is used to describe the relationship of these points, just as we might think of one point as being the mirror image of another.

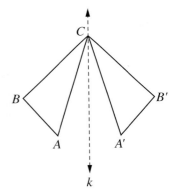

In Symbols

$A \rightarrow A'$, and $A' \rightarrow A$.
$B \rightarrow B'$, and $B' \rightarrow B$.
$C \rightarrow C$.

In Words

The image of A is A', and the image of A' is A.
The image of B is B', and the image of B' is B.
The image of C is C.

If the image of A is A', we may also say that the ***preimage*** of A' is A.

A reflection in line k is indicated in symbols as r_k. Thus, to show that the images are formed under a reflection in line k, we can write:

$r_k(A) = A'$. Under a reflection in line k, the image of A is A'.
$r_k(B) = B'$. Under a reflection in line k, the image of B is B'.
$r_k(C) = C$. Under a reflection in line k, the image of C is C.

In the diagram, $\overline{AA'}$ and $\overline{BB'}$ are drawn to connect two points and their images. We note:

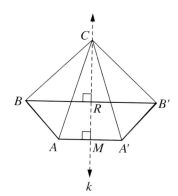

1. Line k is perpendicular to each segment, $\overline{AA'}$ and $\overline{BB'}$.

2. Line k bisects each of these segments. If M is the intersection of $\overline{AA'}$ and line k, them $AM = MA'$. Similarly, if R is the intersection of $\overline{BB'}$ and line k, then $BR = RB'$.

● **DEFINITION.** A *reflection in a line* k is a transformation of the plane such that:

1. If point P is not on line k, the image of P is P', where line k is the perpendicular bisector of $\overline{PP'}$.

2. If point P is on line k, the image of P is P.

Under a line reflection, the image of a segment is another segment, as in $\overline{AB} \rightarrow \overline{A'B'}$, or $r_k(\overline{AB}) = \overline{A'B'}$. Also, the image of an angle is another angle, as in $\angle ABC \rightarrow \angle A'B'C$, or $r_k(\angle ABC) = \angle A'B'C$.

Point Reflections

In the diagram that follows, $\triangle ABC$ is reflected through point P, and its image, $\triangle A'B'C'$, is formed. To find this image under a reflection through point P, the following steps are taken:

Step 1: A segment is drawn from vertex A to its image, A', through point P such that $AP = PA'$. A second segment is drawn from vertex B to its image, B', through point P such that $BP = PB'$. A third segment is drawn from vertex C to its image, C', through P such that $CP = PC'$.

Step 2: Images A', B', and C' are connected to form $\triangle A'B'C'$, which is the reflection of $\triangle ABC$ through point P.

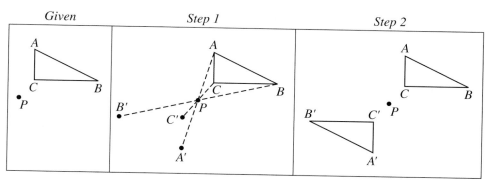

A reflection in a point P is indicated in symbols as R_P. To name the specific images under a reflection in point P, we write:

In Symbols	*In Words*
$R_P(A) = A'$.	Under a reflection in point P, the image of A is A'.
$R_P(B) = B'$.	Under a reflection in point P, the image of B is B'.
$R_P(C) = C'$.	Under a reflection in point P, the image of C is C'.

Under the point reflection just described, point P is the midpoint of each of the segments of $\overline{AA'}$, $\overline{BB'}$, and $\overline{CC'}$, leading to our definition. We note, however, that one point remains fixed in the plane, namely, point P itself.

- **DEFINITION.** A *reflection in a point* P is a transformation of the plane such that:

    1. The image of the fixed point P is P.

    2. For all other points, the image of K is K', where P is the midpoint of $\overline{KK'}$.

Rotations

As the steering wheel of a car is turned, every point on the wheel (except the fixed point in the center) moves through an arc so that the position of each point is changed by the same number of degrees. This transformation is called a *rotation*.

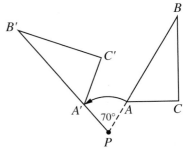

At the right, $\triangle ABC$ is rotated 70° counterclockwise about fixed point P to form its image, $\triangle A'B'C'$. By drawing $\overrightarrow{PA}$ and $\overrightarrow{PA'}$, we see that m$\angle APA' = 70$. We notice that the distance from P to A is equal to the distance from P to A', or $PA = PA'$. Also, m$\angle BPB' = 70$ and $PB = PB'$. In the same way, if $\overrightarrow{PC}$ and $\overrightarrow{PC'}$ were drawn, we would see that m$\angle CPC' = 70$ and $PC = PC'$.

This rotation of 70° counterclockwise about point P is written in symbols as $R_{P,70°}$. Thus, $R_{P,70°}(A) = A'$ indicates that the image of A is A' under the rotation. It is understood in this symbolism that a counterclockwise direction is being taken.

In the diagrams at the right, we observe the following:

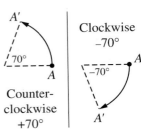

1. The measure of the angle of rotation is positive when the rotation is counterclockwise.

2. The measure of the angle of rotation is negative when the rotation is clockwise.

- **DEFINITION.** A ***rotation*** is a transformation of the plane about a point P, called the *center of rotation*, and through an angle of ϕ degrees such that:

  1. The image of the fixed point P is P.
  2. For all other points, the image of K is K', where m$\angle KPK' = \phi$ and $PK = PK'$.

Note: Since a rotation of 180° about a point P is equivalent to a reflection in point P, we abbreviate $R_{P,180°}$ as R_P, the symbol for a point reflection.

Translations

If a line reflection is like a flip, and a point reflection is like a half-turn, then a *translation* is like a slide or a shift.

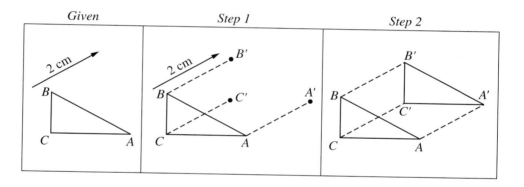

In the preceding diagram, $\triangle ABC$ is moved 2 centimeters in the direction indicated by the arrow, and its image, $\triangle A'B'C'$, is formed.

Step 1: From each vertex of $\triangle ABC$, a segment 2 centimeters long is drawn parallel to the arrow that indicates the direction of this shift. Thus, $AA' = BB' = CC' = 2$ centimeters, and also $\overline{AA'} \parallel \overline{BB'} \parallel \overline{CC'}$.

Step 2: Images A', B', and C' are connected to form $\triangle A'B'C'$.

Any transformation of the plane that slides a figure as shown here is called a *translation*, symbolized as T. Under a translation, if one point moves, then all points move and *no* point remains fixed.

- **DEFINITION.** A ***translation*** is a transformation of the plane that shifts every point in the plane the same distance in the same direction to its image.

Transformations of the Plane as Functions

In Chapter 12, we studied functions. Since a transformation of the plane is a one-to-one correspondence between the points in the plane, it is true that:

- **Every transformation of the plane is a one-to-one function**.

For example, let us compare a familiar transformation of the plane, such as a line reflection, with a one-to-one algebraic function.

f: *A one-to-one algebraic function*	r_m: *A reflection in line m*
$f(x) = 2x - 3$	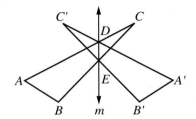

<table>
<tr><td>

1. For every x in the domain, there is one and only one corresponding $f(x)$ in the range.
   For example:

$$f(10) = 17$$
$$f(6) = 9$$
$$f(3) = 3$$

   Therefore, f is a *function*.

</td><td>

1. For every point in the plane, there is one and only one corresponding point (or image) in the plane.
   For example:

$$r_m(A) = A'$$
$$r_m(C) = C'$$
$$r_m(E) = E$$

   Therefore, r_m is a *function*.

</td></tr>
<tr><td>

2. Since every $f(x)$ corresponds to a unique value of x, that is, one and only one x, the function f is *one-to-one*.
   For example, if $f(x) = 5$, then $x = 4$.

</td><td>

2. Since every image has a unique preimage, that is, one and only one preimage, the function r_m is *one-to-one*.
   For example, given image B', its preimage is B.

</td></tr>
<tr><td>

3. For function f:

   domain = {real numbers}

   range = {real numbers}

   Thus, function f is a one-to-one correspondence between elements of the set of real numbers.

</td><td>

3. For function r_m:

   domain = {points in plane}

   range = {points in plane}

   Thus, transformation r_m or function r_m is a one-to-one correspondence between the points in the plane.

</td></tr>
</table>

Just as r_m, the reflection in line m, is a function, it is also true that every transformation of the plane is a function. For example:

R_P: A reflection in point P is a function.

$R_{M,\phi}$: A rotation about point M, through an angle of measure ϕ, is a function.

T: A translation is a function.

EXERCISES WITH OPEN-RESPONSE PROBLEMS

In 1–8, the reflection of △ABC in line k is △DEC.

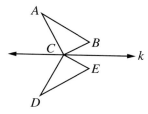

1. What is the image of point A under the line reflection?
2. $r_k(B) = ?$ 3. $r_k(C) = ?$ 4. $r_k(D) = ?$
5. What is the preimage of point B under the line reflection?
6. $r_k(\angle ABC) = ?$ 7. $r_k(\overline{DE}) = ?$ 8. $r_k(?) = \overline{EC}$

Ex. 1–8

In 9–16, the reflection of △PQR through point P is △PST.

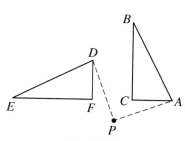

9. What is the image of point R under the point reflection?
10. $R_P(Q) = ?$ 11. $R_P(T) = ?$ 12. $R_P(P) = ?$
13. What is the preimage of point S under the point reflection?
14. $R_P(\angle STP) = ?$ 15. $R_P(\overline{TP}) = ?$ 16. $R_P(?) = \overline{QS}$

17. **a.** On your paper, draw any triangle and label it ABC.
    b. Locate point M, the midpoint of $\overline{AC}$.
    c. Draw the reflection of △ABC through point M.
    d. Explain why the image of A is C, and the image of C is A.
    e. If the image of B is B′, what type of quadrilateral is ABCB′? Explain your answer.

In 18–26, △ABC → △DEF by a quarter-turn about P, that is, by a rotation of 90° about point P.

18. What is the image of A under the quarter-turn?
19. $R_{P,90°}(B) = ?$ 20. $R_{P,90°}(C) = ?$ 21. $R_{P,90°}(P) = ?$
22. What is the preimage of $\overline{FE}$ under the quarter-turn?
23. $R_{P,90°}(\overline{CA}) = ?$ 24. $R_{P,90°}(?) = \angle EDF$
25. $m\angle APD = ?$
26. Does $m\angle BPE = m\angle CPF$? Explain your answer.

In 27–30, in each case, select *one or more* of these transformations that fit the given conditions: line reflection, point reflection, rotation, translation.

27. In the transformation $A \rightarrow A'$, where $A \neq A'$ and *no* point maps to itself.
28. In the transformation $A \rightarrow A'$, where $A \neq A'$ and *exactly one* point maps to itself.
29. In the transformation $A \rightarrow A'$, where $A \neq A'$ and *at least one* point maps to itself.
30. In the transformation $A \rightarrow A'$, where $A \neq A'$ and *at least two* points map to themselves.

In 31–34, use the accompanying diagram of nine congruent rectangles whose vertices are lettered.

31. Under a given line reflection, if the image of Q is G, find the image of:
   a. P **b.** L **c.** $\overline{RQ}$ **d.** $\overline{NR}$ **e.** $\angle LPQ$

32. Under a given reflection in a point, if the image of Q is G, find the image of:
   a. P **b.** L **c.** $\overline{RQ}$ **d.** $\overline{NR}$ **e.** $\angle LPQ$

33. Under a given translation, if the image of Q is G, find the image of:
   a. P **b.** L **c.** $\overline{RQ}$ **d.** $\overline{NR}$ **e.** $\angle LPQ$

34. Under a given translation, if the image of D is M, find the image of:
   a. C **b.** F **c.** $\overline{DH}$ **d.** $\overline{FG}$ **e.** $\overline{BD}$ **f.** $\angle BCG$

| | A | B | C | D |

Ex. 31–34

13-2 TRANSFORMATIONS AND COORDINATE GEOMETRY

Many transformations in the coordinate plane can be described by rules involving the variables x and y. Rules for the most common transformations, discovered by inductive reasoning in Math A, are reviewed here.

Line Reflections

1. *Reflection in the y-axis*
   Here, the vertices of $\triangle ABC$ are $A(1, 6)$, $B(4, 3)$, and $C(2, -1)$. These vertices are reflected in the y-axis; and their images, when connected, form $\triangle A'B'C'$.

$$A(1, 6) \rightarrow A'(-1, 6)$$
$$B(4, 3) \rightarrow B'(-4, 3)$$
$$C(2, -1) \rightarrow C'(-2, -1)$$

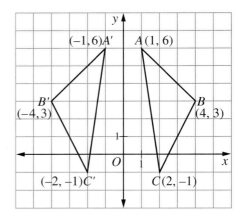

This example illustrates a general rule.

- **Under a reflection in the y-axis:**

$$P(x, y) \rightarrow P'(-x, y) \quad \text{or} \quad r_{y\text{-axis}}(x, y) = (-x, y)$$

2. *Reflection in the line* $y = x$

Here, the endpoints of $\overline{AB}$ are $A(3, 0)$ and $B(4, 3)$. These endpoints are reflected in the line whose equation is $y = x$ and are connected to form $\overline{A'B'}$.

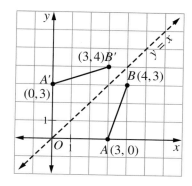

$$A(3, 0) \rightarrow A'(0, 3)$$
$$B(4, 3) \rightarrow B'(3, 4)$$

Another general rule can be stated.

- **Under a reflection in the line $y = x$:**

$$P(x, y) \rightarrow P'(y, x) \qquad \text{or} \qquad r_{y=x}(x, y) = (y, x)$$

3. *Reflection in the line* $y = -x$

Here, the endpoints of $\overline{AB}$ are $A(-1, 2)$ and $B(3, 0)$. The endpoints are reflected in the line whose equations is $y = -x$ and are connected to form $\overline{A'B'}$.

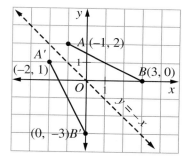

$$A(-1, 2) \rightarrow A'(-2, 1)$$
$$B(3, 0) \rightarrow B'(0, -3)$$

These coordinates illustrate a third general rule.

- **Under a reflection in the line $y = -x$:**

$$P(x, y) \rightarrow P'(-y, -x) \qquad \text{or} \qquad r_{y=-x}(x, y) = (-y, -x)$$

4. *Reflection in the x-axis*

Here, the vertices of quadrilateral $ABCD$ are $A(1, 3)$, $B(2, 1)$, $C(7, 1)$, and $D(5, 5)$. These vertices are reflected in the x-axis; and their images, when connected, form quadrilateral $A'B'C'D'$.

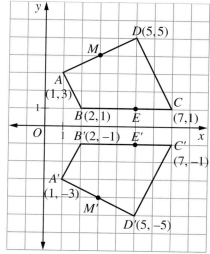

$$A(1, 3) \rightarrow A'(1, -3)$$
$$B(2, 1) \rightarrow B'(2, -1)$$
$$C(7, 1) \rightarrow C'(7, -1)$$
$$D(5, 5) \rightarrow D'(5, -5)$$

This example illustrates a fourth general rule.

- **Under a reflection in the x-axis:**

$$P(x, y) \rightarrow P'(x, -y) \qquad \text{or} \qquad r_{x\text{-axis}}(x, y) = (x, -y)$$

Properties Under a Line Reflection

In Math A, we studied properties preserved under certain transformations. Let us review the properties by studying the last example above, in which $ABCD \rightarrow A'B'C'D'$ by a reflection in the x-axis.

1. *Distance is preserved*; that is, each segment and its image are equal in length.
   The **distance** d between points (x_1, y_1) and (x_2, y_2) is given by the formula

$$d = \sqrt{(x_1 - x_2)^2 + (y_1 - y_2)^2}$$

Under the reflection in the x-axis, $\overline{AB} \rightarrow \overline{A'B'}$.

For $A(1, 3)$ and $B(2, 1)$:
$$AB = \sqrt{(1 - 2)^2 + (3 - 1)^2}$$
$$= \sqrt{(-1)^2 + 2^2}$$
$$= \sqrt{1 + 4} = \sqrt{5}$$

For $A'(1, -3)$ and $B'(2, -1)$:
$$A'B' = \sqrt{(1 - 2)^2 + [-3 - (-1)]^2}$$
$$= \sqrt{(-1)^2 + (-2)^2}$$
$$= \sqrt{1 + 4} = \sqrt{5}$$

Thus, when the image of $\overline{AB}$ is $\overline{A'B'}$, the lengths are equal; $AB = A'B' = \sqrt{5}$. Similarly, $\overline{BC} \rightarrow \overline{B'C'}$, and $BC = B'C' = 5$.

2. *Angle measure is preserved*; that is, each angle and its image are equal in measure.
   Under the reflection in the x-axis, $\angle DAB \rightarrow \angle D'A'B'$.
   The **slope** m of a line containing (x_1, y_1) and (x_2, y_2), where $x_1 \neq x_2$, is given by the formula $\qquad m = \frac{y_2 - y_1}{x_2 - x_1}$

Since
slope of $\overline{DA} = \frac{5 - 3}{5 - 1} = \frac{2}{4} = \frac{1}{2}$, and

slope of $\overline{AB} = \frac{3 - 1}{1 - 2} = \frac{2}{-1} = -2$,

then $\overline{DA} \perp \overline{AB}$ and m$\angle DAB = 90$.

Also,
slope of $\overline{D'A'} = \frac{-5 - (-3)}{5 - 1} = \frac{-2}{4} = -\frac{1}{2}$, and

slope of $\overline{A'B'} = \frac{-3 - (-1)}{1 - 2} = \frac{-2}{-1} = 2$.

Thus, $\overline{D'A'} \perp \overline{A'B'}$ and m$\angle D'A'B' = 90$.

Just as m$\angle DAB = $ m$\angle D'A'B'$, each angle and its image are equal in measure.

3. *Parallelism is preserved*; that is, if two lines are parallel, their images will be parallel lines.
   In our example, since the slope of $\overline{AB} = $ slope of $\overline{DC} = -2$, then $\overline{AB} \parallel \overline{DC}$. Under the reflection in the x-axis, $\overline{AB} \rightarrow \overline{A'B'}$, and $\overline{DC} \rightarrow \overline{D'C'}$. Since slope of $\overline{A'B'} = $ slope of $\overline{D'C'} = +2$, then $\overline{A'B'} \parallel \overline{D'C'}$, and parallelism is preserved.

4. *Collinearity is preserved*; that is, if three or more points lie on a straight line, their images will also lie on a straight line.
   In our example, B, E, and C are collinear points that lie on the line whose equation is $y = 1$. Their images, B', E', and C', are also collinear since these points lie on the line whose equation is $y = -1$.

5. *A midpoint is preserved*; that is, given three points such that one is the midpoint of the line segment whose endpoints are the other two points, then the images of these points will be related in the same way.

The **midpoint** of a line segment whose endpoints are (x_1, y_1) and (x_2, y_2) is given by the expression

$$\left(\frac{x_1 + x_2}{2}, \frac{y_1 + y_2}{2}\right)$$

Under the reflection in the x-axis, $\overline{AD} \rightarrow \overline{A'D'}$.

The midpoint M of $\overline{AD}$, where $A = (1, 3)$ and $D = (5, 5)$, is

$$\left(\frac{1+5}{2}, \frac{3+5}{2}\right) = \left(\frac{6}{2}, \frac{8}{2}\right) = (3, 4)$$

The midpoint M' of $\overline{A'D'}$, where $A' = (1, -3)$ and $D' = (5, -5)$, is

$$\left(\frac{1+5}{2}, \frac{-3-5}{2}\right) = \left(\frac{6}{2}, \frac{-8}{2}\right) = (3, -4)$$

Since $M \rightarrow M'$ under the reflection in the x-xis, the midpoint is preserved.

The *properties preserved under every line reflection* include the five properties just demonstrated: distance, angle measure, parallelism, collinearity, and midpoint.

Point Reflections and Rotations

Although it is possible to use any point on the coordinate plane as a point of reflection or a point of rotation, the most commonly used point is the origin.

1. *Point reflection in the origin, or half-turn, or rotation of 180°*

Here, the vertices of $\triangle ABC$ are $A(1, 2)$, $B(5, 5)$, and $C(5, 2)$. These vertices are reflected in the origin (point O). Their images are connected to form $\triangle A'B'C'$.

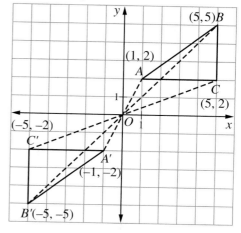

$$A(1, 2) \rightarrow A'(-1, -2)$$
$$B(5, 5) \rightarrow B'(-5, -5)$$
$$C(5, 2) \rightarrow C'(-5, -2)$$

This example illustrates a general rule

● **Under a reflection in point O, the origin:**

$$P(x, y) \rightarrow P'(-x, -y)$$

or $\qquad R_o(x, y) = (-x, -y)$

or $\qquad R_{180°}(x, y) = (-x, -y)$

2. *Rotation of 90°, counterclockwise about the origin*

Here, the vertices of $\triangle ABC$ are $A(1, 3)$, $B(5, 1)$, and $C(1, 1)$. These vertices are rotated counterclockwise about the origin (point O) through an angle of 90°, and their images are connected to form $\triangle A'B'C'$.

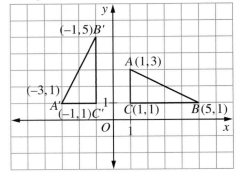

$$A(1, 3) \rightarrow A'(-3, 1)$$
$$B(5, 1) \rightarrow B'(-1, 5)$$
$$C(1, 1) \rightarrow C'(-1, 1)$$

The coordinates illustrate another general rule.

- **Under a rotation of 90° counterclockwise about point O, the origin:**

$$P(x, y) \rightarrow P'(-y, x) \qquad \text{or} \qquad R_{90°}(x, y) = (-y, x)$$

3. *Rotation of 270°, counterclockwise about the origin*

Similar examples can be used to demonstrate a third general rule.

- **Under a rotation of 270° counterclockwise about point O, the origin:**

$$P(x, y) \rightarrow P'(y, -x) \qquad \text{or} \qquad R_{270°}(x, y) = (y, -x)$$

Note: If no point is mentioned, it is assumed that the rotation is taken about the origin. Thus, $R_{50°}$ means a 50° rotation about O, the origin.

The *properties preserved under a point reflection* and *under a rotation* include all five properties listed previously for a line reflection, namely, distance, angle measure, parallelism, collinearity, and midpoint.

Translations

A rule for a translation is easily stated in coordinate geometry. At the right, the segment $\overline{AB}$ is translated onto its image, $\overline{A'B'}$, by moving each point 3 units to the right and 2 units down. Thus, by counting, we form the rule for the translation:

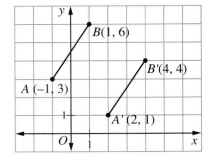

$$P(x, y) \rightarrow P'(x + 3, y - 2)$$
$$\text{or}$$
$$T_{3,-2}(x, y) = (x + 3, y - 2)$$

- **Under a translation of a units horizontally and b units vertically:**

$$P(x, y) \rightarrow P'(x + a, y + b) \qquad \text{or} \qquad T_{a,b}(x, y) = (x + a, y + b)$$

The *properties preserved under a translation* include all five properties listed previously for a line reflection, namely, distance, angle measure, parallelism, collinearity, and midpoint.

EXAMPLES

1. Given $\triangle ABC$, whose vertices are $A(1, 3)$, $B(-2, 0)$, $C(4, -3)$.
   a. On one set of axes, draw $\triangle ABC$ and its image, $\triangle A'B'C'$, under a reflection in the y-axis.
   b. Find the coordinates of all points on the sides of $\triangle ABC$ that remain fixed under the given line reflection.

Solutions a. In step 1, draw and label $\triangle ABC$.
In step 2, find the images of the vertices of $\triangle ABC$ by using the rule $P(x, y) \rightarrow P'(-x, y)$. Then draw and label $\triangle A'B'C'$.

$$A(1, 3) \rightarrow A'(-1, 3)$$
$$B(-2, 0) \rightarrow B'(2, 0)$$
$$C(4, -3) \rightarrow C'(-4, -3)$$

Step 1

Step 2

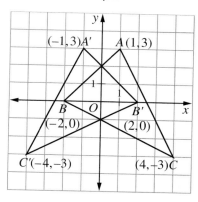

b. Under a reflection in the y-axis, points on the y-axis remain fixed. The sides of $\triangle ABC$ intersect the y-axis at $(0, 2)$ and $(0, -1)$. As seen in the graph, only these two points are common to both triangles.

Answers: **a.** See the graph labeled *Step 2*.   **b.** $(0, 2)$ and $(0, -1)$

---

2. A translation maps $A(2, 1)$ onto $A'(10, -4)$. Find the coordinates of B', the image of $B(8, 7)$, under the same translation.

Solution (1) Use the coordinates of A and A' to discover the number of units shifted horizontally and vertically.

$$A(2, 1) \rightarrow A'(10, -4)$$
$$(x, y) \rightarrow (x + 8, y - 5)$$

(2) Substitute the coordinates of B in the rule determined for the translation.

$$B(8, 7) \rightarrow B'(16, 2)$$

Answer: $B'(16, 2)$

3. The vertices of parallelogram $ABCD$ are $A(1, 1)$, $B(3, 5)$, $C(9, 5)$, and $D(7, 1)$.

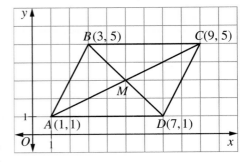

a. Find the coordinates of the point of symmetry for $\square ABCD$.

b. Find the image of $\angle CAD$ under this point reflection.

Solutions **a.** Since the diagonals of a parallelogram bisect each other, the point of symmetry is the intersection point of the two diagonals, or the midpoint of either diagonal.

For $\overline{AC}$, the coordinates of midpoint M are:

$$\left(\frac{1+9}{2}, \frac{1+5}{2}\right) = \left(\frac{10}{2}, \frac{6}{2}\right) = (5, 3)$$

For $\overline{BD}$, the coordinates of midpoint M are:

$$\left(\frac{3+7}{2}, \frac{5+1}{2}\right) = \left(\frac{10}{2}, \frac{6}{2}\right) = (5, 3)$$

b. Under a reflection in point M: $C \rightarrow A$, $A \rightarrow C$, and $D \rightarrow B$. Therefore, $R_M(\angle CAD) = \angle ACB$.

Answers: **a.** $(5, 3)$ **b.** $\angle ACB$

EXERCISES WITH OPEN-RESPONSE PROBLEMS

In 1–5, find the image of each point under a reflection in the *x*-axis.

1. $(3, 10)$ **2.** $(6, -4)$ **3.** $(-1, 8)$ **4.** $(3, 0)$ **5.** $(-2.7, 0)$

In 6–10, find the image of each point under a reflection in the *y*-axis.

6. $(3, 10)$ **7.** $(6, -4)$ **8.** $(-1, 8)$ **9.** $(0, 6)$ **10.** $(-8, -1.3)$

In 11–15, find the image of each point under a reflection in the line $y = x$.

11. $(3, 10)$ **12.** $(6, -4)$ **13.** $(-1, 8)$ **14.** $(-1.5, -7)$ **15.** $(8, 8)$

In 16–20, find the image of each point under a reflection in the origin.

16. $(3, 10)$ **17.** $(6, -4)$ **18.** $(-1, 8)$ **19.** $(0, 0)$ **20.** $(-10, -5)$

In 21–25, find the image of point $(-3, 2)$ under each given translation.

21. $T_{1,2}$ **22.** $T_{3,-6}$ **23.** $T_{-4,0}$ **24.** $T_{0,-7}$ **25.** $T_{3,-2}$

26. Under function f: $(x, y) \rightarrow (x, -y)$.
  a. Function f is a reflection
    (1) in the x-axis   (2) in the y-axis   (3) in the line $x = y$ (4) in the line $x = -y$
  b. State the domain of f.   **c.** State the range of f.

27. a. If function g is a reflection in the line $y = -x$, the rule of g is
    (1) $(x, y) \rightarrow (x, -y)$ (2) $(x, y) \rightarrow (-x, y)$ (3) $(x, y) \rightarrow (y, x)$ (4) $(x, y) \rightarrow (-y, -x)$
  b. Write the coordinates of three points that remain fixed under this reflection.

28. Match the name of the transformation of the plane in Column A with its function rule in Column B.

Column A	Column B
1. A reflection in the y-axis	a. $(x, y) \rightarrow (x + 3, y)$
2. A point reflection in the origin	b. $(x, y) \rightarrow (x, -y)$
3. A reflection in the line $y = -x$	c. $(x, y) \rightarrow (-x, y)$
4. A reflection in the x-axis	d. $(x, y) \rightarrow (-y, x)$
5. A translation of 3 to the right	e. $(x, y) \rightarrow (-x, -y)$
6. A reflection in the line $y = x$	f. $(x, y) \rightarrow (-y, -x)$
7. A counterclockwise rotation of 90° about the origin	g. $(x, y) \rightarrow (y, x)$

In 29–34, in each case find the rule for the translation so that the image of A is A'.

29. $A(3, 8) \rightarrow A'(4, 6)$ **30.** $A(1, 0) \rightarrow A'(0, 1)$ **31.** $A(2, 5) \rightarrow A'(-1, 1)$
32. $A(-1, 2) \rightarrow A'(-2, -3)$ **33.** $A(0, -3) \rightarrow A'(-7, -3)$ **34.** $A(4, -7) \rightarrow A'(4, -2)$

35. A translation maps $B(0, 2)$ onto $B'(5, 0)$. Find the coordinates of C', the image of $C(-3, 1)$, under the same translation.

36. A translation maps the origin to point $(-1, 7)$. What is the image of $(3, -7)$ under the same translation?

37. Translation $T_{-4,6}$ maps point $A(7, -4)$ to point B, and a second translation maps points B to the origin. What is the rule for the second translation?

In 38–40, the vertices of $\triangle ABC$ are $A(1, 4)$, $B(3, 0)$, and $C(-3, -4)$. In each case:
  a. Find the coordinates of A', B', and C', the images of the vertices of $\triangle ABC$ under the given transformation.
  b. On one set of axes, draw $\triangle ABC$ and $\triangle A'B'C'$.
  c. Find the coordinates of all points on the sides of $\triangle ABC$ that remain fixed under the given transformation.

38. $r_{x\text{-axis}}$ **39.** $r_{y\text{-axis}}$ **40.** $r_{y=x}$

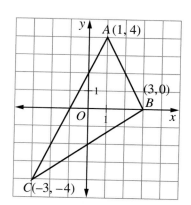

Ex. 38–40

41. The vertices of $\triangle RST$ are $R(0, 0)$, $S(1, 2)$, and $T(4, 1)$. If $\triangle RST$ is reflected in the line whose equation is $y = 3$, find the coordinates of the images, R', S', and T'.

In 42–45, the image of $\triangle ABC$ under a line reflection is $\triangle A'B'C'$. In each case:

a. On one set of axes, use the given coordinates to draw $\triangle ABC$ and $\triangle A'B'C'$, and draw the line of reflection.

b. Write the equation of the line of reflection.

42. $\triangle ABC$: $A(2, 4)$, $B(2, 1)$, $C(-1, 1)$
$\triangle A'B'C'$: $A'(4, 4)$, $B'(4, 1)$, $C'(7, 1)$

43. $\triangle ABC$: $A(1, 3)$, $B(2, 5)$, $C(5, 3)$
$\triangle A'B'C'$: $A'(1, 1)$, $B'(2, -1)$, $C'(5, 1)$

44. $\triangle ABC$: $A(1, 4)$, $B(2, 1)$, $C(4, 2)$
$\triangle A'B'C'$: $A'(-5, 4)$, $B'(-6, 1)$, $C'(-8, 2)$

45. $\triangle ABC$: $A(4, 2)$, $B(6, 2)$, $C(2, -1)$
$\triangle A'B'C'$: $A'(2, 4)$, $B'(2, 6)$, $C'(-1, 2)$

46. The vertices of rhombus $ABCD$ are $A(0, 1)$, $B(3, 5)$, $C(8, 5)$, and $D(5, 1)$.

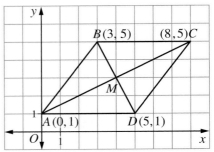

a. Find the coordinates of M, the point of symmetry for rhombus $ABCD$.

b. $R_M(A) = ?$ **c.** $R_M(\overline{BC}) = ?$ **d.** $R_M(M) = ?$

e. $R_M(\angle BCD) = ?$ **f.** $R_M(\angle MCB) = ?$

g. Find the length of $\overline{AB}$ and the length of its image. Is distance preserved in the given transformation?

47. a. Using the rule $(x, y) \rightarrow (-y, x)$, find the images of $T(1, 1)$, $U(2, 4)$, $R(5, 3)$, and $N(7, -1)$, namely, T', U', R', and N'.

b. On one set of axes, draw quadrilaterals $TURN$ and $T'U'R'N'$.

c. Describe, in words, the transformation that maps quadrilateral $TURN$ onto $T'U'R'N'$.

d. Using TU and $T'U'$, demonstrate that distance is preserved.

e. Using $\angle RUT$ and $\angle R'U'T'$, demonstrate that angle measure is preserved.

f. Using $\overline{UR}$ and $\overline{TN}$ and their images, demonstrate that parallelism is preserved.

g. Using $\overline{RN}$ and $\overline{R'N'}$, demonstrate that midpoints of segments are preserved.

In 48–51, the image of $\triangle ABC$ under a point reflection is $\triangle A'B'C'$. In each case:

a. Using the given coordinates, draw $\triangle ABC$ and $\triangle A'B'C'$ on one set of axes.

b. Find the coordinate of the point of reflection.

48. $\triangle ABC$: $A(2, 2)$, $B(5, 2)$, $C(5, 4)$
$\triangle A'B'C'$: $A'(0, 2)$, $B'(-3, 2)$, $C'(-3, 0)$

49. $\triangle ABC$: $A(2, 5)$, $B(5, 6)$, $C(2, 3)$
$\triangle A'B'C'$: $A'(2, 1)$, $B'(-1, 0)$, $C'(2, 3)$

50. $\triangle ABC$: $A(3, 1)$, $B(5, 5)$, $C(6, 3)$
$\triangle A'B'C'$: $A'(3, 7)$, $B'(1, 3)$, $C'(0, 5)$

51. $\triangle ABC$: $A(-3, 6)$, $B(1, 7)$, $C(2, 4)$
$\triangle A'B'C'$: $A'(-1, 0)$, $B'(-5, -1)$, $C'(-6, 2)$

52. The vertices of $\triangle DEF$ are $D(4, 3)$, $E(8, 1)$, and $F(8, 3)$. If $\triangle DEF$ is reflected through point $(4, 1)$, find the coordinates of the images, D', E', and F'.

53. a. On graph paper, draw the line whose equation is $y = \frac{1}{2}x + 2$.

b. Name the coordinates of three points on this line, and call these points A, B, and C.

c. Under a point reflection in the origin, name the coordinates of A', B', and C', the images of the three points found in part **b**.

d. On graph paper, draw the line containing A', B', and C'.

e. What is the equation of the line drawn in part **d**?

In 54–61, a line whose equation is given is reflected through the origin. In each case, what is the equation of the line that is its image? (*Hint*: See procedures in Exercise 53.)

54. $x = 3$ **55.** $y = -8$ **56.** $y = x + 5$ **57.** $y = -x + 1$
58. $y = x$ **59.** $y = 2x - 3$ **60.** $y = 3x$ **61.** $y = -x$

62. Let $f(x, y) = (x, 0)$, where the domain is the set of points in the plane.
  a. Find $f(5, 2)$.
  b. Find $f(3, 7)$.
  c. Find $f(3, 4)$.
  d. The range of f is
    (1) the x-axis   (2) the y-axis   (3) the set of points in the plane   (4) the line $y = x$
  e. Is f a function?   **f.** Is f a one-to-one function?
  g. Explain why f is *not* a transformation of the plane.

63. Given the rule $g(x, y) = (2, y)$.
  a. Find $g(5, 6)$.
  b. Find $g(9, 7)$.
  c. Find $g(-8, 7)$.
  d. State the domain of g.
  e. State the range of g.
  f. Explain why g is a function.
  g. Explain why g is *not* a transformation of the plane.

13-3   COMPOSITIONS AND DILATIONS

In Chapter 12, we learned that composition is an operation performed on a set of functions. Since every transformation of the plane is a one-to-one function, composition can be performed on these transformations.

Compositions of Transformations

When two transformations occur, one following another, we have a *composition of transformations*. The first transformation produces an image, and the second transformation is performed on that image.

For example, let us start with $\triangle ABC$ whose vertices are $A(1, 2)$, $B(5, 5)$, and $C(5, 2)$. To demonstrate a composition of transformations, let us use two line reflections. First, by reflecting $\triangle ABC$ in the y-axis, we form $\triangle A'B'C'$, or $\triangle$I. Then, by reflecting $\triangle A'B'C'$ in the x-axis, we form $\triangle A''B''C''$, or $\triangle$II.

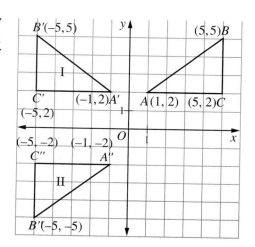

$$A(1, 2) \rightarrow A'(-1, 2) \rightarrow A''(-1, -2)$$
$$B(5, 5) \rightarrow B'(-5, 5) \rightarrow B''(-5, -5)$$
$$C(5, 2) \rightarrow C'(-5, 2) \rightarrow C''(-5, -2)$$

As we compare the original triangle, $\triangle ABC$, with its final image, $\triangle A''B''C''$, in the graph just drawn, we observe another familiar transformation:

- **The composition of a line reflection in the *y*-axis, followed by a line reflection in the *x*-axis, is equivalent to a single transformation, namely, a reflection through point *O*, the origin.**

In symbols, we write:

$$r_{x\text{-axis}} \circ r_{y\text{-axis}} = R_o$$

In Chapter 12, we learned two ways to write the composition "f *following* g":

$$f(g(x))$$

or

$$(f \circ g)(x)$$

Here, function g is applied before function f.

In the same way, the composition "a reflection in the *x*-axis *following* a reflection in the *y*-axis" may be written as

$$r_{x\text{-axis}}(r_{y\text{-axis}}(A))$$

or

$$r_{x\text{-axis}} \circ r_{y\text{-axis}}(A)$$

Here, a point is reflected in the *y*-axis before its image is reflected in the *x*-axis.

Therefore, when performing the composition just described, we may use either symbolism, but we must reflect in the *y*-axis *first*.

$$r_{x\text{-axis}}(r_{y\text{-axis}}(A)) = r_{x\text{-axis}}(A') = A''$$

or

$$A \xrightarrow{\;r_{y\text{-axis}}\;} A' \xrightarrow{\;r_{x\text{-axis}}\;} A''$$

$$r_{x\text{-axis}} \circ r_{y\text{-axis}}(A) = A''$$

If we had reflected the triangle first in the *x*-axis and then in the *y*-axis, would this composition be equivalent to a reflection through point *O*, the origin? The answer is yes. However, not all compositions will act in the same way. In general, compositions of transformations are *not* commutative.

Dilations

When a photograph is enlarged or reduced, a change, or transformation, takes place in its size. There is a constant ratio of the distances between points in the original photograph compared to the distances between their images in the enlargement or reduction. This type of transformation is called a *dilation*.

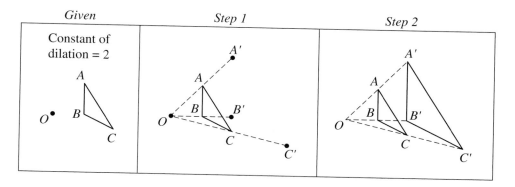

In the diagram, $\triangle ABC$ is to be dilated so that the *center of dilation* is point O and the *constant of dilation* is 2.

Step 1:   From O, the center of dilation, rays are drawn to pass through each of the vertices of $\triangle ABC$. Then, the constant of dilation, 2, is used to locate the images, A', B', and C', on these rays so that $OA' = 2 \cdot OA$, $OB' = 2 \cdot OB$, and $OC' = 2 \cdot OC$.

Step 2:   The images, A', B', and C', are connected to form $\triangle A'B'C'$.

This dilation, with a constant factor of 2, is written in symbols as D_2.
    Although any point may be chosen as the center of dilation, we usually limit dilations to those where point O, the origin, is the center of dilation.

- **DEFINITION.** A *dilation* of k, where k is a positive number called the *constant of dilation*, is a transformation of the plane such that:

1. The image of point O, the center of dilation, is O.
2. For all other points, the image of P is P', where $\overrightarrow{OP}$ and $\overrightarrow{OP'}$ name the same ray and $OP' = k \cdot OP$.

A rule for a dilation is stated in coordinate geometry as follows:

- **Under a dilation of k (a positive number) whose center of dilation is the origin:**

$$P(x, y) \rightarrow P'(kx, ky) \qquad \text{or} \qquad D_k(x, y) = (kx, ky)$$

Compositions Involving Dilations

On page 578, $\triangle ABC \rightarrow \triangle A'B'C'$ by a point reflection in the origin. Then, $\triangle A'B'C' \rightarrow \triangle A''B''C''$ by a dilation of 2. This composition of a point reflection followed by a dilation of 2 is equivalent to multiplying the x and y values in each of the coordinates by -2.
    Let us apply the two transformations to $A(1, 3)$, $B(3, 1)$ and $C(2, 0)$ and then compare each original vertex to its final image.

$$(x, y) \overset{R_O}{\rightarrow} (-x, -y) \overset{D_2}{\rightarrow} (-2x, -2y)$$

$$A(1, 3) \rightarrow A'(-1, -3) \rightarrow A''(-2, -6)$$

$$B(3, 1) \rightarrow B'(-3, -1) \rightarrow B''(-6, -2)$$

$$C(2, 0) \underbrace{\rightarrow C'(-2, 0) \quad \rightarrow C''(-4, 0)}$$

$$D_2 \circ R_O = D_{-2}$$

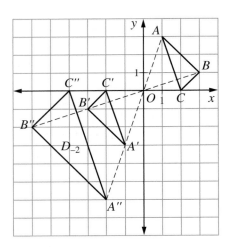

Since these coordinates follow the rule $(x, y) \rightarrow (-2x, -2y)$ we will symbolize this composition of transformations as D_{-2}.

- **A composition of transformations consisting of a point reflection about the origin and a dilation of k, where k is a positive number, is equivalent to the single transformation**

$$D_{-k}(x, y) = (-kx, -ky)$$

Under a dilation there is generally only one fixed point, namely, the center of dilation. If the constant of dilation is 1, however, all points are fixed.

The *properties preserved under a dilation* include only four of the properties listed for the other transformations studied earlier in this chapter, namely, angle measure, parallelism, collinearity, and midpoint.

- **Distance is *not* preserved under a dilation.**

EXAMPLES

In 1 and 2, in each case, write a single rule for a dilation, or a composition involving a dilation, by which A maps to A'.

1. $A(3, -1) \rightarrow A'(-12, 4)$

2. $A(9, 0) \rightarrow A'(6, 0)$

Solutions   In each case, write and solve an equation to find the constant of dilation, k.

1. $(3, -1) \rightarrow (-12, 4)$

$$\begin{array}{ccc} 3k = -12 & \text{or} & -1k = 4 \\ k = -4 & & k = -4 \end{array}$$

Answer: $(x, y) \rightarrow (-4x, -4y)$

or

$$D_{-4}(x, y) = (-4x, -4y)$$

2. $(9, 0) \rightarrow (6, 0)$

$$9k = 6$$

$$k = \frac{6}{9} = \frac{2}{3}$$

Answer: $(x, y) \rightarrow \left(\frac{2}{3}x, \frac{2}{3}y\right)$

or

$$D_{\frac{2}{3}}(x, y) = \left(\frac{2}{3}x, \frac{2}{3}y\right)$$

EXERCISES WITH OPEN-RESPONSE PROBLEMS

In 1–5, use the rule $(x, y) \rightarrow (4x, 4y)$ to find the image of each given point.

1. $(3, 5)$ **2.** $(-3, 2)$ **3.** $(7, 0)$ **4.** $(-4, 9)$ **5.** $(0.125, 0.5)$

In 6–10, find the image of each given point under a dilation of 5.

6. $(12, 20)$ **7.** $(-9, -7)$ **8.** $(0, -8)$ **9.** $\left(\frac{3}{10}, -\frac{1}{5}\right)$ **10.** $(\sqrt{2}, 0)$

In 11–15, $D_{-3}(x, y) = (-3x, -3y)$ is a composition of a half-turn about the origin and a dilation of 3. Using D_{-3}, find the image of each given point.

11. $(9, 4)$ **12.** $(-3, 0)$ **13.** $(-5, -6)$ **14.** $\left(\frac{2}{3}, -\frac{5}{6}\right)$ **15.** $(0.\overline{3}, 0.\overline{6})$

In 16–24, in each case, write a single rule for a dilation, or a composition involving a dilation, by which the image of A is A'.

16. $A(2, 5) \rightarrow A'(4, 10)$ **17.** $A(3, -1) \rightarrow A'(21, -7)$ **18.** $A(-2, 5) \rightarrow A'(8, -20)$

19. $A(10, 4) \rightarrow A'(5, 2)$ **20.** $A(-20, 8) \rightarrow A'(-5, 2)$ **21.** $A(0, 9) \rightarrow A'(0, -3)$

22. $A(4, 6) \rightarrow A'(6, 9)$ **23.** $A(4, -3) \rightarrow A'(-8, 6)$ **24.** $A(4, 0) \rightarrow A'(-5, 0)$

In 25–30, as shown in the accompanying diagram, O is the center of dilation and $D_k(\triangle OQR) = \triangle OPS$.

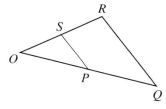

25. What is the image of R under the dilation?

26. $D_k(Q) = ?$ **27.** $D_k(?) = \overline{SP}$ **28.** $D_k(\overline{OR}) = ?$

29. If $OP = PQ$, what is the constant of dilation k?

30. Using the value of k from Exercise 29, find the value of $RQ:SP$.

Ex. 25–30

31. a. On graph paper, draw $\triangle ACE$ with vertices $A(2, 3)$, $C(2, -1)$, and $E(-1, -1)$.

     b. Using the same axes, graph $\triangle A'C'E'$ such that $D_3(\triangle ACE) = \triangle A'C'E'$.

     c. Using EA and $E'A'$, demonstrate that distance is *not* preserved under the dilation.

     d. Show that $\triangle ACE \sim \triangle A'C'E'$.

32. The vertices of quadrilateral $TRAP$ are $T(-2, 1)$, $R(0, 4)$, $A(5, 4)$, and $P(3, 1)$. Under a dilation of 2, $TRAP$ maps to $T'R'A'P'$.

     a. On one set of axes, draw and label quadrilaterals $TRAP$ and $T'R'A'P'$.

     b. True or False: Since $D_2(TRAP) = T'R'A'P'$, the area of quadrilateral $T'R'A'P'$ is twice the area of quadrilateral $TRAP$.

     c. Explain your answer to part **b**, providing work to support your reasoning.

13-4 COMPOSITIONS AND SYMMETRIES

Symmetry occurs in a figure when the figure is its own image under a given transformation. In Math A, we studied three types of symmetries.

1. **Line symmetry** occurs in a figure when the figure is its own image under a reflection in a line. Such a line is called the **axis of symmetry**, or line of symmetry.

   In line symmetry, every point in a figure moves to its image through a reflection in the axis of symmetry, and the figure appears to be unchanged. As shown here, isosceles triangle RST has line symmetry with respect to $\overleftrightarrow{SM}$, a vertical line, and the word CHECK has line symmetry with respect to a horizontal line.

2. **Point symmetry** occurs in a figure when the figure is its own image under a reflection in a point. Such a point is called the **point of reflection**, or point of symmetry.

   Figures that have point symmetry also appear to look the same when turned upside down, as if moved through a half-turn. Let us turn this book upside down and examine the figures with point symmetry.

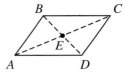

   In parallelogram $ABCD$, diagonals $\overline{AC}$ and $\overline{BD}$ intersect at E, the point of reflection. We note that parallelogram $ABCD$ has point symmetry but it does *not* have line symmetry.

3. **Rotational symmetry** occurs in a figure when the figure is its own image under a rotation of ϕ degrees, and only the center point remains fixed.

   The degree measure of the *smallest* angle needed to rotate a regular polygon of n sides to be its own image is $\frac{360°}{n}$.

   An equilateral triangle is its own image if it rotated through 120° because $\frac{360°}{3} = 120°$, or through 240° (a multiple of 120°).

   A regular pentagon is its own image if it is rotated through 72° because $\frac{360°}{5} = 72°$, or through any multiple of 72°, such as 144°, 216°, and 288°.

Certain figures, such as the square and the circle, possess all three types of symmetry.

As shown here, square $ABCD$ has:

1. *Line symmetry*, using r_k, r_n, r_p, or r_q.
2. *Point symmetry*, using R_M.
3. *Rotational symmetry*, using $R_{M,90°}$, $R_{M,180°}$, or $R_{M,270°}$.

In the examples that follow, we will use square $ABCD$ and its symmetries to study compositions involving transformations.

EXAMPLES

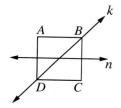

1. In the accompanying figure, k and n are lines of symmetry for square $ABCD$. Find $r_n \circ r_k(A)$.

How to Proceed:

(1) First, reflect point A in line k to find its image, C.
(2) Then, reflect C in line n to find the image B.

Answer: B

Solution:

$$A \xrightarrow{r_k} C \xrightarrow{r_n} B$$

$$r_n \circ r_k(A) = B$$

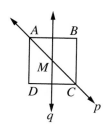

2. In the accompanying diagram, p and q are lines of symmetry for square $ABCD$, and M is the midpoint of diagonal $\overline{AC}$. Find $R_M \circ r_p \circ r_q(D)$.

How to Proceed:

(1) First, reflect point D in line q to find its image, C.
(2) Note that, since C is a point on line p, the image of C under a reflection in line p is still C.
(3) Finally, reflect C through point M to find the image A.

Answer: A

Solution:

$$R_M \circ r_p \circ r_q(D) = A$$

Note: As seen in this example, we omit parentheses when writing the composition of three or more transformations in order to reduce the symbolism involved.

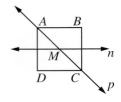

3. In square $ABCD$, p and n are lines of symmetry, and M is the midpoint of $\overline{AC}$. What is $r_n \circ R_{M,90°} \circ r_p(\overline{AB})$?

(1) $\overline{AB}$ (2) $\overline{BC}$ (3) $\overline{CD}$ (4) $\overline{DA}$

How to Proceed:

Reflect $\overline{AB}$ in line p to find its image, $\overline{AD}$.

Rotate $\overline{AD}$ counterclockwise through a 90° angle about M to find its image, $\overline{DC}$.

Reflect $\overline{DC}$ in line n to find the image $\overline{AB}$.

Answer: (1)

Solution:

$$\overline{AB} \xrightarrow{r_p} \overline{AD} \xrightarrow{R_{M,90°}} \overline{DC} \xrightarrow{r_n} \overline{AB}$$

$$r_n \circ R_{M,90°} \circ r_p(\overline{AB}) = \overline{AB}$$

EXERCISES WITH OPEN-RESPONSE PROBLEMS

In 1–10, for each given figure: **a.** Tell whether the figure has *line symmetry*; and, if so, sketch the figure and its line(s) of symmetry on your paper. **b.** Tell whether the figure has *point symmetry*; and, if so, sketch the figure and locate its point of reflection on your paper. **c.** Tell whether the figure has *rotational symmetry*; and, if so, write the degree measure of the smallest angle of rotation for which the figure is its own image.

1.

2.

Parabola

3.

Star

4.

Regular octagon

5. Rectangle   **6.** Rhombus   **7.** Parallelogram

8. Isosceles triangle   **9.** Line segment   **10.** Ellipse

In 11–16, regular hexagon $ABCDEF$ is inscribed in circle O, and O is the center of rotation.

11. Find $R_{60°} \circ R_{180°}(A)$.

12. Find $R_{240°} \circ R_{120°}(E)$.

13. Find $R_{300°} \circ R_{120°}(B)$.

14. Find $R_{120°} \circ R_{-240°}(F)$.

15. Find $R_{-120°} \circ R_{180°} \circ R_{-300°} \circ R_{240°}(C)$.

16. The composition $R_{-240°} \circ R_{180°} \circ R_{-60°}$ is equivalent to the transformation

(1) $R_{-120°}$ (2) $R_{180°}$ (3) $R_{240°}$ (4) $R_{300°}$

Ex. 11–16

In 17–20, p and q are lines of symmetry for rectangle $ABCD$.

17. Find $r_p \circ r_q(A)$.
19. Find $r_q \circ r_p \circ r_q(C)$.

18. Find $r_q \circ r_p(D)$.
20. Find $r_p \circ r_q \circ r_p(B)$.

Ex. 17–20

In 21–28, k and m are lines of symmetry for equilateral triangle ABC, and points A, B, and C are equidistant from point P.

21. Find $r_k \circ r_m(C)$.
23. Find $r_m \circ r_k \circ r_m(A)$.
25. Find $R_{P,120°} \circ R_{P,120°}(A)$.

22. Find $r_m \circ r_k(C)$.
24. Find $r_k \circ r_m \circ r_k(B)$.
26. Find $r_m \circ R_{P,240°}(A)$.

27. Which of the vertices, A, B, or C, is its own image under the composition $r_k \circ R_{P,120°}$?

28. a. Find the image of each vertex, A, B, and C, under the composition $r_k \circ R_{P,120°} \circ r_m$.
 b. The composition $r_k \circ R_{P,120°} \circ r_m$ is equivalent to the single transformation
 (1) r_k (2) r_m (3) $R_{P,120°}$ (4) $R_{P,240°}$

Ex. 21–28

In 29–37, k and g are lines of symmetry for square $ABCD$, and M is the midpoint of diagonal $\overline{AC}$.

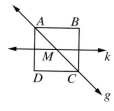

29. a. Find $r_g \circ r_k(B)$.
 b. Find $r_k \circ r_g(B)$.
 c. What conclusion regarding commutativity can be drawn from the answers to parts **a** and **b**?

30. Find $r_k \circ r_g \circ r_k(D)$.
32. Find $R_M \circ r_k \circ r_g(D)$.
34. Find $r_k \circ r_g(\overline{DA})$.
36. Find $r_g \circ R_M \circ r_g(\overline{BC})$.

31. Find $r_g \circ r_k \circ r_g(A)$.
33. Find $r_g \circ R_M \circ r_k(A)$.
35. Find $r_g \circ r_k(\overline{BC})$.
37. Find $r_k \circ r_g \circ R_M(\overline{AB})$.

Ex. 29–37

In 38–46, m and p are lines of symmetry for regular hexagon $ABCDEF$.

38. Find $r_p \circ r_m(D)$.
40. Find $r_m \circ r_p \circ r_m(B)$.
42. Find $r_m \circ r_p(\overline{AB})$.
44. Find $r_p \circ r_m \circ r_p(\overline{ED})$.

39. Find $r_m \circ r_p(E)$.
41. Find $r_p \circ r_m \circ r_p(C)$.
43. Find $r_p \circ r_m(\overline{AB})$.
45. Find $r_m \circ r_p \circ r_m(\overline{CB})$.

46. *True* or *False*: The composition $r_m \circ r_p$ is equivalent to a counterclockwise rotation of $120°$ about the center of regular hexagon $ABCDEF$. (*Hint:* Find the image of each vertex by using $r_m \circ r_p$.)

Ex. 38–46

In 47–53, h and n are two of the five possible lines of symmetry for regular pentagon $ABCDE$.

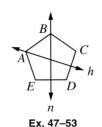

47. Find $r_h \circ r_n(E)$.

48. Find $r_n \circ r_h(E)$.

49. Find $r_h \circ r_n(C)$.

50. Find $r_n \circ r_h \circ r_n(D)$.

51. Find $r_n \circ r_h \circ r_n(\overline{CB})$.

52. Find $r_h \circ r_n \circ r_h(\overline{BA})$.

53. Every point on the pentagon is its own image under the composition

   (1) $r_h \circ r_n$ (2) $r_n \circ r_h$ (3) $r_n \circ r_n$ (4) $r_h \circ r_h \circ r_h$

Ex. 47–53

In 54–60, p, q, and m are lines of symmetry for the figure shown at the right.

54. Find $r_p \circ r_q(B)$.

55. Find $r_q \circ r_m(A)$.

56. Find $r_m \circ r_p(C)$.

57. Find $r_m \circ r_q(D)$.

58. Find $r_q \circ r_p \circ r_m(D)$.

59. Find $r_p \circ r_q \circ r_m(B)$.

60. Under the composition $r_m \circ r_q \circ r_p$, which point $(A, B, C, D, \text{ or } E)$ is its own image?

Ex. 54–60

In 61–68, $ABCD$ is a square. The midpoints of sides $\overline{AB}$, $\overline{BC}$, $\overline{CD}$, and $\overline{DA}$ are E, F, G, and H, respectively. Lines $\overleftrightarrow{AC}$, $\overleftrightarrow{BD}$, $\overleftrightarrow{EG}$, and $\overleftrightarrow{HF}$ are drawn.

61. Find $r_{\overleftrightarrow{EG}} \circ r_{\overleftrightarrow{AC}}(B)$.

62. Find $r_{\overleftrightarrow{BD}} \circ r_{\overleftrightarrow{HF}}(D)$.

63. Find $r_{\overleftrightarrow{AC}} \circ r_{\overleftrightarrow{HF}} \circ r_{\overleftrightarrow{BD}}(A)$.

64. Find $r_{\overleftrightarrow{EG}} \circ r_{\overleftrightarrow{BD}} \circ r_{\overleftrightarrow{AC}}(H)$.

65. Find $r_{\overleftrightarrow{AC}} \circ r_{\overleftrightarrow{HF}} \circ r_{\overleftrightarrow{BD}}(F)$.

66. Find $r_{\overleftrightarrow{AC}} \circ r_{\overleftrightarrow{EG}} \circ r_{\overleftrightarrow{HF}}(\overline{AE})$.

67. Find $r_{\overleftrightarrow{EG}} \circ r_{\overleftrightarrow{BD}} \circ r_{\overleftrightarrow{AC}}(\overline{BF})$.

68. Find $r_{\overleftrightarrow{BD}} \circ r_{\overleftrightarrow{EG}} \circ r_{\overleftrightarrow{HF}}(\overline{AB})$.

69. Determine whether the graph of each equation is symmetric with respect to the y-axis. Explain your reasoning.
   a. $y = |3x + 2|$
   b. $y = |5x - 8|$
   c. $y = x^2 + 6x + 3$
   d. $y = x^2 + 4$

70. Determine whether the graph of each equation is symmetric with respect to the x-axis. Explain your reasoning.
   a. $x^2 + 4y^2 = 4$
   b. $x^2 + y^2 = 25$
   c. $(x - 4)^2 + (y + 2) = 9$
   d. $x = y^2 - 2y$

13-5 COMPOSITION RULES

Finding Coordinate Rules

The composition of two or more functions, each of which is one-to-one, is also a one-to-one function. Since every transformation of the plane is a one-to-one function, the composition of two or more such transformations is a single transformation of the plane.

In Section 13-3, we studied compositions of transformations and saw that the composition of a reflection in the y-axis followed by a reflection in the x-axis was equivalent to a reflection through the origin. In the same way that $r_{x\text{-axis}} \circ r_{y\text{-axis}} = R_O$, we can determine a coordinate rule for the composition of many transformations.

We will consider a composition consisting of a dilation and a translation:

Let $D_4(x, y) = (4x, 4y)$. | Let $T_{3, 0}(x, y) = (x + 3, y)$.

To find the rule for $T_{3,0} \circ D_4$, we *first* dilate the point by a factor of 4. Then, we translate its image 3 units to the right.

$$(x, y) \xrightarrow{\;D_4\;} (4x, 4y) \xrightarrow{\;T_{3,0}\;} (4x + 3, 4y)$$
$$\underbrace{\qquad\qquad\qquad\qquad}_{T_{3,0} \circ D_4}$$

Thus:

$$T_{3,0} \circ D_4(x, y) = (4x + 3, 4y)$$

To find the rule for $D_4 \circ T_{3,0}$, we *first* translate the point 3 units to the right. Then, we dilate its image by a factor of 4.

$$(x, y) \xrightarrow{\;T_{3,0}\;} (x + 3, y) \xrightarrow{\;D_4\;} (4x + 12, 4y)$$
$$\underbrace{\qquad\qquad\qquad\qquad}_{D_4 \circ T_{3,0}}$$

Thus:

$$D_4 \circ T_{3,0}(x, y) = (4x + 12, 4y)$$

These rules demonstrate clearly that $T_{3,0} \circ D_4 \neq D_4 \circ T_{3,0}$. In general, it is true that:

- **Composition of transformations is *not* commutative.**

Glide Reflections

As stated in Section 13-1, a line reflection is like a flip, and a translation is like a shift or a glide. The pattern of footsteps seen in the following diagram represents a composition of a line reflection and a translation, called a *glide reflection*.

From footstep 1 to 2, we reflect the step in line m, then translate this image to the right. From footstep 2 to 3, we again reflect the step in line m, then translate this image to the right. We note that the translation is parallel to the line of reflection.

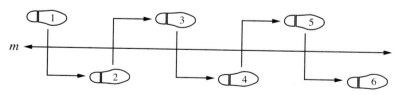

If we had first translated the footstep to the right and then reflected its image in line m, the same pattern would occur. Thus, the composition of these specific transformations is commutative.

- **DEFINITION. A *glide reflection* is a transformation of the plane that represents the composition, in either order, of a line reflection and a translation that is parallel to the line of reflection.**

KEEP IN MIND ———

The composition of any two transformations of the plane is itself a transformation of the plane.

EXAMPLES

1. The coordinates of the vertices of $\triangle ABC$ are $A(2, -6)$, $B(2, -2)$, and $C(4, -5)$.
   a. On graph paper, draw and label $\triangle ABC$.
   b. Find the coordinates of the vertices of $\triangle A'B'C'$, the image of $\triangle ABC$ after a translation of $T_{0,7}$.
   c. Find the coordinates of the vertices of $\triangle A''B''C''$, the image of $\triangle A'B'C'$ after a reflection in the y-axis.
   d. The single transformation that maps $\triangle ABC$ onto $\triangle A''B''C''$ is a
   (1) line reflection   (2) glide reflection   (3) point reflection   (4) rotation

Solutions   **a.** $\triangle ABC$ is graphed at the right.

b. Under the given translation:

$$T_{0,7}(x, y) = (x, y + 7)$$

Thus: $A(2, -6) \rightarrow A'(2, 1)$
$B(2, -2) \rightarrow B'(2, 5)$
$C(4, -5) \rightarrow C'(4, 2)$

$\triangle A'B'C'$ is graphed at the right.

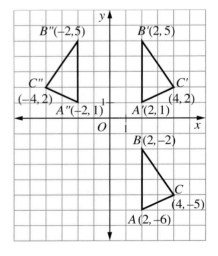

c. Under a reflection in the y-axis:

$$r_{y\text{-axis}}(x, y) = (-x, y)$$

Thus: $A'(2, 1) \rightarrow A''(-2, 1)$
$B'(2, 5) \rightarrow B''(-2, 5)$
$C'(4, 2) \rightarrow C''(-4, 2)$

$\triangle A''B''C''$ is graphed at the right.

d. Translation $T_{0,7}$ is parallel to the y-axis, which is the line of reflection. The composition of a line reflection and a translation parallel to the line of reflection is a *glide reflection*.

Answers: **a.** See graph.   **b.** $A'(2, 1)$, $B'(2, 5)$, and $C'(4, 2)$
c. $A''(-2, 1)$, $B''(-2, 5)$, and $C''(-4, 2)$ **d.** (2)

2. Triangle ABC has vertices $A(0, 3)$, $B(2, 3)$, and $C(4, 5)$.
   a. Graph $\triangle ABC$ and its image, $\triangle A'B'C'$, after a reflection in the line $y = x$.
   b. Graph $\triangle A''B''C''$, the image of $\triangle A'B'C'$ after a translation of $T_{-3,3}$.
   c. Name the single transformation that maps $\triangle ABC$ onto $\triangle A''B''C''$.
   d. Find the rule of the transformation equivalent to $T_{-3,3} \circ r_{y=x}$.

Solutions   **a.** Under a reflection in the line $y = x$:

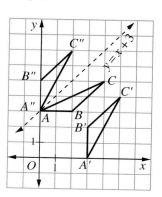

$$r_{y=x}(x, y) = (y, x)$$

   Thus: $A(0, 3) \rightarrow A'(3, 0)$
            $B(2, 3) \rightarrow B'(3, 2)$
            $C(4, 5) \rightarrow C'(5, 4)$

   $\triangle ABC$ and $\triangle A'B'C'$ are graphed at the right.

   b. Under the given translation:

$$T_{-3,3}(x, y) = (x - 3, y + 3)$$

   Thus: $A'(3, 0) \rightarrow A''(0, 3)$
            $B'(3, 2) \rightarrow B''(0, 5)$
            $C'(5, 4) \rightarrow C''(2, 7)$

   $\triangle A''B''C''$ is graphed at the right.

   c. $\triangle ABC$ maps onto $\triangle A''B''C''$ by a reflection in the line $y = x + 3$, as sketched in the coordinate graph.

   Note: The composition of a reflection in the line $y = x$, followed by translation $T_{-3,3}$, is *not* a glide reflection because the translation is *not parallel* to the line of reflection. In this specific case, the composition is a line reflection. In other cases, other transformations may occur.

   d. The coordinate rule is true for any point:

$$(x, y) \xrightarrow{\;r_{y=x}\;} (y, x) \xrightarrow{\;T_{-3,3}\;} (y - 3, x + 3)$$

$$T_{-3,3} \circ r_{y=x}(x, y) = (y - 3, x + 3)$$

Answers: **a, b.** See graph.   **c.** A reflection in the line $y = x + 3$.
   d. $T_{-3,3} \circ r_{y=x}(x, y) = (y - 3, x + 3)$ OR $(x, y) \rightarrow (y - 3, x + 3)$

---

3. In the accompanying diagram, the equation of line k is $y = -x$, the equation of line m is $y = 2$, and point $A = (-3, -2)$. Find the coordinates of $r_m \circ r_k(A)$.

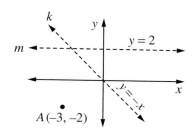

How to Proceed:

Solution:

Use graph paper (*not shown*), or use the basic definitions and rules for transformations.

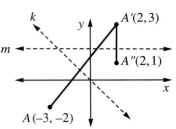

(1) First, reflect point A in line k $(y = -x)$ using the rule $(x, y) \rightarrow (-y, -x)$.

(2) Then, reflect this image in line m $(y = 2)$ using the definition of a line reflection.

$$(-3, -2) \xrightarrow{r_k} (2, 3) \xrightarrow{r_m} (2, 1)$$

$$r_m \circ r_k(-3, -2) = (2, 1)$$

Answer: $(2, 1)$

---

4. Name the single transformation that is equivalent to the composition $r_{x\text{-axis}} \circ r_{y=x}$.

How to Proceed:

Solution:

(1) First, reflect point (x, y) in the line $y = x$.

(2) Then, reflect the image found in the x-axis.

$$(x, y) \xrightarrow{r_{y=x}} (y, x) \xrightarrow{r_{x\text{-axis}}} (y, -x)$$

$$r_{x\text{-axis}} \circ r_{y=x} = R_{270°}$$

The transformation that maps (x, y) to $(y, -x)$ is a rotation of $270°$ about the origin.

Answer: $R_{270°}$, or a rotation of $270°$ about the origin

EXERCISES WITH OPEN-RESPONSE PROBLEMS

1. The coordinates of the vertices of $\triangle ABC$ are $A(1, 3)$, $B(1, 6)$, and $C(3, 3)$.
   a. Find the coordinates of the vertices of $\triangle A'B'C'$, the image of $\triangle ABC$ under a point reflection in the origin.
   b. Find the coordinates of $\triangle A''B''C''$, the image of $\triangle A'B'C'$ after a reflection in the y-axis.
   c. On graph paper, draw and label $\triangle ABC$, $\triangle A'B'C'$, and $\triangle A''B''C''$.
   d. Name the single transformation that maps $\triangle ABC$ onto $\triangle A''B''C''$.

2. The vertices of $\triangle ABC$ are $A(-6, -2)$, $B(-4, 4)$, and $C(-1, 4)$.
   a. Graph $\triangle ABC$ and its image, $\triangle A'B'C'$, under translation $T_{6,0}$.
   b. Graph $\triangle A''B''C''$, the image of $\triangle A'B'C'$ after a reflection in the x-axis.
   c. Write the rule of the transformation equivalent to the composition described in parts **a** and **b**.

3. The coordinates of the vertices of $\triangle CDE$ are $C(0, 1)$, $D(4, 1)$, and $E(4, 3)$.

    a. Graph $\triangle CDE$ and its image, $\triangle C'D'E'$, under a reflection in the x-axis.

    b. Graph $C''D''E''$, the image of $\triangle C'D'E'$ under a reflection in the line $y = x$.

    c. The composition $r_{y=x} \circ r_{x\text{-axis}}$, which maps $\triangle CDE$ onto $\triangle C''D''E''$, is equivalent to the transformation

        (1) $r_{y\text{-axis}}$ (2) $r_{y=-x}$ (3) $R_{90°}$ (4) $R_{270°}$

4. The vertices of $\triangle ABC$ are $A(0, 2)$, $B(5, 4)$, and $C(6, 2)$.

    a. Graph $\triangle ABC$ and $\triangle A'B'C'$, where $R_{90°}(\triangle ABC) = \triangle A'B'C'$, using the rule $(x, y) \rightarrow (-y, x)$.

    b. Graph $\triangle A''B''C''$ such that $R_{180°}(\triangle A'B'C') = \triangle A''B''C''$.

    c. Graph $\triangle A'''B'''C'''$ such that $r_{x\text{-axis}}(\triangle A''B''C'') = \triangle A'''B'''C'''$.

    d. The composition $r_{x\text{-axis}} \circ R_{180°} \circ R_{90°}$ is equivalent to the single transformation

        (1) $r_{y=x}$ (2) $r_{y=-x}$ (3) $r_{y\text{-axis}}$ (4) $R_{270°}$

5. The coordinates of the vertices of $\triangle BUG$ are $B(1, 1)$, $U(1, 4)$, and $G(7, 1)$. Let $r_{y\text{-axis}}(\triangle BUG) = \triangle B'U'G'$, and $r_{y=x}(\triangle B'U'G') = \triangle B''U''G''$.

    a. On graph paper, draw and label $\triangle BUG$, $\triangle B'U'G'$, and $\triangle B''U''G''$.

    b. State the coordinates of the vertices of $\triangle B'U'G'$.

    c. State the coordinates of the vertices of $\triangle B''U''G''$.

    d. Name the single transformation that maps $\triangle BUG$ onto $\triangle B''U''G''$.

6. Triangle BCD has the vertices $B(-1, 2)$, $C(-1, 4)$, and $D(3, 2)$.

    a. Graph $\triangle BCD$ and its image, $\triangle B'C'D'$, after a reflection in the line $y = -x$.

    b. Graph $\triangle B''C''D''$, the image of $\triangle B'C'D'$, after translation $T_{5,5}$.

    c. The single transformation that maps $\triangle BCD$ onto $\triangle B''C''D''$ is a

        (1) line reflection   (2) glide reflection   (3) point reflection   (4) rotation

7. The vertices of $\triangle JAM$ have the coordinates $J(1, 0)$, $A(1, 4)$, and $M(3, 1)$.

    a. Let $\triangle JAM \rightarrow \triangle I$ by a dilation of 2 with the origin as the center of dilation. Let $\triangle I \rightarrow \triangle II$ by a reflection in the y-axis. On graph paper, draw and label $\triangle JAM$, $\triangle I$, and $\triangle II$.

    b. Let $\triangle JAM \rightarrow \triangle III$ by a reflection in the y-axis, and let $\triangle III \rightarrow \triangle IV$ by a dilation of 2 with the origin as center of dilation. On a new set of axes, draw and label $\triangle JAM$, $\triangle III$, and $\triangle IV$.

    c. *True* or *False*: $r_{y\text{-axis}} \circ D_2 = D_2 \circ r_{y\text{-axis}}$.

In 8–10, the coordinates of point P are $(1, -2)$, and the equations of lines m and q are stated in the accompanying diagrams. In each case, find the coordinates of: **a.** $r_m \circ r_q(P)$ **b.** $r_q \circ r_m(P)$

8.

9.

10.

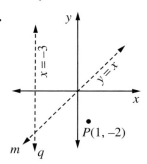

11. a. Copy and complete the rule for the composition $T_{c,d} \circ T_{a,b}$:

$$(x, y) \xrightarrow{\ T_{a,b}\ } (\quad , \quad) \xrightarrow{\ T_{c,d}\ } (\quad , \quad)$$

b. Write a similar rule for the composition $T_{a,b} \circ T_{c,d}$.
c. What observation, if any, can be made regarding the solutions to parts **a** and **b**?

12. a. Copy and complete the rule for $r_{x\text{-axis}} \circ T_{5,-2}$:

$$(x, y) \xrightarrow{\ T_{5,-2}\ } (\quad , \quad) \xrightarrow{\ r_{x\text{-axis}}\ } (\quad , \quad)$$

b. Write a similar rule for the composition $T_{5,-2} \circ r_{x\text{-axis}}$.
c. What observation, if any, can be made regarding the solutions to parts **a** and **b**?

In 13–21, in each case, write the rule of the single transformation that is equivalent to the stated composition.

13. $R_{90°} \circ R_{90°}$ **14.** $T_{6,0} \circ T_{-6,7}$ **15.** $T_{-a,-b} \circ T_{a,b}$
16. $r_{x\text{-axis}} \circ D_3$ **17.** $r_{y=x} \circ T_{2,5}$ **18.** $T_{5,-4} \circ r_{y\text{-axis}}$
19. $T_{1,-6} \circ D_4$ **20.** $D_2 \circ T_{-1,2} \circ R_{180°}$ **21.** $R_{180°} \circ T_{-1,2} \circ D_2$

In 22–27, in each case: **a.** Write the rule of the single transformation that is equivalent to the given composition.   **b.** Name the transformation whose rule was found in part **a**.

22. $r_{x\text{-axis}} \circ r_{y\text{-axis}}$ **23.** $R_{180°} \circ R_{90°}$ **24.** $R_{180°} \circ r_{x\text{-axis}}$
25. $r_{y=x} \circ r_{y=-x}$ **26.** $r_{y=x} \circ R_{90°}$ **27.** $R_{180°} \circ r_{y=-x}$

13-6 ISOMETRIES, ORIENTATION, AND OTHER PROPERTIES

In Section 13-2, we learned that under a *line reflection*, a *point reflection*, a *rotation*, and a *translation* the following five properties are preserved:

1. Distance is preserved.
2. Angle measure is preserved.
3. Parallelism is preserved.
4. Collinearity is preserved.
5. A midpoint is preserved.

It can be shown that two other properties are also preserved under these transformations:

6. Betweenness of points is preserved.
7. Area is preserved.

Under a *dilation*, distance is *not* preserved, and area is *not* preserved, while the other properties mentioned are preserved.

- **DEFINITION.** A transformation that preserves distance is called an *isometry*.

Thus, every line reflection, point reflection, rotation, and translation is an isometry. Since, however, a dilation does not preserve distance, a dilation is *not* an isometry.

Orientation (or Order)

In each of the figures that follow, the vertices of △*ABC* appear in a *clockwise orientation* or *order*. In other words, going from vertex *A* to vertex *B* to vertex *C*, we follow a clockwise direction, indicated in the figures by the symbol ↻.

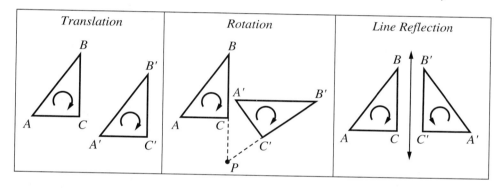

Under the translation and under the rotation, orientation is preserved because the images *A′*, *B′*, and *C′* appear in the same clockwise order as points *A*, *B*, and *C*.

Under the line reflection, however, orientation is *not* preserved because the images *A′*, *B′*, and *C′* appear in a *counterclockwise order*, indicated in the figure by the symbol ↺.

- **DEFINITION.** A *direct isometry* is one that preserves orientation (order).

Every translation, rotation, and point reflection is a direct isometry. In other words, each of these transformations preserves both order (orientation) and distance.

- **DEFINITION.** An *opposite isometry* is one that changes the order, or orientation, from clockwise to counterclockwise, or vice versa.

Every line reflection is an opposite isometry; that is, every line reflection preserves distance but fails to preserve order.

Note: A dilation preserves orientation (order); but, as observed previously, a dilation is not an isometry because it fails to preserve distance.

Properties Under a Composition

We recall that a glide reflection is a *composition* of a line reflection and a translation parallel to the line of reflection. At the right, $\triangle ART \to \triangle A''R''T''$ by a glide reflection.

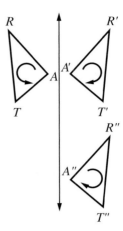

It can be shown that a glide reflection preserves distance, angle measure, parallelism, collinearity, and midpoint. Since these properties are preserved by both a line reflection and a translation, it should be clear that the composition of such transformations will also preserve these same properties.

Orientation is *not* preserved, however, under a glide reflection. In the figure at the right, vertices A, R, and T are in a counterclockwise order, while their images, A'', R'', and T'', are in a clockwise order. Therefore, a *glide reflection is an opposite isometry*.

Since a translation is a direct isometry and both a line reflection and a glide reflection are opposite isometries, the example just studied illustrates that:

● **The composition of a direct isometry and an opposite isometry is an opposite isometry**.

In the next section, we will examine many other compositions and will study properties preserved under different given conditions.

EXAMPLES

1. Which transformation is an example of a direct isometry?
  (1) line reflection   (2) glide reflection   (3) point reflection   (4) dilation

Solution   Since an isometry preserves distance, eliminate choice (4), dilation. A direct isometry preserves orientation (or order) as well as distance.

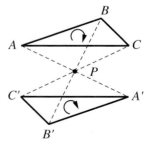

As illustrated in the point reflection at the right, vertices A, B, C, and their images, A', B', and C', appear in the same clockwise order. Thus, a point reflection is a direct isometry.

Answer: (3)

2. The coordinates of the vertices of $\triangle ABC$ are $A(0, 3)$, $B(1, 1)$, and $C(4, 1)$.

Let $\triangle ABC \rightarrow \triangle A'B'C'$ under transformation $K(x, y) \rightarrow (x, 3y)$.
Let $\triangle ABC \rightarrow \triangle A''B''C''$ under transformation $L(x, y) \rightarrow (-x - 2, y - 3)$.
Let $\triangle ABC \rightarrow \triangle A'''B'''C'''$ under transformation $M(x, y) \rightarrow (-y - 2, x + 3)$.

a. On one set of axes, sketch and label $\triangle ABC$, $\triangle A'B'C'$, $\triangle A''B''C''$, and $\triangle A'''B'''C'''$.
b. Which transformation, K, L, or M, is *not* an isometry?
c. Which transformation, K, L, or M, does *not* preserve orientation?

Solutions   **a.** Under $K(x, y) \rightarrow (x, 3y)$:
$A(0, 3) \rightarrow A'(0, 9)$
$B(1, 1) \rightarrow B'(1, 3)$
$C(4, 1) \rightarrow C'(4, 3)$

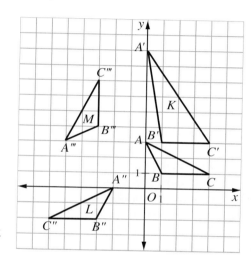

Under $L(x, y) \rightarrow (-x - 2, y - 3)$:
$A(0, 3) \rightarrow A''(-2, 0)$
$B(1, 1) \rightarrow B''(-3, -2)$
$C(4, 1) \rightarrow C''(-6, -2)$

Under $M(x, y) \rightarrow (-y - 2, x + 3)$:
$A(0, 3) \rightarrow A'''(-5, 3)$
$B(1, 1) \rightarrow B'''(-3, 4)$
$C(4, 1) \rightarrow C'''(-3, 7)$

b. Distance is not preserved under transformation K. For example, $AB = \sqrt{5}$ but image $A'B' = \sqrt{37}$. Therefore, K is *not* an isometry.

c. Vertices A, B, and C appear in a counterclockwise order. Under transformation L, their images, A'', B'', and C'', appear in a clockwise order. Therefore, L does *not* preserve orientation.

Answers: **a.** See graph.   **b.** K **c.** L

EXERCISES WITH OPEN-RESPONSE PROBLEMS

1. The vertices of $\triangle ABC$ are $A(1, 2)$, $B(2, 5)$, and $C(5, 2)$. Under transformation P, $(x, y) \rightarrow (2 - x, 3 - y)$.
a. Sketch $\triangle ABC$ and its image, $\triangle A'B'C'$, after transformation P.
b. Transformation P preserves
   (1) distance only
   (2) order only
   (3) both distance and order
   (4) neither distance nor order

2. The vertices of $\triangle RST$ are $R(-1, 2)$, $S(0, 5)$, and $T(3, 2)$. Under transformation K, $(x, y) \rightarrow (y + 2, x - 4)$.
   a. Sketch $\triangle RST$ and its image, $\triangle R'S'T'$, after transformation K.
   b. Is K a direct isometry, an opposite isometry, or no isometry? Explain your answer.

3. Triangle ABC has the vertices $A(1, 1)$, $B(-1, 2)$, and $C(1, 6)$.
   Let $\triangle ABC \rightarrow \triangle A'B'C'$ under transformation $F(x, y) = (2x, 2y)$.
   Let $\triangle ABC \rightarrow \triangle A''B''C''$ under transformation $G(x, y) = (2y - 1, x - 1)$.
   a. On one set of axes, sketch and label $\triangle ABC$, $\triangle A'B'C'$, and $\triangle A''B''C''$.
   b. Which of the transformations given above is an isometry (are isometries)?
   (1) F only   (2) G only   (3) both F and G (4) neither F nor G

4. The coordinates of the vertices of $\triangle ABC$ are $A(-3, -4)$, $B(-2, -1)$, and $C(0, -5)$. Under transformation X, $\triangle ABC \rightarrow \triangle A'B'C'$ by a reflection in the x-axis. Under transformation Y, $\triangle ABC \rightarrow \triangle A''B''C''$ by a reflection in the origin. Under transformation Z, $\triangle ABC \rightarrow \triangle A'''B'''C'''$ by a reflection in point C.
   a. Graph and label $\triangle ABC$, $\triangle A''B''C''$, and $\triangle A'''B'''C'''$.
   b. Which transformation, X, Y, or Z, is *not* a direct isometry?

5. The coordinates of the vertices of $\triangle ACE$ are $A(1, 3)$, $C(2, 0)$, and $E(3, 6)$.
   a. Graph and label $\triangle ACE$.
   b. Find the coordinates of the vertices of $\triangle A'C'E'$, the image of $\triangle ACE$ under a reflection in the line $y = x$. Graph $\triangle A'C'E'$.
   c. Find the coordinates of the vertices of $\triangle A''C''E''$, the image of $\triangle ACE$ under the composition $r_{x\text{-axis}} \circ r_{y\text{-axis}}$. Graph $\triangle A''C''E''$.
   d. Find the coordinates of the vertices of $\triangle A'''C'''E'''$, the image of $\triangle ACE$ after a translation that maps $P(0, 0)$ to $P'''(2, -5)$. Graph $\triangle A'''C'''E'''$.
   e. Which of the given transformations is an opposite isometry?

6. The vertices of $\triangle ABC$ are $A(2, 1)$, $B(4, 1)$, and $C(0, -3)$. Given these transformations:
   $$P(x, y) = (1 - x, 5 - y) \qquad Q(x, y) = (4 - y, x + 1) \qquad R(x, y) = (-2x, y - 2)$$
   a. Graph $\triangle ABC$ and its image, $\triangle A'B'C'$, after transformation P.
   b. Graph $\triangle A''B''C''$, the image of $\triangle ABC$ after transformation Q.
   c. Graph $\triangle A'''B'''C'''$, the image of $\triangle ABC$ after transformation R.
   d. Which transformation, P, Q, or R, is *not* an isometry?
   e. Which transformation, P, Q, or R, does *not* preserve order?

7. Given: Y is the transformation $(x, y) \rightarrow (-y, -x)$.
   E is the transformation $(x, y) \rightarrow (x - 1, -y)$.
   S is the transformation $(x, y) \rightarrow (2x, 2y)$.
   The coordinates of the vertices of $\triangle ABC$ are $A(1, 2)$, $B(5, 1)$, and $C(3, -1)$.
   a. Sketch $\triangle ABC$ and its image, $\triangle A'B'C'$, after the transformation Y.
   b. Sketch $\triangle A''B''C''$, the image of $\triangle A'B'C'$ after transformation E.
   c. Sketch $\triangle A'''B'''C'''$, the image of $\triangle A''B''C''$ after transformation S.
   d. Which transformation, Y, E, or S, is *not* an isometry?
   e. Which transformation, Y, E, or S, preserves orientation?

In 8–14, select the *numeral* preceding the expression that best answers the question.

8. Which transformation is *not* an example of an isometry?
(1) line reflection   (2) rotation   (3) translation   (4) dilation

9. Which transformation does *not* preserve orientation?
(1) line reflection   (2) rotation   (3) translation   (4) dilation

10. Which property is *not* preserved under a glide reflection?
(1) collinearity   (2) distance   (3) orientation   (4) betweenness

11. Which property is *not* preserved under a dilation?
(1) angle measure   (2) parallelism   (3) area   (4) midpoint

12. Which property is (properties are) preserved under a rotation?
(1) distance only
(3) both distance and angle measure
(2) angle measure only
(4) neither distance nor angle measure

13. Which transformation is an example of a direct isometry?
(1) $r_{x\text{-axis}}$ (2) $r_{y=x}$ (3) $R_{90°}$ (4) D_5

14. Which rule indicates a transformation that is a direct isometry?
(1) $(x, y) \rightarrow (x, -y)$ (2) $(x, y) \rightarrow (-x, -y)$ (3) $(x, y) \rightarrow (-x, y)$ (4) $(x, y) \rightarrow (y, x)$

15. The coordinates of the vertices of rectangle *SEAN* are $S(1, 1)$, $E(1, 3)$, $A(5, 3)$, and $N(5, 1)$. Transformation *B* maps (x, y) to $(x + y, -y)$.
  a. Graph rectangle *SEAN*.
  b. Graph quadrilateral $S'E'A'N'$, the image of $\square SEAN$ after transformation *B*, and state the coordinates of S', E', A', and N'.
  c. Which of the following seven properties are preserved by transformation *B*: distance, angle measure, collinearity, parallelism, midpoint, orientation, area?
  d. For each property from part **c** that is *not* preserved by transformation *B*, cite an example to show that the property does not hold.

16. Given $P(3, 2)$ and $Q(7, 4)$ and transformations *A*, *B*, *C*, *D*, whose rules are as follows:
$$A: (x, y) \rightarrow (x + 2, y - 4)$$
$$B: (x, y) \rightarrow (4 - y, x)$$
$$C: (x, y) \rightarrow (-x, y)$$
$$D: (x, y) \rightarrow (y, x + 1)$$
  a. Graph $\overline{PQ}$ and its image $\overline{P'Q'}$ after transformation *A*.
  b. Graph $\overline{P''Q''}$, the image of $\overline{PQ}$ after transformation *B*.
  c. Graph $\overline{P'''Q'''}$, the image of $\overline{PQ}$ after transformation *C*.
  d. Graph $\overline{P''''Q''''}$, the image of $\overline{PQ}$ after transformation *D*.
  e. Compare the slopes of the pairs of segments listed below, and tell whether these slopes are equal, reciprocals, additive inverses, or negative reciprocals.
    (1) $\overline{PQ}$ and $\overline{P'Q'}$ *(2)* $\overline{PQ}$ and $\overline{P''Q''}$ *(3)* $\overline{PQ}$ and $\overline{P'''Q'''}$ *(4)* $\overline{PQ}$ and $\overline{P''''Q''''}$

13-7 COMPOSITIONS WITH LINE REFLECTIONS

In this section, we will limit all compositions of transformations to those involving line reflections only. Why? The reason may be surprising, but in the next few pages we will demonstrate that:

- **Every isometry (or distance-preserving transformation) can be expressed as the composition of either two or three line reflections.**

Case 1: Translations

In Figure 1, line k is *parallel* to line m, $r_k(\triangle ABC) = \triangle A'B'C'$, and $r_m(\triangle A'B'C') = \triangle A''B''C''$. Therefore:

$$r_m \circ r_k(\triangle ABC) = \triangle A''B''C''$$

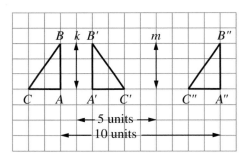

Figure 1

By studying the diagram, we can observe certain facts:

1. Since $\triangle ABC \to \triangle A''B''C''$, so that every point in the plane moves the same distance in the same direction to its image, the composition $r_m \circ r_k$, where $k \parallel m$, is a *translation*.

2. The distance between lines k and m is 5 units. The distance of the translation measured from A to A'', or from B to B'', or from C to C'', is 10 units. Thus, the distance of the translation is twice the distance between the parallel lines of reflection.

3. The direction of the translation is perpendicular to lines k and m, and this direction is the same as the direction from the first line of reflection, k, to the second, m.

These three facts will be true for the composition of any two line reflections in which the lines are parallel to each other. Let us suppose that we had reflected first in line m and then in line k. This situation is illustrated in Figure 2 on the next page.

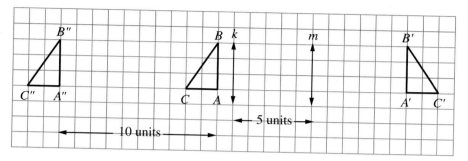

Figure 2

Here, $k \parallel m$, $r_m(\triangle ABC) = \triangle A'B'C'$, and $r_k(\triangle A'B'C') = \triangle A''B''C''$. Therefore, $r_k \circ r_m(\triangle ABC) = \triangle A''B''C''$.

Using Figure 2, we again observe:

1. The composition $r_k \circ r_m$, where $k \parallel m$, is a *translation*.
2. The distance of the translation is twice the distance between the parallel lines of reflection.
3. The direction of the translation is perpendicular to lines k and m, but the direction of the translation is now the same as the direction from the first line of reflection, m, to the second, k.

The General Case for Translations. In Figure 3, we observe a general situation where $k \parallel m$ and where $r_m \circ r_k(\triangle ABC) = \triangle A''B''C''$. To understand why this composition is a translation, we will study its direction and distance.

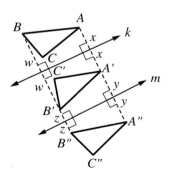

Figure 3

Direction: In Figure 3, by the definition of a line reflection, $\overline{AA'} \perp k$, $\overline{BB'} \perp k$, and $\overline{CC'} \perp k$. Also, $\overline{A'A''} \perp m$, $\overline{B'B''} \perp m$, and $\overline{C'C''} \perp m$. Since $k \parallel m$, certain points must be collinear: $\overline{AA'A''}$, $\overline{BB'B''}$, and $\overline{CC'C''}$. Each of these segments is perpendicular to lines k and m, and each indicates the direction of the translation (as in A to A'').

Distance: In Figure 3, if x represents the distance from A to line k, then x is also the distance from A' to k. If y represents the distance from A' to line m, then y is also the distance from A'' to m.

Therefore, the distance between lines k and m is $(x + y)$, and the distance of the translation from A to A'' is $x + x + y + y = 2x + 2y = 2(x + y)$.

In a similar way, it can be shown that $BB' = 2w$, $B'B'' = 2z$, and the distance of the translation from B to $B'' = 2w + 2z = 2(w + z)$. We note, however, that $(w + z) = (x + y)$. Therefore, the distance of the translation from B to B'', shown to be $2(w + z)$, is equal to $2(x + y)$. By a similar argument, the distance of the translation from C to C'' is also $2(x + y)$.

These examples demonstrate that every composition of two line reflections in parallel lines is a translation. Conversely, it can be shown that:

- **Every translation is equivalent to the composition of two line reflections, $r_m \circ r_k$, where $k \parallel m$.**

For example in Figure 4, $\triangle ABC \rightarrow \triangle A''B''C''$ by a translation. By choosing two lines, k and m, such that $k \perp \overleftrightarrow{AA''}$, $m \perp \overline{AA''}$, and the distance between lines k and m is $\frac{1}{2}(AA'')$, we illustrate that the translation is equivalent to the composition $r_m \circ r_k$, where $k \parallel m$. We notice that lines k and m are *not unique*.

In other words, there are many lines k and m that allow us to map $\triangle ABC$ onto $\triangle A''B''C''$ by a composition of two line reflections.

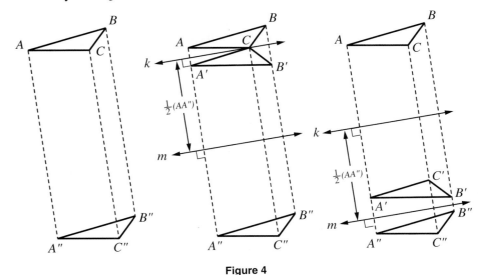

Figure 4

The examples we have just studied illustrate another truth concerning order, or orientation. Since a line reflection is an opposite isometry and a translation is a direct isometry, we observe that:

- **The composition of two opposite isometries is a direct isometry.**

Case 2: Rotations

In Figure 5, lines k and m intersect at point P, $r_k(\triangle ABC) = \triangle A'B'C'$, and $r_m(\triangle A'B'C') = \triangle A''B''C''$. Therefore:

$$r_m \circ r_k(\triangle ABC) = \triangle A''B''C''$$

We will consider the case where k and m intersect to form an acute angle.

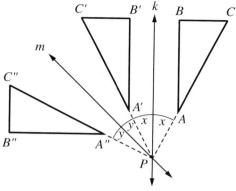

Figure 5

1. The composition $r_m \circ r_k$, where lines k and m intersect at point P, is a *rotation* about P.

   Hint: To prove that $\triangle ABC \rightarrow \triangle A''B''C''$ by a rotation about P:
   a. Show that $PA = PA''$, $PB = PB''$, and $PC = PC''$. For example, since P is a point on each line of reflection, $PA = PA'$ and $PA' = PA''$. Thus, $PA = PA''$.
   b. Show that m$\angle APA'' = $ m$\angle BPB'' = $ m$\angle CPC''$. See step 3 below for the start of this proof; then use a plan similar to the one shown for the general case involving translations.
   (The proof is left to the student.)

2. The direction of the rotation is the same as the direction from the first line of reflection to the second. Going from line k to line m, we move in a counterclockwise direction; the rotation from $\triangle ABC$ to $\triangle A''B''C''$ is also in a counterclockwise direction.

3. The measure of the angle of rotation is twice the measure of the acute angle formed by the intersecting lines k and m.
   In Figure 5, if x is the measure of the angle formed by $\overrightarrow{PA}$ and line k, then x is also the measure of the angle formed by $\overrightarrow{PA'}$ and k. If y is the measure of the angle formed by $\overrightarrow{PA'}$ and line m, then y is also the measure of the angle formed by $\overrightarrow{PA''}$ and m. Therefore, the measure of the acute angle formed by lines k and m is $(x + y)$, and the measure of the angle of rotation, $\angle APA''$, is $x + x + y + y = 2x + 2y = 2(x + y)$.

Conversely, it can be shown that:

- **Every rotation about a point P is equivalent to the composition of two line reflections, $r_m \circ r_k$, where lines k and m intersect at P.**

Therefore, given a rotation of $x°$ about point P, we can demonstrate that $R_{P,x°}$ is equivalent to $r_m \circ r_k$ by choosing lines k and m so that k and m intersect at P to form an angle whose measure is $\frac{1}{2}x°$. We note that lines k and m are not unique.

Note: In Figure 6, lines x and y are perpendicular; that is, they intersect at an angle of 90°. Thus, $r_x \circ r_y$ is a rotation of 180° about O, the point where lines x and y intersect. From this example, which is a special case involving rotations, we conclude that:

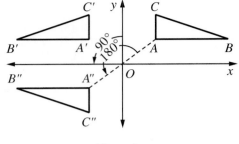

Figure 6

- **Every reflection through a point P is equivalent to the composition of two line reflections, $r_m \circ r_k$, where $k \perp m$ at point P.**

Case 3: Glide Reflections

In Figure 7, $\triangle ABC \rightarrow \triangle A'''B'''C'''$ by a glide reflection. This glide reflection is a composition of a line reflection, r_{k_1}, a translation parallel to the line of reflection. Since the translation mapping $\triangle A'B'C'$ to $\triangle A'''B'''C'''$ is itself the composition of two line reflections, $r_{k_3} \circ r_{k_2}$, we conclude that:

$$r_{k_3} \circ r_{k_2} \circ r_{k_1}(\triangle ABC) = \triangle A'''B'''C'''$$

- **Every glide reflection is equivalent to the composition of three line reflections.**

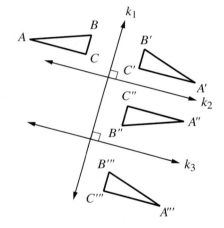

Figure 7

As seen in Figure 7, two of these lines of reflection are parallel ($k_2 \parallel k_3$), and the remaining line is perpendicular to the first two ($k_1 \perp k_2$, and $k_1 \perp k_3$). Lines k_1, k_2, and k_3 are not unique.

Case 4: Any Isometry (Distance-Preserving Transformation)

Every isometry (or distance-preserving transformation) can be displayed by showing the effect of the transformation on three noncollinear points.

In Figure 8, for example, there is one and only one isometry by which $A \rightarrow A'''$, $B \rightarrow B'''$, and $C \rightarrow C'''$. The following sequence of steps and diagrams shows that $\triangle ABC \rightarrow \triangle A'''B'''C'''$ by a composition of no more than three line reflections. This procedure is called the Three-Line Reflection Theorem.

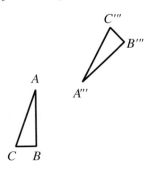

Figure 8

●   **The Three-Line Reflection Theorem. Every isometry is equivalent to the composition of no more than three line reflections.**

Given: $\triangle ABC \cong \triangle A'''B'''C'''$ (as shown on page 600, Figure 8).

Step 1:   Let $A \rightarrow A'''$ by a reflection in line k_1. Construct k_1 as the perpendicular bisector of $\overline{AA'''}$. Thus, $r_{k_1}(\triangle ABC) = \triangle A'''B'C'$.

Step 2:   Let $B' \rightarrow B'''$ by a reflection in line k_2. Construct k_2 as the perpendicular bisector of $\overline{B'B'''}$. Since $A'''B' = A'''B'''$, then A''' is a point on line k_2. Thus, $r_{k_2}(\triangle A'''B'C') = \triangle A'''B'''C''$.

Step 3:   Let $C'' \rightarrow C'''$ by a reflection in line k_3. Construct k_3 as the perpendicular bisector of $\overline{C''C'''}$. Since $A'''C'' = A'''C'''$ and $B'''C'' = B'''C'''$, then both A''' and B''' are points on line k_3. Thus, $r_{k_3}(\triangle A'''B'''C'') = \triangle A'''B'''C'''$.

We conclude that: $r_{k_3} \circ r_{k_2} \circ r_{k_1}(\triangle ABC) = \triangle A'''B'''C'''$

The lines of reflection, k_1, k_2, and k_3, are not unique. This fact can be demonstrated by mapping B to B''' as the first step.

We note that $\triangle ABC$ has clockwise orientation, while $\triangle A'''B'''C'''$ has counterclockwise orientation. This fact demonstrates that the composition of three line reflections, or three opposite isometries, is an opposite isometry.

If $\triangle A'''B'''C'''$ had the same order or orientation as $\triangle ABC$, then $\triangle ABC$ could map onto $\triangle A'''B'''C'''$ by a composition of only two line reflections.

KEEP IN MIND _____

Every transformation that preserves distance can be expressed as the composition of no more than three line reflections.

EXERCISES WITH OPEN-RESPONSE PROBLEMS

In 1–5, select the *numeral* preceding the expression that best completes the sentence.

1. If line $g \parallel$ line h, then the composition $r_g \circ r_h$ is equivalent to a
  (1) translation   (2) point reflection   (3) glide reflection   (4) line reflection

2. If line $g \perp$ line h, then the composition $r_g \circ r_h$ is equivalent to a
   (1) translation   (2) point reflection   (3) glide reflection   (4) line reflection

3. If line g intersects line h, then the composition $r_g \circ r_h$ is equivalent to a
   (1) translation   (2) glide reflection   (3) rotation   (4) line reflection

4. The composition of two line reflections is *always*
   (1) a translation   (2) a rotation   (3) a direct isometry   (4) an opposite isometry

5. If the composition $r_p \circ r_q$ is equivalent to a rotation of $80°$, then lines p and q intersect to form an angle whose measure is
   (1) $40°$ (2) $80°$ (3) $90°$ (4) $160°$

In 6–14, copy $\triangle ABC$ and the appropriate lines onto graph paper. The coordinates of the vertices of $\triangle ABC$ are $A(0, 4)$, $B(1, 2)$, and $C(3, 2)$. The equation of line k is $x = 3$, of line m is $x = 6$, and of line p is $y = 4$. Let r_x represent a reflection in the x-axis, and let r_y represent a reflection in the y-axis.

Ex. 6–14

6. **a.** Find the coordinates of the vertices of $\triangle A''B''C''$, the image of $\triangle ABC$ under the composition $r_m \circ r_k$.
   b. The composition $r_m \circ r_k$ is equivalent to isometry
   (1) $T_{0,6}$ (2) $T_{6,0}$ (3) $T_{0,-6}$ (4) $T_{-6,0}$

7. **a.** Find the coordinates of the vertices of $\triangle A''B''C''$, the image of $\triangle ABC$ under the composition $r_k \circ r_m$.
   b. The composition $r_k \circ r_m$ is equivalent to translation
   (1) $T_{0,6}$ (2) $T_{6,0}$ (3) $T_{0,-6}$ (4) $T_{-6,0}$

8. **a.** Find the coordinates of the vertices of $\triangle A''B''C''$, the image of $\triangle ABC$ under the composition $r_x \circ r_p$.
   b. The composition $r_x \circ r_p$ is equivalent to translation
   (1) $T_{0,8}$ (2) $T_{8,0}$ (3) $T_{0,-8}$ (4) $T_{-8,0}$

9. **a.** If $r_p \circ r_x(\triangle ABC) = \triangle A''B''C''$, find the coordinates of A'', B'', and C''.
   b. Name the single transformation equivalent to $r_p \circ r_x$.

10. **a.** If $r_x \circ r_y(\triangle ABC) = \triangle A''B''C''$, find the coordinates of A'', B'', and C''.
    b. Name the single transformation equivalent to $r_x \circ r_y$.

11. **a.** If $r_p \circ r_k(\triangle ABC) = \triangle A''B''C''$, find the coordinates of A'', B'', and C''.
    b. The composition $r_p \circ r_k$ is equivalent to a reflection through point
    (1) $(3, 4)$ (2) $(4, 3)$ (3) $(6, 4)$ (4) $(0, 0)$

12. A point reflection through A is equivalent to the composition
    (1) $r_x \circ r_y$ (2) $r_y \circ r_p$ (3) $r_x \circ r_p$ (4) $r_p \circ r_x$

13. Which composition is *not* a translation to the right?
    (1) $r_m \circ r_k$ (2) $r_m \circ r_y$ (3) $r_k \circ r_y$ (4) $r_y \circ r_k$

14. **a.** If $r_p \circ r_m \circ r_k(\triangle ABC) = \triangle A'''B'''C'''$, find the coordinates of A''', B''', and C'''.
    b. The isometry equivalent to $r_p \circ r_m \circ r_k$ is a
    (1) translation   (2) point reflection   (3) glide reflection   (4) line reflection

In 15–17, in each case, copy the two given congruent triangles onto your paper in their given positions. Demonstrate that one triangle maps onto the other by a composition of *no more than three* line reflections by locating and drawing the lines of reflection.

15. Demonstrate how $\triangle ABC \rightarrow \triangle A'''B'''C'''$.

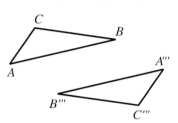

16. Demonstrate how $\triangle DEF \rightarrow \triangle D''E''F''$.

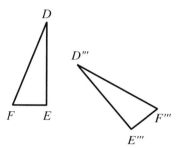

17. Demonstrate how $\triangle RST \rightarrow \triangle R'''S'''T'''$.

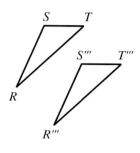

18. a. On graph paper, draw and label congruent triangles $\triangle ABC$ and $\triangle A'''B'''C'''$, whose vertices have the coordinates $A(3, 6)$, $B(1, 6)$, $C(0, 3)$, $A'''(7, 2)$, $B'''(7, 4)$, and $C'''(10, 5)$.

   b. Demonstrate that $\triangle ABC \rightarrow \triangle A'''B'''C'''$ by a composition of three line reflections by locating reflection lines.

   c. *Challenge*: If $A \rightarrow A'''$ by the first line of reflection and $B' \rightarrow B'''$ by the second, find the equations of the three lines of reflection.

19. *True* or *False*: If $\triangle RST \rightarrow \triangle R'S'T'$ by a direct isometry, then $\triangle RST$ can map onto $\triangle R'S'T'$ by a composition of *exactly two* line reflections. Explain your reasoning.

13-8 GROUPS OF TRANSFORMATIONS

In Section 12-12, we learned that the set of one-to-one functions, under the operation of composition, is a group. Since every transformation of the plane is a one-to-one function, we may say:

● **The set of transformations of the plane, under the operation of composition, is a group.**

In symbols, we write (Transformations of the plane, ∘) is a group. This statement indicates that four properties are true:

1. *Closure*. The composition of two transformations is a single transformation.

2. *Associativity*. For all transformations f, g, and h, and for any point P:

$$f \circ (g \circ h)(P) = (f \circ g) \circ h(P)$$

3. *Identity*. There is an identity transformation I that leaves every point on the plane fixed. Thus, $I(P) = P$, or $I(x, y) = (x, y)$.

The identity transformation I may be expressed in various forms:

As a translation:	As a dilation whose center is the origin:	As a rotation about a point P:
$I = T_{0,0}$,	$I = D_1$,	$I = R_{P,0°}$,
where	where	where
$T_{0,0}(x, y) = (x + 0, y + 0)$	$D_1(x, y) = (1x, 1y)$	$R_{P,0°}(x, y) = (x, y)$

4. *Inverses.* For every transformation f, there is an inverse transformation f^{-1} such that:

$$f^{-1} \circ f(P) = P \qquad \text{and} \qquad f \circ f^{-1}(P) = P$$

In addition to the group of (Transformations of the plane, ∘), other selected transformations form groups under composition, including:

1. The set of all isometries, or distance-preserving transformations, is a group under composition. In symbols, (Isometries, ∘) is a group.
2. (Direct isometries, ∘) is a group.
3. (Translations, ∘) is a group.
4. (Rotations about a point P, ∘) is a group.

● **DEFINITION.** If S is a *subset* of G and both $(S, *)$ and $(G, *)$ are *groups*, then $(S, *)$ is called a ***subgroup*** of $(G, *)$.

For example, because both systems are groups, and the set of translations is a subset of the set of transformations of the plane, we say:

(Translations, ∘) is a *subgroup* of (Transformations of the plane, ∘)

EXAMPLES

1. Give as many reasons as possible to indicate why the set of half-turns about a point P is *not* a group under composition.

Solution   (Half-turns about point P, ∘) is *not* a group because:

(1) It is *not closed*. The composition of two half-turns about point P is equivalent to $(x, y) \rightarrow (x, y)$, which is *not* a half-turn.

(2) There is *no identity* in the set of half-turns. In other words, there is no half-turn whose rule is $(x, y) \rightarrow (x, y)$, leaving every point on the plane fixed.

(3) If a system has no identity, then it also has *no inverses*.

2. Demonstrate that the set of translations under the operation of composition is a group.

Solution   To demonstrate that (Translations, $\circ$) is a group, we must verify four properties in general terms:

(1) *Closure.*

$$(x, y) \xrightarrow{T_{a,b}} (x + a, y + b) \xrightarrow{T_{c,d}} (x + a + c, y + b + d)$$

$$T_{c,d} \circ T_{a,b} = T_{a+c,b+d}$$

Therefore, the composition of two translations is a translation.

(2) *Associativity.* Since the set of all one-to-one functions is associative under composition, and translations are one-to-one functions, the set of translations is associative under composition.

(3) *Identity.* The identity translation is $T_{0,0}(x, y) = (x + 0, y + 0)$, or simply $T_{0,0}(x, y) = (x, y)$, as demonstrated below.

$$(x, y) \xrightarrow{T_{a,b}} (x + a, y + b) \xrightarrow{T_{0,0}} (x + a, y + b) \qquad (x, y) \xrightarrow{T_{0,0}} (x, y) \xrightarrow{T_{a,b}} (x + a, y + b)$$

$$T_{0,0} \circ T_{a,b} = T_{a,b} \qquad\qquad\qquad T_{a,b} \circ T_{0,0} = T_{a,b}$$

(4) *Inverses.* The inverse translation of $T_{a,b}(x, y) = (x + a, y + b)$ is $T_{-a,-b}(x, y) = (x - a, y - b)$, as demonstrated below.

$$(x, y) \xrightarrow{T_{a,b}} (x + a, y + b) \xrightarrow{T_{-a,-b}} (x, y) \qquad (x, y) \xrightarrow{T_{-a,-b}} (x - a, y - b) \xrightarrow{T_{a,b}} (x, y)$$

$$T_{-a,-b} \circ T_{a,b} = T_{0,0} \qquad\qquad\qquad T_{a,b} \circ T_{-a,-b} = T_{0,0}$$

EXERCISES WITH OPEN-RESPONSE PROBLEMS

1. Let $(R, \circ)$ represent the set of all rotations about the origin under the operation of composition.
  a. Find $R_{40°} \circ R_{80°}$ **b.** Find $R_{-75°} \circ R_{184°}$
  c. Name the group property that is demonstrated by the statement $R_\theta \circ R_\gamma = R_{\theta+\gamma}$.
  d. Explain why $(R, \circ)$ is associative.
  e. Name the identity rotation in $(R, \circ)$.   **f.** Find $R_\theta \circ R_{-\theta}$ **g.** Explain why $(R, \circ)$ is a group.

2. Let $D_k(x, y) = (kx, ky)$, where $k > 0$. Then, $(D_k, \circ)$ represents the set of all dilations under the operation of composition.
  a. Find $D_5 \circ D_3$.   **b.** Find $D_8 \circ D_{1/4}$.   **c.** Find $D_2 \circ D_{5/2}$.
  d. *True* or *False*: $D_a \circ D_b = D_{ab}$, where $a > 0$ and $b > 0$, demonstrates that the set of dilations is closed under composition.
  e. What is the identity element in $(D_k, \circ)$?
  f. What is the inverse for D_a in this system?   **g.** Is $(D_k, \circ)$ a group? Explain why.

In 3–6: **a.** Is the given set of transformations closed under the operation of composition?
b. If the answer to part **a** is no, explain why.

3. Isometries   **4.** Direct isometries   **5.** Line reflections   **6.** Glide reflections

7. Let R_{60k}, where k is an integer, represent the set of rotations about the origin through angles whose measures are $60k$ degrees. Included in this set are $R_{-60°}$, $R_{0°}$, $R_{60°}$, $R_{120°}$, and so forth. Demonstrate that this set of rotations under the operation of composition is a group.

8. Let R_{30k}, where k is an integer, represent the set of rotations about the origin through angles whose measures are $30k$ degrees.
    a. Is $(R_{30k}, \circ)$ a group? Explain why.
    b. Is $(R_{60k}, \circ)$ a subgroup of $(R_{30k}, \circ)$? Explain why.

9. Give as many reasons as possible to indicate why the set of line reflections is *not* a group under composition.

10. Give as many reasons as possible to indicate why the set of opposite isometries is *not* a group under composition.

11. a. Let $D_a(x, y) = (ax, ay)$, where a is any real number. Find the reason why $(D_a, \circ)$ is *not* a group.
    b. Let $D_b(x, y) = (bx, by)$, where $b \neq 0$. Is $(D_b, \circ)$ a group? Explain your answer.

12. *True* or *False*: (Translations, $\circ$) is a subgroup of (Isometries, $\circ$).

13. *True* or *False*: (Rotations, $\circ$) is a subgroup of (Direct isometries, $\circ$).

14. *True* or *False*: (Opposite isometries, $\circ$) is a subgroup of (Isometries, $\circ$).

CHAPTER SUMMARY

A ***transformation of the plane*** is a one-to-one correspondence between the points in a plane that demonstrates a change in position or a fixed position for every point in the plane.

Every transformation of the plane is a *one-to-one function*. The function rules for the most common transformations are often stated in terms of coordinates, including the following:

Line Reflections:
1. A reflection in the x-axis: $r_{x\text{-axis}}(x, y) = (x, -y)$
2. A reflection in the y-axis: $r_{y\text{-axis}}(x, y) = (-x, y)$
3. A reflection in the line $y = x$: $r_{y=x}(x, y) = (y, x)$
4. A reflection in the line $y = -x$: $r_{y=-x}(x, y) = (-y, -x)$

Point Reflection in the Origin:
5. A reflection in the origin, or a half-turn,
    or a rotation of $180°$: $R_O(x, y) = (-x, -y)$

Rotation About the Origin:
6. A counterclockwise rotation of 90° about O: $\qquad R_{90°}(x, y) = (-y, x)$
7. A counterclockwise rotation of 180° about O: $\qquad R_{180°}(x, y) = (-x, -y)$
8. A counterclockwise rotation of 270° about O: $\qquad R_{270°}(x, y) = (y, -x)$

Translation:
9. A translation of a units horizontally and
   b units vertically: $\qquad T_{a,b}(x, y) = (x + a, y + b)$

Dilation:
10. A dilation of k, where $k > 0$, and the origin
    is the center of dilation: $\qquad D_k(x, y) = (kx, ky)$

Symmetry occurs in a figure when the figure is its own image under a given transformation. Three basic types of symmetry are line symmetry, point symmetry, and rotational symmetry.

Under a *line reflection*, a *point reflection*, a *rotation*, and a *translation*, the following **properties are preserved**: distance, angle measure, parallelism, collinearity, midpoint, betweenness of points, and area. Under a *dilation*, distance and area are *not* preserved but the other listed properties are.

A transformation that preserves distance is called an **isometry**.

1. A **direct isometry** preserves distance and **orientation** (that is, the order in which points are named). Direct isometries include translations, point reflections, and rotations.

2. An **opposite isometry** preserves distance but changes the orientation from a clockwise to a counterclockwise order, or vice versa. A line reflection is an opposite isometry.

The **composition of transformations** is a composition of one-to-one functions. Under the composition "f *following* g," written as f ∘ g, first point P is mapped to its image P', using transformation g, then point P' is mapped to its image P'', using transformation f. Composition of transformations is *not* commutative.

A **glide reflection** is a transformation of the plane formed by the composition, in either order, of a line reflection and a translation that is parallel to the line of reflection.

By the **Three-Line Reflection Theorem**, every isometry is equivalent to the composition of no more than three line reflections.

VOCABULARY

13-1   Transformation of the plane   Line of reflection   Fixed point
        Image   Preimage   Reflection in a line   Reflection in a point
        Rotation   Translation

13-2   Distance   Slope   Midpoint

13-3   Composition of transformations   Dilation

13-4   Symmetry   Line symmetry   Axis of symmetry   Point symmetry
        Point of reflection   Rotational symmetry

13-5   Glide reflection

13-6   Isometry   Orientation (clockwise or counterclockwise order)
        Direct isometry   Opposite isometry

13-7   Three-Line Reflection Theorem

13-8   Subgroup

REVIEW EXERCISES WITH OPEN-RESPONSE PROBLEMS

1. Let k represent any transformation of the plane.
   a. State the domain of k.   **b.** State the range of k.
   c. *True* or *False*: Transformation k is a one-to-one function.

In 2–8, for each figure drawn or named:
a. Does the figure have *line symmetry*? If yes, how many lines of symmetry does
     the figure have?
b. Does the figure have *point symmetry*?
c. Does the figure have *rotational symmetry*? If yes, find the degree measure of the
     smallest angle of rotation for which the figure is its own image.

2.   **3.**   **4.**   **5.**

6. Parallelogram   **7.** Regular pentagon   **8.** Equilateral triangle

In 9–20, find the image of $(6, -5)$ under each given transformation.

9. Reflection in the x-axis.   **10.** Reflection in the y-axis.
11. Reflection in the line $x = 4$.   **12.** Reflection in the line $y = 2$.
13. Reflection in the line $y = x$.   **14.** Reflection in the origin.
15. Quarter-turn about the origin.   **16.** Dilation of $1\frac{1}{2}$, center at origin.

17. $T_{3,-8}$ **18.** $T_{-6,5}$ **19.** D_{-4} **20.** $R_{270°}$

In 21–24, in each case, write the coordinate rule of the composition using the transformations $F(x, y) = (2x, y)$ and $G(x, y) = (x + 3, -y)$.

21. $G \circ F$ **22.** $F \circ G$ **23.** $G \circ G$ **24.** $F \circ F$

In 25–37, k and n are lines of symmetry for square $ABCD$, and M is the midpoint of diagonal $\overline{BD}$. In each case, find the image under the given composition.

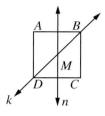

Ex. 25–37

25. $r_k \circ r_n(B)$ **26.** $r_n \circ r_k(B)$ **27.** $r_n \circ r_k \circ r_n(D)$
28. $r_k \circ r_n \circ r_k(D)$ **29.** $R_M \circ r_k(C)$ **30.** $r_n \circ R_M(A)$
31. $R_M \circ r_n \circ r_k(A)$ **32.** $r_k \circ r_n(\overline{BC})$ **33.** $r_n \circ r_k(\overline{BC})$
34. $R_{M,270°} \circ r_k(\overline{DA})$ **35.** $r_n \circ R_{M,90°}(\overline{BA})$ **36.** $r_n \circ R_{M,-90°}(\overline{BC})$

37. By finding the image for each vertex of the square under the given composition, we can show that $R_M \circ r_k \circ r_n$ is equivalent to
(1) $R_{M,90°}$ (2) $R_{M,270°}$ (3) r_k (4) r_n

38. The vertices of $\triangle ABC$ are $A(1, -4)$, $B(3, 1)$, and $C(3, -3)$.
   a. On graph paper, draw and label $\triangle ABC$.
   b. Find the coordinates of the vertices of $\triangle A'B'C'$, the image of $\triangle ABC$ reflected over the y-axis. Graph $\triangle A'B'C'$.
   c. Find the coordinates of the vertices of $\triangle A''B''C''$, the image of $\triangle A'B'C'$ reflected over the line $y = -x$. Graph $\triangle A''B''C''$.
   d. Find the coordinates of the vertices of $\triangle A'''B'''C'''$, the image of $\triangle A''B''C''$ under translation $T_{7,-2}$. Graph $\triangle A'''B'''C'''$.

39. The coordinates of point P are $(5, 2)$, the equation of line k is $x = 3$, and the equation of line g is $y = x$. Find the coordinates of:
   a. $r_k \circ r_g(P)$ **b.** $r_k \circ r_{x\text{-axis}}(P)$
   c. $r_g \circ r_{y\text{-axis}}(P)$ **d.** $r_g \circ r_k(P)$

In 40–43, in each case, write the rule of the single transformation that is equivalent to the stated composition.

Ex. 39

40. $r_{y\text{-axis}} \circ T_{2,3}$ **41.** $D_2 \circ r_{y=x}$
42. $r_{y=-x} \circ R_{180°}$ **43.** $r_{x\text{-axis}} \circ T_{-1,-2} \circ D_3$

44. The vertices of $\triangle ABC$ are $A(1, 2)$, $B(4, 4)$, and $C(4, 2)$.

$$\triangle ABC \rightarrow \triangle A'B'C' \text{ under transformation } F(x, y) = (4 - x, -y).$$
$$\triangle ABC \rightarrow \triangle A''B''C'' \text{ under transformation } G(x, y) = (-x, y - 1).$$
$$\triangle ABC \rightarrow \triangle A'''B'''C''' \text{ under transformation } H(x, y) = (2x, y + 3).$$

   a. On one set of axes, graph and label $\triangle ABC$, $\triangle A'B'C'$, $\triangle A''B''C''$, and $\triangle A'''B'''C'''$.
   b. Which transformation, F, G, or H, does *not* preserve order?
   c. Which transformation, F, G, or H, is *not* an isometry?

In 45–47, select the *numeral* preceding the expression that best completes the sentence or answers the question.

45. If lines a and b are parallel, then the composition $r_a \circ r_b$ is equivalent to a
    (1) rotation   (2) translation   (3) glide reflection   (4) dilation

46. If line c intersects line d, the composition $r_c \circ r_d$ is equivalent to a
    (1) rotation   (2) translation   (3) glide reflection   (4) dilation

47. The single transformation that is equivalent to the composition $r_{y=x} \circ r_{x\text{-axis}}$ is
    (1) $R_{90°}$ (2) $R_{180°}$ (3) $R_{270°}$ (4) $r_{y=-x}$

In 48–50, in each case: **a.** Tell whether the given set of transformations is a group under the operation of composition.   **b.** If the system is *not* a group, explain why.

48. (Isometries, °)   **49.** (Translations, °)   **50.** (Line reflections, °)

CUMULATIVE REVIEW WITH OPEN-RESPONSE PROBLEMS

1. Simplify: $\dfrac{4 - \frac{1}{x^2}}{2 + \frac{1}{x}}$.

2. Sove and check: $x - \sqrt{2x + 1} = 7$.

3. Two secants, $\overline{PAB}$ and $\overline{PCD}$, are drawn to a circle from P. Chord $\overline{DE}$ bisects $\overline{AB}$ at F. $DF = 9$, $FE = 4$, $AP = 8$, and CD is 4 less than PC.
    Find   **a.** AB **b.** PC **c.** CD

4. Let $f(x) = 3x - 4$ and $g(x) = x^2$. Find:
    a. $f(0)$ **b.** $g(-2)$ **c.** $f(g(-1))$ **d.** $f \circ g(x)$ **e.** $g \circ f(x)$ **f.** $f^{-1}(x)$

5. a. Write an equation of the circle whose center is at $(0, 3)$ and passes through the point $(-6, 0)$.

    b. Find the area of the circle in part **a.**

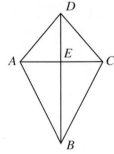

6. In the diagram, $AD = CD$ and $AB = CB$.
    a. Prove that $\overline{BD}$ is the perpendicular bisector of $\overline{AC}$.
    b. If $BD = 20$ and $BE : ED = 3 : 2$, find BE and ED.

Ex. 6

Exploration

The line $\overleftrightarrow{AB}$ is tangent to circle O at B.

    a. Prove that under a reflection in $\overleftrightarrow{AO}$, the image of the tangent line $\overleftrightarrow{AB}$ is a line tangent to circle O.

    b. Prove that under a reflection in any line through O, the image of the tangent line $\overleftrightarrow{AB}$ is a line tangent to circle O.

Trigonometric Functions

All airspace over our country is covered by radar stations. Areas are divided into air corridors that link major airports, and a portion of each area is assigned to an air traffic controller, who monitors the movement of planes in that space.

The controller keeps aircraft at safe distances from each other by studying images on a radar screen. A continuously moving ray whose endpoint is at the center of the screen represents the radar sweep of the area. The position of an airplane is shown on the screen as a spot of light, which is intense at first but then begins to fade. Within seconds, another radar sweep shows a new spot of light for the same plane.

The air traffic controller uses the information thus obtained to determine the range or distance of the plane, its angle from the radar station, and its movement to or from that station. A plane may be landing, taking off, or flying at a constant elevation. As the skies become more congested and the screen fills with many spots of light, tension in the radar station builds.

In this chapter, we study angles, similar to those on the radar screen, covering a full 360-degree range, and we learn that trigonometry is more than the study of indirect measure of angles and segments in a right triangle.

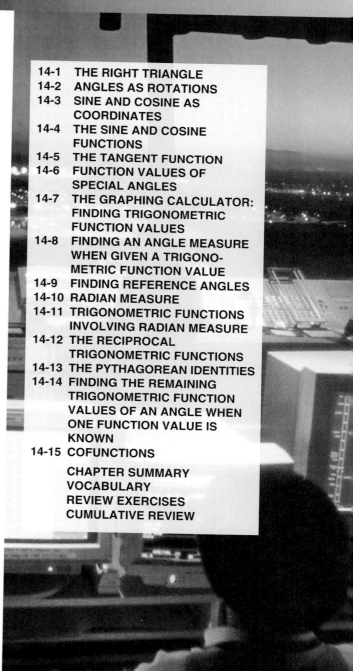

14-1 THE RIGHT TRIANGLE

The word *trigonometry*, which is Greek in origin, means "measurement of triangles." Although the study of trigonometry includes much more than the measurement of triangles, we will begin by recalling some relationships in the right triangle.

In a right triangle, the **hypotenuse**, which is the longest side, is opposite the right angle. The other two sides, which are contained in the rays of the right angle, are called **legs**. These legs are identified as the **opposite leg** and the **adjacent leg** to describe their positions relative to the acute angles of the triangle.

The same triangle, $\triangle ABC$, is shown in the two diagrams below. In both diagrams, $\angle C$ is the right angle and $\overline{AB}$ is the hypotenuse.

At the left, opposite and adjacent legs are labeled in relation to $\angle A$.

At the right, opposite and adjacent legs are labeled in relation to $\angle B$.

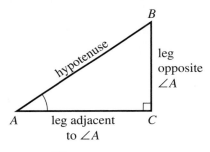

$\overline{BC}$ is opposite $\angle A$.
$\overline{AC}$ is adjacent to $\angle A$.

$\overline{AC}$ is opposite $\angle B$.
$\overline{BC}$ is adjacent to $\angle B$.

To see how a comparison of the lengths of two sides of a right triangle leads to a trigonometric ratio, we will consider the following diagram.

Here, $\triangle ACB$, $\triangle AED$, and $\triangle AGF$ are right triangles. Since each triangle contains $\angle A$ and a right angle, the triangles are similar by a.a. $\cong$ a.a.

$$\triangle ACB \sim \triangle AED \sim \triangle AGF$$

Then, since corresponding sides of similar triangles are in proportion, we may write:

$$\frac{BC}{CA} = \frac{DE}{EA} = \frac{FG}{GA}$$

Each of these three equal ratios compares the length of a leg opposite $\angle A$ to the length of a leg adjacent to $\angle A$ in one of the triangles.

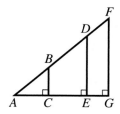

In the three similar triangles, the lengths of the legs may vary but the measure of ∠A remains constant and the ratio is constant. This is the first of three basic trigonometric ratios:

1. *Tangent ratio.* In a right triangle, the **tangent** of an acute angle is the ratio of the length of the leg opposite the acute angle to the length of the leg adjacent to that angle.

- tangent of $\angle A = \dfrac{\text{length of side opposite } \angle A}{\text{length of side adjacent to } \angle A}$ or $\tan A = \dfrac{\text{opp}}{\text{adj}}$

Using the three similar triangles shown at the left, we may write:

$$\tan A = \frac{BC}{CA} \qquad \tan A = \frac{DE}{EA} \qquad \tan A = \frac{FG}{GA}$$

2. *Sine ratio.* In a right triangle, the **sine** of an acute angle is the ratio of the length of the leg opposite the acute angle to the length of the hypotenuse.

- sine of $\angle A = \dfrac{\text{length of side opposite } \angle A}{\text{length of hypotenuse}}$ or $\boxed{\sin A = \dfrac{\text{opp}}{\text{hyp}}}$

Using the three similar triangles shown at the left, we may write:

$$\sin A = \frac{CB}{BA} \qquad \sin A = \frac{ED}{DA} \qquad \sin A = \frac{GF}{FA}$$

3. *Cosine ratio.* In a right triangle, the **cosine** of an acute angle is the ratio of the length of the leg adjacent to the acute angle to the length of the hypotenuse.

- cosine of $\angle A = \dfrac{\text{length of side adjacent to } \angle A}{\text{length of hypotenuse}}$ or $\boxed{\cos A = \dfrac{\text{adj}}{\text{hyp}}}$

Using the three similar triangles shown at the left, we may write:

$$\cos A = \frac{AC}{AB} \qquad \cos A = \frac{AE}{AD} \qquad \cos A = \frac{AG}{AF}$$

EXAMPLES

In 1–6, △ABC is a right triangle with m∠C = 90, AC = 5, BC = 12, and AB = 13. Write each trigonometric ratio as a fraction.

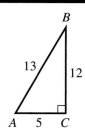

1. tan A   **2.** sin A   **3.** cos A
4. tan B   **5.** sin B   **6.** cos B

Solutions   **1.** $\tan A = \dfrac{\text{opp}}{\text{adj}} = \dfrac{BC}{AC} = \dfrac{12}{5}$ *Answer*   **4.** $\tan B = \dfrac{\text{opp}}{\text{adj}} = \dfrac{AC}{BC} = \dfrac{5}{12}$ *Answer*

2. $\sin A = \dfrac{\text{opp}}{\text{hyp}} = \dfrac{BC}{AB} = \dfrac{12}{13}$ *Answer*   **5.** $\sin B = \dfrac{\text{opp}}{\text{hyp}} = \dfrac{AC}{AB} = \dfrac{5}{13}$ *Answer*

3. $\cos A = \dfrac{\text{adj}}{\text{hyp}} = \dfrac{AC}{AB} = \dfrac{5}{13}$ *Answer*   **6.** $\cos B = \dfrac{\text{adj}}{\text{hyp}} = \dfrac{BC}{AB} = \dfrac{12}{13}$ *Answer*

EXERCISES WITH OPEN-RESPONSE PROBLEMS

In 1–6, $\triangle RST$ is a right triangle with $m\angle S = 90$, $RS = 15$, $ST = 8$, and $RT = 17$. Give the value of each ratio as a fraction.

1. $\sin R$ **2.** $\cos R$ **3.** $\tan R$
4. $\sin T$ **5.** $\cos T$ **6.** $\tan T$

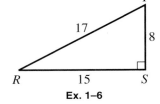

Ex. 1–6

In 7–18, $\triangle ABC$ is an equilateral triangle with $AB = 10$ and $\overline{BD} \perp \overline{AC}$. In each case, find the *exact* value of the measure or trigonometric ratio, expressing the value in simplest radical form if necessary.

7. AC **8.** AD **9.** BD
10. $\sin A$ **11.** $\cos A$ **12.** $\tan A$
13. $\cos 60°$ **14.** $m\angle ABC$ **15.** $m\angle DBC$
16. $\sin 30°$ **17.** $\cos 30°$ **18.** $\tan 30°$

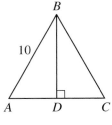

Ex. 7–18

14-2 ANGLES AS ROTATIONS

In our study of geometry, we limited the measures of angles to values greater than $0°$ and less than or equal to $180°$. There are, however, many situations in which the measure of an angle can be less than $0°$ or greater than $180°$.

Let us consider, for example, a bicycle wheel and a spoke that acts as a radius. When the wheel turns, the change in position for the spoke generates an angle. In the diagram at the left, as the wheel makes $\frac{5}{8}$ of a complete rotation in the counterclockwise direction, a spoke that was initially in position $\overrightarrow{OA}$ is rotated to position $\overrightarrow{OA'}$. The rotation, $\angle AOA'$, measures $225°$ $\left(\frac{5}{8} \text{ of } 360°, \text{ a complete rotation}\right)$.

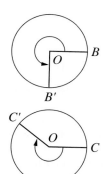

In the diagram at the left, as the wheel makes $\frac{3}{4}$ of a complete rotation in the counterclockwise direction, a spoke that was initially in position $\overrightarrow{OB}$ is rotated in position $\overrightarrow{OB'}$. The rotation, $\angle BOB'$, measures 270° $\left(\frac{3}{4} \text{ of } 360°\right)$.

In the next diagram, shown at the left, as the wheel makes $\frac{2}{3}$ of a complete rotation in the clockwise direction, a spoke that was initially in position $\overrightarrow{OC}$ is rotated to position $\overrightarrow{OC'}$. This is a rotation through 240°, but in the direction *opposite* to that of $\angle AOA'$ and $\angle BOB'$. Just as we use positive and negative values to indicate opposite directions on a number line, we do the same with angles. Thus, this rotation, $\angle COC'$, measures −240°.

- **An angle formed by a counterclockwise rotation has a positive measure. An angle formed by a clockwise rotation has a negative measure.**

Classifying Angles by Quadrant

The ray from which a rotation begins is called the *initial side* of the angle, and the ray at which the rotation ends is the *terminal side* of the angle. The diagrams that follow reexamine the three angles shown above and identify the initial and the terminal side of each angle.

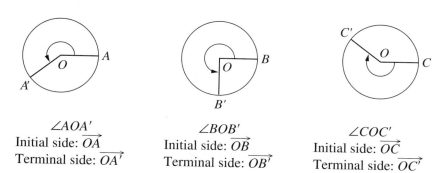

$\angle AOA'$
Initial side: $\overrightarrow{OA}$
Terminal side: $\overrightarrow{OA'}$

$\angle BOB'$
Initial side: $\overrightarrow{OB}$
Terminal side: $\overrightarrow{OB'}$

$\angle COC'$
Initial side: $\overrightarrow{OC}$
Terminal side: $\overrightarrow{OC'}$

To study angles as rotations, we often use the coordinate plane. An angle on the coordinate plane is in *standard position* when its vertex is at the origin and its initial side coincides with the nonnegative ray of the x-axis.

The x-axis and y-axis divide the plane into four *quadrants*, labeled I, II, III, and IV, as shown in the diagram at the right. An angle in standard position is classified by the quadrant in which the terminal side lies.

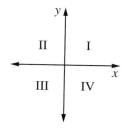

Examples of four angles in standard position are shown below.

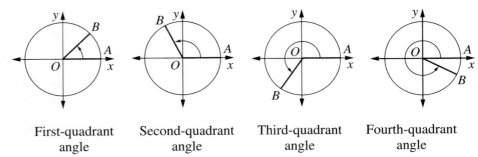

First-quadrant angle   Second-quadrant angle   Third-quadrant angle   Fourth-quadrant angle

If $0 < m\angle AOB < 90$, $\angle AOB$ is in the *first* quadrant.
If $90 < m\angle AOB < 180$, $\angle AOB$ is in the *second* quadrant.
If $180 < m\angle AOB < 270$, $\angle AOB$ is in the *third* quadrant.
If $270 < m\angle AOB < 360$, $\angle AOB$ is in the *fourth* quadrant.

An angle in standard position whose terminal side lies on one of the axes is a *quadrantal angle*. The measure of a quadrantal angle is a multiple of 90°.

An angle of 90°   An angle of 180° or 2(90°)   An angle of 270° or 3(90°)

Coterminal Angles

When ray $\overrightarrow{OD}$ is rotated 300° in the counterclockwise direction (+300°), the terminal side of the angle, $\overrightarrow{OD'}$, lies in the fourth quadrant, as shown in the diagram. When $\overrightarrow{OD}$ is rotated 60° in the clockwise direction (−60°), the terminal side of the angle is again $\overrightarrow{OD'}$. In standard position, an angle of 300° and an angle of −60° have the same terminal side. Angles in standard position having the same terminal side are *coterminal angles*.

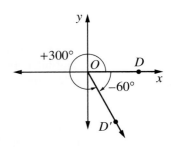

If two angles are coterminal, the difference in their measures is 360° or a multiple of 360°. For the angle above, $300° - (-60°) = 360°$.

When a wheel continues to turn, it makes more than one rotation, thus generating angles with measures greater than 360°.

An angle of 430° is coterminal with an angle of 70° because:	An angle of 870° is coterminal with an angle of −210° because:	An angle of 320° is coterminal with an angle of −400° because:
$430° - 70° = 360°$	$870° - (-210°) = 1{,}080°$ $= 3(360°)$	$320° - (-400°) = 720°$ $= 2(360°)$

If x and y are the measures of coterminal angles, then $x - y = 360k$ for some integer, k. Therefore, $x - 360k = y$. For example, to find angles coterminal with an angle of 910°, we add or subtract multiples of 360°.

By subtraction: $\quad 910° - 360° = 550°$
$\quad\quad\quad\quad\quad\quad 550° - 360° = 190°,\quad$ or $\quad 910° - 360°(2) = 190°$
$\quad\quad\quad\quad\quad\quad 190° - 360° = -170°,\quad$ or $\quad 910° - 360°(3) = -170°$

By addition: $\quad\quad 910° + 360° = 1{,}270°,\quad$ or $\quad 910° - 360°(-1) = 1{,}270°$
$\quad\quad\quad\quad\quad 1{,}270° + 360° = 1{,}630°,\quad$ or $\quad 910° - 360°(-2) = 1{,}630°$

Thus, all angles of the form $(910 \pm 360k)°$, where k is a whole number, are coterminal angles, including 1,630°, 1,270°, 910°, 550°, 190°, and −170°.

EXAMPLES

In 1 and 2, in each case, in which quadrant does an angle of the given measure lie?

1. 200°   **2.** −40°

Solutions
1. Since $180 < 200 < 270$, the angle is in the third quadrant. *Answer*

2. An angle whose measure is $-40 + 360 = 320$, or 320° is coterminal with an angle of −40°. Since $270 < 320 < 360$, the angle is in the fourth quadrant. *Answer*

In 3 and 4, in each case, find the angle of smallest positive measure that is cotermi-nal with an angle of the given measure.

3. 790°   **4.** −100°

| Solutions | **3.** Subtract 360° or a multiple of 360° from the given measure until a measure between 0° and 360° is obtained. | 790° − 360° = 430° 430° − 360° = 70°   *Answer* |
| | **4.** Add 360° to the given measure. | −100° + 360° = 260°   *Answer* |

EXERCISES WITH OPEN-RESPONSE PROBLEMS

In 1–15, in each case, determine the quadrant in which an angle of the given measure lies.

1. 140°	**2.** 210°	**3.** 97°	**4.** 315°	**5.** 80°
6. 240°	**7.** −168°	**8.** −200°	**9.** −260°	**10.** 175°
11. −340°	**12.** −380°	**13.** 500°	**14.** −475°	**15.** 420°

In 16–30, in each case, find the angle of smallest positive measure coterminal with an angle of the given measure.

16. 400°	**17.** 520°	**18.** 710°	**19.** 375°	**20.** 580°
21. 450°	**22.** 790°	**23.** 840°	**24.** −30°	**25.** −110°
26. −370°	**27.** −540°	**28.** −400°	**29.** −75°	**30.** −800°

In 31–40, draw an angle of each given measure, indicating the direction of the rotation by an arrow.

| **31.** 100° | **32.** 210° | **33.** 270° | **34.** 315° | **35.** 360° |
| **36.** 540° | **37.** 700° | **38.** −50° | **39.** −140° | **40.** −200° |

14-3 SINE AND COSINE AS COORDINATES

The coordinate system enables us to extend trigonometry beyond the study of right triangles. In trigonometry, we often use a Greek letter to represent the measure of an angle. In the development that follows, the Greek letter θ (theta) is an angle measure; other commonly used letters are ϕ (phi), and ρ (rho).

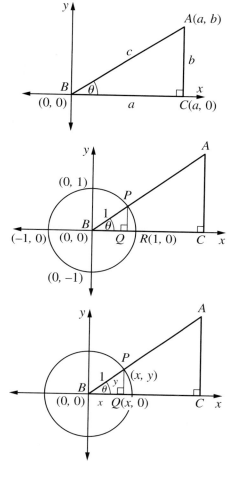

Step 1. Right triangle *ABC* is placed on the coordinate plane with vertex *B* at the origin and the vertex of the right angle *C* on the positive *x*-axis.

Step 2. A ***unit circle***, which is a circle with radius of length 1 and center at the origin, is placed over $\triangle ABC$. Since $\overrightarrow{BA}$ intersects the unit circle at *P*, $\overline{BP}$ is a radius of the circle and $BP = 1$. Then $\overline{PQ}$ is drawn perpendicular to the *x*-axis at *Q*.

Step 3. Points $P(x, y)$, $Q(x, 0)$, and $B(0, 0)$ are the vertices of a right triangle with $PB = 1$, $BQ = x$, and $PQ = y$. In right triangle *PBQ*, $m\angle B = \theta$. Then:

$$\sin \theta = \frac{\text{opp}}{\text{hyp}} = \frac{y}{1} = y$$

and

$$\cos \theta = \frac{\text{adj}}{\text{hyp}} = \frac{x}{1} = x$$

Therefore: the coordinates of *P* are $(x, y) = (\cos \theta, \sin \theta)$.

Alternative Approach. Here, we use transformation geometry. After following steps 1 and 2 shown above, we apply the dilation $D_{\frac{1}{c}}$.

We will let $BC = a$, $AC = b$, $AB = c$, and $m\angle B = \theta$. The coordinates of the vertices of $\triangle ABC$ are then $B(0, 0)$, $C(a, 0)$, and $A(a, b)$. Therefore:

$$\sin \theta = \frac{\text{opp}}{\text{hyp}} = \frac{b}{c} \quad \text{and} \quad \cos \theta = \frac{\text{adj}}{\text{hyp}} = \frac{a}{c}$$

Then:

$$A(a, b) \overset{D_{\frac{1}{c}}}{\rightarrow} P\left(\frac{a}{c}, \frac{b}{c}\right) = P(\cos \theta, \sin \theta)$$

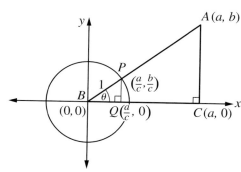

Both the first presentation and this alternative approach lead to the same conclusion.

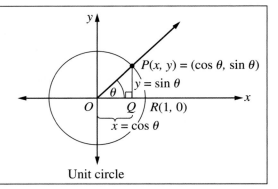

Conclusion: If an angle with measure θ is in standard position, such as $\angle ROP$ in the diagram, then the point at which the terminal side of the angle intersects the unit circle has the coordinates $(\cos \theta, \sin \theta)$.

Unit circle

This relationship between the coordinates of a point on the terminal side of the angle and the sine and cosine of the angle makes it possible to define sine and cosine for angles, like those shown below, that are not the angles of a right triangle.

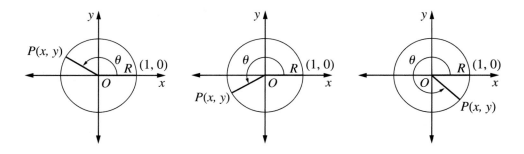

● **In a unit circle, if m$\angle ROP = \theta$, then sin $\theta = y$, and cos $\theta = x$.**

In geometry, the length of a line segment is always regarded as positive. In trigonometry, however, the length of a line segment is treated as a *directed distance*. As trigonometric functions are defined, the lengths of line segments will be associated with the coordinates of a point. Therefore, in a ***directed distance***:

1. A vertical line segment will be considered positive if it is above the *x*-axis and negative if it is below the *x*-axis.

2. A horizontal line segment will be considered positive if it is to the right of the *y*-axis and negative if it is to the left of the *y*-axis.

EXERCISES WITH OPEN-RESPONSE PROBLEMS

All exercises refer to the diagram of the unit circle showing $\angle ROP$ in standard position with m$\angle ROP = \theta$.

1. What is the length of the radius of the unit circle?

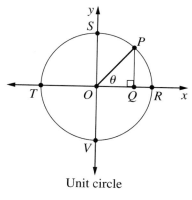

In 2–7, write the coordinates of each given point.

2. O **3.** R **4.** S **5.** T **6.** V **7.** P

In 8–13, in each case, tell whether the directed distance named is positive or negative.

8. OQ **9.** QP **10.** OT **11.** OR **12.** OS **13.** OV

Unit circle

Ex. 1–13

14-4   THE SINE AND COSINE FUNCTIONS

The Sine Function

A circle with a radius of measure 1 (a unit circle) has its center, O, at the origin of the coordinate plane. We will let R be the point $(1, 0)$ at which the circle intersects the x-axis, and let P be any point on the circle. In the diagram, angle ROP is an angle in standard position, and $\overline{PQ}$ is drawn perpendicular to the x-axis so that Q is the foot of the perpendicular. If the coordinates of P are (a, b), then $PQ = b$.

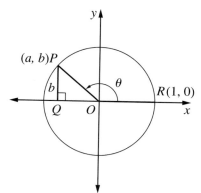

- **The sine function assigns to every θ that is the measure of an angle in standard position a unique value, b, that is the y-coordinate of the point where the terminal side of the angle intersects a unit circle.**

$$\theta \xrightarrow{\text{sine}} b$$

The value b is called the "sine of the angle whose measure is θ," written as

$$b = \sin \theta$$

In the diagram, $\angle ROP$ is an angle of 143°, and the coordinates of point P on circle O are, to the nearest tenth, $(-0.8, 0.6)$. Therefore:

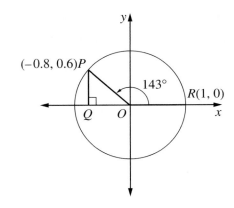

$$\sin 143° = 0.6$$

Thus, $PQ = 0.6$, or $PQ = \sin 143°$.

The diagrams that follow show an angle in each quadrant, where $m\angle ROP = \theta$ and $\sin \theta = PQ$.

   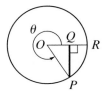

Quadrant I	Quadrant II	Quadrant III	Quadrant IV
PQ is *positive*.	PQ is *positive*.	PQ is *negative*.	PQ is *negative*.
Sin θ is *positive*.	Sin θ is *positive*.	Sin θ is *negative*.	Sin θ is *negative*.

The Cosine Function

Let us look again at the unit circle with its center, O, at the origin and points $R(1, 0)$ and $P(a, b)$ on the circle. PQ is drawn perpendicular to the x-axis so that Q is the foot of the perpendicular. The x-coordinate of P is $a = OQ$, a directed distance.

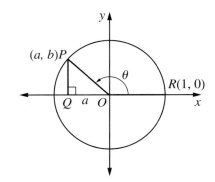

- **The cosine function assigns to every θ that is the measure of an angle in standard position a unique value, a, that is the x-coordinate of the point where the terminal side of the angle intersects a unit circle.**

$$\theta \xrightarrow{\text{cosine}} a$$

The value a is called "the cosine of the angle whose measure is θ," written

$$a = \cos \theta$$

In the diagram, $\angle ROP$ is an angle of 143°, and the coordinates of P on circle O are, to the nearest tenth, $(-0.8, 0.6)$. Therefore:

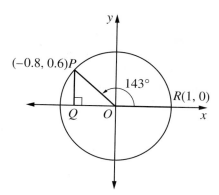

$$\cos 143° = -0.8$$

We note that $OQ = -0.8$, a negative value, because it is measured to the left of the origin.

The diagrams that follow show an angle in each quadrant, where $m\angle ROP = \theta$ and $\cos \theta = OQ$.

   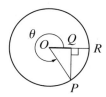

Quadrant I	Quadrant II	Quadrant III	Quadrant IV
OQ is *positive*.	OQ is *negative*.	OQ is *negative*.	OQ is *positive*.
Cos θ is *positive*.	Cos θ is *negative*.	Cos θ is *negative*.	Cos θ is *positive*.

EXAMPLES

Find: **a.** $\sin 180°$ **b.** $\cos 180°$

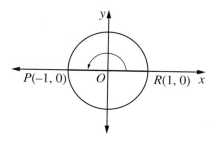

Solutions In the diagram, $\angle ROP$ is an angle of 180°, and the coordinates of point P on the unit circle are $(x, y) = (-1, 0)$.

Therefore:
a. $\sin 180° = y$
$\sin 180° = 0$ *Answer*
b. $\cos 180° = x$
$\cos 180° = -1$ *Answer*

EXERCISES

In 1–4, $m\angle ROP = \theta$ and $OR = 1$. Given the coordinates of point P on circle O, in each case, find:
a. $\sin \theta$ **b.** $\cos \theta$

Ex. 1

Ex. 2

Ex. 3

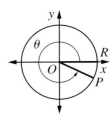

Ex. 4

1. $P(0.96, 0.28)$

2. $P\left(-\frac{3}{4}, \frac{\sqrt{7}}{4}\right)$

3. $P(-0.6, -0.8)$

4. $P\left(\frac{2\sqrt{6}}{5}, -\frac{1}{5}\right)$

5. Name the quadrants in which an angle of measure θ could lie when:
  a. $\cos \theta > 0$ **b.** $\cos \theta < 0$
6. Name the quadrants in which an angle of measure θ could lie when:
  a. $\sin \theta > 0$ **b.** $\sin \theta < 0$
7. Name the quadrant in which an angle of measure θ could lie when:
  a. $\sin \theta > 0$ and $\cos \theta > 0$ **b.** $\sin \theta < 0$ and $\cos \theta > 0$
  c. $\sin \theta < 0$ and $\cos \theta < 0$ **d.** $\sin \theta > 0$ and $\cos \theta < 0$
8. Circle O is a unit circle that intersects the x-axis at
  $R(1, 0)$ and $S(-1, 0)$ and the y-axis at $P(0, 1)$ and
  $V(0, -1)$. Find:

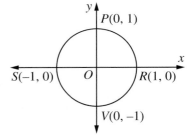

  a. $m\angle ROR$ **b.** $\cos 0°$ **c.** $\sin 0°$
  d. $m\angle ROP$ **e.** $\cos 90°$ **f.** $\sin 90°$
  g. $m\angle ROS$ **h.** $\cos 180°$ **i.** $\sin 180°$
  j. $m\angle ROV$ **k.** $\cos 270°$ **l.** $\sin 270°$

14-5 THE TANGENT FUNCTION

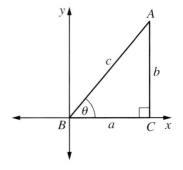

In the diagram at the right, right triangle ABC is placed on the coordinate plane with vertex B at the origin and the vertex of right angle C on the positive ray of the x-axis. If $AB = c$, $AC = b$, $BC = a$, and $m\angle B = \theta$, then:

$$\tan \theta = \frac{\text{opp}}{\text{adj}} = \frac{b}{a}$$

In this diagram, a unit circle with radius of length 1 and center at the origin is placed over △ABC, and △PQB is drawn, where P is the intersection of $\overrightarrow{BA}$ and the unit circle, and $\overline{PQ}$ is perpendicular to the x-axis at Q.

A line is drawn tangent to the unit circle at point R. Since $\overrightarrow{BA}$ intersects this tangent line at T and $\overline{TR}$ is perpendicular to $\overline{BR}$, right triangle TBR is formed.

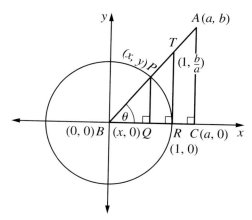

Under a dilation, $D_{\frac{1}{a}}$:

$A(a, b) \rightarrow T\left(1, \frac{b}{a}\right)$

$C(a, 0) \rightarrow R(1, 0)$

$B(0, 0) \rightarrow B(0, 0)$

Also, under a dilation, $D_{\frac{1}{c}}$:

$A(a, b) \rightarrow P(x, y)$ or $A(a, b) \rightarrow P\left(\frac{a}{c}, \frac{b}{c}\right)$

$C(a, 0) \rightarrow Q(x, 0)$ or $C(a, 0) \rightarrow Q\left(\frac{a}{c}, 0\right)$

$B(0, 0) \rightarrow B(0, 0)$ or $B(0, 0) \rightarrow B(0, 0)$

Since right triangle ABC ~ right triangle TBR ~ right triangle PBQ, tan θ can be expressed in terms of the lengths of the sides of any of these triangles.

In △ABC, $\tan \theta = \frac{\text{opp}}{\text{adj}} = \frac{AC}{BC} = \frac{b}{a}$.

In △TBR, $\tan \theta = \frac{\text{opp}}{\text{adj}} = \frac{TR}{BR} = \frac{\left(\frac{b}{a}\right)}{1} = \frac{b}{a}$.

In △PBQ, $\tan \theta = \frac{\text{opp}}{\text{adj}} = \frac{PQ}{BQ} = \frac{\left(\frac{b}{c}\right)}{\left(\frac{a}{c}\right)} = \frac{b}{a}$, or $\frac{PQ}{BQ} = \frac{y}{x}$, where $\frac{y}{x} = \frac{b}{a}$.

This ratio of the coordinates of the point where the terminal side of an angle intersects the unit circle is used to define the tangent.

Let us look again at the unit circle studied in Section 14-4, with its center, O, at the origin and points R(1, 0) and P(a, b) on the circle. $\overline{PQ}$ is drawn perpendicular to the x-axis so that Q is the foot of the perpendicular. Then the x-coordinate of P is a = OQ, the y-coordinate of P is b = PQ, and m∠ROP = θ.

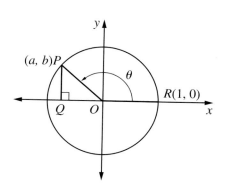

- **The tangent function assigns to every θ that is the measure of an angle in standard position a unique value, $\frac{b}{a}$, that is the ratio of the y-coordinate to the x-coordinate of the point where the terminal side of the angle intersects a unit circle with its center at the origin.**

$$\theta \xrightarrow{\ \text{tangent}\ } \frac{b}{a}$$

The value $\frac{b}{a}$ is called "the tangent of the angle whose measure is θ," written

$$\frac{b}{a} = \tan \theta$$

The tangent function is defined for all values of θ where $a \neq 0$.

In the diagram, $\angle ROP$ is an angle of $143°$, and the coordinates of point P on circle O, to the nearest tenth, are $(-0.8, 0.6)$. Therefore:

$$\tan 143° = \frac{0.6}{-0.8} = -\frac{3}{4} = -0.75$$

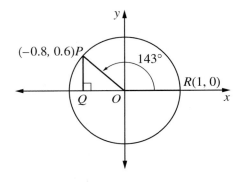

The diagrams that follow show $\angle ROP$ in each of the four quadrants. A tangent is drawn to unit circle O at $R(1, 0)$. Line $\overleftrightarrow{OP}$ intersects the tangent line at T.

  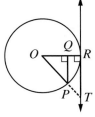

Quadrant I   Quadrant II   Quadrant III   Quadrant IV

In each of the four diagrams above, right triangle $POQ \sim$ right triangle TOR by a.a. $\cong$ a.a. Thus, $\frac{QP}{OQ} = \frac{RT}{OR}$. This proportion is used to develop two observations regarding the tangent of an angle.

In each diagram, $\angle ROP$ is in standard position in the unit circle, and $m\angle ROP = \theta$. A *tangent segment* $\overline{RT}$ is a segment of the tangent line from R, the point of tangency on the initial side of the angle, to T, the point where the line of the terminal side of the angle intersects the tangent. (*Note:* Observe where $\overline{RT}$ lies in each of the four diagrams.)

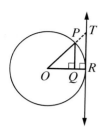

Observation 1: The length of the tangent segment $\overline{RT}$, when considered as a directed distance, is equal to tan θ.

1. Since $\triangle POQ \sim \triangle TOR$, corresponding sides of these similar triangles are in proportion.

1. $\dfrac{QP}{OQ} = \dfrac{RT}{OR}$

2. If $m\angle ROP = \theta$, then $\dfrac{QP}{OQ} = \tan \theta$ by definition.

2. $\tan \theta = \dfrac{RT}{1}$

Also, in the unit circle, $OR = 1$. Substitute these values in the given proportion.

3. Simplify.

3. $\boxed{\tan \theta = RT}$

Observation 2: For an angle of measure θ, $\dfrac{\sin \theta}{\cos \theta} = \tan \theta$.

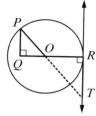

1. Corresponding sides of similar triangles are in proportion.

1. $\dfrac{QP}{OQ} = \dfrac{RT}{OR}$

2. In the unit circle, $OR = 1$.

2. $\dfrac{QP}{OQ} = \dfrac{RT}{1}$

3. If $m\angle ROP = \theta$, then, by definition, $\sin \theta = QP$, $\cos \theta = OQ$, and $\tan \theta = RT$. Substitute these values in the proportion, and simplify.

3. $\boxed{\dfrac{\sin \theta}{\cos \theta} = \tan \theta}$

(*Note:* If $\cos \theta = 0$, then $\tan \theta$ is undefined.)

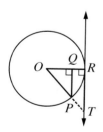

In the table that follows, note the signs of the trigonometric functions for angles in each quadrant. Compare these values with the direction of $\overline{RT}$, as shown in each of the four diagrams at the left.

Quadrant	Sin θ	Cos θ	$\dfrac{\text{Sin } \theta}{\text{Cos } \theta}$	Tan θ	Direction of $\overline{RT}$
I	$+$	$+$	$\dfrac{+}{+}$	$+$	above the x-axis
II	$+$	$-$	$\dfrac{+}{-}$	$-$	below the x-axis
III	$-$	$-$	$\dfrac{-}{-}$	$+$	above the x-axis
IV	$-$	$+$	$\dfrac{-}{+}$	$-$	below the x-axis

Quadrantal Angles

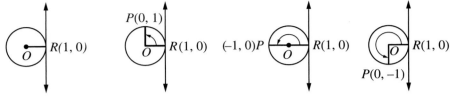

Angle of 0°
$\sin 0° = 0$
$\cos 0° = 1$
$\tan 0° = \frac{0}{1} = 0$

Angle of 90°
$\sin 90° = 1$
$\cos 90° = 0$
$\tan 90° = \frac{1}{0}$
(undefined)

Angle of 180°
$\sin 180° = 0$
$\cos 180° = -1$
$\tan 180° = \frac{0}{-1} = 0$

Angle of 270°
$\sin 270° = -1$
$\cos 270° = 0$
$\tan 270° = \frac{-1}{0}$
(undefined)

For an angle of 0° (such as $\angle ROR$ in the first diagram above), and an angle of 180° (such as $\angle ROP$ in the third diagram) the line of the terminal side of the angle is the x-axis. Since this line intersects the tangent to circle O at R, $\tan 0° = 0$ and $\tan 180° = 0$.

For angles of 90° and 270°, shown in the second and fourth diagrams, the line of the terminal side of the angle is the y-axis. Since the y-axis is parallel to the tangent line drawn to circle O at R, the y-axis does not intersect the tangent line, and $\tan 90°$ and $\tan 270°$ are undefined.

Function Values of Coterminal Angles

Since we have defined the sine, cosine, and tangent of an angle in terms of the co-ordinates of the point at which the terminal side intersects the unit circle, it follows that two angles that are coterminal have the same function values.

In the diagram, $\overrightarrow{OP}$ is the terminal side of both an angle of 210° and an angle of $-150°$.

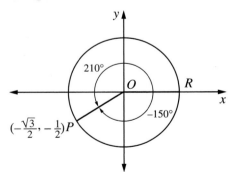

Therefore:

$$\sin 210° = \sin(-150°) = -\frac{1}{2}$$

$$\cos 210° = \cos(-150°) = -\frac{\sqrt{3}}{2}$$

$$\tan 210° = \tan(-150°) = \frac{-\frac{1}{2}}{-\frac{\sqrt{3}}{2}} = +\frac{\frac{1}{2} \cdot 2\sqrt{3}}{\frac{\sqrt{3}}{2} \cdot 2\sqrt{3}} = \frac{\sqrt{3}}{3}$$

EXAMPLES

1. A circle whose center is at the origin intersects the x-axis at $A(1, 0)$ and $\overrightarrow{OB}$ at $B\left(\frac{5}{13}, -\frac{12}{13}\right)$. If m$\angle AOB = \theta$, find:

  a. $\sin \theta$ **b.** $\cos \theta$ **c.** $\tan \theta$

Solutions   Sketch the circle.

a. Since $\sin \theta$ is the y-coordinate of point B, $\sin \theta = -\frac{12}{13}$.

b. Since $\cos \theta$ is the x-coordinate of point B, $\cos \theta = \frac{5}{13}$.

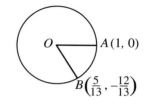

c. Then $\tan \theta = \frac{\sin \theta}{\cos \theta} = \dfrac{-\frac{12}{13}}{\frac{5}{13}} \cdot \frac{13}{13} = -\frac{12}{5}$.

Answers: **a.** $-\frac{12}{13}$ **b.** $\frac{5}{13}$ **c.** $-\frac{12}{5}$

---

2. In what quadrant is an angle of measure θ if $\sin \theta > 0$ and $\cos \theta < 0$?

Solution   If $\sin \theta > 0$, the angle could be in Quadrant I or II.
If $\cos \theta < 0$, the angle could be in Quadrant II or III.
Therefore, only in Quadrant II are both conditions satisfied.

Answer: II

EXERCISES WITH OPEN-RESPONSE PROBLEMS

1. In the diagram, a unit circle is drawn in which radius $\overline{OA}$ has a length of 1, $\overline{AD} \perp \overline{OC}$, $\overline{BC} \perp \overline{OC}$, and m$\angle COA = \theta$. In each case, name the line segment whose length (directed distance) is equal to:

  a. $\sin \theta$ **b.** $\cos \theta$ **c.** $\tan \theta$

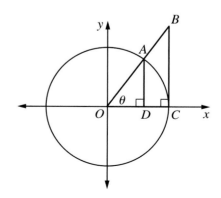

In 2–5, copy each circle and central angle shown below. If, in each case, the measure of the radius of the circle is 1, draw and name the line segments that represent: **a.** sin θ   **b.** cos θ   **c.** tan θ

2.

3.

4.

5.

6. In the diagram shown, $OA = 1$, m∠$AOB = θ$, and m∠$AOC = -θ$. Name the line segment whose directed measure is the value of:

a. sin θ   **b.** cos θ

c. tan θ   **d.** sin (−θ)

e. cos (−θ)   **f.** tan (−θ)

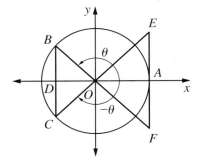

In 7–12, in each case, name two quadrants in which ∠A may lie.

7. Sin A is positive.   **8.** Cos A is positive.   **9.** Tan A is positive.

10. Sin A is negative.   **11.** Cos A is negative.   **12.** Tan A is negative.

In 13–18, in each case, name the quadrant in which ∠A lies.

13. $\tan A > 0$, $\cos A < 0$ **14.** $\sin A < 0$, $\cos A > 0$

15. $\cos A < 0$, $\tan A < 0$ **16.** $\sin A > 0$, $\tan A > 0$

17. $\tan A < 0$, $\sin A < 0$ **18.** $\cos A < 0$, $\sin A < 0$

19. Copy and complete the following table, giving the sign of the function value in each quadrant.

Quadrant	Sin A	Cos A	Tan A
I			
II			
III			
IV			

20. Copy and complete the following table, giving the function value of each quadrantal angle. If a function is not defined for an angle measure, write "undefined."

A	0°	90°	180°	270°	360°
Sin A					
Cos A					
Tan A					

21. If $0° \le θ \le 360°$, for what values of θ is tan θ *not* defined?

22. If (sin θ)(cos θ) > 0, name all quadrants in which an angle of measure θ can lie.

23. Points $A(1, 0)$ and $B(0.6, -0.8)$ are on a unit circle O. If m∠$AOB = θ$, find:

a. sin θ   **b.** cos θ   **c.** tan θ

24. A circle with center O intersects the x-axis at $C(1, 0)$ and $D(-1, 0)$. If m$\angle COD = \phi$, find:
   a. sin ϕ **b.** cos ϕ **c.** tan ϕ

25. Points $R(1, 0)$ and $P\left(-\frac{4}{5}, -\frac{3}{5}\right)$ are on a unit circle O. If m$\angle ROP = \theta$, find:
   a. sin θ **b.** cos θ **c.** tan θ

In 26–29, select the *numeral* preceding the expression that best completes the sentence or answers the question.

26. If tan $\phi < 0$ and sin $\phi = 0.7$, the angle of measure ϕ is in Quadrant
   (1) I   (2) II   (3) III   (4) IV

27. Points A and B are on unit circle O. The coordinates of A are $(1, 0)$ and of B are $\left(-\frac{1}{2}, \frac{\sqrt{3}}{2}\right)$.
   If m$\angle AOB = 120°$, then tan $120°$ equals
   (1) $-\sqrt{3}$ (2) $-\frac{\sqrt{3}}{2}$ (3) $-\frac{\sqrt{3}}{3}$ (4) $\frac{\sqrt{3}}{2}$

28. If cos $A = \frac{\sqrt{2}}{2}$ and tan $A = 1$, the value of sin A is
   (1) $\frac{1}{2}$ (2) 2   (3) $\frac{\sqrt{2}}{2}$ (4) $\sqrt{2}$

29. Which of the following is *false*?
   (1) sin $300° =$ sin $(-60°)$ (2) cos $210° =$ cos $(-150°)$
   (3) cos $90° =$ cos $(-90°)$ (4) sin $90° =$ sin $(-90°)$

14-6 FUNCTION VALUES OF SPECIAL ANGLES

Some angles, such as those with measures that are multiples of $30°$ and $45°$, occur frequently in the application of trigonometry. We can use some of the relationships that we learned in the study of geometry to find exact function values for these angles.

Angles of 30° and 60°

In equilateral triangle ABC, if $\overline{CD}$ is drawn perpendicular to $\overline{AB}$, two congruent right triangles, $\triangle ACD$ and $\triangle BCD$, are formed. Thus, in $\triangle ACD$, m$\angle A = 60$, m$\angle ACD = 30$, and m$\angle CDA = 90$.

If $AC = 1$, then $AD = \frac{1}{2}$.

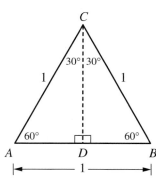

Then, using the Pythagorean Theorem, we can write:

$$(CD)^2 + (AD)^2 = (AC)^2$$

$$(CD)^2 + \left(\frac{1}{2}\right)^2 = (1)^2$$

$$(CD)^2 + \frac{1}{4} = 1$$

$$(CD)^2 = \frac{3}{4}$$

$$CD = \pm\frac{\sqrt{3}}{2}$$

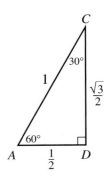

In geometry, the measure of every line segment is positive. In trigonometry, however, since a length represents a trigonometric function value that may be positive or negative, *directed* line segments are used.

We will let $\angle ROP$ be a central angle of a unit circle with its center at the origin. If $m\angle ROP = 30$, and $OP = 1$, then $PQ = \frac{1}{2}$ and $OQ = \frac{\sqrt{3}}{2}$. Here:

$$\sin 30° = \frac{1}{2}$$

$$\cos 30° = \frac{\sqrt{3}}{2}$$

$$\tan 30° = \frac{\frac{1}{2}}{\frac{\sqrt{3}}{2}} \cdot \frac{2}{2} = \frac{1}{\sqrt{3}} \cdot \frac{\sqrt{3}}{\sqrt{3}} = \frac{\sqrt{3}}{3}$$

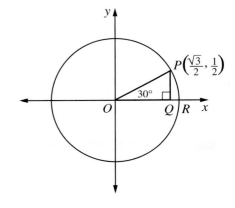

Again, we will let $\angle ROP$ be a central angle of a unit circle with its center at the origin. If $m\angle ROP = 60$, and $OP = 1$, then $PQ = \frac{\sqrt{3}}{2}$ and $OQ = \frac{1}{2}$. Here:

$$\sin 60° = \frac{\sqrt{3}}{2}$$

$$\cos 60° = \frac{1}{2}$$

$$\tan 60° = \frac{\frac{\sqrt{3}}{2}}{\frac{1}{2}} \cdot \frac{2}{2} = \frac{\sqrt{3}}{1} = \sqrt{3}$$

Angles of 45°

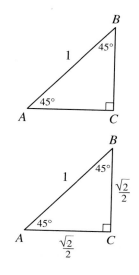

In the diagram, $\triangle ABC$ is an isosceles right triangle with a right angle at C. Therefore, $m\angle A = m\angle B = 45$, and $AC = BC$. If $AB = 1$, we will let $AC = x$ and $BC = x$.

Then, using the Pythagorean Theorem, we can write:

$$(AC)^2 + (BC)^2 = (AB)^2$$

$$x^2 + x^2 = 1^2$$

$$2x^2 = 1$$

$$x^2 = \frac{1}{2}$$

$$x = \pm\sqrt{\frac{1}{2}} = \pm\frac{\sqrt{1}}{\sqrt{2}}$$

$$x = \pm\frac{1}{\sqrt{2}} \cdot \frac{\sqrt{2}}{\sqrt{2}} = \pm\frac{\sqrt{2}}{2}$$

In trigonometry, a directed line segment may have a positive or a negative length. For a third time, we will let $\angle ROP$ be a central angle of a unit circle with its center at the origin. If $m\angle ROP = 45$ and $OP = 1$, then $PQ = \frac{\sqrt{2}}{2}$ and $OQ = \frac{\sqrt{2}}{2}$. Here:

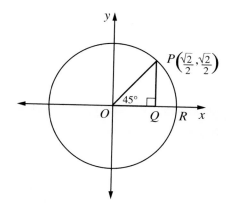

$$\sin 45° = \frac{\sqrt{2}}{2}$$

$$\cos 45° = \frac{\sqrt{2}}{2}$$

$$\tan 45° = \frac{\frac{\sqrt{2}}{2}}{\frac{\sqrt{2}}{2}} = 1$$

Summary

θ	0°	30°	45°	60°	90°
$\sin \theta$	0	$\frac{1}{2}$	$\frac{\sqrt{2}}{2}$	$\frac{\sqrt{3}}{2}$	1
$\cos \theta$	1	$\frac{\sqrt{3}}{2}$	$\frac{\sqrt{2}}{2}$	$\frac{1}{2}$	0
$\tan \theta$	0	$\frac{\sqrt{3}}{3}$	1	$\sqrt{3}$	undefined

EXAMPLE

Find the exact numerical value of $(\sin 60°)(\cos 30°) + \tan 60°$.

How to Proceed:	*Solution:*
(1) Write the expression.	$(\sin 60°)(\cos 30°) + \tan 60°$
(2) Substitute values.	$\left(\frac{\sqrt{3}}{2}\right)\left(\frac{\sqrt{3}}{2}\right) + \sqrt{3}$
(3) Multiply.	$\frac{3}{4} + \sqrt{3}$
(4) To add, express the terms with a common denominator.	$\frac{3}{4} + \frac{4\sqrt{3}}{4}$
	$\frac{3 + 4\sqrt{3}}{4}$ *Answer*

EXERCISES

In 1–27, in each case, find the exact numerical value of the expression.

1. $\sin 30°$ **2.** $\cos 45°$ **3.** $\tan 60°$ **4.** $\cos 30°$

5. $\tan 45°$ **6.** $\sin 60°$ **7.** $\cos 60°$ **8.** $\sin 45°$

9. $\sin 30° + \cos 60°$ **10.** $\tan 45° + \sin 30°$ **11.** $\sin 45° + \cos 45°$

12. $(\tan 60°)(\tan 30°)$ **13.** $(\sin 60°)(\cos 60°)$ **14.** $\tan 45° + 2 \cos 60°$

15. $(\cos 45°)^2$ **16.** $(\tan 30°)^2$ **17.** $(\cos 30°)^2 + (\sin 30°)^2$

18. $(\sin 30° + \tan 60°)^2$ **19.** $2 \sin 30°$ **20.** $(\tan 45° + \tan 30°)^2$

21. $\sin 90° + \cos 0°$ **22.** $\cos 180° + \sin 270°$ **23.** $(\tan 60°)^2 + \sin 180°$

24. $(\sin 0°)(\tan 30°) + \cos 0°$

26. $\cos 60°(\cos 0° - \cos 180°)$

25. $(\cos 180° + 2 \tan 45°)^2$

27. $(\sin 30°)(\cos 60°) + (\cos 30°)(\sin 60°)$

In 28–32, select the *numeral* preceding the expression that best completes the sentence or answers the question.

28. If θ is the measure of an acute angle and $\sin \theta = \frac{\sqrt{3}}{2}$, then

(1) $\cos \theta = \frac{\sqrt{3}}{2}$
(2) $\tan \theta = 1$
(3) $\cos \theta = \frac{1}{2}$
(4) $\tan \theta = \frac{\sqrt{3}}{3}$

29. If $\phi = 30°$, which expression has the largest numerical value?

(1) $\sin \phi$
(2) $\cos \phi$
(3) $\tan \phi$
(4) $(\cos \phi)(\tan \phi)$

30. If $\sin \theta = \sqrt{3} \cos \theta$, then θ can equal

(1) $0°$
(2) $30°$
(3) $45°$
(4) $60°$

31. The value of $2(\sin 30°)(\cos 30°)$ is equal to the value of

(1) $\sin 60°$
(2) $\cos 60°$
(3) $\sin 90°$
(4) $\tan 30°$

32. Which expression has the smallest numerical value?

(1) $\cos 180°$
(2) $2 \sin 270°$
(3) $3 \sin 180°$
(4) $\frac{1}{2} \cos 60°$

14-7   THE GRAPHING CALCULATOR: FINDING TRIGONOMETRIC FUNCTION VALUES

Mathematicians once compiled tables to show the function values of the sine, cosine, and tangent of angle measures from 0° to 90°. In our present world, however, a graphing calculator is capable of displaying these trigonometric function values for any angle measure.

When a graphing calculator is turned on, it is usually operating in degrees. Check by pressing [MODE] [↓] [↓] [→] [ENTER]. When working with degree measures, the calculator should be set to Degree mode.

Special Angles

In Section 14-6, *exact* trigonometric function values were found for the sine, cosine, and tangent of angles with measures of 30°, 45°, and 60°. Let us compare these values to function values displayed on a calculator.

Exact value
$\sin 30° = \frac{1}{2}$

To find $\sin 30°$ on a calculator, use the following sequence of keys.

Enter: SIN 30 ENTER

Display: `.5`

The calculator displays the decimal form of $\frac{1}{2}$.

Exact value
$\sin 45° = \frac{\sqrt{2}}{2}$

Again, find sin 45°.

Enter: SIN 45 ENTER

Display: `.7071067812`

The calculator displays a rational approximation of $\frac{\sqrt{2}}{2}$. This can be verified by evaluating the irrational number, $\frac{\sqrt{2}}{2}$.

Enter: 2nd √ 2) ÷ 2 ENTER

Display: `.7071067812`

Exact value
$\sin 60° = \frac{\sqrt{3}}{2}$

Use the key sequence shown below to find sin 60°.

Enter: SIN 60 ENTER

Display: `.8660254038`

The calculator display is a rational approximation of $\frac{\sqrt{3}}{2}$.

By using the COS and TAN keys and the sequence correct for the calculator, similar approximations can be found for cosine and tangent functions. When a calculator is used to find an undefined term, such as tan 90°, an ERROR message will appear in the display.

The tables shown below compare exact function values found by algebraic methods to rational approximations obtained by using a graphing calculator. Each approximation is rounded to the *nearest ten-thousandth* (four decimal places).

Exact Function Values

	sin	cos	tan
0°	0	1	0
30°	$\frac{1}{2}$	$\frac{\sqrt{3}}{2}$	$\frac{\sqrt{3}}{3}$
45°	$\frac{\sqrt{2}}{2}$	$\frac{\sqrt{2}}{2}$	1
60°	$\frac{\sqrt{3}}{2}$	$\frac{1}{2}$	$\sqrt{3}$
90°	1	0	undefined

Approximations of Function Values

	sin	cos	tan
0°	0.	1.	0.
30°	0.5000	0.8660	0.5774
45°	0.7071	0.7071	1.
60°	0.8660	0.5000	1.7321
90°	1.	0.	undefined

The table of trigonometric function values expressed as decimals helps us to see that:

- **As the angle measure θ increases from 0° to 90°, sin θ increases (from 0 to 1), cos θ decreases (from 1 to 0), and tan θ increases (from 0 to increasingly larger positive numbers).**

Angle Measures to the Nearest Degree

A graphing calculator is capable of displaying trigonometric function values for any angle measure. Here are two examples:

To find cos 50°:

Enter: [COS] 50 [ENTER]

Display: [.6427876097]

To find tan 87°:

Enter: [TAN] 87 [ENTER]

Display: [19.08113669]

In Section 14-2, as we studied angles as rotations, we learned that angle measures greater than 180° and less than 0° exist. The graphing calculator is used to find trigonometric function values for these angles as well.

In the following examples, cosine and sine function values are found for an angle of 283° and rounded to four decimal places.

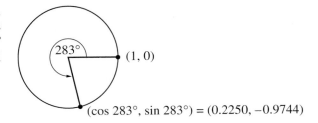

$(\cos 283°, \sin 283°) = (0.2250, -0.9744)$

To find cos 283°:

Enter: COS 283 ENTER

Display: .2249510543

To the nearest ten-thousandth: $\cos 283° = 0.2250$ *Answer*

To find sin 283°:

Enter: SIN 283 ENTER

Display: −.9743700648

To the nearest ten-thousandth: $\sin 283° = -0.9744$ *Answer*

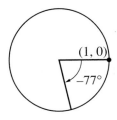

We have learned that an angle with a clockwise direction of rotation has a negative measure. When a calculator is used to find a trigonometric function value for a negative angle measure, the sign-change key, (−), must be utilized.

To find cos (−77°):

Enter: COS (−) 77 ENTER

Display: .2249510543

To the nearest ten-thousandth: $\cos (-77°) = 0.2250$ *Answer*

To find sin (−77°):

Enter: SIN (−) 77 ENTER

Display: −.9743700648

To the nearest ten-thousandth: $\sin (-77°) = -0.9744$ *Answer*

We note that cos (−77°) = cos 283°, and sin (−77°) = sin 283°, because these two angles are coterminal.

More Precise Angle Measure

There are two ways to show angle measures with greater precision than that of the nearest degree.

1. *Using fractional and decimal parts of a degree.* Midway between two angles whose measures are 20° and 21°, there is an angle whose measure is $20\frac{1}{2}^{\circ}$ or 20.5°. By using the procedure shown on page 638, we can find trigonometric function values for angle measures such as 20.5°, 32.65°, and $74\frac{1}{3}^{\circ}$. Here are two examples:

To find sin 20.5° to four decimal places:

Enter: [**SIN**] 20.5 [**ENTER**]

Display: [.3502073813]

To the nearest ten-thousandth: sin 20.5° = 0.3502   *Answer*

To find tan $74\frac{1}{3}^{\circ}$ to four decimal places:

Enter: [**TAN**] 74 [**+**] 1 [**÷**] 3 [**ENTER**]

Display: [3.565574877]

To the nearest ten-thousandth: tan $74\frac{1}{3}^{\circ}$ = 3.5656   *Answer*

2. *Using minutes and seconds.* Just as 1 hour can be divided into smaller *units of time* called minutes and seconds, 1 degree can be divided into smaller *units of angle measure* also called minutes and seconds.

There are 60 equal parts, each called 1 ***minute***, in 1 degree. Thus, 1 degree equals 60 minutes of angle measure (in symbols: 1° = 60′). For greater precision, 1 minute equals 60 *seconds* of angle measure, or 1′ = 60″. An angle measure of 17 degrees 43 minutes 5 seconds is written as 17°43′05″.

In this textbook, we will limit the precision of angle measure to degrees and minutes.

Since each minute of angle measure equals $\frac{1}{60}$ degree, or $1' = \frac{1}{60}^\circ$, a measure such as 17 degrees 43 minutes can be expressed as follows:

$$17^\circ 43' = 17^\circ + 43\left(\frac{1}{60}^\circ\right) = \left(17 + \frac{43}{60}\right)^\circ = 17\frac{43^\circ}{60}$$

This example leads to the following procedure, which can be used with a graphing calculator.

PROCEDURE. To find the trigonometric function value of any angle whose measure is given in degrees and minutes, use the sequence of keys and enter the angle measure as follows:

1. Enter the number of degrees as a whole number.
2. To this entry, add the number of minutes divided by 60 to show minutes as a portion of 1 degree.

To find cos 17°43′ to four decimal places:

Enter: | COS | 17 | + | 43 | ÷ | 60 | ENTER |

Display: | .9525730013 |

To the nearest ten-thousandth: cos 17°43′ = 0.9526

Special Conversion Keys

Graphing calculators can convert angle measures from degrees/minutes/seconds (DMS) to decimal degrees (DD), and vice versa.

Conversion keys are usually accessed by first pressing | 2nd | or | SHIFT |.

- To change an angle measure from decimal degrees to degrees/minutes/seconds, the key sequence shown at the right is used to convert 20.5° to 20°30′0″.

  Enter: 20.5 | 2nd | ANGLE | 4 | ENTER |

  Display: | 20°30′0″ |

- To change from degrees/minutes/seconds to decimal degrees, use the key sequence shown.

  Enter: 20 | + | 30 | ÷ | 60 | ENTER |

  Display: | 20.5 |

Caution: As shown above, the angle measure 20°30′ is entered as the decimal 20.30, but 20°30′ does *not* equal 20.30°. The display shows that 20°30′ is converted to 20.5°.

On calculators with special conversion keys, a trigonometric function value can be found for an angle measure displayed in either format. We have just seen that $20.5° = 20°30'$; to find the sine of this angle, we start with either measure.

Decimal Degrees	Degrees/Minutes/Seconds
To find sin 20.5°:	To find sin 20°30':

Enter: `SIN` 20.5 `ENTER`

Enter: `SIN` 20 `2nd` `ANGLE`
`ENTER` 30 `2nd` `ANGLE`
2 `ENTER`

Display: `.3502073813`

Display: `.3502073813`

KEEP IN MIND

A graphing calculator can display the sine, cosine, and tangent function values for *any* angle measure, whether positive or negative, and to any degree of precision, provided that the function value is defined.

EXAMPLES

In 1–3, in the unit circle shown at the right, $OR = 1$, $\overline{PQ} \perp \overline{OQ}$, $\overline{RT} \perp \overline{OR}$, and $m\angle ROP = 131°$. Find each indicated length (directed distance) to the *nearest ten-thousandth*:

1. PQ **2.** OQ **3.** RT

Solutions **1.** Since $PQ = \sin 131°$:

Enter: `SIN` 131 `ENTER`
Display: `.7547095802`

Round to four decimal places: 0.7547

2. Since $OQ = \cos 131°$:

Enter: `COS` 131 `ENTER`
Display: `-.656059029`

Round to: −0.6561

3. Since $RT = \tan 131°$:

Enter: `TAN` 131 `ENTER`
Display: `-1.150368407`

Round to: −1.1504

Answers: **1.** $PQ = 0.7547$ **2.** $OQ = -0.6561$ **3.** $RT = -1.1504$

4. Which of the following expressions has the greatest function value?
(1) sin 23°50′   (2) cos 66.2°   (3) tan 28°17′   (4) cos 138°

Solution   Evaluate each trigonometric expression; select the one with the greatest value.

(1) sin 23°50′ → *Enter:*   [SIN] 23 [+] 50 [÷] 60 [ENTER]

Display: ⎡.40407753⎤

(2) cos 66.2° → *Enter:*   [COS] 66.2 [ENTER]

Display: ⎡.4035452964⎤

(3) tan 28°17′ → *Enter:*   [TAN] 28 [+] 17 [÷] 60 [ENTER]

Display: ⎡.538069359⎤

(4) cos 138° → *Enter:*   [COS] 138 [ENTER]

Display: ⎡−.743144825⎤

Of the four choices, tan 28°17′ has the greatest function value, 0.538069359.

Answer: (3)

---

5. Michael and Lisa want to measure the distance across a lake, but cannot do it directly. They take some measurements and make and label a diagram. Explain how Michael and Lisa can use this information to find the required measure. Find the distance across the lake to the *nearest meter.*

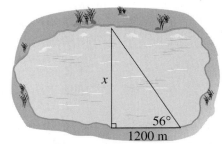

Solution   The angle indicated in the diagram is 56°. Based on the given information, use the tangent ratio.

$$\tan 56° = \frac{\text{opp}}{\text{adj}} = \frac{x}{1200}$$

$$x = 1200 \tan 56°$$

Enter: 1200 [TAN] 56 [ENTER]

Display: ⎡1779.073162⎤

Answer: The distance across the lake is 1779 meters.

EXERCISES WITH OPEN-RESPONSE PROBLEMS

In 1–20, express each function value to the *nearest ten-thousandth* (four decimal places).

1. sin 19°   **2.** sin 86°   **3.** cos 70°   **4.** cos 8°
5. tan 51°   **6.** tan 16°   **7.** sin 31.5°   **8.** cos 25.8°
9. tan 6.75°   **10.** sin 115°   **11.** cos 115°   **12.** tan 105°
13. sin 200°   **14.** cos 193°   **15.** cos 310°   **16.** sin 347°
17. cos (−20°)   **18.** sin (−82°)   **19.** tan (−95°)   **20.** tan (−85°)

In 21–40, each angle measure is stated in degrees and minutes. Express each function value rounded to four decimal places.

21. sin 12°40′   **22.** sin 82°50′   **23.** cos 51°30′   **24.** cos 85°10′
25. tan 3°20′   **26.** tan 71°30′   **27.** sin 80°00′   **28.** cos 6°00′
29. sin 56°17′   **30.** cos 45°54′   **31.** tan 61°23′   **32.** sin 123°45′
33. cos 123°45′   **34.** tan 123°45′   **35.** sin 210°00′   **36.** cos 251°34′
37. tan 263°06′   **38.** sin (−8°23′)   **39.** cos (−15°47′)   **40.** tan (−118°03′)

In 41–44, in each unit circle, $OR = 1$, $PQ \perp OQ$, and $RT \perp OR$. For the given measure of $\angle ROP$, find each indicated length (directed distance) to the *nearest ten-thousandth:*
  a. PQ **b.** OQ **c.** RT

41. m$\angle ROP = 48$ **42.** m$\angle ROP = 125$ **43.** m$\angle ROP = 237$ **44.** m$\angle ROP = 319$

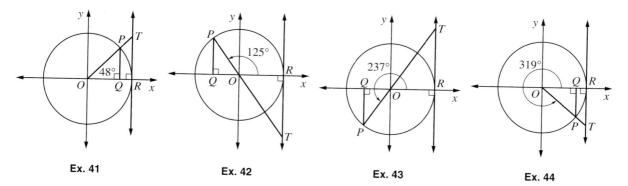

Ex. 41   Ex. 42   Ex. 43   Ex. 44

45. As the measure of $\angle A$ increases from 0° to 90°, tell whether: **a.** sin A increases or decreases   **b.** cos A increases or decreases   **c.** tan A increases or decreases

In 46–51, select the *numeral* preceding the choice that best completes the sentence or answers the question.

46. Which statement correctly shows the relationship between degrees and minutes?

(1) $1° = 60'$ (2) $1° = 100'$ (3) $1' = 60°$ (4) $1' = 100°$

47. An angle of $26\frac{1}{2}°$ is equal in measure to an angle of

(1) $26°5'$ (2) $26°30'$ (3) $26°50'$ (4) $26°60'$

48. An angle of $75.3°$ is equal in measure to an angle of

(1) $75°03'$ (2) $75°30'$ (3) $75°18'$ (4) $75\frac{1}{3}°$

49. Which expression has the greatest function value?

(1) $\sin 52°$ (2) $\cos 52°$ (3) $\tan 52°$ (4) $\sin 80°$

50. Which expression is equal in value to $\sin 41°$?

(1) $\cos 41°$ (2) $\cos 49°$ (3) $\tan 41°$ (4) $\tan 49°$

51. Which expression has the smallest function value?

(1) $\sin 5°05'$ (2) $\cos 89°20'$ (3) $\tan 100°$ (4) $\cos 140°$

In 52–55, in each case: **a.** Tell whether the given statement is true or false.   **b.** Explain your answer.

52. If $\angle A$ is an acute angle, then $\sin A < \cos A$.
53. If θ is the measure of an acute angle and θ is greater than $45°$, then $\tan \theta > 1$.
54. If $\angle B$ is an acute angle, then $\sin B < \tan B$.
55. If θ and ϕ are the measures of acute angles and $\theta < \phi$, then $\cos \theta < \cos \phi$.

56. a. On your paper, copy and complete the table of sine and cosine function values for angle measures that are multiples of $10°$ from $0°$ to $90°$. Write each function value as a four-place decimal.
   b. *True* or *false*: $\sin 10° = \cos 80°$
   c. *True* or *false*: $\sin 20° = \cos 70°$
   d. *True* or *false:* For any angle measure θ in the table, $\sin \theta = \cos (90° - \theta)$ and $\cos \theta = \sin (90° - \theta)$.
   e. Copy and complete the statement: $\sin 37° = \cos$ _____
   f. Copy and complete the statement: $\sin 15°10' = \cos$ _____

θ	$\sin \theta$	$\cos \theta$
$0°$		
$10°$		
$20°$		
$30°$		
$40°$		
$50°$		
$60°$		
$70°$		
$80°$		
$90°$		

57. A tethered balloon is fastened to the ground with a cable 1,000 feet long. It is blown by the wind so that the cable makes an angle of $62°$ with the ground. Find to the *nearest foot* the height of the balloon.
58. The angle of elevation of the top of the building (the upward angle from the ground) is $25°$ from a point 150 feet from the base of a building. Find the height of the building to the *nearest foot*.

14-8   FINDING AN ANGLE MEASURE WHEN GIVEN A TRIGONOMETRIC FUNCTION VALUE

In Section 14-7, when given an angle measure and a trigonometric function, we used a calculator and the [**SIN**], [**COS**], or [**TAN**] key to find the function value. The function value was usually displayed as a rational *approximation*, which we rounded to four decimal places. For example:

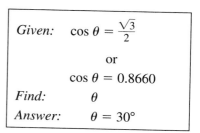

Given: $\cos 30° = x$
Find: function value x
Answer: $\cos 30° = 0.8660$
or
$\cos 30° = \dfrac{\sqrt{3}}{2}$

To find cos 30° → *Enter:*   [**COS**] 30 [**ENTER**]
Display: [.8660254038]

By rounding: cos 30° = 0.8660

For special angles, such as those with measures of 30°, 45°, and 60°, *exact* function values were also found by algebraic techniques. For example, $\cos 30° = \dfrac{\sqrt{3}}{2}$.

Finding an Angle Measure

Now, we will reverse the process. When given a trigonometric function value, we use a calculator to find the angle measure. To do this, we utilize the [**SIN⁻¹**], [**COS⁻¹**], or [**TAN⁻¹**] key, usually accessed by first pressing [**2nd**] or [**SHIFT**], and follow the sequences shown in the two examples that follow. The calculator must be set in DEG mode to display the angle measure in degrees.

Given: $\cos \theta = \dfrac{\sqrt{3}}{2}$
or
$\cos \theta = 0.8660$
Find: θ
Answer: $\theta = 30°$

☐   Given $\cos \theta = \dfrac{\sqrt{3}}{2}$ (an *exact* function value), find θ.

Enter: [**2nd**] [**COS⁻¹**] [**2nd**] [**√**] 3 [**)**] [**÷**] 2 [**ENTER**]
Display: [30.]

In this case, the angle measure is *exact*: $\theta = 30°$.   *Answer*

☐   Given $\cos \theta = 0.8660$ (an *approximate* function value), find θ.

Enter: [**2nd**] [**COS⁻¹**] .8660 [**ENTER**]
Display: [30.00291093]

Here, an *approximate* angle measure is displayed. By rounding to the *nearest degree*: $\theta = 30°$.   *Answer*

The following observations are based on the two examples shown on page 645:

1. We think of $\cos^{-1}$ as "the angle whose cosine is." For example, given $\cos \theta = 0.8660$, then θ is the angle whose cosine is 0.8660, and θ is found by using the $\boxed{\text{COS}^{-1}}$ key. Similar meanings exist for $\sin^{-1}$ and $\tan^{-1}$.

   Caution: $\cos^{-1}$ does *not* mean $\frac{1}{\cos}$, or the inverse of the cosine function.

2. An angle measure is sometimes displayed exactly, as in 30°, or as an approximate value, as in 30.00291093°. In most cases, we round approximate angle measures to the nearest degree but a greater precision of measurement can also be used if required.

   When we enter a real number greater than 1 or less than -1 as the value of $\sin \theta$ or of $\cos \theta$, the calculator displays an error message.

☐ Given $\sin \theta = 2.5$, find θ.

   Enter: $\boxed{\text{2nd}}$ $\boxed{\text{SIN}^{-1}}$ 2.5 $\boxed{\text{ENTER}}$
   Display: $\boxed{\text{ERROR}}$

   There is no angle measure such that $\sin \theta = 2.5$.   *Answer*

Positive Function Values and Acute Angles

We have learned trigonometric function values for quadrantal angles, including:

$\sin 0° = 0$ $\cos 0° = 1$ $\tan 0° = 0$
$\sin 90° = 1$ $\cos 90° = 0$ $\tan 90°$ is undefined.

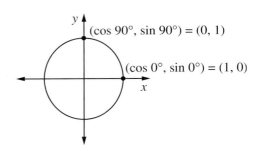

Every angle whose measure lies between 0° and 90° is an acute angle that, when placed in standard position, is in Quadrant I.

If θ is the measure of an acute angle, the function values for $\sin \theta$ and $\cos \theta$ are positive real numbers that range between 0 and 1. In turn, we see that:

● **For any positive real number between 0 and 1 entered as a function value for $\sin \theta$ or $\cos \theta$, a graphing calculator will display θ as the measure of an acute angle in Quadrant I.**

☐ Given $\sin \theta = 0.2545$, find θ.

   Enter: $\boxed{\text{2nd}}$ $\boxed{\text{SIN}^{-1}}$ .2545 $\boxed{\text{ENTER}}$
   Display: $\boxed{\text{14.74395983}}$

To the *nearest degree*, $\theta = 15°$.   *Answer*

☐   Given $\cos \theta = 0.4$, find θ.

Enter: | 2nd | | COS⁻¹ | .4 | ENTER |

Display: | 66.42182152 |

To the *nearest degree*, $\theta = 66°$.   *Answer*

If θ is the measure of an acute angle, the range of function values for $\tan \theta$ is the set of all positive real numbers. In turn, we see that:

● **For any positive real number entered as a function value for $\tan \theta$, a graphing calculator will display θ as the measure of an acute angle in Quadrant I.**

☐   Given $\tan \theta = 5.1116$, find θ.

Enter: | 2nd | | TAN⁻¹ | 5.1116 | ENTER |

Display: | 78.93083006 |

To the *nearest degree*, $\theta = 79°$.   *Answer*

In Section 14-9, we will study procedures to find the measures of angles in quadrants other than Quadrant I.

More Precise Angle Measure

There are two ways to show angle measures with greater precision than that of the nearest degree:

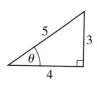

1.   *Using fractional and decimal parts of a degree.* What is the measure of the smallest angle in a 3-4-5 right triangle? Since the smallest angle is opposite the smallest side, we can find the measure θ by solving any of these three equations:

$$\sin \theta = \frac{\text{opp}}{\text{hyp}} = \frac{3}{5} \qquad \cos \theta = \frac{\text{adj}}{\text{hyp}} = \frac{4}{5} \qquad \tan \theta = \frac{\text{opp}}{\text{adj}} = \frac{3}{4}$$

Let us solve the first equation, $\sin \theta = \frac{3}{5}$ or $\sin \theta = 0.6$.

METHOD 1: *Enter:* | 2nd | | SIN⁻¹ | 3 | ÷ | 5 | ENTER |

METHOD 2: *Enter:* | 2nd | | SIN⁻¹ | .6 | ENTER |

Display: | 36.86989765 |

Then, depending on the degree of precision desired, we use rounding to show the measure of the angle. In this case:

$\theta = 37°$ (to the *nearest degree*)

$\theta = 36.9°$ (to the *nearest tenth of a degree*)

$\theta = 36.87°$ (to the *nearest hundredth of a degree*)

2. *Using degrees and minutes.* The angle measure $15.6° = 15° + 0.6°$. Since $0.6°$ indicates a portion of 1 degree, and 1 degree equals 60 minutes of angle measure, this decimal measure is converted to minutes when multiplied by $60'$:

$$15.6° = 15° + 0.6° = 15° + (0.6)(1°) = 15° + (0.6)(60') = 15° + 36'$$

This example leads to the following procedure, which can be used with *all* graphing calculators.

PROCEDURE. When given the trigonometric function value of an angle, use the sequence correct for your calculator to find the angle measure expressed as a decimal degree. The decimal degree is converted to degrees and minutes as follows:

1. Record the whole-number portion of the decimal degree as degrees.

2. Without clearing the display, subtract the whole number and multiply the decimal remaining by 60 to show this portion of 1 degree as minutes.

3. If necessary, round to the nearest minute.

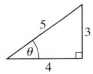

In a problem shown above, $\sin \theta = \frac{3}{5}$ or $\sin \theta = 0.6$. We can now find θ expressed in degrees and minutes.

(1) Enter the appropriate expression, and obtain the angle measure in decimal degrees.

Enter: [2nd] [SIN⁻¹] .6 [ENTER]

Display: [36.86989765]

(2) Record the whole number as degrees. Thus, $\theta = $ ___36°___ _____

(3) Without clearing the display, subtract the whole number.

Enter: [−] 36 [ENTER]

Display: [.8698976458]

(4) Without clearing the new display, multiply by 60 to convert the decimal degree to minutes.

Enter: [×] 60 [ENTER]

Display: [52.19385875]

(5) Round the final display to the nearest whole number, and record this result as the number of minutes.

This rounds to $52'$.

Answer: $\theta = 36°52'$

At times, a solution may call for an angle measure to the *nearest ten minutes*. Rounding is again used to determine the precision of the angle measure. In this case:

$$\theta = 37° \quad \text{(to the } nearest\ degree\text{)}$$
$$\theta = 36°50' \quad \text{(to the } nearest\ ten\ minutes\text{)}$$
$$\theta = 36°52' \quad \text{(to the } nearest\ minute\text{)}$$

Special Conversion Keys

Graphing calculators are able to convert angle measures from decimal degrees (DD) to degrees/minutes/seconds (DMS). When working with a given trigonometric function value, a calculator can display the angle measure in degrees, minutes, and seconds.

☐　Given $\sin \theta = 0.6$, find θ to the *nearest minute*.

Enter:　[2nd]　[SIN⁻¹]　.6　[2nd]　[ANGLE]　4　[ENTER]

Display:　$\boxed{36°52'11.632''}$

To the *nearest minute*, $\theta = 36°52'$.　　*Answer*

If the angle measure displayed contains 30 seconds (30″) or more, the nearest minute is found by rounding upward.

☐　Given $\cos \phi = 0.1234$, find ϕ to the *nearest minute*.

Enter:　[2nd]　[COS⁻¹]　0.1234　[2nd]　[ANGLE]　4　[ENTER]

Display:　$\boxed{82°54'41.878''}$

To the *nearest minute*, $\phi = 82°55'$.　　*Answer*

KEEP IN MIND

When any positive real number is entered as a function value for $\tan \theta$, or any positive real number between 0 and 1 is entered as $\sin \theta$ or $\cos \theta$, a graphing calculator will display θ as the measure of an acute angle in Quadrant I.

EXAMPLE

Find, at a time when a flagpole 15 feet high casts a shadow 4 feet in length, the measure of the angle of elevation of the sun:　**a.** to the *nearest degree*　**b.** to the *nearest minute*　**c.** to the *nearest ten minutes*

Solutions　**a.** The angle of elevation is indicated in the diagram as θ. Based on the given information, use the tangent ratio.

$$\tan \theta = \frac{\text{opp}}{\text{adj}} = \frac{15}{4} \quad \text{or} \quad \tan \theta = 3.75$$

Enter either $\frac{15}{4}$ or 3.75 on a calculator as $\tan \theta$, and find θ by using the $\tan^{-1}$ function.

Enter:　[2nd]　[TAN⁻¹]　15　[÷]　4　[ENTER]

Display:　$\boxed{75.06858282}$

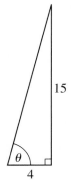

15

θ

4

To the *nearest degree*, $\theta = 75°$

b. (1) Start with the display from part **a.**

(2) Convert from DD format to DMS format.

Display: `75.06858282`

Enter: `2nd` `ANGLE` `4` `ENTER`

Display: `75°4'6.898"`

Therefore, to the *nearest minute*, $\theta = 75°04'$

c. Between 75° and 76°, angle measures to the nearest ten minutes are as follows:

$$75°10', \; 75°20', \; 75°30', \; 75°40', \; 75°50'$$

Since 75°04' lies between 75°00' and 75°10', and $\frac{04'}{10'}$ is less than $\frac{1}{2}$, round down to 75°00'.

Thus, to the *nearest ten minutes*, $\theta = 75°00'$

Answers: **a.** 75°   **b.** 75°04'   **c.** 75°00'

EXERCISES WITH OPEN-RESPONSE PROBLEMS

In 1–12, find the measure of each acute angle ϕ to the *nearest degree.*

1. $\sin \phi = 0.2478$ **2.** $\sin \phi = 0.5281$ **3.** $\cos \phi = 0.2249$ **4.** $\cos \phi = 0.6355$

5. $\tan \phi = 0.3987$ **6.** $\tan \phi = 2.1111$ **7.** $\sin \phi = 0.85$ **8.** $\tan \phi = 1.5$

9. $\cos \phi = 0.85$ **10.** $\cos \phi = 0.9$ **11.** $\tan \phi = 19.$ **12.** $\sin \phi = 0.025$

In 13–16, for each given right triangle: **a.** Write a trigonometric ratio using the angle measure θ. **b.** Find θ to the *nearest degree.*

13.

14.

15.

16.

In 17–24, express the measure of each acute angle A: **a.** to the *nearest degree*   **b.** to the *nearest tenth of a degree*

17. $\tan A = 0.1175$ **18.** $\sin A = 0.3213$ **19.** $\sin A = 0.7486$ **20.** $\cos A = 0.5905$

21. $\cos A = 0.8215$ **22.** $\tan A = 0.8387$ **23.** $\tan A = 4.5$ **24.** $\sin A = 0.3578$

In 25–32, express each angle measure shown in degrees and minutes to the *nearest ten minutes.*

25. 35°42'   **26.** 16°27'   **27.** 44°36'   **28.** 62°13'

29. 83°03'   **30.** 82°57'   **31.** 23°05'   **32.** 1°08'

In 33–40, express the measure of each acute angle θ: **a.** to the *nearest degree* **b.** to the *nearest minute* **c.** to the *nearest ten minutes*

33. $\sin \theta = 0.5505$ **34.** $\sin \theta = 0.8811$ **35.** $\cos \theta = 0.8811$ **36.** $\cos \theta = 0.7454$
37. $\tan \theta = 0.2456$ **38.** $\tan \theta = 1.3579$ **39.** $\sin \theta = 0.3$ **40.** $\tan \theta = 3$

In 41–44, for each right triangle ABC, the lengths of two sides are given. **a.** Write a trigonometric ratio using $\angle A$. **b.** Find $m\angle A$ to the *nearest degree*.

41.   **42.**   **43.**   **44.**

45. A ladder 15 feet long rests against the side of a building, with the foot of the ladder 4 feet from the base of the building. Find the measure of the angle that the ladder makes with the horizontal ground:
  a. to the *nearest degree* **b.** to the *nearest minute*
46. A standard rectangular sheet of paper measures $8\frac{1}{2}$ inches by 11 inches. A diagonal is drawn, connecting opposite corners of the paper. Find, to the *nearest minute*, the measures of the two acute angles formed by the diagonal.
47. A 20-foot ladder leans against a wall. The top of the ladder reaches 18.5 feet up the side of the building. Find the measure of the angle the ladder makes with the ground.
  a. to the *nearest degree* **b.** to the *nearest minute* **c.** to the *nearest ten minutes*
48. If $\sin A = 0.4$ and $\sin B = 0.2$, does $m\angle A = 2(m\angle B)$? Explain your answer.

14-9 FINDING REFERENCE ANGLES

   When given a positive trigonometric function value, the graphing calculator will display only an angle measure in Quadrant I, that is, an angle whose measure is between 0° and 90°. In this section, we will now learn how to relate function values of angles in Quadrants II, III, and IV to values of trigonometric functions of angles in Quadrant I.

Second-Quadrant Angles

   In Figure 1, we will let $\angle ROP$ be any Quadrant II angle in standard position in the unit circle. If $m\angle ROP = \theta$ and P is a point on the unit circle, then the coordinates of P are $(\cos \theta, \sin \theta)$, or $(-a, b)$, indicating that $\cos \theta$ is negative and $\sin \theta$ is positive.

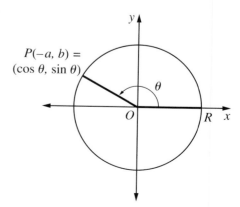

Figure 1

In Figure 2, we draw $\overline{PQ} \perp \overleftrightarrow{RO}$, and we reflect $\triangle POQ$ in the y-axis. The image of $\triangle POQ$ is $\triangle P'OQ'$ with P' a point on the unit circle. We note that $\angle ROP'$, called the *reference angle*, is formed in Quadrant I.

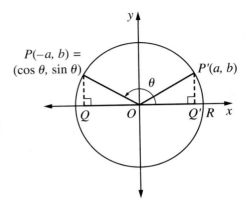

Figure 2

To find the measure of the reference angle, let us study Figure 3. Since $\angle ROP$ and $\angle QOP$ are supplementary, $m\angle QOP = 180° - m\angle ROP = 180° - \theta$. Because angle measure is preserved under a line reflection, $m\angle ROP' = m\angle QOP = 180° - \theta$. Therefore:

- **For every angle in the second quadrant whose degree measure is θ, there is a reference angle in the first quadrant whose measure is $180° - \theta$.**

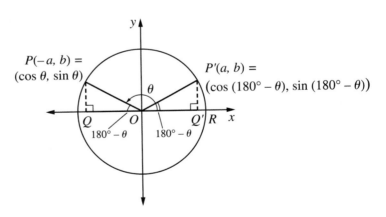

Figure 3

Under a reflection in the y-axis, $P(-a, b) \rightarrow P'(a, b)$. The coordinates of $P'(a, b) = (\cos (180° - \theta), \sin (180° - \theta))$, as shown in Figure 3. Using the definitions of sine, cosine, and tangent, we find that the following relationships hold:

Since $\sin \theta = b$ and $\sin (180° - \theta) = b$: $\sin \theta = \sin (180° - \theta)$

Since $\cos \theta = -a$ and $\cos (180° - \theta) = a$: $\cos \theta = -\cos (180° - \theta)$

Since $\tan \theta = \frac{b}{-a}$ and $\tan (180° - \theta) = \frac{b}{a}$: $\tan \theta = -\tan (180° - \theta)$

To demonstrate these rules, we select an angle in Quadrant II. Let $\theta = 140°$. Then $(180° - \theta) = 40°$, the measure of the reference angle.

1. For θ in Quadrant II: **sin θ = sin (180° − θ)**

Since the sine value is positive in Quadrant II and in Quadrant I:

$$\sin 140° = \sin 40°$$

$\sin 140° \rightarrow$ ***Enter:*** [SIN] 140 [ENTER]

          Display: $.6427876097$

$\sin 40° \rightarrow$ ***Enter:*** [SIN] 40 [ENTER]

          Display: $.6427876097$

2. For θ in Quadrant II: **cos θ = −cos (180° − θ)**

Since the cosine value is negative in Quadrant II and positive in Quadrant I:

$$\cos 140° = -\cos 40°$$

$\cos 140° \rightarrow$ ***Enter:*** [COS] 140 [ENTER]

          Display: $-.7660444431$

$-\cos 40° \rightarrow$ ***Enter:*** [(−)] [COS] 40 [ENTER]

          Display: $-.7660444431$

3. For θ in Quadrant II: **tan θ = −tan (180° − θ)**

Since the tangent value is negative in Quadrant II and positive in Quadrant I:

$$\tan 140° = -\tan 40°$$

$\tan 140° \rightarrow$ ***Enter:*** [TAN] 140 [ENTER]

          Display: $-.8390996312$

$-\tan 40° \rightarrow$ ***Enter:*** [(−)] [TAN] 40 [ENTER]

          Display: $-.8390996312$

These examples illustrate that a trigonometric function of 140° can be written as a function of 40°, or as a *function of a positive acute angle*.

Third-Quadrant Angles

In Figure 1, we will let $\angle ROP$ be any Quadrant III angle in standard position in the unit circle. If m$\angle ROP = \theta$ and P is a point on the unit circle, the coordinates of P are $(\cos \theta, \sin \theta)$, or $(-a, -b)$, indicating that $\cos \theta$ and $\sin \theta$ are both negative.

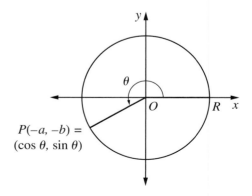

Figure 1

In Figure 2, we draw $\overline{PQ} \perp \overleftrightarrow{RO}$, and we reflect $\triangle POQ$ in the origin, O. The image of $\triangle POQ$ is $\triangle P'OQ'$ with P' a point on the unit circle. We note that $\angle ROP'$, the *reference angle*, is formed in Quadrant I.

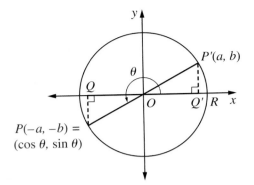

Figure 2

To find the measure of the reference angle, let us study Figure 3. Since $m\angle ROP = 180 + m\angle QOP$, then $m\angle QOP = \theta - 180$. Because angle measure is preserved under a point reflection, $m\angle ROP' = m\angle QOP = \theta - 180$. Therefore:

- **For every angle in the third quadrant whose degree measure is θ, there is a reference angle in the first quadrant whose measure is $\theta - 180°$.**

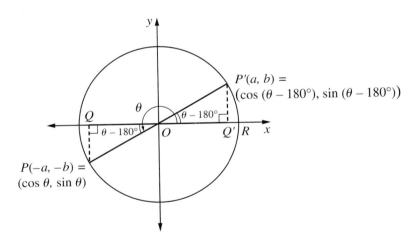

Figure 3

Under a reflection in the origin, $P(-a, -b) \rightarrow P'(a, b)$. The coordinates of $P'(a, b) = (\cos(\theta - 180°), \sin(\theta - 180°))$, as shown in Figure 3. Using the definitions of sine, cosine, and tangent, we find that the following relationships hold:

Since $\sin \theta = -b$ and $\sin(\theta - 180°) = b$: $\qquad$ **$\sin \theta = -\sin(\theta - 180°)$**

Since $\cos \theta = -a$ and $\cos(\theta - 180°) = a$: $\qquad$ **$\cos \theta = -\cos(\theta - 180°)$**

Since $\tan \theta = \frac{-b}{-a} = \frac{b}{a}$ and $\tan(\theta - 180°) = \frac{b}{a}$: $\qquad$ **$\tan \theta = \tan(\theta - 180°)$**

To demonstrate these rules, we select an angle in Quadrant III. Let $\theta = 250°$. Then $(\theta - 180°) = 70°$, the measure of the reference angle.

1. For θ in Quadrant III: $\sin \theta = -\sin (\theta - 180°)$

Since the sine value is negative in Quadrant III and positive in Quadrant I:	$\sin 250° \rightarrow$ **Enter:** ⬛ SIN ⬜ 250 ⬛ ENTER ⬛
	Display: ⬛ $-.9396926208$ ⬛
$\sin 250° = -\sin 70°$	$-\sin 70° \rightarrow$ **Enter:** ⬛ (−) ⬛ SIN ⬜ 70 ⬛ ENTER ⬛
	Display: ⬛ $-.9396926208$ ⬛

2. For θ in Quadrant III: $\cos \theta = -\cos (\theta - 180°)$

Since the cosine value is negative in Quadrant III and positive in Quadrant I:	$\cos 250° \rightarrow$ **Enter:** ⬛ COS ⬜ 250 ⬛ ENTER ⬛
	Display: ⬛ $-.3420201433$ ⬛
$\cos 250° = -\cos 70°$	$-\cos 70° \rightarrow$ **Enter:** ⬛ (−) ⬛ COS ⬜ 70 ⬛ ENTER ⬛
	Display: ⬛ $-.3420201433$ ⬛

3. For θ in Quadrant III: $\tan \theta = \tan (\theta - 180°)$

Since the tangent value is positive in Quadrant III and in Quadrant I:	$\tan 250° \rightarrow$ **Enter:** ⬛ TAN ⬜ 250 ⬛ ENTER ⬛
	Display: ⬛ 2.747477419 ⬛
$\tan 250° = \tan 70°$	$\tan 70° \rightarrow$ **Enter:** ⬛ TAN ⬜ 70 ⬛ ENTER ⬛
	Display: ⬛ 2.747477419 ⬛

These examples illustrate that a trigonometric function of 250° can be written as a function of 70°, that is, as a function of a positive acute angle.

Fourth-Quadrant Angles

In Figure 1, we will let $\angle ROP$ be any Quadrant IV angle in standard position in the unit circle. If m$\angle ROP = \theta$ and P is a point on the unit circle, then the coordinates of P are $(\cos \theta, \sin \theta)$ or $(a, -b)$, indicating that $\cos \theta$ is positive and $\sin \theta$ is negative.

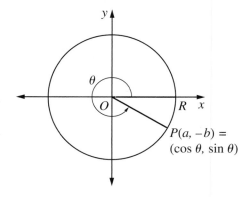

$$P(a, -b) = (\cos \theta, \sin \theta)$$

Figure 1

In Figure 2, we draw $\overline{PQ} \perp \overleftrightarrow{RO}$, and we reflect $\triangle POQ$ in the x-axis. The image of $\triangle POQ$ is $\triangle P'OQ$ with P' a point on the unit circle. Notice that $\angle ROP'$, the *reference angle*, is formed in Quadrant I.

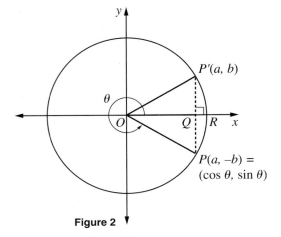

Figure 2

To find the measure of the reference angle, let us study Figure 3. Here the counterclockwise rotations $\angle ROP$ and $\angle POQ$ make a complete rotation of $360°$. Thus, $m\angle ROP + m\angle POQ = 360$, or $m\angle POQ = 360 - m\angle ROP = 360 - \theta$. Since angle measure is preserved under a line reflection, $m\angle ROP' = m\angle POQ = 360 - \theta$. Therefore:

- **For every angle in the fourth quadrant whose degree measure is θ, there is a reference angle in the first quadrant whose measure is $360° - \theta$.**

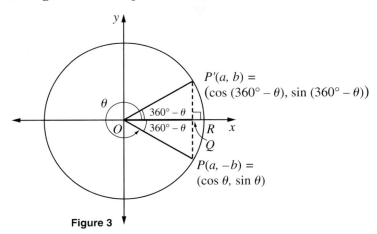

Figure 3

Under a reflection in the x-axis, $P(a, -b) \rightarrow P'(a, b)$. The coordinates of $P'(a, b) = (\cos(360° - \theta), \sin(360° - \theta))$, as shown in Figure 3. Using the definitions of sine, cosine, and tangent, we find that the following relationships hold:

Since $\sin \theta = -b$ and $\sin(360° - \theta) = b$: $\sin \theta = -\sin(360° - \theta)$

Since $\cos \theta = a$ and $\cos(360° - \theta) = a$: $\cos \theta = \cos(360° - \theta)$

Since $\tan \theta = \frac{-b}{a}$ and $\tan(360° - \theta) = \frac{b}{a}$: $\tan \theta = -\tan(360° - \theta)$

To demonstrate these rules, we select an angle in Quadrant IV. Let $\theta = 343°$. Then $(360° - \theta) = 17°$, the measure of the reference angle.

1. For θ in Quadrant IV: $\sin \theta = -\sin (360° - \theta)$

Since the sine value is negative in Quadrant IV and positive in Quadrant I:

$\sin 343° = -\sin 17°$

$\sin 343° \rightarrow$ ***Enter:***   `SIN` 343 `ENTER`

Display: $\boxed{-.2923717047}$

$-\sin 17° \rightarrow$ ***Enter:***   `(−)` `SIN` 17 `ENTER`

Display: $\boxed{-.2923717047}$

2. For θ in Quadrant IV: $\cos \theta = \cos (360° - \theta)$

Since the cosine value is positive in Quadrant IV and in Quadrant I:

$\cos 343° = \cos 17°$

$\cos 343° \rightarrow$ ***Enter:***   `COS` 343 `ENTER`

Display: $\boxed{.956304756}$

$\cos 17° \rightarrow$ ***Enter:***   `COS` 17 `ENTER`

Display: $\boxed{.956304756}$

3. For θ in Quadrant IV: $\tan \theta = -\tan (360° - \theta)$

Since the tangent value is negative in Quadrant IV and positive in Quadrant I:

$\tan 343° = -\tan 17°$

$\tan 343° \rightarrow$ ***Enter:***   `TAN` 343 `ENTER`

Display: $\boxed{-.3057306815}$

$-\tan 17° \rightarrow$ ***Enter:***   `(−)` `TAN` 17 `ENTER`

Display: $\boxed{-.3057306815}$

These examples illustrate that a trigonometric function of 343° can be written as a function of 17°, that is, as a function of a positive acute angle.

Summary

On the basis of the angles studied for Quadrants II, III, and IV, we form a general definition.

- **DEFINITION.** The ***reference angle*** for any angle in standard position is an acute angle formed by the terminal side of the given angle and the x-axis.

The following table summarizes the relationships of the trigonometric function values of any angle and its reference angle.

$90° < \theta < 180°$ **Quadrant II**	$180° < \theta < 270°$ **Quadrant III**	$270° < \theta < 360°$ **Quadrant IV**
$\sin \theta = \sin (180° - \theta)$ $\cos \theta = -\cos (180° - \theta)$ $\tan \theta = -\tan (180° - \theta)$	$\sin \theta = -\sin (\theta - 180°)$ $\cos \theta = -\cos (\theta - 180°)$ $\tan \theta = \tan (\theta - 180°)$	$\sin \theta = -\sin (360° - \theta)$ $\cos \theta = \cos (360° - \theta)$ $\tan \theta = -\tan (360° - \theta)$

If θ is the measure of an angle greater than $360°$ or less than $0°$, we first find a coterminal angle whose measure is between $0°$ and $360°$. In this way, we can find the value of a trigonometric function of an angle of any degree measure.

EXAMPLES

1. Express $\cos 260°$ as a function of a positive acute angle.

Solution In an algebraic approach, three items must be determined.

(1) Determine the quadrant.   Since $180° < 260° < 270°$, the angle lies in Quadrant III.

(2) Determine the sign.   In Quadrant III, the cosine of an angle is *negative*.

(3) Determine the reference angle.   In Quadrant III, use the rule $\theta - 180° = 260° - 180° = 80°$.

(4) Use the sign and reference angle to write the function. $\cos 260° = -\cos 80°$

Calculator Solution In a calculator approach, there is no need to identify the quadrant.

(1) Enter $\cos 260°$ to find its function value; the minus $(-)$ sign indicates that $\cos 260°$ is *negative*.

Enter: | COS | 260 | ENTER |
Display: $\boxed{-.1736481777}$

(2) Change the display to a positive function value.

Enter: | × | (−) | 1 | ENTER |
Display: $\boxed{.1736481777}$

(3) Use the | COS⁻¹ | key to find the measure of the acute angle whose cosine value is displayed; this is the reference angle.

Enter: | 2nd | COS⁻¹ | 2nd |
| ANS | ENTER |
Display: $\boxed{80.}$

Answer: $\cos 260° = -\cos 80°$ Write: $\cos 260° = -\cos 80°$

In 2 and 3, write each expression for an angle measure greater than 360° or less than 0° as a function of a positive acute angle.

2. tan 545°   **3.** tan (−250°)

Solutions

(1) First find an angle between 0° and 360° coterminal with the given angle.

2. 545° = 545° − 360°
　　　= 185°

3. −250° = −250° + 360°
　　　= 110°

(2) Determine the quadrant.

Quadrant III

Quadrant II

(3) Determine the sign.

Tan is positive.

Tan is negative.

(4) Determine the reference angle.

θ − 180° = 185° − 180°
　　　= 5°

180° − θ = 180° − 110°
　　　= 70°

(5) Write the function.

tan 545° = tan 5°

tan (−250°) = −tan 70°

Calculator Solutions

Follow these steps:

(1) Find the tan function value and note its sign.

(2) If the sign is negative, change it to positive.

(3) Use the ┃ **TAN⁻¹** ┃ key to find the reference angle for the positive function value.

2. *Enter:* ┃ **TAN** ┃ 545 ┃ **ENTER** ┃
　　Display: |.0874886635|

Enter: ┃ **2nd** ┃ ┃ **TAN⁻¹** ┃
　　　┃ **2nd** ┃ ┃ **ANS** ┃
　　　┃ **ENTER** ┃
Display: |　　　5.|

3. *Enter:* ┃ **TAN** ┃ ┃ **(−)** ┃ 250 ┃ **ENTER** ┃
　　Display: |−2.747477419|

Enter: ┃ **×** ┃ ┃ **(−)** ┃ 1 ┃ **ENTER** ┃
　　Display: |2.747477419|

Enter: ┃ **2nd** ┃ ┃ **TAN⁻¹** ┃ ┃ **2nd** ┃
　　　┃ **ANS** ┃ ┃ **ENTER** ┃
Display: |　　　70.|

Answers: **2.** tan 545° = tan 5°   **3.** tan (−250°) = −tan 70°

4. Find the exact function value of sin 420°.

Solution Find a coterminal angle between 0° and 360°: 420° = 420° − 360° = 60°.

Then: $\sin 420° = \sin 60° = \frac{\sqrt{3}}{2}$

Calculator
Solution

Enter: | SIN | 420 | ENTER |

This is *not* an *exact* value; it is an approximation. Find the reference angle.

Display: .8660254038

Enter: | 2nd | SIN⁻¹ | 2nd |
| ANS | ENTER |

Write the exact value for the function of the positive acute angle.

Display: 60.

$\sin 420° = \sin 60° = \frac{\sqrt{3}}{2}$

Answer: $\frac{\sqrt{3}}{2}$

---

5. If ϕ is an angle in Quadrant III and $\tan \phi = 3.75$, find ϕ to the *nearest degree*.

Solution (1) Find the reference angle.

Enter: | 2nd | TAN⁻¹ | 3.75 | ENTER |

Display: 75.06858282

(2) Use the rule for an angle in Quadrant III, and solve for ϕ.

$\phi - 180° = $ reference angle

$\phi - 180° = 75°$

$\phi = 75° + 180° = 255°$

Answer: 255°

EXERCISES

In 1–24, express each given function as a function of a positive acute angle.

1. sin 100°   **2.** cos 150°   **3.** sin 340°   **4.** tan 300°
5. cos 190°   **6.** tan 215°   **7.** cos 290°   **8.** tan 145°
9. sin 248°   **10.** cos 305°   **11.** sin 200°   **12.** tan 237°
13. sin 98°   **14.** tan 345°   **15.** sin 500°   **16.** cos 690°
17. tan 620°   **18.** sin 650°   **19.** sin (−20°)   **20.** cos (−200°)
21. sin (−340°)   **22.** cos (−250°)   **23.** tan (−80°)   **24.** sin (−158°)

In 25–32: In each case: **a.** Express the given function as a function of a positive acute angle. **b.** Find the exact function value.

25. sin 150°   **26.** cos 300°   **27.** tan 225°   **28.** cos 240°
29. tan 120°   **30.** cos 405°   **31.** sin 495°   **32.** tan 675°

In 33–48, find each exact function value.

33. tan 330°

34. sin 240°

35. sin 390°

36. tan 600°

37. cos 570°

38. sin (−45°)

39. cos (−30°)

40. tan (−120°)

41. cos (−300°)

42. sin (−135°)

43. cos 810°

44. sin 900°

45. −cos 315°

46. −sin 135°

47. −sin 630°

48. −tan 540°

In 49–54, find the exact value of each expression.

49. sin 210° + cos 120°

50. tan 135° + sin 330°

51. cos 135° + cos 225°

52. sin 300° + sin (−240°)

53. tan (−315°) + tan 135°

54. (sin 60°)(cos 150°) − tan (−45°)

In 55–66, for each indicated value and quadrant, find the angle measure θ to the *nearest degree*.

55. sin θ = 0.2756, Quadrant II

56. tan θ = 0.5095, Quadrant III

57. cos θ = 0.9816, Quadrant IV

58. sin θ = −0.8746, Quadrant III

59. tan θ = −4.7047, Quadrant IV

60. cos θ = −0.1392, Quadrant III

61. sin θ = −0.0698, Quadrant III

62. cos θ = −0.9336, Quadrant II

63. tan θ = −7, Quadrant II

64. sin θ = −0.8, Quadrant IV

65. cos θ = $\frac{3}{4}$, Quadrant IV

66. tan θ = $\frac{3}{4}$, Quadrant III

In 67–71, select the *numeral* preceding the expression that best completes the sentence or answers the question.

67. The value of tan 150° is equal to the value of

(1) tan 30°

(2) tan 60°

(3) −tan 30°

(4) −tan 60°

68. The value of tan 135° is equal to the value of

(1) cos 90°

(2) sin 90°

(3) cos 270°

(4) sin 270°

69. The value of cos 390° is equal to the value of

(1) sin 30°

(2) sin 60°

(3) −sin 30°

(4) −sin 60°

70. Which of the following has the largest numerical value?

(1) sin 150°

(2) cos 225°

(3) cos 270°

(4) tan 315°

71. Which of the following has the smallest numerical value?

(1) cos 120°

(2) tan 225°

(3) sin 240°

(4) cos 315°

14-10   RADIAN MEASURE

Just as we can measure a line segment by using different units of length, such as inches and centimeters, so we can measure an angle by using a unit of measure other than a degree.

● **DEFINITION.** A *radian* is the measure of an angle that, when drawn as a central angle of a circle, intercepts an arc whose length is equal to the length of a radius of the circle.

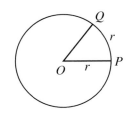

In the figure at the right, the measure of a radius of circle O is r. The distance from P to Q along the circle is r. The measure of $\angle POQ$ is *1 radian*.

In a unit circle, an angle of 1 radian intercepts an arc whose length is 1.

In the unit circle O at the left, radius $\overline{OA}$ has a length of 1, $\angle AOB$ is a central angle, and the intercepted arc $\widehat{AB}$ has a length of 3. Since $\widehat{AB}$ can be divided into three parts, the length of each being equal to the length of the radius, 1, then m$\angle AOB = 3$ radians.

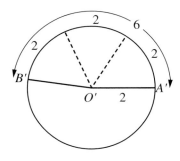

In the larger circle O' at the right, radius $\overline{O'A'}$ has a length of 2, $\angle A'O'B'$ is a central angle, and the intercepted arc $\widehat{A'B'}$ has a length of 6. Since $\widehat{A'B'}$ can be divided into three parts, the length of each being equal to the length of the radius, 2, then m$\angle A'O'B' = 3$ radians.

These two examples illustrate the following relationship:

$$\text{measure of an angle in radians} = \frac{\text{length of the intercepted arc}}{\text{length of the radius}}$$

In general, if θ is the measure in radians of a central angle, s is the length of the intercepted arc, and r is the length of a radius, then:

$$\theta = \frac{s}{r}$$

If both members of this equation are multiplied by r, the rule is stated as $s = r\theta$.

A Relationship Between Degrees and Radians

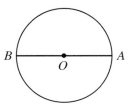

If $\overline{AOB}$ is a diameter of circle O with a radius of length r, the points A and B separate the circle into two semicircles. The circumference of a circle is equal to 2π times the length of its radius, or $C = 2\pi r$. The length of each semicircle is the length of an arc equal to one-half the circumference, or:

$$s = \tfrac{1}{2} C = \tfrac{1}{2} (2\pi r) = \pi r$$

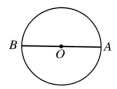

To find the measure of straight angle AOB in radians, we write:

$$\theta = \frac{s}{r}$$

and then substitute:

$$m\angle AOB = \frac{\pi r}{r} = \pi \text{ radians}$$

Since the measure of a straight angle, such as $\angle AOB$, is π radians and since the measure of a straight angle is also expressed as 180°, the following relationship is true:

$$\boxed{\pi \textbf{ radians} = \textbf{180°}}$$

To find the degree measure of an angle of 1 radian, we can divide both sides of the equation just stated by π. Thus:

$$1 \text{ radian} = \frac{180°}{\pi} \text{ (an irrational number)}$$

An approximate degree measure for an angle of 1 radian is found by using a calculator.

Enter: 180 $\boxed{\div}$ $\boxed{\textbf{2nd}}$ $\boxed{\pi}$ $\boxed{\textbf{ENTER}}$

Display: $\boxed{57.29577951}$

Therefore, by rounding or converting, we see:

1 radian $= \frac{180°}{\pi} =$ **57°** (to the *nearest degree*)

or   **57.3°** (to the *nearest tenth of a degree*)

or   **57°18'** (to the *nearest minute*)

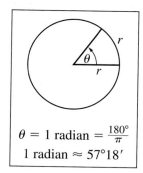

$\theta = 1 \text{ radian} = \frac{180°}{\pi}$

$1 \text{ radian} \approx 57°18'$

Changing from Degrees to Radians

We have seen that π radians = 180°. Just as the measure of a straight angle can be expressed in degrees or in radians, the measure of any angle (such as $\angle A$) can be expressed in degrees or in radians. Thus, we form the proportion:

$$\frac{m\angle A \text{ in degrees}}{m\angle A \text{ in radians}} = \frac{\text{measure of a straight angle in degrees}}{\text{measure of a straight angle in radians}}$$

Since 180° and π radians are the measures of a straight angle, the proportion can be rewritten as follows:

$$\frac{\text{m}\angle A \text{ in degrees}}{\text{m}\angle A \text{ in radians}} = \frac{180°}{\pi \text{ radians}}$$

or

$$\frac{\text{measure in degrees}}{\text{measure in radians}} = \frac{180}{\pi}$$

This proportion is used to find the radian measure of an angle whose degree measure is known, for example:

☐ Express an angle of 75° in radian measure.

How to Proceed:	*Solution:*
(1) Identify the variable.	Let x = measure in radians of an angle of 75°.
(2) Write the proportion.	$\dfrac{\text{measure in degrees}}{\text{measure in radians}} = \dfrac{180}{\pi}$
(3) Substitute 75° and x radians for the angle in question.	$\dfrac{75}{x} = \dfrac{180}{\pi}$
(4) Solve for x.	$180x = 75\pi$
	$x = \dfrac{75}{180}\pi$
(5) Simplify.	$= \dfrac{5}{12}\pi$

Answer: $\dfrac{5}{12}\pi$ radians

Note: Although the measure of the angle is $\dfrac{5}{12}\pi$ radians, mathematicians generally agree that the word *radian* or any symbol for the word need not be written when stating a radian measure. Thus, the radian measure of the angle is written simply as $\dfrac{5}{12}\pi$.

This agreement can cause some confusion. For example, if m$\angle A = 2$, do we mean 2° or 2 radians? To ease this confusion, we observe that

1. If an angle measure is found by using the rule $\theta = \frac{s}{r}$, then a radian measure is being determined.

2. If the situation is unclear, we will identify the type of angle measure being used, either by words or by symbols, as in m$\angle A = 2°$ and m$\angle B = 2$ radians.

Changing from Radians to Degrees

To find the degree measure of an angle whose radian measure is known, we may use either of two approaches.

1. *Proportion.* Use the same proportion developed earlier.

For example, to convert an angle of $\frac{\pi}{4}$ radians to degrees, let x = degree measure of the angle. Then:

$$\frac{\text{measure in degrees}}{\text{measure in radians}} = \frac{180}{\pi} \rightarrow \frac{x}{\left(\frac{\pi}{4}\right)} = \frac{180}{\pi}$$

Solve for x:

$$\pi x = \frac{\pi}{4}(180)$$

$$\pi x = 45\pi$$

$$x = 45$$

The measure of the angle is 45°.

2. *Substitution.* Since π radians = 180°, substitute 180° for π radians and simplify the expression. For example:

$$\frac{\pi}{4} \text{ radians} = \frac{1}{4}(\pi \text{ radians}) = \frac{1}{4}(180°) = 45°$$

EXAMPLES

1. In a circle, the length of a radius is 4 centimeters. Find the length of an arc intercepted by a central angle whose measure is 1.5 radians.

How to Proceed:	*Solution:*
(1) Write the rule that shows that the radian measure θ of a central angle is equal to the length s of the intercepted arc divided by the length r of a radius.	$\theta = \frac{s}{r}$
(2) Substitute the given values.	$1.5 = \frac{s}{4}$
(3) Solve for s.	$s = 4(1.5)$
	$= 6$

Answer: 6 cm

2. Express in radian measure an angle of 135°.

How to Proceed:	*Solution:*
(1) Identify the variable.	Let x = radian measure of an angle of 135°.
(2) Write the proportion.	$\dfrac{\text{measure of degrees}}{\text{measure in radians}} = \dfrac{180}{\pi}$
(3) Substitute 135° and x radians for the angle in question.	$\dfrac{135}{x} = \dfrac{180}{\pi}$
(4) Solve for x.	$180x = 135\pi$
	$x = \dfrac{135}{180}\pi$
(5) Express in simplest form.	$= \dfrac{3}{4}\pi$

Answer: $\dfrac{3}{4}\pi$, or $\dfrac{3\pi}{4}$

---

3. Express $\dfrac{7\pi}{3}$ radians in degrees.

METHOD 1: *Proportion*

Let y = degree measure of an angle of $\dfrac{7\pi}{3}$ radians.

$$\frac{\text{measure in degrees}}{\text{measure in radians}} = \frac{180}{\pi}$$

$$\frac{y}{\dfrac{7\pi}{3}} = \frac{180}{\pi}$$

$$\pi y = \frac{7\pi}{3}(180)$$

$$\pi y = 420\pi$$

$$y = 420$$

METHOD 2: *Substitution*

Substitute 180° for π radians, and simplify.

$$\frac{7\pi}{3} \text{ radians} = \frac{7}{3}(180°)$$

$$= \frac{7}{\overset{}{3}}(\overset{60°}{\cancel{180°}}) = 420°$$

Answer: 420°

EXERCISES WITH OPEN-RESPONSE PROBLEMS

In 1–15, find the radian measure of each angle whose degree measure is given.

1. 30°
2. 90°
3. 45°
4. 120°
5. 160°

6. 180°
7. 210°
8. 225°
9. 270°
10. 300°

11. 315°
12. 100°
13. 198°
14. 99°
15. 396°

In 16–30, find the degree measure of each angle whose radian measure is given.

16. $\frac{\pi}{3}$
17. $\frac{\pi}{9}$
18. $\frac{\pi}{10}$
19. $\frac{2\pi}{5}$
20. $\frac{\pi}{2}$

21. $\frac{5\pi}{6}$
22. π
23. $\frac{4\pi}{3}$
24. $\frac{10\pi}{9}$
25. $\frac{3\pi}{4}$

26. $\frac{11\pi}{6}$
27. 3π
28. $\frac{7\pi}{2}$
29. $\frac{5\pi}{18}$
30. $\frac{2\pi}{27}$

In 31–38, θ is the measure of a central angle that intercepts an arc of length s in a circle with a radius of length r.

31. If $s = 12$ and $r = 4$, find θ.
32. If $s = 6$ and $r = 1$, find θ.

33. If $s = 10$ and $r = 2.5$, find θ.
34. If $s = 12$ and $\theta = 6$, find r.

35. If $s = 12$ and $\theta = 0.5$, find r.
36. If $\theta = 2.5$ and $r = 4$, find s.

37. If $\theta = \frac{1}{3}$ and $s = 3$, find r.
38. If $\theta = 4$ and $r = 1.25$, find s.

39. In a circle, a central angle of $\frac{1}{3}$ radian intercepts an arc of 3 centimeters. Find the length, in centimeters, of a radius of the circle.

40. A circle has a radius of 1.7 inches. Find the length of an arc intercepted by a central angle whose measure is 2 radians.

41. In a circle whose radius measures 5 feet, a central angle intercepts an arc of length 12 feet. Find the radian measure of the central angle.

42. In a circle, a central angle of 4.2 radians intercepts an arc whose length is 6.3 meters. Find the length, in meters, of a radius of the circle.

43. A central angle intercepts an arc on a circle equal in length to a diameter of the circle. Find the measure, in radians, of the central angle.

44. On a clock, the length of the pendulum is 30 centimeters. A swing of the pendulum determines an angle of 0.8 radian. Find, in centimeters, the distance traveled by the tip of the pendulum during this swing.

45. As the pendulum of a clock swings through an angle of 30°, the tip of the pendulum travels along an arc whose length is 4π inches.
 a. Express the angle of 30° in radian measure.
 b. Find the length, in inches, of the pendulum.

46. Copy and complete the table.

Amount of rotation	$\frac{1}{2}$	$\frac{1}{12}$	$\frac{1}{8}$	$\frac{1}{6}$	$\frac{1}{4}$	$\frac{3}{4}$
Degree measure	180°					
Radian measure	π					

47. Express $\frac{10\pi}{3}$ radians in degrees.

48. Find the radian measure of an angle of 306°.

In 49–53, select the *numeral* preceding the expression that best completes the sentence.

49. One radian is approximately equal to
 (1) 45° (2) 50° (3) 57° (4) 60°

50. The number of radians in a complete rotation is approximately
 (1) 6.28 (2) 3.14 (3) 10 (4) 36

51. Two-thirds of a rotation determines an angle whose radian measure is
 (1) $\frac{2\pi}{3}$ (2) $\frac{4\pi}{3}$ (3) $\frac{8\pi}{3}$ (4) $\frac{3\pi}{2}$

52. Three-eighths of a rotation determines an angle whose measure is
 (1) $\frac{3\pi}{8}$ (2) 140° (3) $\frac{3\pi}{4}$ (4) 150°

53. A wheel whose radius measures 10 inches is rotated. If a point on the circumference of the wheel moves a distance of 5 feet, the point travels through an angle whose radian measure is
 (1) $\frac{1}{2}$ (2) 2 (3) $\frac{1}{6}$ (4) 6

14-11 TRIGONOMETRIC FUNCTIONS INVOLVING RADIAN MEASURE

Since angle measure can be expressed in radians as well as in degrees, we can find values of trigonometric functions of angles expressed in radian measure. This can be done in either of two ways.

1. *Use radian measures.* A graphing calculator can determine the function value for an angle in radian measure. To do this, use the [**MODE**] key to change the calculator setting from degrees to radians. Then, enter the trigonometric function and the radian measure. For example, to find $\sin \frac{\pi}{3}$:

| Radian |

Enter: [**SIN**] [**2nd**] [π] [$\div$] 3 [**ENTER**]

Display: $\fbox{.8660254038}$

> Therefore, $\sin \frac{\pi}{3} = 0.8660$ to four decimal places.

Caution: Some graphing calculators, when the display is cleared, will automatically return to the Degree setting. Thus, if a series of function values involving radian measures are to be found, it will be necessary to set the calculator to Radian mode before determining each trigonometric function value.

2. *Convert radians to degrees; use degree measures.*

An algebraic approach: To find the function value of $\sin \frac{\pi}{3}$, use either the proportion method or substitution to express $\frac{\pi}{3}$ radians in degree measure.

$$\frac{\pi}{3} \text{ radians} = \frac{1}{3} (\pi \text{ radians}) = \frac{1}{3} (180°) = 60°$$

Then determine the function value for the degree measure.

$$\sin \frac{\pi}{3} = \sin 60° = \frac{\sqrt{3}}{2}$$

A calculator approach: Calculator usage involves the same steps shown above for the algebraic approach. Since the radian measure is to be converted to degrees, the calculator must be set to Degree mode and π radians is replaced by 180°. Thus, to find $\sin \frac{\pi}{3}$:

| Degree |

Enter: [**SIN**] 180 [$\div$] 3 [**ENTER**]

Display: $\fbox{.8660254038}$

> Therefore, $\sin \frac{\pi}{3} = 0.8660$ to four decimal places.

Note: If an *exact* function value is sought, the only acceptable value for $\sin \frac{\pi}{3}$ is $\frac{\sqrt{3}}{2}$. If we simply seek *a* function value for $\sin \frac{\pi}{3}$, then both $\frac{\sqrt{3}}{2}$ and 0.8660 are acceptable solutions.

EXAMPLES

1. Find the value of $\sin \frac{2\pi}{5}$ to four decimal places.

Solution

Radian

(1) Set the calculator to radian mode, and evaluate $\sin \frac{2\pi}{5}$.

Enter: [SIN] [2] [×] [2nd] [π] [÷] [5] [ENTER]

Display: [.9510565163]

(2) Round to the nearest ten-thousandth.

$\sin \frac{2\pi}{5} = 0.9511$

Alternative Solution

Degree

(1) Change radian measure to degrees.

$\frac{2\pi}{5}$ radians $= \frac{2}{5}(180°) = 72°$

(2) With the calculator set in degree mode, evaluate $\sin \frac{2\pi}{5}$ by evaluating $\sin 72°$.

Enter: [SIN] [72] [ENTER]

Display: [.9510565163]

(3) Round to the nearest ten-thousandth.

$\sin \frac{2\pi}{5} = \sin 72° = 0.9511$

Answer: $\sin \frac{2\pi}{5} = 0.9511$

---

2. If a function f is defined as $f(x) = \cos 2x + \sin x$, find the numerical value of $f\left(\frac{\pi}{2}\right)$.

How to Proceed:	*Solution:*
(1) Write the function.	$f(x) = \cos 2x + \sin x$
(2) Let $x = \frac{\pi}{2}$, and simplify the terms in the expression.	$f\left(\frac{\pi}{2}\right) = \cos\left(2 \cdot \frac{\pi}{2}\right) + \sin\left(\frac{\pi}{2}\right)$
	$= \cos \pi + \sin \frac{\pi}{2}$
(3) Change radian measures to degrees in the expression.	$= \cos 180° + \sin 90°$
(4) Evaluate and simplify.	$= -1 + 1 = 0$

Answer: $f\left(\frac{\pi}{2}\right) = 0$

EXERCISES WITH OPEN RESPONSE PROBLEMS

In 1–15, find the exact value of each trigonometric function.

1. $\cos \frac{\pi}{3}$

2. $\tan \frac{\pi}{4}$

3. $\sin \frac{2\pi}{3}$

4. $\cos \frac{4\pi}{3}$

5. $\sin \frac{5\pi}{4}$

6. $\sin \frac{7\pi}{6}$

7. $\tan \frac{4\pi}{3}$

8. $\cos \frac{11\pi}{6}$

9. $\tan \frac{5\pi}{6}$

10. $\cos \frac{3\pi}{4}$

11. $\sin \frac{5\pi}{3}$

12. $\tan 3\pi$

13. $\sin \frac{15\pi}{4}$

14. $\cos \left(\frac{-\pi}{6}\right)$

15. $\sin \left(\frac{-5\pi}{6}\right)$

In 16–30, find the value of each trigonometric function to four decimal places.

16. $\sin \frac{\pi}{4}$

17. $\cos \frac{\pi}{6}$

18. $\tan \frac{11\pi}{6}$

19. $\sin \frac{7\pi}{6}$

20. $\cos \frac{5\pi}{4}$

21. $\cos \frac{\pi}{5}$

22. $\sin \frac{\pi}{10}$

23. $\tan \frac{2\pi}{5}$

24. $\tan \frac{7\pi}{10}$

25. $\sin \frac{3\pi}{8}$

26. $\cos \frac{17\pi}{12}$

27. $\tan \left(\frac{-\pi}{3}\right)$

28. $\cos \left(\frac{-\pi}{10}\right)$

29. $\sin \left(\frac{-2\pi}{9}\right)$

30. $\tan \left(\frac{-6\pi}{5}\right)$

In 31–33, if a function f is defined as $f(x) = \cos 3x$, find the numerical value of:

31. $f\left(\frac{\pi}{2}\right)$

32. $f\left(\frac{\pi}{6}\right)$

33. $f(\pi)$

In 34–36, if a function f is defined as $f(x) = \sin \left(\frac{x}{2}\right)$, find the numerical value of:

34. $f(3\pi)$

35. $f\left(\frac{\pi}{2}\right)$

36. $f\left(\frac{5\pi}{3}\right)$

In 37–42, for each given function f, find the numerical value of $f(\pi)$.

37. $f(x) = \sin 2x$

38. $f(x) = \cos \frac{1}{4} x$

39. $f(x) = \sin x + \cos 2x$

40. $f(x) = \tan \left(\frac{x}{3}\right)$

41. $f(x) = \tan 2x - \sin \left(\frac{x}{2}\right)$

42. $f(x) = \sin x \cos 2x$

In 43–48, for each given function f, find the numerical value of $f\left(\frac{\pi}{3}\right)$.

43. $f(x) = \sin 2x$

44. $f(x) = \tan 5x$

45. $f(x) = \cos \frac{1}{2} x$

46. $f(x) = \sin \left(\frac{7x}{2}\right)$

47. $f(x) = \sin \frac{1}{2} x + \cos 5x$

48. $f(x) = \tan x \tan 2x$

49. If $\theta = 3$ radians, find the value of $\sin \theta$ to four decimal places.

50. If $\phi = 1$ radian, find the value of $\cos \phi$ to the *nearest ten-thousandth*.

51. a. Which, if either, is the measure of the larger angle: $15°$ or 15 radians? Explain your answer.
   b. Which, if either, is the greater function value: $\tan 15°$ or $\tan 15$? Explain your answer.

   In 52–55, select the *numeral* preceding the expression that best completes the sentence or answers the question.

52. If $f(x) = \tan 5x + \cos 2x$, then $f\left(\frac{\pi}{4}\right)$ equals

   (1) 1   (2) 2   (3) 0   (4) $\frac{\sqrt{2}}{2}$

53. If $f(x) = \cos x + \tan \frac{x}{3}$, then $f(\pi)$ is

   (1) $\frac{\sqrt{3} + 3}{3}$ (2) $\frac{\sqrt{3} - 3}{3}$ (3) $\sqrt{3} + 1$ (4) $\sqrt{3} - 1$

54. Which of the following functions has the largest numerical value when $x = 2\pi$?

   (1) $f(x) = \sin \frac{x}{2}$ (2) $g(x) = \cos \frac{x}{2}$ (3) $h(x) = \sin \frac{x}{4}$ (4) $k(x) = \cos \frac{x}{4}$

55. What is the value of $\sin \frac{4\pi}{3} \sin \frac{\pi}{3}$?

   (1) $-\frac{3}{4}$ (2) $\frac{3}{4}$ (3) $-\frac{3}{2}$ (4) $\frac{3}{2}$

14-12   THE RECIPROCAL TRIGONOMETRIC FUNCTIONS

We have defined three trigonometric functions, namely, the sine, cosine, and tangent functions. Three other trigonometric functions can be defined in terms of the cosine, sine, and tangent.

Secant, Cosecant, and Cotangent

- The *secant function* assigns to every angle measure θ, for which $\cos \theta \neq 0$, a unique value that is the reciprocal of $\cos \theta$.

$$\theta \xrightarrow{\text{secant}} \frac{1}{\cos \theta}$$

Using "sec" for secant, we write the reciprocal identity as follows:

$$\sec \theta = \frac{1}{\cos \theta}$$

When $\cos \theta \neq 0$, a function value can be found for $\sec \theta$. For example, $\cos 60° = \frac{1}{2}$. Then $\sec 60°$ is the reciprocal of $\frac{1}{2}$, or 2.

$$\sec 60° = \frac{1}{\cos 60°} = \frac{1}{\left(\frac{1}{2}\right)} = 2$$

Although there is no secant key on a graphing calculator, we can find function values for secant by using the reciprocal of the cosine.

PROCEDURE. To display the secant function on a graphing calculator, use the cosine function key $\boxed{\text{COS}}$ followed by the reciprocal or multiplicative inverse key $\boxed{x^{-1}}$.

To find $\sec 60°$:

Enter: $\boxed{\text{COS}}$ 60 $\boxed{\text{ENTER}}$ $\boxed{x^{-1}}$ $\boxed{\text{ENTER}}$

Display: $\boxed{\qquad\qquad 2.}$

Since $\sec \theta$ is the reciprocal of $\cos \theta$, $\sec \theta$ is undefined when $\cos \theta = 0$, that is, when $\theta = 90°$, $270°$, and so on. For example, $\sec 90°$ is undefined because

$$\sec 90° = \frac{1}{\cos 90°} = \frac{1}{0} \text{ (undefined)}$$

An attempt to evaluate an undefined term such as $\sec 90°$ on a calculator will result in an $\boxed{\text{ERROR}}$ message in the display.

● The *cosecant function* assigns to every θ for which $\sin \theta \neq 0$ a unique value that is the reciprocal of $\sin \theta$.

$$\theta \xrightarrow{\text{cosecant}} \frac{1}{\sin \theta}$$

The abbreviation for cosecant is "csc," not the first three letters of the word as for the other functions. This reciprocal identity is as follows:

$$\boxed{\csc \theta = \frac{1}{\sin \theta}}$$

When $\sin \theta \neq 0$, a function value can be found for $\csc \theta$. For example, $\sin 20° = 0.342020143$ as displayed on a calculator. Since $\sin 20°$ is approximately $\frac{1}{3}$, then $\csc 20°$ should be close to the reciprocal of $\frac{1}{3}$, or to 3. To verify this estimate, let us evaluate $\csc 20°$ on a calculator.

PROCEDURE.   To display the cosecant function on a graphing calculator, use the sine function key SIN followed by the reciprocal key x^{-1}.

To find csc 20°:

Enter: SIN 20 ENTER x^{-1} ENTER

Display: $\boxed{2.9238044}$

Thus, csc 20° = 2.9238 to four decimal places, a value close to 3.

Since csc θ is the reciprocal of sin θ, csc θ is undefined when sin θ = 0, that is, when θ = 0°, 180°, 360°, and so on. For example, csc 180° is undefined because

$$\csc 180° = \frac{1}{\sin 180°} = \frac{1}{0} \text{ (undefined)}$$

● **The *cotangent function* assigns to every θ for which tan $\theta \neq 0$ a unique value that is the reciprocal of tan θ.**

$$\theta \xrightarrow{\text{cotangent}} \frac{1}{\tan \theta}$$

Using "cot" for cotangent, we write the reciprocal identity as follows:

$$\boxed{\cot \theta = \frac{1}{\tan \theta}}$$

Since tan $\theta = \frac{\sin \theta}{\cos \theta}$, the reciprocal function cot θ is also expressed as

$$\cos \theta = \frac{1}{\tan \theta} = \frac{1}{\frac{\sin \theta}{\cos \theta}} = \frac{\cos \theta}{\sin \theta}$$

PROCEDURE.   To enter the cotangent function on a graphing calculator:

1. *Either* enter the tangent function key TAN followed by the reciprocal key x^{-1}.

2. *Or* enter the cosine of the angle using COS and divide by the sine of the same angle using SIN.

To find cot 75°:

METHOD 1: *Enter:* | TAN | 75 | ENTER | x^{-1} | ENTER |

METHOD 2: *Enter:* | COS | 75 |) | ÷ | SIN | 75 | ENTER |

Display: | .2679491924 |

With either method, cot 75° = 0.2679 to four decimal places. Since $\cot \theta = \frac{1}{\tan \theta}$ or $\cot \theta = \frac{\cos \theta}{\sin \theta}$, it follows that cot θ is undefined when tan $\theta = 0$ or sin $\theta = 0$, that is, when $\theta = 0°, 180°, 360°$, and so on.

$$\cot 180° = \frac{1}{\tan 180°} = \frac{\cos 180°}{\sin 180°} = \frac{1}{0} \text{ (undefined)}$$

Function Values as Lengths of Line Segments

In the following diagrams, each trigonometric function value is represented as the length of a line segment. In each diagram, $\angle ROP$ is an angle in standard position in a unit circle whose center is at the origin. The tangent to the circle at $R(1, 0)$ intersects the line of the terminal ray at T. Point C is the point of intersection of the circle with the nonnegative ray of the y-axis. The tangent to the circle at C intersects the line of the terminal ray at S.

Also, in each diagram $\overline{CS} \perp y$-axis, $\overline{RT} \perp x$-axis, $\overline{PQ} \perp x$-axis, and m$\angle ROP = \theta$. Since $\angle OSC \cong \angle POQ \cong \angle TOR$ and $\angle OCS \cong \angle PQO \cong \angle TRO$, then $\triangle OSC \sim \triangle POQ \sim \triangle TOR$ by a.a. $\cong$ a.a.

In Quadrant I, we know that:

$$\sin \theta = QP$$
$$\cos \theta = OQ$$
$$\tan \theta = RT$$

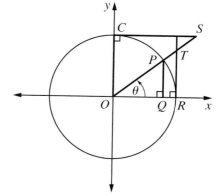

Quadrant I

It follows that:

$$\sec \theta = OT \text{ since } \frac{OP}{OQ} = \frac{1}{\cos \theta}, \text{ and } \frac{OP}{OQ} = \frac{OT}{OR}\left(\frac{1}{\cos \theta} = \frac{\sec \theta}{1}\right)$$

$$\csc \theta = OS \text{ since } \frac{OP}{QP} = \frac{1}{\sin \theta}, \text{ and } \frac{OP}{QP} = \frac{OS}{OC}\left(\frac{1}{\sin \theta} = \frac{\csc \theta}{1}\right)$$

$$\cot \theta = CS \text{ since } \frac{OR}{RT} = \frac{1}{\tan \theta}, \text{ and } \frac{OR}{RT} = \frac{CS}{OC}\left(\frac{1}{\tan \theta} = \frac{\cot \theta}{1}\right)$$

In Quadrants II, III, and IV, the same lengths represent the trigonometric functions, that is:

$$\sin \theta = QP \qquad \cos \theta = OQ \qquad \tan \theta = RT$$
$$\sec \theta = OT \qquad \csc \theta = OS \qquad \cot \theta = CS$$

Quadrant II

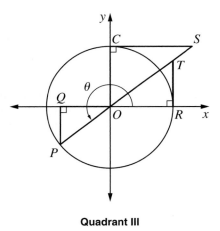

Quadrant III

Quadrant IV

By applying the definition of directed distance given in Section 14-3 to the diagrams shown above, we can determine the signs for vertical and horizontal line segments.

Vertical segments: QP(sin θ) *and RT*(tan θ)
  Positive if above the *x*-axis
  Negative if below the *x*-axis

Horizontal segments: OQ(cos θ) *and CS*(cot θ)
  Positive to the right of the *y*-axis
  Negative to the left of the *y*-axis

The definition of directed distance is now extended to the two remaining trigonometric functions, which lie neither on horizontal nor vertical lines, but on the line formed by $\overrightarrow{OP}$, the terminal side or terminal ray of $\angle\theta$.

Segments on the line of the terminal ray: OT(sec θ) *and OS*(csc θ)
  Positive if the segment is part of the terminal ray $\overrightarrow{OP}$
  Negative if the segment is part of the ray opposite $\overrightarrow{OP}$

In the table at the right, each trigonometric function is paired with its reciprocal function. Sign values are shown for these functions in all four quadrants. The table helps to illustrate the fact that:

● **For any given angle, a trigonometric function and its reciprocal function have values with the same sign.**

Quadrant	I	II	III	IV
$\sin \theta = QP$	+	+	−	−
$\csc \theta = OS$	+	+	−	−
$\cos \theta = OQ$	+	−	−	+
$\sec \theta = OT$	+	−	−	+
$\tan \theta = RT$	+	−	+	−
$\cot \theta = CS$	+	−	+	−

EXAMPLES

In 1 and 2, write each expression in terms of $\sin \theta$, $\cos \theta$, or both. Simplify wherever possible.

1. $\sec \theta \cdot \cot \theta$

Solution   Since $\sec \theta = \dfrac{1}{\cos \theta}$ and $\cot \theta = \dfrac{\cos \theta}{\sin \theta}$, substitute these values in the expression.

$$\sec \theta \cdot \cot \theta = \frac{1}{\cos \theta} \cdot \frac{\cos \theta}{\sin \theta} = \frac{1}{\cancel{\cos \theta}} \cdot \frac{\cancel{\cos \theta}^{1}}{\sin \theta} = \frac{1}{\sin \theta} \quad Answer$$

2. $\dfrac{\tan \theta}{\csc \theta}$

Solution   Since $\tan \theta = \dfrac{\sin \theta}{\cos \theta}$ and $\csc \theta = \dfrac{1}{\sin \theta}$, substitute these values in the expression. Then, simplify the complex fraction.

$$\frac{\tan \theta}{\csc \theta} = \frac{\left(\dfrac{\sin \theta}{\cos \theta}\right)}{\left(\dfrac{1}{\sin \theta}\right)} = \frac{\left(\dfrac{\sin \theta}{\cos \theta}\right) \cdot \sin \theta}{\left(\dfrac{1}{\cancel{\sin \theta}}\right) \cdot \cancel{\sin \theta}} = \frac{\dfrac{\sin^2 \theta}{\cos \theta}}{1} = \frac{\sin^2 \theta}{\cos \theta} \quad Answer$$

Note: The product $\sin \theta \cdot \sin \theta$ is equal to $(\sin \theta)^2$, which is usually written as $\sin^2 \theta$ to indicate that the sine function value is being squared.

In 3 and 4, find the exact numerical value of each expression.

3. $\cot^2 30°$

Solution   Evaluate either $\cot^2 30° = \dfrac{1}{\tan^2 30°}$ or $\cot^2 30° = \dfrac{\cos^2 30°}{\sin^2 30°}$.

$$\cot^2 30° = \frac{\cos^2 30°}{\sin^2 30°} = \frac{(\cos 30°)^2}{(\sin 30°)^2} = \frac{\left(\dfrac{\sqrt{3}}{2}\right)^2}{\left(\dfrac{1}{2}\right)^2} = \frac{\dfrac{3}{4} \cdot 4}{\dfrac{1}{4} \cdot 4} = \frac{3}{1} = 3$$

Calculator Solution   Enter $\cot 30°$ as the reciprocal of $\tan 30°$, and square the value.

Enter: TAN | 30 | ENTER | x^{-1} | ENTER | x^2 | ENTER

Display: [3.]

Answer: 3

---

4. $\cot 45° \cdot \csc 45°$

Solution   (1) Use reciprocal functions: Since $\tan 45° = 1$, $\cot 45° = 1$.

Since $\sin 45° = \dfrac{\sqrt{2}}{2}$, $\csc 45° = \dfrac{2}{\sqrt{2}}$.

(2) Substitute these values in the expression, and simplify.

$$\cot 45° \cdot \csc 45° = 1 \cdot \frac{2}{\sqrt{2}} = \frac{2}{\sqrt{2}}$$

$$= \frac{2}{\sqrt{2}} \cdot \frac{\sqrt{2}}{\sqrt{2}} = \frac{2\sqrt{2}}{2} = \sqrt{2}$$

Answer: $\sqrt{2}$

Note: A calculator solution will *not* result in an exact numerical value for this expression.

EXERCISES WITH OPEN-RESPONSE PROBLEMS

In 1–12, write each expression in terms of $\sin \theta$, $\cos \theta$, or both. Simplify wherever possible.

1. $\tan \theta$ **2.** $\cot \theta$ **3.** $\sec \theta$ **4.** $\csc \theta$

5. $\tan \theta \cdot \csc \theta$ **6.** $\dfrac{\tan \theta}{\sec \theta}$ **7.** $\dfrac{\cot \theta}{\csc \theta}$ **8.** $\dfrac{\cos \theta}{\sec \theta}$

9. $\dfrac{\sin \theta}{\csc \theta}$ **10.** $\dfrac{\tan \theta}{\cot \theta}$ **11.** $\dfrac{\sec \theta}{\cot \theta}$ **12.** $\dfrac{\sec \theta}{\csc \theta}$

13. Copy and complete the following table. If a function is undefined for an angle measure, write "undefined."

θ	0°	30°	45°	60°	90°
sec θ					
csc θ					
cot θ					

In 14–31, find the exact numerical value of each expression.

14. csc 150°

15. sec 240°

16. cot 315°

17. csc 120°

18. sec 2π

19. cot $\frac{\pi}{6}$

20. csc $\frac{3\pi}{2}$

21. sec $\frac{5\pi}{4}$

22. sin 30° • csc 30°

23. tan 45° • sec 30°

24. sec^2 60° + csc^2 60°

25. tan^2 60° + cot 45°

26. sin $\frac{\pi}{3}$ • tan $\frac{\pi}{6}$

27. cot $\frac{\pi}{4}$ + sec^2 $\frac{\pi}{6}$

28. cos^2 $\frac{\pi}{4}$ + sec^2 $\frac{\pi}{4}$

29. csc $\frac{\pi}{2}$ + sec π

30. cot $\frac{\pi}{2}$ + sec 0

31. cot^2 $\frac{\pi}{3}$ + csc $\frac{\pi}{2}$

In 32–37, in each case, name the quadrants in which $\angle A$ may lie.

32. csc $A > 0$

33. cot $A < 0$

34. sec $A < 0$

35. cot $A > 0$

36. csc $A < 0$

37. sec $A > 0$

In 38–43, in each case, name the quadrant in which $\angle B$ must lie.

38. cot $B < 0$ and sin $B > 0$

39. sec $B < 0$ and tan $B > 0$

40. sec $B < 0$ and csc $B > 0$

41. cot $B < 0$ and sec $B > 0$

42. csc $B < 0$ and tan $B > 0$

43. csc $B < 0$ and sec $B > 0$

44. If sin $A = \frac{3}{5}$ and cos $A = -\frac{4}{5}$, find: **a.** the quadrant in which $\angle A$ lies

    b. tan A **c.** sec A **d.** csc A **e.** cot A

45. If sin $\theta = -\frac{2}{3}$ and cos $\theta = -\frac{\sqrt{5}}{3}$, find:

    a. the quadrant in which the angle whose measure is θ lies

    b. tan θ **c.** sec θ **d.** csc θ **e.** cot θ

46. If sin $\phi = -\frac{1}{\sqrt{5}}$ and cos $\phi = \frac{2}{\sqrt{5}}$, find:

    a. the quadrant in which the angle whose measure is ϕ lies

    b. tan ϕ **c.** sec ϕ **d.** csc ϕ **e.** cot ϕ

47. If sec $\theta = \sqrt{3}$ and csc $\theta = \frac{\sqrt{6}}{2}$, find:

    a. the quadrant in which the angle whose measure is θ lies

    b. cos θ **c.** sin θ **d.** tan ϕ **e.** cot θ

In 48–55, select the *numeral* preceding the expression that best completes the sentence or answers the question.

48. If $\cos A > 0$, then which must always be true?

(1) $\sin A > 0$ (2) $\tan A > 0$ (3) $\sec A > 0$ (4) $\csc A > 0$

49. If $\csc B < 0$, then which must always be true?

(1) $\sin B < 0$ (2) $\cos B < 0$ (3) $\tan B < 0$ (4) $\cot B < 0$

50. In which quadrant are cotangent and cosecant both negative?

(1) I   (2) II   (3) III   (4) IV

51. If $\cot x > 0$ and $\sec x < 0$, which must be true?

(1) $\tan x < 0$ (2) $\sin x > 0$ (3) $\cos x > 0$ (4) $\sin x < 0$

52. If $\sin y \sec y > 0$ and $\sin y < 0$, which is true?

(1) $\cos y < 0$ (2) $\tan y < 0$ (3) $\cot y < 0$ (4) $\sec y > 0$

53. If $\sin A \cot A > 0$ and $\sin A < 0$, which must be true?

(1) $\cos A > 0$ (2) $\tan A > 0$ (3) $\sec A < 0$ (4) $\csc A > 0$

54. The value of $\sec \frac{\pi}{6} \div \cot \frac{\pi}{6}$ is

(1) $\frac{1}{3}$ (2) $\frac{2}{3}$ (3) $\sqrt{3}$ (4) $\frac{\sqrt{3}}{3}$

55. The value of $\csc \frac{\pi}{3} + \sec \frac{\pi}{3}$ is

(1) $\frac{2\sqrt{3} + 2}{3}$ (2) $\frac{2\sqrt{3} + 6}{3}$ (3) $\frac{2 + \sqrt{6}}{3}$ (4) $\frac{4\sqrt{3}}{3}$

14-13 THE PYTHAGOREAN IDENTITIES

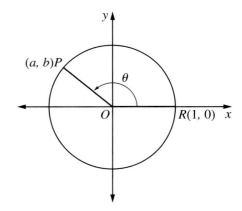

If circle O is a unit circle whose center is at the origin, the equation of the circle is

$$x^2 + y^2 = 1$$

In the diagram, P is any point on the circle O. If the coordinates of point P are (a, b), then:

$$a^2 + b^2 = 1$$

Since $m\angle ROP = \theta$, we know that $a = \cos \theta$ and $b = \sin \theta$. Therefore, the equation becomes:

$$(\cos \theta)^2 + (\sin \theta)^2 = 1 \quad \text{or} \quad \boxed{\cos^2 \theta + \sin^2 \theta = 1}$$

We recall that the square of the sine of an angle $(\sin \theta)^2$ is written without parentheses as $\sin^2 \theta$ to emphasize the fact that it is the function value, not the measure of the angle, that is being squared. Similarly, $(\cos \theta)^2 = \cos^2 \theta$, $(\tan \theta)^2 = \tan^2 \theta$, $(\sec \theta)^2 = \sec^2 \theta$, and so on.

● **DEFINITION.** An *identity* is an equation that is true for all values of the variable.

To demonstrate that $\cos^2 \theta + \sin^2 \theta = 1$ is an identity, we may select any values for θ and show that the equation is true. For example:

If $\theta = 60°$, $\cos \theta = \frac{1}{2}$ and $\sin \theta = \frac{\sqrt{3}}{2}$.

$$\text{Then, } \cos^2 \theta + \sin^2 \theta = \left(\tfrac{1}{2}\right)^2 + \left(\tfrac{\sqrt{3}}{2}\right)^2 = \tfrac{1}{4} + \tfrac{3}{4} = 1.$$

If $\theta = \frac{3\pi}{4}$, $\cos \theta = -\frac{\sqrt{2}}{2}$ and $\sin \theta = \frac{\sqrt{2}}{2}$.

$$\text{Then, } \cos^2 \theta + \sin^2 \theta = \left(-\tfrac{\sqrt{2}}{2}\right)^2 + \left(\tfrac{\sqrt{2}}{2}\right)^2 = \tfrac{2}{4} + \tfrac{2}{4} = 1.$$

Let us select any measure for θ and evaluate the expression $\sin^2 \theta + \cos^2 \theta$ on a calculator. For example, if $\theta = 19°$, we evaluate $\sin^2 19° + \cos^2 19°$ as follows:

Enter: [SIN] 19 [ )] [x^2] [+] [COS] 19 [ )] [x^2] [ENTER]

Display: [_____ 1.]

From this basic identity, $\cos^2 \theta + \sin^2 \theta = 1$, we can derive other identities.

Derivation 1

1. Write the identity involving $\cos^2 \theta$ and $\sin^2 \theta$.

$$\cos^2 \theta + \sin^2 \theta = 1$$

2. Divide both sides of the equation by $\cos^2 \theta$. Here, $\cos \theta \neq 0$.

$$\frac{\cos^2 \theta + \sin^2 \theta}{\cos^2 \theta} = \frac{1}{\cos^2 \theta}$$

$$\frac{\cos^2 \theta}{\cos^2 \theta} + \frac{\sin^2 \theta}{\cos^2 \theta} = \frac{1}{\cos^2 \theta}$$

3. Rewrite the equation in terms of other trigonometric functions, and simplify. The identity is true for all values of θ for which $\tan \theta$ and $\sec \theta$ are defined.

$$\left(\frac{\cos \theta}{\cos \theta}\right)^2 + \left(\frac{\sin \theta}{\cos \theta}\right)^2 = \left(\frac{1}{\cos \theta}\right)^2$$

$$(1)^2 + (\tan \theta)^2 = (\sec \theta)^2$$

$$\boxed{\mathbf{1 + \tan^2 \theta = \sec^2 \theta}}$$

Derivation 2

1. Write the identity involving $\cos^2 \theta$ and $\sin^2 \theta$.

$$\cos^2 \theta + \sin^2 \theta = 1$$

2. Divide both sides of the equation by $\sin^2 \theta$. Here, $\sin \theta \neq 0$.

$$\frac{\cos^2 \theta + \sin^2 \theta}{\sin^2 \theta} = \frac{1}{\sin^2 \theta}$$

$$\frac{\cos^2 \theta}{\sin^2 \theta} + \frac{\sin^2 \theta}{\sin^2 \theta} = \frac{1}{\sin^2 \theta}$$

3. Rewrite the equation in terms of other trigonometric functions, and simplify. The identity is true for all values of θ for which $\cot \theta$ and $\csc \theta$ are defined.

$$\left(\frac{\cos \theta}{\sin \theta}\right)^2 + \left(\frac{\sin \theta}{\sin \theta}\right)^2 = \left(\frac{1}{\sin \theta}\right)^2$$

$$(\cot \theta)^2 + (1)^2 = (\csc \theta)^2$$

$$\boxed{\cot^2 \theta + 1 = \csc^2 \theta}$$

Function Values, Lengths, and the Pythagorean Theorem

If we look at these function values as lengths of line segments, we can see how these identities can be found by using the Pythagorean Theorem.

The diagram shows a unit circle with its center at the origin, where $\overleftrightarrow{RT}$ is tangent to the circle at R, $\overleftrightarrow{CS}$ is tangent to the circle at C, and $\overline{PQ} \perp x$-axis at Q. If $m\angle ROP = \theta$, then:

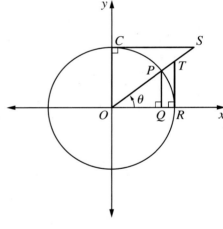

$$PQ = \sin \theta \qquad OQ = \cos \theta \qquad RT = \tan \theta$$

$$OS = \csc \theta \qquad OT = \sec \theta \qquad CS = \cot \theta$$

Also:

In right triangle OPQ, $(OQ)^2 + (PQ)^2 = (OP)^2$

$$\cos^2 \theta + \sin^2 \theta = 1$$

In right triangle OTR, $(OR)^2 + (RT)^2 = (OT)^2$

$$1 + \tan^2 \theta = \sec^2 \theta$$

In right triangle OSC, $(CS)^2 + (OC)^2 = (OS)^2$

$$\cot^2 \theta + 1 = \csc^2 \theta$$

We can verify that these identities are true for an angle in any quadrant by using the diagrams shown in Section 14-12 for angles in Quadrants II, III, and IV.

Summary

In this chapter, we have defined eight basic trigonometric identities.

Reciprocal Identities	Quotient Identities	Pythagorean Identities
$\csc \theta = \dfrac{1}{\sin \theta}$	$\tan \theta = \dfrac{\sin \theta}{\cos \theta}$	$\cos^2 \theta + \sin^2 \theta = 1$
$\sec \theta = \dfrac{1}{\cos \theta}$	$\cot \theta = \dfrac{\cos \theta}{\sin \theta}$	$1 + \tan^2 \theta = \sec^2 \theta$
$\cot \theta = \dfrac{1}{\tan \theta}$		$\cot^2 \theta + 1 = \csc^2 \theta$

EXAMPLES

1. If $\sec A = -3$ and $\angle A$ is in Quadrant II, find $\tan A$.

How to Proceed:	*Solution:*
(1) Use the Pythagorean identity.	$1 + \tan^2 A = \sec^2 A$
(2) Substitute the given value.	$1 + \tan^2 A = (-3)^2$
(3) Solve for $\tan A$.	$1 + \tan^2 A = 9$
	$\tan^2 A = 8$
(4) Since, in Quadrant II, the tangent is negative, use the negative root.	$\tan A = -\sqrt{8}$ or $-2\sqrt{2}$

Answer: $-\sqrt{8}$, or $-2\sqrt{2}$

---

2. Express $1 + \cot^2 \theta$ in terms of $\sin \theta$, $\cos \theta$, or both in simplest form.

How to Proceed:	*Solution:*
(1) Write an equivalent expression for $\cot^2 \theta$.	$1 + \cot^2 \theta = 1 + \dfrac{\cos^2 \theta}{\sin^2 \theta}$
(2) To add fractions, obtain like denominators. Then, add the numerators and maintain the common denominator.	$= \dfrac{\sin^2 \theta}{\sin^2 \theta} + \dfrac{\cos^2 \theta}{\sin^2 \theta}$ $= \dfrac{\sin^2 \theta + \cos^2 \theta}{\sin^2 \theta}$
(3) Since $\sin^2 \theta + \cos^2 \theta = 1$, replace the numerator with 1.	$= \dfrac{1}{\sin^2 \theta}$

Answer: $\dfrac{1}{\sin^2 \theta}$

EXERCISES WITH OPEN-RESPONSE PROBLEMS

In 1–12, in each case, name the trigonometric function of $\angle A$ that, when written in the blank, will make the equation an identity.

1. $\sin^2 A + (\underline{\hspace{1cm}})^2 = 1$ **2.** $1 + (\underline{\hspace{1cm}})^2 = \sec^2 A$ **3.** $(\underline{\hspace{1cm}})^2 + 1 = \csc^2 A$

4. $(\underline{\hspace{1cm}})^2 = 1 - \cos^2 A$ **5.** $\sin A \cot A = \underline{\hspace{1cm}}$ **6.** $\sec A \cos^2 A = \underline{\hspace{1cm}}$

7. $\pm\sqrt{1 + \tan^2 A} = \underline{\hspace{1cm}}$ **8.** $\underline{\hspace{1cm}} = \pm\sqrt{\cot^2 A + 1}$ **9.** $\csc A \tan A = \underline{\hspace{1cm}}$

10. $\sin A \sec A = \underline{\hspace{1cm}}$ **11.** $\cos A \div \cot A = \underline{\hspace{1cm}}$ **12.** $\cot A \sec A = \underline{\hspace{1cm}}$

In 13–20, use a Pythagorean identity to find each required function value.

13. If $\sin A = 0.6$ and $\angle A$ is in Quadrant II, find $\cos A$.

14. If $\tan B = -\frac{3}{4}$ and $\angle B$ is in Quadrant IV, find $\sec B$.

15. If $\csc C = \frac{13}{5}$ and $\angle C$ is in Quadrant I, find $\cot C$.

16. If $\cos A = -\frac{1}{3}$ and $\angle A$ is in Quadrant III, find $\sin A$.

17. If $\sec B = -\sqrt{5}$ and $\angle B$ is in Quadrant II, find $\tan B$.

18. If $\cot C = -\sqrt{15}$ and $\angle C$ is in Quadrant IV, find $\csc C$.

19. If $\tan A = 3$ and $\angle A$ is in Quadrant III, find $\sec A$.

20. If $\cos B = \frac{\sqrt{5}}{3}$ and $\angle B$ is in Quadrant I, find $\sin B$.

21. a. If $\theta = \frac{\pi}{6}$ radians, find the values of $\sin \theta$ and $\cos \theta$.
    b. Demonstrate that $\sin^2 \theta + \cos^2 \theta = 1$ when $\theta = \frac{\pi}{6}$ radians.

22. a. If $\theta = 225°$, find the values of $\tan \theta$ and $\sec \theta$.
    b. Demonstrate that $\tan^2 \theta + 1 = \sec^2 \theta$ when $\theta = 225°$.

23. a. If $\theta = 300°$, find the values of $\cot \theta$ and $\csc \theta$.
    b. Demonstrate that $\cot^2 \theta + 1 = \csc^2 \theta$ when $\theta = 300°$.

24. a. What is the value of $\sin^2 63° + \cos^2 63°$?
    b. Write the sequence of calculator keys that will verify your answer to part **a**.

In 25–36, write each given expression in terms of $\sin A$, $\cos A$, or both. Then express the result in simplest form.

25. $\sec A \cot A$ **26.** $\csc A \tan A$ **27.** $\sec A \cos^2 A$

28. $\cot^2 A \tan A$ **29.** $1 + \tan^2 A$ **30.** $\tan A + \cot A$

31. $\sec^2 A + \csc^2 A$ **32.** $\sec^2 A - 1$ **33.** $\csc^2 A - 1$

34. $\frac{\tan A}{\sec A}$ **35.** $\frac{\cot A}{\csc A}$ **36.** $\frac{\sec A \cos A}{\tan A \cot A}$

In 37–40, select the *numeral* preceding the expression that best completes the statement.

37. The expression $\frac{1}{\sec\theta}$ (tan θ + sec θ) equals
  (1) sin θ (2) sin θ + 1   (3) cos θ (4) cos θ + 1

38. The product $(1 + \csc\theta)(1 - \csc\theta)$ equals
  (1) $\tan^2\theta$ (2) $-\tan^2\theta$ (3) $\cot^2\theta$ (4) $-\cot^2\theta$

39. The expression $\frac{\sec\theta - \csc\theta}{\sec\theta}$ is equal to
  (1) $\frac{\sin\theta - \cos\theta}{\sin\theta}$ (2) $\frac{\sin\theta - \cos\theta}{\cos\theta}$ (3) $\frac{\cos\theta - \sin\theta}{\sin\theta}$ (4) $\frac{\cos\theta - \sin\theta}{\cos\theta}$

40. The product $(1 - \sec B)(1 + \cos B)$ equals
  (1) 0   (2) 2   (3) $\frac{\cos^2 B - 1}{\cos B}$ (4) $\frac{\cos B - 1}{\cos B}$

14-14 FINDING THE REMAINING TRIGONOMETRIC FUNCTION VALUES OF AN ANGLE WHEN ONE FUNCTION VALUE IS KNOWN

If we know one trigonometric function value and the quadrant in which the angle lies, it is possible to find the remaining five trigonometric function values of the angle.

METHOD 1: *Using Identities*

For example, if $\sin\theta = \frac{5}{13}$ and θ is the measure of an angle in Quadrant II, find the values of: **a.** cos θ **b.** tan θ **c.** csc θ **d.** sec θ **e.** cot θ

a. (1) Use the Pythagorean identity:

(2) Substitute the given value.

(3) Solve for cos θ.

(4) Since an angle in the second quadrant has a negative cosine, cos θ is the negative square root of $\frac{144}{169}$.

$$\cos^2\theta + \sin^2\theta = 1$$

$$\cos^2\theta + \left(\frac{5}{13}\right)^2 = 1$$

$$\cos^2\theta + \frac{25}{169} = 1$$

$$\cos^2\theta + \frac{25}{169} = \frac{169}{169}$$

$$\cos^2\theta = \frac{144}{169}$$

$$\cos\theta = -\frac{12}{13}$$

b. (1) Write the quotient identity (shown below) for tan θ.

(2) Substitute the known values, and simplify.

$$\tan\theta = \frac{\sin\theta}{\cos\theta} = \frac{\frac{5}{13}}{-\frac{12}{13}} = \frac{\frac{5}{13}}{-\frac{12}{13}} \cdot \frac{13}{13} = \frac{5}{-12} = -\frac{5}{12}$$

c, d, and **e**: (1) Write a reciprocal identity (shown below).
(2) Substitute the known value, and simplify.

c. $\csc \theta = \dfrac{1}{\sin \theta} = \dfrac{1}{\dfrac{5}{13}} = \dfrac{1}{\dfrac{5}{13}} \cdot \dfrac{13}{13} = \dfrac{13}{5}$

d. $\sec \theta = \dfrac{1}{\cos \theta} = \dfrac{1}{-\dfrac{12}{13}} = \dfrac{1}{-\dfrac{12}{13}} \cdot \dfrac{13}{13} = \dfrac{13}{-12} = -\dfrac{13}{12}$

e. $\cot \theta = \dfrac{1}{\tan \theta} = \dfrac{1}{-\dfrac{5}{12}} = \dfrac{1}{-\dfrac{5}{12}} \cdot \dfrac{12}{12} = \dfrac{12}{-5} = -\dfrac{12}{5}$

Answers: Quadrant II, when $\sin \theta = \dfrac{5}{13}$:

a. $\cos \theta = -\dfrac{12}{13}$ **b.** $\tan \theta = -\dfrac{5}{12}$ **c.** $\csc \theta = \dfrac{13}{5}$

d. $\sec \theta = -\dfrac{13}{12}$ **e.** $\cot \theta = -\dfrac{12}{5}$

METHOD 2: *Using Right Triangles and Directed Distances*

In Section 14-3, we saw that a dilation can be used to transform a given right triangle into a similar right triangle in the unit circle. The hypotenuse of the right triangle in the unit circle has a length of 1 because the radius of the circle has a length of 1.

We can also use a dilation to transform a right triangle in the unit circle into a similar right triangle whose hypotenuse does not have a length of 1. Just as the lengths of sides of a right triangle in the unit circle are treated as directed distances, so too are the lengths of sides in the newly formed similar triangle treated as *directed distances* in a coordinate plane.

For example, if θ is the measure of an angle in Quadrant IV where $\cos \theta = \dfrac{3}{5}$ and $\sin \theta = -\dfrac{4}{5}$, we can construct right triangle OQP in the unit circle.

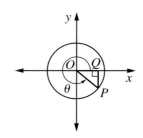

Here:

$$\cos \theta = OQ = \dfrac{3}{5}$$

$$\sin \theta = QP = -\dfrac{4}{5}$$

$$OP = 1$$

Under a dilation of 5 with the origin as the fixed point, right triangle OQP will have as its image right triangle $OQ'P'$. The length of each side of $\triangle OQ'P'$ will be *five times* the length of its corresponding side in $\triangle OQP$.

Here, under a dilation of 5, or under D_5:

$\overline{OQ} \to \overline{OQ'}$, or $D_5\left(\frac{3}{5}\right) \to 3$.   Thus: $OQ' = 3$

$\overline{QP} \to \overline{Q'P'}$, or $D_5\left(-\frac{4}{5}\right) \to -4$. $Q'P' = -4$

$\overline{OP} \to \overline{OP'}$, or $D_5(1) \to 5$. $OP' = 5$

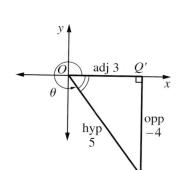

In right triangle $OQ'P'$, the acute angle whose vertex is at the origin, that is, $\angle Q'OP'$, is directly related to the Quadrant IV angle whose measure is θ. Using acute $\angle Q'OP'$, we can identify the sides of right triangle $OQ'P'$ as follows:

$\overline{Q'P'}$ is *opposite* the acute $\angle Q'OP'$.

$\overline{OQ'}$ is *adjacent* to the acute $\angle Q'OP'$.

$\overline{OP'}$ is the *hypotenuse* of the triangle.

The sine, cosine, and tangent functions were originally defined as ratios involving the lengths of the sides of a right triangle. We now extend these definitions to include **directed distances** for any right triangle. We name the sides of the right triangle as they relate to the acute angle whose vertex is at the origin and that is determined by the angle of any given measure θ. Thus, using right triangle $OQ'P'$, we now state:

$$\cos \theta = \frac{\text{adj}}{\text{hyp}} = \frac{3}{5} \qquad \sin \theta = \frac{\text{opp}}{\text{hyp}} = -\frac{4}{5} \qquad \tan \theta = \frac{\text{opp}}{\text{adj}} = -\frac{4}{3}$$

Since $\sec \theta = \frac{1}{\cos \theta}$, $\csc \theta = \frac{1}{\sin \theta}$, and $\cot \theta = \frac{1}{\tan \theta}$, these reciprocal identities allow us to redefine these functions as ratios involving the lengths of the sides of a right triangle. Thus, for right triangle $OQ'P'$:

$$\sec \theta = \frac{\text{hyp}}{\text{adj}} = \frac{5}{3} \qquad \csc \theta = \frac{\text{hyp}}{\text{opp}} = -\frac{5}{4} \qquad \cot \theta = \frac{\text{adj}}{\text{opp}} = -\frac{3}{4}$$

Let us now apply this method to solving the problem stated earlier in this section, for example:

If $\sin \theta = \frac{5}{13}$ and θ is the measure of an angle in the second quadrant, find the values of: **a.** $\cos \theta$ **b.** $\tan \theta$ **c.** $\csc \theta$ **d.** $\sec \theta$ **e.** $\cot \theta$

(1) Draw right triangle $OQ'P'$ in Quadrant II. Since $\sin \theta = \frac{5}{13} = \frac{\text{opp}}{\text{hyp}}$, let $Q'P' = 5$ and $OP' = 13$. Also, let $OQ' = x$. $\left(\text{Note that right triangle } OQ'P'\right.$ is the image under a dilation of 13 of $\triangle OQP$, a right triangle in Quadrant II of the unit circle, where $\sin \theta = \frac{5}{13}.\Big)$

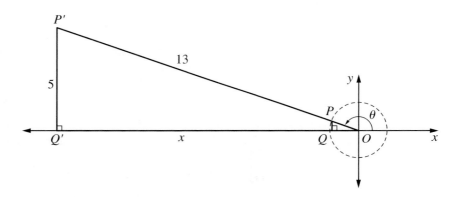

(2) Solve for x by using the Pythagorean Theorem:
$$x^2 + 5^2 = 13^2$$
$$x^2 + 25 = 169$$
$$x^2 = 144$$
$$x = -12$$

In Quadrant II, x is a negative value.

(3) To find the remaining trigonometric functions, use the definitions involving ratios of lengths of sides in a right triangle. Remember to use directed distances.

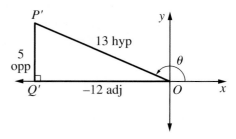

Answers: **a.** $\cos \theta = \dfrac{\text{adj}}{\text{hyp}} = \dfrac{-12}{13}$ **b.** $\tan \theta = \dfrac{\text{opp}}{\text{adj}} = \dfrac{5}{-12} = -\dfrac{5}{12}$

c. $\csc \theta = \dfrac{\text{hyp}}{\text{opp}} = \dfrac{13}{5}$ **d.** $\sec \theta = \dfrac{\text{hyp}}{\text{adj}} = \dfrac{13}{-12} = -\dfrac{13}{12}$

e. $\cot \theta = \dfrac{\text{adj}}{\text{opp}} = \dfrac{-12}{5}$

EXAMPLES

1. If $\tan A = \frac{\sqrt{7}}{3}$ and $\sin A < 0$, find $\cos A$.

Solution   (1) Since $\tan A$ is positive and $\sin A$ is negative, the terminal side of $\angle A$ must lie in Quadrant III.

(2) Draw right triangle $OQ'P'$ in Quadrant III. Here, x and y are both negative values. Since $\tan A = \frac{\sqrt{7}}{3}$ and x and y are negative, let $\tan A = \frac{-\sqrt{7}}{-3} = \frac{\text{opp}}{\text{adj}}$.

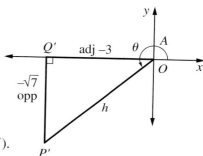

Then:

$Q'P' = -\sqrt{7}$ (opposite acute angle $Q'OP'$).

$OQ' = -3$ (adjacent to acute angle $Q'OP'$).

(3) Let $h = $ length of hypotenuse $\overline{OP'}$. Use the Pythagorean Theorem to find the value of h.

$$h^2 = (-\sqrt{7})^2 + (-3)^2$$
$$= 7 + 9$$
$$= 16$$
$$h = 4$$

(4) Therefore, $\cos A = \frac{\text{adj}}{\text{hyp}} = \frac{-3}{4}$

Alternative Solution

(1) Use the Pythagorean identity that includes $\tan A$.

$$\tan^2 A + 1 = \sec^2 A$$

(2) Substitute the value of $\tan A$.

$$\left(\frac{\sqrt{7}}{3}\right)^2 + 1 = \sec^2 A$$

(3) Simplify the left member of the equation.

$$\frac{7}{9} + \frac{9}{9} = \sec^2 A$$

(4) Since $\tan A$ is positive and $\sin A$ is negative, $\angle A$ lies in Quadrant III. Thus, $\sec A$ is negative. Solve for the negative value of $\sec A$.

$$\frac{16}{9} = \sec^2 A$$

$$-\frac{4}{3} = \sec A$$

(5) Use the reciprocal identity to find $\cos A$.

$$\cos A = \frac{1}{\sec A} = \frac{1}{-\frac{4}{3}} = -\frac{3}{4}$$

Answer: $\cos A = -\frac{3}{4}$

2. Express each of the five remaining trigonometric functions in terms of $\sin \theta$.

Solution   To express one function in terms of another, we make use of the *identities* for trigonometric functions.

(1) Use the Pythagorean identity that includes $\sin \theta$, and solve for $\cos \theta$. Since no quadrant is specified, $\cos \theta$ may be positive or negative.

$$\cos^2 \theta + \sin^2 \theta = 1$$
$$\cos^2 \theta = 1 - \sin^2 \theta$$
$$\cos \theta = \pm\sqrt{1 - \sin^2 \theta}$$

(2) Use reciprocal identities to find $\csc \theta$ and $\sec \theta$.

$$\csc \theta = \frac{1}{\sin \theta} \qquad \sec \theta = \frac{1}{\cos \theta} = \frac{1}{\pm\sqrt{1 - \sin^2 \theta}}$$

(3) Use quotient identities to find $\tan \theta$ and $\cot \theta$.

$$\tan \theta = \frac{\sin \theta}{\cos \theta} = \frac{\sin \theta}{\pm\sqrt{1 - \sin^2 \theta}} \qquad \cot \theta = \frac{\cos \theta}{\sin \theta} = \frac{\pm\sqrt{1 - \sin^2 \theta}}{\sin \theta}$$

Answer: $\cos \theta = \pm\sqrt{1 - \sin^2 \theta} \qquad \csc \theta = \frac{1}{\sin \theta} \qquad \sec \theta = \pm\frac{1}{\sqrt{1 - \sin^2 \theta}}$

$\tan \theta = \pm\frac{\sin \theta}{\sqrt{1 - \sin^2 \theta}} \qquad \cot \theta = \pm\frac{\sqrt{1 - \sin^2 \theta}}{\sin \theta}$

EXERCISES WITH OPEN-RESPONSE PROBLEMS

In 1–4, in each case, a right triangle is drawn in one of the quadrants relating to an angle whose measure is θ. Using the lengths of the sides of the triangle, indicated as directed distances, find:
a. $\sin \theta$ **b.** $\cos \theta$ **c.** $\tan \theta$ **d.** $\csc \theta$ **e.** $\sec \theta$ **f.** $\cot \theta$

1.

2.

3.

4.

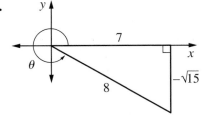

5. If $\cos \theta = \frac{3}{5}$ and $\sin \theta < 0$, find:

    a. $\sin \theta$ **b.** $\sec \theta$ **c.** $\csc \theta$ **d.** $\tan \theta$ **e.** $\cot \theta$

6. If $\tan A = -\frac{3}{4}$ and $\cos A < 0$, find:

    a. $\sec A$ **b.** $\cos A$ **c.** $\sin A$ **d.** $\csc A$ **e.** $\cot A$

7. If $\tan \theta = \frac{\sqrt{11}}{5}$ and $\sec \theta > 0$, find:

    a. $\sec \theta$ **b.** $\cos \theta$ **c.** $\sin \theta$ **d.** $\csc \theta$ **e.** $\cot \theta$

8. If $\sin B = -\frac{5}{13}$ and $\tan B > 0$, find:

    a. $\cos B$ **b.** $\tan B$ **c.** $\cot B$ **d.** $\csc B$ **e.** $\sec B$

9. If $\cot \theta = \frac{3}{2}$ and $\csc \theta < 0$, find:

    a. $\csc \theta$ **b.** $\tan \theta$ **c.** $\sin \theta$ **d.** $\cos \theta$ **e.** $\sec \theta$

10. If $\csc A = -\frac{\sqrt{10}}{3}$ and $\cot A < 0$, find:

    a. $\cot A$ **b.** $\sin A$ **c.** $\tan A$ **d.** $\sec A$ **e.** $\cos A$

    In 11–15, in each case, express each of the five remaining trigonometric functions in terms of the given function.

11. $\cos \theta$ **12.** $\tan \theta$ **13.** $\cot \theta$ **14.** $\sec \theta$ **15.** $\csc \theta$

16. If $\sin A = \frac{\sqrt{3}}{2}$ and $\tan A$ is negative, find $\cos A$.

17. If $\cos A = -\frac{\sqrt{2}}{2}$ and $\cot A > 0$, find $\sin A$.

18. If $\tan B = -\frac{6}{8}$ and $\sin B < 0$, find $\cos B$.

19. If $\sin A = \frac{\sqrt{24}}{7}$ and $\sec A > 0$, find $\tan A$.

    In 20 and 21, select the *numeral* preceding the expression that best completes the sentence.

20. If $\tan \theta = \frac{2}{5}$ and $\sin \theta < 0$, then $\cos \theta$ is equal to

    (1) $\frac{5}{\sqrt{29}}$ (2) $-\frac{\sqrt{29}}{5}$ (3) $-\frac{5}{\sqrt{29}}$ (4) $-\frac{5}{29}$

21. If $\tan A = -\frac{1}{3}$ and $\cos A < 0$, then $\sin A$ equals

    (1) $\frac{\sqrt{10}}{10}$ (2) $-\frac{3}{\sqrt{10}}$ (3) $-\frac{\sqrt{10}}{10}$ (4) $\frac{3\sqrt{10}}{10}$

14-15 COFUNCTIONS

In Figure 1, $\angle ROP$ is a central angle of a unit circle whose center is at the origin. Points $R(1, 0)$ and $P(a, b)$ are on the circle. If the measure of acute angle ROP is θ, then $\cos \theta = a$ and $\sin \theta = b$.

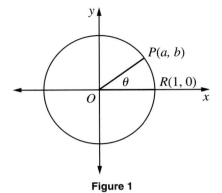

Figure 1

In Figure 2, $\angle ROP$ is reflected in the line $y = x$:

$$r_{y=x}(x, y) = (y, x)$$
$$P(a, b) \rightarrow P'(b, a)$$
$$R(1, 0) \rightarrow R'(0, 1)$$
$$O(0, 0) \rightarrow O(0, 0)$$

Since a line reflection preserves distance, $OP' = OP = 1$ and P' is a point on the unit circle. Also, since a line reflection preserves angle measure, $m\angle R'OP' = m\angle ROP = \theta$. Thus:

$$m\angle ROP' = m\angle ROR' - m\angle ROP$$
$$= 90° \qquad - \theta$$

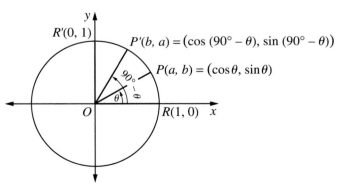

Figure 2

In Figure 3, we see that $\angle ROP'$ is an angle in standard position, and the coordinates of P' are (b, a). Therefore, $\cos (90° - \theta) = b$ and $\sin (90° - \theta) = a$.

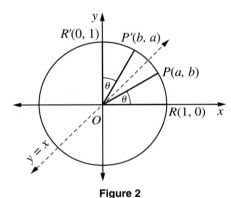

Figure 3

Since $b = \sin \theta$ and
$b = \cos (90° - \theta)$:

$$\boxed{\sin \theta = \cos (90° - \theta)}$$

Since $a = \cos \theta$ and
$a = \sin (90° - \theta)$:

$$\boxed{\cos \theta = \sin (90° - \theta)}$$

Thus, the sine of an acute angle is equal to the cosine of its complement, and the cosine of an acute angle is equal to the sine of its complement. The sine and cosine functions are called *cofunctions*.

Other cofunctions exist in trigonometry. For example:

Since $\tan \theta = \frac{b}{a}$ and $\cot (90° - \theta) = \frac{b}{a}$: $\boxed{\tan \theta = \cot (90° - \theta)}$

Since $\cot \theta = \frac{a}{b}$ and $\tan (90° - \theta) = \frac{a}{b}$: $\boxed{\cot \theta = \tan (90° - \theta)}$

Thus, the tangent of an acute angle is equal to the cotangent of its complement, and the cotangent of an acute angle is equal to the tangent of its complement. The tangent and cotangent functions are cofunctions.

Since $\sec \theta = \frac{1}{a}$ and $\csc (90° - \theta) = \frac{1}{a}$: $\boxed{\sec \theta = \csc (90° - \theta)}$

Since $\csc \theta = \frac{1}{b}$ and $\sec (90° - \theta) = \frac{1}{b}$: $\boxed{\csc \theta = \sec (90° - \theta)}$

Thus, the secant of an acute angle is equal to the cosecant of its complement, and the cosecant of an acute angle is equal to the secant of its complement.

These observations allow us to make the following general statement:

- **Any trigonometric function of an acute angle is equal to the cofunction of its complement.**

The prefix *co-* allows us to identify easily the pairs of functions that are cofunctions:

Sine and *co*sine are *co*functions.
Tangent and *co*tangent are *co*functions.
Secant and *co*secant are *co*functions.

We note that the prefix *co-* matches the first two letters of the word *complement*, a concept that is basic in the definition of cofunctions.

EXAMPLES

1. If $\sin x = \cos (x + 20°)$, and x and $(x + 20°)$ are the measure of two acute angles, find x.

Solution   If the function of one acute angle is equal to the cofunction of another acute angle, then the angles are complementary. Thus:

$$x + (x + 20) = 90$$
$$2x + 20 = 90$$
$$2x = 70$$
$$x = 35$$

Calculator Check: If $x = 35°$, then $x + 20° = 55°$. Evaluate $\sin 35°$ and $\cos 55°$ to see that the same function value is displayed.

Enter: [SIN] 35 [ENTER]   *Enter:* [COS] 55 [ENTER]
Display: [.5735764364]   *Display:* [.5735764364]

Alternative Calculator Check: Enter $\sin 35°$. Without clearing the display, use the [$\cos^{-1}$] key to find the measure of the angle whose cosine is shown. The display should indicate an angle of 55°.

Enter: [SIN] 35 [ENTER] [2nd] [$\cos^{-1}$] [2nd] [ANS] [ENTER]
Display: [55.]

Answer: $x = 35°$

---

2. Express $\sin 285°$ as the function of an angle whose measure is less than 45°.

Solution   Use the procedure to express $\sin 285°$ as a function of a positive acute angle:

(1) Determine the quadrant.   Quadrant IV

(2) Determine the sign.   Sine is negative.

(3) Determine the reference angle.
$$360° - \theta = 360° - 285°$$
$$= 75°$$

Thus, $\sin 285° = -\sin 75°$

(4) Since 75° is *not* less than 45°, use cofunctions.

$$\sin 285° = -\sin 75° = -\cos 15°$$

Answer: $-\cos 15°$

EXERCISES WITH OPEN-RESPONSE PROBLEMS

In 1–12, write each expression as a function of an acute angle whose measure is less than 45°.

1. sin 80°   **2.** tan 72°   **3.** sin 50°   **4.** cos 67°
5. sec 83°   **6.** cot 65°   **7.** csc 58°   **8.** cos 75°
9. sin 88°   **10.** tan 56°30′   **11.** cot 87°20′   **12.** cos 63°50′

In 13–27, each equation contains the measures of two acute angles. Find a value of θ for which the statement is true.

13. $\sin 10° = \cos \theta$ **14.** $\tan 48° = \cot \theta$ **15.** $\sec 70° = \csc \theta$
16. $\cot 8.6° = \tan \theta$ **17.** $\csc 85°06′ = \sec \theta$ **18.** $\cos 17°42′ = \sin \theta$
19. $\sin \theta = \cos 2\theta$ **20.** $\tan \theta = \cot 5\theta$ **21.** $\sin \theta = \cos \theta$
22. $\sec \theta = \csc (\theta + 60°)$ **23.** $\sec 2\theta = \csc (\theta + 15°)$
24. $\cos (\theta + 10°) = \sin (3\theta + 8°)$ **25.** $\tan (\theta + 8°) = \cot (90° - 2\theta)$
26. $\cot (\theta + 7°) = \tan (2\theta + 7°)$ **27.** $\csc (47° - \theta) = \sec (9 - 3\theta)$

In 28–47, write each expression as the function of an acute angle whose measure is less than 45°.

28. sin 280°   **29.** cos 110°   **30.** tan 265°   **31.** sec 125°
32. cot 95°   **33.** tan 310°   **34.** sin 115.5°   **35.** tan 98.6°
36. cos 258°   **37.** sin 420°   **38.** sec 100°20′   **39.** cos 253°17′
40. sec 490°   **41.** cos 635°   **42.** tan 600°   **43.** cos (−50°)
44. sin (−80°)   **45.** sin (−100°)   **46.** cot (−277°)   **47.** tan (−75°50′)

In 48–52, select the *numeral* preceding the expression that best completes the sentence.

48. If x and y are the measures of two acute angles and $\tan x = \cot y$, then
(1) $x = y + 90°$ (2) $x = y - 90°$
(3) $x = 90° - y$ (4) $y = x - 90°$

49. If θ is the measure of an acute angle and $\cos \theta = \sin 60°$, then $\cos \theta$ equals
(1) 30°   (2) 60°   (3) $\frac{\sqrt{3}}{2}$ (4) $\frac{1}{2}$

50. If x is the measure of an acute angle and $\sin (x + 15°) = \cos 45°$, then $\sin x$ equals
(1) $\frac{1}{2}$ (2) $\frac{\sqrt{2}}{2}$ (3) $\frac{\sqrt{3}}{2}$ (4) 30°

51. If r and t are the measures of two acute angles so that $r + t = 90°$, then $\cos r$ equals
(1) $\sin (90° - t)$ (2) $\sin (t + 90°)$ (3) $\sin (t - 90°)$ (4) $\sin t$

52. If b is the measure of an acute angle and $\cos b = 0.75$, then
(1) $\sin (b - 90°) = 0.75$ (2) $\sin (90° - b) = 0.75$
(3) $\sin b = 0.75$ (4) $\sin b = 0.25$

53. If k is the measure of an acute angle and $\cos k = \sin (2k + 30°)$, demonstrate that k may equal 20° or 60°.

CHAPTER SUMMARY

Trigonometry involves the indirect measure of angles and lengths of line segments.

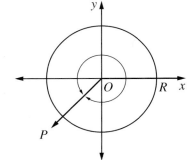

In a right triangle, three basic trigonometric ratios are defined for the measure of an acute angle θ and the lengths of sides related to that angle, namely, the opposite and adjacent legs and the hypotenuse. These are the *sine* (sin), *cosine* (cos), and *tangent* (tan) ratios.

$$\sin \theta = \frac{\text{opp}}{\text{hyp}} \qquad \cos \theta = \frac{\text{adj}}{\text{hyp}} \qquad \tan \theta = \frac{\text{opp}}{\text{adj}}$$

The measure of an angle may be defined in terms of rotation. The ray from which the rotation begins is called the *initial side*, and the ray at which the rotation ends is the *terminal side*.

1. An *angle* is in *standard position* when its vertex is at the origin of the coordinate system and its initial side is the nonnegative ray of the x-axis.

2. The measure of an angle formed by a counterclockwise rotation is positive; angle measure formed by a clockwise rotation is negative.

3. An angle is identified by the quadrant in which its terminal side lies.

4. Two angles in standard position with the same terminal side are called *coterminal angles*.

5. *Sine*, *cosine*, and *tangent* are functions that assign to any angle measure a value that is a real number.

6. The range of the sine function and the range of the cosine function include all real numbers from -1 to 1; the range of the tangent function includes all real numbers.

7. Sine, cosine, and tangent functions can be defined by the coordinates of the point at which the terminal side of an angle in standard position intersects the unit circle.

An angle may be measured in *degrees* and, more precisely, in either decimal degrees or degrees/minutes/seconds. An angle may also be measured in radians. If an angle is drawn as the central angle of a circle, the *radian* measure θ is the ratio of the intercepted arc length s to the radius length r of the circle:

$$\theta = \frac{s}{r} \qquad \text{or} \qquad s = r\theta$$

Angle measures are converted from degrees to radians, and from radians to degrees, by using the relationship established for the measure of a straight angle:

$$\pi \text{ radians} = 180°$$

In the diagrams below, $\angle ROP$ is an angle in standard position with $R(1, 0)$ on the x-axis and $P(a, b)$ the point at which the terminal ray of $\angle ROP$ intersects the unit circle. From P, $\overline{PQ}$ is drawn perpendicular to the x-axis, with Q on the x-axis. The line tangent to the circle at $R(1, 0)$ intersects the terminal ray of the angle at T. If $m\angle ROP = \theta$, then:

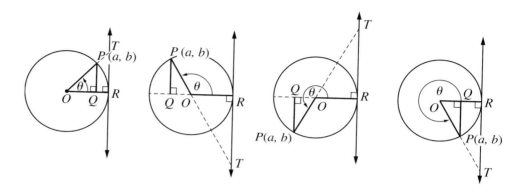

$$\sin \theta = PQ = b \qquad \cos \theta = OQ = a \qquad \tan \theta = RT = \frac{a}{b}$$

The function value of any angle can be expressed in terms of a positive acute angle called the **reference angle**, which is formed by the terminal side of the given angle and the x-axis.

Let ρ = the measure of a reference angle for an angle whose measure is θ. The relationships of these angle measures are shown by quadrants in the diagram at the right.

II	I
$\rho = 180° - \theta$	$\rho = \theta$
III	IV
$\rho = \theta - 180°$	$\rho = 360° - \theta$

Exact function values are determined for special angles such as those with measures of 30°, 45°, and 60° and for **quadrantal angles** (those terminating on the x- or y-axis) by using algebraic methods. *Approximate* function values for the measure of any angle are found by using a graphing calculator.

For any given positive function value from the correct range, the calculator will display the degree measure of the first quadrant angle for that function.

Reciprocal trigonometric functions include the *secant* (sec), *cosecant* (csc), and *cotangent* (cot). An *identity*, or an equation that is true for all values of the variable that are defined, can be written to define each of these functions:

$$\sec \theta = \frac{1}{\cos \theta} \qquad \csc \theta = \frac{1}{\sin \theta} \qquad \cot \theta = \frac{1}{\tan \theta}$$

Quotient identities include $\tan \theta = \frac{\sin \theta}{\cos \theta}$ and $\cot \theta = \frac{\cos \theta}{\sin \theta}$.

Pythagorean identities also exist in trigonometry: $\sin^2 \theta + \cos^2 \theta = 1$

$$1 + \tan^2 \theta = \sec^2 \theta$$
$$\cot^2 \theta + 1 = \csc^2 \theta$$

Cofunctions are two trigonometric functions such that the trigonometric function of an acute angle θ is equal to the cofunction of its complement, $90° - \theta$. Cofunctions include sine and cosine, tangent and cotangent, secant and cosecant.

$$\sin \theta = \cos (90° - \theta) \qquad \tan \theta = \cot (90° - \theta) \qquad \sec \theta = \csc (90° - \theta)$$
$$\cos \theta = \sin (90° - \theta) \qquad \cot \theta = \tan (90° - \theta) \qquad \csc \theta = \sec (90° - \theta)$$

VOCABULARY

14-1   Hypotenuse   Legs   Opposite leg   Adjacent leg   Tangent
Sine   Cosine

14-2   Initial side (of angle)   Terminal side (of angle)
Standard position (of angle)   Quadrants   Quadrantal angle
Coterminal angles

14-3   Unit circle   Directed distance

14-4   Sine function   Cosine function

14-5   Tangent function   Tangent segment

14-7   Minute (of angle measure)

14-9   Reference angle

14-10   Radian

14-12   Secant function   Cosecant function   Cotangent function

14-13   Identity

14-15   Cofunctions

REVIEW EXERCISES

1. In the diagram, $\overleftrightarrow{CA}$ is tangent to circle O at $A(1, 0)$ and $\overleftrightarrow{ED}$ is tangent to circle O at $E(0, 1)$. Point B is on circle O, points D and C are on $\overrightarrow{OB}$, and $\overline{BF} \perp \overrightarrow{OA}$. If $m\angle AOB = \theta$, name the line segment whose measure is each of the following:

   a. $\sin \theta$ **b.** $\cos \theta$
   c. $\tan \theta$ **d.** $\sec \theta$
   e. $\csc \theta$ **f.** $\cot \theta$

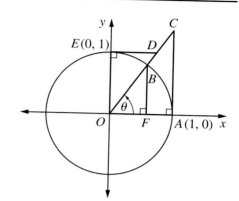

In 2–11, express each given degree measure in radian measure.

2. $90°$ **3.** $120°$ **4.** $30°$ **5.** $100°$ **6.** $135°$
7. $-180°$ **8.** $240°$ **9.** $315°$ **10.** $450°$ **11.** $-200°$

In 12–21, express each given radian measure in degree measure.

12. 2π **13.** $\frac{2\pi}{5}$ **14.** $\frac{5\pi}{6}$ **15.** $\frac{3\pi}{2}$ **16.** $\frac{11\pi}{12}$

17. $\frac{7\pi}{3}$ **18.** $-\frac{3\pi}{4}$ **19.** $-\frac{9\pi}{10}$ **20.** $\frac{17\pi}{6}$ **21.** $\frac{8\pi}{15}$

In 22–33, find the exact value of each expression.

22. $\sin 60°$ **23.** $\cos 300°$ **24.** $\tan 405°$ **25.** $\cos 135°$

26. $\tan 210°$ **27.** $\tan(-120°)$ **28.** $\sin \frac{5\pi}{3}$ **29.** $\sec(-\pi)$

30. $\cot \frac{3\pi}{2}$ **31.** $\csc 330°$ **32.** $\sec\left(-\frac{\pi}{3}\right)$ **33.** $\csc\left(\frac{7\pi}{3}\right)$

In 34–39, in a circle whose radius has length r, a central angle whose radian measure is θ intercepts an arc of length s. In each case, find the missing measure.

34. If $s = 10$ and $r = 2$, find θ.   **35.** If $s = 5\pi$ and $r = 10$, find θ.
36. If $\theta = 3$ and $s = 9$, find r.   **37.** If $\theta = \pi$ and $s = 2\pi$, find r.
38. If $\theta = \frac{1}{2}$ and $r = 3$, find s.   **39.** If $\theta = \frac{\pi}{3}$ and $r = 9$, find s.

In 40–48, write each expression as a function of a positive acute angle.

40. $\sin 138°$ **41.** $\cos 190°$ **42.** $\tan 305°$
43. $\tan(-142°20')$ **44.** $\cos(-284°)$ **45.** $\csc 350°$
46. $\sin(-165°)$ **47.** $\sec 92.6°$ **48.** $\cot(-12.6°)$

In 49–60, find each function value rounded to four decimal places.

49. cos 39°   **50.** sin 64°   **51.** tan 106°30′   **52.** cos 172°10′
53. sec 39°   **54.** csc 111°   **55.** cot 193.5°   **56.** sin 333°50′
57. cos (−51°)   **58.** tan (−104°) **59.** sin 199°28′   **60.** sec (−2°17′)

In 61–66, for each given function value, where $0° \leq \theta \leq 90°$, find the value of θ: **a.** to the *nearest degree*   **b.** to the *nearest minute*   **c.** to the *nearest ten minutes*

61. sin θ = 0.9390   **62.** tan θ = 0.2732   **63.** cos θ = 0.4472
64. cos θ = 0.1113   **65.** sin θ = 0.85   **66.** tan θ = 1.2345

In 67–72, for each given function value, find *two* values of θ, $0° \leq \theta \leq 360°$, each to the *nearest minute*.

67. sin θ = 0.1492   **68.** cos $\theta = \frac{1}{8}$ **69.** tan θ = 3

70. sin θ = −0.3420   **71.** cos θ = −0.4462   **72.** tan θ = −5.2011

In 73–78, write each given expression in terms of sin θ, cos θ, or both. Express the result in simplest form.

73. csc θ sin^2 θ **74.** sec θ cot θ **75.** cot^2 θ + 1

76. $\frac{\sec \theta}{\tan \theta}$ **77.** $\frac{\tan \theta}{\cot \theta}$ **78.** sec^2 θ + csc^2 θ

In 79–81, if $g(x) = \cos 2x$, find the exact value of:

79. $g(\pi)$ **80.** $g\left(\frac{\pi}{4}\right)$ **81.** $g\left(\frac{\pi}{12}\right)$

In 82–84, if $f(x) = \sin x$, express each of the following function values to the *nearest ten-thousandth:*

82. $f\left(\frac{4\pi}{3}\right)$ **83.** $f\left(\frac{\pi}{5}\right)$ **84.** $f\left(\frac{13\pi}{20}\right)$

In 85–94, select the *numeral* preceding the expression that best completes the sentence or answers the question.

85. If sin x cos x < 0, x must be the measure of an angle in Quadrant
      (1) I or III   (2) II or IV   (3) I or IV   (4) II or III

86. An angle whose measure is $\frac{\pi}{3}$ has the same terminal side as an angle whose

measure is

      (1) $\frac{2\pi}{3}$ (2) $\frac{5\pi}{3}$ (3) $-\frac{\pi}{3}$ (4) $-\frac{5\pi}{3}$

87. The degree measure of an angle of 1 radian is

(1) $57°$ (2) between $57°$ and $58°$ (3) $\frac{1°}{\pi}$ (4) $\frac{\pi°}{180}$

88. If $\sin x < 0$, which must also be true?

(1) $\cos x < 0$ (2) $\tan x < 0$ (3) $\sec x < 0$ (4) $\csc x < 0$

89. The value of $\tan \frac{3\pi}{4}$ is equal to the value of

(1) $\sin \frac{\pi}{2}$ (2) $\cos \frac{\pi}{2}$ (3) $\sin \frac{3\pi}{2}$ (4) $\cos \frac{3\pi}{2}$

90. The expression $\frac{\csc \theta - \sin \theta}{\cot \theta}$ is equivalent to

(1) $\cos \theta$ (2) $\sin \theta$ (3) $1 - \sin^2 \theta$ (4) $\cos^2 \theta$

91. Which expression is undefined?

(1) $\sin \frac{\pi}{2}$ (2) $\cos \frac{\pi}{2}$ (3) $\tan \frac{\pi}{2}$ (4) $\csc \frac{\pi}{2}$

92. The expression $\frac{1 + \tan^2 \theta}{1 + \cot^2 \theta}$ is equal to

(1) $(1 + \tan^2 \theta)^2$ (2) 1 (3) $\tan^2 \theta$ (4) $\cot^2 \theta$

93. Which expression is not always equal to 0?

(1) $\cos \theta - \sin \left(\frac{\pi}{2} - \theta \right)$

(2) $\sin \theta - \sin (-\theta)$

(3) $\sin \theta + \sin (-\theta)$

(4) $\cos \theta - \cos (-\theta)$

94. Which expression is not always true?

(1) $\sin \theta = \sin (2\pi - \theta)$ (2) $\cos \theta = \cos (2\pi - \theta)$

(3) $\cos^2 \theta = \cos^2 (-\theta)$ (4) $\sin^2 \theta = \sin^2 (-\theta)$

In 95–98, each equation contains the degree measures of two acute angles. In each case, find a value of x for which the statement is true.

95. $\sin x = \cos (2x + 45)$ **96.** $\sec (x + 12) = \csc (x + 8)$

97. $\cot (x + 10) = \tan 3x$ **98.** $\cos (28 - x) = \sin 5x$

In 99–102, write each expression as a function of a positive acute angle whose measure is less than $45°$.

99. $\sin 125°$ **100.** $\cos 108°$

101. $\tan 297°$ **102.** $\sin (-105°20')$

103. If $\tan \theta = -\frac{3}{4}$ and $\sin \theta > 0$, find:

a. $\sec \theta$ **b.** $\cos \theta$ **c.** $\sin \theta$ **d.** $\csc \theta$ **e.** $\cot \theta$

104. a. If $\cos \theta = -\frac{2}{3}$ and $\sin \theta < 0$, find $\tan \theta$.

b. Express each of the five remaining trigonometric functions in terms of $\cos \theta$.

105. BriAnna lets out 300 feet of string while she is flying her kite. Assuming that the string is stretched taut and makes an angle of $48°$ with the ground, find to the *nearest foot* the height of the kite above the ground.

CUMULATIVE REVIEW

1. The vertices of quadrilateral $ABCD$ are $A(-2, 4)$, $B(3, 5)$, $C(4, -2)$, and $D(-3, -1)$.
   a. Prove that the diagonals are perpendicular.
   b. Prove that $ABCD$ has two pairs of congruent sides.
   c. Prove that $ABCD$ is not a parallelogram.

2. The length of an altitude of an equilateral triangle is 12 centimeters.
   a. Find the length of a side of the triangle to the *nearest centimeter*.
   b. Find the area of the triangle to the *nearest square centimeter*.

3. Prove that the midpoint of the hypotenuse of a right triangle is equidistant from the three vertices. (Use an indirect proof. Show that $m\angle MCA > m\angle A$ and $m\angle MCA < m\angle A$ lead to contradictions.)

4. Under transformation T, the image of $A(-1, -2)$ is $A'(2, 2)$, the image of $B(-3, -1)$ is $B'(0, 1)$, and the image of $C(-3, -4)$ is $C'(0, 4)$.
   a. Draw $\triangle ABC$ and $\triangle A'B'C'$ on the same set of axes.
   b. What are the coordinates of the image of point $D(-2, -3)$ under transformation T?
   c. If the coordinates of E are (a, b), write the coordinates of the image of E under transformation T in terms of a and b.
   d. Which of the following describes the transformation T?
   (*1*) a line reflection   (*2*) a point reflection
   (*3*) a glide reflection   (*4*) a translation

5. If $f(x) = 4x^2 - 1$ and $g(x) = \frac{1}{x}$, find $g \circ f(-1)$.

6. In the diagram, $\overline{PQ}$ is a tangent to circle O and $\overline{PRS}$ is a secant to circle O. If $PQ = RS$ and $PR = 4$, find PQ in radical form.

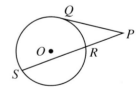

7. For what values of the variable is the fraction $\dfrac{x + 3}{x^2 - 7x - 30}$ undefined?

8. Write the fraction $\dfrac{3 + \sqrt{6}}{3 - \sqrt{6}}$ as an equivalent expression in simplest form.

In 9–12:　**a.** Identify the graph of each relation as a circle, an ellipse, a hyperbola, or a parabola.　**b.** Find the coordinates of the points, if any, at which the graph of each relation intersects the x- and y-axes.　**c.** Is the relation a function?

9. $x^2 + 12y^2 = 36$ 　　　　　　　　　 10. $x^2 - 12y^2 = 36$
11. $x^2 - 12y = 36$ 　　　　　　　　　　 12. $xy = 36$

Exploration

Point $P(0.52, 3.36)$ lies on a circle whose center is at the origin. Write the coordinates of P in the form $(r \cos \theta, r \sin \theta)$, expressing r and θ to the *nearest tenth*.

Trigonometric Graphs

Each of us is surrounded by sounds every day. Examples of these sounds include the voices of other persons, soothing or stimulating music, and the crash produced when two hard objects collide. Each sound is the effect of energy transmitted to our ears in a wave pattern.

The vibrating strings of a piano produce sound waves. The pitch of the sound is determined by the frequency of the sound wave, that is, the number of complete waves in a given period of time. For example, the frequency of middle C is 256 waves per second. Strings of different lengths produce sound waves with different frequencies and therefore different pitches.

Sound waves can be patterned by the sine function. In this chapter we will study the graphs of the trigonometric functions that are basic to the representation of sound and other physical phenomena characterized by wave patterns.

15-1 THE WRAPPING FUNCTION

Let us think of a vertical number line that is tangent to a unit circle so that the point representing 0 on the number line coincides with point (1, 0) on the unit circle. Now, let us imagine that we can wrap the number line about the circle so that each point on the line coincides with a point on the circle. The diagram shows some corresponding points as the positive ray of the number line makes a single rotation about the circle.

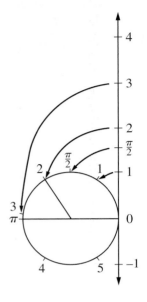

Each point on the circle determines the terminal ray of a central angle of the circle. The radian measure of an angle in standard position is equal to the coordinate of the corresponding point on the number line.

For example, a point whose coordinate is 2 on the number line corresponds to a point on the unit circle that determines an angle whose radian measure is 2. Similarly, a point whose coordinate is $\frac{\pi}{2}$ (approximately 1.5708) on the number line corresponds to a point on the unit circle that determines an angle whose radian measure is $\frac{\pi}{2}$, that is, a right angle.

We can continue to wrap the positive ray of the number line about the circle in a counterclockwise direction. In the same way, we can wrap the negative ray of the number line about the circle in a clockwise direction. Under this **wrapping function**, every point on the real-number line corresponds to one and only one point on the unit circle.

There is, however, an infinite number of points on the real-number line that correspond to the same point on the unit circle. For example, the points that represent the real numbers 0, 2π, -2π, 4π, -4π, 6π, -6π, and so on, all correspond to point (1, 0) on the circle, that is, the point that determines a central angle of 0 radian. This set of real numbers is indicated by the expression $2\pi k$, where k represents any integer.

In the same way, the set of points whose real numbers are of the form $2 + 2\pi k$ for all integral values of k corresponds to a point on the unit circle that determines a central angle of 2 radians.

We will use this correspondence between points on the real-number line and the radian measures of angles of a unit circle to graph trigonometric functions.

EXERCISES WITH OPEN-RESPONSE PROBLEMS

In 1 and 2, select the *numeral* preceding the expression that best answers the question.

1. Which number does *not* have a point on the real-number line corresponding to the point on the unit circle that determines an angle measure of 0 radian?
   (1) 6π (2) 2π (3) 3π (4) 4π

2. A point P on the unit circle determines an angle of 3 radians. Which real number does *not* have a point on the number line that corresponds to point P on the circle?
   (1) $3 + 2\pi$ (2) $3 - 2\pi$ (3) $3 + \pi$ (4) $3 + 10\pi$

3. Name four real numbers whose points on the number line correspond to the point on the unit circle whose coordinates are $(-1, 0)$.

In 4–8, in each case name five real numbers whose points on the number line correspond to the point on the unit circle that determines an angle whose radian measure is given.

4. $\frac{\pi}{2}$ 5. 5   6. $\frac{\pi}{3}$ 7. 1.23   8. $\frac{7\pi}{6}$

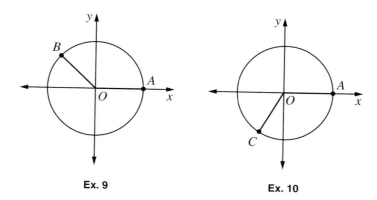

Ex. 9   Ex. 10

9. In a unit circle, $\angle AOB$ indicates an angle associated with $\frac{3}{8}$ of a rotation, A and B are points on the circle, and A lies on the positive x-axis, as shown in the accompanying diagram. Name four real numbers whose points on the number line correspond to point B on the circle.

10. In a unit circle, $\angle AOC$ indicates an angle associated with $\frac{2}{3}$ of a rotation, and point C is on the circle, as shown in the accompanying diagram. If k represents any integer, which of the following expressions names the infinite set of real numbers that correspond to point C on the circle?

   (1) $\frac{2}{3} + 2\pi k$ (2) $\frac{2\pi}{3} + 2\pi k$ (3) $\frac{4\pi}{3} + 2\pi k$ (4) $\frac{4}{3} + 2\pi k$

In 11–18, in each case three of the four given numbers have points on the real-number line that correspond to the same point on the unit circle. Which real number has a point that does *not* belong to this set?

11. $8\pi, 10\pi, 11\pi, 12\pi$

12. $5\pi, 10\pi, 15\pi, -5\pi$

13. $\dfrac{3\pi}{2}, \dfrac{5\pi}{2}, \dfrac{7\pi}{2}, \dfrac{15\pi}{2}$

14. $\dfrac{-\pi}{6}, \dfrac{-13\pi}{6}, \dfrac{5\pi}{6}, \dfrac{11\pi}{6}$

15. $\dfrac{\pi}{4}, \dfrac{9\pi}{4}, \dfrac{-7\pi}{4}, \dfrac{-3\pi}{4}$

16. $\dfrac{5\pi}{3}, \dfrac{-5\pi}{3}, \dfrac{-\pi}{3}, \dfrac{11\pi}{3}$

17. $4 - 2\pi, 4 + \pi, 4 + 2\pi, 4 - 4\pi$

18. $\dfrac{1}{3}, \dfrac{2\pi + 1}{3}, \dfrac{6\pi + 1}{3}, \dfrac{1 - 12\pi}{3}$

15-2 GRAPH OF $y = \sin x$

A function is a set of ordered pairs and can be represented as a set of points in the coordinate plane when the domain and range of the function are subsets of the real numbers. This set of points is called the *graph* of the function. In Math A, we learned to graph algebraic functions such as $y = 2x - 1$ and $y = x^2 - 3x + 7$. Now we will learn to graph $y = \sin x$.

To graph this trigonometric function, we will use as the x-axis the number line that we have associated with points on the unit circle. We can select from the domain that is the set of all real numbers any convenient set of values for x and then find the corresponding value of $\sin x$ or y. One possible set with which to begin is the multiples of $\dfrac{\pi}{6}$ from 0 to 2π, which includes the measure of each of the quadrantal angles and measures of two angles in each quadrant. A table of values for $y = \sin x$ is shown below:

x	0	$\dfrac{\pi}{6}$	$\dfrac{\pi}{3}$	$\dfrac{\pi}{2}$	$\dfrac{2\pi}{3}$	$\dfrac{5\pi}{6}$	π	$\dfrac{7\pi}{6}$	$\dfrac{4\pi}{3}$	$\dfrac{3\pi}{2}$	$\dfrac{5\pi}{3}$	$\dfrac{11\pi}{6}$	2π
$\sin x$	0	0.5	0.87	1	0.87	0.5	0	-0.5	-0.87	-1	-0.87	-0.5	0

The value of $\sin \dfrac{\pi}{6} = \dfrac{1}{2}$ or 0.5, and the value of $\sin \dfrac{\pi}{3} = \dfrac{\sqrt{3}}{2} = 0.87$, to the nearest hundredth.

After choosing a scale along the y-axis, we let 3 be an approximation for π on the x-axis as a convenient way to present the graph on the next page as closely as possible to its actual scale.

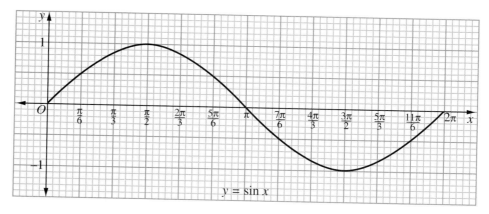

The curve shown above is the **basic sine curve**, or **sine wave**. If we divide the interval from 0 to 2π into four equal parts, the curve increases from 0 to 1 in the first quarter, decreases from 1 to 0 and from 0 to -1 in the second and third quarters, and then increases from -1 to 0 in the fourth quarter. In the unit circle, we see this same pattern for $\sin \theta$.

As θ increases from 0 to $\frac{\pi}{2}$ radians in Quadrant I, $\sin \theta$ increases from 0 to 1. In Quadrant II, as θ increases from $\frac{\pi}{2}$ to π radians, $\sin \theta$ decreases from 1 to 0. The similarities continue for Quadrants III and IV.

This, of course, is only part of the graph of $y = \sin x$. If we choose values of x from -2π to 0, we have the following set of values:

x	-2π	$-\frac{11\pi}{6}$	$-\frac{5\pi}{3}$	$-\frac{3\pi}{2}$	$-\frac{4\pi}{3}$	$-\frac{7\pi}{6}$	$-\pi$	$-\frac{5\pi}{6}$	$-\frac{2\pi}{3}$	$-\frac{\pi}{2}$	$-\frac{\pi}{3}$	$-\frac{\pi}{6}$	0
$\sin x$	0	0.5	0.87	1	0.87	0.5	0	-0.5	-0.87	-1	-0.87	-0.5	0

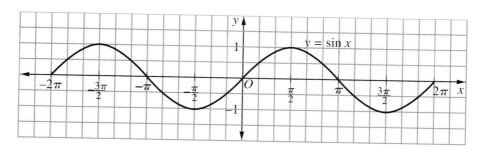

The graph of $y = \sin x$ is drawn over an interval from -2π to 2π. The set of values for $\sin x$ from $x = -2\pi$ to $x = 0$ duplicates the values for $\sin x$ from $x = 0$ to $x = 2\pi$. Thus, the graph of $y = \sin x$ in the interval $-2\pi \le x \le 0$ repeats the basic sine curve. We observe:

$$\sin x = \sin (x + 2\pi k) \text{ for any integer } k$$

The graph of $y = \sin x$ has translational symmetry under the translation $T_{2\pi,0}$; that is, the graph of $y = \sin x$ is its own image under the translation $T_{2\pi,0}$.

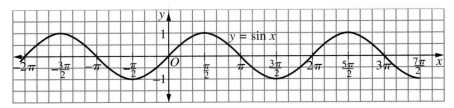

$$y = \sin x$$
$$\text{Domain} = \{x \,|\, x \in \text{Real numbers}\}$$
$$\text{Range} = \{y \,|\, -1 \leq y \leq 1\}$$

A function, f, is a *periodic function* if there exists a nonzero constant, p, such that, for every x in the domain of f, $f(x + p) = f(x)$. The smallest positive value of p is called the *period* of the function. In other words, the period is the length of the interval between successive repetitions of the curve. For example, when $x = \frac{\pi}{2}$, $\sin x = 1$. Then, when $x = \frac{5\pi}{2}$, $\sin x = 1$. Therefore, the difference between $\frac{5\pi}{2}$ and $\frac{\pi}{2}$ shows an interval length of $\frac{5\pi}{2} - \frac{\pi}{2} = \frac{4\pi}{2} = 2\pi$; in other words, 2π is the period of function $y = \sin x$.

Each of the graphs shown in this section can be drawn by a graphing calculator. To do this, we begin by putting the calculator in radian mode.

Enter: | MODE | | ▼ | | ▼ | | ENTER |

Next, we enter the equation of the function to be graphed.

Enter: | Y= | | SIN | | X,T,θ,n | | ENTER |

Finally, we set the | WINDOW | to include values of x from 0 to 2π and values of y from -2 to 2. On some calculators, 2 | 2nd | | π | can be used in place of 6.28.

Enter: | WINDOW | 0 | ENTER | 6.28 | ENTER | 1
| ENTER | | (−) | 2 | ENTER | 2 | ENTER | 1 | GRAPH |

Display:

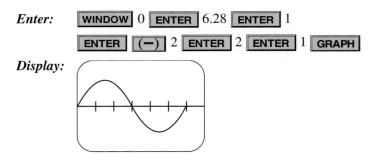

This is the basic sine curve.

Now, leaving all other settings as entered for the preceding graph of $y = \sin x$, we change the x values to Xmin = -6.28 and Xmax = 6.28 to display two periods of the graph.

Enter: WINDOW   (−) 6.28 ENTER 6.28 GRAPH

Display:

We notice that, because we have changed the scale for x without changing the scale for y, each period of the graph is smaller in the horizontal direction but not in the vertical direction. One unit along the x-axis is smaller than one unit along the y-axis so that the graph is somewhat distorted. We must keep this fact in mind whenever we use a graphing calculator to display the graph of a trigonometric function.

We can continue to display as many periods of the graph as we wish by changing the values of Xmin and Xmax. If we let Xmin = -6.28, Xmax = 11, and keep all other settings unchanged, the calculator will display two full periods and three quarters of a third period of a sine curve. This graph is shown at the top of page 708.

EXAMPLE

From the graph of $y = \sin x$, determine whether $\sin x$ increases or decreases in each quadrant.

Solution

Sketch the graph, and divide the interval from 0 to 2π into quadrants. Study the change in the y-values in each quadrant.

Answer: In Quadrant I, $\sin x$ increases from 0 to 1.
In Quadrant II, $\sin x$ decreases from 1 to 0.
In Quadrant III, $\sin x$ decreases from 0 to -1.
In Quadrant IV, $\sin x$ increases from -1 to 0.

EXERCISES WITH OPEN-RESPONSE PROBLEMS

1. Sketch the graph of $y = \sin x$ from $x = -2\pi$ to $x = 2\pi$.

2. What is the period of $y = \sin x$?

3. a. What is the largest value of $\sin x$?
   b. What is the smallest value of $\sin x$?

4. What is the range of $y = \sin x$?

5. For what values of x in the interval $-2\pi \le x \le 2\pi$ is $\sin x = 1$?

6. For what values of x in the interval $-2\pi \le x \le 2\pi$ is $\sin x = -1$?

7. Between what values of x in the interval $-2\pi \le x \le 2\pi$ is $\sin x$:
   a. increasing?   **b.** decreasing?

8. Name three real numbers that are *not* elements of the range of the function $y = \sin x$.

9. An oscilloscope can produce a visual image of a sound wave.
   The function $y = 0.001 \sin (100\pi x)$ represents the sound produced by a tuning fork,
   where x represents the time in seconds.
   a. Make a table of values for $y = 0.001 \sin (100\pi x)$ for values of $x = 0, \frac{1}{400}, \frac{2}{400}, \ldots, \frac{8}{400}$ second.
      Find the values of y to four decimal places.
   b. Draw the graph of the sine curve produced by the tuning fork.
   c. How many complete sine waves will the tuning fork produce in 1 second?

10. Waves are rhythmic disturbances that carry energy. As a wave travels through a medium, such
   as water, particles of the medium are displaced. If two or more waves move simultaneously
   through a medium, the displacements they create are added together. For example, if a wave
   with a 1-millimeter displacement overlaps a wave with a 2-millimeter displacement,
   a wave with a 3-millimeter displacement would be produced at that instant.

   a. The graphs shown below represent two waves. Assume the waves start from the point at the same
      time and travel in the same direction.

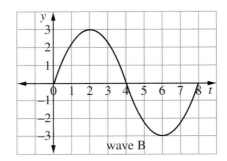

   Draw the graph of the wave that results from the interaction of the two waves.

   b. Draw a graph of a wave that would "cancel" wave A, resulting in no displacement.

15-3   GRAPH OF $y = \cos x$

We can sketch the graph of $y = \cos x$ by making a table of values, as we did for $y = \sin x$, using multiples of $\frac{\pi}{6}$ from 0 to 2π.

x	0	$\frac{\pi}{6}$	$\frac{\pi}{3}$	$\frac{\pi}{2}$	$\frac{2\pi}{3}$	$\frac{5\pi}{6}$	π	$\frac{7\pi}{6}$	$\frac{4\pi}{3}$	$\frac{3\pi}{2}$	$\frac{5\pi}{3}$	$\frac{11\pi}{6}$	2π
$\cos x$	1	0.87	0.5	0	-0.5	-0.87	-1	-0.87	-0.5	0	0.5	0.87	1

Once again, we have chosen a scale along the y-axis and we let 3 be an approximation for π on the x-axis as a convenient way to present the graph as closely as possible to its actual scale.

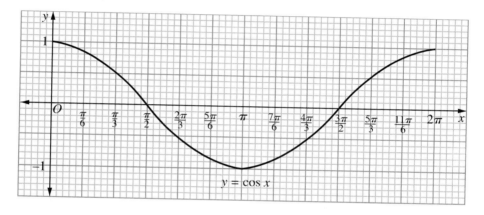

The curve shown above is the **basic cosine curve**.

Let us study the curve $y = \cos x$. If we divide the interval from 0 to 2π into four equal parts, the curve decreases from 1 to 0 and then from 0 to -1 in the first and second quarters and then increases from -1 to 0 and from 0 to 1 in the third and fourth quarters. In the unit circle, we see the same pattern of values for $\cos \theta$. As θ increases from 0 to $\frac{\pi}{2}$ radians in Quadrant I, $\cos \theta$ decreases from 1 to 0. Then, in Quadrant II, as θ increases from $\frac{\pi}{2}$ to π radians, $\cos \theta$ decreases from 0 to -1. The similarities continue for Quadrants III and IV.

Like the sine function, the cosine function is a periodic function with a period of 2π.

$$\cos x = \cos (x + 2\pi k) \text{ for any integer } k$$

When $x = \pi$, $\cos x = -1$, and when $x = 3\pi$, $\cos x = -1$. The difference between 3π and π shows an integral length of $3\pi - \pi = 2\pi$; in other words, 2π is the period of the function $y = \cos x$.

The graph of $y = \cos x$ has translational symmetry with respect to the translation $T_{2\pi,0}$, and its graph is an endless repetition of the basic cosine curve above.

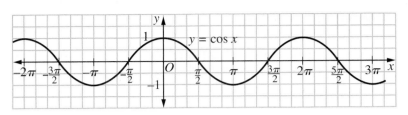

$$y = \cos x$$
$$\text{Domain} = \{x \mid x \in \text{Real numbers}\}$$
$$\text{Range} = \{y \mid -1 \le y \le 1\}$$

We can display the graph of the cosine function on a graphing calculator. We begin by putting the calculator in radian mode.

Enter: | MODE | | ▼ | | ▼ | | ENTER |

Next, we enter the equation of the function to be graphed.

Enter: | Y= | | COS | | X,T,θ,n | | ENTER |

Finally, we set the | WINDOW | to include values of x from 0 to 2π and values of y from -2 to 2. On some calculators, 2 | 2nd | | π | can be used in place of 6.28.

Enter: | WINDOW | 0 | ENTER | 6.28 | ENTER | 1

| ENTER | | (−) | 2 | ENTER | 2 | ENTER | 1 | GRAPH |

Display:

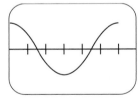

This is the basic cosine curve.

EXAMPLE

From the graph of $y = \cos x$, determine whether $\cos x$ increases or decreases in each quadrant.

Solution

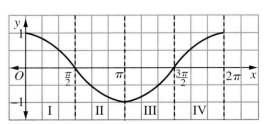

Sketch the graph, and divide the interval from 0 to 2π into quadrants. Study the change in the y-values in each quadrant.

Answer: In Quadrant I, cos x decreases from 1 to 0.
In Quadrant II, cos x decreases from 0 to -1.
In Quadrant III, cos x increases from -1 to 0.
In Quadrant IV, cos x increases from 0 to 1.

EXERCISES WITH OPEN-RESPONSE PROBLEMS

1. Sketch the graph of $y = \cos x$ from $x = -2\pi$ to $x = 2\pi$.
2. What is the period of $y = \cos x$?
3. **a.** What is the largest value of cos x?
   b. What is the smallest value of cos x?
4. What is the range of $y = \cos x$?
5. For what values of x in the interval $-2\pi \le x \le 2\pi$ is cos $x = 1$?
6. For what values of x in the interval $-2\pi \le x \le 2\pi$ is cos $x = -1$?
7. Between what values of x in the interval $-2\pi \le x \le 2\pi$ is cos x:
   a. increasing?   **b.** decreasing?
8. **a.** Sketch the graph of $y = \cos x$ in the interval $-2\pi \le x \le 2\pi$.
   b. On the same set of axes, sketch the graph of $y = \sin x$.
   c. For what value of q is $y = \sin x$ the image of $y = \cos x$ under the translation $T_{q,0}$?

15-4 AMPLITUDE

To draw the graph of $y = a \sin x$ for some constant, a, we must first find the values of sin x and then multiply these values by a. For example, the table at the right shows us how to find four rational approximations for y when the function is $y = 2 \sin x$.

To facilitate our task, we prepare the following compact table that we might use to graph $y = 2 \sin x$ and $y = \frac{1}{2} \sin x$ over the interval $0 \le x \le 2\pi$.

x	2 sin x	=	y
0	$2 \sin 0 = 2(0)$	=	0
$\frac{\pi}{6}$	$2 \sin \frac{\pi}{6} = 2(0.5)$	=	1.0
$\frac{\pi}{3}$	$2 \sin \frac{\pi}{3} = 2(0.866)$	=	1.732
$\frac{\pi}{2}$	$2 \sin \frac{\pi}{2} = 2(1)$	=	2

x	0	$\frac{\pi}{6}$	$\frac{\pi}{3}$	$\frac{\pi}{2}$	$\frac{2\pi}{3}$	$\frac{5\pi}{6}$	π	$\frac{7\pi}{6}$	$\frac{4\pi}{3}$	$\frac{3\pi}{2}$	$\frac{5\pi}{3}$	$\frac{11\pi}{6}$	2π
sin x	0	0.5	0.866	1	0.866	0.5	0	-0.5	-0.866	-1	-0.866	-0.5	0
2 sin x	0	1.0	1.732	2	1.732	1.0	0	-1.0	-1.732	-2	-1.732	-1.0	0
$\frac{1}{2}$ sin x	0	0.25	0.433	0.5	0.433	0.25	0	-0.25	-0.433	-0.5	-0.433	-0.25	0

After finding the values of sin x in row 2, we multiply these values by 2 to find the values of 2 sin x in row 3. To draw the graph of $y = 2$ sin x, we use values of x from row 1 with the corresponding values of y from row 3. In the same way, we multiply the values of sin x in row 2 by $\frac{1}{2}$ to find the values of $\frac{1}{2}$ sin x in row 4. To draw the graph of $y = \frac{1}{2}$ sin x, we use values of x from row 1 with the corresponding values of y from row 4. The graphs of $y = $ sin x, $y = 2$ sin x, and $y = \frac{1}{2}$ sin x are shown below.

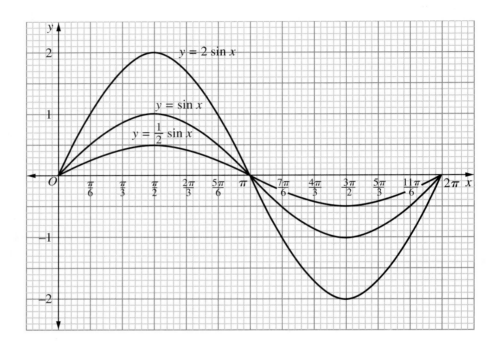

We see that each graph follows the pattern of the basic sine curve. Each graph intersects the x-axis at 0, π, and 2π; reaches its highest point at $\frac{\pi}{2}$, and reaches its lowest point at $\frac{3\pi}{2}$. Like the graph of y sin x, the graph of $y = a$ sin x has translational symmetry under the translation $T_{2\pi,0}$, and the complete graph repeats the basic pattern endlessly.

The following observations are true for the three graphs shown above:

- For $y = $ sin x, the maximum value of y is 1, the minimum value of y is -1, and the range is $-1 \leq y \leq 1$.

- For $y = 2$ sin x, the maximum value of y is 2, the minimum value of y is -2, and the range is $-2 \leq y \leq 2$.

- For $y = \frac{1}{2}$ sin x, the maximum value of y is $\frac{1}{2}$, the minimum value of y is $-\frac{1}{2}$, and the range is $-\frac{1}{2} \leq y \leq \frac{1}{2}$.

As shown in the figure below, the graph of $y = -2 \sin x$ is the reflection in the x-axis of the graph of $y = 2 \sin x$. Here, the maximum value of y is 2, the minimum value of y is -2, and the range is $-2 \le y \le 2$.

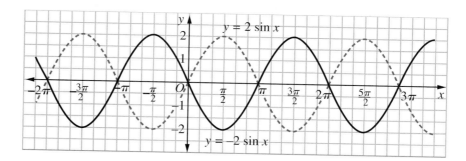

The **amplitude** of a periodic function is one-half the difference between the maximum value and the minimum value.

$$\text{If } y = -2 \sin x, \text{ amplitude} = \frac{2 - (-2)}{2} = 2.$$

$$\text{If } y = a \sin x, \text{ amplitude} = \frac{|a| - (-|a|)}{2} = |a|.$$

The cosine function, like the sine function, has as its range the set of real numbers from -1 to 1. The same principles that were discussed for $y = a \sin x$ apply to functions of the form $y = a \cos x$. For example, if $y = 4 \cos x$, the range of the function is $-4 \le y \le 4$ and the amplitude is 4.

A graphing calculator can be used to compare the graph of $y = \cos x$, whose amplitude is 1, to the graph of $y = 4 \cos x$, whose amplitude is 4. We set the WINDOW to include values of x from 0 to 2π and values of y from -4.5 to 4.5.

Enter:

Display:

● **In general, for the functions $y = a \sin x$ and $y = a \cos x$:**

amplitude $= |a|$.

EXAMPLE

Sketch the graph of $y = 2 \cos x$ in the interval $0 \leq x \leq 2\pi$.

Solution Choose a convenient scale on the y-axis; and, using the same scale, locate points that are convenient approximations of $\frac{\pi}{2}$, π, $\frac{3\pi}{2}$, and 2π on the x-axis. These four values and 0 can be used to find the maximum, minimum, and 0 values of $2 \cos x$, as shown in the table. Plot the points, using values from the table. Then, using the shape of the basic cosine curve as a guide, sketch the curve.

x	$2 \cos x$	$=$	y
0	$2 \cos 0 = 2(1)$	$=$	2
$\frac{\pi}{2}$	$2 \cos \frac{\pi}{2} = 2(0)$	$=$	0
π	$2 \cos \pi = 2(-1)$	$=$	-2
$\frac{3\pi}{2}$	$2 \cos \frac{3\pi}{2} = 2(0)$	$=$	0
2π	$2 \cos 2\pi = 2(1)$	$=$	2

Answer:

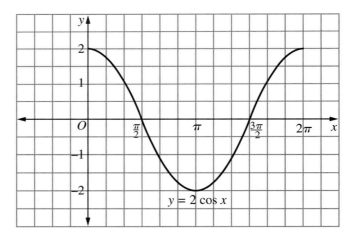

$y = 2 \cos x$

Note: The five points selected identify the maximum, minimum, and 0 y-values of the graph. To draw a more accurate sketch, we include more points in the interval.

Values for x commonly include multiples of $\frac{\pi}{6}$ (such as $\frac{\pi}{6}$, $\frac{\pi}{3}$, $\frac{2\pi}{3}$, $\frac{5\pi}{6}$), and/or multiples of $\frac{\pi}{4}$ (such as $\frac{\pi}{4}$, $\frac{3\pi}{4}$, $\frac{5\pi}{4}$, $\frac{7\pi}{4}$). The values in the table shown here are the coordinates of points of the graph of $y = 2 \cos x$ shown above.

x	$2 \cos x$	$=$	y
$\frac{\pi}{6}$	$2 \cos \frac{\pi}{6} = 2(0.866)$	$=$	1.732
$\frac{\pi}{4}$	$2 \cos \frac{\pi}{4} = 2(0.707)$	$=$	1.414
$\frac{\pi}{3}$	$2 \cos \frac{\pi}{3} = 2(0.5)$	$=$	1.0

EXERCISES WITH OPEN-RESPONSE PROBLEMS

In 1–6, state the amplitude of each given function.

1. $y = 3 \sin x$

2. $y = \frac{1}{2} \cos x$

3. $y = 2 \cos x$

4. $y = \frac{1}{4} \sin x$

5. $y = -3 \sin x$

6. $y = -0.6 \cos x$

In 7–12, sketch each graph from $x = 0$ to $x = 2\pi$.

7. $y = \frac{1}{2} \cos x$

8. $y = 2 \sin x$

9. $y = 3 \cos x$

10. $y = 0.8 \sin x$

11. $y = 4 \cos x$

12. $y = -2 \sin x$

In 13–18, state the range of each given function.

13. $y = \sin x$

14. $y = \cos x$

15. $y = 2 \sin x$

16. $y = \frac{1}{2} \cos x$

17. $y = 8 \cos x$

18. $y = -3 \sin x$

19. a. State three values of x in the interval $0 \le x \le 2\pi$ for which $3 \sin x = 0$.
   b. For what value of x in the interval $0 \le x \le 2\pi$ is $3 \sin x$ a maximum value?
   c. For what value of x in the interval $0 \le x \le 2\pi$ is $3 \sin x$ a minimum value?

15-5   PERIOD

We saw that the graphs of $y = a \sin x$ have different amplitudes as the value of a changes but that the period remains 2π. Now we shall study the graph of a function of the form $y = \sin bx$ and observe what changes result when we multiply x by some constant before finding the sine value. For example, the table at the right shows us how to find four rational approximations for y when the function is $y = \sin 2x$.

To facilitate our task, we might use the values from the table at the top of page 718 to graph $y = \sin 2x$.

x	$\sin 2x$	=	y
0	$\sin 2 \cdot 0 = \sin 0$	=	0
$\frac{\pi}{6}$	$\sin 2 \cdot \frac{\pi}{6} = \sin \frac{\pi}{3}$	=	0.87
$\frac{\pi}{4}$	$\sin 2 \cdot \frac{\pi}{4} = \sin \frac{\pi}{2}$	=	1
$\frac{\pi}{3}$	$\sin 2 \cdot \frac{\pi}{3} = \sin \frac{2\pi}{3}$	=	0.87

x	0	$\frac{\pi}{6}$	$\frac{\pi}{4}$	$\frac{\pi}{3}$	$\frac{\pi}{2}$	$\frac{2\pi}{3}$	$\frac{3\pi}{4}$	$\frac{5\pi}{6}$	π	$\frac{7\pi}{6}$	$\frac{5\pi}{4}$	$\frac{4\pi}{3}$	$\frac{3\pi}{2}$	$\frac{5\pi}{3}$	$\frac{7\pi}{4}$	$\frac{11\pi}{6}$	2π
$2x$	0	$\frac{\pi}{3}$	$\frac{\pi}{2}$	$\frac{2\pi}{3}$	π	$\frac{4\pi}{3}$	$\frac{3\pi}{2}$	$\frac{5\pi}{3}$	2π	$\frac{7\pi}{3}$	$\frac{5\pi}{2}$	$\frac{8\pi}{3}$	3π	$\frac{10\pi}{3}$	$\frac{7\pi}{2}$	$\frac{11\pi}{3}$	4π
$\sin 2x$	0	0.87	1	0.87	0	-0.87	-1	-0.87	0	0.87	1	0.87	0	-0.87	-1	-0.87	0

To draw the graph of $y = \sin 2x$, we use values of x from row 1 with the corresponding values of y from row 3.

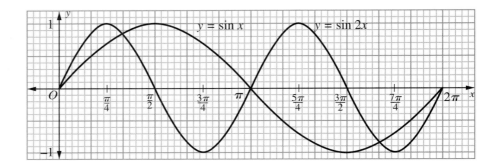

For $y = \sin x$, the basic sine curve appears once over an interval of 2π. For $y = \sin 2x$, the sine curve appears twice over an interval from 0 to 2π. In other words, given $y = \sin 2x$, the frequency of the curve is 2 and its period is π. In general, the *frequency* of a periodic function is the number of times the function repeats itself in a given interval. Let us agree that the interval to be considered is 2π for all trigonometric functions.

The period of a function is equal to the length of the interval, 2π, divided by the frequency. Thus, for $y = \sin 2x$, the frequency is 2 and period $= \frac{2\pi}{2} = \pi$.

This relationship can also be seen by studying translations. Since the graph of $y = \sin 2x$ completes a full cycle in a period of π, we can write:

$$\sin 2x = \sin (2x + 2\pi) = \sin 2(x + \pi)$$

$$T_{\pi,0}: \sin 2x \rightarrow \sin 2(x + \pi)$$

The curve $y = \sin 2x$ has translational symmetry under $T_{\pi,0}$ and has a period of π.

In general, if $y = \sin bx$ where b is positive:

$$\sin bx = \sin (bx + 2\pi) = \sin b\left(x + \frac{2\pi}{b}\right)$$

$$T_{\frac{2\pi}{b},0} : \sin bx \rightarrow \sin b\left(x + \frac{2\pi}{b}\right)$$

Also, if $y = \cos bx$, where b is positive:

$$\cos bx = \cos (bx + 2\pi) = \cos b\left(x + \tfrac{2\pi}{b}\right)$$

$$T_{\frac{2\pi}{b}, 0} : \cos bx \rightarrow \cos b\left(x + \tfrac{2\pi}{b}\right)$$

Therefore, $y = \sin bx$ and $y = \cos bx$ have translational symmetry under $T_{\frac{2\pi}{b}, 0}$.

They are periodic functions with period $\frac{2\pi}{b}$.

● **In general, for the functions $y = \sin bx$ and $y = \cos bx$:**

$$\text{frequency} = |b| \qquad \text{and} \qquad \text{period} = \tfrac{2\pi}{|b|}.$$

Note: The absolute-value symbol is used in writing $|b|$ and $\frac{2\pi}{|b|}$ to ensure that both the frequency and the period are stated as positive numbers.

EXAMPLES

1. Which is the equation of the function sketched in the accompanying diagram?

(1) $y = \sin 2x$ (2) $y = \cos 2x$

(3) $y = \sin \frac{1}{2}x$ (4) $y = \cos \frac{1}{2}x$

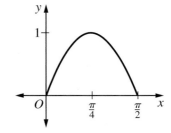

Solution   Since the sketch above is the start of the *sine* curve, choices (2) and (4) can be rejected.

Since the first half of the sine curve occurs over an interval from 0 to $\frac{\pi}{2}$, the

period of the full curve is $2 \cdot \frac{\pi}{2} = \pi$. In choice (1), $y = \sin 2x$, the

period $= \frac{2\pi}{|b|} = \frac{2\pi}{2} = \pi$.

Answer: (1)

2. a. Sketch the graph of $y = \cos \frac{1}{2}x$ from $x = 0$ to $x = 4\pi$.

b. Find the value(s) of x in the interval $0 \le x \le 4\pi$ such that the value of $\cos \frac{1}{2}x$ is: *(1)* a maximum   *(2)* a minimum   *(3)* 0

Solution   **a.**   (1) Compare $y = \cos \frac{1}{2}x$ to $y = \cos bx$ to find $b = \frac{1}{2}$.

Thus, the period $= \frac{2\pi}{|b|} = \frac{2\pi}{\frac{1}{2}} = \frac{2\pi}{\frac{1}{2}} \cdot \frac{2}{2} = 4\pi.$

(2) Since a complete cycle occurs over a period of 4π, divide the period into quarters and find the values of y for the values of x shown in the table.

(3) Plot these points, and draw a smooth curve through them.

x	$\cos \frac{1}{2}x$	$=$	y
0	$\cos \frac{1}{2} \cdot 0 = \cos 0$	$=$	1
π	$\cos \frac{1}{2} \cdot \pi = \cos \frac{\pi}{2}$	$=$	0
2π	$\cos \frac{1}{2} \cdot 2\pi = \cos \pi$	$=$	-1
3π	$\cos \frac{1}{2} \cdot 3\pi = \cos \frac{3\pi}{2}$	$=$	0
4π	$\cos \frac{1}{2} \cdot 4\pi = \cos 2\pi$	$=$	1

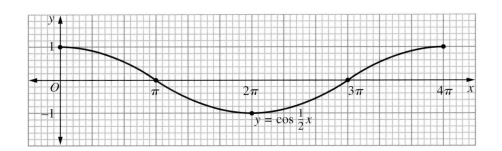

$y = \cos \frac{1}{2}x$

b. Maximum, minimum, and 0 values can be read from the graph.

(1) The maximum value of $\cos \frac{1}{2}x$ occurs when $x = 0$ and when $x = 4\pi$.

(2) The minimum value of $\cos \frac{1}{2}x$ occurs when $x = 2\pi$.

(3) The expression $\cos \frac{1}{2}x$ equals 0 when $x = \pi$ and when $x = 3\pi$.

Answers: **a.** See the graph.
          b. *(1)* 0 and 4π *(2)* 2π *(3)* π and 3π

EXERCISES WITH OPEN-RESPONSE PROBLEMS

In 1–8, give the period of each function.

1. $y = \cos 2x$ **2.** $y = \sin \frac{1}{2}x$ **3.** $y = \cos 3x$ **4.** $y = \cos x$

5. $y = \sin 4x$ **6.** $y = \sin x$ **7.** $y = 3 \sin 2x$ **8.** $y = \frac{1}{2} \cos 6x$

In 9–14, sketch the graph of each function from $x = 0$ to $x = 2\pi$.

9. $y = \cos 2x$ **10.** $y = \sin \frac{1}{2}x$ **11.** $y = \sin 3x$

12. $y = \sin 2x$ **13.** $y = \cos \frac{1}{2}x$ **14.** $y = \cos 3x$

15. Find the values of x between 0 and 2π inclusive for which $y = \sin 2x$ is:
   a. a maximum   **b.** a minimum   **c.** 0

16. Find the values of x between 0 and 2π inclusive for which $y = \cos 2x$ is:
   a. a maximum   **b.** a minimum   **c.** 0

17. The graph of $y = \sin 4x$ is drawn for values of x in the interval $0 \le x \le 2\pi$.
   a. How many times will the basic sine curve appear?
   b. What is the frequency of the graph of $y = \sin 4x$?

18. The graph of $y = \cos \frac{1}{3}x$ is drawn for values of x in the interval $0 \le x \le 2\pi$.
   a. What fractional part of the basic cosine curve will appear?
   b. What is the frequency of the graph of $y = \cos \frac{1}{3}x$?

In 19–24, in each case the graph shows $y = \sin bx$ or $y = \cos bx$.   **a.** What is the frequency of the curve?   **b.** What is the equation of the function?

19.

20.

21.

22.

23.

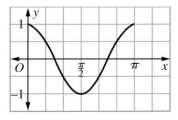

24.

25. In an experiment, a ball bobs up and down (oscillates) on the end of a spring as shown in the figure. Suppose that the maximum distance (or displacement) as the ball moves vertically up or down from its equilibrium (at rest) position is 10 centimeters. It takes about 4 seconds for the ball to move from a maximum point to a minimum point and back to a maximum. Assume that the conditions of the experiment are ideal and there is no friction or air resistance. Then the ball will continue this motion without stopping.

a. Sketch a graph that represents the motion of the ball/spring system.

b. Write an equation that models the motion.

15-6 SKETCHING SINE AND COSINE CURVES

- **For every function $y = a \sin bx$ and $y = a \cos bx$, we have learned:**

    $$\text{amplitude} = |a|, \qquad \text{frequency} = |b|, \qquad \text{period} = \frac{2\pi}{|b|}.$$

EXAMPLES

1. Sketch the graph of $y = 3 \sin 2x$ in the interval $0 \leq x \leq 2\pi$.

Solution   (1) Determine the amplitude and the period of the curve $y = 3 \sin 2x$. Comparison to $y = a \sin bx$ shows that $a = 3$ and $b = 2$.

$$\text{Amplitude} = |a| = |3| = 3 \qquad \text{Period} = \frac{2\pi}{|b|} = \frac{2\pi}{|2|} = \frac{2\pi}{2} = \pi$$

(2) Then, since the amplitude is 3, the maximum value of the curve is 3 and the minimum value is -3.

(3) Since the period is π, divide the interval on the x-axis from 0 to π into four quarters at points $0, \frac{\pi}{4}, \frac{\pi}{2}, \frac{3\pi}{4}$, and π. In a sine curve, the 0's occur at the first, middle, and last of these points. For $y = 3 \sin 2x$, the maximum value, 3, occurs when $x = \frac{\pi}{4}$; and the minimum value, -3, occurs when $x = \frac{3\pi}{4}$.

(4) Repeat the process in step 3 for the interval π to 2π.

(5) Draw a smooth curve through the points that have been plotted.

Answer:

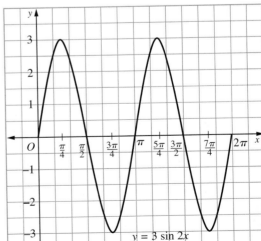

2. a. Sketch, on the same set of axes, the graphs of $y = 2 \cos x$ and $y = \sin \frac{1}{2}x$ as x varies from 0 to 2π.

b. Determine the number of values of x between 0 and 2π that satisfy the equation $2 \cos x = \sin \frac{1}{2}x$.

Solutions

a.

$y = 2 \cos x$

Amplitude = 2

Frequency = 1

Period = $\frac{2\pi}{1} = 2\pi$

$y = \sin \frac{1}{2}x$

Amplitude = 1

Frequency = $\frac{1}{2}$

Period = $\frac{2\pi}{\frac{1}{2}} = 4\pi$

Sketch and label each graph.

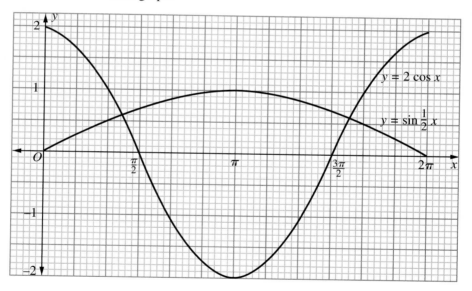

b. The values of x that satisfy the equation $2 \cos x = \sin \frac{1}{2}x$ are the x-coordinates of the points of intersection of $y = 2 \cos x$ and $y = \sin \frac{1}{2}x$. Therefore, there are two values of x between 0 and 2π that satisfy the equation.

Answers: **a.** See the graph. **b.** Two

EXERCISES WITH OPEN-RESPONSE PROBLEMS

In 1–6, in each case: **a.** State the amplitude of the graph.   **b.** State the period of the graph.

1. $y = 3 \sin 2x$

2. $y = \frac{1}{2} \sin x$

3. $y = 2 \cos \frac{1}{2} x$

4. $y = 2 \cos 2x$

5. $y = \sin \frac{1}{2} x$

6. $y = -2 \cos x$

7. If $f(x) = \sin 2x$, find: **a.** $f(\pi)$ **b.** $f\left(\frac{\pi}{2}\right)$ **c.** $f\left(\frac{\pi}{6}\right)$

8. If $f(x) = \cos \frac{1}{2} x$, find: **a.** $f(\pi)$ **b.** $f\left(\frac{\pi}{2}\right)$ **c.** $f(3\pi)$

9. a. Sketch the graph of $y = \sin 2x$ from $x = 0$ to $x = 2\pi$.

b. On the same set of axes, sketch the graph of $y = \frac{1}{2} \cos x$.

c. For how many values of x in the interval $0 \le x \le 2\pi$ does $\sin 2x = \frac{1}{2} \cos x$?

10. a. Sketch the graph of $y = 2 \cos \frac{1}{2} x$ for values of x in the interval $-2\pi \le x \le 2\pi$.

b. On the same set of axes, sketch the graph of $y = 2 \sin x$.

c. For how many values of x in the interval $-2\pi \le x \le 2\pi$ does $2 \cos \frac{1}{2} x = 2 \sin x$?

11. a. On the same set of axes, sketch the graphs of $y = \cos 2x$ and $y = \sin x$ for values of x in the interval $0 \le x \le 2\pi$.

b. For what values of x in the interval $0 \le x \le 2\pi$ does $\cos 2x = \sin x$?

In 12–17:   **a.** In each case, sketch the graphs of the two functions on one set of axes, using the interval $0 \le x \le 2\pi$.   **b.** Solve each given equation for x in the interval $0 \le x \le 2\pi$.

12. a. Graph $y = \sin x$
   $y = \cos x$.
   b. Solve $\sin x = \cos x$.

13. a. Graph $y = \cos \frac{1}{2} x$
   $y = -\sin x$.
   b. Solve $\cos \frac{1}{2} x = -\sin x$.

14. a. Graph $y = 3 \cos x$
   $y = \sin 2x$.
   b. Solve $3 \cos x = \sin 2x$.

15. a. Graph $y = -\cos x$
   $y = \sin x$.
   b. Solve $-\cos x = \sin x$.

16. a. Graph $y = \frac{1}{2} \sin x$
   $y = -2 \sin x$.
   b. Solve $\frac{1}{2} \sin x = -2 \sin x$.

17. a. Graph $y = \sin \frac{x}{2}$
   $y = -\cos x$.
   b. Solve $\sin \frac{x}{2} = -\cos x$.

18 a. On the same set of axes, sketch the graphs of $y = \cos x$ and $y = 2 \sin 2x$ for values of x in the interval $-\pi \leq x \leq \pi$.

  b. For how many values of x in the interval $-\pi \leq x \leq \pi$ does $\cos x = 2 \sin 2x$?

19. a. On the same set of axes, sketch the graph of $y = \sin \frac{1}{2} x$ and $y = 2 \cos x$ for values of x in the interval $-2\pi \leq x \leq 0$.

  b. For how many values of x in the interval $-2\pi \leq x \leq 0$, does $\sin \frac{1}{2} x = 2 \cos x$?

20. a. Sketch the graph of $y = 2 \cos 2x$ in the interval $0 \leq x \leq 2\pi$.

  b. On the same set of axes, draw the graph of $y = 1$.

  c. What are the coordinates of the points of intersection of the graphs drawn in parts **a** and **b**?

21. An oscilloscope is a device that presents pictures of sound waves.
The function $y = 0.002 \sin (200\pi x)$ describes the sound produced by a tuning fork, where x represents the time in seconds.

  a. What is the amplitude of the given function?

  b. What is its period?

  c. Copy and complete the table, finding values of y to four decimal places:

x	0	$\frac{1}{800}$	$\frac{2}{800}$	$\frac{3}{800}$	$\frac{4}{800}$	$\frac{5}{800}$	$\frac{6}{800}$	$\frac{7}{800}$	$\frac{8}{800}$
y									

  d. Graph the picture of the sine wave produced by the tuning fork over an interval of time from 0 to $\frac{8}{800}$ $\left(\text{or } \frac{1}{100}\right)$ second.

  e. How many complete sine waves will be produced by the tuning fork in an interval of one second?

22. Research the terms *amplitude modulation* and *frequency modulation*, commonly abbreviated as AM and FM, and explain the terms in relation to practical applications of trigonometric graphs.

15-7   GRAPH OF $y = \tan x$

We can draw the graph of $y = \tan x$, as we did the graphs of $y = \sin x$ and $y = \cos x$, by making a table of values. We recall from our work with the unit circle that the tangent function is undefined at $\pm \frac{\pi}{2}, \pm \frac{3\pi}{2}$, or any odd multiple of $\frac{\pi}{2}$. Each undefined function value is indicated in the following table by a dash (—).

x	-2π	$\frac{-11\pi}{6}$	$\frac{-7\pi}{4}$	$\frac{-5\pi}{3}$	$\frac{-3\pi}{2}$	$\frac{-4\pi}{3}$	$\frac{-5\pi}{4}$	$\frac{-7\pi}{6}$	$-\pi$	$\frac{-5\pi}{6}$	$\frac{-3\pi}{4}$	$\frac{-2\pi}{3}$	$\frac{-\pi}{2}$	$\frac{-\pi}{3}$	$\frac{-\pi}{4}$	$\frac{-\pi}{6}$	0
$\tan x$	0	0.58	1	1.7	—	-1.7	-1	-0.58	0	0.58	1	1.7	—	-1.7	-1	-0.58	0

x	0	$\frac{\pi}{6}$	$\frac{\pi}{4}$	$\frac{\pi}{3}$	$\frac{\pi}{2}$	$\frac{2\pi}{3}$	$\frac{3\pi}{4}$	$\frac{5\pi}{6}$	π	$\frac{7\pi}{6}$	$\frac{5\pi}{4}$	$\frac{4\pi}{3}$	$\frac{3\pi}{2}$	$\frac{5\pi}{3}$	$\frac{7\pi}{4}$	$\frac{11\pi}{6}$	2π
$\tan x$	0	0.58	1	1.7	—	-1.7	-1	-0.58	0	0.58	1	1.7	—	-1.7	-1	-0.58	0

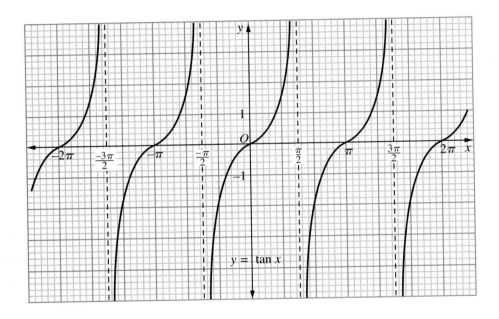

$$y = \tan x$$

Domain $= \{x \mid x \in \text{Real numbers and } x \neq \frac{(2k + 1)\pi}{2} \text{ for integral values of } k\}$

Range $= \{y \mid y \in \text{Real numbers}\}$

Unlike the sine and cosine curves, which are continuous, the graph of $y = \tan x$ is discontinuous at $x = \frac{\pi}{2}$, $x = \frac{3\pi}{2}$, $x = \frac{-\pi}{2}$, and at any value of $x = \frac{(2k + 1)\pi}{2}$ for integral values of k. By choosing points with x-coordinates sufficiently close to these odd multiples of $\frac{\pi}{2}$, we can make the value of $\tan x$ as large or as small as we choose. Therefore, $y = \tan x$ has no maximum or minimum value. The tangent function does not have an amplitude.

Like the sine and cosine functions, the tangent function is periodic. We see in the graph on page 726 that the shape of the tangent curve from $x = \frac{-3\pi}{2}$ to $x = \frac{-\pi}{2}$ is repeated in the interval from $x = \frac{-\pi}{2}$ to $x = \frac{\pi}{2}$ and again from $\frac{\pi}{2}$ to $\frac{3\pi}{2}$. Since $\frac{3\pi}{2} - \frac{\pi}{2} = \frac{2\pi}{2} = \pi$, the period of the tangent function is π.

$$\tan x = \tan (x + \pi) \text{ for all } x$$

The graph of $y = \tan x$ has translational symmetry with respect to the translation $T_{\pi,0}$.

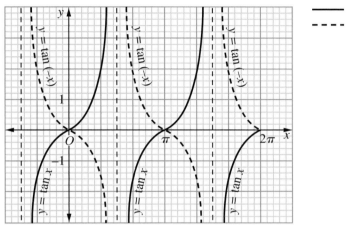

The graph shows the reflection of the curve $y = \tan x$ in the x-axis. If this image is reflected in the y-axis, the image is the curve $y = \tan x$. Since a reflection in the x-axis followed by a reflection in the y-axis is a reflection in the origin, the graph of $y = \tan x$ has point symmetry with respect to a reflection in the origin.

EXERCISES WITH OPEN-RESPONSE PROBLEMS

1. Sketch the graph of $y = \tan x$ from $x = -2\pi$ to $x = 2\pi$.
2. What is the period of $y = \tan x$?
3. What is the domain of $y = \tan x$?   4. What is the range of $y = \tan x$?
5. Between what values of x in the interval $-\frac{\pi}{2} < x < \frac{\pi}{2}$ is $\tan x$:   **a.** increasing?   **b.** decreasing?
6. Which is *not* an element of the domain of $y = \tan x$?
   (1) π (2) 2π (3) $\frac{\pi}{2}$ (4) $-\pi$

7. **a.** On the same set of axes, sketch the graphs of $y = 2 \sin x$ and $y = \tan x$ for values of x in the interval $-\pi \leq x \leq \pi$.
   b. State how many values of x in the interval $-\pi \leq x \leq \pi$ are solutions of $\tan x = 2 \sin x$.

15-8 GRAPHS OF RECIPROCAL FUNCTIONS

The graphs of $y = \csc x$, $y = \sec x$, and $y = \cot x$ can be sketched by comparing each function with its reciprocal function. We recall that the reciprocal of a number whose absolute value is less than or equal to 1 is a number whose absolute value is greater than or equal to 1. Therefore, since $|\sin x| \leq 1$, $|\csc x| \geq 1$. The reciprocal of 0 is undefined. Therefore, when $\sin x = 0$, $\csc x$ is undefined. For comparison, the graph of $y = \csc x$ is shown in Figure 1 as a solid line, and the graph of $y = \sin x$ as a dotted line.

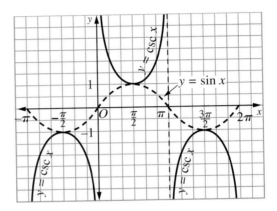

Figure 1

When $x = 0$, $\sin x = 0$, and $\csc x$ is undefined. For $0 < x \leq \frac{\pi}{2}$, $\sin x$ increases through values greater than 0 to 1, and $\csc x$ decreases from large positive values to 1. When $\sin x = 1$, $\csc x = 1$. Then, for $\frac{\pi}{2} < x < \pi$, $\sin x$ decreases from 1 to values close to 0, and $\csc x$ increases from 1 to large positive values. When $x = \pi$, $\sin x$ is again 0, and $\csc x$ is undefined. When $\pi < x < 2\pi$, a similar pattern is observed for negative values of $\sin x$ and $\csc x$.

$$y = \csc x$$

Domain $= \{x \mid x \in \text{Real numbers and } x \neq k\pi \text{ for integral values of } k\}$

Range $= \{y \mid |y| \geq 1\}$

In Figure 2 on page 729, $y = \cos x$ is shown as a dotted line and $y = \sec x$ as a solid line. We can make observations about these functions similar to those made about the graphs of the sine and the cosecant functions. For all odd multiples of $\frac{\pi}{2}$, $\cos x$ is 0 and $\sec x$ is undefined.

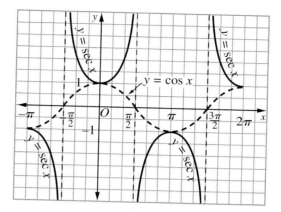

Figure 2

$$y = \sec x$$
Domain $= \{x \mid x \in \text{Real numbers and } x \neq \frac{(2k + 1)\pi}{2} \text{ for integral values of } k\}$
Range $= \{y \mid |y| \geq 1\}$

In Figure 3, $y = \tan x$ is shown as a dotted line and $y = \cot x$ as a solid line. When $\tan x$ is 0, $\cot x$ is undefined; and when $\tan x$ is undefined, $\cot x$ is 0. Therefore, $\cot x$ is 0 for all odd multiples of $\frac{\pi}{2}$ and is undefined for all multiples of π.

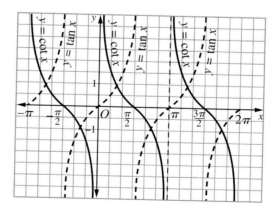

Figure 3

$$y = \cot x$$
Domain $= \{x \mid x \in \text{Real numbers and } x \neq k\pi \text{ for integral values of } k\}$
Range $= \{y \mid y \in \text{Real numbers}\}$

Most graphing calculators do not have keys for the secant, cosecant, and cotangent functions. These functions can be evaluated or graphed by using the reciprocals of the cosine, sine, and tangent functions. For example, to use a graphing calculator to draw the graph of $y = \sec x$, we put the calculator in radian mode and set the $\boxed{\text{WINDOW}}$ from -2π to 2π for x and from -10 to 10 for y.

Enter: $\boxed{\text{Y=}}$ $\boxed{1}$ $\boxed{\div}$ $\boxed{\text{COS}}$ $\boxed{\text{X,T,}\theta\text{,}n}$ $\boxed{\text{ENTER}}$ $\boxed{\text{GRAPH}}$

Display:

EXERCISES WITH OPEN-RESPONSE PROBLEMS

1. If $f(x) = \sec x$, find: **a.** $f(0)$ **b.** $f\left(\frac{\pi}{3}\right)$ **c.** $f(\pi)$

2. If $f(x) = \csc x$, find: **a.** $f\left(\frac{\pi}{2}\right)$ **b.** $f\left(\frac{7\pi}{6}\right)$ **c.** $f(-\pi)$

3. If $f(x) = \cot x$, find: **a.** $f\left(\frac{\pi}{4}\right)$ **b.** $f\left(\frac{\pi}{2}\right)$ **c.** $f\left(\frac{-\pi}{2}\right)$

4. State two values of x in the interval $\frac{-\pi}{2} \leq x \leq \frac{3\pi}{2}$ for which $\csc x$ is undefined.

5. For what value of x in the interval $0 \leq x \leq \pi$ is the value of $\csc x$ a minimum?

6. State two values of x in the interval $0 \leq x \leq 2\pi$ for which $\sec x$ is undefined.

7. State two values of x in the interval $\frac{-\pi}{2} \leq x \leq \frac{3\pi}{2}$ for which $\cos x = \sec x$.

8. State two values of x in the interval $0 \leq x \leq \pi$ for which $\tan x = \cot x$.

9. State two values of x in the interval $-\pi \leq x \leq \pi$ for which $\cot x = 0$.

In 10–12, select the *numeral* preceding the expression that best answers the question.

10. Which is *not* an element of the domain of $y = \cot x$?

(1) 0 (2) $\frac{\pi}{2}$ (3) $\frac{3\pi}{2}$ (4) $\frac{-\pi}{2}$

11. Which is *not* an element of the range of $y = \sec x$?
(1) 1 (2) 2 (3) -1 (4) $\frac{1}{2}$

12. Which is *not* an element of the range of $y = \csc x$?
(1) $\sqrt{2}$ (2) -2 (3) $\frac{\sqrt{2}}{2}$ (4) 4

15-9   REFLECTIONS OVER THE LINE $y = x$

In Chapter 13, we discussed the reflection of a set of points in the line $y = x$:

$$P(x, y) \rightarrow P'(y, x) \quad \text{OR} \quad r_{y=x}(x, y) = (y, x)$$

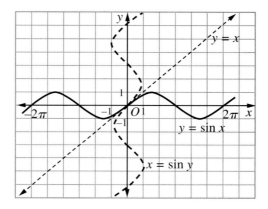

When the set of points that is the graph of $y = \sin x$ is reflected in the line $y = x$, the set of image points is the graph of $x = \sin y$. We can see from the graph that each x does not have a unique y. In other words, the set of ordered pairs defined by $x = \sin y$ is not a function of x since many ordered pairs have the same first element.

When we express a set of ordered pairs in terms of its equation, it is usually convenient to define the second element, y, in terms of the first element x. Therefore, we want to rewrite $x = \sin y$ so that it is solved for y. We will begin by expressing the relationship in words:

$$x = \sin y$$

y is the angle whose sine is x.

Since the measure of a central angle of a unit circle is equal to the measure of the arc, we can also say:

y is the arc whose sine is x.

To abbreviate this statement and write it in symbolic form, we will pick out essential words:

y is the **arc** whose **sine** is **x**.

Using just these essential words, we can write the sentence as $y = $ arc sin x:

$$y = \text{arc} \sin x \leftrightarrow x = \sin y$$

For example, $\frac{\pi}{2} = $ arc sin 1 is equivalent to $1 = \sin\frac{\pi}{2}$. Also, $90° = $ arc sin 1 is equivalent to $1 = \sin 90°$. Since $\frac{\pi}{2}$ radians and $90°$ are measures of the same angle, the two statements express the same equality.

Similarly, $\frac{\pi}{6} = $ arc sin $\frac{1}{2}$ is equivalent to $\frac{1}{2} = \sin\frac{\pi}{6}$. Also, $30° = $ arc sin $\frac{1}{2}$ is equivalent to $\frac{1}{2} = \sin 30°$. Since $\frac{\pi}{6}$ radians and $30°$ are measures of the same angle, the two statements express the same equality.

If we consider the values of θ for which $\theta = \sin\frac{1}{2}$, there are infinitely many solutions.

$$\theta = \text{arc sin } \tfrac{1}{2} \leftrightarrow \sin\theta = \tfrac{1}{2}$$

Since θ is the measure of an angle whose sine is positive, θ can be the measure of an angle in Quadrant I or in Quadrant II.

In Quadrant I

$\theta = 30°$

In Quadrant II

$\theta = (180 - 30)° = 150°$

The angle whose measure is θ can also be any angle whose measure differs from $30°$ or from $150°$ by a multiple of $360°$.

In Quadrant I

$\theta = 30° + 1(360)° = 390°$
$\theta = 30° + 2(360)° = 750°$
$\theta = 30° + (-1)(360)° = -330°$

In Quadrant II

$\theta = 150° + 1(360)° = 510°$
$\theta = 150° + 2(360)° = 870°$
$\theta = 150° + (-1)(360)° = -210°$

In *degree measure*, the solution of the equation $\theta = $ arc sin $\frac{1}{2}$ is:

$\theta = 30° + 360°k$ OR $\theta = 150° + 360°k$ $(k \in \text{Integers})$

In *radian measure*, the solution of the equation $\theta = $ arc sin $\frac{1}{2}$ is:

$\theta = \frac{\pi}{6} + 2\pi k$ OR $\theta = \frac{5\pi}{6} + 2\pi k$ $(k \in \text{Integers})$

We use notation similar to arc sin for the reflection of the other trigonometric functions over the line $y = x$.

Function	Reflection in the line $y = x$
$y = \cos x$	$x = \cos y \leftrightarrow y = \text{arc cos } x$
$y = \tan x$	$x = \tan y \leftrightarrow y = \text{arc tan } x$

An expression such as $y = \text{arc cos}\,(-0.2249)$ has two solutions in the interval $0° \le y \le 360°$, one in Quadrant II and the other in Quadrant III. When we use a calculator to evaluate this expression, the calculator will return just one value of y.

Enter: 2nd   cos⁻¹   (−)   .2249   ENTER

Display: `102.9969979`

The measure of a second-quadrant angle whose cosine is -0.2249 is approximately equal to 103°. To find another value of y, we must first find the measure of the reference angle, R. Then we use the measure of R to find the measure of the third-quadrant angle.

$$\text{m}\angle R = 180° - 103° = 77°$$
$$y = 180° + 77° = 257°$$

Therefore, if $y = \text{arc cos}\,(-0.2249)$ and $0° \le y \le 360°$, then $y = 103°$ or $y = 257°$.

EXAMPLES

1. If $\theta = \text{arc tan}\,(-1)$ and $0° \le \theta \le 360°$, find θ.

Solution   (1) Rewrite $\theta = \text{arc tan}\,(-1)$ as $\tan \theta = -1$.

(2) Since $\tan \theta$ is negative, θ is the measure of a second- or a fourth-quadrant angle.

(3) Since $\tan 45° = 1$, the measure of the reference angle is 45°.

(4) In Quadrant II, $\theta = 180° - 45° = 135°$.
    In Quadrant IV, $\theta = 360° - 45° = 315°$.

Answer: $\theta = 135°$ or $\theta = 315°$

---

2. Find $\cos\,(\text{arc sin}\,0.6)$.

Solution   Let $\theta = \text{arc sin}\,0.6$. Then find $\cos \theta$ when $\sin \theta = 0.6$.

(1) Use the Pythagorean identity. $\cos^2 \theta = 1 - \sin^2 \theta$

(2) Substitute. $= 1 - (0.6)^2$

(3) Simplify. $= 1 - 0.36$

   $= 0.64$

(4) Take the square root of each side. $\cos \theta = \pm 0.8$

Answer: ± 0.8

---

3. Find $\cot\left(\text{arc tan } \frac{8}{5}\right)$.

Solution Let $\phi = \text{arc tan } \frac{8}{5}$. Then find $\cot\phi$ when $\tan\phi = \frac{8}{5}$.

Since $\cot\phi = \frac{1}{\tan\phi}$,

$$\cot\phi = \frac{1}{\frac{8}{5}} = \frac{1}{\frac{8}{5}} \cdot \frac{5}{5} = \frac{5}{8}$$

Answer: $\frac{5}{8}$

Note: Cotangent and tangent are inverse functions. If $\tan\theta = k$, then $\cot\theta = \frac{1}{k}$. Thus, if it is known that $\tan\theta = \frac{8}{5}$, then $\cot\theta = \frac{5}{8}$.

EXERCISES WITH OPEN-RESPONSE PROBLEMS

In 1–6, rewrite each statement as an equivalent statement, using arc sin, arc cos, or arc tan.

1. $\sin\theta = \frac{1}{2}$
2. $\cos\theta = -\frac{\sqrt{3}}{2}$
3. $\tan\theta = 2$

4. $\sin\theta = 0.1$
5. $\tan\theta = -\frac{4}{5}$
6. $\cos\theta = 1$

In 7–12, rewrite each statement as an equivalent statement, using $\sin\theta$, $\cos\theta$, or $\tan\theta$.

7. $\theta = \text{arc cos } \frac{1}{2}$
8. $\theta = \text{arc tan }\left(-\sqrt{3}\right)$
9. $\theta = \text{arc sin } \frac{\sqrt{2}}{2}$
10. $\theta = \text{arc tan } 1$
11. $\theta = \text{arc sin }(-1)$
12. $\theta = \text{arc cos } 0$

In 13–21:   **a.** Rewrite each statement as an equivalent statement, using $\sin\theta$, $\cos\theta$, or $\tan\theta$.   **b.** Find, to the *nearest degree*, all values of θ in the interval $0° \leq \theta \leq 360°$.

13. $\theta = \text{arc sin } 1$
14. $\theta = \text{arc cos }\left(-\frac{\sqrt{3}}{2}\right)$
15. $\theta = \text{arc tan } 0$

16. $\theta = \text{arc cos } \frac{\sqrt{2}}{2}$
17. $\theta = \text{arc sin }(0.9903)$
18. $\theta = \text{arc cos }(0.7314)$

19. $\theta = \text{arc tan }(-3.7321)$
20. $\theta = \text{arc cos }(-0.8988)$
21. $\theta = \text{arc sin }(-0.3907)$

In 22–27, find all values of θ, in radians, in the interval $0 \le \theta \le 2\pi$.

22. $\theta = \text{arc sin} \left(-\frac{1}{2} \right)$

23. $\theta = \text{arc tan} \, (-1)$

24. $\theta = \text{arc cos} \, \frac{\sqrt{3}}{2}$

25. $\theta = \text{arc sin} \, \frac{\sqrt{3}}{2}$

26. $\theta = \text{arc tan} \, \sqrt{3}$

27. $\theta = \text{arc cos} \left(-\frac{\sqrt{2}}{2} \right)$

28. Find $\sin \left(\text{arc cos} \, \frac{1}{2} \right)$.

29. Find $\tan \, (\text{arc sin} \, 0)$.

30. Find $\cos \, (\text{arc sin} \, (-1))$.

31. Find $\sec \, (\text{arc cos} \, 0.3)$.

32. Find $\sin \, (\text{arc csc} \, 4)$.

33. Find $\tan \left(\text{arc cot} \, \frac{3}{2} \right)$.

34. Find the positive value of $\cos \left(\text{arc sin} \, \frac{4}{5} \right)$.

35. Find the positive value of $\sin \left(\text{arc cos} \left(-\frac{5}{13} \right) \right)$.

36. Find the positive value of $\cos \, (\text{arc sin} \, 0.28)$.

37. Express $\cos \, (\text{arc sin} \, a)$ in terms of a.

38. Express $\sin \, (\text{arc sin} \, b)$ in terms of b.

In 39–42, select the *numeral* preceding the expression that best completes the sentence or answers the question.

39. If $x = \text{arc sin} \left(-\frac{1}{2} \right)$, then x can be equal to

(1) 30°   (2) 60°   (3) 300°   (4) 330°

40. If $y = \text{arc cos} \left(-\frac{1}{2} \right)$, then y can be equal to

(1) $\frac{\pi}{6}$ (2) $\frac{\pi}{3}$ (3) $\frac{2\pi}{3}$ (4) $\frac{5\pi}{6}$

41. If $\theta = \text{arc sin} \, \frac{\sqrt{2}}{2}$, then θ can *not* equal

(1) 45°   (2) 135°   (3) 405°   (4) 585°

42. If $\theta = \text{arc cos} \, 1$, then θ can *not* equal which radian measure?

(1) 0   (2) π (3) 2π (4) -4π

15-10   INVERSE TRIGONOMETRIC FUNCTIONS

When the sets of points $y = \sin x$, $y = \cos x$, and $y = \tan x$ are reflected in the line $y = x$, the images are the sets of points $y = \text{arc sin} \, x$, $y = \text{arc cos} \, x$, and $y = \text{arc tan} \, x$. These sets of image points are not functions of x since each value of x is paired with many values of y. However, by limiting the range, that is, the allowable values of y, we can define functions that are inverse functions of the trigonometric functions.

Inverse Sine Function

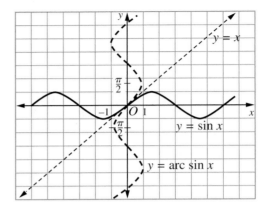

Figure 1

In Figure 1, two graphs are drawn: $y = \sin x$ and $y = \text{arc sin } x$ (the image of $y = \sin x$ under a reflection in the line $y = x$). We observe that $y = \sin x$ is a function with domain $= \{x \mid x \in \text{Real numbers}\}$ and range $= \{y \mid -1 \leq y \leq 1\}$.

However, $y = \text{arc sin } x$ is *not* a function of x. For $y = \text{arc sin } x$, we see that the domain $= \{x \mid -1 \leq x \leq 1\}$ and the range $= \{y \mid y \in \text{Real numbers}\}$.

If we select values of y so that each value of x is assigned to a single value of y by the equation $y = \text{arc sin } x$, the resulting set of points will be a function. To do this, we can limit the range to the values of y from $-\frac{\pi}{2}$ to $\frac{\pi}{2}$ so that the values of x will vary from -1 to 1 just once. This set of points (seen as the solid portion of the graph of $y = \text{arc sin } x$ in Figure 1 and reproduced in Figure 2) is a function.

To distinguish the relation $y = \text{arc sin } x$ from the function $y = \text{Arc sin } x$ just formed, we use the capital letter A to write the word *arc* in the expression ***Arc sin***. Just as the range in $y = \text{Arc sin } x$ is restricted, we must work with only a portion of the domain of the sine function (that is, a **restricted domain** of $y = \sin x$) to define the inverse sine function.

Figure 2

A Subset of the Sine Function	Inverse Sine Function
$y = \sin x$	$y = \textbf{Arc sin } x$
Restricted Domain $= \left\{x \mid -\frac{\pi}{2} \leq x \leq \frac{\pi}{2}\right\}$	Domain $= \{x \mid -1 \leq x \leq 1\}$
Range $= \{y \mid -1 \leq y \leq 1\}$	Range $= \left\{y \mid -\frac{\pi}{2} \leq y \leq \frac{\pi}{2}\right\}$

Another notation for $y = \text{Arc sin } x$ is $y = \text{Sin}^{-1} x$, but we must be careful not to confuse this notation with the exponent -1 that indicates a reciprocal.

Notice how Arc sin is evaluated in the following example.

☐   Find Arc sin $\left(-\frac{\sqrt{2}}{2}\right)$.

Using algebra: If $\theta = \text{Arc sin } \left(-\frac{\sqrt{2}}{2}\right)$, then $\sin \theta = -\frac{\sqrt{2}}{2}$ and $-\frac{\pi}{2} \le \theta \le \frac{\pi}{2}$. Since $\sin \frac{\pi}{4} = \frac{\sqrt{2}}{2}$, the measure of the reference angle is $\frac{\pi}{4}$. Since $\sin \theta$ is negative, $\sin \left(-\frac{\pi}{4}\right) = -\frac{\sqrt{2}}{2}$ and $\theta = -\frac{\pi}{4}$. Thus, Arc sin $\left(-\frac{\sqrt{2}}{2}\right) = -\frac{\pi}{4}$.   *Answer*

Using a calculator: Evaluate Arc sin $\left(-\frac{\sqrt{2}}{2}\right)$ by making this entry:

Enter:

If the calculator is set to a radian (RAD) mode, then:

Display: $\boxed{-.7853981634}$

Although -0.7853981634 is a rational approximation of $-\frac{\pi}{4}$, this fact is not evident.

Answer: Arc sin $\left(-\frac{\sqrt{2}}{2}\right) = -\frac{\pi}{4}$

If the calculator is set to a degree (DEG) mode, then:

Display: $\boxed{-45.}$

Convert $-45°$ to $-\frac{\pi}{4}$ radians, and write the value as a real number:

$$\text{Arc sin } \left(-\frac{\sqrt{2}}{2}\right) = -\frac{\pi}{4}$$

Inverse Cosine Function

In Figure 3, two graphs are drawn: $y = \cos x$ and $y = \text{arc cos } x$ (the image of $y = \cos x$ under a reflection in the line $y = x$).

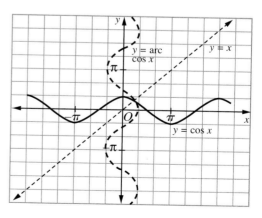

Figure 3

We know that $y = \cos x$ is a function. We observe in Figure 3 on page 737 that the function $y = \cos x$ has domain = $\{x \mid x \in$ Real numbers$\}$ and range = $\{y \mid -1 \leq y \leq 1\}$.

However, $y = \text{arc} \cos x$ is *not* a function of x. For $y = \text{arc} \cos x$, we see that the domain = $\{x \mid -1 \leq x \leq 1\}$ and the range = $\{y \mid y \in$ Real numbers$\}$.

As we did with the relation $y = \text{arc} \sin x$, we can select values of y so that each value of x is assigned to a single value of y by the equation $y = \text{arc} \cos x$. The resulting set of points will be a function. To do this, we must limit the range to the values of y from 0 to π so that the values of x will vary from -1 to 1 just once. This set of points (seen as the solid portion of the graph of $y = \text{arc} \cos x$ in Figure 3 and reproduced in Figure 4) is a function.

Figure 4

Just as with the inverse sine function, we use the capital A in writing the word *arc* in the expression (*Arc cos*) to distinguish the relation $y = \text{arc} \cos x$ from the function $y = \text{Arc} \cos x$. The function $y = \text{Arc} \cos x$ is the inverse of a subset of the cosine function, $y = \cos x$, formed by restricting the domain.

A Subset of the Cosine Function	Inverse Cosine Function
$y = \cos x$	$y = \text{Arc} \cos x$
Restricted Domain = $\{x \mid 0 \leq x \leq \pi\}$	Domain = $\{x \mid -1 \leq x \leq 1\}$
Range = $\{y \mid -1 \leq y \leq 1\}$	Range = $\{y \mid 0 \leq y \leq \pi\}$

The Arc cos function appears in the following example.

☐ Find $\sin\left(\text{Arc} \cos \frac{1}{2}\right)$.

Using algebra: We are asked to find $\sin \theta$ when $\theta = \text{Arc} \cos \frac{1}{2}$, that is, when $\cos \theta = \frac{1}{2}$ and $0 \leq \theta \leq \pi$. Since $\cos \frac{\pi}{3} = \frac{1}{2}$, then $\theta = \frac{\pi}{3}$ and $\sin \frac{\pi}{3} = \frac{\sqrt{3}}{2}$. Therefore,

$\sin\left(\text{Arc} \cos \frac{1}{2}\right) = \sin\left(\frac{\pi}{3}\right) = \frac{\sqrt{3}}{2}$.   *Answer*

Using a calculator: Work with a degree setting; evaluate Arc cos $\frac{1}{2}$.

Enter: [2nd] [cos⁻¹] 1 [÷] 2 [ENTER]

Display: [60.]

Then, $\sin\left(\text{Arc} \cos \frac{1}{2}\right) = \sin(60°) = \frac{\sqrt{3}}{2}$.   *Answer*

Inverse Tangent Function

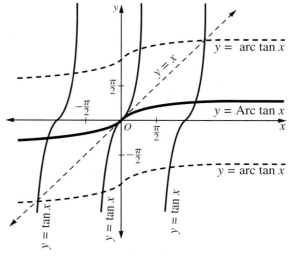

Figure 5

In Figure 5, two graphs are drawn: $y = \tan x$ and $y = \text{arc tan } x$ (the image of $y = \tan x$ under a reflection in the line $y = x$). We recall that $\tan x$ is not defined for values of x that are odd multiples of $\frac{\pi}{2}$. Therefore, $y = \tan x$ is a function whose domain is

$$\left\{ x \mid x \in \text{Real numbers and } x \neq \frac{(2k + 1)\pi}{2} \text{ for integral values of } k \right\}$$

and whose range $= \{ y \mid y \in \text{Real numbers} \}$. However, $y = \text{arc tan } x$ is *not* a function of x.

For $y = \text{arc tan } x$, the domain $= \{ x \mid x \in \text{Real numbers} \}$ and the range is

$$\left\{ y \mid y \in \text{Real numbers and } y \neq \frac{(2k + 1)\pi}{2} \text{ for integral values of } k \right\}.$$

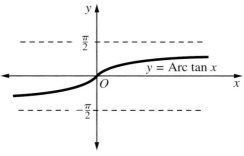

Figure 6

If we select values of y so that each value of x is assigned to a single value of y by the equation $y = $ arc tan x, the resulting set of points will be a function. To do this, we must limit the range to the values of y from $-\frac{\pi}{2}$ to $\frac{\pi}{2}$, but not including those values, so that the values of x will assume every real number as a value just once. This set of points (seen as a heavy line in Figure 5 and reproduced in Figure 6) is a function whose second elements are indicated by the expression **Arc tan**. The function $y = $ Arc tan x is the inverse of a subset of the tangent function, $y = \tan x$, formed by restricting the domain.

A Subset of the Tangent Function	Inverse Tangent Function
$y = \tan x$	$y = $ **Arc tan** x
Restricted Domain $= \left\{ x \mid -\frac{\pi}{2} < x < \frac{\pi}{2} \right\}$	Domain $= \{ x \mid x \in$ Real numbers$\}$
Range $= \{ y \mid y \in$ Real numbers$\}$	Range $= \left\{ y \mid -\frac{\pi}{2} < y < \frac{\pi}{2} \right\}$

The following example involves the Arc tan function.

☐ Find $\cos \left(\text{Arc tan} \left(-\sqrt{3} \right) \right)$.

Using algebra: We are asked to find $\cos \theta$ when $\theta = $ Arc tan $\left(-\sqrt{3} \right)$, that is, when $\tan \theta = -\sqrt{3}$ and $-\frac{\pi}{2} < \theta < \frac{\pi}{2}$. Since $\tan \frac{\pi}{3} = \sqrt{3}$, the measure of the reference angle is $\frac{\pi}{3}$. But, since $\tan \theta$ is negative, $\tan \left(-\frac{\pi}{3} \right) = -\sqrt{3}$ and $\theta = -\frac{\pi}{3}$. Thus, $\cos \left(\text{Arc tan} \left(-\sqrt{3} \right) \right) = \cos \left(-\frac{\pi}{3} \right) = \frac{1}{2}$.   *Answer*

Using a calculator: In each of two approaches, a degree (DEG) setting is utilized.

Enter: [2nd] [TAN⁻¹] [(−)] [2nd] [√] 3 [ENTER]

Display: [−60.]

Then, $\cos \left(\text{Arc tan} \left(-\sqrt{3} \right) \right) = \cos \left(-60° \right)$

and $\cos \left(-60° \right) = \frac{1}{2}$.   *Answer*

Enter: [COS] [2nd] [TAN⁻¹] [(−)] [2nd] [√] 3 [ENTER]

Display: [.5]

Here, it is directly shown that

$$\cos \left(\text{Arc tan} \left(-\sqrt{3} \right) \right) = 0.5 = \frac{1}{2}.   \text{Answer}$$

The functions $y = \text{Arc sec } x$, $y = \text{Arc csc } x$, and $y = \text{Arc cot } x$ can be defined by similar restrictions of the ranges of the corresponding relations. In turn, we must restrict the domains of the functions $y = \sec x$, $y = \csc x$, and $y = \cot x$ to define these inverse trigonometric functions.

The restricted domains and ranges are listed here for students who wish to investigate these functions.

A Subset of the Secant Function	Inverse Secant Function
$y = \sec x$	$y = \text{Arc sec } x$
Restricted Domain $= \left\{x \mid 0 \le x \le \pi, \text{ and } x \ne \frac{\pi}{2}\right\}$	Domain $= \{x \mid \lvert x \rvert \ge 1\}$
Range $= \{y \mid \lvert y \rvert \ge 1\}$	Range $= \left\{y \mid 0 \le y \le \pi, \text{ and } y \ne \frac{\pi}{2}\right\}$
A Subset of the Cosecant Function	Inverse Cosecant Function
$y = \csc x$	$y = \text{Arc csc } x$
Restricted Domain $= \left\{x \mid 0 < \lvert x \rvert \le \frac{\pi}{2}\right\}$	Domain $= \{x \mid \lvert x \rvert \ge 1\}$
Range $= \{y \mid \lvert y \rvert \ge 1\}$	Range $= \left\{y \mid 0 < \lvert y \rvert \le \frac{\pi}{2}\right\}$
A Subset of the Cotangent Function	Inverse Cotangent Function
$y = \cot x$	$y = \text{Arc cot } x$
Restricted Domain $= \left\{x \mid 0 < \lvert x \rvert \le \frac{\pi}{2}, \text{ and } x \ne -\frac{\pi}{2}\right\}$	Domain $= \{x \mid x \in \text{Real numbers}\}$
Range $= \{y \mid y \in \text{Real numbers}\}$	Range $= \left\{y \mid 0 < \lvert y \rvert \le \frac{\pi}{2}, \text{ and } y \ne -\frac{\pi}{2}\right\}$

Degree Measures of the Inverse Trigonometric Functions

When the expression Arc sin a, Arc cos a, or Arc tan a is evaluated, the value may be expressed in degrees as well as in radians.

$$\theta = \text{Arc sin } a \leftrightarrow \sin \theta = a \text{ and } -\frac{\pi}{2} \leq \theta \leq \frac{\pi}{2} \text{ in radians}$$

$$\sin \theta = a \text{ and } -90° \leq \theta \leq 90° \text{ in degrees}$$

$$\theta = \text{Arc cos } a \leftrightarrow \cos \theta = a \text{ and } 0 \leq \theta \leq \pi \text{ in radians}$$

$$\cos \theta = a \text{ and } 0° \leq \theta \leq 180° \text{ in degrees}$$

$$\theta = \text{Arc tan } a \leftrightarrow \tan \theta = a \text{ and } -\frac{\pi}{2} < \theta < \frac{\pi}{2} \text{ in radians}$$

$$\tan \theta = a \text{ and } -90° < \theta < 90° \text{ in degrees}$$

☐   Evaluate Arc tan (-1).

Using algebra: If Arc tan $(-1) = \theta$, then $\tan \theta = -1$ and either $-\frac{\pi}{2} < \theta < \frac{\pi}{2}$ (in radians) or $-90° < \theta < 90°$ (in degrees).

Since $\tan \frac{\pi}{4} = 1$ and $\tan 45° = 1$, the measure of the reference angle is $\frac{\pi}{4}$ radians or 45°. Therefore, $\tan \left(-\frac{\pi}{4}\right) = -1$ and $\tan (-45°) = -1$.

Thus, Arc tan $(-1) = -\frac{\pi}{4}$ radians, or Arc tan $(-1) = -45°$.   *Answer*

Using a calculator: Evaluate Arc tan (-1) with a degree (DEG) setting, and answer either directly in degrees or convert to radians.

Enter: | 2nd | | TAN⁻¹ | | (−) | 1 | ENTER |

Display: | _____ −45. |

Thus, Arc tan $(-1) = -45°$, or Arc tan $(-1) = -\frac{\pi}{4}$.   *Answer*

EXAMPLES

1. If $\theta = \text{Arc cos } 0$, what is the value of θ in radians?

Solution   We are asked to find the value of θ when $\cos \theta = 0$ and $0 \leq \theta \leq \pi$.

Since $\cos \frac{\pi}{2} = 0$, $\theta = \frac{\pi}{2}$.

Answer: $\frac{\pi}{2}$

2. If $\theta = \text{Arc} \sin \left(-\frac{1}{2}\right)$, find the value of θ in degrees.

Solution   We are asked to find θ when $\sin \theta = -\frac{1}{2}$ and $-90° \leq \theta \leq 90°$.

Since $\sin 30° = \frac{1}{2}$, the measure of the reference angle is $30°$.

Therefore, $\sin (-30°) = -\frac{1}{2}$ and $\theta = -30°$.

Calculator
Solution

Enter: [**2nd**] [**SIN⁻¹**] [**(−)**] 1 [**÷**] 2

Display: [−30.   ]

Answer: $-30°$

---

3. Find the value of $\text{Arc} \tan \frac{\sqrt{3}}{3}$.

Solution   We are asked to find the angle measure θ when $\tan \theta = \frac{\sqrt{3}}{3}$ and either

$-\frac{\pi}{2} < \theta < \frac{\pi}{2}$ (in radians) or $-90° < \theta < 90°$ (in degrees).

Since $\tan \frac{\pi}{6} = \frac{\sqrt{3}}{3}$ and $\tan 30° = \frac{\sqrt{3}}{3}$, here $\text{Arc} \tan \frac{\sqrt{3}}{3} = \frac{\pi}{6}$ radians or $30°$.

Calculator
Solution

Evaluate $\text{Arc} \tan \frac{\sqrt{3}}{3}$ in a degree (DEG) setting, and answer either directly in degrees or convert to radians.

Enter: [**2nd**] [**TAN⁻¹**] [**2nd**] [**√**] 3 [**)**] [**÷**] 3 [**ENTER**]

Display: [30.   ]

Thus, $\text{Arc} \tan \frac{\sqrt{3}}{3} = 30°$, or $\text{Arc} \tan \frac{\sqrt{3}}{3} = \frac{\pi}{6}$ radians.

Answer: $\frac{\pi}{6}$ radians or $30°$

EXERCISES

In 1–12, in each case find the value of θ in degrees.

1. $\theta = \text{Arc} \cos \frac{1}{2}$

2. $\theta = \text{Arc} \sin 0$

3. $\theta = \text{Arc} \tan 1$

4. $\theta = \text{Arc} \sin \frac{1}{2}$

5. $\theta = \text{Arc} \cos (-1)$

6. $\theta = \text{Arc} \cos \left(-\frac{\sqrt{3}}{2}\right)$

7. $\theta = \text{Arc tan}\left(-\sqrt{3}\right)$ **8.** $\theta = \text{Arc sin}\left(-1\right)$ **9.** $\theta = \text{Arc tan } 0$

10. $\theta = \text{Arc sin}\left(-\frac{\sqrt{2}}{2}\right)$ **11.** $\theta = \text{Arc cos } 0$ **12.** $\theta = \text{Arc cos } 1$

In 13–24, in each case find the value of θ in radians.

13. $\theta = \text{Arc sin } \frac{\sqrt{3}}{2}$ **14.** $\theta = \text{Arc tan } \sqrt{3}$ **15.** $\theta = \text{Arc cos}\left(-\frac{\sqrt{2}}{2}\right)$

16. $\theta = \text{Arc sin } 1$ **17.** $\theta = \text{Arc sin}\left(-\frac{1}{2}\right)$ **18.** $\theta = \text{Arc tan}\left(-1\right)$

19. $\theta = \text{Arc cos } \frac{\sqrt{2}}{2}$ **20.** $\theta = \text{Arc tan}\left(-\frac{\sqrt{3}}{3}\right)$ **21.** $\theta = \text{Arc cos}\left(-\frac{1}{2}\right)$

22. $\theta = \text{Arc sec } 2$ **23.** $\theta = \text{Arc cot}\left(-\sqrt{3}\right)$ **24.** $\theta = \text{Arc csc } \sqrt{2}$

In 25–33, find the value of each expression.

25. $\sin\left(\text{Arc cos}\left(-1\right)\right)$ **26.** $\tan\left(\text{Arc sin } 0\right)$ **27.** $\tan\left(\text{Arc cos } \frac{4}{5}\right)$

28. $\cos\left(\text{Arc tan}\left(-\frac{5}{12}\right)\right)$ **29.** $\sec\left(\text{Arc cos } \frac{1}{6}\right)$ **30.** $\sin\left(\text{Arc csc}\left(-\sqrt{2}\right)\right)$

31. $\cot\left(\text{Arc tan } 1\right)$ **32.** $\cos\left(\text{Arc sin } \frac{1}{3}\right)$ **33.** $\sec\left(\text{Arc tan } \sqrt{3}\right)$

In 34–39, select the *numeral* preceding the expression that best completes the sentence.

34. If $\theta = \text{Arc sec } \sqrt{2}$, then θ equals
     (1) $30°$ (2) $45°$ (3) $60°$ (4) $90°$

35. The value of $\frac{1}{2}\cot\left(\text{Arc tan } \frac{8}{5}\right)$ is
     (1) $\frac{5}{4}$ (2) $\frac{5}{16}$ (3) $\frac{4}{5}$ (4) $\frac{8}{5}$

36. A value of y that is *not* in the range of the function $y = \text{Arc sin } x$ is
     (1) 0 (2) $\frac{\pi}{2}$ (3) π (4) $-\frac{\pi}{2}$

37. The value of $2 \cos\left(\text{Arc sin}\left(-0.6\right)\right)$ is
     (1) 1.6 (2) -1.6 (3) 0.8 (4) -0.8

38. If $f(x) = \text{Arc sin } x$, then $f\left(-\frac{1}{2}\right)$ is
     (1) $\frac{\pi}{3}$ (2) $-\frac{\pi}{3}$ (3) $\frac{7\pi}{6}$ (4) $-\frac{\pi}{6}$

39. A number that is *not* an element of the range of $y = \text{Arc tan } x$ is
     (1) $\frac{\pi}{3}$ (2) $\frac{\pi}{2}$ (3) 0 (4) $-\frac{\pi}{6}$

40. In a children's park, a slide 27 feet long is built over a horizontal distance of 16 feet along the ground. Determine to the *nearest degree* the measure of the angle the slide makes with the horizontal.

41. From a lighthouse window 190 feet above the water, the keeper sights a boat in distress. The lighthouse keeper, having years of experience, estimates that the boat is 2,000 feet away. Determine to the nearest *tenth of a degree* the angle of depression from the lighthouse window to the boat.

CHAPTER SUMMARY

The ***wrapping function*** maps every point on the real-number line to a point on the unit circle.

The graph of a trigonometric function is a periodic curve; that is, the basic curve repeats and the graph is its own image under the translation $T_{\text{period},0}$.

$y = \sin x$

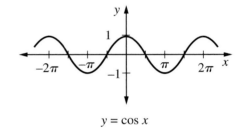

$y = \cos x$

For $y = \sin x$ and $y = \cos x$: Domain $= \{x \mid x \in \text{Real numbers}\}$
Range $= \{y \mid -1 \le y \le 1\}$
Period $= 2\pi$

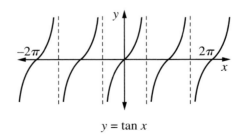

$y = \tan x$

For $y = \tan x$:
Domain $= \{x \mid x \in \text{Real numbers and } x \ne \dfrac{(2k+1)\pi}{2} \text{ for } k \in \text{Integers}\}$
Range $= \{y \mid y \in \text{Real numbers}\}$
Period $= \pi$

For $y = a \sin bx$ and $y = a \cos bx$, each graph has an **amplitude** of $|a|$, a **frequency** of $|b|$, **period** of $\frac{2\pi}{|b|}$, and **translational symmetry** under translation $T_{\frac{2\pi}{|b|}, 0}$.

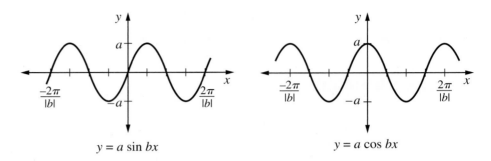

$$y = a \sin bx \qquad\qquad y = a \cos bx$$

When the graph of a trigonometric function is reflected over the line $y = x$, the relations formed are *not* functions. The trigonometric functions have inverses under composition of functions only for a restricted domain.

Function	Reflection in $y = x$	Restricted Domain	Inverse Function
$y = \sin x$	$y = \arcsin x$	$\left\{ x \mid -\frac{\pi}{2} \leq x \leq \frac{\pi}{2} \right\}$	$y = \text{Arc } \sin x$
$y = \cos x$	$y = \arccos x$	$\left\{ x \mid 0 \leq x \leq \pi \right\}$	$y = \text{Arc } \cos x$
$y = \tan x$	$y = \arctan x$	$\left\{ x \mid -\frac{\pi}{2} < x < \frac{\pi}{2} \right\}$	$y = \text{Arc } \tan x$

The equation $\theta = \arcsin a$ is equivalent to $\sin \theta = a$, where θ is an angle measure in degrees or radians. Similar equivalent equations exist for the other trigonometric functions.

VOCABULARY

15-1	Wrapping function
15-2	Basic sine curve (sine wave) Periodic function Period
15-3	Basic cosine curve
15-4	Amplitude
15-5	Frequency
15-10	Restricted domain Arc sin Arc cos Arc tan

REVIEW EXERCISES WITH OPEN-RESPONSE PROBLEMS

In 1–9, for each function, state: **a.** its amplitude, if possible   **b.** its period

1. $y = \sin x$

2. $y = 3 \cos 2x$

3. $y = \tan x$

4. $y = \frac{1}{2} \sin x$

5. $y = 2 \cos \frac{1}{2} x$

6. $y = 4 \sin 3x$

7. $y = -2 \cos \frac{x}{3}$

8. $y = -\frac{1}{2} \sin 2x$

9. $y = -5 \sin \frac{1}{2} x$

10. If the period of $y = \sin bx$ is $\frac{\pi}{2}$, and $b > 0$, state the value of b.

In 11–16, for each function, state: **a.** the domain   **b.** the range

11. $y = 2 \cos x$

12. $y = \tan x$

13. $y = 3 \sin 2x$

14. $y = \text{Arc} \sin x$

15. $y = \text{Arc} \cos x$

16. $y = \text{Arc} \tan x$

17. a. Sketch the graph of $y = 2 \sin x$ for values of x in the interval $0 \le x \le 2\pi$.
  b. On the same set of axes, sketch the graph of $y = \cos 2x$.
  c. How many values of x in the interval $0 \le x \le 2\pi$ are solutions of the equation $2 \sin x = \cos 2x$?

18. a. Sketch the graph of $y = \cos \frac{1}{2} x$ for values of x in the interval $-2\pi \le x \le 2\pi$.
  b. On the same set of axes, sketch the graph of $y = \tan x$.
  c. For how many values of x in the interval $-2\pi \le x \le 2\pi$ does $\cos \frac{1}{2} x = \tan x$?

19. a. On the same set of axes, sketch the graphs of $y = \sin 2x$ and $y = 2 \cos x$ for values of x in the interval $-\pi \le x \le \pi$.
  b. For what values of x in the interval $-\pi \le x \le \pi$ does $\sin 2x = 2 \cos x$?

In 20–28, find all values of θ in the interval $0° \le \theta \le 360°$ that make each statement true.

20. $\theta = \arcsin 0.5$

21. $\theta = \arccos(-1)$

22. $\theta = \arctan 1$

23. $\theta = \arccos 0$

24. $\theta = \arcsin\left(-\frac{\sqrt{3}}{2}\right)$

25. $\theta = \arctan\left(-\sqrt{3}\right)$

26. $\theta = \text{arc sec}(-2)$

27. $\theta = \text{arc csc}\left(-\sqrt{2}\right)$

28. $\theta = \text{arc cot } 0$

In 29–34, write the value of each expression in radian measure.

29. $\text{Arc} \cos \frac{1}{2}$

30. $\text{Arc} \sin(-1)$

31. $\text{Arc} \tan(-1)$

32. $\text{Arc} \cos\left(-\frac{\sqrt{3}}{2}\right)$

33. $\text{Arc cot } 0$

34. $\text{Arc csc } 1$

In 35–40, find the value of each given expression.

35. sin (Arc cos (−1))   **36.** cos (Arc sin 0.6)   **37.** tan (Arc cos 0.8)

38. csc $\left(\text{Arc sin } \frac{1}{3}\right)$ **39.** sec $\left(\text{Arc cos }\left(-\frac{2}{3}\right)\right)$ **40.** tan (Arc cot (−4))

In 41–51, select the *numeral* preceding the expression that best completes the sentence or answers the question.

41. When x increases from $x = 0$ to $x = \pi$, the value of cos x
(1) decreases   (2) decreases, then increases
(3) increases   (4) increases, then decreases

42. When x increases from $x = 0$ to $x = \pi$, the value of sin x
(1) decreases   (2) decreases, then increases
(3) increases   (4) increases, then decreases

43. When x increases from $x = -\frac{\pi}{3}$ to $x = \frac{\pi}{3}$, the value of tan x
(1) decreases   (2) decreases, then increases
(3) increases   (4) increases, then decreases

44. If $x = \text{arc cos }\left(-\frac{\sqrt{2}}{2}\right)$, then x can be equal to
(1) −45°   (2) 45°   (3) 135°   (4) 315°

45. If f(x) = 2 sin 2x, then the value of f$\left(\frac{\pi}{4}\right)$ is
(1) 1   (2) 2   (3) 0   (4) $2\sqrt{2}$

46. Which is *not* an element of the domain of $y = \tan x$?
(1) π (2) 0   (3) $-\pi$ (4) $-\frac{\pi}{2}$

47. The period of the curve whose equation is $y = \frac{1}{3} \cos 2x$ is
(1) $\frac{1}{3}$ (2) 2   (3) π (4) 4π

48. Under which translation is the graph of $y = \sin x$ the image of the graph of $y = \cos x$?
(1) $T_{\frac{\pi}{2},0}$ (2) $T_{\pi,0}$ (3) $T_{2\pi,0}$ (4) $T_{-\pi,0}$

49. What is the maximum value of the function $y = 3 \sin 2x$?
(1) 1   (2) 2   (3) 3   (4) 6

50. The diagram shows the graph of
(1) $y = \sin x$ (2) $y = \sin 2x$
(3) $y = \cos x$ (4) $y = \cos 2x$

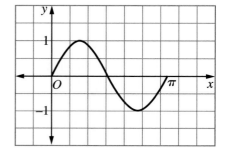

51. The diagram shows the graph of
   (1) $y = 2 \sin x$ (2) $y = \cos 2x$
   (3) $y = \sin 2x$ (4) $y = 2 \cos x$

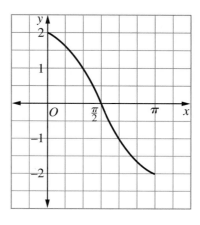

52. The Ferris wheel at an amusement park measures 100 feet in diameter. When running at full speed, the wheel completes one rotation in 30 seconds. The bottom of the wheel is 4 feet above the ground.
   a. Sketch a graph that represents a rider's height above the ground with respect to time (t). Begin when the rider is at the lowest point on the wheel.
   b. Find a trigonometric equation that models the situation.
   c. Determine the rider's height above the ground when $t = 42$ seconds.

CUMULATIVE REVIEW WITH OPEN-RESPONSE PROBLEMS

1. The lengths of the sides of a triangle are 10, 11, and 15. Is the triangle acute, right, or obtuse? Explain your answer.

2. The altitude to the hypotenuse of a right triangle divides the hypotenuse into segments whose lengths are in the ratio $3:2$. The length of the altitude is 18 feet. Find:
   a. the length of the hypotenuse in simplest radical form.
   b. the length of the hypotenuse to the *nearest inch.*
   c. the length of each leg of the triangle in simplest radical form.
   d. the length of each leg of the triangle to the *nearest inch.*

3. Let $f(x) = \frac{1}{x} - 1$.
   a. What is the domain of f?
   b. What is the range of f?
   c. Find $f^{-1}(x)$.
   d. What is the domain of f^{-1}?
   e. What is the range of f^{-1}?

4. Solve and check: $3 + \sqrt{2x - 1} = x + 1$

5. If $\tan \theta = -\frac{7}{24}$ and θ is the measure of an angle in Quadrant II, find $\csc \theta$.

6. If $f(x) = 3 \sin 2x$, find $f\left(\frac{\pi}{12}\right)$.

7. Simplify: $\dfrac{1 - \frac{1}{x^2}}{\frac{1}{x} - 1}$

Exploration

Use an almanac to find the time of sunrise at intervals of one week for a period of one (non-leap) year. Let December 21 be day 0 and December 21 of the next year be day 365. Round the time of sunrise to the *nearest quarter of an hour*. For example, let 6:17 be $6\frac{1}{4}$ and 7:26 be $7\frac{1}{2}$. Draw a graph using the horizontal axis to represent days and the vertical axis to represent time. What trigonometric function most closely resembles the graph that you drew?

Chapter *16*

Exponential Functions

A store owner wants to employ some high school students for 10 days during the winter holidays to help with inventory. To encourage them to work for the full 10 days, he offers two different wage scales: he will pay either $40 a day for each day worked, or $1 for 1 day of work, $2 for 2 days of work, $4 for 3 days of work, and so on, so that the amount earned will double for each additional day worked.

Kyle chooses to work for $40 a day, and Roscoe decides on the other plan. If each boy works for only 5 days, who will be paid more? If each boy works for 10 days, who will be paid more? If they fail to finish the work in 10 days and each works for an extra day, how much does each boy earn for the 11 days? And why did the store owner think that the second wage plan would encourage the students he hired to work for the full 10 days?

The wage scales described above are examples of two different types of functions: the first is a linear function, and the second an exponential function. Exponential functions occur frequently in problems of investment, population growth or decline, radioactive decay, and other examples of financial, business, and scientific change. In this chapter, we will study functions in which the elements of the domain occur as exponents.

16-1 LAWS OF EXPONENTS

In Chapter 8, we reviewed some laws of exponents learned in earlier courses. The following rules summarize operations on powers with like bases:

- **If *a*, *b*, and *c* are positive integers:**

  1. *Multiplication Law.* $x^a \cdot x^b = x^{a+b}$
  2. *Division Law.* $x^a \div x^a = x^{a-b}$ ($x \neq 0$ and $a > b$)
  3. *Power Law.* $(x^a)^c = x^{ac}$

For example:

1. $x^3 \cdot x^2 = x^5$ and $4^3 \cdot 4^2 = 4^5$
2. $y^7 \div y^4 = y^3$ and $3^7 \div 3^4 = 3^3$
3. $(\sin^2 \theta)^3 = \sin^6 \theta$ and $(10^2)^3 = 10^6$

In each of these examples, we were working with powers of like bases. Now, let us consider some examples of powers that have unlike bases, such as xy^3 and $(xy)^3$. We recall that

$$xy^3 = x \cdot y \cdot y \cdot y,$$

while

$$(xy)^3 = (xy)(xy)(xy) = x \cdot x \cdot x \cdot y \cdot y \cdot y = x^3 y^3$$

For example, if $x = 2$ and $y = 3$, then:

1. $xy^3 = 2 \cdot 3^3 = 2 \cdot 3 \cdot 3 \cdot 3 = 54$
2. $(xy)^3 = (2 \cdot 3)^3 = 6^3 = 6 \cdot 6 \cdot 6 = 216$, or
   $(xy)^3 = x^3 y^3 = 2^3 \cdot 3^3 = 8 \cdot 27 = 216$

When we evaluate an expression that includes a power, we must remember that the base of the power does not include the coefficient or the sign of the number or variable that immediately precedes the exponent unless that coefficient or sign is included in parentheses. For example, in the expression $-x^4$, the base is x, not $-x$, and $-x^4 = -1 \cdot x^4$. If we want to raise $-x$ to the fourth power, we write $(-x)^4$, and $(-x)^4 = (-x)(-x)(-x)(-x) = x^4$.

For example, if $x = 2$, then:

1. $-x^4 = -1 \cdot x^4 = -1 \cdot 2^4 = -1 \cdot 2 \cdot 2 \cdot 2 \cdot 2 = -16$
2. $(-x)^4 = (-1 \cdot x^4) = (-1 \cdot 2)^4 = (-2)^4 = (-2)(-2)(-2)(-2) = 16$, or
   $(-x)^4 = (-1 \cdot x)^4 = (-1)^4 \cdot (x)^4 = (-1)^4 \cdot (2)^4 = 1 \cdot 16 = 16$

When dividing powers with unlike bases, we observe a similar pattern. We have learned that

$$\frac{a^3}{b} = \frac{a \cdot a \cdot a}{b},$$

while

$$\left(\frac{a}{b}\right)^3 = \left(\frac{a}{b}\right)\left(\frac{a}{b}\right)\left(\frac{a}{b}\right) = \frac{a^3}{b^3}$$

For example, if $a = 6$ and $b = 4$, then:

1. $\dfrac{a^3}{b} = \dfrac{6^3}{4} = \dfrac{6 \cdot 6 \cdot 6}{4} = \dfrac{216}{4} = 54$

2. $\left(\dfrac{a}{b}\right)^3 = \dfrac{a^3}{b^3} = \dfrac{6^3}{4^3} = \dfrac{6 \cdot 6 \cdot 6}{4 \cdot 4 \cdot 4} = \dfrac{216}{64} = \dfrac{27}{8}$

From the examples we have just seen, we now formulate two more laws of exponents.

- **In general, if a is a positive integer:**

  4. *Power-of-a-Product Law.* $(xy)^a = x^a y^a$

  5. *Power-of-a-Quotient Law.* $\left(\dfrac{x}{y}\right)^a = \dfrac{x^a}{y^a}$ $(y \neq 0)$

EXAMPLES

1. Simplify: $\dfrac{2^8 \cdot 2^4}{(2^5)^2}$.

How to Proceed:

(1) Use the rule for multiplying powers with like bases to simplify the numerator. Use the rule for finding the power of a power to simplify the denominator.

(2) Use the rule for dividing powers with like bases, and simplify.

Solution:

$\dfrac{2^8 \cdot 2^4}{(2^5)^2} = \dfrac{2^{12}}{2^{10}}$

$= 2^2$
$= 4$

Answer: 4

2. Find the value of $\dfrac{(xy)^4}{xy^3}$ when $x = 3$ and $y = 5$.

How to Proceed:

(1) Write the numerator without parentheses.

(2) Divide powers with like bases.

(3) Substitute

(4) Simplify.

Solution:

$\dfrac{(xy)^4}{xy^3} = \dfrac{x^4 y^4}{xy^3}$

$= x^3 y$

$= 3^3 \cdot 5$

$= 27 \cdot 5$
$= 135$

Answer: 135

EXERCISES

In 1–40, simplify each expression. The literal exponents represent positive integers; $x \neq 0$ and $y \neq 0$.

1. $x^7 \cdot x^2$ **2.** $x \cdot x^5$ **3.** $x^9 \div x^4$ **4.** $a^5 \div a$

5. $(a^3)^2$ **6.** $(y^4)^3$ **7.** $2^5 \cdot 2^2$ **8.** $3^4 \div 3^3$

9. $\dfrac{x^8 \cdot x^2}{x^7}$ **10.** $\dfrac{10^5 \cdot 10^4}{10^6}$ **11.** $\dfrac{(x^5)^3}{x^{10}}$ **12.** $\dfrac{(7^3)^4}{7^{10}}$

13. $\dfrac{y^4 \cdot y^3}{(y^2)^3}$ **14.** $\dfrac{5^4 \cdot 5^7}{(5^3)^3}$ **15.** $\dfrac{-x^5}{(-x)^4}$ **16.** $\dfrac{-9^{10}}{(-9^2)^3}$

17. $\dfrac{(xy)^5}{xy^3}$ **18.** $\dfrac{(2x)^5}{2x^3}$ **19.** $\dfrac{(3a)^5}{3^3}$ **20.** $\dfrac{-4y^7}{(2y)^2}$

21. $5^a \cdot 5^b$ **22.** $3^4 \cdot 3^a$ **23.** $x^b \cdot x$ **24.** $y^{n+2} \cdot y^{n+1}$

25. $\dfrac{6^c}{6^b}$ **26.** $\dfrac{10^3}{10^a}$ **27.** $\dfrac{y^{4c}}{y^c}$ **28.** $\dfrac{x^{k+2}}{x^k}$

29. $\left(\dfrac{1}{2}x^2\right)^3$ **30.** $(4y^b)^2$ **31.** $(-x^c)^2$ **32.** $(x^2y)^k$

33. $\dfrac{(2 \cdot 5)^4}{5^4}$ **34.** $\dfrac{2 \cdot 5^4}{5^4}$ **35.** $\dfrac{(3 \cdot 7)^a}{7^a}$ **36.** $\dfrac{3 \cdot 7^a}{7^a}$

37. $3^4 \cdot 2^4$ **38.** $2^c \cdot 5^c$ **39.** $\dfrac{12^4}{6^4}$ **40.** $\dfrac{6^a}{2^a}$

In 41–48, evaluate each expression when $a = 5$ and $b = 2$.

41. ab^2 **42.** $(ab)^2$ **43.** $-ab^2$ **44.** $(-ab)^2$

45. $-(ab)^2$ **46.** $ab(ab)^3$ **47.** $-a^4$ **48.** $-a^3 \div (-a)^2$

In 49–53, express each number as a power of 10.

49. 100   **50.** 1,000   **51.** 1,000,000   **52.** $10^5 \cdot 100^2$ **53.** $100^3 \div 10^4$

In 54–58, express each number as a power of 4.

54. 64   **55.** 256   **56.** $4^5 \cdot 16$ **57.** $4^{10} \div 16$ **58.** 16^3

In 59–62, select the *numeral* preceding the choice that best completes the sentence.

59. The expression 2^6 is equal to
    (1) 4^5 (2) 4^2 (3) 4^3 (4) 4^4

60. The expression $3 \cdot 3^7$ is equal to
    (1) 3^8 (2) 3^7 (3) 9^8 (4) 9^7

61. If $3^a = b$, then 3^{a+1} equals
    (1) $b + 1$ (2) $3b$ (3) $b + 3$ (4) b^2

62. If $10^x = c$, then $100c$ equals
    (1) 10^{x+2} (2) 10^{2x} (3) $1{,}000^x$ (4) 100^{2x}

16-2 EXTENDING THE LAWS OF EXPONENTS

We have defined a power as the product of equal factors. This definition requires that the exponent be a positive integer. Now we will define powers having exponents that are not positive, that is, **zero exponents** and **negative exponents**, in a way that is consistent with the rules for powers already established.

Zero Exponents

We recall the rule for dividing powers with like bases:

$$x^a \div x^b = x^{a-b} \quad (x \neq 0)$$

If we do not require $a > b$, then a may be equal to b. When $a = b$:

$$x^a \div x^b = x^a \div x^a = x^{a-a} = x^0$$

but

$$x^a \div x^a = 1$$

Therefore, in order for x^0 to be meaningful, we must make the following definition:

$$x^0 = 1 \quad (x \neq 0)$$

Since the definition $x^0 = 1$ is based upon division, and division by 0 is not possible, we have stated that $x \neq 0$. Actually, the expression 0^0 (0 to the zero power) is one of several *indeterminate* expressions in mathematics. It is not possible to assign a value to an indeterminate expression.

Before we accept x^0 as a power, we must show that it satisfies the rules for powers. For example:

1. $x^a \cdot x^0 = x^{a+0} = x^a$ and $x^a \cdot x^0 = x^a \cdot 1 = x^a$

2. $x^a \div x^0 = x^{a-0} = x^a$ and $x^a \div x^0 = x^a \div 1 = x^a$

3. $(x^0 \cdot x^a)^b = (x^{a+0})^b = x^{ab}$ and $(x^0 \cdot x^a)^b = (1 \cdot x^a)^b = x^{ab}$

Since x can be any base except 0, any nonzero base to the zero power is 1.

$$4^0 = 1 \qquad 12^0 = 1 \qquad (2ab)^0 = 1 \quad \text{if } a \neq 0 \text{ and } b \neq 0$$

Care must be taken when using the zero exponent, as seen in the following examples:

1. $(-4)^0 = 1$ **2.** $-4^0 = -1 \cdot 4^0 = -1 \cdot 1 = -1$

3. $(3x)^0 = 1$ **4.** $3x^0 = 3 \cdot x^0 = 3 \cdot 1 = 3$

Most graphing calculators will evaluate a power with a zero exponent. For example, to evaluate 5^0:

Enter: 5 $\boxed{\wedge}$ 0 $\boxed{\text{ENTER}}$

Display: $\boxed{\qquad\qquad 1.}$

Negative Exponents

We recall again the rule for dividing powers with like bases:

$$x^a \div x^b = x^{a-b} \quad (x \neq 0)$$

If we do not require $a > b$, then a may be less than b. When $a < b$ and $x \neq 0$, we may use the division law as follows:

$$\frac{x^3}{x^5} = x^{3-5} = x^{-2}$$

It is also true that

$$\frac{x^3}{x^5} = \frac{\overset{1}{\cancel{x}} \cdot \overset{1}{\cancel{x}} \cdot \overset{1}{\cancel{x}}}{\underset{1}{\cancel{x}} \cdot \underset{1}{\cancel{x}} \cdot \underset{1}{\cancel{x}} \cdot x \cdot x} = \frac{1}{x^2}$$

Therefore, $x^{-2} = \frac{1}{x^2}$.

We can use the division law for powers with like bases and the definition of the zero exponent to show that this relationship holds for any exponent b and any base $x \neq 0$.

$$\frac{1}{x^b} = \frac{x^0}{x^b} = x^{0-b} = x^{-b}$$

We can therefore make the following definition:

$$x^{-b} = \frac{1}{x^b} \quad (x \neq 0)$$

To accept this as a valid definition, we must show that powers with negative exponents satisfy the rules for exponents. For example:

1. $x^5 \cdot x^{-3} = x^{5+(-3)} = x^2$ and $x^5 \cdot x^{-3} = x^5 \cdot \frac{1}{x^3} = x^2$

2. $x^4 \div x^{-2} = x^{4-(-2)} = x^6$ and $x^4 \div x^{-2} = x^4 \div \frac{1}{x^2} = x^4 \cdot x^2 = x^6$

3. $(x^{-3})^2 = x^{-3(2)} = x^{-6}$ and $(x^{-3})^2 = \left(\frac{1}{x^3}\right)^2 = \frac{1}{x^6} = x^{-6}$

4. Since x^{-b} is the reciprocal of x^b, the base $x \neq 0$. Just as $x^{-b} = \frac{1}{x^b}$, it can be shown that $\frac{1}{x^{-n}} = x^n$. Here is an example:

$$\frac{1}{x^{-4}} = \frac{x^0}{x^{-4}} = x^{0-(-4)} = x^4$$

or

$$\frac{1}{x^{-4}} = 1 \div x^{-4} = 1 \div \frac{1}{x^4} = 1 \cdot x^4 = x^4$$

5. $\left(\frac{2}{3}\right)^{-n} = \frac{2^{-n}}{3^{-n}} = 2^{-n} \div 3^{-n} = \frac{1}{2^n} \div \frac{1}{3^n} = \frac{1}{2^n} \cdot 3^n = \frac{3^n}{2^n} = \left(\frac{3}{2}\right)^n$

Examples 4 and 5 illustrate the truth of the following generalization:

$$\left(\frac{a}{b}\right)^{-n} = \left(\frac{b}{a}\right)^{n} \quad (a \neq 0, b \neq 0)$$

We can demonstrate the truth of this generalization by evaluating $\left(\frac{2}{5}\right)^{-3}$ and $\left(\frac{5}{2}\right)^{3}$ on a calculator.

Enter: $\boxed{(}$ 2 $\boxed{\div}$ 5 $\boxed{)}$ $\boxed{\wedge}$ 3 $\boxed{(-)}$ $\boxed{\text{ENTER}}$

Display: $\boxed{\qquad 15.625}$

Enter: $\boxed{(}$ 5 $\boxed{\div}$ 2 $\boxed{)}$ $\boxed{y^x}$ 3 $\boxed{=}$

Display: $\boxed{\qquad 15.625}$

EXAMPLES

1. Find the value of $3a^0 + a^{-2}$ if $a = 4$.

How to Proceed: *Solution:*

(1) Use the definitions $a^0 = 1$ and $a^{-2} = \frac{1}{a^2}$. $3a^0 + a^{-2} = 3(1) + \frac{1}{a^2}$

(2) Substitute the value of a. $= 3(1) + \frac{1}{4^2}$

(3) Simplify. $= 3 + \frac{1}{16} = 3\frac{1}{16}$

Calculator   *Enter:* 3 $\boxed{\times}$ 4 $\boxed{\wedge}$ 0 $\boxed{+}$ 4 $\boxed{\wedge}$ $\boxed{(-)}$ 2 $\boxed{\text{ENTER}}$
Solution   *Display:* $\boxed{\qquad 3.0625}$

Answer: $3\frac{1}{16}$ or 3.0625

---

2. Write the expression $\frac{2c^2}{a^3 c^{-2}}$ without a denominator.

How to Proceed: *Solution:*

(1) Rewrite the expression, grouping powers with like bases. $\frac{2c^2}{a^3 c^{-2}} = 2 \cdot \frac{1}{a^3} \cdot \frac{c^2}{c^{-2}}$

(2) Use the definition of a negative exponent and the rule for dividing powers with like bases. $= 2a^{-3}c^{2-(-2)}$

(3) Simplify. $= 2a^{-3}c^4$

Answer: $2a^{-3}c^4$

3. Using only positive exponents, write an expression equivalent to $\frac{5x^{-4}}{y^{-2}}$.

How to Proceed:	*Solution:*
(1) Rewrite the expression, using a separate factor for each base.	$\frac{5x^{-4}}{y^{-2}} = 5 \cdot x^{-4} \cdot \frac{1}{y^{-2}}$
(2) Rewrite each power that has a negative exponent, using the rules $x^{-b} = \frac{1}{x^b}$ and $\frac{1}{x^{-n}} = x^n$.	$= 5 \cdot \frac{1}{x^4} \cdot y^2$
	$= \frac{5y^2}{x^4}$

Answer: $\frac{5y^2}{x^4}$

EXERCISES WITH OPEN-RESPONSE PROBLEMS

In 1–16, find the value of each expression if $a \neq 0$, $y \neq 0$.

1. a^0 **2.** $2a^0$ **3.** $(2a)^0$ **4.** 4^0

5. -4^0 **6.** $(-4)^0$ **7.** $(5y)^0$ **8.** $5y^0$

9. $-5y^0$ **10.** $(-5y)^0$ **11.** 10^0 **12.** -10^0

13. $(-10)^0$ **14.** $\left(\frac{1}{4}\right)^0$ **15.** 0.2^0 **16.** $\left(\frac{2}{3}\right)^0$

In 17–44, in each case, write an equivalent expression, using only positive exponents. The bases are *not* equal to 0.

17. x^{-2} **18.** a^{-5} **19.** c^{-1} **20.** $4b^{-2}$

21. $3k^{-4}$ **22.** $7y^{-1}$ **23.** $8x^{-3}$ **24.** $(2b)^{-1}$

25. $(3a)^{-3}$ **26.** $(9r)^{-2}$ **27.** $(2x)^{-4}$ **28.** $(0.1b)^{-5}$

29. $\frac{1}{a^{-9}}$ **30.** $\frac{1}{x^{-4}}$ **31.** $\frac{1}{c^{-7}}$ **32.** $\frac{1}{d^{-3}}$

33. $\frac{3}{x^{-1}}$ **34.** $\frac{5}{y^{-10}}$ **35.** $\frac{x}{y^{-2}}$ **36.** $\frac{a}{c^{-6}}$

37. $\frac{b^2}{a^{-8}}$ **38.** $\frac{a^{-3}}{b^{-5}}$ **39.** $\frac{b^{-7}}{b^{-2}}$ **40.** $\frac{x^{-1}}{x^{-3}}$

41. $\frac{2y^{-4}}{y^4}$ **42.** $\frac{c^{-3}}{3c}$ **43.** $\frac{3d^{-5}}{6d}$ **44.** $\frac{x^{10}}{2x^{-1}}$

In 45–56, simplify each fraction and write the quotient without a denominator. The variables represent nonzero real numbers.

45. $\frac{ab^2}{a^5b^4}$ **46.** $\frac{x^3}{x^3y^5}$ **47.** $\frac{(x^3y)^3}{xy^3}$ **48.** $\frac{12x^2}{3x^{-7}}$

49. $\frac{4b^{-2}}{4b^{-3}}$ **50.** $\frac{9x^{-5}}{3x^{-8}}$ **51.** $\frac{4d^{-3}}{cd^{-1}}$ **52.** $\frac{(a^{-1})^{-2}}{a^4b^2}$

53. $\frac{(x^{-2})^{-3}}{x^3y^6}$ **54.** $\frac{12(y^2)^{-1}}{(12y)^{-1}}$ **55.** $\frac{(12y^2)^{-1}}{(12y)^{-1}}$ **56.** $\frac{3^{-2}}{(3a^2)^{-2}}$

In 57–84,   **a.** Write each expression as an integer or as the ratio of integers.   **b.** Use a calculator to find the value of each expression as an integer or as a repeating decimal.

57. 7^{-1}

58. 2^{-3}

59. 3^{-2}

60. 3^{-3}

61. $\left(\frac{1}{4}\right)^2$

62. $\left(\frac{1}{4}\right)^{-2}$

63. $\left(\frac{1}{10}\right)^{-3}$

64. $\left(-\frac{1}{10}\right)^3$

65. $5^0(2)^{-1}$

66. $12^0(4)^{-3}$

67. $8^{-1}(7)^0$

68. $10^{-2}(5)^2$

69. $(-8)^{-2}$

70. -8^{-2}

71. $(-9)^{-1}$

72. -9^{-1}

73. $(-5)^{-3}$

74. -5^{-3}

75. $(-10)^{-4}$

76. -10^{-4}

77. $\dfrac{8^0}{8^{-2}}$

78. $\dfrac{3^0}{3^{-4}}$

79. $\dfrac{5^0}{5^{-3}}$

80. $\dfrac{4^{-4}}{4^{-5}}$

81. $\dfrac{(2 \cdot 3)^2}{2 \cdot 3^{-1}}$

82. $\dfrac{(5 \cdot 2)^3}{5 \cdot 2^{-2}}$

83. $\dfrac{(5 \cdot 3)^{-1}}{5 \cdot 3^{-4}}$

84. $\dfrac{3 \cdot 8^{-2}}{(3 \cdot 8)^{-3}}$

85. Find the value of $7a^0 + (5a)^0$ if $a \neq 0$.

86. Find the value of $3b^{-2} + 3b^0$ when $b = 6$.

87. Find the value of $\left(\frac{3}{4}\right)^{-2} \cdot (4)^{-3}$.

88. If $f(x) = 2x^{-1}$, find $f\left(\frac{2}{3}\right)$.

89. If $f(x) = 2x^{-1} + (2x)^{-1}$, find $f(8)$.

90. If $f(x) = 3x^{-2}$, find $f(6)$.

91. If $f(x) = x^{-1} + (2x)^{-1}$, find $f(3)$.

92. If the function $g(x) = 2x^{-2} + x^{-1} + 3x^0$, find $g(2)$.

In 93–97, select the *numeral* preceding the choice that best completes the sentence.

93. The expression $2a^{-2}b^3$ is equivalent to

(1) $\dfrac{b^3}{2a^2}$

(2) $\dfrac{a^{-2}}{2b^{-3}}$

(3) $\dfrac{1}{2a^2b^{-3}}$

(4) $\dfrac{2b^3}{a^2}$

94. The expression $\dfrac{12x^{-2}}{(3x)^{-1}}$ is equivalent to

(1) $4x^{-3}$

(2) $36x^{-3}$

(3) $36x^{-1}$

(4) $4x^{-1}$

95. The expression $(9a^{-1})(3a)^{-2}$ is equivalent to

(1) a^{-3}

(2) $81a^{-3}$

(3) $27a^{-3}$

(4) $27a$

96. The expression $4a^0 + 4^{-1}$ is equal to

(1) 1

(2) $1\frac{1}{4}$

(3) $4\frac{1}{4}$

(4) $\frac{1}{4}$

97. The expression $\dfrac{(2a)^0}{2a^{-2}}$, when $a = 3$, is equal to

(1) 9

(2) $\frac{9}{2}$

(3) $\frac{1}{18}$

(4) 18

16-3 SCIENTIFIC NOTATION

To write and compute with very large or very small numbers, we find it convenient to use *scientific notation*.

- A number is in **scientific notation** if it is written in the form $a \times 10^n$, where $1 \leq a < 10$ and n is an integer.

The number $93{,}000{,}000 = 9.3 \times 10{,}000{,}000$ and is written in scientific notation as 9.3×10^7. The number $0.000562 = 5.62 \times 0.0001$ and is written in scientific notation as 5.62×10^{-4}.

Some Integral Powers of 10		
$10^8 = 100{,}000{,}000$	$10^3 = 1{,}000$	$10^{-2} = \frac{1}{100} = 0.01$
$10^7 = 10{,}000{,}000$	$10^2 = 100$	$10^{-3} = \frac{1}{1{,}000} = 0.001$
$10^6 = 1{,}000{,}000$	$10^1 = 10$	$10^{-4} = \frac{1}{10{,}000} = 0.0001$
$10^5 = 100{,}000$	$10^0 = 1$	$10^{-5} = \frac{1}{100{,}000} = 0.00001$
$10^4 = 10{,}000$	$10^{-1} = \frac{1}{10} = 0.1$	$10^{-6} = \frac{1}{1{,}000{,}000} = 0.000001$

Conversions between numbers in decimal notation and in scientific notation are aided by integral powers of 10 shown in the table above. Each time a number is multiplied by 10, the decimal point in the number is moved one place to the right. Also, each time a number is divided by 10 (that is, multiplied by 10^{-1} or by 0.1), the decimal point in the number is moved one place to the left.

In the examples shown below, a caret ($\wedge$) indicates the original placement of the decimal point.

$$3.46 \times 10^4 = 3{\wedge}4600. = 34{,}600$$
$$\text{4 places}$$

$$1.89 \times 10^{-2} = \frac{1.89}{10^2} = 0.01{\wedge}89 = 0.0189$$
$$\text{2 places}$$

To change a number from ordinary decimal notation to scientific notation, we must first divide it by a power of 10 to obtain a, the factor that is greater than or equal to 1, but less than 10. To do this, we use the place value of the first nonzero digit.

For example, to write 8,790 in scientific notation:

1. Change 8,790 to a number between 1 and 10. To do this, divide by the place value of the first digit, 8. Since 8 is in the 1,000 or 10^3 place, divide by 10^3.

$$\frac{8,790}{10^3} = 8.790$$

2. After 8,790 is divided by 10^3, multiply by 10^3 to keep the number unchanged.

$$8,790 = \frac{8,790}{10^3} \times 10^3 = 8.790 \times 10^3$$

To write 0.0546 in scientific notation, the same procedure is followed.

1. Divide 0.0546 by the place value of the first nonzero digit. Since 5 is in the $\frac{1}{100}$ or 10^{-2} place, divide 0.0546 by 10^{-2}.

$$\frac{0.0546}{10^{-2}} = 0.0546 \times 10^2 = 5.46$$

2. After 0.0546 is divided by 10^{-2}, multiply by 10^{-2} to keep the number unchanged.

$$0.0546 = \frac{0.0546}{10^{-2}} \times 10^{-2} = 5.46 \times 10^{-2}$$

The number of places that the decimal point is moved is the absolute value of the exponent of 10 in the scientific notation.

$$8{,}790. = 8.79 \times 10^3$$
3 places

$$0.05\,46 = 5.46 \times 10^{-2}$$
2 places

We will use this concept to change numbers from ordinary decimal notation to scientific notation, and vice versa, as seen in the examples at the end of this section.

Most graphing calculators will display the result of a computation in scientific notation when the number of digits needed to display the number in ordinary notation exceeds the display capability of the calculator.

For example, to find the product $120,000 \times 3,000,000$:

Enter: 120000 $\boxed{\times}$ 3000000 $\boxed{\text{ENTER}}$

Display: $\boxed{\qquad 3.6\,\text{E}11}$

On some calculators, an $\boxed{\text{EE}}$ key is used to enter a number in scientific notation. For example, we can enter the product of 120,000 or 1.2×10^5 and 3,000,000 or 3×10^6 as shown below.

Enter: 1.2 $\boxed{\text{2nd}}$ $\boxed{\text{EE}}$ 5 $\boxed{\times}$ 3 $\boxed{\text{2nd}}$ $\boxed{\text{EE}}$ 6 $\boxed{\text{ENTER}}$

Display: $\boxed{\qquad 3.6\,\text{E}11}$

If a calculator does not have an $\boxed{\text{EE}}$ key, the calculator manual may provide instructions to enter a number in scientific notation using a different process or mode. On all graphing calculators, it is always possible to enter the product of 1.2×10^5 and 3×10^6 by using the $\boxed{\wedge}$ or the $\boxed{y^x}$ key as shown here.

Enter: 1.2 $\boxed{\times}$ 10 $\boxed{\wedge}$ 5 $\boxed{\times}$ 3 $\boxed{\times}$ 10 $\boxed{\wedge}$ 6 $\boxed{\text{ENTER}}$

Display: $\boxed{\qquad 3.6\,\text{E}11}$

Some calculators have a procedure that changes ordinary decimal notation to scientific notation. This may be accomplished by changing the mode to SCI or by using a second function key labeled $\boxed{\text{SCI}}$.

For example, to change 8,790 to scientific notation, put the calculator in SCI mode:

Enter: $\boxed{\text{MODE}}$ $\boxed{\blacktriangleright}$ $\boxed{\text{ENTER}}$ 8790 $\boxed{\text{ENTER}}$

Display: $\boxed{\qquad 8.79\,\text{E}03}$

If a calculator does not have a $\boxed{\text{SCI}}$ mode or key, the manual may provide instructions to convert decimal notation to scientific notation through a different process.

EXAMPLES

1. Write 42,700 in scientific notation.

How to Proceed:

(1) Place a caret after the first nonzero digit. Count the number of places from the caret to the decimal point.

(2) Replace the caret with a decimal point so that 4.27 is the first factor. Since you counted 4 places to the right, the exponent of 10 is positive 4; that is, the second factor is 10^4.

Solution:

4 2700.

4 places to the right

$= 4.27 \times 10^4$

Answer: 4.27×10^4

---

2. Write 8.63×10^{-2} in ordinary decimal notation.

How to Proceed:

In 10^{-2}, the exponent, -2, is negative. To multiply by 10^{-2}, move the decimal point in the factor 8.63 two places to the left, annexing as many 0's to the left of the number as necessary.

Solution:

8.63×10^{-2}

$= .08 63$

2 places to the left

$= 0.0863$

Answer: 0.0863

---

3. Express $\dfrac{(7.5 \times 10^5) \times (2.8 \times 10^{-8})}{1.5 \times 10^{-5}}$ as a single number in scientific notation.

How to Proceed:

(1) Use the commutative and associative properties of multiplication.

(2) Use the rules for powers with like bases to multiply and divide powers of 10.

(3) Change 14.0 to scientific notation and multiply the powers of 10.

Solution:

$\dfrac{(7.5 \times 2.8) \times (10^5 \times 10^{-8})}{1.5 \times 10^{-5}}$

$= \dfrac{21.00 \times 10^{-3}}{1.5 \times 10^{-5}}$

$= 14.0 \times 10^2$

$= 1.4 \times 10^1 \times 10^2$

$= 1.4 \times 10^3$

Calculator Solution To simplify $\dfrac{(7.5 \times 10^5) \times (2.8 \times 10^{-8})}{1.5 \times 10^{-5}}$, use one of the methods shown below. Unless the calculator being used is set to display an answer in scientific notation, the answer may be displayed in decimal notation as shown below.

METHOD 1: *Enter:* 7.5 | 2nd | | EE | 5 | × | 2.8 | 2nd | | EE | | (−) | 8
| ENTER | | ÷ | 1.5 | 2nd | | EE | | (−) | 5 | ENTER |

METHOD 2: *Enter:* 7.5 | × | 10 | ∧ | 5 | × | 2.8 | × | 10 | ∧ | | (−) | 8
| ÷ | | (| 1.5 | × | 10 | ∧ | | (−) | 5 |) | | ENTER |

Display: | 1400. |

Convert the answer in the display to scientific notation: 1.4×10^3.

Answer: 1.4×10^3

EXERCISES WITH OPEN-RESPONSE PROBLEMS

In 1–6, the number can be written in scientific notation as 6.93×10^n. Find the value of n for each number.

1. 693 **2.** 69.3 **3.** 0.0693 **4.** 0.000693 **5.** 693,000 **6.** 6.93

In 7–12, write each number in scientific notation.

7. 40.7 **8.** 0.0053 **9.** 0.81 **10.** 3,920 **11.** 9.05 **12.** 0.00000007

In 13–21, write each number in ordinary decimal notation.

13. 1.87×10^4 **14.** 5.2×10^1 **15.** 2.91×10^{-6}
16. 3.55×10^{-1} **17.** 7.6×10^2 **18.** 6.82×10^{-3}
19. 8.76×10^0 **20.** 1.25×10^{-8} **21.** 3.6×10^7

In 22–29, calculate and express each result: **a.** in scientific notation **b.** in ordinary decimal notation.

22. $(1.5 \times 10^3)(3 \times 10^2)$ **23.** $(1.2 \times 10^5)(1.5 \times 10^{-3})$

24. $\dfrac{7.2 \times 10^4}{6 \times 10^2}$ **25.** $\dfrac{1.25 \times 10^{-3}}{2.5 \times 10^{-7}}$

26. $\dfrac{(5.4 \times 10^3)(3 \times 10^2)}{1.8 \times 10^4}$ **27.** $\dfrac{(2.4 \times 10^{-7})(7.5 \times 10^{-2})}{2 \times 10^{-3}}$

28. $\dfrac{(9 \times 10^{-5})^2}{3 \times 10^{-8}}$ **29.** $\dfrac{(1.2 \times 10^{-3})^2}{4 \times 10^3}$

In 30–34, change each number written in scientific notation to decimal notation.

30. Light travels 3×10^8 meters per second.
31. The rest mass of a proton is 1.67×10^{-24} gram.
32. There are 6.02×10^{23} molecules in 1 mole.
33. The mass of Earth is 6×10^{27} grams.
34. There are 3.6×10^3 seconds in 1 hour.

In 35–41, write each decimal number in scientific notation.

35. In a year, light travels approximately 9,500,000,000,000,000 meters.
36. The approximate distance from Earth to the sun is 93,000,000 miles.
37. One gram is about 0.035 ounce.
38. The wavelength of violet light is 0.000016 inch.
39. The Pacific Ocean covers 70,000,000 square miles of Earth's surface.
40. One micron equals 0.00003937 inch.
41. A *googol* is a large number defined in mathematics as 1 followed by 100 zeros.

16-4 FRACTIONAL EXPONENTS

In Chapter 10, we defined the nth root of a number as one of the n equal factors of the number so that, if $x > 0$ and $x^n = k$, then $\sqrt[n]{k} = x$. Since this definition implies a connection between roots and powers, we will look for a way to express a root as a power.

Case 1.

1. For $x \geq 0$, we have learned that:

$$\sqrt{x} \cdot \sqrt{x} = x$$

2. If there exists a number, p, such that $x^p = \sqrt{x}$, then it must be true that:

$$x^p \cdot x^p = x$$

3. In order for this statement to be consistent with the multiplication law for powers with like bases:

$$x^{p+p} = x^1$$
$$x^{2p} = x^1$$
$$2p = 1$$
$$p = \frac{1}{2}$$

4. Therefore, we conclude for $x \geq 0$:

$$x^{\frac{1}{2}} = \sqrt{x}$$

For example, $3^{\frac{1}{2}} = \sqrt{3}$ because

$$3^{\frac{1}{2}} \cdot 3^{\frac{1}{2}} = 3^{\frac{1}{2}+\frac{1}{2}} = 3^{\frac{2}{2}} = 3$$

and

$$\sqrt{3} \cdot \sqrt{3} = 3$$

Case 2.

1. For any real number x:

$$\sqrt[3]{x} \cdot \sqrt[3]{x} \cdot \sqrt[3]{x} = \sqrt[3]{x^3} = x$$

2. If there exists a number, q, such that $x^q = \sqrt[3]{x}$, then:

$$x^q \cdot x^q \cdot x^q = x$$

3. In order for this statement to be consistent with the multiplication law for powers with like bases:

$$x^{q+q+q} = x^1$$
$$x^{3q} = x^1$$
$$3q = 1$$
$$q = \frac{1}{3}$$

4. Therefore, we conclude:

$$x^{\frac{1}{3}} = \sqrt[3]{x}$$

For example, $(-2)^{\frac{1}{3}} = \sqrt[3]{-2}$ because

$$(-2)^{\frac{1}{3}} \cdot (-2)^{\frac{1}{3}} \cdot (-2)^{\frac{1}{3}} = (-2)^{\frac{1}{3}+\frac{1}{3}+\frac{1}{3}} = (-2)^1 = -2$$

and

$$\sqrt[3]{-2} \cdot \sqrt[3]{-2} \cdot \sqrt[3]{-2} = \sqrt[3]{-8} = -2$$

These two cases lead to a definition of a power with the exponent $\frac{1}{n}$.

● In general, if n is a counting number, then:

$$x^{\frac{1}{n}} = \sqrt[n]{x}$$

Note: There is no real number that is an even root of a negative number. For example, $\sqrt{-9} = \sqrt[2]{-9}$ is not an element of the set of real numbers. Therefore, *if n is even, the base, x, must be nonnegative*, that is, $x \geq 0$. If n is odd, however, the base, x, can be negative. For example:

$$(-8)^{\frac{1}{3}} = \sqrt[3]{-8} = -2$$

We can verify that a ***fractional exponent*** can be used to express a radical by comparing the use of radicals and the use of fractional exponents in the following multiplication example.

Multiply $\sqrt{2} \cdot \sqrt{3}$.

Radicals	*Fractional Exponents*
$\sqrt{2} \cdot \sqrt{3} = \sqrt{2 \cdot 3} = \sqrt{6}$	$2^{\frac{1}{2}} \cdot 3^{\frac{1}{2}} = (2 \cdot 3)^{\frac{1}{2}} = 6^{\frac{1}{2}}$

Now let us compare the use of radicals and the use of fractional exponents in the following division examples.

Divide: $\dfrac{3}{\sqrt{3}}$.

Radicals	*Fractional Exponents*
$\dfrac{3}{\sqrt{3}} = \dfrac{3}{\sqrt{3}} \cdot \dfrac{\sqrt{3}}{\sqrt{3}} = \dfrac{3\sqrt{3}}{3} = \sqrt{3}$	$\dfrac{3}{3^{\frac{1}{2}}} = 3^{1-\frac{1}{2}} = 3^{\frac{1}{2}}$

Divide: $\dfrac{2}{\sqrt[3]{2}}$.

Radicals	*Fractional Exponents*
$\dfrac{2}{\sqrt[3]{2}} = \dfrac{2}{\sqrt[3]{2}} \cdot \dfrac{\sqrt[3]{4}}{\sqrt[3]{4}} = \dfrac{2\sqrt[3]{4}}{\sqrt[3]{8}}$ $= \dfrac{2\sqrt[3]{4}}{2}$ $= \sqrt[3]{4}$	$\dfrac{2}{2^{\frac{1}{3}}} = 2^{1-\frac{1}{3}} = 2^{\frac{2}{3}}$

We can show that $\sqrt[3]{4}$ and $2^{\frac{2}{3}}$ represent the same real number by rewriting $2^{\frac{2}{3}}$ and using the rule for the power of a power:

$$2^{\frac{2}{3}} = 2^{2 \cdot \frac{1}{3}} = (2^2)^{\frac{1}{3}} = \sqrt[3]{2^2} = \sqrt[3]{4}$$

We can also verify that $\sqrt[3]{4} = 2^{\frac{2}{3}}$ by evaluating each expression on a calculator.

1. To evaluate $\sqrt[3]{4}$, use the [$\sqrt[x]{\,}$] key, which is usually accessed by first pressing [**2nd**], [**MATH**] 5, or [**INV**]. Some calculators require the radicand 4 to be entered second (see Method 1), while others require the radicand to be entered first (see Method 2). Check to see which sequence is correct for your calculator.

METHOD 1: *Enter:*　3 [**MATH**] 5　4 [**ENTER**]

METHOD 2: *Enter:*　4 [**2nd**] [$\sqrt[x]{\,}$] 3 [**=**]

Display:　[1.587401052]

In this book, Method 1 is used.

2. To evaluate $2^{\frac{2}{3}}$, enclose the exponent $\frac{2}{3}$ in parentheses.

Enter:　2 [$\wedge$] [**(**] 2 [**÷**] 3 [**)**] [**ENTER**]

Display:　[1.587401052]

This example leads to the following general definition, where *n* is a counting number:

$$x^{\frac{a}{n}} = \sqrt[n]{x^a} \qquad \text{and} \qquad x^{\frac{a}{n}} = (\sqrt[n]{x})^a$$

Note: If *n* is even, then $x \geq 0$.

This rule suggests the two methods that we can use to evaluate an expression such as $125^{\frac{2}{3}}$.

METHOD 1: $125^{\frac{2}{3}} = \sqrt[3]{125^2}$

$= \sqrt[3]{15,625}$

$= 25$

METHOD 2: $125^{\frac{2}{3}} = (\sqrt[3]{125})^2$

$= (5)^2$

$= 25$

In most cases, it is easier to perform a computation involving roots and powers by finding the root before raising to a power, since the resulting numbers are smaller.

EXAMPLES

1. Evaluate $a^0 + a^{\frac{1}{3}} + a^{-2}$ when $a = 8$.

How to Proceed:

(1) Use the definitions of zero, negative, and fractional exponents.

(2) Substitute the value of a.

(3) Simplify.

Solution:

$a^0 + a^{\frac{1}{3}} + a^{-2}$

$= 1 + \sqrt[3]{a} + \dfrac{1}{a^2}$

$= 1 + \sqrt[3]{8} + \dfrac{1}{8^2}$

$= 1 + 2 + \dfrac{1}{64}$

$= 3\dfrac{1}{64}$

Alternative Solution

It is possible to interchange steps 1 and 2 in the process shown above.

$a^0 + a^{\frac{1}{3}} + a^{-2} = 8^0 + 8^{\frac{1}{3}} + 8^{-2} = 1 + \sqrt[3]{8} + \dfrac{1}{8^2} = 1 + 2 + \dfrac{1}{64} = 3\dfrac{1}{64}$

Answer: $3\dfrac{1}{64}$

---

2. If $f(x) = x^{-\frac{3}{2}}$, find $f(16)$.

Solution

$$f(16) = 16^{-\frac{3}{2}} = \dfrac{1}{16^{\frac{3}{2}}} = \dfrac{1}{(16^{\frac{1}{2}})^3} = \dfrac{1}{(\sqrt{16})^3} = \dfrac{1}{4^3} = \dfrac{1}{64}$$

Calculator Solution

Enter: 16 $\boxed{\wedge}$ $\boxed{(}$ $\boxed{(-)}$ 3 $\boxed{\div}$ 2 $\boxed{)}$ $\boxed{\text{ENTER}}$

Display: $\boxed{\text{0.015625}}$

Answer: $\dfrac{1}{64}$ or 0.015625

---

3. If $m = 8$, find the value of $(8m^0)^{\frac{2}{3}}$.

Solution $(8m^0)^{\frac{2}{3}} = (8 \cdot 8^0)^{\frac{2}{3}} = (8 \cdot 1)^{\frac{2}{3}} = 8^{\frac{2}{3}} = (\sqrt[3]{8})^2 = 2^2 = 4$

Answer: 4

---

4. Write $x^{-\frac{3}{4}}$, using radicals and positive integral exponents $(x > 0)$.

How to Proceed:	*Solution:*
(1) Use the definition of a negative exponent.	$x^{-\frac{3}{4}} = \dfrac{1}{x^{\frac{3}{4}}}$
(2) Use the definition of a fractional exponent.	$= \dfrac{1}{\sqrt[4]{x^3}}$

Answer: $\dfrac{1}{\sqrt[4]{x^3}}$

EXERCISES WITH OPEN-RESPONSE PROBLEMS

In 1–8, write each given expression, using a radical sign. Let the variables represent positive numbers.

1. $x^{\frac{1}{2}}$
5. $3a^{\frac{1}{2}}$

2. $a^{\frac{1}{3}}$
6. $(3a)^{\frac{1}{2}}$

3. $b^{\frac{1}{5}}$
7. $ab^{\frac{1}{4}}$

4. $y^{\frac{2}{3}}$
8. $(ab)^{\frac{1}{4}}$

In 9–16, use exponents to write each radical expression. Let the variables represent positive numbers.

9. $\sqrt{2}$
13. $7\sqrt{5}$

10. $\sqrt{3a}$
14. $x\sqrt{y^3}$

11. $\sqrt[3]{5x}$
15. $-\sqrt{8}$

12. $2(\sqrt[5]{b})$
16. $-\sqrt[3]{2}$

In 17–48, evaluate each given expression.

17. $25^{\frac{1}{2}}$
21. $125^{-\frac{1}{3}}$
25. $9^{\frac{3}{2}}$
29. $64^{\frac{2}{3}}$
33. $-4^{\frac{5}{2}}$
37. $\left(\frac{4}{25}\right)^{\frac{1}{2}}$
41. $2^{\frac{1}{2}} \cdot 2^{\frac{3}{2}}$
45. $5^0 + 5^{-1}$

18. $27^{\frac{1}{3}}$
22. $(-125)^{\frac{1}{3}}$
26. $1,000^{\frac{2}{3}}$
30. $64^{\frac{3}{2}}$
34. $81^{\frac{3}{4}}$
38. $\left(\frac{9}{16}\right)^{-\frac{1}{2}}$
42. $4^2 \cdot 4^{\frac{1}{2}}$
46. $-4^0 + 4^{-\frac{1}{2}}$

19. $16^{\frac{1}{4}}$
23. $100^{-\frac{1}{2}}$
27. $32^{\frac{3}{5}}$
31. $4^{-\frac{3}{2}}$
35. $(36^{-1})^{\frac{1}{2}}$
39. $\left(-\frac{1}{27}\right)^{\frac{1}{3}}$
43. $9^{\frac{3}{2}} \cdot 9^{-\frac{1}{2}}$
47. $(8^0 + 8)^{\frac{1}{2}}$

20. $16^{-\frac{1}{2}}$
24. $81^{-\frac{1}{4}}$
28. $(-8)^{\frac{2}{3}}$
32. $27^{-\frac{2}{3}}$
36. $(8^0)^{\frac{1}{3}}$
40. $\left(\frac{1}{27}\right)^{-\frac{1}{3}}$
44. $8^{\frac{1}{3}} \cdot 8^{-\frac{2}{3}}$
48. $(3^0 + 3)^{-\frac{1}{2}}$

49. Find the value of $2a^{\frac{1}{3}}$ when $a = \frac{27}{8}$.

50. Evaluate $a^0 + a^{-\frac{1}{2}}$ when $a = 9$.

51. If $k = 4$, find the value of $(9k^0)^{\frac{3}{2}}$.

52. Find the value of $(m^{-1})^{\frac{3}{4}}$ when $m = 16$.

53. If $f(x) = x^{\frac{2}{3}}$, find the value of $f(-216)$.

54. If $f(x) = x^{-\frac{3}{2}}$, find the value of $f(100)$.

55. If the function $g(x) = 4x^{-\frac{1}{2}}$, find the value of $g(25)$.

In 56–60, select the *numeral* preceding the choice that best completes the sentence.

56. The expression $\dfrac{2x^{-\frac{1}{2}}}{x^{-1}}$ is equivalent to

(1) $2\sqrt{x}$ (2) $\sqrt{2x}$ (3) $2\sqrt{x^3}$ (4) $\sqrt{2x^3}$

57. The expression $3\sqrt[4]{3}$ can be written as

(1) $3^{\frac{3}{4}}$ (2) $3^{\frac{4}{3}}$ (3) $3^{\frac{5}{4}}$ (4) $3^{\frac{4}{5}}$

58. If $b = -64$, then $b^{-\frac{1}{3}}$ is equal to

(1) 4 (2) -4 (3) $\frac{1}{4}$ (4) $-\frac{1}{4}$

59. If $a = -9$, then $a^{-\frac{1}{2}}$ is

(1) 3 (2) $\frac{1}{3}$ (3) $-\frac{1}{3}$ (4) not a real number

60. If $x = \frac{8}{9}$, then $x^{-\frac{1}{3}}$ is equal to

(1) $\frac{2}{3}$ (2) $\frac{3}{2}$ (3) $\frac{\sqrt[3]{9}}{2}$ (4) $\frac{2}{\sqrt[3]{9}}$

16-5 EXPONENTIAL FUNCTIONS

Linear Growth

A piece of paper is one layer thick. If we place another paper on top of it, the total is two layers thick. If we place a third paper on top, the total is now three layers thick.

As this process continues, we can describe the number of layers (y) in terms of the number of sheets added (x) by the *linear equation* $y = 1 + x$. For example, by adding five sheets, we have a total of six sheets of paper. This is an example of **linear growth** because the growth is described by means of a linear function.

Exponential Growth

Let us consider another experiment. A piece of paper is one layer thick. If the paper is folded in half, it is now two layers thick. If it is folded in half again, the paper is now four layers thick. If it is folded in half again, the paper is now eight layers thick.

0 folds	1 fold	2 folds	3 folds
1 layer	2 layers	4 layers	8 layers

Although we will reach a point where it is impossible to fold the paper, let us imagine that this process can continue. We can describe the number of layers of paper (y) in terms of the number of folds (x) by means of an **exponential function**, namely, $y = 2^x$. The table at the right shows some values for the exponential function $y = 2^x$.

For example, after five folds, the paper is 2^5 or 32 layers thick. After ten folds, the paper is 2^{10} or 1,024 layers thick. This is an example of **exponential growth** because the growth is described by means of an exponential function.

x	$2^x =$	y
0	$2^0 =$	1
1	$2^1 =$	2
2	$2^2 =$	4
3	$2^3 =$	8
4	$2^4 =$	16
5	$2^5 =$	32

There are many examples of exponential growth in the world around us. Over an interval of time, certain populations—for instance, of bacteria or rabbits or the people of a nation—grow exponentially. Compound interest is based on exponential growth. In all these cases, growth is defined by an equation that involves a power b^x, where b is a positive number and the exponent x is a variable.

In the paper-folding experiment described by the exponential function $y = 2^x$, we let the domain of x values be whole numbers. To study the function $y = 2^x$ in general, we can expand the domain to include all *rational values* of x, as defined earlier in Section 16-4. Here, we expand the table of values for $y = 2^x$ by considering some convenient negative and fractional values of x.

x	2^x	$=$	y
-3	$2^{-3} = \frac{1}{2^3}$	$=$	$\frac{1}{8}$
-2	$2^{-2} = \frac{1}{2^2}$	$=$	$\frac{1}{4}$
-1	$2^{-1} = \frac{1}{2^1}$	$=$	$\frac{1}{2}$
0	$2^0 = 1$	$=$	1
$\frac{1}{2}$	$2^{\frac{1}{2}} = \sqrt{2}$	$=$	$\sqrt{2} \approx 1.4$
1	$2^1 = 2$	$=$	2
$\frac{3}{2}$	$2^{\frac{3}{2}} = \sqrt{2^3}$	$=$	$\sqrt{8} \approx 2.8$
2	$2^2 = 4$	$=$	4
$\frac{5}{2}$	$2^{\frac{5}{2}} = \sqrt{2^5}$	$=$	$\sqrt{32} \approx 5.7$
3	$2^3 = 8$	$=$	8

x	y
-3	$\frac{1}{8}$
-2	$\frac{1}{4}$
-1	$\frac{1}{2}$
0	1
$\frac{1}{2}$	$\sqrt{2} \approx 1.4$
1	2
$\frac{3}{2}$	$\sqrt{8} \approx 2.8$
2	4
$\frac{5}{2}$	$\sqrt{32} \approx 5.7$
3	8

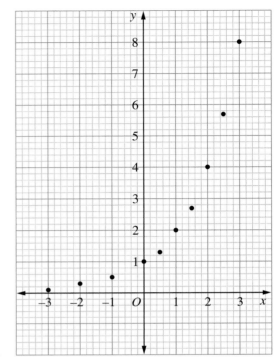

Figure 1

In Figure 1, the pairs of numbers $(x, 2^x)$ or (x, y) are represented as points in the coordinate plane. They lie in a pattern that suggests a smooth curve. If we assume that the curve drawn through these points in Figure 2 is the graph of $y = 2^x$, then 2^x is defined for all real values of x.

The length of the diagonal of a square each of whose sides measure 1 is used to locate $\sqrt{2}$ on the x-axis, as shown below.

In Figure 2, we locate a point on the curve whose x-coordinate is $\sqrt{2}$ and whose y-coordinate is $2^{\sqrt{2}}$. The exponent $\sqrt{2}$ is an *irrational number*, and the value of $2^{\sqrt{2}}$, as seen on the graph, is approximately 2.7.

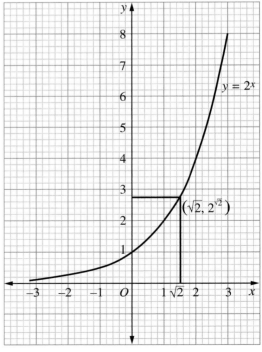

Figure 2

Now, let us consider a different exponential function, $y = 5^x$. The table below shows some pairs that were used to draw the graph of $y = 5^x$.

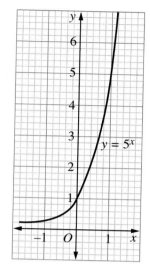

x	5^x	$=$	y
-1	$5^{-1} = \frac{1}{5}$	$=$	0.2
0	5^0	$=$	1
$\frac{1}{2}$	$5^{\frac{1}{2}} = \sqrt{5}$	$\approx$	2.24
1	5^1	$=$	5

We notice, in Figure 3, that the graph of $y = 5^x$ has the same basic shape as the graph of $y = 2^x$.

Figure 3

Let us consider an exponential function in which the value of base b is positive but less than 1. The graph of $y = \left(\frac{1}{2}\right)^x$ can be drawn, using the pairs of values shown in the table below.

x	$\left(\frac{1}{2}\right)^x$	$=$	y
-3	$\left(\frac{1}{2}\right)^{-3} = 2^3$	$=$	8
-2	$\left(\frac{1}{2}\right)^{-2} = 2^2$	$=$	4
-1	$\left(\frac{1}{2}\right)^{-1} = 2^1$	$=$	2
0	$\left(\frac{1}{2}\right)^0$	$=$	1
1	$\left(\frac{1}{2}\right)^1$	$=$	$\frac{1}{2}$
2	$\left(\frac{1}{2}\right)^2$	$=$	$\frac{1}{4}$
3	$\left(\frac{1}{2}\right)^3$	$=$	$\frac{1}{8}$

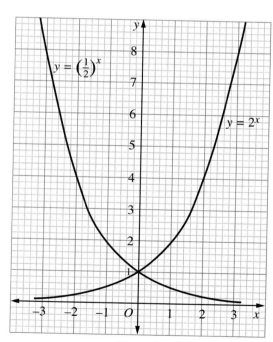

Figure 4

Figure 4 shows the graph of $y = \left(\frac{1}{2}\right)^x$ and the reflection of this graph over the y-axis. Since $r_{y\text{-axis}}(x, y) = (-x, y)$, the equation of the reflection of $y = \left(\frac{1}{2}\right)^x$ over the y-axis is $y = \left(\frac{1}{2}\right)^{-x}$. Also, since $\left(\frac{1}{2}\right)^{-x} = \left(\frac{2}{1}\right)^x = 2^x$, the reflection over the y-axis of $y = \left(\frac{1}{2}\right)^x$ is $y = 2^x$.

On a graphing calculator, we can draw the graphs of several exponential functions and compare them. We set the [WINDOW] for Xmin $= -3$, Xmax $= 3$, Xscl $= 1$, Ymin $= -1$, Ymax $= 9$, Yscl $= 1$. Then we enter four exponential graphs with different values of b, for example, $b = 8$, $b = 3$, $b = 2$, and $b = 1.5$.

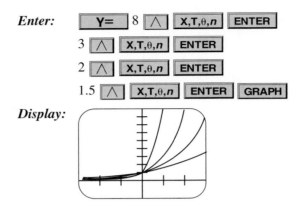

Enter: [Y=] 8 [∧] [X,T,θ,n] [ENTER]

3 [∧] [X,T,θ,n] [ENTER]

2 [∧] [X,T,θ,n] [ENTER]

1.5 [∧] [X,T,θ,n] [ENTER] [GRAPH]

Display:

The calculator display shows us that each graph intersects the y-axis at $(0, 1)$ and that the larger the value of b, the more rapidly the graph rises as the positive values of x increase. For negative values of x, as the value of x decreases, each graph approaches but does not intersect the x-axis.

A function $f(x)$ has a ***horizontal asymptote*** whose equation is $y = c$ if there exists a constant, c, such that, as x increases or decreases without limit, $f(x)$ approaches but never equals c. The line $y = 0$ (the x-axis) is the horizontal asymptote of every exponential function $f(x) = b^x$ for $b > 0$ and $b \neq 1$.

EXAMPLE

a. Sketch the graph of $y = \left(\frac{3}{2}\right)^x$ in the interval $-3 \leq x \leq 3$.

b. Sketch the graph of $y = \left(\frac{2}{3}\right)^x$ in the interval $-3 \leq x \leq 3$.

c. Use the graph to find an approximate rational value of $\left(\frac{3}{2}\right)^{1.4}$ to the *nearest tenth*.

How to Proceed:

a. (1) Make a table of values for integral values of x from $x = -3$ to $x = 3$.

Solution:

x	$\left(\frac{3}{2}\right)^{x}$		$=$	y
-3	$\left(\frac{3}{2}\right)^{-3}$	$= \left(\frac{2}{3}\right)^{3}$	$=$	$\frac{8}{27}$
-2	$\left(\frac{3}{2}\right)^{-2}$	$= \left(\frac{2}{3}\right)^{2}$	$=$	$\frac{4}{9}$
-1	$\left(\frac{3}{2}\right)^{-1}$	$= \left(\frac{2}{3}\right)^{1}$	$=$	$\frac{2}{3}$
0	$\left(\frac{3}{2}\right)^{0}$		$=$	1
1	$\left(\frac{3}{2}\right)^{1}$		$=$	$\frac{3}{2}$
2	$\left(\frac{3}{2}\right)^{2}$		$=$	$\frac{9}{4}$
3	$\left(\frac{3}{2}\right)^{3}$		$=$	$\frac{27}{8}$

(2) Plot the points that correspond to the pairs of values in the table.

(3) Draw a smooth curve through these points.

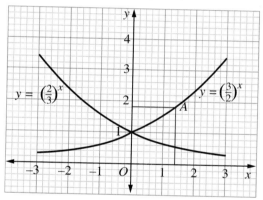

$y = \left(\frac{2}{3}\right)^{x}$ $y = \left(\frac{3}{2}\right)^{x}$

b. (1) The graph of $y = \left(\frac{2}{3}\right)^{x}$ is the reflection in the y-axis of the graph of $y = \left(\frac{3}{2}\right)^{x}$. For each point (x, y) on the graph of $y = \left(\frac{3}{2}\right)^{x}$, locate a point $(-x, y)$ on the graph of $y = \left(\frac{2}{3}\right)^{x}$.

(2) Draw a smooth curve through these points.

c. (1) Draw a vertical line at $x = 1.4$ to locate point $\left(1.4, \left(\frac{3}{2}\right)^{1.4}\right)$ on the graph (point A).

(2) Draw a horizontal line from point A to the y-axis. Approximate the value to the nearest tenth.

Answers: **a, b.** See graph.   **c.** 1.8

EXERCISES WITH OPEN-RESPONSE PROBLEMS

1. a. Sketch the graph of $y = 3^x$ in the interval $-3 \le x \le 3$.
   b. From the graph, approximate the value of $3^{2.2}$ to the *nearest tenth*, and compare this value to a calculator value.

2. a. Sketch the graph of $y = 4^x$ in the interval $-2 \le x \le 2$.
   b. From the graph, approximate the value of $4^{\sqrt{2}}$ to the *nearest tenth*, and compare this value to a calculator value.

3. a. Sketch the graph of $y = \left(\frac{1}{4}\right)^x$ in the interval $-2 \le x \le 2$.

   b. For the domain of real numbers, what is the range of the function $y = \left(\frac{1}{4}\right)^x$?

   c. In what quadrants does the graph of $y = \left(\frac{1}{4}\right)^x$ lie?

4. a. Sketch the graph of $y = \left(\frac{5}{2}\right)^x$ in the interval $-3 \le x \le 3$.

   b. Sketch the reflection in the y-axis of the graph of $y = \left(\frac{5}{2}\right)^x$.

   c. What is an equation of the graph drawn in answer to part **b**?

In 5–8, find each function value when $f(x) = 6^x$.

5. $f(-1)$ **6.** $f(0)$ **7.** $f\left(\frac{1}{2}\right)$ **8.** $f\left(\frac{3}{2}\right)$

9. For what values of b does $y = b^x$ define an exponential function?
10. Name the coordinates of the point at which the graphs of $y = 5^x$ and $y = 8^x$ intersect.

In 11–13, select the *numeral* preceding the choice that best completes the sentence.

11. The equation $y = a^x$ defines an exponential function when a equals
   (1) 1   (2) 2   (3) 0   (4) -1

12. The graph of $y = b^x$, where $b > 0$ and $b \ne 1$, lies in Quadrants
   (1) I and II   (2) I and IV   (3) II and III   (4) II and IV

13. If $b > 0$, then the graph of $y = b^x$ must contain point
   (1) $(-1, 0)$ (2) $(1, 0)$ (3) $(0, 1)$ (4) $(0, 0)$

14. If $f(x) = -2^x$, find: **a.** $f(0)$ **b.** $f(2)$ **c.** $f(-2)$.

15. a. Sketch the graph of $y = 2^x$ in the interval $-3 \le x \le 3$.
   b. On the same set of axes, sketch the graph of $y = -2^x$.
   c. What is the equation of the line of reflection such that the graph of $y = -2^x$ is the image of the graph of $y = 2^x$?

16. a. In 1970, the population of a city was 10,000 people. If the population has doubled every 10 years since that time, find the population of this city:
   (1) in 1980   *(2)* in 1990   *(3)* in 2000
   b. If this exponential growth continues, what will be the population of the city in the year 2020?

17. If a bank compounds interest annually (once each year), then the amount of money, A, in a bank account is determined by the formula $A = P(1 + r)^x$. Here, $P =$ the principal, or the amount invested, $r =$ the rate of interest, and $x =$ the number of years involved. If $100 is invested at 6% interest compounded annually, the amount, A, in the account is found by using the formula $A = \$100(1.06)^x$. Find the amount of money in this account at the end of:
   a. 1 year   **b.** 2 years   **c.** 3 years   **d.** 4 years.

18. The thickness of a sheet of paper is 0.004 inch. If x represents the number of times that this sheet of paper is folded in half over itself, then $y = 2^x$ determines the number of layers of paper, and $y = 0.004(2)^x$ determines the thickness of all the layers of paper. What is the total thickness of the layers if such a sheet of paper is folded in half over itself exactly 15 times?

19. In January 1995, the population of a small town was 8,000 people. Each year after 1995, the population decreased by 1%. If P represents the population t years after January 1995, then $P = 8,000(1 - 0.01)^t$ or $P = 8,000(0.99)^t$.
   a. Find the population of the town in January 2000.
   b. If this rate of decrease continues unchanged, what is the expected population of the town in January 2010?

16-6   EQUATIONS WITH FRACTIONAL OR NEGATIVE EXPONENTS

In raising a power to a power, we multiply exponents.

$$(x^a)^c = x^{ac}$$

If a and c are reciprocals, their product is 1 and the resulting power is x^1 or x. For example:

$$(x^2)^{\frac{1}{2}} = x^1 = x$$

$$(x^{\frac{3}{4}})^{\frac{4}{3}} = x^1 = x$$

$$(x^{-\frac{1}{2}})^{-2} = x^1 = x$$

This observation will simplify the solution of equations containing powers with fractional or negative exponents.

EXAMPLES

Solve for x and check: **1.** $2x^{-\frac{1}{3}} = 6$ **2.** $x^{\frac{3}{2}} + 1 = 9$

How to Proceed: *Solutions:*

(1) Change the equation into an equivalent equation that has only the variable term with coefficient 1 on the left member.

1. $2x^{-\frac{1}{3}} = 6$
$x^{-\frac{1}{3}} = 3$

2. $x^{\frac{3}{2}} + 1 = 9$
$x^{\frac{3}{2}} = 8$

(2) Raise both members of the equation to a power, using the reciprocal of the given exponent.

$(x^{-\frac{1}{3}})^{-3} = 3^{-3}$

$(x^{\frac{3}{2}})^{\frac{2}{3}} = 8^{\frac{2}{3}}$

(3) Simplify both members of the equation.

$x^1 = \dfrac{1}{3^3}$

$x = \dfrac{1}{27}$

$x^1 = \sqrt[3]{8^2}$
$x = (2)^2$
$= 4$

(4) Check the solution in the original equation.

$2x^{-\frac{1}{3}} = 6$

$2\left(\dfrac{1}{27}\right)^{-\frac{1}{3}} \overset{?}{=} 6$

$2\sqrt[3]{27} \overset{?}{=} 6$

$2(3) \overset{?}{=} 6$

$6 = 6$ ✔

$x^{\frac{3}{2}} + 1 = 9$

$4^{\frac{3}{2}} + 1 \overset{?}{=} 9$

$(\sqrt{4})^3 + 1 \overset{?}{=} 9$

$8 + 1 \overset{?}{=} 9$

$9 = 9$ ✔

Answers: **1.** $\dfrac{1}{27}$ **2.** 4

EXERCISES WITH OPEN-RESPONSE PROBLEMS

In 1–4, find the value of a for which each expression is equal to x.

1. $(x^{\frac{1}{2}})^a$ **2.** $(x^{\frac{3}{4}})^a$ **3.** $(x^{-6})^a$ **4.** $(x^{-\frac{3}{5}})^a$

In 5–16, solve each equation and check. All variables represent positive numbers.

5. $x^{\frac{1}{2}} = 7$

6. $x^{\frac{1}{3}} = 5$

7. $x^{\frac{2}{3}} = 4$

8. $y^{-2} = 9$

9. $a^{-\frac{1}{4}} = 2$

10. $b^{-\frac{1}{2}} = \dfrac{1}{3}$

11. $x^{\frac{4}{3}} - 1 = 15$

12. $y^{-\frac{3}{2}} + 2 = 10$

13. $2x^{\frac{4}{3}} = 162$

14. $2x^{-\frac{1}{2}} = 3$

15. $2x^{-\frac{1}{4}} + 3 = 4$

16. $4x^{\frac{2}{3}} - 5 = 20$

17. Find the root of the equation $x \cdot x^{\frac{1}{2}} = 8$. (Simplify the left side by using the rule for multiplying powers with like bases.)

18. Solve for y and check: $2y \cdot y^{\frac{1}{3}} = 0.0002$.

In 19 and 20, select the *numeral* preceding the choice that best completes the sentence.

19. A root of $(x + 2)^{\frac{2}{3}} = 4$ is

(1) 6   (2) 2   (3) 8   (4) 4

20. A root of $3y^{\frac{3}{2}} = 6$ is

(1) $\sqrt{8}$ (2) $\sqrt[3]{2}$ (3) $\sqrt[3]{12}$ (4) $\sqrt[3]{4}$

In 21–26, solve each equation, in which the variable represents a positive number. (*Hint:* Before solving, change the radical expression to a power having a fractional exponent.)

21. $\sqrt[3]{x^2} = 16$ **22.** $\sqrt{x^3} = 64$ **23.** $\sqrt[3]{y^4} = 625$

24. $\sqrt{y^5} = 32$ **25.** $\sqrt{m} = 15$ **26.** $\sqrt[4]{b} = 9$

16-7 EXPONENTIAL EQUATIONS

An equation in which the variable appears in an exponent is called an **exponential equation**. Simple exponential equations involving powers of like bases can be solved by using the following observation:

$$\text{For } b \neq 0 \text{ and } b \neq 1, \ b^x = b^y \leftrightarrow x = y.$$

In the examples that follow, we will solve each equation by equating exponents of like bases. If the bases in the given equation are not equal (see Examples 2, 3, and 4), we will change one or both bases as a first step.

EXAMPLES

1. Solve and check: $5^{x+1} = 5^4$

How to Proceed:	Solution:	Check:
(1) Write the equation.	$5^{x+1} = 5^4$	$5^{x+1} = 5^4$
(2) Since the bases are alike, equate the exponents.	$x + 1 = 4$	$5^{3+1} \overset{?}{=} 5^4$ $5^4 = 5^4$
(3) Solve the resulting equation.	$x = 3$	(True)

Answer: $x = 3$

2. Solve and check: $2^{x-1} = 8^2$

How to Proceed:	*Solution:*	*Check:*
(1) Write the equation.	$2^{x-1} = 8^2$	$2^{x-1} = 8^2$
(2) Change the right member to base 2, using $8 = 2^3$.	$2^{x-1} = (2^3)^2$	$2^{7-1} \stackrel{?}{=} 8^2$
	$2^{x-1} = 2^6$	$2^6 \stackrel{?}{=} 8^2$
(3) Simplify the right member.	$x - 1 = 6$	$64 = 64$
(4) Equate the exponents of like bases.	$x = 7$	(True)
(5) Solve the resulting equation.		

Answer: $x = 7$

---

3. Solve and check: $9^{x+1} = 27^x$

How to Proceed:	*Solution:*	*Check:*
(1) Write the equation.	$9^{x+1} = 27^x$	$9^{x+1} = 27^x$
(2) Change each member to base 3, using $9 = 3^2$ and $27 = 3^3$.	$(3^2)^{x+1} = (3^3)^x$	$9^{2+1} \stackrel{?}{=} 27^2$
		$9^3 \stackrel{?}{=} 27^2$
(3) Simplify each member.	$3^{2x+2} = 3^{3x}$	$729 = 729$
(4) Equate exponents of like bases.	$2x + 2 = 3x$	(True)
(5) Solve the resulting equation.	$2 = x$	

Answer: $x = 2$

---

4. Solve and check: $\left(\frac{1}{4}\right)^x = 8^{1-x}$

How to Proceed:	*Solution:*	*Check:*
(1) Write the equation.	$\left(\frac{1}{4}\right)^x = 8^{1-x}$	$\left(\frac{1}{4}\right)^x = 8^{1-x}$
(2) Change each member to base 2, using $\frac{1}{4} = \frac{1}{2^2} = 2^{-2}$ and $8 = 2^3$.	$(2^{-2})^x = (2^3)^{1-x}$	$\left(\frac{1}{4}\right)^3 \stackrel{?}{=} 8^{1-3}$
	$2^{-2x} = 2^{3-3x}$	$\left(\frac{1}{4}\right)^3 \stackrel{?}{=} 8^{-2}$
(3) Simplify each member.	$-2x = 3 - 3x$	$\frac{1}{64} = \frac{1}{64}$
(4) Equate exponents of like bases.	$x = 3$	(True)
(5) Solve the resulting equation.		

Answer: $x = 3$

Note: It is not always possible to express each member as an integral power of the same base. We will learn how to solve equations such as $2^x = 3$ in Chapter 17.

EXERCISES WITH OPEN-RESPONSE PROBLEMS

In 1–15, express each number as a power with an integral exponent and the smallest possible positive integral base.

1. 36 **2.** 25 **3.** 16 **4.** 27 **5.** 64

6. 81 **7.** 125 **8.** 32 **9.** 1,000 **10.** 0.1

11. $\frac{1}{3}$ **12.** $\frac{1}{2}$ **13.** $\frac{1}{8}$ **14.** $\frac{1}{25}$ **15.** $\frac{1}{27}$

In 16–36, solve each equation and check.

16. $4^{x+2} = 4^3$ **17.** $3^{2x-1} = 3^{x+2}$ **18.** $7^{x-4} = 7$

19. $12^{2x-10} = 12^{x-5}$ **20.** $4^{x-2} = 4^{3x}$ **21.** $2^x = 4$

22. $5^{x-1} = 125$ **23.** $49^x = 7^{x+1}$ **24.** $36^x = 6^{x-1}$

25. $64^x = 4^{x+2}$ **26.** $9^{2x} = 3^{3x+1}$ **27.** $8^{2x} = 2^{2x+2}$

28. $5^{3x} = 25^{x+1}$ **29.** $16^{x-3} = 4^{x-3}$ **30.** $9^{x+1} = 3^x$

31. $8^x = 4^{x-1}$ **32.** $27^x = 9^{x+2}$ **33.** $\left(\frac{1}{2}\right)^x = 8^{2-x}$

34. $\left(\frac{1}{3}\right)^{1-x} = 9^x$ **35.** $125^x = 25$ **36.** $32^x = 4$

In 37 and 38, select the *numeral* preceding the choice that best completes the sentence.

37. The solution set of $2^{x^2+2} = 2^{3x}$ is
(1) $\{1\}$ (2) $\{2\}$ (3) $\{1, 2\}$ (4) $\{8, 64\}$

38. The solution set of $3^{x^2-3} = 3^{2x}$ is
(1) $\{-1\}$ (2) $\{3, -1\}$ (3) $\{3\}$ (4) $\left\{729, \frac{1}{9}\right\}$

CHAPTER SUMMARY

The rules for operations with powers can be extended to include exponents that are real numbers. For $x \neq 0$ and $y \neq 0$:

1. $x^a \cdot x^b = x^{a+b}$ **2.** $x^a \cdot y^a = (xy)^a$

3. $\frac{x^a}{x^b} = x^{a-b}$ **4.** $\frac{x^a}{y^a} = \left(\frac{x}{y}\right)^a$

5. $(x^a)^b = x^{ab}$ **6.** $x^0 = 1$ **7.** $x^{-a} = \dfrac{1}{x^a}$

8. $\left(\dfrac{x}{y}\right)^{-a} = \left(\dfrac{y}{x}\right)^a = \dfrac{y^a}{x^a}$ **9.** $x^{\frac{1}{a}} = \sqrt[a]{x}$ **10.** $x^{\frac{a}{b}} = \sqrt[b]{x^a}$

A number is in **scientific notation** if it is written in the form $a \times 10^n$, where $1 \le a < 10$ and n is an integer. To change a number to scientific notation, we divide the number by the place value of the first nonzero digit and then multiply the result by that same place value written as a power of 10.

An **exponential function** is a function whose graph is of the form $y = b^x$, where $b > 0$ and $b \ne 1$. The domain of an exponential function is the set of real numbers, and the range is the set of positive real numbers. The x-axis is a **horizontal asymptote**, and $(0, 1)$ is a point of the graph of $y = b^x$ for all $b > 0$ and $b \ne 1$. The graph of $y = b^{-x}$ or $y = \left(\dfrac{1}{b}\right)^x$ is the reflection over the y-axis of the graph of $y = b^x$.

An **exponential equation** is an equation in which the variable appears in an exponent. If $b \ne 0$ and $b \ne 1$, $b^x = b^y$ if and only if $x = y$.

VOCABULARY

16-2   Zero exponent   Negative exponent

16-3   Scientific notation

16-4   Fractional exponent

16-5   Linear growth   Exponential function   Exponential growth
          Horizontal asymptote

16-7   Exponential equation

REVIEW EXERCISES WITH OPEN-RESPONSE PROBLEMS

In 1–6, simplify each expression and write it without a denominator. All variables represent positive numbers.

1. $\dfrac{a^2 b^{-1}}{ab^{-3}}$ **2.** $\dfrac{20x^{-2}y^5}{4x^{-2}y^4}$ **3.** $(2c^{\frac{1}{2}}d)(c^{\frac{3}{2}}d^{-1})$

4. $(4x^{-1}y^{\frac{2}{3}})^{\frac{3}{2}}$ **5.** $\dfrac{(2a^2 b^4)^2}{2a^3 b^{-5}}$ **6.** $\left(\dfrac{1}{x^2 y}\right)^{-3}$

In 7–18, find the value of each expression.

7. 25^0 **8.** 15^{-1} **9.** $100^{\frac{1}{2}}$ **10.** -8^{-2}

11. $(-8)^{-2}$ **12.** $64^{\frac{2}{3}}$ **13.** $0.008^{\frac{1}{3}}$ **14.** $-64^{\frac{1}{2}}$

15. $\left(\dfrac{3}{4}\right)^{-2}$ **16.** $125^{-\frac{2}{3}}$ **17.** $4^{-\frac{3}{2}}$ **18.** $(12\frac{1}{5})^0$

19. Find the value of $3a^0 + a^{\frac{1}{2}}$ when $a = 9$.

20. Find the value of $(5b)^0 + (2b)^{\frac{3}{2}}$ when $b = 8$.

21. Find the value of $2c^{-\frac{1}{3}} + c^0$ when $c = 27$.

22. Find the value of $(x + 1)^{-1} + (x + 2)^{\frac{3}{4}} + (x + 3)^0$ when $x = 14$.

23. If $f(x) = x^{-\frac{2}{3}}$, find $f(27)$.

24. If $f(x) = 9x^{-2}$, find $f\left(\frac{3}{5}\right)$.

25. a. Sketch the graph of $y = 3^x$ in the interval $-2 \le x \le 2$.
   b. Use the graph of $y = 3^x$ to determine the value of $3^{1.6}$ to the *nearest tenth*.

26. For what value of b is the graph of $y = b^x$ the reflection in the y-axis of the graph of $y = 6^x$?

In 27 and 28, select the *numeral* preceding the choice that best completes the sentence.

27. The equation that defines the same function as $y = 5^x$ is
   (1) $y = 5^{-x}$ (2) $y = -5^{-x}$ (3) $y = \left(\frac{1}{5}\right)^{-x}$ (4) $y = \left(\frac{1}{5}\right)^x$

28. The graphs of $y = 3^x$ and $y = 3^{-x}$ intersect at
   (1) $(0, 1)$ only   (2) $(1, 0)$ only
   (3) $(0, 1)$ and $(1, 3)$ (4) no point

In 29–40, solve and check each equation.

29. $x^{\frac{5}{3}} = 32$

30. $a^{-2} + 2 = 27$

31. $y^{\frac{3}{4}} = 0.008$

32. $4x^{\frac{1}{3}} = 12$

33. $3b^{-\frac{1}{2}} = 10$

34. $2c^{\frac{3}{4}} + 1 = 55$

35. $6^{x-1} = 6^{2x-4}$

36. $5^{x+1} = 25^x$

37. $32^x = 8$

38. $8^x = 4^{x+1}$

39. $1{,}000^x = 100^{x-1}$

40. $\left(\frac{1}{3}\right)^{x-1} = 9$

41. When Jordan was born, his grandparents invested $1,000 for him in an account that doubled in value every 6 years. The value, A, of the investment at any time is given by the equation $A = 1{,}000(2)^{\frac{t}{6}}$, where t represents the number of years that the money was invested.
   a. What was the value of the investment when Jordan was ready to go to college at age 18?
   b. Jordan won a scholarship to college and did not need to use the money his grandparents had invested for him. He kept the money invested until he was ready to retire at age 60. What was the value of the investment at that time?

42. When tickets for a popular music group were to go on sale, the first person arrived to wait in line 1 hour before the box office opened. Then the number of persons in the line tripled every 10 minutes for the next hour. How many persons were in line when the box office opened?

In 43–49, select the *numeral* preceding the choice that best completes the sentence or answers the question.

43. The expression $\frac{2\sqrt{x}}{x}$ is equivalent to

(1) $2x^{\frac{1}{2}}$ (2) $(2x)^{\frac{1}{2}}$ (3) $2x^{-\frac{1}{2}}$ (4) $(2x)^{-\frac{1}{2}}$

44. The expression $(4 - x)^{-\frac{1}{2}}$ represents a real number
(1) for all x (2) for $x > 4$ only
(3) for $x \leq 4$ only   (4) for $x < 4$ only

45. Which of the following is *not* a real number?

(1) $-64^{\frac{1}{2}}$ (2) $(-64)^{\frac{1}{2}}$ (3) -64^0 (4) $-64^{\frac{1}{3}}$

46. The product $8 \cdot 8^5$ is *not* equal to
(1) 2^{18} (2) 4^9 (3) 8^6 (4) 64^5

47. The product $2^{\frac{1}{2}} \cdot 8^{\frac{1}{3}}$ is *not* equal to

(1) $16^{\frac{1}{6}}$ (2) $8^{\frac{1}{2}}$ (3) $2^{\frac{3}{2}}$ (4) $2\sqrt{2}$

48. If $x^n = 3x^{n-1}$ for all n, what is the value of x?

49. If $n^x = (n + 1)^x$ for all $n \neq 0$, what is the value of x?

CUMULATIVE REVIEW WITH OPEN-RESPONSE PROBLEMS

1. Write $\dfrac{1 - \sqrt{2}}{2 + \sqrt{2}}$ as an equivalent fraction with a rational denominator.

2. If $f(x) = 1 - \frac{1}{x}$ and $g(x) = \frac{1}{1 - x}$, show that $f \circ g(x) = g \circ f(x)$.

3. Points $A(4, 0)$ and $B(-2\sqrt{3}, 2)$ are on circle O whose center is at the origin.
  a. Find m$\angle AOB$.
  b. Find the coordinates of the image of B under a rotation of $30°$ about the origin.

4. Find $\tan (\text{Arc cos} (-0.5))$.

5. **a.** What is the period of the graph of $y = 2 \cos 3x$?
  b. What is the amplitude of the graph of $y = 2 \cos 3x$?

6. **a.** Simplify: $\dfrac{x^3 + 3x^2 - 4x - 12}{x^2 + 5x + 6}$

  b. For what values of x is $\dfrac{x^3 + 3x^2 - 4x - 12}{x^2 + 5x + 6}$ undefined?

Exploration

Prove that $\dfrac{2^n + 2^{n+2}}{2^{n+2} - 2^n} = \dfrac{5}{3}$ for all n.

Chapter 17

Logarithmic Functions

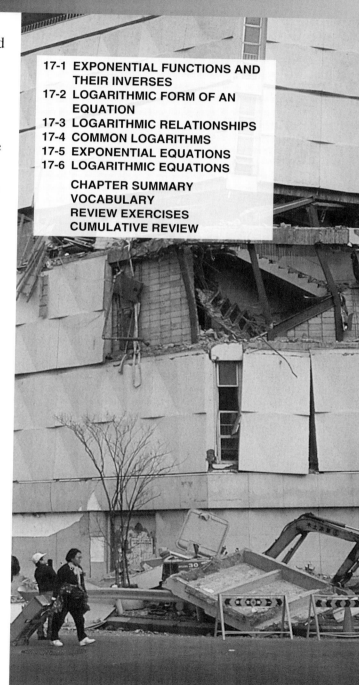

Throughout the ages, humankind has attempted to understand and control the forces of nature by finding ways to measure and moderate them. Earthquakes are one such force that has wrought destructive effects on Earth.

Charles Richter devised a scale by which the magnitude of an earthquake can be measured. The Richter scale computes the magnitude of a quake by using the amplitude of the waves as recorded by seismographs and then registers this magnitude in terms of a *common logarithm* or exponent to the base 10.

In the twentieth century, San Francisco has experienced two major earthquakes. In 1906 the city was devastated by an earthquake that registered 8.3 on the Richter scale, and in 1989 by one that registered 7.1. Since the difference between these two measurements is 1.2, the 1906 earthquake was $10^{1.2}$ or almost 16 times as powerful as the one in 1989.

The Richter scale for measuring earthquakes is just one way in which logarithms are used. Before devices such as computers and calculators were available as computational aids, the development of logarithms simplified complex computations and led to the advancement of sciences such as astronomy that require accurate computation with very large numbers. Logarithms continue to be an important concept in advanced mathematics.

17-1 EXPONENTIAL FUNCTIONS AND THEIR INVERSES

In Chapter 16, we studied the graphs of exponential functions of the form $y = b^x$. In this section, we will study the inverses of these exponential functions.

The figure below shows the graph of $y = 2^x$ and its reflection in the line $y = x$. Since $r_{y=x}(x, y) = (y, x)$, the equation of the reflection of $y = 2^x$ is $x = 2^y$. This equation defines a function that is the inverse of $y = 2^x$ under composition of functions.

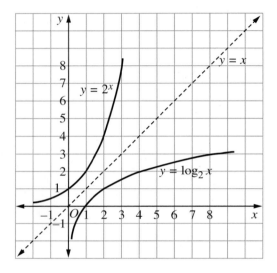

We prefer to write the equation that defines a function by expressing y in terms of x. Therefore, we want to rewrite $x = 2^y$ so that it is solved for y. We begin by describing y in the equation $x = 2^y$ in words:

y is the exponent to the base 2 needed to obtain x.

Since the word ***logarithm*** means "exponent," we can write this sentence as follows:

y is the logarithm to the base 2 of x.

To abbreviate this sentence and write it in symbolic form, we will pick out essential parts, using "log" for "logarithm."

<u>y is</u> the <u>log</u>arithm to the base <u>2</u> of <u>x</u>.

or simply: $\qquad\qquad\qquad\qquad y = \log_2 x$

The base, 2, is written a half-line below the word *log*.

Therefore:
$$x = 2^y \quad\leftrightarrow\quad y = \log_2 x$$

Thus, the equation $x = 2^y$ is *equivalent* to the equation $y = \log_2 x$.

These two equations name the same set of points, some of which are included in the table that follows and can also be seen in the graph shown earlier.

Point (x, y)	Exponential Form $x = 2^y$	Logarithmic Form $y = \log_2 x$	Logarithmic Form Is Read As
$(8, 3)$	$8 = 2^3$	$3 = \log_2 8$	3 is the log to the base 2 of 8.
$(4, 2)$	$4 = 2^2$	$2 = \log_2 4$	2 is the log to the base 2 of 4.
$\left(\frac{1}{2}, -1\right)$	$\frac{1}{2} = 2^{-1}$	$-1 = \log_2 \frac{1}{2}$	-1 is the log to the base 2 of $\frac{1}{2}$.
$\left(\frac{1}{4}, -2\right)$	$\frac{1}{4} = 2^{-2}$	$-2 = \log_2 \frac{1}{4}$	-2 is the log to the base 2 of $\frac{1}{4}$.

The graph of the exponential function $y = 2^x$ lies entirely in Quadrants I and II because the x values consist of all real numbers and the y values are positive. Under a reflection in the line $y = x$, the graph of its inverse function (that is, $x = 2^y$ or $y = \log_2 x$) lies entirely in Quadrants I and IV because the x values are positive and the y values now consist of all real numbers.

We can see from the graph of $y = \log_2 x$ that, since no vertical line can intersect the curve in more than one point, no two pairs have the same first element. The set of ordered pairs defined by $y = \log_2 x$ is a function whose domain is the set of positive real numbers and whose range is the set of all real numbers.

What we have observed using the base 2 can be applied to any base, b, for which the exponential function $y = b^x$ is defined.

$$\text{For } b > 0 \text{ and } b \neq 1: x = b^y \leftrightarrow y = \log_b x.$$

The equation $y = \log_b x$ defines a logarithmic function that is the inverse under composition of the exponential function $y = b^x$.

A function f(x) is an *exponential function*:	Its inverse f$^{-1}(x)$ is a *logarithmic function*:
$$\mathbf{f}(x) = \boldsymbol{b^x}$$ or $$\boldsymbol{y = b^x}$$	$$\mathbf{f}^{-1}(x) = \log_b x$$ or $$\boldsymbol{y = \log_b x}$$
Domain $= \{x \mid x \in \text{Real numbers}\}$	Domain $= \{x \mid x > 0\}$
Range $\ = \{y \mid y > 0\}$	Range $\ = \{y \mid y \in \text{Real numbers}\}$

EXAMPLE

a. Sketch the graph of $y = 5^x$ to include the points whose ordered pairs are found in the table at the right.

x	-2	-1	0	1	2
$y = 5^x$	$\frac{1}{25}$	$\frac{1}{5}$	1	5	25

b. Name the ordered pairs that are the images of the pairs in the table of part **a**, under a reflection in the line $y = x$.

c. Sketch the graph of the inverse of $y = 5^x$, using the pairs from part **b**.

d. State the equation of the curve graphed in part **c**, using some form of the word *logarithm*.

Solutions
a. Plot the points whose ordered pairs are given in the table, and draw a smooth curve through them.

b. Under a reflection in the line $y = x$, $(x, y) \rightarrow (y, x)$.

x	$\frac{1}{25}$	$\frac{1}{5}$	1	5	25
y	-2	-1	0	1	2

The equation formed is $x = 5^y$.

c. Plot the points whose ordered pairs are given in the table in part **b**. Draw a smooth curve through these points, as shown on the graph above.

d. Since $x = b^y \leftrightarrow y = \log_b x$ and here $b = 5$, then $x = 5^y \leftrightarrow y = \log_5 x$.

Answers: **a, b, c.** See graph and table above.   **d.** $y = \log_5 x$

EXERCISES WITH OPEN-RESPONSE PROBLEMS

1. a. Copy and complete the table at the right by finding, for each given value of x, the corresponding value of $y = 3^x$.

x	-2	-1	0	1	2
$y = 3^x$					

b. Sketch the graph of $y = 3^x$ to include the points whose ordered pairs were found in part **a**.

c. Name the ordered pairs that are the images of the pairs in the table of part **a**, under a reflection in the line $y = x$.

d. Sketch the graph of the inverse of $y = 3^x$ by using the pairs from part **c**.

e. State the equation of the curve graphed in part **d**, using some form of the word *logarithm*.

2. a. Copy and complete the table at the right by finding, for each given value of x, the corresponding value of $y = 4^x$.

x	$-\frac{3}{2}$	-1	$-\frac{1}{2}$	0	$\frac{1}{2}$	1	$\frac{3}{2}$
$y = 4^x$							

b. Sketch the graph of $y = 4^x$ to include the points whose ordered pairs were found in part **a**.

c. Name seven ordered pairs found in the graph of the inverse of $y = 4^x$.

d. Sketch the graph of $y = \log_4 x$ to include the points named in part **c**.

3. The table at the right lists three selected pairs of the function $y = 5^x$. Note that values of y are stated as rational approximations to the nearest tenth.

a. Sketch the graph of $y = 5^x$ in the interval $-1 \le x \le \frac{3}{2}$, including points where $x = -1, -\frac{1}{2}, 0, \frac{1}{2}, 1$, and $\frac{3}{2}$.

x	5^x	$= y$
$-\frac{1}{2}$	$5^{-\frac{1}{2}} = \frac{1}{\sqrt{5}} = \frac{\sqrt{5}}{5}$	≈ 0.4
$\frac{1}{2}$	$5^{\frac{1}{2}} = \sqrt{5}$	≈ 2.2
$\frac{3}{2}$	$5^{\frac{3}{2}} = (\sqrt{5})^3 = 5\sqrt{5}$	≈ 11.2

b. Sketch the graph of $y = \log_5 x$ (that is, the reflection of $y = 5^x$ in the line $y = x$).

4. a. Name five ordered pairs in the function $y = 6^x$.

b. Name five pairs in the function $y = \log_6 x$.   **c.** Sketch the graph of $y = \log_6 x$.

5. a. Sketch the graph of $y = 8^x$, including points for which $x = -1, -\frac{2}{3}, -\frac{1}{3}, 0, \frac{1}{3}, \frac{2}{3}, 1$.

b. Sketch the graph of $y = \log_8 x$, including the images of the ordered pairs in part **a** under a reflection in the line $y = x$.

6. a. Sketch the graph of $y = \left(\frac{5}{2}\right)^x$ in the interval $-1 \le x \le 2$.

b. Sketch the graph of $y = \log_{\frac{5}{2}} x$ in the interval $\frac{2}{5} \le x \le \frac{25}{4}$.

c. What is the y-intercept of $y = \left(\frac{5}{2}\right)^x$?   **d.** What is the x-intercept of $y = \log_{\frac{5}{2}} x$?

7. a. Sketch the graph of $y = \log_{10} x$ in the interval $\frac{1}{10} \le x \le 10$. (It will be helpful to choose $\sqrt{10} \approx 3.2$ as a value of x.)

b. On the same set of axes, draw the graph of $y = 1$.

c. What are the coordinates of the point of intersection of the graphs of $y = \log_{10} x$ and $y = 1$?

d. In what quadrants does the graph of $y = \log_{10} x$ lie?

8. The graph of $y = 7^x$ is reflected in the line $y = x$. What is the equation of the set of image points?

9. When drawn on the same set of axes, at what point, if any, do the graphs of $y = \log_5 x$ and $y = \log_3 x$ intersect?

In 10–15, in each case, write the equation of $f^{-1}(x)$, the inverse of $f(x)$.

10. $f(x) = 2^x$ **11.** $f(x) = 6^x$ **12.** $f(x) = 12^x$

13. $f(x) = \log_3 x$ **14.** $f(x) = \log_7 x$ **15.** $f(x) = \log_9 x$

In 16–23, select the *numeral* preceding the expression that best completes each sentence or answers the question.

16. The graph of $y = \log_8 x$ lies entirely in Quadrants
  (1) I and II   (2) II and III   (3) I and III   (4) I and IV

17. The function that is the inverse of $y = 5^x$ under composition is
  (1) $y = -5^x$ (2) $y = 5^{-x}$ (3) $y = \log_5 x$ (4) $x = \log_5 y$

18. At what point does the graph of $y = \log_5 x$ intersect the *x*-axis?
  (1) $(1, 0)$ (2) $(0, 1)$ (3) $(5, 0)$ (4) There is no point of intersection.

19. A number that is *not* in the domain of the function $y = \log_{10} x$ is
  (1) 1   (2) 0   (3) $\frac{1}{2}$ (4) 10

20. If $y = \log_{10} x$ and $x > 1$, then y is
  (1) positive   (2) zero   (3) negative   (4) not a real number

21. If $y = \log_{10} x$ and $x = 1$, then y is
  (1) positive   (2) zero   (3) negative   (4) not a real number

22. If $y = \log_{10} x$ and $0 < x < 1$, then y is
  (1) positive   (2) zero   (3) negative   (4) not a real number

23. If $y = \log_{10} x$ and $x \leq 0$, then y is
  (1) positive   (2) zero   (3) negative   (4) not a real number

17-2 LOGARITHMIC FORM OF AN EQUATION

In Section 17-1, we saw that an exponential equation and a logarithmic equation are two ways of expressing a statement about a power. The basic statement made by the equation $\log_5 125 = 3$ is that the log (that is, the exponent) is 3.

$$\log_5 125 \;\; = 3$$
$$\downarrow \qquad\quad \downarrow\;\downarrow$$
$$\text{Exponent is 3.}$$

Here, the base is 5, written to the right of and a half-line below the word *log*.

$$\log_5 125 = 3 \quad\leftrightarrow\quad 5^3 = 125$$

Other equivalent *logarithmic* equations and *exponential* equations are:

$$\log_7 49 = 2 \quad\leftrightarrow\quad 7^2 = 49$$
$$\log_{10} 0.1 = -1 \quad\leftrightarrow\quad 10^{-1} = 0.1$$
$$\log_4 2 = \frac{1}{2} \quad\leftrightarrow\quad 4^{\frac{1}{2}} = 2$$

● In general: $\mathbf{\log_b c = a} \quad\leftrightarrow\quad \mathbf{b^a = c}\ (b > 0 \text{ and } b \neq 1)$

EXAMPLES

1. Write $8^2 = 64$ in logarithmic form.

Solution
(1) The basic statement is that the logarithm (or exponent) is 2.

$\log = 2$

(2) The base, 8, is written to the right of and a half-line below the word *log*.

$\log_8 = 2$

(3) The power, 64, follows the word *log*.

$\log_8 64 = 2$

Answer: $\log_8 64 = 2$

---

2. Write $\log_3 81 = 4$ in exponential form.

Solution Since $\log_b c = a$ is equivalent to $b^a = c$, then $\log_3 81 = 4$ is equivalent to $3^4 = 81$.

Answer: $3^4 = 81$

---

3. Solve for x: $\log_x 8 = 3$

How to Proceed:	*Solution:*
(1) Rewrite the logarithmic equation in exponential form. The base is x, and the exponent is 3.	$\log_x 8 = 3$ $x^3 = 8$
(2) Use the reciprocal of the exponent to solve for x.	$(x^3)^{\frac{1}{3}} = 8^{\frac{1}{3}}$
(3) Simplify.	$x = \sqrt[3]{8}$

Answer: $x = 2$

$= 2$

---

4. Find the value of $\log_{25} 125$.

How to Proceed:	*Solution:*
(1) Write an equation in logarithmic form.	$\log_{25} 125 = a$
(2) Rewrite the equation in exponential form. The base is 25, and the exponent is a.	$25^a = 125$
(3) Change each power to base 5: $25 = 5^2$ and $125 = 5^3$.	$(5^2)^a = 5^3$
(4) Equate exponents of like bases.	$2a = 3$
(5) Solve for a	$a = \frac{3}{2}$

Answer: $\log_{25} 125 = \frac{3}{2}$

EXERCISES WITH OPEN-RESPONSE PROBLEMS

In 1–12, write each exponential equation in logarithmic form.

1. $2^4 = 16$ **2.** $3^2 = 9$ **3.** $10^{-2} = 0.01$ **4.** $12^0 = 1$

5. $8^{\frac{1}{3}} = 2$ **6.** $5^{\frac{1}{2}} = \sqrt{5}$ **7.** $6^{-1} = \frac{1}{6}$ **8.** $9^{-\frac{1}{2}} = \frac{1}{3}$

9. $4^a = b$ **10.** $x^3 = y$ **11.** $5^c = d$ **12.** $b^a = 8$

In 13–24, write each logarithmic equation in exponential form.

13. $\log_2 64 = 6$ **14.** $\log_7 49 = 2$ **15.** $\log_{10} 1{,}000 = 3$

16. $\log_{27} 9 = \frac{2}{3}$ **17.** $\log_4 32 = \frac{5}{2}$ **18.** $\log_{15} 1 = 0$

19. $\log_{\frac{1}{9}} 3 = -\frac{1}{2}$ **20.** $\log_{\frac{1}{8}} 2 = -\frac{1}{3}$ **21.** $\log_{10} 0.001 = -3$

22. $\log_a \sqrt[3]{a} = \frac{1}{3}$ **23.** $\log_a \frac{1}{a} = -1$ **24.** $\log_b c = \frac{1}{5}$

In 25–33, solve each equation for x.

25. $\log_2 x = 4$ **26.** $\log_5 x = 2$ **27.** $\log_3 x = -2$

28. $\log_7 x = 0$ **29.** $\log_{81} x = \frac{1}{2}$ **30.** $\log_9 x = -\frac{1}{2}$

31. $\log_6 x = -2$ **32.** $\log_{10} x = 7$ **33.** $\log_{64} x = \frac{2}{3}$

In 34–42, evaluate each expression.

34. $\log_3 27$ **35.** $\log_2 16$ **36.** $\log_{10} 10{,}000$

37. $\log_5 \frac{1}{25}$ **38.** $\log_8 32$ **39.** $\log_{100} 0.1$

40. $\log_{36} 216$ **41.** $\log_{49} \frac{1}{7}$ **42.** $\log_{27} \frac{1}{9}$

In 43–51, solve each equation for b.

43. $\log_b 27 = 3$ **44.** $\log_b 49 = 2$ **45.** $\log_b \frac{1}{2} = -1$

46. $\log_b 125 = \frac{3}{2}$ **47.** $\log_b 4 = \frac{1}{2}$ **48.** $\log_b 6 = \frac{1}{3}$

49. $\log_b 0.1 = -\frac{1}{2}$ **50.** $\log_b 8 = -3$ **51.** $\log_b \sqrt{5} = \frac{1}{4}$

52. If $f(x) = \log_4 x$, find f(64).   **53.** If $f(x) = \log_3 x$, find f(1).

54. If $f(x) = \log_2 x$, find f($\sqrt{2}$).   **55.** If $\log_{10} x = -3$, find x.

In 56–58, select the *numeral* preceding the expression that best completes each sentence.

56. The value of $\log_{25} 5$ is

(1) $\frac{1}{2}$　　　　(2) 2　　　　(3) $\frac{1}{5}$　　　　(4) 5

57. If $\log_8 x = \frac{2}{3}$, then x equals

(1) $\frac{16}{3}$　　　　(2) $\frac{64}{3}$　　　　(3) $16\sqrt{2}$　　　　(4) 4

58. If $\log_2 a = \log_3 a$, then a equals

(1) 1　　　　(2) 2　　　　(3) 3　　　　(4) 0

17-3 LOGARITHMIC RELATIONSHIPS

In Chapter 16, we learned rules for working with powers with like bases, such as the powers of 2 in the table at the right. Since a logarithm is an exponent, we can use those rules for exponents to develop rules that will be useful when we work with logarithms with like bases.

In the table, each exponential equation in the left column is rewritten as an equivalent log equation in the right column. After we have developed the rules for logarithms, we will use the entries in this table to demonstrate the truth of the general rules for logarithms to the base 2.

Powers of 2	Logarithms to the Base 2
$2^0 = 1$	$\log_2 1 = 0$
$2^1 = 2$	$\log_2 2 = 1$
$2^2 = 4$	$\log_2 4 = 2$
$2^3 = 8$	$\log_2 8 = 3$
$2^4 = 16$	$\log_2 16 = 4$
$2^5 = 32$	$\log_2 32 = 5$
$2^6 = 64$	$\log_2 64 = 6$
$2^7 = 128$	$\log_2 128 = 7$
$2^8 = 256$	$\log_2 256 = 8$
$2^9 = 512$	$\log_2 512 = 9$
$2^{10} = 1{,}024$	$\log_2 1{,}024 = 10$
$2^{11} = 2{,}048$	$\log_2 2{,}048 = 11$
$2^{12} = 4{,}096$	$\log_2 4{,}096 = 12$

Product Rule

If $b > 0$ and $b \neq 1$:

$$b^x = A \leftrightarrow \log_b A = x$$

$$b^y = B \leftrightarrow \log_b B = y$$

$$b^{x+y} = AB \leftrightarrow \log_b AB = x + y$$

By substitution:

$$\log_b AB = \log_b A + \log_b B$$

The product rule, $\log_b AB = \log_b A + \log_b B$, is illustrated in the following example.

If $N = 8 \cdot 32$, find N.

METHOD 1: *Exponential Form*

1. Write the expression to be evaluated. $N = 8 \cdot 32$
2. Express each number as a power of 2. $= 2^3 \cdot 2^5$
3. Add exponents when multiplying powers with like bases. $= 2^{3+5}$
   $= 2^8$
4. Evaluate, or find the value from the table. $= 256$

METHOD 2: *Logarithmic Form*

1. Write the expression to be evaluated. $N = 8 \cdot 32$
2. Write the logarithm to the base 2 of each side of the equation. $\log_2 N = \log_2 (8 \cdot 32)$
3. Use the product rule. $= \log_2 8 + \log_2 32$
4. Evaluate the right-hand side (see the table), and simplify. $= 3 + 5$
   $\log_2 N = 8$
5. Find N by referring to the table. (Since $\log_2 256 = 8$, $N = 256$.) $N = 256$

METHOD 3: *Arithmetic Computation*

A calculator or mental arithmetic can be used to compute the product:
$N = 8 \cdot 32 = 256$

Answer: $N = 256$

Quotient Rule

If $b > 0$ and $b \neq 1$:

$$b^x = A \leftrightarrow \log_b A = x$$
$$b^y = B \leftrightarrow \log_b B = y$$

$$b^{x-y} = \frac{A}{B} \leftrightarrow \log_b \frac{A}{B} = x - y$$

By substitution: $\log_b \frac{A}{B} = \log_b A - \log_b B$

The quotient rule is illustrated in the following example.

Evaluate $\frac{128}{512}$.

METHOD 1: *Exponential Form*

$$\frac{128}{512} = \frac{2^7}{2^9}$$
$$= 2^{7-9}$$
$$= 2^{-2}$$
$$= \frac{1}{2^2}$$
$$= \frac{1}{4}$$

METHOD 2: *Logarithmic Form*

Let $A = \frac{128}{512}$.

$$\log_2 A = \log_2\left(\frac{128}{512}\right)$$
$$= \log_2 128 - \log_2 512$$
$$= 7 - 9$$
$$= -2$$

Although -2 is not given as a log to the base 2 in the table, the log expression can be rewritten in exponential form.

$$\log_2 A = -2$$
$$A = 2^{-2}$$
$$= \frac{1}{2^2} = \frac{1}{4}$$

METHOD 3: *Arithmetic Computation*

A calculator will return the quotient 0.25, the decimal form of $\frac{1}{4}$.

Answer: $\frac{128}{512} = \frac{1}{4}$

Power Rule

If $b > 0$ and $b \neq 1$:

$$b^x = A \leftrightarrow \log_b A = x$$
$$b^{xc} = A^c \leftrightarrow \log_b A^c = xc = cx$$

By substitution: $\log_b A^c = c \log_b A$

We can find the values of some logarithmic expressions by two methods. For example, the product rule tells us that

$$\log_2 (4^3) = \log_2 (4 \cdot 4 \cdot 4) = \log_2 4 + \log_2 4 + \log_2 4 = 2 + 2 + 2 = 6$$

Also, by the power rule, we know that

$$\log_2 (4^3) = 3 \log_2 4 = 3 \cdot 2 = 6$$

Therefore, $\log_2 4 + \log_2 4 + \log_2 4 = 3 \log_2 4$.

Not all logarithmic expressions involving powers can be evaluated by the product rule. For example, $\log_2 \sqrt[3]{2}$ can be simplified only by using the power rule. Here, $\log_2 \sqrt[3]{2} = \log_2 (2^{\frac{1}{3}}) = \frac{1}{3} \log_2 2 = \frac{1}{3} \cdot 1 = \frac{1}{3}$.

The computations that have been used to illustrate the logarithmic relationships derived in this section have been limited to numbers that are the integral powers of 2. The rules, however, apply to logarithms with any base.

EXAMPLES

1. Find the value of $\log_6 12 + \log_6 3$.

How to Proceed:	*Solution:*
(1) Write the given expression.	$\log_6 12 + \log_6 3$
(2) Use the product rule.	$= \log_6 (12 \cdot 3)$
(3) Simplify.	$= \log_6 36$
(4) Evaluate the result.	$= 2$

Answer: $\log_6 12 + \log_6 3 = 2$

---

2. If $2 \log_3 9 + \log_3 x = \log_3 27$, find x.

How to Proceed:	*Solution:*
(1) Write the given equation.	$2 \log_3 9 + \log_3 x = \log_3 27$
(2) Simplify the left-hand side. Use the power rule, and use the product rule.	$\log_3 9^2 + \log_3 x = \log_3 27$ $\log_3 (9^2 \cdot x) = \log_3 27$ $\log_3 (81x) = \log_3 27$
(3) Equate the powers, and solve for x.	$81x = 27$ $x = \frac{27}{81} = \frac{1}{3}$

Alternative Solution		
(1) Write the given equation.	$2 \log_3 9 + \log_3 x = \log_3 27$
(2) Evaluate each term if possible.	$2 \cdot 2 + \log_3 x = 3$ $4 + \log_3 x = 3$
(3) Subtract 4 from each side of the equation.	$\log_3 x = -1$
(4) Rewrite in exponential form, and simplify.	$3^{-1} = x$ $\frac{1}{3} = x$

Answer: $x = \frac{1}{3}$

3. If $x = \frac{a}{\sqrt{b}}$, express $\log_{10} x$ in terms of $\log_{10} a$ and $\log_{10} b$.

How to Proceed:	*Solution:*
(1) Express $\sqrt{b}$ as a power.	$x = \frac{a}{\sqrt{b}}$
	$= \frac{a}{b^{\frac{1}{2}}}$
(2) Write the logarithm to the base 10 of each side of the equation.	$\log_{10} x = \log_{10}\left(\frac{a}{b^{\frac{1}{2}}}\right)$
(3) Use the quotient rule.	$= \log_{10} a - \log_{10} b^{\frac{1}{2}}$
(4) Use the power rule.	$= \log_{10} a - \frac{1}{2} \log_{10} b$

Answer: $\log_{10} x = \log_{10} a - \frac{1}{2} \log_{10} b$.

---

4. The expression $\log_3 a^5 b$ is equivalent to

(1) $5 \log_3 ab$ (2) $5 \log_3 a + \log_3 b$

(3) $\log_3 5ab$ (4) $\log_3 5a + \log_3 b$

How to Proceed:	*Solution:*
Use the product rule.	$\log_3 a^5 b = \log_3 a^5 + \log_3 b$
Use the power rule.	$= 5 \log_3 a + \log_3 b$

Answer: (2)

EXERCISES WITH OPEN-RESPONSE PROBLEMS

In 1–8, evaluate each expression by using: **a.** powers of 2 in exponential form   **b.** logarithms to the base 2   **c.** a calculator (*Note:* The table on page 793 may be used for these exercises.)

1. $64 \cdot 16$ **2.** $1{,}024 \div 256$ **3.** 16^3 **4.** $\sqrt[5]{32}$

5. $\frac{128 \cdot 4^2}{512}$ **6.** $\frac{64\sqrt[3]{64}}{256}$ **7.** $\sqrt{\frac{4{,}096}{16}}$ **8.** $32\sqrt[3]{\frac{512}{64}}$

In 9–16, write each expression in terms of $\log_{10} a$ and $\log_{10} b$.

9. $\log_{10} ab$ **10.** $\log_{10}(a \div b)$ **11.** $\log_{10}(a^2 b)$ **12.** $\log_{10}(a^2 b)^3$

13. $\log_{10} \frac{\sqrt{a}}{b}$ **14.** $\log_{10} a\sqrt{b}$ **15.** $\log_{10}(ab)^2$ **16.** $\log_{10} \sqrt{\frac{a}{b}}$

In 17–22, solve each equation for n.

17. $\log_3 9 + \log_3 3 = \log_3 n$

18. $\log_4 64 - \log_4 16 = \log_4 n$

19. $3 \log_2 4 = \log_2 n$

20. $\log_6 216 - \frac{1}{2} \log_6 36 = \log_6 n$

21. $\log_{10} 1{,}000 - 2 \log_{10} 100 = \log_{10} n$

22. $\log_3 n - \log_3 \frac{1}{3} = \log_3 9$

In 23–26, select the *numeral* preceding the expression that best completes each sentence.

23. The expression $\log_5 \frac{a}{c^2}$ is equivalent to

(1) $\log_5 a - \frac{1}{2} \log_5 c$

(2) $\frac{\log_5 a}{2 \log_5 c}$

(3) $2 (\log_5 a - \log_5 c)$

(4) $\log_5 a - 2 \log_5 c$

24. If $x = (ab)^2$, then $\log_{10} x$ equals

(1) $2 \log_{10} a + \log_{10} b$

(2) $2 \log_{10} a + 2 \log_{10} b$

(3) $\log_{10} a + 2 \log_{10} b$

(4) $\log_{10} 2a + \log_{10} 2b$

25. The expression $\log_{10} \sqrt{\frac{x}{y}}$ is equivalent to

(1) $\frac{1}{2} \log_{10} x - \log_{10} y$

(2) $\frac{1}{2} \left(\frac{\log_{10} x}{\log_{10} y} \right)$

(3) $\log_{10} \frac{1}{2} x - \log_{10} \frac{1}{2} y$

(4) $\frac{1}{2} (\log_{10} x - \log_{10} y)$

26. The value of $\log_4 8 + \log_4 2$ is

(1) 1   (2) 2   (3) 16   (4) 4

17-4 COMMON LOGARITHMS

Since the earliest use of numbers, people have devised aids in computation. One of the first such tools was the abacus, still in use today in some parts of the world. In the seventeenth century, the development of logarithms greatly facilitated the calculations necessary in the study of astronomy and helped advance that science. The slide rule, a mechanical device that uses a scale based on logarithms, was for many years the familiar tool of scientists and engineers.

Although calculators and computers have now replaced many older calculating devices, the logarithmic functions remain important in mathematics, science, engineering, and business. Understanding logarithms helps us to use the functions and equations needed to solve problems in these areas.

Finding Common Logarithms

A *common logarithm* is an exponent to the base 10. When no base is written in the logarithmic form of a number, the base is understood to be 10; that is, $\log a = \log_{10} a$.

On a graphing calculator, the [**LOG**] key is used to display the common logarithm of a number. To find log 2.53 on a calculator, one of two methods is used. Each sequence of keys should be tested to determine which is correct for use in your calculator. In this book we will use Method 1.

METHOD 1: *Enter:*   [**LOG**] 2.53 [**ENTER**]

METHOD 2: *Enter:*   2.53 [**LOG**]

Display: $\boxed{.4031205212}$

This calculator response can be written as follows:

$$\log 2.53 \approx 0.4031205212 \quad \text{or} \quad 10^{0.4031205212} \approx 2.53.$$

Since $1 < 2.53 < 10$, and since exponents to the base 10, or common logarithms, increase as the corresponding numbers increase:

$$\log 1 < \log 2.53 < \log 10 \quad \text{or} \quad 0 < \log 2.53 < 1.$$

If we know that, to the nearest ten-thousandth, $\log 2.53 = 0.4031$, then we can write the following:

$$\log 25.3 = \log (2.53 \times 10^1) = \log 2.53 + \log 10^1 = 0.4031 + 1 = 1.4031$$
$$\log 253 = \log (2.53 \times 10^2) = \log 2.53 + \log 10^2 = 0.4031 + 2 = 2.4031$$
$$\log 2{,}530 = \log (2.53 \times 10^3) = \log 2.53 + \log 10^3 = 0.4031 + 3 = 3.4031$$

In general:

If $1 < a < 10$, then $0 < \log a < 1$ and $\log (a \times 10^n) = n + \log a$.

This statement can be verified on a calculator. For example, let us find, to the *nearest ten-thousandth*, log 7.83, log 78.3, log 7,830, and log 783,000.

Enter: [**LOG**] 7.83 [**ENTER**]

Display: $\boxed{.8937617621}$

To the *nearest ten-thousandth*,
$$\log 7.83 = 0.8938.$$

Enter: [**LOG**] 78.3 [**ENTER**]

Display: $\boxed{1.893761762}$

To the *nearest ten-thousandth*,
$$\log 78.3 = 1.8938.$$

Enter: [**LOG**] 7830 [**ENTER**]

Display: $\boxed{3.893761762}$

To the *nearest ten-thousandth*,
$$\log 7{,}830 = 3.8938.$$

Enter: [**LOG**] 783000 [**ENTER**]

Display: $\boxed{5.893761762}$

To the *nearest ten-thousandth*,
$$\log 783{,}000 = 5.8938.$$

Finding Powers from Logarithms

If we know the common logarithm of a number, we can use a calculator to find the number. If log $N = a$, then $N = 10^a$. Therefore, the key that is used to find N is usually labeled $\boxed{10^x}$ and is accessed by first pressing $\boxed{\textbf{2nd}}$ or $\boxed{\text{INV}}$.

For example, if log $N = 2.5716$, to find N to the *nearest tenth* we use one of the following sequences of keys and round the number in the display to the nearest tenth.

METHOD 1: *Enter:* $\boxed{\textbf{2nd}}$ $\boxed{10^x}$ 2.5716 $\boxed{\textbf{ENTER}}$

METHOD 2: *Enter:*   2.5716 $\boxed{\textbf{2nd}}$ $\boxed{10^x}$

Display: $\boxed{372.90654}$

To the *nearest tenth*, $N = 372.9$

Each method should be tested to see which is right for your calculator. In this book, we will use Method 1.

Note: Since log $N = 2.5716$ becomes log $372.9 = 2.5716$, it follows that $10^{2.5716} = 372.9$. A sense of estimation verifies this answer because $10^2 < 10^{2.5716} < 10^3$, or $100 < 372.9 < 1,000$.

EXAMPLES

1. Find log 0.01277 to the *nearest ten-thousandth*.

Solution   Use a calculator.

Enter: $\boxed{\textbf{LOG}}$ .01277 $\boxed{\textbf{ENTER}}$

Display: $\boxed{-1.893809103}$

Answer: -1.8938

2. If log $x = 3.78860$, find x to the *nearest integer*.

Solution   Use a calculator.

Enter: $\boxed{\textbf{2nd}}$ $\boxed{10^x}$ 3.7886 $\boxed{\textbf{ENTER}}$

Display: $\boxed{6146.105347}$

Answer: 6,146

3. Use logarithms to show that $\frac{12.6 \times 0.824}{0.336} = 30.9$.

Solution (1) Let $N = \frac{12.6 \times 0.824}{0.336}$, and write a log equation.

$$\log N = \log \frac{12.6 \times 0.824}{0.336}$$
$$= \log 12.6 + \log 0.824 - \log 0.336$$

(2) Substitute the logs of the numbers, and perform the computation with logs.

Enter:

Display: ⌐1.489958479⌐

(3) Find N, the number whose log is the number in the display. With the result of step 2 in the calculator display:

Enter:

Display: [30.9]

Thus, the left side N equals 30.9, the value on the right side.

Alternative Solution Show that each side of the equation has the same logarithmic value. By steps 1 and 2 above, the logarithm of the left side equals 1.489958479. Then demonstrate that log 30.9 also equals 1.489958479.

---

4. If $\log a = 0.5733$, find $\log 0.001a$.

Solution
$$\log 0.001a = \log 0.001 + \log a$$
$$= \log 10^{-3} + \log a$$
$$= -3 + 0.5733$$
$$= -2.4267$$

Answer: -2.4267

---

5. If $\log N = 3.36486$, find N to three significant digits.

Solution *Enter:* [2nd] [10ˣ] 3.36486 [ENTER]

Display: [2316.647731]

Answer: 2,320

EXERCISES WITH OPEN-RESPONSE PROBLEMS

In 1–12, find the common logarithm of each number to four decimal places.

1. 279   **2.** 56.8   **3.** 9,280   **4.** 7.65
5. 0.824   **6.** 0.00039   **7.** 0.021   **8.** 42,800
9. 7.8   **10.** 12.7   **11.** 0.005   **12.** 97

In 13–21, find to three significant digits each number N whose common logarithm is given.

13. $\log N = 0.6884$ **14.** $\log N = 3.9294$ **15.** $\log N = 1.7612$
16. $\log N = -1.7799$ **17.** $\log N = -0.3635$ **18.** $\log N = 2.0170$
19. $\log N = -3.0057$ **20.** $\log N = 1.4942$ **21.** $\log N = 4.3856$

22. If $\log x = 1.8650$, find x to the *nearest tenth*.   **23.** If $10^{3.7924} = a$, find $\log a$.

In 24–27, in each case, express x in terms of a, b, and c.

24. $\log x = \frac{1}{2}(\log a + \log b - \log c)$ **25.** $\log x = \frac{1}{2}(\log a - (\log b + \log c))$

26. $\log x = 2\log a - \frac{1}{2}(\log b + \log c)$ **27.** $\log x = \frac{1}{2}\log a - \left(\log b + \frac{1}{2}\log c\right)$

In 28–35, in each case, express $\log N$ in terms of $\log x$, $\log y$, and $\log z$.

28. $N = xyz$ **29.** $N = \sqrt{xyz}$ **30.** $N = \frac{xy}{z}$ **31.** $N = x^2 y\sqrt{z}$

32. $N = \frac{x^2 y}{z^3}$ **33.** $N = \sqrt{\frac{xy}{z}}$ **34.** $N = \frac{x\sqrt{y}}{z^2}$ **35.** $N = \frac{x^2}{y\sqrt{z}}$

In 36–45, select the *numeral* preceding the expression that best completes each sentence or answers the question.

36. If $\log a = c$, then $\log 100a$ equals
(1) $100c$ (2) $2c$ (3) $2 + c$ (4) $2 + \log c$
37. If $\log 7.11 = b$, then $\log 7,110$ equals
(1) $1,000b$ (2) $3b$ (3) $3 + b$ (4) $1,000 + b$
38. The expression $\log\sqrt{\frac{a}{b}}$ is equivalent to

(1) $\frac{1}{2}\log a - \log b$ (2) $\frac{1}{2}(\log a - \log b)$

(3) $\log\frac{1}{2}a - \log b$ (4) $\log\frac{1}{2}a - \log\frac{1}{2}b$

39. The expression $2\log a + \frac{1}{3}\log b$ is equivalent to

(1) $\log\frac{a^2 b}{3}$ (2) $\log\frac{2ab}{3}$ (3) $\log\sqrt[3]{a^2 b}$ (4) $\log a^2(\sqrt[3]{b})$

40. If $x = a\sqrt{b}$, then $\log x$ is equivalent to

(1) $\log a + \log \frac{1}{2} b$

(2) $\frac{1}{2}(\log a + \log b)$

(3) $\log a + \frac{1}{2}\log b$

(4) $\log\left(a + \frac{1}{2}b\right)$

41. If $x = \frac{a}{2b}$, then $\log x$ is equivalent to

(1) $\log a - 2\log b$

(2) $\log a - \log 2 + \log b$

(3) $\frac{1}{2}(\log a - \log b)$

(4) $\log a - (\log 2 + \log b)$

42. If $K = \frac{\sqrt[3]{6}}{5^2}$, which of the following is equivalent to $\log K$?

(1) $3\log 6 - 2\log 5$

(2) $\frac{1}{3}\log 6 - 2\log 5$

(3) $\dfrac{\frac{1}{3}\log 6}{2\log 5}$

(4) $\dfrac{3\log 6}{2\log 5}$

43. If $N = \sqrt{\frac{5}{12}}$, then $\log N$ is equivalent to

(1) $\frac{1}{2}(\log 5 - \log 12)$

(2) $\frac{1}{2}\log 5 - \log 12$

(3) $\frac{1}{2}\cdot\dfrac{\log 5}{\log 12}$

(4) $\sqrt{\dfrac{\log 5}{\log 12}}$

44. The expression $\log\sqrt{7^3}$ is equivalent to

(1) $\frac{2}{3}\log 7$

(2) $\frac{3}{2}\log 7$

(3) $3\log\frac{7}{2}$

(4) $\frac{1}{2}\log 3\cdot 7$

45. The expression $\log 5^{n+1}$ is equivalent to

(1) $n\log 5 + 5$

(2) $5\log 5^n$

(3) $n\log 5 + 1$

(4) $n\log 5 + \log 5$

In 46–57, if $\log 2 = a$, $\log 3 = b$, and $\log 10 = 1$, write each given expression in terms of a and b.

46. $\log 6$

47. $\log 9$

48. $\log 4$

49. $\log 12$

50. $\log \frac{2}{3}$

51. $\log \frac{3}{2}$

52. $\log \frac{6}{10}$

53. $\log \frac{20}{3}$

54. $\log \frac{30}{2}$

55. $\log \frac{10}{3}$

56. $\log \frac{9}{20}$

57. $\log \frac{10}{9}$

In 58–60, show that the left and right sides of each expression are equal by using: **a.** logarithms   **b.** arithmetic computation.

58. $\dfrac{15.96 \times 3.8}{2.527} = 24$

59. $\sqrt{\dfrac{25.6 \times 62.4}{15 \times 1.664}} = 8$

60. $\dfrac{18.9\sqrt{7.84}}{(0.6)^2} = 3(7)^2$

17-5 EXPONENTIAL EQUATIONS

In Chapter 16, we solved equations in which the exponent was a variable, such as $4^x = 8$. After writing each side of the equation as a power to the same base, we used this relationship:

$$\textbf{For } b > 0 \textbf{ and } b \neq 1, b^x = b^y \rightarrow x = y.$$

At that time, we were not able to solve an equation such as $3^x = 5$ because 3 and 5 are not integral powers of the same base. However, since common logarithms make it possible to write any number as an approximate power to the base 10, we can now solve any exponential equation.

Compare the solutions of $4^x = 8$ and $3^x = 5$ shown below.

$$4^x = 8$$
$$(2^2)^x = 2^3$$
$$2^{2x} = 2^3$$
$$2x = 3$$
$$x = \frac{3}{2} = 1.5$$

Check: $\quad 4^{1.5} = 8$

Enter: $\quad 4 \;\boxed{\wedge}\; 1.5 \;\boxed{\text{ENTER}}$

Display: $\boxed{8.}$

$$3^x = 5$$
$$\log 3^x = \log 5$$
$$x \log 3 = \log 5$$
$$x = \frac{\log 5}{\log 3} \approx 1.465$$

Check: $\quad 3^{1.465} = 5$

Enter: $\quad 3 \;\boxed{\wedge}\; 1.465 \;\boxed{\text{ENTER}}$

Display: $\boxed{\text{5.000145454}}$

EXAMPLES

1. If $9^x = 14$, find x to the *nearest tenth*.

How to Proceed:	*Solution:*

(1) Write the equation. $\qquad\qquad\qquad\qquad\qquad\qquad\qquad\qquad 9^x = 14$

(2) Write the log of each side of the equation. $\qquad\qquad \log 9^x = \log 14$

(3) Use the power rule to simplify the left side. $\qquad\quad x \log 9 = \log 14$

(4) Solve the equation for x. $\qquad\qquad\qquad\qquad\qquad\qquad x = \dfrac{\log 14}{\log 9}$

(5) Evaluate on a calculator.

Enter:

Display: $\boxed{\text{1.201086751}}$

(6) Round to the nearest tenth. $\qquad\qquad\qquad\qquad\qquad\qquad x = 1.2$

Answer: To the *nearest tenth*, $x = 1.2$.

2. Solve for x to the *nearest tenth*: $12 \cdot 12^x = 500$.

Solution   METHOD 1:

$$12 \cdot 12^x = 500$$

$$\log (12 \cdot 12^x) = \log 500$$

$$\log 12 + x \log 12 = \log 500$$

$$x \log 12 = \log 500 - \log 12$$

$$x = \frac{\log 500 - \log 12}{\log 12}$$

Enter: 500 12 ⟩ ⟩ ÷
LOG 12 ENTER

Display: $\boxed{1.500942278}$

METHOD 2:

$$12 \cdot 12^x = 500$$

$$12^x = \frac{500}{12}$$

$$\log 12^x = \log \left(\frac{500}{12}\right)$$

$$x \log 12 = \log 500 - \log 12$$

$$x = \frac{\log 500 - \log 12}{\log 12}$$

The calculator sequence and the result are the same as for Method 1.

METHOD 3:

$$12 \cdot 12^x = 500$$

$$12^{1+x} = 500$$

$$\log 12^{1+x} = \log 500$$

$$(1 + x) \log 12 = \log 500$$

$$1 + x = \frac{\log 500}{\log 12}$$

$$x = \frac{\log 500}{\log 12} - 1$$

Enter: (LOG 500 ⟩ ÷ 12 ⟩ ⟩ − 1 ENTER

Display: $\boxed{1.500942278}$

Answer: To the *nearest tenth*, $x = 1.5$.

EXERCISES WITH OPEN-RESPONSE PROBLEMS

In 1–12, in each case, find x to the *nearest tenth*.

1. $2^x = 7$

2. $3^x = 15.6$

3. $7^x = 615$

4. $5^x = 47.6$

5. $15^x = 295$

6. $4.7^x = 10.2$

7. $1.06^x = 1.14$

8. $4.5^x = 1.57$

9. $3.8^x = 2.9$

10. $2.5^x = 9.88$

11. $4.08^x = 2.02$

12. $2.75^x = 3.72$

In 13–15, the amount of money, A, in a bank account is determined by the formula $A = P\left(1 + \frac{r}{n}\right)^{nt}$, where P is the principal (or the amount invested), r is the yearly rate of interest, n is the number of times each year that interest is compounded, and t is the number of years involved.

13. How long must \$500 be left in an account that pays 7% interest compounded annually in order for the value of the account to be \$750? (*Hint:* The equation $750 = 500\left(1 + \frac{0.07}{1}\right)^{1t}$ may be simplified to $750 = 500(1.07)^t$ before solving by using logarithms.)

14. How long must a sum of money be left in an account at 6% interest compounded semiannually (twice a year) in order to double? (*Hint:* Let $P = 1$ and $A = 2$.)

15. How long must \$100 be left at 8% interest compounded quarterly (four times a year) in order to acquire the value \$1,000?

16. The thickness of a sheet of paper is 0.004 inch. If x represents the number of times that this sheet of paper is folded in half over itself, then $y = 2^x$ determines the number of layers of paper, and $y = 0.004(2)^x$ determines the thickness of all the layers of paper. Calculate the number of folds that would produce a stack of paper closest to 1 mile high.
(*Hint:* 1 mile = 63,360 inches.)

17. When Patty was in kindergarten, her mother gave her 10 cents a week to spend. In the first grade, Patty received 20 cents a week, double her kindergarten allowance. In the third grade, Patty suggested to her mother that her allowance be doubled every year, but her mother was wise enough to refuse. If Patty's suggestion had been followed, in what grade would her weekly allowance have been more than \$200? (*Hint:* Use the formula $y = 0.10(2)^x$.)

18. If $\log_4 3 = x$:   **a.** Rewrite the equation in exponential form.   **b.** Solve the equation written in part **a**, using common logarithms. State the value of x to the *nearest ten-thousandth*.

In 19–21, solve each equation for x. Use the method of Exercise 18.

19. $\log_8 12 = x$

20. $\log_6 4 = x$

21. $\log_5 2 = x$

22. Use the method of Exercise 18 to prove that $\log_a n = \frac{\log n}{\log a}$.

17-6 LOGARITHMIC EQUATIONS

Since the function $y = \log_b x$ is a one-to-one function for $b > 0$ and $b \neq 1$, it follows that, if $\log_b A = \log_b C$, then $A = C$. We can use this relationship to solve equations that involve the logarithm of a variable, as shown in the examples that follow.

EXAMPLES

1. Solve for x: $\log_b 3 + \log_b x = \log_b 12$.

How to Proceed:	*Solution:*
(1) Write the equation.	$\log_b 3 + \log_b x = \log_b 12$
(2) Use the rule $\log_b A + \log_b C = \log_b AC$.	$\log_b 3x = \log_b 12$
(3) Use the rule $\log_b A = \log_b C \rightarrow A = C$.	$3x = 12$
(4) Solve for x.	$x = 4$

Answer: $x = 4$

2. Solve for x: $\log x + \log (x - 3) = 1$.

How to Proceed:	*Solution:*
(1) Write the equation.	$\log x + \log (x - 3) = 1$
(2) Simplify the left side.	$\log x (x - 3) = 1$
(3) Write the equation in exponential form.	$x (x - 3) = 10^1$
(4) Solve for x.	

$$x^2 - 3x = 10$$
$$x^2 - 3x - 10 = 0$$
$$(x - 5)(x + 2) = 0$$

(5) Reject the negative root; the log of a negative number does not exist.

$$x - 5 = 0 \quad \bigg| \quad x + 2 = 0$$
$$x = 5 \quad \bigg| \quad x = -2$$
$$\text{(reject)}$$

Alternative Solution

(1) Write the equation.

$$\log x + \log (x - 3) = 1$$

(2) Write each side as a common log.

$$\log x (x - 3) = \log 10$$

(3) Use the rule $\log_b A = \log_b C \rightarrow A = C$.

$$x(x - 3) = 10$$

Follow steps 4 and 5 as shown above.

Answer: $x = 5$

EXERCISES

In 1–10 solve each equation for the positive value of x.

1. $\log_2 x + \log_2 4 = \log_2 32$

2. $\log x + \log 14 = \log 98$

3. $2 \log_5 x - \log_5 5 = \log_5 125$

4. $\frac{1}{2} (\log_3 80 - \log_3 5) = \log_3 x$

5. $\log x + \log (x + 1) = \log 12$

6. $\log_4 (x - 2) + \log_4 5 = \log_4 70$

7. $2 \log x - \log (x - 1) = \log 4$

8. $3 \log_8 2 - \log_8 x = \log_8 16$

9. $\log_4 x - \log_4 8 = 1$

10. $\log x + \log 5 = 2$

In 11–16, solve each equation for the positive value of x, to the *nearest hundredth*.

11. $3 \log x = \log 15$

12. $\log x + \log 20 - \log 3 = \log 7$

13. $\frac{1}{2} \log x + \log 36 = \log 18$

14. $\frac{2}{3} \log x - \log 4 = \log 15$

15. $4 \log 2 + 3 \log x = 1$

16. $2 \log x - 3 \log 5 = 0$

17. Show that the equation $\log (x - 2) + \log (x - 1) = 2 \log x$ has no solution in the set of real numbers.

18. The time t required for a sum of money invested at 6% interest compounded monthly to double in value is given by the equation $t(12 \log 1.005) = \log 2$.
  a. Find t to the *nearest hundredth* of a year.
  b. If a sum of money was invested in January 1998, find the year and month in which the value of the investment is closest to doubling.

19. Show that $\log_b a = \dfrac{1}{\log_a b}$.

CHAPTER SUMMARY

The inverse of the function $f(x) = b^x$ or $y = b^x$ ($b > 0$, $b \neq 1$) is the function $f^{-1}(x) = \log_b x$ or $y = \log_b x$ ($b > 0$, $b \neq 1$). The domain of function $y = \log_b x$ is $\{x \mid x \in \text{Positive real numbers}\}$, and the range is $\{y \mid y \in \text{Real numbers}\}$.

A *logarithm* is an exponent. If $b^a = c$, then $\log_b c = a$. The rules for operations with powers having like bases can be used to derive the rules for operations with logarithms.

	Powers	Logarithms
Product rule:	$a^x \cdot a^y = a^{x+y}$	$\log_a xy = \log_a x + \log_a y$
Quotient rule:	$\dfrac{a^x}{a^y} = a^{x-y}$	$\log_a \dfrac{x}{y} = \log_a x - \log_a y$
Power rule:	$(a^x)^c = a^{cx}$	$\log_a x^c = c \log_a x$

Common logarithms are logarithms to the base 10. When no base is written in the logarithmic form of a number, the base is understood to be 10. Thus, $\log x = \log_{10} x$. Graphing calculators give the common log of a number when the LOG key is pressed. When the log of a number is known, the number can be found by using the 10^x key on a calculator.

Equations that involve exponents or logarithms can be solved by using the relationships $a^x = a^y \rightarrow x = y$ and $\log_a x = \log_a y \rightarrow x = y$.

VOCABULARY

17-1   Logarithm

17-4   Common logarithm

REVIEW EXERCISES WITH OPEN-RESPONSE PROBLEMS

1. a. Sketch the graph of $y = \log_{1.5} x$ in the interval $0 < x \le 6$.
   b. On the same set of axes, sketch the graph that is the reflection in the line $y = x$ of the graph drawn in part **a**.
   c. What is the equation of the graph drawn in part **b**?

2. a. State the domain of the function $y = \log_5 x$.
   b. State the range of the function $y = \log_5 x$.

In 3–8, write each equation in exponential form.

3. $3 = \log_2 8$

4. $0 = \log_7 1$

5. $\log 0.01 = -2$

6. $\log_5 0.2 = -1$

7. $1.5 = \log_4 8$

8. $\log_3 \sqrt{3} = \frac{1}{2}$

In 9–14, write each equation in logarithmic form.

9. $7^2 = 49$

10. $5^3 = 125$

11. $27^{\frac{1}{3}} = 3$

12. $0.001 = 10^{-3}$

13. $(\sqrt{5})^4 = 25$

14. $6^{-1} = \frac{1}{6}$

In 15–20, for each equation, find the value of x.

15. $x = \log 0.0001$

16. $\log_9 3 = x$

17. $\log_x \frac{1}{5} = -1$

18. $\log_2 x = 6$

19. $\log_x 9 = \frac{2}{3}$

20. $\log_6 x = 2$

21. If $f(x) = \log x$, find f(100).

22. If $g(x) = \log_4 x$, find g(8).

In 23–26, in each case, express x in terms of a and b.

23. $\log_2 x = 2 \log_2 a + \log_2 b$

24. $\log_5 x = 3 \log_5 a - \frac{1}{2} \log_5 b$

25. $\log x = \frac{1}{2} (\log a - \log b)$

26. $\log x = \log b + \frac{1}{3} \log a$

In 27–34, if $\log_b 2 = p$ and $\log_b 5 = q$, express each log in terms of p and q.

27. $\log_b \frac{2}{5}$ **28.** $\log_b 2.5$ **29.** $\log_b 20$ **30.** $\log_b 0.01$

31. $\log_b 50$ **32.** $\log_b \sqrt[3]{10}$ **33.** $\log_b \frac{\sqrt{5}}{4}$ **34.** $\log_b \frac{\sqrt{8}}{25}$

35. Find the solution set of $\log (x - 1) + \log (x + 2) = 1$.

In 36–41, solve each equation for x to the *nearest hundredth*.

36. $15 \cdot 15^x = 114$ **37.** $2^x \cdot 8^x = 12$
38. $\log_3 5 + \log_3 x = \log_3 (7 + x)$ **39.** $\log (x - 3) + \log x = \log 7$
40. $\log (x + 2) + \log (x - 2) = 1$ **41.** $2 \log_2 x - \log_2 (x - 1) = 3$

42. Show that $a^{\log_a b} = b$.
43. If $\log a = 1.7866$, find: **a.** $\log \sqrt{a}$ **b.** $\log 100a$ **c.** $\log a^2$
44. If $10^{1.6184} = x$, find x to the *nearest hundredth*.

In 45–50, in each case, find x to the *nearest tenth*.

45. $3^x = 4$ **46.** $5^x = 3.6$ **47.** $x^{1.5} = 15$
48. $2^x = 1.5$ **49.** $4^x = 21$ **50.** $x^{0.4} = 1.6$

51. Find, to the *nearest tenth*, $\log_2 7$.
52. The length of time needed for the value of a bank deposit to double is given by the equation $2 = \left(1 + \frac{r}{n}\right)^{nt}$, where r is the yearly rate of interest and n is the number of times each year that interest is compounded. How long will the value of a deposit take to double if interest is compounded quarterly (four times a year) at an annual rate of 8%? Express your answer to the nearest quarter of a year.

In 53–57, select the *numeral* preceding the expression that best completes each sentence.

53. If $A = \pi r^2$, then $\log A$ equals
   (1) $2\pi \log r$ (2) $\log \pi + 2 \log r$
   (3) $2 (\log \pi + \log r)$ (4) $\log 2 + \log \pi + \log r$

54. If $C = 2\pi r$, then $\log C$ equals
   (1) $2\pi \log r$ (2) $\log \pi + 2 \log r$
   (3) $2 \log \pi + \log r$ (4) $\log 2 + \log \pi + \log r$

55. If $\log 3.87 = a$, then $\log 387$ equals
   (1) $100a$ (2) $a + 2$ (3) $a + 100$ (4) $2a$

56. If $\log 3 = a$, then $\log 90$ equals
   (1) $10 + 2a$ (2) $10a^2$ (3) $1 + 2a$ (4) $1 + a^2$

57. If $10^{2.5527} = 357$, then $10^{0.5527}$ equals
   (1) 355 (2) $35,700$ (3) $\frac{357}{2}$ (4) 3.57

CUMULATIVE REVIEW WITH OPEN-RESPONSE PROBLEMS

1. In $\triangle RST$ the measure of an exterior angle at S is 85 and $m\angle R = 2m\angle T$. Which angle is the smallest angle of the triangle?

2. A trapezoid has three congruent sides. The fourth side is congruent to a diagonal. Find the measures of the upper and the lower base angles.

3. The lengths of the sides of a triangle are 14 centimeters, 17 centimeters, and 26 centimeters. Find the lengths of the sides of a similar triangle if the measure of the shortest side is 21 centimeters.

4. The diagonals of a trapezoid divide the trapezoid into four triangles that do not overlap. Prove that two of these triangles are similar.

5. Write $\dfrac{(a^3b)^2}{a^{-1}b^4}$ in simplest form with positive exponents.

6. **a.** Sketch the graph of $y = 2 \cos 2x$ in the interval $-\pi \le x \le \pi$.
   b. On the same set of axes, sketch the graph of $y = 1$.
   c. What are the coordinates of the points at which the graphs intersect?

7. Under a rotation about the origin, the image of $A(-\sqrt{2}, \sqrt{2})$ is $A'(0, -2)$. Find $m\angle AOA'$.

8. Points A and B are on circle O and C is on the major arc, $\overset{\frown}{ACB}$. If $m\angle ACB = 5x$ and $m\angle AOB = 3x + 21$, find:
   a. the value of x **b.** $m\overset{\frown}{AB}$ **c.** $m\overset{\frown}{ACB}$

9. If $f(x) = \sin 2x$, find $f\left(\dfrac{2\pi}{3}\right)$ in radical form.

10. Solve for x: $\sqrt{3x + 1} - 1 = x - 2$.

Exploration

Before calculators were in common use, scientists and engineers performed calculations on a *slide rule*. Research the construction and use of the slide rule and investigate how it is related to logarithms. Write a report of your findings.

Chapter *18*

Trigonometric Applications

In an emergency situation, a few minutes can often mean the difference between a successful outcome and a disaster. Therefore, accurate information about the exact position of any persons in need of help is essential. For example, a distress signal may be received at two coast guard stations from a ship unable to determine its exact location. The distance between the stations and the direction from which the ship's signal is received at each station can be used to determine exactly where the ship is, which coast guard station is closer, and from which station help can arrive more quickly.

In the situation described above, the two coast guard stations and the ship in distress can be represented by the vertices of a triangle. The distance between the stations is the length of one side, and the directions from which the two stations are receiving the distress signal can be used to determine the measures of two angles of the triangle. In this chapter we will derive the formulas that can be used to determine distances and angle measures when sufficient information is available for this purpose.

18-1　REVIEW OF BASIC CONCEPTS

Triangle Congruence

In the study of geometry, we learned that the congruence of certain pairs of sides and angles of two given triangles can be used to prove that the triangles are congruent. This means that these triangles can have exactly one size and one shape.

The size and shape of a triangle are determined by any one of the following:

1. Two sides and the included angle (s.a.s.).
2. Three sides (s.s.s.).
3. Two angles and the included side (a.s.a.).
4. Two angles and a side opposite one of them (a.a.s.).

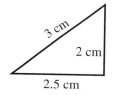

For example, if every student in a mathematics class were to construct a triangle with sides that measure 2 centimeters, 2.5 centimeters, and 3 centimeters, all of the triangles would have the same size and shape as the triangle at the left because the measures of three sides determine the size and shape of a triangle.

In this chapter, we will derive and use laws or formulas that enable us to find the measures of the other sides and angles of a triangle when any of the combinations listed above is known.

Rectangular Coordinates in Trigonometric Form

Before we derive the formulas that enable us to determine the measures of the sides and angles of a triangle, we should recall the relationship between the trigonometric function values of the measure of an angle in standard position and the coordinates of a point on the terminal ray of that angle.

In Chapter 14, we learned that, if P is a point of the unit circle on the terminal ray of an angle in standard position whose measure is θ, then the coordinates of P are $(\cos \theta, \sin \theta)$.

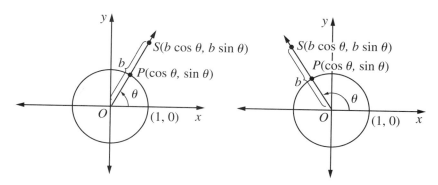

In the diagrams above, by a dilation $D_b(x, y) = (bx, by)$, point P is mapped to point S. Therefore, $(b \cos \theta, b \sin \theta)$ are the coordinates of point S. In other words, point S is at a distance b from the origin and on a ray that makes an angle of measure θ with the positive x-axis.

We can also write rectangular coordinates in a trigonometric form by using similar triangles. We will let P be a point of the unit circle with center at the origin, O, and S be a point at a distance r from O on $\overrightarrow{OP}$. We draw $\overline{PQ}$ perpendicular to the x-axis at Q, and $\overline{SR}$ perpendicular to the x-axis at R.

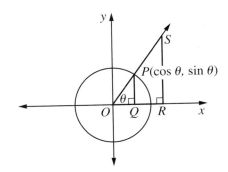

In $\triangle QOP$,
$\text{m}\angle QOP = \theta$,
$\text{m}\angle PQO = 90$,
$\quad OP = 1$,
$\quad PQ = \sin \theta$,
$\quad OQ = \cos \theta$.

In $\triangle ROS$,
$\text{m}\angle ROS = \theta$,
$\text{m}\angle SRO = 90$,
$\quad OS = r$.

Therefore: $\triangle QOP \sim \triangle ROS$ by a.a. $\cong$ a.a.

Since the lengths of corresponding sides of similar triangles are in proportion, we can say:

$$\frac{OQ}{OP} = \frac{OR}{OS}$$

$$\frac{\cos \theta}{1} = \frac{OR}{r}$$

$$OR = r \cos \theta$$

$$\frac{PQ}{OP} = \frac{SR}{OS}$$

$$\frac{\sin \theta}{1} = \frac{SR}{r}$$

$$SR = r \sin \theta$$

Therefore, if S is a point r units from the origin, O, and $\overrightarrow{OS}$ makes an angle with the positive x-axis whose measure is θ, then S is the point whose coordinates are

$$(r \cos \theta, r \sin \theta)$$

EXAMPLE

Point A is 4 units from the origin on the terminal ray of a $150°$ angle in standard position. Find the coordinates of A: **a.** in radical form   **b.** to the *nearest hundredth*.

Solutions   The coordinates of any point at a distance r from the origin on the terminal side of an angle whose measure is θ are $(r \cos \theta, r \sin \theta)$. Since $r = 4$ and $\theta = 150°$, the coordinates of A are $(4 \cos 150°, 4 \sin 150°)$.

a. (1) Determine the exact values of $\cos 150°$ and $\sin 150°$.

$\cos 150° = -\cos (180° - 150°)$
$\qquad = -\cos 30° = -\dfrac{\sqrt{3}}{2}$

$\sin 150° = \sin (180° - 150°)$
$\qquad = \sin 30° = \dfrac{1}{2}$

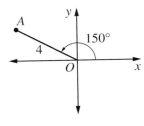

(2) Use substitution to find the coordinates of A.

The x-coordinate of A is $4 \cos 150° = 4\left(-\dfrac{\sqrt{3}}{2}\right) = -2\sqrt{3}$.

The y-coordinate of A is $4 \sin 150° = 4\left(\dfrac{1}{2}\right) = 2$.

Therefore, the coordinates of A in radical form are $(-2\sqrt{3}, 2)$.

b. Use a calculator to find approximate values of the coordinates of A. Make sure your calculator is in degree mode.

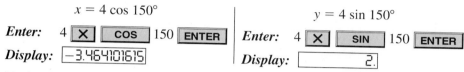

$$x = 4 \cos 150° \qquad\qquad y = 4 \sin 150°$$

Enter: 4 $\boxed{\times}$ $\boxed{\text{COS}}$ 150 $\boxed{\text{ENTER}}$ | *Enter:* 4 $\boxed{\times}$ $\boxed{\text{SIN}}$ 150 $\boxed{\text{ENTER}}$

Display: $\boxed{-3.464101615}$ | *Display:* $\boxed{\qquad\qquad 2.}$

To the *nearest hundredth*, the coordinates of A are $(-3.46, 2.00)$.

Answers: **a.** $(-2\sqrt{3}, 2)$ **b.** $(-3.46, 2.00)$

Note: Accuracy in using measures is very important since a small error can cause a significant difference in the answer. For example, in the problem above the difference of ten degrees will make a large difference in the answer since the sine of the angle is multiplied by 4 ($4 \sin 160° = 1.37$ to the *nearest hundredth*). You start with an error in measurement of about 7 percent and the error in the answer increases to about 37 percent.

EXERCISES WITH OPEN-RESPONSE PROBLEMS

In 1–9, in each case, find the rectangular coordinates (x, y) of a point that is r units from the origin and on the terminal ray of an angle in standard position whose measure is θ. Write irrational values in simplest radical form.

1. $r = 6, \theta = 30°$

2. $r = 3, \theta = 90°$

3. $r = 8, \theta = 135°$

4. $r = 9, \theta = 180°$

5. $r = 2, \theta = 240°$

6. $r = \frac{1}{2}, \theta = 270°$

7. $r = 1, \theta = 300°$

8. $r = 10, \theta = \text{Arc sin } \frac{3}{5}$

9. $r = 5, \theta = \text{Arc cos } \left(\frac{-7}{25}\right)$

In 10–15:   **a.** Write the coordinates of each point, expressing irrational values to the *nearest hundredth*.
b. Locate the point on a coordinate graph.

10. $A(6 \cos 60°, 6 \sin 60°)$

11. $B(2 \cos 90°, 2 \sin 90°)$

12. $C(\sqrt{2} \cos 135°, \sqrt{2} \sin 135°)$

13. $D(4 \cos \pi, 4 \sin \pi)$

14. $E\left(8 \cos \frac{7\pi}{6}, 8 \sin \frac{7\pi}{6}\right)$

15. $F\left(3 \cos \frac{3\pi}{2}, 3 \sin \frac{3\pi}{2}\right)$

In 16–19, △*ABC* is drawn in the coordinate plane with point *A* at the origin and point *B* on the positive ray of the *x*-axis. In each case, state the coordinates of point *C*, expressing irrational values in simplest radical form.

16. m∠*A* = 45, *AC* = 14

17. m∠*A* = 120, *AC* = 10

18. *A* = Arc sin $\frac{5}{13}$, *AC* = 39

19. *A* = Arc cos $\left(\frac{-3}{5}\right)$, *AC* = 15

20. The locus of points at a distance *r* from the origin is a circle whose center is the origin and whose radius is *r*. Demonstrate that the coordinates of all such points where $(x, y) = (r \cos \theta, r \sin \theta)$ satisfy the equation of the circle, $x^2 + y^2 = r^2$.

18-2 THE LAW OF COSINES

When the measures of two sides and the included angle of a triangle *ABC* are known, the size and shape of the triangle are determined, and we should be able to find the measure of the third side. To do this, we draw △*ABC* so that *A* is at the origin of the coordinate plane, and *B* is on the positive ray of the *x*-axis. In Figure 1, where ∠*A* is acute, point *C* lies in the first quadrant. In Figure 2, where ∠*A* is obtuse, point *C* lies in the second quadrant.

Figure 1

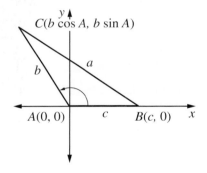

Figure 2

In each triangle *ABC* shown above, *AB* = *c*, *AC* = *b*, and *BC* = *a*. Therefore:

● The coordinates of *A* = (0, 0) because *A* is at the origin.

● The coordinates of *B* = (*c*, 0) because *AB* = *c* and *B* is on the positive ray of the *x*-axis.

● The coordinates of *C* = (*b* cos *A*, *b* sin *A*) because *C* is at a distance *b* from the origin and on the terminal ray of ∠*A* in standard position.

Thus, the coordinates of points *B* and *C* are given in terms of the measures of two sides and the included angle of the triangle. The distance formula can be used to express *a*, the distance from *B* to *C* in the coordinate plane, in terms of *b*, *c*, and m∠*A*.

Proof: In $\triangle ABC$, $B(x_1, y_1) = (c, 0)$ and $C(x_2, y_2) = (b \cos A, b \sin A)$.

1. Write the distance formula.

$$d^2 = (x_2 - x_1)^2 + (y_2 - y_1)^2$$

2. Substitute the given coordinates of points B and C to write an expression for a^2.

$$a^2 = (b \cos A - c)^2 + (b \sin A - 0)^2$$
$$a^2 = (b \cos A - c)^2 + (b \sin A)^2$$

3. Square each term on the right-hand side.

$$a^2 = b^2 \cos^2 A - 2bc \cos A + c^2 + b^2 \sin^2 A$$

4. Group the terms containing b^2, and factor.

$$a^2 = b^2 \cos^2 A + b^2 \sin^2 A + c^2 - 2bc \cos A$$
$$a^2 = b^2(\cos^2 A + \sin^2 A) + c^2 - 2bc \cos A$$

5. Apply the identity $\cos^2 A + \sin^2 A = 1$ to simplify the equation.

$$a^2 = b^2(1) + c^2 - 2bc \cos A$$
$$a^2 = b^2 + c^2 - 2bc \cos A$$

This result, $a^2 = b^2 + c^2 - 2bc \cos A$, is called the **Law of Cosines**. It states that the square of the measure of one side of a triangle is equal to the sum of the squares of the measures of the other two sides minus twice the product of the measures of these two sides and the cosine of the angle between them.

This formula can be rewritten in terms of any two sides and their included angle.

Law of Cosines

$$a^2 = b^2 + c^2 - 2bc \cos A$$
$$b^2 = a^2 + c^2 - 2ac \cos B$$
$$c^2 = a^2 + b^2 - 2ab \cos C$$

Note: If $\triangle ABC$ is a right triangle with $m\angle C = 90$, then:

$$c^2 = a^2 + b^2 - 2ab \cos 90°$$
$$c^2 = a^2 + b^2 - 2ab(0)$$
$$c^2 = a^2 + b^2 - 0$$
$$c^2 = a^2 + b^2$$

Thus, if $\triangle ABC$ is a right triangle, the Law of Cosines gives us the familiar relationship of the Pythagorean Theorem, $c^2 = a^2 + b^2$. This is not an unexpected result since the Pythagorean Theorem was used to prove both the distance formula and the basic identity $\cos^2 A + \sin^2 A = 1$, which were used to prove the Law of Cosines.

EXAMPLES

1. In $\triangle ABC$, if $a = 4$, $c = 6$, and $\cos B = \frac{1}{16}$, find b.

How to Proceed:

(1) Write the Law of Cosines, expressing b^2 in terms of a, c, and $\cos B$.

(2) Substitute the given values.

(3) Simplify.

(4) Express b as a positive length.

Solution:

$$b^2 = a^2 + c^2 - 2ac \cos B$$

$$= 4^2 + 6^2 - 2(4)(6)\left(\tfrac{1}{16}\right)$$

$$= 16 + 36 - 3$$
$$= 49$$

$$b = 7$$

Answer: 7

---

2. In $\triangle RST$, $r = 11$, $s = 12$, and m$\angle T = 120$. Find t to the *nearest integer*.

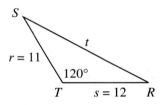

How to Proceed:

(1) Write the Law of Cosines, expressing t^2 in terms of r, s, and $\cos T$.

(2) Substitute the given values.

(3) Since $\angle T$ is obtuse, $\cos 120° = -\cos 60°$
$$= -\tfrac{1}{2}.$$

(4) Simplify.

(5) Express t as a positive length.

(6) Find the square root to the nearest integer.

Solution:

$$t^2 = r^2 + s^2 - 2rs \cos T$$

$$= 11^2 + 12^2 - 2(11)(12)(\cos 120°)$$

$$= 11^2 + 12^2 - 2(11)(12)\left(-\tfrac{1}{2}\right)$$

$$= 121 + 144 + 132$$
$$= 397$$

$$t = \sqrt{397}$$

$$\approx 20$$

Calculator Solution   (1) Write the Law of Cosines for t^2, using given values, and compute t^2.

$$t^2 = r^2 + s^2 - 2rs \cos T$$
$$= 11^2 + 12^2 - 2(11)(12)(\cos 120°)$$

Enter: 11 $\boxed{x^2}$ $\boxed{+}$ 12 $\boxed{x^2}$ $\boxed{-}$ 2 $\boxed{\times}$
11 $\boxed{\times}$ 12 $\boxed{\times}$ $\boxed{\text{COS}}$ 120 $\boxed{\text{ENTER}}$

Display: $\boxed{\qquad 397.}$

(2) Find the square root of t^2, and round to the nearest integer.

Enter: $\boxed{\text{2nd}}$ $\boxed{\sqrt{}}$ $\boxed{\text{2nd}}$ $\boxed{\text{ANS}}$ $\boxed{\text{ENTER}}$

Display: $\boxed{19.92485885}$

Answer: 20

EXERCISES WITH OPEN-RESPONSE PROBLEMS

1. In $\triangle PAT$, express p^2 in terms of a, t, and $\cos P$.

2. In $\triangle CAR$, express r^2 in terms of c, a, and $\cos R$.

3. In $\triangle SAD$, express a^2 in terms of s, d, and $\cos A$.

4. In $\triangle ABC$, if $a = 2$, $b = 3$, and $\cos C = \frac{1}{3}$, find c.

5. In $\triangle ABC$, if $b = 8$, $c = 5$, and $\cos A = \frac{1}{10}$, find a.

6. In $\triangle ABC$, if $a = 10$, $c = 7$, and $\cos B = \frac{1}{5}$, find b.

7. In $\triangle PQR$, if $p = 12$, $q = 8$, and $\cos R = \frac{1}{3}$, find r.

8. In $\triangle CAP$, if $c = 7$, $a = 6$, and $\cos P = \left(-\frac{3}{7}\right)$, find p.

9. In $\triangle QRS$, if $s = 5$, $r = 7$, and $\cos Q = \left(-\frac{1}{10}\right)$, find q.

10. In $\triangle ABC$, if $a = 5$, $b = 6$, and $\cos C = \left(-\frac{1}{3}\right)$, find c.

11. In $\triangle BAD$, if $b = 3\sqrt{3}$, $a = 6$, and $m\angle D = 30$, find d.

In 12–14, select the *numeral* preceding the expression that best completes each statement.

12. In $\triangle BCD$, if $b = 5$, $c = 4$, and $m\angle D = 60$, then d is

(1) $\frac{1}{2}$ (2) $\sqrt{21}$ (3) 3   (4) $\sqrt{41}$

13. In $\triangle BAR$, if $b = 1$, $a = \sqrt{3}$, and $m\angle R = 30$, then r is

(1) 1   (2) $\sqrt{2}$ (3) $\sqrt{3}$ (4) $\frac{1}{2}\sqrt{3}$

14. In $\triangle ABC$, if $b = 3$, $c = 6$, and $m\angle A = 120$, then a is

(1) $\sqrt{63}$ (2) $\sqrt{53}$ (3) $\sqrt{37}$ (4) $\sqrt{27}$

15. In $\triangle CDE$, if $c = 2$, $d = \sqrt{2}$, and $m\angle E = 45$, find e in simplest radical form.

16. In $\triangle PQR$, if $p = 3$, $q = 5$, and $m\angle R = 120$, find r.

17. In $\triangle RST$, if $r = 3\sqrt{2}$, $s = 1$, and $m\angle T = 135$, find t.

18. Using the Law of Cosines, find the length of a diagonal of a rectangle if the lengths of two adjacent sides are 5 and 12.

19. Find the length of the longer diagonal of a parallelogram if the lengths of two adjacent sides are 6 and 10 and the measure of an angle is 120°.

20. Find to the *nearest integer* the measure of the base of an isosceles triangle if the measure of the vertex angle is 84° and the measure of each leg is 12.

21. The measures of two sides of a triangle are 20.0 and 12.0, and the measure of the included angle is 58.7°. Find to the *nearest tenth* the measure of the third side of the triangle.

22. Find the length of one side of an equilateral triangle inscribed in a circle if the measure of a radius of the circle is $10\sqrt{3}$.

23. The vertices of a triangle inscribed in a circle separate the circle into arcs whose measures are in the ratio $2:3:4$. If the measure of a radius of the circle is 10, find to the *nearest integer* the measure of the longest side of the triangle.

24. A kite is in the shape of a quadrilateral with two pairs of congruent adjacent sides. If the measures of two sides of the kite are 25 inches and 40 inches, and the measure of the angle between the sides that are not congruent is 140°, find to the *nearest inch* the length of the kite (i.e., the length of the longer diagonal).

18-3 USING THE LAW OF COSINES TO FIND ANGLE MEASURE

If you are given the measures of the three sides of a triangle you can determine the size and shape of the triangle. You can use the Law of Cosines to express the cosine of any angle of a triangle in terms of the measures of the sides of the triangle. Compare the steps that are used below to express $\cos C$ in terms of a, b, and c with those used to find the value of $\cos C$ when $a = 3$, $b = 4$, and $c = 2$.

The General Case

$$c^2 = a^2 + b^2 - 2ab \cos C$$

$$\underline{+ 2ab \cos C - c^2 = \qquad\qquad + 2ab \cos C - c^2}$$

$$2ab \cos C = a^2 + b^2 \qquad\qquad - c^2$$

$$\frac{2ab \cos C}{2ab} = \frac{a^2 + b^2 - c^2}{2ab}$$

$$\cos C = \frac{a^2 + b^2 - c^2}{2ab}$$

A Specific Example

$$c^2 = a^2 + b^2 - 2ab \cos C$$

$$2^2 = 3^2 + 4^2 - 2(3)(4) \cos C$$

$$2^2 = 3^2 + 4^2 - 24 \cos C$$

$$\frac{+ 24 \cos C - 2^2 =}{24 \cos C = 3^2 + 4^2} \qquad \frac{+ 24 \cos C - 2^2}{-2^2}$$

$$\frac{24 \cos C}{24} = \frac{3^2 + 4^2 - 2^2}{24}$$

$$\cos C = \frac{9 + 16 - 4}{24} = \frac{21}{24} = \frac{7}{8}$$

The formula in the last line of the general case expresses the value of cos C in terms of the measures of the sides of a triangle ABC. The equation in the last line of the specific example gives the cosine of the smallest angle of a triangle whose sides measure 2, 3, and 4. Since $\angle C$ is an angle of a triangle, $0° < m\angle C < 180°$. In this example, since the cosine of $\angle C$ is positive, $\angle C$ must be an acute angle. We use a calculator to find the measure of $\angle C$.

Enter: [2nd] [COS⁻¹] 7 [÷] 8 [ENTER]

Display: [28.95502437]

Therefore, to the *nearest degree*, the measure of $\angle C$ is 29°.

This relationship can be stated for the cosine of any angle in $\triangle ABC$, as illustrated in the following rules:

$$\cos A = \frac{b^2 + c^2 - a^2}{2bc}$$

$$\cos B = \frac{a^2 + c^2 - b^2}{2ac}$$

$$\cos C = \frac{a^2 + b^2 - c^2}{2ab}$$

In any triangle ABC, $\angle C$ may be acute, right, or obtuse, depending on the measures of the sides. We can illustrate this fact in the following cases, where each angle measure is given to the nearest degree.

CASE 1: $a^2 + b^2 > c^2$, and $\angle C$ is an acute angle.

In $\triangle ABC$, $a = 3$, $b = 4$, $c = 2$.

$$\cos C = \frac{a^2 + b^2 - c^2}{2ab} = \frac{3^2 + 4^2 - 2^2}{2(3)(4)} = \frac{9 + 16 - 4}{24} = \frac{21}{24} = \frac{7}{8}$$

Since $\cos C$ is positive, $\angle C$ is acute. The measure of $\angle C \approx 29°$.

CASE 2: $a^2 + b^2 = c^2$, and $\angle C$ is a right angle.

In $\triangle ABC$, $a = 3$, $b = 4$, $c = 5$.

$$\cos C = \frac{a^2 + b^2 - c^2}{2ab} = \frac{3^2 + 4^2 - 5^2}{2(3)(4)} = \frac{9 + 16 - 25}{24} = \frac{0}{24} = 0$$

Since $\cos C$ is 0, $\angle C$ is a right angle. The measure of $\angle C = 90°$.

CASE 3: $a^2 + b^2 < c^2$, and $\angle C$ is an obtuse angle.

In $\triangle ABC$, $a = 3$, $b = 4$, $c = 6$.

$$\cos C = \frac{a^2 + b^2 - c^2}{2ab} = \frac{3^2 + 4^2 - 6^2}{2(3)(4)} = \frac{9 + 16 - 36}{24} = \frac{-11}{24}$$

Since $\cos C$ is negative, $\angle C$ is obtuse. The measure of $\angle C = 117°$.

If $\angle C$ is a right angle, then $\triangle ABC$ is a right triangle where:

(1) c is the measure of the hypotenuse;

(2) a is the measure of the leg adjacent to $\angle B$; and

(3) b is the measure of the leg adjacent to $\angle A$.

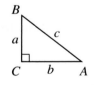

In right triangle ABC, $c^2 = a^2 + b^2$. Let us observe what happens when $a^2 + b^2$ is substituted for c^2 in the following situations:

$$\cos A = \frac{b^2 + c^2 - a^2}{2bc}$$

$$\cos A = \frac{b^2 + (a^2 + b^2) - a^2}{2bc}$$

$$\cos A = \frac{2b^2}{2bc}$$

$$\cos A = \frac{b}{c}$$

$$\cos A = \frac{\text{measure of leg adjacent to } \angle A}{\text{measure of hypotenuse}}$$

$$\cos B = \frac{a^2 + c^2 - b^2}{2ac}$$

$$\cos B = \frac{a^2 + (a^2 + b^2) - b^2}{2ac}$$

$$\cos B = \frac{2a^2}{2ac}$$

$$\cos B = \frac{a}{c}$$

$$\cos B = \frac{\text{measure of leg adjacent to } \angle B}{\text{measure of hypotenuse}}$$

EXAMPLES

1. In $\triangle ABC$, $a = 5$, $b = 7$, and $c = 10$. Find $\cos B$.

How to Proceed:

(1) Write the Law of Cosines solved for $\cos B$.

(2) Substitute the given values.

(3) Express the value of $\cos B$ as a fraction in simplest form or as a decimal.

Solution:

$$\cos B = \frac{a^2 + c^2 - b^2}{2ac}$$

$$= \frac{5^2 + 10^2 - 7^2}{2(5)(10)}$$

$$= \frac{25 + 100 - 49}{100}$$

$$= \frac{76}{100} = \frac{19}{25}$$

Answer: $\cos B = \frac{19}{25}$, or $\cos B = 0.76$

---

2. In isosceles triangle RED, $RE = ED = 5$ and $RD = 8$. Find the measure of the vertex angle, $\angle E$, to the *nearest degree*.

Solution: Let $RE = d = 5$

$ED = r = 5$

$RD = e = 8$

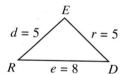

$$\cos E = \frac{d^2 + r^2 - e^2}{2dr}$$

$$= \frac{5^2 + 5^2 - 8^2}{2(5)(5)} = \frac{25 + 25 - 64}{50} = \frac{-14}{50} = -0.28$$

$$m\angle E \approx 106$$

The computation can be done on a calculator and the number in the display rounded to the nearest degree. Since the value of $\cos E$ is negative, the calculator returns the degree measure of an angle in Quadrant II, an obtuse angle.

Enter:

Display: $\boxed{106.2602047}$

Answer: $m\angle E = 106$ to the *nearest degree*

EXERCISES WITH OPEN-RESPONSE PROBLEMS

1. In $\triangle PQR$, express $\cos P$ in terms of p, q, and r.
2. In $\triangle SAD$, express $\cos D$ in terms of s, a, and d.
3. In $\triangle ABC$, $a = 5$, $b = 7$, and $c = 8$. Find $\cos C$.
4. In $\triangle ABC$, $a = 5$, $b = 9$, and $c = 12$. Find $\cos A$.
5. In $\triangle ABC$, $a = 5$, $b = 12$, and $c = 13$. Find $\cos B$.
6. Find the cosine of the largest angle of a triangle if the measures of the sides of the triangle are 5, 6, and 7.
7. Find the cosine of the largest angle of a triangle if the measures of the sides of the triangle are 2, 3, and 4.
8. In $\triangle RST$, $r = 5$, $s = 7$, and $t = 8$. Find m$\angle S$.
9. In $\triangle CDE$, $c = 1$, $d = 2$, and $e = \sqrt{3}$. Find m$\angle E$.
10. In $\triangle ABC$, the measures of the sides are 3, 5, and 7. Find the measure of the largest angle in the triangle.

In 11–13, select the *numeral* preceding the expression that best completes each sentence or answers each question.

11. In $\triangle BDE$, $b = 3$, $e = 5$, and $d = \sqrt{7}$. What is the value of $\cos D$?

    (1) $-\frac{1}{2}$　　　　(2) $\frac{1}{30}$　　　　(3) $\frac{9}{10}$　　　　(4) $\frac{4}{5}$

12. In $\triangle RPM$, $r = 9$, $p = 12$, and $m = 15$. The cosine of the largest angle in the triangle is

    (1) 1　　　　(2) 0　　　　(3) $\frac{4}{5}$　　　　(4) 90

13. In $\triangle ABC$, $a = 6$, $b = 6$, and $c = 6\sqrt{2}$. The measure of $\angle B$ is
    (1) 45°　　　(2) 60°　　　(3) 120°　　　(4) 135°

14. In $\triangle FTG$, $t = 10$, $g = 14$, and $f = 20$. Find to the *nearest degree* the measure of $\angle T$.

15. Find to the *nearest degree* the measure of the vertex angle of a triangle whose sides measure 3, 3, and 5.

16. Find to the *nearest degree* the measure of a base angle of an isosceles triangle whose equal sides each measure 3 and whose base measures 4.

17. Find to the *nearest degree* the measure of the largest angle of a triangle whose sides measure 7, 9, and 12.

18. The lengths of the sides of a triangle are 9, 40, and 41. Find the measure of the largest angle.

19. A cross-country ski trail is laid out in the shape of a triangle. The lengths of the three paths that make up the trail are 2000 meters, 1200 meters, and 1800 meters. Find to the *nearest degree* the measure of the smallest angle of the trail.

20. The lengths of the sides of a triangle inscribed in a circle are 9, 5, and 10. Find to the *nearest degree* the measure of: **a.** the smallest angle in the triangle   **b.** the smallest arc of the circle whose endpoints are vertices of the triangle

21. The diagram shows the side of a small shed with vertical walls of equal height and a roof that is formed by two slanted sections. The shed is 15 feet wide and the two sections of the roof measure 5 feet and 12 feet. Find, to the *nearest degree*, the measure of the angle between the two sections of the roof.

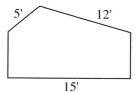

22. Use the formula $\cos A = \dfrac{b^2 + c^2 - a^2}{2bc}$ to show that the measure of an angle of an equilateral triangle is 60°. (*Hint:* Let the measure of each side of the triangle equal s.)

18-4 AREA OF A TRIANGLE

Since the measures of two sides and the included angle of a triangle determine the size and shape of the triangle, we are able to use these measures to find the area, K, of a triangle.

Let us draw $\triangle ABC$ in three positions in the coordinate plane. In each case, we will place one vertex at the origin and another vertex on the positive x-axis.

In Figure 1, point C is a distance b from the origin on the terminal ray of $\angle A$. Therefore, the coordinates of C are $(b \cos A, b \sin A)$. The measure of the base, $\overline{AB}$, of the triangle is c. The measure of the altitude, h, is the y-coordinate of point C, namely, $b \sin A$. Therefore:

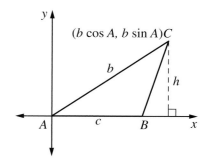

Figure 1

$$\text{Area of } \triangle ABC = \tfrac{1}{2}\,(\text{base})(\text{height})$$

$$K = \tfrac{1}{2}\,c \cdot b \sin A$$

In Figures 2 and 3, $\triangle ABC$ is repositioned so that the sides whose measures are a and b, respectively, act as the base. In each case, we again find the area of the triangle.

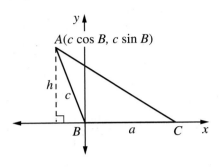

Figure 2

Figure 3

Area of $\triangle ABC = \frac{1}{2}$ (base)(height)	Area of $\triangle ABC = \frac{1}{2}$ (base)(height)
$K = \frac{1}{2} a \cdot c \sin B$	$K = \frac{1}{2} b \cdot a \sin C$

The area of a triangle, K, is equal to one-half the product of the measures of two sides and the sine of the angle between them.

$$\textbf{Area of } \triangle ABC = \frac{1}{2} \, ab \, \sin C = \frac{1}{2} \, bc \, \sin A = \frac{1}{2} \, ca \, \sin B$$

We can use this formula for the area of a triangle to consider two cases, one in which the given angle is acute and the other in which the given angle is obtuse.

CASE 1: The given angle is acute.

Find the area of $\triangle ABC$ if $c = 8$, $a = 6$, and $m\angle B = 30$.

$K = \frac{1}{2} ac \sin B$

$= \frac{1}{2} (6)(8) \sin 30°$

$= \frac{1}{2} (6)(8)\left(\frac{1}{2}\right) = 12$

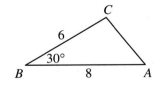

CASE 2: The given angle is obtuse.

Find the area of $\triangle BAD$ if $BA = 8$, $AD = 6$, and $m\angle A = 150$.

$K = \frac{1}{2} (BA)(AD) \sin A$

$= \frac{1}{2} (8)(6) \sin 150°$

$= \frac{1}{2} (8)(6)\left(\frac{1}{2}\right) = 12$

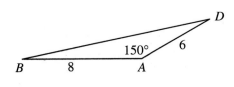

Each diagonal of a parallelogram divides the parallelogram into two congruent
triangles. For example, in parallelogram
ABCD, adjacent sides measure 6 and 8
and consecutive angles measure 30° and
150°. In the diagrams below, diagonal $\overline{AC}$ forms two triangles congruent to the
triangle in Case 1 on page 826, and diagonal $\overline{BD}$ forms two triangles congruent to
the triangle in Case 2 on page 826.

Area of $\triangle ABC = \frac{1}{2}(AB)(BC)\sin B$

Area of $\square ABCD = 2\left(\frac{1}{2}\right)(AB)(BC)\sin B$
$\qquad = (AB)(BC)\sin B$

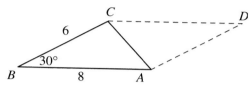

Case 1

Area of $\triangle BAD = \frac{1}{2}(BA)(AD)\sin A$

Area of $\square ABCD = 2\left(\frac{1}{2}\right)(BA)(AD)\sin A$
$\qquad = (BA)(AD)\sin A$

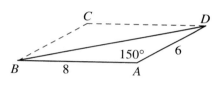

Case 2

These examples illustrate that the area of a parallelogram is equal to the product of
the measures of two adjacent sides and the sine of the angle between them.

EXAMPLES

1. Find the exact value of the area of an equilateral triangle if the measure of one
side is 4.

Solution   The measure of each side of the equilateral triangle is 4, and the measure of each
angle is 60°.

$$K = \frac{1}{2} ab \sin C$$

$$= \frac{1}{2}(4)(4)\sin 60°$$

$$= \frac{1}{2}(4)(4)\left(\frac{\sqrt{3}}{2}\right)$$

$$= 4\sqrt{3}$$

Answer: $4\sqrt{3}$

2. Find to the *nearest hundred* the number of square feet in the area of a triangular lot at the intersection of two streets if the angle of intersection is 76°10′ and the frontages along the streets are 220 feet and 156 feet.

Solution   Draw and label a diagram. Write the formula in terms of the diagram, and substitute the given values.

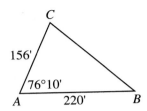

$$K = \tfrac{1}{2}\, bc \sin A$$

$$= \tfrac{1}{2}\,(156)(220) \sin 76°10'$$

Use a calculator for the computation. Round the number in the display to the nearest hundred.

Enter: 1 ÷ 2 × 156 × 220 SIN 76 + 10 ÷
60 ENTER

Display: 16662.28008

Answer: 16,700 square feet

---

3. The area of a parallelogram is 20. Find the measures of the angles of the parallelogram if the measures of two adjacent sides are 8 and 5.

Solution   Let *ABCD* be the parallelogram with *AB* = 8 and *BC* = *AD* = 5. Here, ∠*A* is acute and ∠*B* is obtuse.

$K = (AB)(AD)(\sin A)$

$20 = (8)(5)(\sin A)$

$20 = 40 \sin A$

$\dfrac{20}{40} = \dfrac{40 \sin A}{40}$

$0.5 = \sin A$

Since ∠*A* is acute, m∠*A* = 30.

$K = (AB)(BC)(\sin B)$

$20 = (8)(5)(\sin B)$

$20 = 40 \sin B$

$\dfrac{20}{40} = \dfrac{40 \sin B}{40}$

$0.5 = \sin B$

Since ∠*B* is obtuse,
m∠*B* = 180 − 30 = 150.

Answer: 30° and 150°

EXERCISES WITH OPEN-RESPONSE PROBLEMS

In 1–10, in each case, find the area of $\triangle ABC$.

1. $a = 6, b = 7, \sin C = \frac{1}{3}$

2. $b = 12, c = 14, \sin A = \frac{3}{4}$

3. $a = 9, b = 10, \sin C = \frac{2}{3}$

4. $a = 15, c = 12, \sin B = \frac{3}{5}$

5. $b = 13, c = 21, \sin A = \frac{2}{7}$

6. $b = 8, c = 20, \text{m}\angle A = 30$

7. $a = 7, b = 5, \text{m}\angle C = 90$

8. $a = \sqrt{3}, b = 8, \text{m}\angle C = 60$

9. $a = 2\sqrt{3}, c = 3, \text{m}\angle B = 120$

10. $a = 12, c = 9, \text{m}\angle B = 150$

11. In $\triangle ABC$, $a = 3\sqrt{2}$, $b = 5$, and $\text{m}\angle C = 45$. Find the area of $\triangle ABC$.

12. In $\triangle DEF$, $d = 8$, $f = 4\sqrt{2}$, and $\text{m}\angle E = 135$. Find the area of $\triangle DEF$.

13. In isosceles triangle RST, $RS = ST = 6$. If the measure of the vertex angle is 150°, what is the area of $\triangle RST$?

14. Find the area of an isosceles triangle if the measure of a base angle is 75° and the measure of each of the congruent sides is 10.

15. Find to the *nearest integer* the area of an isosceles triangle if the measure of the vertex angle is 42° and the measure of each of the congruent sides is 12.

16. Find to the *nearest tenth* the area of a triangle if the measures of two sides and the included angle are 2.6, 5.2, and 67°.

17. Find to the *nearest integer* the number of square meters in the area of a triangle if the lengths of two adjacent sides are 71.9 and 14.3 and the measure of the angle between them is 38.7°.

18. In right triangle ABC, $\text{m}\angle C = 90$, $a = 5$, and $b = 12$. Find the area of the triangle, using:

    a. $K = \frac{1}{2} \text{ base} \cdot \text{height}$ **b.** $K = \frac{1}{2} ab \sin C$

19. In parallelogram $ABCD$, $AB = 4$, $AD = 5\sqrt{3}$, and $\text{m}\angle A = 60$. The area of $\square ABCD$ is
  (1) 15   (2) 30   (3) $5\sqrt{3}$ (4) $20\sqrt{3}$

20. In rhombus $PQRS$, the length of each side is 8 and $\text{m}\angle PQR = 30$. Find the area of rhombus $PQRS$.

21. Find to the *nearest integer* the area of a parallelogram if the measures of a pair of adjacent sides are 20.0 and 24.0 and the measure of an angle is 32°20′.

22. If the area of $\triangle ABC$ is 12, find $\sin C$ when $a = 5$ and $b = 6$.

23. If the area of $\triangle CAP$ is 75, find $\sin A$ when $c = 30$ and $p = 20$.

24. Find to the *nearest degree* the measure of the acute angle of a triangle between two sides of measures 10 and 15 if the area of the triangle is 50.

25. In $\triangle ROC$, $\angle O$ is an obtuse angle, $OR = 32$, $OC = 36$, and the area of the triangle is 240. Find the measure of $\angle O$ to the *nearest degree*.

26. If the measure of the side of an equilateral triangle is represented by s, show that the area of the triangle is $\frac{s^2}{4}\sqrt{3}$.

In 27–30, in each case the lengths, in centimeters, of the sides of a triangle are given.   **a.** Find the measure of the largest angle of the triangle to the *nearest degree*.   **b.** Using the answer from part **a**, find the area of the triangle to the *nearest square centimeter*.

27. 5, 6, 7   **28.** 5, 6, 4   **29.** 5, 6, 2   **30.** 5, 6, 8

31. In a parallelogram, two consecutive sides measure 2 centimeters and 10 centimeters, and the length of the longer diagonal is 11 centimeters.   **a.** Find the measure of the largest angle of the parallelogram to the *nearest degree*.   **b.** Using the answer from part **a**, find the area of the parallelogram to the *nearest square centimeter*.

18-5 THE LAW OF SINES

In Section 18-4, we derived three forms for the area of a triangle.

$$\text{Area of } \triangle ABC = \tfrac{1}{2}\, bc \sin A = \tfrac{1}{2}\, ac \sin B = \tfrac{1}{2}\, ab \sin C$$

If we divide each of the last three terms of the equality by $\frac{1}{2}\, abc$, the result is a triple equality.

$$\frac{\tfrac{1}{2}\, bc \sin A}{\tfrac{1}{2}\, abc} = \frac{\tfrac{1}{2}\, ac \sin B}{\tfrac{1}{2}\, abc} = \frac{\tfrac{1}{2}\, ab \sin C}{\tfrac{1}{2}\, abc}$$

$$\frac{\sin A}{a} = \frac{\sin B}{b} = \frac{\sin C}{c}$$

This equality, also written in terms of the reciprocals of these ratios, is called the *Law of Sines*.

$$\frac{a}{\sin A} = \frac{b}{\sin B} = \frac{c}{\sin C}$$

The Law of Sines can be used to find the measure of a side of a triangle when the measures of two angles and a side are known (a.a.s. or a.s.a.).

For example, in $\triangle ABC$, $a = 10$, $m\angle A = 30$, and $m\angle B = 50$. We can use the Law of Sines to find b to the *nearest integer*.

1. Choose the ratios that use a and b.

$$\frac{a}{\sin A} = \frac{b}{\sin B}$$

2. Substitute the given values, and solve for b.

$$\frac{10}{\sin 30°} = \frac{b}{\sin 50°}$$

$$b \sin 30° = 10 \sin 50°$$

$$b = \frac{10 \sin 50°}{\sin 30°}$$

3. Use a calculator to find b.

Enter: 10 $\boxed{\times}$ $\boxed{\text{SIN}}$ 50 $\boxed{)}$ $\boxed{\div}$ $\boxed{\text{SIN}}$ 30 $\boxed{\text{ENTER}}$

Display: $\boxed{15.32088886}$

4. Round as directed.

To the nearest integer, $b = 15$.

Answer: 15

If $\angle C$ is a right angle, then $\triangle ABC$ is a right triangle where:

(1) c is the measure of the hypotenuse;

(2) a is the measure of the leg opposite $\angle A$; and

(3) b is the measure of the leg opposite $\angle B$.

Let us observe what happens when $\sin C = \sin 90° = 1$.

$$\frac{c}{\sin C} = \frac{a}{\sin A}$$
$$c \sin A = a \sin C$$
$$\frac{c \sin A}{c} = \frac{a \sin C}{c}$$
$$\sin A = \frac{a \sin 90°}{c}$$
$$\sin A = \frac{a(1)}{c}$$
$$\sin A = \frac{a}{c}$$
$$\sin A = \frac{\text{measure of leg opposite } \angle A}{\text{measure of hypotenuse}}$$

$$\frac{c}{\sin C} = \frac{b}{\sin B}$$
$$c \sin B = b \sin C$$
$$\frac{c \sin B}{c} = \frac{b \sin C}{c}$$
$$\sin B = \frac{b \sin 90°}{c}$$
$$\sin B = \frac{b(1)}{c}$$
$$\sin B = \frac{b}{c}$$
$$\sin B = \frac{\text{measure of leg opposite } \angle B}{\text{measure of hypotenuse}}$$

In Section 18-3, we showed that in right triangle ABC with $m\angle C = 90$:

$$\cos A = \frac{b}{c} = \frac{\text{measure of leg adjacent to } \angle A}{\text{measure of hypotenuse}}$$

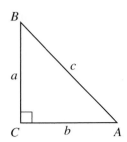

Therefore:

$$\tan A = \frac{\sin A}{\cos A} = \frac{\frac{a}{c}}{\frac{b}{c}} = \frac{a}{c} \cdot \frac{c}{b} = \frac{a}{b} = \frac{\text{measure of leg opposite } \angle A}{\text{measure of leg adjacent to } \angle A}$$

If we let "opp" represent measure of the leg opposite the angle, "adj" represent measure of the leg adjacent to the angle, and "hyp" represent measure of the hypotenuse, then:

In right triangle ABC with $m\angle C = 90$:

$$\sin A = \frac{a}{c} = \frac{\text{opp}}{\text{hyp}} \qquad \cos A = \frac{b}{c} = \frac{\text{adj}}{\text{hyp}} \qquad \tan A = \frac{a}{b} = \frac{\text{opp}}{\text{adj}}$$

EXAMPLES

1. In $\triangle DAT$, $m\angle D = 27$, $m\angle A = 105$, and $t = 21$. Find d to the *nearest integer*.

How to Proceed:

(1) Since the ratios involving t and d must be used, find $m\angle T$.

(2) Write a proportion, using the two ratios of the Law of Sines in terms of t and d.

(3) Substitute the given values.

(4) Solve for d.

(5) Use a calculator to find d.

(6) Round the result.

Answer: 13

Solution:

$m\angle T = 180 - (m\angle A + m\angle D)$

$\qquad = 180 - (105 + 27)$

$\qquad = 48$

$$\frac{d}{\sin D} = \frac{t}{\sin T}$$

$$\frac{d}{\sin 27°} = \frac{21}{\sin 48°}$$

$$d = \frac{21 \sin 27°}{\sin 48°}$$

Enter: 21 [×] [SIN] 27 [)] [÷]

[SIN] 48 [ENTER]

Display: 12.82899398

To the nearest integer, $d = 13$

2. In $\triangle ABC$, $a = 12$, $\sin A = \frac{1}{3}$, and $\sin C = \frac{1}{4}$. Find c.

How to Proceed:

Solution:

(1) Choose the two ratios of the Law of Sines that use a, the side whose measure is given, and c, the side whose measure must be found.

$$\frac{c}{\sin C} = \frac{a}{\sin A}$$

(2) Substitute the given values.

$$\frac{c}{\left(\frac{1}{4}\right)} = \frac{12}{\left(\frac{1}{3}\right)}$$

(3) Solve for c.

$$\frac{1}{3}c = \frac{1}{4}(12)$$

$$\frac{1}{3}c = 3$$

$$c = 9$$

Answer: 9

---

3. In $\triangle ABC$, $m\angle A = 30$ and $m\angle B = 45$. Find the ratio $a:b$.

How to Proceed:

Solution:

(1) Write the two ratios of the Law of Sines that use a and b.

$$\frac{a}{\sin A} = \frac{b}{\sin B}$$

(2) Substitute the given values.

$$\frac{a}{\sin 30°} = \frac{b}{\sin 45°}$$

(3) Write the values for $\sin 30°$ and $\sin 45°$.

$$\frac{a}{\left(\frac{1}{2}\right)} = \frac{b}{\left(\frac{\sqrt{2}}{2}\right)}$$

(4) Solve for $\frac{a}{b}$, and simplify the result.

$$\frac{\sqrt{2}}{2}a = \frac{1}{2}b$$

$$\frac{\frac{\sqrt{2}}{2}a}{\frac{\sqrt{2}}{2}b} = \frac{\frac{1}{2}b}{\frac{\sqrt{2}}{2}b}$$

$$\frac{a}{b} = \frac{\frac{1}{2}}{\frac{\sqrt{2}}{2}} = \frac{\frac{1}{2} \cdot \sqrt{2}}{\frac{\sqrt{2}}{2} \cdot \sqrt{2}}$$

$$= \frac{\frac{\sqrt{2}}{2}}{\frac{2}{2}} = \frac{\sqrt{2}}{2}$$

Answer: $\sqrt{2}: 2$

4. In right triangle ABC, $m\angle C = 90$, $m\angle A = 56$, and $BC = 8.7$. Find AB to the *nearest tenth*.

How to Proceed: *Solution:*

Method 1: Law of Sines

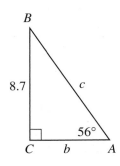

(1) Since $BC = a$ and $AB = c$, using triangle ABC write the Law of Sines in terms of a and c.

$$\frac{c}{\sin C} = \frac{a}{\sin A}$$

(2) Substitute the given values.

$$\frac{c}{\sin 90°} = \frac{8.7}{\sin 56°}$$

(3) Solve for c.

$$c \sin 56° = 8.7 \sin 90°$$

$$c = \frac{8.7 \sin 90°}{\sin 56°}$$

(4) Perform the computation, and round the value of c to the nearest tenth.

$$= 10.49409615$$
$$= 10.5$$

Method 2: Sine Ratio of a Right Triangle

(1) Write the sine ratio for a right triangle.

$$\sin A = \frac{a}{c}$$

(2) Substitute the given values.

$$\sin 56° = \frac{8.7}{c}$$

(3) Solve for c.

$$c \sin 56° = 8.7$$

$$c = \frac{8.7}{\sin 56°}$$

(4) Perform the computation, and round the value of c to the nearest tenth.

$$= 10.49409615$$
$$= 10.5$$

Answer: 10.5

EXERCISES WITH OPEN-RESPONSE PROBLEMS

1. In $\triangle ABC$, $a = 6$, $\sin A = 0.2$, and $\sin B = 0.3$. Find b.

2. In $\triangle ABC$, $b = 12$, $\sin B = 0.6$, and $\sin C = 0.9$. Find c.

3. In $\triangle ABC$, $c = 8$, $\sin C = \frac{1}{4}$, and $\sin B = \frac{3}{8}$. Find b.

4. In $\triangle ABC$, $b = 30$, $\sin B = 0.6$, and $\sin A = 0.8$. find a.

5. In $\triangle DEN$, $d = 12$, $\sin D = 0.4$, and $\sin N = 0.3$. Find n.

6. In $\triangle CAP$, $c = \sqrt{6}$, $m\angle C = 45$, and $m\angle P = 60$. Find p.

7. In $\triangle REM$, $r = 3\sqrt{2}$, $m\angle R = 135$, and $m\angle M = 30$. Find m.

8. In $\triangle ABC$, $a = 6\sqrt{2}$, $m\angle A = 45$, and $m\angle B = 105$. Find c.

9. In $\triangle CAR$, $a = 24$, $m\angle A = 27$, and $m\angle C = 83$. Find c to the *nearest integer*.

10. In $\triangle PAR$, $p = 8.5$, $m\angle P = 72$, and $m\angle A = 68$. Find r to the *nearest tenth*.

In 11–13, select the *numeral* preceding the expression that best completes each sentence.

11. In an isosceles triangle, the length of each of the congruent sides is 12 and the measure of a base angle is 30°. The length of the base of the triangle is
   (1) $12\sqrt{3}$ (2) $12\sqrt{2}$ (3) 12   (4) $6\sqrt{3}$

12. In an isosceles triangle, the vertex angle measures 90° and the length of each congruent leg is $5\sqrt{2}$. The length of the base of the triangle is
   (1) 5   (2) 10   (3) $10\sqrt{2}$ (4) $10\sqrt{3}$

13. In $\triangle ABC$, m$\angle A = 45$ and m$\angle B = 30$. The ratio of $a:b$ is
   (1) $\sqrt{2}:1$ (2) $2:1$ (3) $\sqrt{2}:2$ (4) $1:2$

14. Find to the *nearest tenth* the length of one of the congruent sides of an isosceles triangle if the measure of the base is 24.6 and the measure of each base angle is 72°10′.

15. Find to the *nearest tenth* the length of one of the congruent sides of an isosceles triangle if the measure of the base is 48.9 and the measure of the vertex angle is 57.6°.

16. A ladder that is 10 feet long leans against a wall so that the top of the ladder just reaches the top of the wall. Find to the *nearest tenth* of a foot the height of the wall if the foot of the ladder makes an angle of 72° with the ground.

17. A wire that is 8.5 meters long runs in a straight line from the top of a telephone pole to a stake in the ground. If the wire makes an angle of 68° with the ground, find to the *nearest tenth* of a meter the height of the pole.

18. A straight road slopes upward at 15° from the horizontal. How long is the section of the road that rises a vertical distance of 250 feet? (Express the answer to the *nearest 10 feet*.)

19. Find to the *nearest integer* the measure of the base of an isosceles triangle if the measure of the vertex angle is 70° and the measure of each of the congruent sides is 15.

20. In $\triangle RST$, sin $R = 0.4$ and m$\angle S = 30$. Find the ratio $r:s$.

21. In $\triangle PQR$, sin $P = 0.15$ and sin $Q = 0.5$. Find the ratio $q:p$.

22. In $\triangle ABC$, m$\angle A = 24°50′$, m$\angle B = 65°30′$, and $BC = 25.6$. Find AC to the *nearest tenth*.

23. In $\triangle DEF$, m$\angle E$ is 31.25 m$\angle F = 18.75$, and $DF = 72.3$. Find DE to the *nearest tenth*.

24. In $\triangle ABC$, the ratio m$\angle A$:m$\angle B$:m$\angle C = 2:3:7$, and $BC = 40.2$. Find: **a.** m$\angle A$ **b.** m$\angle B$ **c.** m$\angle C$ **d.** AC to the *nearest tenth* **e.** AB to the *nearest tenth*

25. In $\triangle ABC$, m$\angle A = 84°25′$, m$\angle C = 17°43′$, and $BC = 245$ meters. Find: **a.** m$\angle B$ **b.** AB to the *nearest meter* **c.** AC to the *nearest meter*

26. Is it possible for $\triangle PQR$ to exist if m$\angle P = 39°40′$, $p = 1$, and $q = 2$? Explain your answer.

18-6   THE AMBIGUOUS CASE

It would seem that, if we know the measures of two sides of a triangle and of the angle opposite one of them, we could use the Law of Sines to solve for the measure of another angle. We know, however, that the measure of two sides and of the angle opposite one of them do not suffice to determine the size and shape of a triangle (see the figures on page 836).

In △ABC and △A′B′C′, m∠A = m∠A′ = 30, AB = A′B′ = 12, and BC = B′C′ = 7. But △ABC is not congruent to △A′B′C′.

 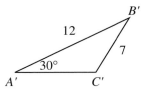

We will use the Law of Sines to study the **ambiguous case**, the number of possible triangles that can be constructed when the measures of two sides of the angle opposite one of them are known.

First, we will consider the cases, like the one shown above, in which the given angle is acute.

CASE 1: c > a > c sin A

If $a = 7$, m∠A = 30, and $c = 12$, find m∠C.

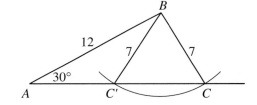

$$\frac{a}{\sin A} = \frac{c}{\sin C}$$

$$\frac{7}{\sin 30°} = \frac{12}{\sin C}$$

$$\frac{7}{\left(\frac{1}{2}\right)} = \frac{12}{\sin C}$$

$$7 \sin C = \frac{1}{2}(12)$$

$$\sin C = \frac{6}{7}$$

There are two possible angles with measures between 0° and 180° whose sine is $\frac{6}{7}$. One is a first-quadrant angle; the other, a second-quadrant angle.

$$m∠C ≈ 59$$
$$\text{and } m∠C' ≈ 180 - 59 = 121$$

Conclusion: In △ABC, if ∠A is acute and c > a > c sin A, then two possible triangles can be drawn.

CASE 2: a = c sin A

If $a = 6$, m$\angle A = 30$, and $c = 12$, find m$\angle C$.

$$\frac{a}{\sin A} = \frac{c}{\sin C}$$

$$\frac{6}{\sin 30°} = \frac{12}{\sin C}$$

$$\frac{6}{\left(\frac{1}{2}\right)} = \frac{12}{\sin C}$$

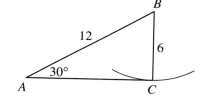

$$6 \sin C = \frac{1}{2}(12)$$

$$\sin C = \frac{6}{6} = 1$$

$$m\angle C = 90$$

Conclusion: In $\triangle ABC$, if $\angle A$ is acute and $a = c \sin A$, then one right triangle can be drawn.

CASE 3: a ≥ c > c sin A

If $a = 15$, m$\angle A = 30$, and $c = 12$, find m$\angle C$.

$$\frac{a}{\sin A} = \frac{c}{\sin C}$$

$$\frac{15}{\sin 30°} = \frac{12}{\sin C}$$

$$\frac{15}{\left(\frac{1}{2}\right)} = \frac{12}{\sin C}$$

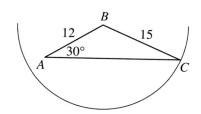

$$15 \sin C = \frac{1}{2}(12)$$

$$\sin C = \frac{6}{15}$$

$$m\angle C \approx 24$$

$$\text{and } m\angle C' \approx 180 - 24 = 156$$

But m$\angle A$ + m$\angle C'$ = 30 + 156 = 186. Therefore, $\angle C'$ is not a possible solution. If $a = c$, it can be shown in a similar way that only one triangle, namely, an isosceles triangle, can be drawn.

Conclusion: In $\triangle ABC$, if $\angle A$ is acute and $a \geq c > c \sin A$, then only one triangle can be drawn.

CASE 4: a < c sin A

If $a = 4$, m$\angle A = 30$, and $c = 12$, find m$\angle C$.

$$\frac{a}{\sin A} = \frac{c}{\sin C}$$

$$\frac{4}{\sin 30°} = \frac{12}{\sin C}$$

$$\frac{4}{\left(\frac{1}{2}\right)} = \frac{12}{\sin C}$$

$$4 \sin C = \frac{1}{2}(12)$$

$$\sin C = \frac{6}{4} = 1.5$$

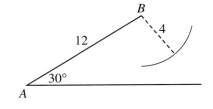

There is no angle whose sine is greater than 1.

Conclusion: In $\triangle ABC$, if $\angle A$ is acute and $a < c \sin A$, then no triangle can be drawn.

If the given angle is obtuse, the measure of the side opposite the obtuse angle must be greater than the measure of any other side. In the next two cases, $\angle A$ is obtuse.

CASE 5: a > c

If $a = 15$, m$\angle A = 150$, and $c = 12$, find m$\angle C$.

$$\frac{a}{\sin A} = \frac{c}{\sin C}$$

$$\frac{15}{\sin 150°} = \frac{12}{\sin C}$$

$$\frac{15}{\left(\frac{1}{2}\right)} = \frac{12}{\sin C}$$

$$15 \sin C = \frac{1}{2}(12)$$

$$\sin C = \frac{6}{15}$$

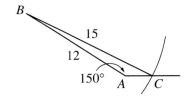

There can be no more than one obtuse angle in a triangle.
Therefore, $\angle C$ must be an acute angle.

$$m\angle C \approx 24$$

Conclusion: In $\triangle ABC$, if $\angle A$ is obtuse and $a > c$, then only one triangle can be drawn.

CASE 6: a ≤ c

If $a = 8$, $m\angle A = 150$, and $c = 12$, find $m\angle C$.

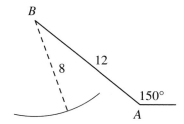

$$\frac{a}{\sin A} = \frac{c}{\sin C}$$

$$\frac{8}{\sin 150°} = \frac{12}{\sin C}$$

$$\frac{8}{\left(\frac{1}{2}\right)} = \frac{12}{\sin C}$$

$$8 \sin C = \tfrac{1}{2}(12)$$

$$\sin C = \tfrac{6}{8}$$

$$m\angle C \approx 49$$

and $m\angle C' \approx 180 - 49 = 131$

$$m\angle A + m\angle C = 150 + 49 = 199$$

$$m\angle A + m\angle C' = 150 + 131 = 281$$

Therefore, neither value is a solution.

If $a = c$, it can also be shown that no triangle can be drawn.

Conclusion: In $\triangle ABC$, if $\angle A$ is obtuse and $a \leq c$, then no triangle can be drawn.

Summary		
∠A is acute.	$c > a > c \sin A$ $a = c \sin A$ $a \geq c > c \sin A$ $a < c \sin A$	2 triangles 1 triangle 1 triangle 0 triangle
∠A is obtuse.	$a > c$ $a \leq c$	1 triangle 0 triangle

In any situation, after applying the Law of Sines to the given data, we can discover the number of possible triangles by:

(1) checking to see that the sum of the measures of two angles of the triangle(s) is less than 180°, or

(2) making an accurate drawing, using the given data.

EXAMPLES

1. State the number of possible triangles that can be constructed if $a = 10$, $b = 12$, and $m\angle B = 20$.

How to Proceed:	*Solution:*

(1) Write the Law of Sines in terms of a and b.

$$\frac{a}{\sin A} = \frac{b}{\sin B}$$

(2) Substitute the given values.

$$\frac{10}{\sin A} = \frac{12}{\sin 20°}$$

(3) Solve for $\sin A$.

$$12 \sin A = 10 \sin 20°$$

$$\sin A = \frac{10 \sin 20°}{12}$$

$$= 0.285016786$$

(4) Find to the nearest degree the measures of an acute angle and an obtuse angle whose sine is approximately equal to 0.285.

$$m\angle A = 17$$

or $m\angle A = 180 - 17 = 163$

(5) Combine the measures of $\angle A$ and $\angle B$ to determine whether a third angle is possible.

$m\angle A = 17$	$m\angle A = 163$
$m\angle B = 20$	$m\angle B = 20$
$m\angle C = 143$	
A triangle is possible using this value for $m\angle A$.	No triangle is possible using this value for $m\angle A$.

Answer: One

---

2. In $\triangle PRQ$, $p = 12$, $\sin P = 0.6$, and $r = 8$. Find $\sin R$.

How to Proceed:	*Solution:*

(1) Write the Law of Sines in terms of p and r.

$$\frac{p}{\sin P} = \frac{r}{\sin R}$$

(2) Substitute the given values.

$$\frac{12}{0.6} = \frac{8}{\sin R}$$

(3) Solve the equation for $\sin R$.

$$12 \sin R = 0.6(8)$$

$$\sin R = \frac{4.8}{12}$$

Note: Since you are asked to find $\sin R$, it is not necessary to determine $m\angle R$ or to decide whether the angle is acute or obtuse.

$$= 0.4$$

Answer: $\sin R = 0.4$

EXERCISES WITH OPEN-RESPONSE PROBLEMS

In 1–8, in each case, how many noncongruent triangles can be constructed with the given measures?

1. $a = 4$, $b = 6$, and m$\angle A = 30$

2. $a = \sqrt{2}$, $b = 3$, and m$\angle A = 45$

3. $a = 4$, $b = 6$, and m$\angle A = 150$

4. $a = 4$, $b = 6$, and m$\angle B = 150$

5. $a = 15$, $b = 12$, and m$\angle B = 45$

6. $a = 15$, $b = 12$, and m$\angle A = 135$

7. $a = 5$, $b = 8$, and m$\angle A = 40$

8. $a = 9$, $b = 12$, and m$\angle A = 35$

9. How many distinct triangles can be constructed if the measures of two sides are to be 35 and 70 and the measure of the angle opposite the smaller of these sides is to be 30°?

In 10–12, select the *numeral* preceding the expression that best completes each sentence.

10. If $a = 6$, $b = 8$, and m$\angle A = 30$, the number of distinct triangles that can be constructed is
  (1) 1   (2) 2   (3) 3   (4) 0

11. In $\triangle ABC$, if m$\angle A = 30$, $a = 5$, and $b = 10$, then $\triangle ABC$
  (1) must be an acute triangle
  (2) must be a right triangle
  (3) must be an obtuse triangle
  (4) may be an acute or an obtuse triangle

12. In $\triangle PQR$, if m$\angle P = 30$, $p = 5$, and $r = 8$, then $\triangle PQR$
  (1) must be an acute triangle
  (2) must be a right triangle
  (3) must be an obtuse triangle
  (4) may be an acute or an obtuse triangle

13. In $\triangle ABC$, $a = 18$, $b = 12$, and sin $A = 0.6$. Find sin B.

14. In $\triangle ABC$, $a = 10$, $c = 15$, and sin $C = 0.3$. Find sin A.

15. In $\triangle ABC$, $b = 8$, $c = 18$, and sin $C = \frac{1}{4}$. Find sin B.

16. In $\triangle ABC$, $b = 24$, $c = 30$, and m$\angle C = 30$. Find sin B.

17. The measures of two sides of a triangle are 34 and 22, and the measure of the angle opposite the smaller of these sides is 30°. Find to the *nearest degree* two possible measures of the angle opposite the larger of these sides.

18. In parallelogram $ABCD$, the measure of one side is 10 centimeters, the measure of a diagonal is 14 centimeters, and the measure of one angle is 130°.
  a. How many parallelograms can be constructed that satisfy the given conditions and are not congruent to each other?
  b. Find to the *nearest degree* all possible measures of the angle between the given side and diagonal of $ABCD$.
  c. Sketch the parallelogram(s) $ABCD$.

19. a. Use the Law of Cosines to find two possible measures of c in $\triangle ABC$ when $a = 7$, $b = 8$, and m$\angle A = 60$.   **b.** Use the Law of Cosines and the results obtained in part **a** to find to the *nearest degree* two possible measures of $\angle B$ in $\triangle ABC$.

18-7 FORCES

If two forces act to push or pull an object in the same direction, such as two children pulling their sled together, the effect is that of a single force equal to the sum of the applied forces and in the direction of the two forces.

If two forces act to push or pull an object in opposite directions, such as two children who want to go in opposite directions with their sled, the effect is that of a single force equal to the difference between the applied forces and in the direction of the larger force.

If the two children pull in directions that form an angle other than a straight angle with each other, the effect is that of a single force acting in a direction in the interior of the angle between the applied forces.

A force is an example of a vector quantity. A *vector quantity* is a quantity that has both magnitude (size) and direction. A force is represented by a directed line segment, or ***vector***, in which the length of the line segment represents the magnitude and an arrowhead indicates the direction. When two forces act at a point, the single force that has the same effect as the combination of the applied forces is called the ***resultant***.

In the accompanying figure, $\overrightarrow{PQ}$ and $\overrightarrow{PS}$ are vectors that represent two forces applied to a body at point P. The resultant of these two forces is represented by the vector $\overrightarrow{PR}$. The figure illustrates the following experimental result for two forces acting on a body at an angle other than a straight angle:

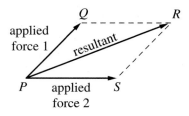

- **The vectors that represent the applied forces form two adjacent sides of a parallelogram, and the vector that represents the resultant force is the diagonal of this parallelogram.**

Note: The resultant does not bisect the angle between two applied forces that are unequal in magnitude.

EXAMPLES

1. Two forces of 25 and 15 pounds act on a body so that the angle between them is 75°. Find to the *nearest pound* the magnitude of the resultant.

How to Proceed: *Solution:*

(1) Draw and label parallelogram *ABCD*. Let $\overrightarrow{AD}$ and $\overrightarrow{AB}$ represent the given forces, and $\overrightarrow{AC}$ represent the resultant. (*Note:* In ☐*ABCD*, *AD* = *BC* = 15.)

(2) Consecutive angles of a parallelogram are supplementary. Find m∠*B*.

$$m\angle B = 180 - m\angle DAB$$
$$= 180 - 75$$
$$= 105$$

(3) In △*ABC*, the measures of two sides and the included angle are known. Use the Law of Cosines to find the measure of the third side of the triangle (i.e., the magnitude of resultant $\overrightarrow{AC}$).

$$b^2 = a^2 + c^2 - 2ac \cos B$$

(4) Substitute given values.

$$= 15^2 + 25^2 - 2(15)(25) \cos 105°$$

(5) Find the value of b^2.

(6) Find *b*, the principal square root of b^2, and round as directed.

Enter: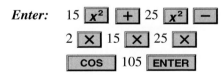

Display: ⌜1044.114284⌝

Enter: 2nd √ 2nd ANS
           ENTER

Display: ⌜32.31275729⌝

To the nearest integer, *b* = 32

Answer: 32 pounds

2. A resultant force of 143 pounds is needed to move a heavy box. Two applied forces act at angles of 35°40′ and 47°30′ with the resultant. Find to the *nearest pound* the magnitude of the larger force.

Solution   (1) Draw and label parallelogram *ABCD*. If $\overrightarrow{AC}$ represents the resultant, then $AC = 143$, m∠*BAC* = 35°40′, and m∠*DAC* = 47°30′.

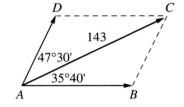

(2) If parallel lines ($\overleftrightarrow{AD}$ and $\overleftrightarrow{BC}$) are cut by a transversal ($\overleftrightarrow{AC}$), the alternate interior angles (∠*DAC* and ∠*ACB*) are congruent. Therefore, m∠*ACB* = m∠*DAC* = 47°30′.

(3) In △*ABC*, the longer of sides $\overline{AB}$ and $\overline{BC}$ is opposite the larger angle. Therefore, $\overrightarrow{AB}$ represents the larger applied force.

(4) To use the Law of Sines, you must know the measure of ∠*B*, the angle opposite side $\overline{AC}$, whose measure is known. Here:

$$\text{m}\angle B = 180° - (\text{m}\angle BAC + \text{m}\angle ACB)$$
$$= 180° - (35°40′ + 47°30′) = 96°50′$$

(5) Write the Law of Sines, and substitute known values.

$$\frac{c}{\sin C} = \frac{b}{\sin B}$$

$$\frac{AB}{\sin 47°30′} = \frac{143}{\sin 96°50′}$$

(6) Solve for *AB*.

$$AB = \frac{143 \sin 47°30′}{\sin 96°50′}$$

(7) Compute, and round the value of *AB* to the nearest integer.

$$= 106$$

Answer: *AB* = 106 pounds

EXERCISES WITH OPEN-RESPONSE PROBLEMS

1. Two forces of 12 pounds and 20 pounds act on a body with an angle of 60° between them. Find to the *nearest pound* the magnitude of the resultant.

2. Find to the *nearest tenth* of a pound the magnitude of the resultant force if two forces of 2.5 and 4.0 pounds act with an angle of 40° between them.

3. If two forces of 30 pounds and 40 pounds act on a body with an angle of 120° between them, find to the *nearest pound* the magnitude of the resultant.

4. Two forces act on a body so that the resultant is a force of 50 pounds. The measures of the angles between the resultant and the forces are 25° and 38°. Find to the *nearest pound* the magnitude of the larger applied force.

5. The measures of the angles between the resultant and two applied forces are 65° and 42°. If the magnitude of the resultant is 24 pounds, find to the *nearest pound* the magnitude of the smaller force.

6. Two forces act on a body. The measure of the angle between the 34-pound force and the 40-pound resultant is 60°. Find to the *nearest pound* the magnitude of the other force.

7. When forces of 12 pounds and 8 pounds act on a body, the magnitude of the resultant is 15 pounds. Find to the *nearest degree* the measure of the angle between the resultant and the larger force.

8. When forces of 20 pounds and 25 pounds act on a body, the magnitude of the resultant is 30 pounds. Find to the *nearest degree* the measure of the angle between the resultant and the smaller force.

9. Find to the *nearest degree* the measure of the angle between two applied forces of 9 and 11 pounds if the resultant is a force of 14 pounds.

10. Find to the *nearest degree* the measure of the angle between two applied forces of 8 and 10 pounds if the resultant is a force of 5 pounds.

11. In still air, Mr. Chafer's plane flies 400 miles per hour. When the wind is blowing to the north at 40 miles per hour, find to the *nearest degree* the angle at which he must set his course east of due north in order to keep to a course that is 30° east of due north. (*Hint:* First determine the measure of the angle between the course he must set and the course along which the plane actually flies.)

12. By setting a course slightly west of due south, Mr. Chafer flew to an airport due south of where he took off. The wind was blowing at 30 miles per hour at an angle of 40° east of due south. If the plane took an hour to fly the 420 miles from takeoff to landing, find to the *nearest 10 miles per hour* the speed at which the plane would have been traveling in still air.

13. For Joe to cross the bay to a point directly east of his camp, he must set a course 6° south of due east to compensate for a current that flows to the northeast, 30° north of due east. If Joe's boat travels 20 miles per hour in still water, what is the rate of the current to the *nearest integer*?

18-8 SOLVING TRIANGLES

In a right triangle, if the measure of one side and an acute angle or the measures of two sides are known, then it is possible to use special ratios to find the measure of the other parts of the triangle.

In right triangle *ABC* with m∠C = 90
$\sin A = \dfrac{a}{c} = \dfrac{\text{measure of leg opposite } \angle A}{\text{measure of hypotenuse}} = \dfrac{\text{opp}}{\text{hyp}}$
$\cos A = \dfrac{b}{c} = \dfrac{\text{measure of leg adjacent to } \angle A}{\text{measure of hypotenuse}} = \dfrac{\text{adj}}{\text{hyp}}$
$\tan A = \dfrac{a}{b} = \dfrac{\text{measure of leg opposite } \angle A}{\text{measure of leg adjacent to } \angle A} = \dfrac{\text{opp}}{\text{adj}}$

If the measure of a side and any two other parts of any triangle are known, the Law of Cosines and the Law of Sines can be used to find the measures of the other sides and angles of the triangle.

Summary of Methods of Solution		
Known Measures	**Law to Be Used**	**Measure to Be Found**
Two sides and the included angle (s.a.s.)	1. First, the Law of Cosines 2. Then, the Law of Sines (or the Law of Cosines) 3. Finally, repeat step 2 (or sum of the angle measures = 180°).	The third side The second angle The third angle
Three sides (s.s.s.)	1. First, the Law of Cosines 2. Then, the Law of Sines (or the Law of Cosines) 3. Finally, repeat step 2 (or sum of the angle measures = 180°).	The first angle The second angle The third angle
Two angles and the included side (a.s.a.)	1. First, sum of the angle measures of a triangle is 180°. 2. Then, the Law of Sines 3. Finally, the Law of Sines (or the Law of Cosines)	The third angle The second side The third side
Two angles and the side opposite one of them (a.a.s.)	Do 1 and 2 in *either order*. 1. First, the Law of Sines 2. Then, sum of the angle measures = 180° 3. Finally, the Law of Sines (or the Law of Cosines)	The second side The third angle The third side
Two sides and an angle opposite one of them (s.s.a.)	1. First, the Law of Sines. If there is a solution, then: 2. Sum of the angle measures = 180° 3. Finally, the Law of Sines (or the Law of Cosines)	The second angle (0, 1, or 2 solutions) The third angle The third side

A right triangle can be solved by using special ratios.

In problems involving angle measures that can be solved using the laws of trigonometry, an angle is often described as an angle of elevation or an angle of depression.

An ***angle of elevation*** is an angle formed by rays that are parts of a horizontal line and a line of sight that is elevated, or raised upward, from the horizontal. If a person standing at point A looks up to point B at the top of a cliff, the angle of elevation of B from A is $\angle CAB$.

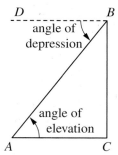

An ***angle of depression*** is an angle formed by rays that are parts of a horizontal line and a line of sight that is depressed, or lowered, from the horizontal. If a person standing at the top of a cliff at point B looks down to point A, the angle of depression of A from B is $\angle DBA$.

PROCEDURE.   To solve a problem involving sides and angles of a triangle:

1. Read the problem carefully.
2. Draw a diagram and label it.
3. Note the relationship of the sides and angles whose measures are given to the side or angle whose measure is to be found.
4. Choose the appropriate law, and write it in terms of the letters used to label the diagram.
5. Determine the required measure.
6. Check that the answer is reasonable.

KEEP IN MIND ──

The laws that follow may be rewritten to include different angles of a triangle. Here, each law is written to include $\angle C$ of $\triangle ABC$.

$$\text{Law of Cosines: } c^2 = a^2 + b^2 - 2ab \cos C$$

$$\text{Law of Cosines: } \cos C = \frac{a^2 + b^2 - c^2}{2ab}$$

$$\text{Law of Sines: } \frac{c}{\sin C} = \frac{b}{\sin B} \quad \text{or} \quad \frac{c}{\sin C} = \frac{a}{\sin A}$$

$$\text{Area of a triangle: } K = \frac{1}{2} ab \sin C$$

EXAMPLES

1. To determine the distance between two points, A and B, on opposite sides of a swampy region, a surveyor chose a point C that was 350 meters from point A and 400 meters from point B. If the measure of $\angle ACB$ was found to be $105°40'$, find to the *nearest meter* the distance, AB, across the swampy region.

Solution

(1) Draw and label a diagram.

(2) Since the measures of two sides and the included angle are known, use the Law of Cosines: $c^2 = a^2 + b^2 - 2ab \cos C$.

(3) Substitute the given values.

$$c^2 = a^2 + b^2 - 2ab \cos C$$
$$= 400^2 + 350^2 - 2(400)(350) \cos 105°40'$$

(4) Use a calculator to find c^2. Express $105°40'$ as $\left(105\frac{40}{60}\right)^\circ$ or $\left(105\frac{2}{3}\right)^\circ$.

Enter: 400 [x²] [+] 350 [x²] [−] 2 [×] 400 [×]
350 [×] [COS] 105 [+] 2 [÷] 3 [ENTER]

Display: | 358111.2921 |

(5) Find c, the principal square root of c^2, and round as directed.

Enter: [2nd] [√] [2nd] [ANS] [ENTER]

Display: | 598.4240069 |

To the nearest integer, $c = 598$.

Answer: 598 meters

2. From a point, *A*, at the edge of a river, the measure of the angle of elevation of the top of a tree on the opposite bank is 37°. From a point, *B*, that is 50 feet from the edge of the river and in line with point *A* and the foot of the tree, the measure of the angle of elevation of the top of the tree is 22°. Find to the *nearest foot* the width of the river.

Solution   (1) Draw and label a diagram. Note that $\overline{AD}$ is the width of the river.

(2) Since $\angle BAC$ and $\angle CAD$ are supplementary, it is possible to determine the measure of the angles of $\triangle ABC$.

$$m\angle BAC = 180 - m\angle CAD$$
$$= 180 - 37 = 143$$
$$m\angle BCA = 180 - (m\angle B + m\angle BAC)$$
$$= 180 - (22 + 143)$$
$$= 180 - 165 = 15$$

(3) Use the Law of Sines to find the measure of $\overline{AC}$, a side common to $\triangle ABC$ and $\triangle ACD$. A calculator can be used for the computation.

$$\frac{AC}{\sin B} = \frac{BA}{\sin \angle BCA}$$
$$\frac{AC}{\sin 22°} = \frac{50}{\sin 15°}$$
$$AC = \frac{50 \sin 22°}{\sin 15°}$$

Enter: 50 [SIN] 22 [ )] [÷]
[SIN] 15 [ENTER]

Display: | 72.36843666 |

(4) Triangle *ACD* is a right triangle. Use the cosine ratio, $\frac{\text{adj}}{\text{hyp}}$, to find *AD*.

$$\cos 37° = \frac{AD}{AC}$$
$$AD = AC \cos 37°$$

With 72.36843666, the value of *AC*, in the calculator display:

Enter: [×] [COS] 37 [ENTER]
Display: | 57.79600332 |

(5) Round as directed.

To the nearest foot, $AD = 58$.

Answer: The width of the river is 58 feet.

EXERCISES WITH OPEN-RESPONSE PROBLEMS

Ex. 1

Ex. 2

Ex. 3

1. In $\triangle ABC$, $a = 10$, $b = 5$, and m$\angle C = 27$. **a.** Find c to the *nearest integer*. **b.** Find m$\angle B$ to the *nearest degree*. **c.** Find m$\angle A$ to the *nearest degree*.

2. In $\triangle DEF$, m$\angle D = 32$, m$\angle E = 54$, and $DE = 22$. **a.** Find m$\angle F$. **b.** Find EF to the *nearest integer*. **c.** Find DF to the *nearest integer*.

3. In $\triangle PQR$, $p = 25$, $q = 12$, and $r = 20$. Find to the *nearest degree* the measure of each angle of the triangle.

4. In $\triangle ABC$, $a = 31.6$, $b = 17.8$, and m$\angle A = 112°40'$.
   a. Find to the *nearest 10 minutes* the measure of $\angle B$.
   b. Find to the *nearest 10 minutes* the measure of $\angle C$. **c.** Find c to the *nearest tenth*.

5. In right triangle ABC, m$\angle C = 90$, m$\angle A = 37$, and $AC = 43$. Find AB to the *nearest integer*.

6. Find to the *nearest foot* the height of a tree that casts a 24-foot shadow when the angle of elevation of the sun is 52°.

7. Find to the *nearest meter* the height that a kite has reached if 120 meters of string have been let out and the string makes an angle of 68° with the ground. (Assume that the string makes a straight line.)

8. Each morning the Beckebredes jog north along a straight path for 0.8 mile, turn at an angle of 60° and jog to the southwest for 1.2 miles, then turn again to the southeast and jog back to their starting point. What is the total distance to the *nearest tenth* of a mile that they jog each morning?

9. In order to know how much seed to buy for a triangular plot of land, Kevin needs to know the area of the plot. The lengths of the sides are 15 feet, 25 feet, and 30 feet.
   a. Find to the *nearest degree* the measure of the smallest angle.
   b. Using the answer found in part **a**, find to the *nearest square foot* the area of the plot of land.

10. The ladder to the top of the slide at the playground is 6 feet long, and the distance down the slide is 16 feet. If the ladder and the slide make an angle of 95° with each other, what is the distance to the *nearest foot* from the bottom of the ladder to the end of the slide?

11. From points A and B, which are 150 meters apart, a third point, C, is sighted such that m$\angle CAB$ is 42°20′ and m$\angle CBA$ is 81°50′. Find to the *nearest meter* the distance from A to C.

12. Birdsong Nature Trail consists of three straight paths forming a triangle. The first two sections of the trail are 0.5 kilometer and 0.8 kilometer in length and make an angle of 100° with each other. Find to the *nearest tenth* of a kilometer the distance back to the starting point from the end of the second section.

13. A young tree is braced by two wires extending in straight lines from the same point on the trunk of the tree to points on the ground on opposite sides of the tree. The wires are fastened to stakes in the ground 32 inches apart and make angles of 35° and 40° with the ground. Find to the nearest inch the lengths of the wires.

14. A pasture gate has begun to sag so that it is now in the shape of a parallelogram with sides that measure 60 inches and 25 inches and an angle of 95°. Find to the *nearest inch* the length of a board needed to brace the gate along its larger diagonal.

15. From points *A* and *B*, which are 150 meters apart, a third point, *C*, is sighted so that m∠*CAB* = 86°40′ and m∠*CBA* = 28°30′. Find to the *nearest meter* the distance from *B* to *C*.

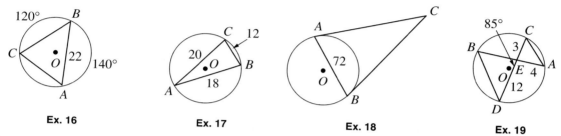

| Ex. 16 | Ex. 17 | Ex. 18 | Ex. 19 |

16. Triangle *ABC* is inscribed in circle *O*. The measure of $\widehat{BC}$ = 120°, the measure of $\widehat{AB}$ = 140°, and *AB* = 22.   **a.** Find *AC* to the *nearest integer*.   **b.** Find the area of △*ABC* to the *nearest integer*.

17. In △*ABC* inscribed in circle *O*, *AB* = 18, *BC* = 12, and *AC* = 20. Find to the *nearest degree* the measures of $\widehat{AB}$, $\widehat{BC}$, and $\widehat{CA}$.

18. From point *C*, two lines are drawn tangent to circle *O* at points *A* and *B*. Chord $\overline{AB}$ is drawn. Points *A* and *B* separate the circle into two arcs whose measures are in the ratio 5:4, and *AB* = 72.
a. Find the measure of ∠*ACB*.   **b.** Find *AC* to the *nearest integer*.
c. Find the area of △*ABC* to the *nearest hundred*.

19. Chords $\overline{AB}$ and $\overline{CD}$ intersect at *E* in circle *O*. The measure of ∠*DEB* is 85°, *DE* = 12, *EC* = 3, and *EA* = 4.   **a.** Find *EB*.   **b.** Find *AC* to the *nearest integer*.   **c.** Find the area of △*DEB* to the *nearest integer*.

20. Quadrilateral *ABCD* is an isosceles trapezoid with diagonal $\overline{BD}$ drawn. The measure of ∠*ADB* is 85°, m∠*DBA* = 20, $\overline{AD} \cong \overline{BC}$, and *DB* = 18.   **a.** Find *BC* to the *nearest integer*.   **b.** Use the answer to part **a** to find the area of trapezoid *ABCD* to the *nearest integer*.

21. From point *A*, the angle of elevation of the top of a building measures 32°10′. From *B*, a point that is 125 feet closer to the building, the angle of elevation at the top of the building measures 46°30′. Find to the *nearest foot* the height of the building.

22. In rhombus *ABCD*, m∠*DAB* = 121°20′ and the length of each side is 20.0.
a. Find to the *nearest tenth* the length of diagonal $\overline{DB}$.
b. Find to the *nearest tenth* the length of diagonal $\overline{AC}$.
c. Using two different methods, find to the *nearest integer* the area of rhombus *ABCD*.

CHAPTER SUMMARY

If P is a point r units from the origin in the coordinate plane on the terminal side of an angle in standard position whose measure is θ, the coordinates of P are $(r\cos\theta, r\sin\theta)$.

When the measures of two sides and an included angle, of three sides, or of two angles and a side of a triangle are known, the ***Law of Cosines*** and the ***Law of Sines*** can be used to find the measures of the other sides and angles.

Law of Cosines: $\quad a^2 = b^2 + c^2 - 2bc\cos A \qquad \cos A = \frac{b^2 + c^2 - a^2}{2bc}$

$$b^2 = a^2 + c^2 - 2ac\cos B \qquad \cos B = \frac{a^2 + c^2 - b^2}{2ac}$$

$$c^2 = a^2 + b^2 - 2ab\cos C \qquad \cos C = \frac{a^2 + b^2 - c^2}{2ab}$$

Law of Sines: $\quad \dfrac{a}{\sin A} = \dfrac{b}{\sin B} = \dfrac{c}{\sin C}$

In $\triangle ABC$:

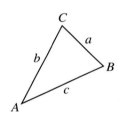

If we know	We can use	To find
$a, b, \mathrm{m}\angle C$	Law of Cosines	c
a, b, c	Law of Cosines	measure of any angle
$a, b, \mathrm{m}\angle A$	Law of Sines	$\mathrm{m}\angle B$ if it exists number of possible triangles
$a, \mathrm{m}\angle A, \mathrm{m}\angle B$	Law of Sines	b

If we know the measures of two sides and the included angle of a triangle, we can find the area of the triangle by using the formula

$$\text{Area of } \triangle ABC = \tfrac{1}{2}\,bc\sin A = \tfrac{1}{2}\,ac\sin B = \tfrac{1}{2}\,ab\sin C$$

An ***angle of elevation*** is an angle between a horizontal line and a line of sight that is raised upward. An ***angle of depression*** is an angle between a horizontal line and a line of sight that is lowered downward.

In right triangle ABC with hypotenuse $\overline{AB}$:

$$\sin A = \frac{BC}{AB}$$

$$\cos A = \frac{AC}{AB}$$

$$\tan A = \frac{BC}{AC}$$

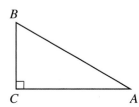

A *vector quantity* has both magnitude and direction. The **vector** that represents the single force equivalent to two applied forces is:

(1) the sum of two forces applied in the same direction,

(2) the difference of two forces applied in opposite directions, or

(3) the diagonal of the parallelogram determined by two forces acting at an angle other than a straight angle.

This vector is called the **resultant**.

VOCABULARY

18-2	Law of Cosines
18-5	Law of Sines
18-6	Ambiguous case
18-7	Vector Resultant
18-8	Angle of elevation Angle of depression

REVIEW EXERCISES WITH OPEN-RESPONSE PROBLEMS

1. In $\triangle ABC$, $b = 12$, $c = 9$, and $\sin B = 0.4$. Find $\sin C$.

2. In $\triangle ABC$, $\sin A = \frac{1}{5}$, $\sin B = \frac{3}{8}$, and $b = 15$. Find a.

3. In $\triangle ABC$, $m\angle A = 30$, $m\angle B = 45$, and $b = 10\sqrt{2}$. Find a.

4. In $\triangle ABC$, $a = 8$, $c = 16$, and $m\angle A = 30$. Find $m\angle C$.

5. In $\triangle ABC$, $a = 5$, $b = 8$, and $m\angle C = 60$. Find c.

6. In $\triangle ABC$, $a = 10$, $b = 4$, and $c = 8$. Find $\cos A$.

7. In $\triangle ABC$, $a = 6$, $c = 2$, and $m\angle B = 120$. Find b.

8. In $\triangle ABC$, $a = 10$, $b = 10\sqrt{3}$, and $c = 10$. Find $m\angle C$.

9. In $\triangle ABC$, $b = 10$, $c = 12$, and $m\angle A = 30$. Find the area of the triangle.

10. Find the area of $\triangle ABC$ if $a = 5$, $b = 3\sqrt{2}$, and $m\angle C = 45$.

11. Find the area of $\triangle ABC$ if $a = 8$, $c = 12$, and $\sin B = \frac{1}{4}$.

12. In right triangle ABC, $m\angle C = 90$, $b = 8$, and $c = 16$. Find the measure of $\angle A$.

13. In right triangle ABC, $m\angle C = 90$, $b = 2\sqrt{2}$, and $c = 4$. Find the measure of $\angle B$.

14. In $\triangle ABC$, $a = 13.7$, $m\angle A = 15°40'$, and $m\angle B = 65°30'$. Find b to the *nearest tenth*.

15. Find to the *nearest degree* the obtuse angle of a parallelogram if the measures of two consecutive sides are 21 and 16 and the measure of the longer diagonal is 28.

16. Two men move a heavy box by pulling on two ropes attached to the box at the same point. The ropes make an angle of 24°30′ with each other, and the applied forces are 15.0 and 21.0 pounds. Find to the *nearest tenth* of a pound the magnitude of the resultant force.

17. Forces of 42 and 53 pounds act on a body so that the angle between the resultant and the larger force is 47°. Find to the *nearest degree* two possible measures of the angle between the resultant and the smaller force.

18. From a point on level ground that is 25 feet from the foot of a flagpole, the angle of elevation of the top of the pole is 62°. Find to the *nearest foot* the height of the flagpole.

19. A signal tower has two lights that are 30 feet apart, one directly above the other. From a boat, the angle of elevation of the lower light is measured to be 14° and the angle of elevation of the upper light is measured to be 32°.
   a. Find to the *nearest foot* the distance from the boat to the lower light.
   b. The boat and the foot of the tower are in the same horizontal plane. Find to the *nearest foot* the distance from the boat to the foot of the tower.

20. Line $\overleftrightarrow{PC}$ is tangent to circle O at C, and secant $\overrightarrow{PAB}$ intersects circle O at A and at B, as shown in the diagram. Chords $\overline{AC}$ and $\overline{BC}$ are drawn. The measure of secant segment $\overline{PB}$ is 18, and the measure of its external segment, $\overline{PA}$, is 8.

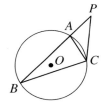

   a. Find the measure of tangent segment $\overline{PC}$.
   b. If m$\overarc{BC}$ is 160, find m$\angle BAC$ and m$\angle CAP$.
   c. Find the measure of $\angle ACP$ to the *nearest degree*.
   d. Find to the *nearest integer* the length of chord $\overline{AC}$.

21. The three sides of a triangular plot of land measure 40.0, 60.0, and 35.0 meters.
   a. Find to the *nearest degree* the measure of the smallest angle between two sides of the plot.
   b. Using the answer from part **a**, find to the nearest 10 *square meters* the area of the plot.

22. Find to the *nearest integer* the radius of a circle if a chord of length 12 intercepts an arc of 42°.

In 23–30, select the *numeral* preceding the expression that best completes the sentence or answers the question.

23. If the measures of two sides of a triangle are to be 16 and 18 and the measure of the angle opposite the shorter of these two sides is to be 30°, then
   (1) one acute triangle can be constructed
   (2) two triangles can be constructed
   (3) no triangle can be constructed
   (4) one right triangle can be constructed

24. If two sides of a triangle are to be 6 and 10 and the measure of the angle opposite the side whose measure is 6 is to be 150°, then
  (1) one obtuse triangle can be constructed
  (2) two triangles can be constructed
  (3) no triangle can be constructed
  (4) one acute triangle can be constructed

25. In $\triangle ABC$, $a = 6$, $c = 6\sqrt{3}$, and $m\angle A = 30$. Then the measure of $\angle C$ is
  (1) 30° only   (2) 60° only   (3) 120° only   (4) 60° or 120°

26. In $\triangle ABC$, if $B = \text{Arc sin } \frac{2}{3}$, $a = 3$, and $b = 2$, then $\triangle ABC$
  (1) must be a right triangle   (2) must be an acute triangle
  (3) must be an obtuse triangle   (4) may be either an acute or an obtuse triangle

27. In $\triangle ABC$, $m\angle A = 40$, $a = 10$, and $b = 5$. Triangle ABC
  (1) must be a right triangle   (2) must be an acute triangle
  (3) must be an obtuse triangle   (4) may be either an acute or an obtuse triangle

28. If, in $\triangle ABC$, $a = 2\sqrt{2}$, $m\angle A = 30$, and $m\angle B = 45$, then b is
  (1) 1   (2) 2   (3) $2\sqrt{2}$ (4) 4

29. In $\triangle ABC$, $a = 4$, $b = 6$, and $c = 8$. What is the value of $\cos C$?
  (1) $-\frac{1}{16}$ (2) $\frac{1}{16}$ (3) $-\frac{1}{4}$ (4) $\frac{1}{4}$

30. In right triangle ABC, $m\angle C = 90$, $a = 12$, and $c = 15$. What is the value of $\sin A$?
  (1) 1   (2) $\frac{4}{5}$ (3) $\frac{3}{5}$ (4) $\frac{5}{4}$

CUMULATIVE REVIEW WITH OPEN-RESPONSE PROBLEMS

1. The length of each side of a square is 8 centimeters. The square is cut along the dotted lines shown in the diagram to form a regular octagon.
  a. What is the length of the side of the octagon?
  b. What is the area of the octagon?

2. The lengths of the diagonals of a rhombus are 12 meters and 18 meters. Find to the *nearest degree* the measure of an acute angle of the rhombus.

3. In the trapezoid $ABCD$, $\overline{AB} \parallel \overline{CD}$, $m\angle A = 90$, $AB = AD = 12$, $DC = 7$.
  a. Find $m\angle B$.
  b. Find the perimeter of the trapezoid.
  c. Find the area of the trapezoid.

4. The vertices of a quadrilateral $ABCD$ are $A(3, 2)$, $B(1, -2)$, $C(7, 0)$, and $D(9, 4)$.
  a. Prove that $ABCD$ is a parallelogram.
  b. Find the coordinates of the point of intersection of the diagonals.

5. The length of a rectangle exceeds three times the width by 3 centimeters and the measure of the diagonal of the rectangle exceeds three times the width by 4 centimeters.

   a. Find the dimensions of the rectangle.

   b. Find the length of a diagonal of the rectangle.

6. Solve for x: $4^x = 8^{x+1}$.

7. Find the exact value of sin (Arc tan (-1)).

8. Simplify the fraction $\dfrac{2 - \dfrac{1}{2x^2}}{2 - \dfrac{1}{x}}$.

9. Solve for x: $\log_3 (x + 3) = 2 + \log_3 (x - 1)$.

10. Find the coordinates of A', the image of $A(3, 1)$ under the compositon $T_{1,-2} \circ D_3$.

11. What is the domain of the function $f(x) = \dfrac{1}{\sqrt{x^2 - 9}}$?

Exploration

   The rectangular coordinate system is commonly used to graph functions. However, other coordinate systems are also used. Research the *polar coordinate system* in which (r, θ) are the coordinates of a point in the plane. Determine the relationship between the rectangular coordinates (x, y) and the polar coordinates (r, θ).

Chapter 19

Trigonometric Equations and Identities

What is a new moon? A crescent moon? A blue moon? To our eyes the moon may appear to differ because what we observe at any given time is the portion of the moon that is lit by the sun. This natural satellite of Earth, however, does not change its shape or mass; the moon is always the same *identical* object, no matter how we view it.

Identities were first studied in Chapter 14. An identity, such as $\sin^2 \theta + \cos^2 \theta = 1$, can be thought of as two different ways of viewing the same quantity, just as moon phases are different ways of viewing the moon. An *identity* contains two equivalent expressions and must be true for all replacements of the variable for which it is defined. By discovering and proving more trigonometric identities in this chapter, we will be able to replace complicated expressions with simpler equivalent ones, and to solve difficult trigonometric equations.

By the way, how does the fact that the moon takes 29 days, 12 hours, 44 minutes, and 2.8 seconds to complete a full revolution about Earth help us to define a blue moon?

19-1 TYPES OF EQUATIONS

In our study of mathematics, we have worked with equations in which the variable represents a real number. That real number may be a trigonometric function value. The set of replacements for the variable that makes the equation true is the solution set of the equation.

An *identity* is an equation whose solution set is the set of all possible replacements of the variable for which each member of the equation is defined.

Algebraic Identities	Trigonometric Identities
$3x + 4x = 7x$	$\sin^2 \theta + \cos^2 \theta = 1$
$\dfrac{5x^2}{x} = 5x \quad (x \neq 0)$	$\dfrac{\cos \theta}{\sin \theta} = \cot \theta \quad (\theta \neq k\pi$ for all integral values of k)

A *conditional equation* is an equation whose solution set does not contain all possible replacements of the variable.

Algebraic Conditional Equations	Trigonometric Conditional Equations
$3x + 4 = 7x$	$2 \sin \theta + 1 = 0$
$\dfrac{x}{3} = x^2$	$\dfrac{\sin \theta}{2} = \sin^2 \theta$

To prove that an equality is *not* an identity, we need to find only one value of the variable for which the statement is not true.

For example, the solution set of $3x + 4 = 7x$ is $\{1\}$ because $3(1) + 4 = 7(1)$, or $7 = 7$. If, however, we choose any value other than 1 as a replacement for x, such as $x = 2$, then $3(2) + 4 \neq 7(2)$, or $10 \neq 14$. Therefore, the equation $3x + 4 = 7x$ is *not* an identity because it is not true for all possible replacements of the variable.

To prove that an equality is an identity, however, it is not practicable to substitute all possible replacements of the variable to show that the statement is always true. In this chapter, we will learn how to use principles of real numbers, valid substitutions, and operations to prove that certain statements are identities.

EXAMPLE

Which of the following three equations is an identity?

(1) $2x + 3 = 5x$ (2) $\sin \theta + \cos \theta = 1$ (3) $2x + 3x = 5x$

Solution   (1) Choose any value other than 1 as a replacement for x.

$$2x + 3 \overset{?}{=} 5x$$

If $x = 2$, then $2(2) + 3 \neq 5(2)$.

Thus, $2x + 3 = 5x$ is *not* an identity.

(2) For $0° \leq \theta \leq 360°$, choose any value as a replacement for θ other than $0°$, $90°$, or $360°$.

$$\sin \theta + \cos \theta \overset{?}{=} 1$$

If $\theta = 30°$, then $\sin 30° + \cos 30° \overset{?}{=} 1$.

$$\frac{1}{2} + \frac{\sqrt{3}}{2} \neq 1$$

Thus, $\sin \theta + \cos \theta = 1$ is *not* an identity.

(3) Choose any value as a replacement for x.

$$2x + 3x \overset{?}{=} 5x$$

If $x = 2$, then $2(2) + 3(2) = 5(2)$ (True)

By the distributive property, $2x + 3x = (2 + 3)x = 5x$. Therefore, the equation is true, not just for $x = 2$, but for all replacements of x. It is proved that $2x + 3x = 5x$ is an identity.

Answer: (3)

EXERCISES WITH OPEN-RESPONSE PROBLEMS

In 1–6, prove that each equation is *not* an identity by giving one value of x that makes the equation false.

1. $x^2 + 1 = (x + 1)^2$

2. $2(x + 1) = 2x + 1$

3. $\frac{3x + 2}{2} = 3x$

4. $\tan x + \cot x = 2$

5. $\sin 2x = 2 \sin x$

6. $\sin x = 1 - \cos x$

In 7–15, state whether each equation is an identity or a conditional equation.

7. $x + 1 = 1 + x$

8. $\sin^2 \theta - 1 = 0$

9. $2x + 1 = 3x$

10. $\tan^2 \theta + 1 = \sec^2 \theta$

11. $3(x + 2) = 3x + 6$

12. $(x + 2)^2 = x^2 + 4$

13. $\frac{\sin \theta}{\cos \theta} = \tan \theta$

14. $\frac{x^2 - 1}{x - 1} = x + 1$

15. $\sin\left(\frac{\pi}{2} - \theta\right) = 1 - \sin \theta$

19-2 BASIC TRIGONOMETRIC IDENTITIES

In Chapter 14, we established eight basic identities involving trigonometric functions. These identities are summarized in the following chart.

Reciprocal Identities	Quotient Identities	Pythagorean Identities
$\sec \theta = \dfrac{1}{\cos \theta}$	$\tan \theta = \dfrac{\sin \theta}{\cos \theta}$	$\cos^2 \theta + \sin^2 \theta = 1$
$\csc \theta = \dfrac{1}{\sin \theta}$	$\cot \theta = \dfrac{\cos \theta}{\sin \theta}$	$1 + \tan^2 \theta = \sec^2 \theta$
$\cot \theta = \dfrac{1}{\tan \theta}$		$\cot^2 \theta + 1 = \csc^2 \theta$

Sometimes, an alternative form of an identity is useful in a proof. For example, let us consider the alternative forms shown in the following chart.

Basic Identity	Alternative Forms		
$\cos^2 \theta + \sin^2 \theta = 1$	$\cos^2 \theta = 1 - \sin^2 \theta$	or	$\sin^2 \theta = 1 - \cos^2 \theta$
$\sec \theta = \dfrac{1}{\cos \theta}$	$\sec \theta \cos \theta = 1$	or	$\cos \theta = \dfrac{1}{\sec \theta}$
$\csc \theta = \dfrac{1}{\sin \theta}$	$\csc \theta \sin \theta = 1$	or	$\sin \theta = \dfrac{1}{\csc \theta}$
$\cot \theta = \dfrac{1}{\tan \theta}$	$\cot \theta \tan \theta = 1$	or	$\tan \theta = \dfrac{1}{\cot \theta}$

By using the eight basic identities or their alternative forms, we can change an expression involving trigonometric functions into an equivalent expression. For example:

$$\frac{\sin^2 \theta}{\cos^2 \theta} = \left(\frac{\sin \theta}{\cos \theta}\right)^2 = \tan^2 \theta$$

Furthermore, the methods we learned to add, subtract, multiply, and divide algebraic expressions can be applied also to trigonometric ones.

Algebraic Examples

1. $x(x + 1) = x^2 + x$

2. $x^2 - 1 = (x - 1)(x + 1)$

3. $\dfrac{1 - \dfrac{1}{b}}{\dfrac{a}{b}} = \left(\dfrac{1 - \dfrac{1}{b}}{\dfrac{a}{b}}\right) \cdot \dfrac{b}{b}$

$= \dfrac{b - 1}{a}$

Trigonometric Examples

1. $\cos \theta \, (\cos \theta + 1) = \cos^2 \theta + \cos \theta$

2. $1 - \sin^2 \theta = (1 - \sin \theta)(1 + \sin \theta)$

3. $\dfrac{1 - \dfrac{1}{\cos \theta}}{\dfrac{\sin \theta}{\cos \theta}} = \left(\dfrac{1 - \dfrac{1}{\cos \theta}}{\dfrac{\sin \theta}{\cos \theta}}\right) \cdot \dfrac{\cos \theta}{\cos \theta}$

$= \dfrac{\cos \theta - 1}{\sin \theta}$

EXAMPLES

1. Express $\sec\theta\cot\theta$ as a single function.

How to Proceed:

Solution:

(1) Use basic identities to express $\sec\theta$ and $\cot\theta$ in terms of $\sin\theta$ and $\cos\theta$.

$$\sec\theta\cot\theta = \frac{1}{\cos\theta}\cdot\frac{\cos\theta}{\sin\theta}$$

(2) Divide the numerator and denominator by the common factor, $\cos\theta$.

$$= \frac{1}{\underset{1}{\cancel{\cos\theta}}}\cdot\frac{\overset{1}{\cancel{\cos\theta}}}{\sin\theta}$$

(3) Use a basic identity to express $\frac{1}{\sin\theta}$ as $\csc\theta$.

$$= \frac{1}{\sin\theta}$$

$$= \csc\theta$$

Answer: $\sec\theta\cot\theta = \csc\theta$

---

2. Show that $(1-\cos\theta)(1+\cos\theta) = \sin^2\theta$.

Solutions **METHOD 1.** Find the product of the binomials. Then, since $\cos^2\theta + \sin^2\theta = 1$, substitute $\cos^2\theta + \sin^2\theta$ for 1, and simplify.

$$(1-\cos\theta)(1+\cos\theta) = 1 - \cos^2\theta$$
$$= (\cos^2\theta + \sin^2\theta) - \cos^2\theta$$
$$(1-\cos\theta)(1+\cos\theta) = \sin^2\theta$$

METHOD 2. Find the product of the binomials. Use an alternative form of the identity $\sin^2\theta + \cos^2\theta = 1$, namely, $\sin^2\theta = 1 - \cos^2\theta$.

$$(1-\cos\theta)(1+\cos\theta) = 1 - \cos^2\theta$$
$$(1-\cos\theta)(1+\cos\theta) = \sin^2\theta$$

EXERCISES WITH OPEN-RESPONSE PROBLEMS

In 1–21, write each expression as a monomial containing a single function or a constant.

1. $1 - \cos^2\theta$

2. $1 - \sin^2\theta$

3. $\tan^2\theta + 1$

4. $\cot^2\theta + 1$

5. $\sin\theta\cot\theta$

6. $\cos\theta\tan\theta$

7. $\sin\theta\sec\theta$

8. $\cos\theta\csc\theta$

9. $\sec\theta\cot\theta\sin\theta$

10. $\cos\theta\tan\theta\csc\theta$

11. $\sin\theta\cot\theta\tan\theta$

12. $\tan\theta\cot\theta\cos\theta$

13. $\sec \theta \sin \theta \csc \theta$

14. $\sec \theta \csc \theta \cos \theta$

15. $\csc \theta \, (1 - \cos^2 \theta)$

16. $\sec \theta \, (1 - \sin^2 \theta)$

17. $\sin \theta \, (\cot^2 \theta + 1)$

18. $\cos \theta \, (\tan^2 \theta + 1)$

19. $\sec \theta \cos \theta - \cos^2 \theta$

20. $\csc \theta \sin \theta - \sin^2 \theta$

21. $\tan \theta \, (\cot \theta + \tan \theta)$

In 22–33, write each expression as a single fraction.

22. $\dfrac{a}{c} + \dfrac{b}{c}$

23. $\dfrac{1}{\cos \theta} + \dfrac{\sin \theta}{\cos \theta}$

24. $\dfrac{1 + a}{b} - \dfrac{a}{b}$

25. $\dfrac{1 + \cos \theta}{\sin \theta} - \dfrac{\cos \theta}{\sin \theta}$

26. $1 - \dfrac{a}{b}$

27. $1 - \dfrac{\sin \theta}{\cos \theta}$

28. $\dfrac{a}{1 - a^2} - \dfrac{1}{1 - a}$

29. $\dfrac{\cos \theta}{1 - \cos^2 \theta} - \dfrac{1}{1 - \cos \theta}$

30. $\dfrac{a}{b} - \dfrac{b}{a}$

31. $\dfrac{\sin \theta}{\cos \theta} - \dfrac{\cos \theta}{\sin \theta}$

32. $\dfrac{1}{a} + \dfrac{1}{a^2}$

33. $\dfrac{1}{\sin \theta} + \dfrac{1}{\sin^2 \theta}$

In 34–39, simplify each complex fraction.

34. $\dfrac{\dfrac{1}{\cos \theta}}{1 - \dfrac{1}{\cos \theta}}$

35. $\dfrac{\dfrac{1}{\cos^2 \theta} - 1}{\dfrac{\sin^2 \theta}{\cos^2 \theta}}$

36. $\dfrac{\dfrac{\sin \theta}{\cos \theta} + \dfrac{\cos \theta}{\sin \theta}}{\dfrac{1}{\sin \theta}}$

37. $\dfrac{\dfrac{1}{\sin \theta} - \dfrac{1}{\cos \theta}}{\dfrac{\cos \theta}{\sin \theta} - \dfrac{\sin \theta}{\cos \theta}}$

38. $\dfrac{\dfrac{1}{\sin \theta \cos \theta}}{\dfrac{1}{\sin \theta} + \dfrac{1}{\cos \theta}}$

39. $\dfrac{1 - \dfrac{1}{\cos \theta}}{1 - \dfrac{1}{\cos^2 \theta}}$

In 40–42, select the *numeral* preceding the expression that best completes each sentence.

40. The expression $\cot \theta \sec \theta$ is equivalent to

(1) $\sin \theta$ (2) $\cos \theta$ (3) $\tan \theta$ (4) $\csc \theta$

41. The expression $(\cos^2 \theta - 1)$ is equivalent to

(1) $\sin^2 \theta$ (2) $\cos^2 \theta$ (3) $-\sin^2 \theta$ (4) $-\cos^2 \theta$

42. The expression $\sin^2 \theta - \cos^2 \theta$ is equivalent to

(1) 1 (2) $(\sin \theta - \cos \theta)^2$

(3) $(1 - \cos^2 \theta)(\sin^2 \theta + 1)$ (4) $(\sin \theta + \cos \theta)(\sin \theta - \cos \theta)$

19-3 PROVING TRIGONOMETRIC IDENTITIES

To prove that an equality is an identity, we need to show that both sides of the equality can be written in the same form. To do this, we use valid substitutions and operations, and follow either of two procedures.

PROCEDURE. To prove that an equality is an identity:

METHOD 1. Transform the expression on one side of the equality (usually the more complicated expression) into the form of the other side.

METHOD 2. Transform both sides of the equality separately into some common form.

In each identity proof that follows, standard algebraic operations and techniques are used to transform expressions involving trigonometric functions.

Simple Substitution

Some identities can be proved by making a substitution based on one or more of the eight basic identities.

IDENTITY PROOF: $\tan^2 \theta + \sin^2 \theta + \cos^2 \theta = \sec^2 \theta$

1. Simplify the more complicated left-hand side of the equation. $\qquad \tan^2 \theta + \sin^2 \theta + \cos^2 \theta = \sec^2 \theta$

First, replace $\cos^2 \theta + \sin^2 \theta$ by 1. $\qquad\qquad \tan^2 \theta + 1 = \sec^2 \theta$

2. Replace $\tan^2 \theta + 1$ by $\sec^2 \theta$. $\qquad\qquad\qquad \sec^2 \theta = \sec^2 \theta$

Since a proof should proceed from a statement that is known to be true to the one that is to be proved, the steps of this proof should really progress in reverse order. However, the form in which the proof is written above is the generally accepted form. This identity is undefined for odd multiples of $\frac{\pi}{2}$.

Products

Some identities are proved by performing an indicated multiplication and simplifying the product that is obtained.

IDENTITY PROOF: $\cos \theta (\sec \theta - \cos \theta) = \sin^2 \theta$

1. Simplify the more complicated left-hand side of the equation. First, perform the indicated multiplication.

$$\cos \theta (\sec \theta - \cos \theta) = \sin^2 \theta$$
$$\cos \theta \sec \theta - \cos^2 \theta =$$

2. Use the reciprocal identity, and simplify.

$$\cos \theta \left(\frac{1}{\cos \theta} \right) - \cos^2 \theta =$$

$$1 - \cos^2 \theta =$$

3. Use the alternative form of the Pythagorean identity.

$$\sin^2 \theta = \sin^2 \theta$$

Note: In proving an identity, *both* sides of the equality are written in the first step. Then, as seen in the proof above, as one side is being transformed, it is not necessary to rewrite the expression on the other side. In the last step, however, *both* the transformed side and the other side are written to show that the identity has been proved.

Factors

Some identities are proved by factoring. This technique is often used to simplify fractions.

☐ IDENTITY PROOF:

$$\frac{\sin^2 \theta}{1 - \cos \theta} = 1 + \cos \theta$$

1. Replace $\sin^2 \theta$ in the more complicated left-hand side of the equality by an expression in terms of $\cos \theta$.

$$\frac{\sin^2 \theta}{1 - \cos \theta} = 1 + \cos \theta$$

$$\frac{1 - \cos^2 \theta}{1 - \cos \theta} =$$

2. Factor the numerator of the fraction.

$$\frac{(1 + \cos \theta)(1 - \cos \theta)}{1 - \cos \theta} =$$

3. Cancel common factors in the numerator and the denominator.

$$\frac{(1 + \cos \theta)(1 - \cos \theta)}{1 - \cos \theta} =$$

$$1 + \cos \theta = 1 + \cos \theta$$

Note: It is incorrect to add terms to both sides or to multiply or divide both sides in order to prove the identity.

For example, it is *not* correct to use the rule that the product of the means equals the product of the extremes in the identity proof just presented. As shown in the incorrect form at the right, the sides of the equation are changed and we are no longer working with the given equality.

Incorrect

$$\frac{\sin^2 \theta}{1 - \cos \theta} = 1 + \cos \theta$$

$$\sin^2 \theta = (1 + \cos \theta)(1 - \cos \theta)$$

$$\sin^2 \theta = 1 - \cos^2 \theta$$

$$\sin^2 \theta = \sin^2 \theta$$

● We prove an identity in the same way as we demonstrate a *check*; that is, we simplify the expression on one side of the equal sign only and never transfer terms from one side of the equality to the other.

Adding Fractions

The quotient and reciprocal identities often transform identities into forms that include fractions. To add fractions, we need a common denominator. This can be seen in the identity proofs that follow.

◻ IDENTITY PROOF: $1 + \sec \theta = \dfrac{\cos \theta + 1}{\cos \theta}$

As shown below, either side of the equality can be transformed to prove an identity.

METHOD 1. Transform the left-hand side.

$$1 + \sec \theta = \frac{\cos \theta + 1}{\cos \theta}$$

$$1 + \frac{1}{\cos \theta} =$$

$$\frac{\cos \theta}{\cos \theta} + \frac{1}{\cos \theta} =$$

$$\frac{\cos \theta + 1}{\cos \theta} = \frac{\cos \theta + 1}{\cos \theta}$$

METHOD 2. Transform the right-hand side.

$$1 + \sec \theta = \frac{\cos \theta + 1}{\cos \theta}$$

$$= \frac{\cos \theta}{\cos \theta} + \frac{1}{\cos \theta}$$

$$1 + \sec \theta = 1 + \sec \theta$$

Sometimes, when proving an identity, we transform the expressions on both sides of the equality to express both as the same form. This process is shown in the following proof.

◻ IDENTITY PROOF: $\tan \theta + \cot \theta = \sec \theta \csc \theta$

$$\tan \theta + \cot \theta \qquad = \qquad \sec \theta \csc \theta$$

$$\frac{\sin \theta}{\cos \theta} + \frac{\cos \theta}{\sin \theta} \qquad\qquad \frac{1}{\cos \theta} \cdot \frac{1}{\sin \theta}$$

$$\frac{\sin \theta}{\sin \theta} \cdot \frac{\sin \theta}{\cos \theta} + \frac{\cos \theta}{\sin \theta} \cdot \frac{\cos \theta}{\cos \theta} \qquad\qquad \frac{1}{\cos \theta \sin \theta}$$

$$\frac{\sin^2 \theta}{\sin \theta \cos \theta} + \frac{\cos^2 \theta}{\sin \theta \cos \theta}$$

$$\frac{\sin^2 \theta + \cos^2 \theta}{\sin \theta \cos \theta}$$

$$\frac{1}{\sin \theta \cos \theta} \qquad = \qquad \frac{1}{\sin \theta \cos \theta}$$

Note: By showing that both sides of the equality reduce to a common form, we have proved the identity. If we wish to show that the left-hand side can be transformed into the form given on the right, however, we can now simply reverse the steps taken on the right and place them at the left. In other words, we add these steps to the identity just shown:

$$\frac{1}{\sin \theta \cos \theta}$$

$$\frac{1}{\cos \theta} \cdot \frac{1}{\sin \theta}$$

$$\sec \theta \csc \theta \qquad = \qquad \sec \theta \csc \theta$$

Simplifying Fractions

A fraction can be simplified in various ways, as illustrated in the following proof.

☐ IDENTITY PROOF: $\dfrac{\sec \theta}{\csc \theta} = \tan \theta$

METHOD 1

The expression on the left is changed to a complex fraction. To clear the denominators, the complex fraction is multiplied by $\dfrac{\sin \theta \cos \theta}{\sin \theta \cos \theta}$, which is a form of the identity element 1.

$$\frac{\sec \theta}{\csc \theta} = \tan \theta$$

$$\frac{\dfrac{1}{\cos \theta}}{\dfrac{1}{\sin \theta}} =$$

$$\frac{\dfrac{1}{\cos \theta}}{\dfrac{1}{\sin \theta}} \cdot \frac{\sin \theta \cos \theta}{\sin \theta \cos \theta} =$$

$$\frac{\sin \theta}{\cos \theta} =$$

$$\tan \theta = \tan \theta$$

METHOD 2

The fraction on the left is expressed as the product of the numerator times the reciprocal of the denominator. This method often is used when the denominator is a monomial.

$$\frac{\sec \theta}{\csc \theta} = \tan \theta$$

$$\sec \theta \cdot \frac{1}{\csc \theta} =$$

$$\frac{1}{\cos \theta} \cdot \sin \theta =$$

$$\frac{\sin \theta}{\cos \theta} =$$

$$\tan \theta = \tan \theta$$

Guidelines for Identity Proofs

There are no rules that can be applied to prove all identities, but the following basic principles can aid in finding a proof.

1. Start with the more complicated side of the equality, and write this expression in simpler terms. If the expressions on both sides are complicated, work with one side of the equality until no further simplification is evident. Then, work with the expression on the other side.

2. Transform different functions into the same function. It is often useful to express each side in terms of sines and cosines.

3. Simplify complex fractions. Look for a common factor in the numerator and denominator of a fraction in order to reduce the fraction to lowest terms.

EXAMPLES

1. Prove the identity $\dfrac{\sin \theta}{1 + \cos \theta} = \csc \theta - \cot \theta$.

How to Proceed:	Identity Proof:
(1) Express the right-hand member in terms of $\sin \theta$ and $\cos \theta$.	$\dfrac{\sin \theta}{1 + \cos \theta} = \csc \theta - \cot \theta$
	$= \dfrac{1}{\sin \theta} - \dfrac{\cos \theta}{\sin \theta}$
(2) Add the fractions.	$= \dfrac{1 - \cos \theta}{\sin \theta}$
(3) The left-hand expression contains $(1 + \cos \theta)$ in the denominator. Multiply the right-hand expression by $\dfrac{1 + \cos \theta}{1 + \cos \theta}$.	$= \dfrac{(1 - \cos \theta)}{\sin \theta} \cdot \dfrac{(1 + \cos \theta)}{(1 + \cos \theta)}$
(4) At the right, the product $(1 - \cos \theta)(1 + \cos \theta)$ equals $1 - \cos^2 \theta$, or $\sin^2 \theta$.	$= \dfrac{1 - \cos^2 \theta}{\sin \theta \,(1 + \cos \theta)}$
	$= \dfrac{\sin^2 \theta}{\sin \theta \,(1 + \cos \theta)}$
(5) Simplify $\dfrac{\sin^2 \theta}{\sin \theta}$.	$\dfrac{\sin \theta}{1 + \cos \theta} = \dfrac{\sin \theta}{1 + \cos \theta}$

2. For what values of θ is the identity in Example 1 undefined?

Solution

$$\text{The identity is } \dfrac{\sin \theta}{1 + \cos \theta} = \csc \theta - \cot \theta$$

$$\text{or} \quad \dfrac{\sin \theta}{1 + \cos \theta} = \dfrac{1}{\sin \theta} - \dfrac{\cos \theta}{\sin \theta}.$$

The left-hand expression is undefined when $1 + \cos \theta = 0$, or $\cos \theta = -1$. This occurs when, in degree measure, $\theta = 180° + 360°k$, where k is any integer, and when, in radians, $\theta = \pi + 2k\pi$ for all integral values of k.	The right-hand expression is undefined when $\sin \theta = 0$. This occurs when, in degree measure, $\theta = 0°, 180°, 360°$, and so on, or when $\theta = 180°k$, where k is any integer, and when, in radians, $\theta = k\pi$ for all integral values of k.

To satisfy all terms in the identity, we use the more restrictive definition shown for the right-hand expression.

Answer: The identity is undefined in degree measure for all multiples of 180°, and in radian measure for all multiples of π.

EXERCISES WITH OPEN-RESPONSE PROBLEMS

In 1–36, prove that each equation is an identity.

1. $\sin \theta \cot \theta = \cos \theta$

2. $\cos \theta \tan \theta = \sin \theta$

3. $\sec \theta \cot \theta = \csc \theta$

4. $\csc \theta \tan \theta = \sec \theta$

5. $\cos \theta (\sec \theta - \cos \theta) = \sin^2 \theta$

6. $\sin \theta (\csc \theta - \sin \theta) = \cos^2 \theta$

7. $\sec \theta (\sec \theta - \cos \theta) = \tan^2 \theta$

8. $\csc \theta (\csc \theta - \sin \theta) = \cot^2 \theta$

9. $\tan^2 \theta (1 + \cot^2 \theta) = \sec^2 \theta$

10. $\sin^2 \theta (\csc^2 \theta - 1) = \cos^2 \theta$

11. $\cos^2 \theta (\sec^2 \theta - 1) = \sin^2 \theta$

12. $\sec^2 \theta (1 - \cos^2 \theta) = \tan^2 \theta$

13. $\sec \theta \sin \theta + \csc \theta \cos \theta = \tan \theta + \cot \theta$

14. $(\sin \theta + \cos \theta)^2 = 1 + 2 \sin \theta \cos \theta$

15. $\dfrac{\sin \theta - \cos \theta}{\sin \theta} = 1 - \cot \theta$

16. $\dfrac{\sin \theta - \cos \theta}{\cos \theta} = \tan \theta - 1$

17. $\dfrac{\cos^2 \theta - \cos \theta}{\cos \theta} = \cos \theta - 1$

18. $\dfrac{\cos \theta - 1}{\cos^2 \theta} = \sec \theta - \sec^2 \theta$

19. $\dfrac{\sec \theta}{\tan \theta} = \csc \theta$

20. $\dfrac{\csc \theta}{\cot \theta} = \sec \theta$

21. $\dfrac{\tan \theta}{\cot \theta} + 1 = \sec^2 \theta$

22. $\dfrac{\cot \theta}{\tan \theta} + 1 = \csc^2 \theta$

23. $\dfrac{\sin \theta}{\cot \theta} + \cos \theta = \sec \theta$

24. $\dfrac{\sin^2 \theta}{1 + \cos \theta} = 1 - \cos \theta$

25. $\dfrac{\sin \theta}{1 + \cos \theta} = \dfrac{1 - \cos \theta}{\sin \theta}$

26. $\dfrac{1 - \sec^2 \theta}{1 + \sec \theta} = \dfrac{\cos \theta - 1}{\cos \theta}$

27. $\dfrac{1 - \csc^2 \theta}{1 - \csc \theta} = \dfrac{1 + \sin \theta}{\sin \theta}$

28. $\dfrac{1 + \sec \theta}{1 - \sec^2 \theta} = \dfrac{\cos \theta}{\cos \theta - 1}$

29. $\sin^4 \theta - \cos^4 \theta = \sin^2 \theta - \cos^2 \theta$

30. $\sec^4 \theta - \tan^4 \theta = \sec^2 \theta + \tan^2 \theta$

31. $\dfrac{1 + 2 \sin \theta \cos \theta}{(\sin \theta + \cos \theta)^2} = 1$

32. $\dfrac{(1 + \sin \theta)^2}{\cos^2 \theta} = \dfrac{1 + \sin \theta}{1 - \sin \theta}$

33. $\sin^2 \theta + \sin^2 \theta \tan^2 \theta = \tan^2 \theta$

34. $\sec^2 \theta + \csc^2 \theta = \sec^2 \theta \csc^2 \theta$

35. $\dfrac{1}{1 + \cos \theta} + \dfrac{1}{1 - \cos \theta} = 2 \csc^2 \theta$

36. $\dfrac{1}{1 + \sin \theta} + \dfrac{1}{1 - \sin \theta} = 2 \sec^2 \theta$

37. a. Prove the identity $\dfrac{(1 - \cos x)(1 + \cos x)}{\sin x} = \sin x$.

  b. For what values of x is the identity proved in part **a** undefined?

38. a. Prove the identity $(1 - \cos \theta)(1 + \sec \theta) = \sin \theta \tan \theta$.

  b. For what values of θ is the identity proved in part **a** undefined?

19-4 COSINE OF THE DIFFERENCE OF TWO ANGLE MEASURES

Which of the following two equalities, if either, is an identity?

$$\cos (A - B) = \cos A - \cos B$$

$$\cos (A - B) = \cos A \cos B + \sin A \sin B$$

As a first step, let us test each equality by selecting replacements for the variables A and B. Let $A = 60°$ and $B = 0°$.

Test equality 1:

$$\cos (A - B) \overset{?}{=} \cos A - \cos B$$

$$\cos (60° - 0°) \overset{?}{=} \cos 60° - \cos 0°$$

$$\cos 60° \overset{?}{=} \cos 60° - \cos 0°$$

$$\frac{1}{2} \overset{?}{=} \frac{1}{2} - 1$$

$$\frac{1}{2} \neq -\frac{1}{2} \qquad \text{(Not an identity)}$$

This first equality is *not* an identity because this equality is not true for all replacements of the variables.

Test equality 2:

$$\cos (A - B) \overset{?}{=} \cos A \cos B + \sin A \sin B$$

$$\cos (60° - 0°) \overset{?}{=} \cos 60° \cos 0° + \sin 60° \sin 0°$$

$$\cos 60° \overset{?}{=} \cos 60° \cos 0° + \sin 60° \sin 0°$$

$$\frac{1}{2} \overset{?}{=} \frac{1}{2} \quad (1) \; + \; \frac{\sqrt{3}}{2} \quad (0)$$

$$\frac{1}{2} \overset{?}{=} \frac{1}{2} + 0$$

$$\frac{1}{2} = \frac{1}{2} \qquad \text{(True)}$$

Although the second equality is true for the chosen replacements, we are still not certain that this equality is an identity. Other replacements for the variable may show that the equality is not always true.

We can, however, apply some mathematical principles and definitions to prove that this second equality is an identity.

☐   IDENTITY PROOF: $\cos (A - B) = \cos A \cos B + \sin A \sin B$

1. Consider a unit circle whose center is at the origin. Let A and B be the measures of two angles in standard position whose terminal rays intersect the unit circle at points P and Q, respectively. Therefore, the coordinates of point P are $(\cos A, \sin A)$, and the coordinates of point Q are $(\cos B, \sin B)$. The measure of $\angle QOP$ is $(A - B)$.

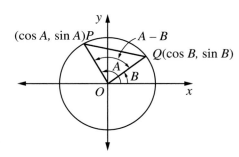

2. Express $(PQ)^2$ by using the *Law of Cosines*.

Consider $\overline{PQ}$ as the side of $\triangle POQ$ that is opposite the angle whose measure is $(A - B)$. Since sides $\overline{OP}$ and $\overline{OQ}$ of $\triangle POQ$ are also radii of a unit circle, $OP = 1$ and $OQ = 1$. Therefore:

$$(PQ)^2 = (OP)^2 + (OQ)^2 - 2(OP)(OQ) \cos (A - B)$$
$$= 1^2 + 1^2 - 2(1)(1) \cos (A - B)$$
$$(PQ)^2 = 1 + 1 - 2 \cos (A - B)$$

3. Express $(PQ)^2$, the square of distance PQ, by using the *distance formula*.

Let $Q(\cos B, \sin B) = (x_1, y_1)$ and $P(\cos A, \sin A) = (x_2, y_2)$. Substitute these coordinate values in the formula, square each binomial, and group terms. Begin by squaring $d = \sqrt{(x_2 - x_1)^2 + (y_2 - y_1)^2}$.

$$d^2 = (x_2 - x_1)^2 + (y_2 - y_1)^2$$
$$(PQ)^2 = (\cos A - \cos B)^2 + (\sin A - \sin B)^2$$
$$= \cos^2 A - 2 \cos A \cos B + \cos^2 B + \sin^2 A - 2 \sin A \sin B + \sin^2 B$$
$$= (\cos^2 A + \sin^2 A) + (\cos^2 B + \sin^2 B) - 2 \cos A \cos B - 2 \sin A \sin B$$
$$(PQ)^2 = 1 + 1 - 2(\cos A \cos B + \sin A \sin B)$$

4. From steps 2 and 3, there are two expressions for $(PQ)^2$, each in terms of the function values of A and B. These two expressions are equal.

$$(PQ)^2 = (PQ)^2$$
$$1 + 1 - 2 \cos (A - B) = 1 + 1 - 2 (\cos A \cos B + \sin A \sin B)$$
$$-2 \cos (A - B) = - 2 (\cos A \cos B + \sin A \sin B)$$
$$\mathbf{\cos (A - B) =} \qquad \mathbf{\cos A \cos B + \sin A \sin B}$$

This equation, which expresses the cosine of the difference of two angle measures, $(A - B)$, in terms of the sines and cosines of the individual angle measures, A and B, is an identity since it is true for all replacements of the variables.

To illustrate this identity, let us use known values for A and B. For example:

☐   Show that $\cos 30° = \frac{\sqrt{3}}{2}$ by finding $\cos (A - B)$ when $A = 90°$ and $B = 60°$.

How to Proceed:	*Solution:*
(1) Write the identity.	$\cos (A - B) = \cos A \cos B \quad + \sin A \quad \sin B$
(2) Substitute the given values.	$\cos (90° - 60°) = \cos 90° \cos 60° + \sin 90° \sin 60°$
(3) Substitute function values on the right-hand side, and simplify both sides.	$\cos 30° = \quad 0 \quad \left(\frac{1}{2}\right) + \quad 1 \quad \left(\frac{\sqrt{3}}{2}\right)$ $= 0 + \frac{\sqrt{3}}{2}$ $\cos 30° = \frac{\sqrt{3}}{2}$

We may also use the procedure just demonstrated to find *exact* function values for many other angles whose values have not yet been determined. For example:

☐   Determine the exact value of cos 15° by finding cos $(A - B)$ when $A = 45°$ and $B = 30°$.

$$\cos (A - B) = \cos A \cos B + \sin A \sin B$$

$$\cos (45° - 30°) = \cos 45° \cos 30° + \sin 45° \sin 30°$$

$$\cos 15° = \frac{\sqrt{2}}{2} \cdot \frac{\sqrt{3}}{2} + \frac{\sqrt{2}}{2} \cdot \frac{1}{2}$$

$$= \frac{\sqrt{6}}{4} + \frac{\sqrt{2}}{4} = \frac{\sqrt{6} + \sqrt{2}}{4}$$

A rational approximation for the exact function value $\frac{\sqrt{6} + \sqrt{2}}{4}$ can be obtained by evaluating this expression on a calculator.

Enter: (| 2nd | √ 6) | + | 2nd | √ 2)) | ÷ 4
ENTER

Display: .9659258263

As a final check, use the calculator to evaluate cos 15° directly.

Enter: COS | 15 | ENTER
Display: .9659258263

Since these two entries produce the same display, we are assured that $\frac{\sqrt{6} + \sqrt{2}}{4}$ is the exact function value of cos 15°.

Answer: $\cos 15° = \dfrac{\sqrt{6} + \sqrt{2}}{4}$

EXAMPLES

1. Use the identity for the cosine of the difference of two angle measures to prove that $\cos (180° - x) = -\cos x$.

How to Proceed:	*Solution:*
(1) Write the identity.	$\cos (A - B) = \cos A \cos B + \sin A \sin B$
(2) Substitute 180° for A and x for B.	$\cos (180° - x) = \cos 180° \cos x + \sin 180° \sin x$
(3) Substitute the values of sin 180° and cos 180°, and simplify.	$= -1 \cdot \cos x + 0 \cdot \sin x$
	$= -\cos x + 0$
	$\cos (180° - x) = -\cos x$

2. If $\sin A$ is $\frac{3}{5}$ and $\angle A$ is in Quadrant II, and $\cos B = \frac{5}{13}$ and $\angle B$ is in Quadrant I, find $\cos (A - B)$.

Solution   (1) To use the identity for $\cos (A - B)$, we must know the sine and cosine values of both A and B. We will use basic identities to find the required values.

$$\sin^2 A + \cos^2 A = 1 \qquad\qquad \sin^2 B + \cos^2 B = 1$$

$$\left(\tfrac{3}{5}\right)^2 + \cos^2 A = 1 \qquad\qquad \sin^2 B + \left(\tfrac{5}{13}\right)^2 = 1$$

$$\tfrac{9}{25} + \cos^2 A = 1 \qquad\qquad \sin^2 B + \tfrac{25}{169} = 1$$

$$\cos^2 A = 1 - \tfrac{9}{25} = \tfrac{16}{25} \qquad\qquad \sin^2 B = 1 - \tfrac{25}{169} = \tfrac{144}{169}$$

$$\cos A = -\tfrac{4}{5} \qquad\qquad\qquad \sin B = \tfrac{12}{13}$$

Since $\angle A$ is in Quadrant II, $\cos A$ is negative. | Since $\angle B$ is in Quadrant I, $\sin B$ is positive.

(2) Write the identity for $\cos (A - B)$, substitute known values, and simplify.

$$\cos (A - B) = \cos A \cos B + \sin A \sin B$$

$$= -\tfrac{4}{5} \cdot \tfrac{5}{13} \quad + \tfrac{3}{5} \cdot \tfrac{12}{13} \quad = -\tfrac{20}{65} + \tfrac{36}{65}$$

$$\cos (A - B) = \tfrac{16}{65}$$

Alternative Solution   (1) Use right triangles, the Pythagorean Theorem, and directed distance to find the values of $\cos A$ and $\sin B$. In Quadrant II, x is negative.

The right triangles may be shown in a unit circle. | The right triangles in the unit circle may be dilated.

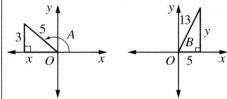

Since $\sin A = \frac{3}{5}$, | Since $\cos B = \frac{5}{13}$, | Here, $x = -4$, and | Here, $y = 12$, and

$x = \cos A = -\frac{4}{5}.$ | $y = \sin B = \frac{12}{13}.$ | $\cos A = -\frac{4}{5}.$ | $\sin B = \frac{12}{13}.$

(2) Using the values found, perform step 2 of the solution above.

Answer: $\cos (A - B) = \frac{16}{65}$

EXERCISES WITH OPEN-RESPONSE PROBLEMS

1. Copy and complete the identity: $\cos(x - y) = \underline{\hspace{1cm}}$.

2. Copy and complete the identity: $\cos(\theta - \phi) = \underline{\hspace{1cm}}$.

3. Demonstrate that $\cos 0° = 1$:   **a.** by using $\cos(60° - 60°) = \cos 60° \cos 60° + \sin 60° \sin 60°$
   b. by using $\cos(45° - 45°)$

4. **a.** Find the exact function value of $\cos 105°$ by using $\cos(135° - 30°)$.
   b. Evaluate the function value from part **a** by using a calculator.
   c. Evaluate $\cos 105°$ directly by using a calculator.
   d. Are the rational approximations found in parts **b** and **c** the same?

5. **a.** Find the exact function value of $\cos 165°$ by using $\cos(225° - 60°)$.
   b. Evaluate, by using a calculator: (*1*) the function value from part **a**   (*2*) $\cos 165°$

6. **a.** Find the exact function value of $\cos(-15°)$ by using $\cos(30° - 45°)$.
   b. Find the exact function value of $\cos(-15°)$ by using $\cos(45° - 60°)$.
   c. Are the function values found in parts **a** and **b** the same?
   d. Evaluate, by using a calculator: (*1*) the function value from part **a**   (*2*) $\cos(-15°)$

In 7–10, use the identity for $\cos(A - B)$ to prove each statement.

7. $\cos(270° - x) = -\sin x$

8. $\cos(90° - x) = \sin x$

9. $\cos(360° - x) = \cos x$

10. $\cos(45° - x) = \frac{\sqrt{2}}{2}(\cos x + \sin x)$

11. If $\sin A = \frac{4}{5}$, $\sin B = \frac{4}{5}$, $\angle A$ is in Quadrant II, and $\angle B$ is in Quadrant I, find the value of $\cos(A - B)$.

12. If $\sin A = -\frac{12}{13}$, $\angle A$ is in Quadrant III, $\sin B = \frac{4}{5}$, and $\angle B$ is in Quadrant II, find:

   a. $\cos(A - B)$ **b.** $\cos(B - A)$

13. If $\sin A = -\frac{1}{2}$, $\cos B = -\frac{1}{4}$, and both $\angle A$ and $\angle B$ are in Quadrant III, find: **a.** $\cos(A - B)$

   b. $\cos(B - A)$

14. If x is the measure of a positive acute angle and $\cos x = \frac{3}{5}$, find the value of $\cos(180° - x)$.

15. If x is the measure of a positive acute angle and $\sin x = 0.8$, find the value of $\cos\left(\frac{\pi}{2} - x\right)$.

In 16–18, select the *numeral* preceding the expression that best completes each sentence.

16. The expression $\cos 30° \cos 12° + \sin 30° \sin 12°$ is equivalent to
   (1) $\cos 42°$ (2) $\cos 18°$ (3) $\cos 42° + \sin 42°$ (4) $\cos^2 42° + \sin^2 42°$

17. The expression $\cos(\pi - x)$ is equivalent to
   (1) $\sin x$ (2) $-\sin x$ (3) $\cos x$ (4) $-\cos x$

18. If $\cos(A - 30°) = \frac{1}{2}$, then the measure of $\angle A$ may be

   (1) $30°$ (2) $60°$ (3) $90°$ (4) $120°$

19-5 COSINE OF THE SUM OF TWO ANGLE MEASURES

The identity $\cos (A - B) = \cos A \cos B + \sin A \sin B$ makes it possible for us to derive many other useful identities, some of which are already familiar. Since an identity is true for all replacements of the variables for which the terms are defined, we can assign special values to A or B or to both.

☐ IDENTITY PROOF: $\cos (90° - B) = \sin B$

Use the identity $\cos (A - B) = \cos A \cos B + \sin A \sin B$, and let $A = 90°$.

Then: $\cos (90° - B) = \cos 90° \cos B + \sin 90° \sin B$

$$= 0 \cdot \cos B \quad\quad + 1 \cdot \sin B$$

$$= 0 + \sin B$$

$$\cos (90° - B) = \sin B$$

☐ IDENTITY PROOF: $\cos A = \sin (90° - A)$

Use the identity $\cos (90° - B) = \sin B$, and let $B = 90° - A$.

Then: $\cos (90° - (90° - A)) = \sin (90° - A)$

$$\cos (90° - 90° + A) = \sin (90° - A)$$

$$\cos A = \sin (90° - A)$$

In Chapter 14, the two identities just proved were derived when A and B were the measures of acute angles. These identities were the basis of the definitions of cofunctions:

$$\boxed{\cos A = \sin (90° - A)} \quad \text{and} \quad \boxed{\sin B = \cos (90° - B)}$$

These identities are true, however, for *all* replacements of the variables, not just for values that are the measures of acute angles.

For example, let $A = 120°$.

Then: $\cos A = \sin (90° - A)$
$\cos 120° = \sin (90° - 120°)$
$\cos 120° = \sin (-30°)$

$$-\tfrac{1}{2} = -\tfrac{1}{2}$$

For example, let $B = 135°$.

Then: $\sin B = \cos (90° - B)$
$\sin 135° = \cos (90° - 135°)$
$\sin 135° = \cos (-45°)$

$$\frac{\sqrt{2}}{2} = \frac{\sqrt{2}}{2}$$

The next two proofs involve $-\theta$, which is the opposite of an angle measure θ.

☐   IDENTITY PROOF: $\cos(-\theta) = \cos\theta$

Use the identity $\cos(A - B) = \cos A \cos B + \sin A \sin B$, and let $A = 0°$ and $B = \theta$.

Then: $\cos(0° - \theta) = \cos 0° \cos\theta + \sin 0° \sin\theta$

$$\cos(-\theta) = 1 \cdot \cos\theta \quad + 0 \cdot \sin\theta$$

$$= \cos\theta + 0$$

$$\cos(-\theta) = \cos\theta$$

☐   IDENTITY PROOF: $\sin(-\theta) = -\sin\theta$

Use the identity $\sin B = \cos(90° - B)$, and let $B = -\theta$.

Then: $\sin(-\theta) = \cos(90° - (-\theta))$

$$= \cos(90° + \theta)$$

$$= \cos(\theta + 90°)$$

$$= \cos(\theta - (-90°))$$

$$= \cos\theta \cos(-90°) + \sin\theta \sin(-90°)$$

$$= \cos\theta \cdot (0) + \sin\theta \cdot (-1)$$

$$= 0 - \sin\theta$$

$$\sin(-\theta) = -\sin\theta$$

The two identities just proved are illustrated in the following diagrams, each of which consists of a unit circle.

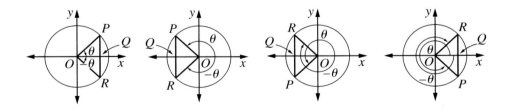

In each of the four diagrams, we observe that:

$$\sin\theta = QP \qquad\qquad \cos\theta = OQ$$

$$\sin(-\theta) = QR \qquad\qquad \cos(-\theta) = OQ$$

$$QR = -QP \qquad\qquad OQ = OQ$$

$$\boxed{\sin(-\theta) = -\sin\theta} \quad \boxed{\cos(-\theta) = \cos\theta}$$

We can use the identity for the cosine of the *difference* of two angle measures, along with the two identities just proved, to find an identity for the *sum* of two angle measures.

☐   IDENTITY PROOF: $\cos (A + B) = \cos A \cos B - \sin A \sin B$

$$\cos (A + B) = \cos (A - (-B))$$
$$= \cos A \cos (-B) + \sin A \sin (-B)$$
$$= \cos A \cos B + \sin A (-\sin B)$$
$$\mathbf{\cos (A + B) = \cos A \cos B - \sin A \sin B}$$

To illustrate the truth of this identity, let us use known values for A and B. For example:

☐   Show that $\cos 90° = 0$ by using $\cos (60° + 30°)$.

How to Proceed:	*Solution:*
(1) Write the identity.	$\cos (A + B) = \cos A \cos B \quad - \sin A \sin B$
(2) Substitute the given values.	$\cos (60° + 30°) = \cos 60° \cos 30° - \sin 60° \sin 30°$
(3) Simplify.	$\cos 90° = \frac{1}{2} \cdot \frac{\sqrt{3}}{2} \quad - \frac{\sqrt{3}}{2} \cdot \frac{1}{2}$
	$= \frac{\sqrt{3}}{4} - \frac{\sqrt{3}}{4}$
	$\cos 90° = 0$

EXAMPLES

1. Find the exact value of $\cos 45° \cos 15° - \sin 45° \sin 15°$.

Solution   Use the identity for the cosine of the sum of two angle measures:

$$\cos 45° \cos 15° - \sin 45° \sin 15° = \cos (45° + 15°)$$
$$= \cos 60° \qquad = \frac{1}{2} \text{ or } 0.5$$

Alternative Solution   *Enter:*

Display: [.5]

Answer: $\frac{1}{2}$ or 0.5

2. a. Find the exact value of cos 75° by using cos (45° + 30°).
  b. Check, by using a calculator, that the function value found equals cos 75°.

Solutions   **a.** Write the general identity, substitute given values, and simplify.

$$\cos (A - B) = \cos A \cos B \quad - \sin A \sin B$$

$$\cos (45° + 30°) = \cos 45° \cos 30° \quad - \sin 45° \sin 30°$$

$$\cos 75° = \frac{\sqrt{2}}{2} \cdot \frac{\sqrt{3}}{2} \quad - \frac{\sqrt{2}}{2} \cdot \frac{1}{2}$$

$$= \frac{\sqrt{6}}{4} - \frac{\sqrt{2}}{4}$$

$$\cos 75° = \frac{\sqrt{6} - \sqrt{2}}{4} \quad Answer$$

b. Evaluate $\frac{\sqrt{6} - \sqrt{2}}{4}$.

Enter: (2nd √ 6) −
  2nd √ 2))
  ÷ 4 ENTER

Display: .2588190451

Evaluate cos 75°.

Enter: COS 75 ENTER

Display: .2588190451

The equal values in the two displays confirm that $\cos 75° = \frac{\sqrt{6} - \sqrt{2}}{4}$.

EXERCISES WITH OPEN-RESPONSE PROBLEMS

1. Copy and complete the identity: cos (x + y) = _____.
2. Copy and complete the identity: cos (θ + φ) = _____.
3. Demonstrate that cos 180° = −1:
   a. by using cos (30° + 150°)   **b.** by using cos (135° + 45°)   **c.** by using cos (60° + 120°)
4. **a.** Find the exact function value of cos 105° by using cos (45° + 60°).
   b. Check, by using a calculator, that the function value found in part **a** equals cos 105°.
5. **a.** Find the exact function value of cos 195° by using cos (135° + 60°).
   b. Find the exact function value of cos 195° by using cos (45° + 150°).
   c. *Without* using an identity rule, write the exact function value of cos (90° + 105°).
   d. Check, by using a calculator, that the function value written in part **c** is equal to cos 195°.

In 6–9, use the identity for cos (A + B) to prove each statement.

6. $\cos (\pi + x) = -\cos x$

7. $\cos \left(\frac{\pi}{2} + x \right) = -\sin x$

8. $\cos \left(\frac{\pi}{4} + x \right) = \frac{\sqrt{2}}{2} (\cos x - \sin x)$

9. $\cos \left(\frac{3\pi}{2} + x \right) = \sin x$

10. If $\sin x = \frac{3}{5}$ and x is the measure of a positive acute angle, find the value of $\cos (x + 180°)$.

11. If $\sin A = \frac{5}{13}$, $\sin B = \frac{5}{13}$, $\angle A$ is in Quadrant II, and $\angle B$ is in Quadrant I, find the value of $\cos (A + B)$.

In 12–16, select the *numeral* preceding the expression that best completes each sentence.

12. If $\cos \theta = -0.6$, then $\cos (-\theta)$ is equal to
   (1) 0.6   (2) -0.6 (3) 0.8   (4) -0.8

13. If $\sin (90° - x) = \frac{1}{2}$, then $\cos x$ is equal to

   (1) $\frac{1}{2}$ (2) $-\frac{1}{2}$ (3) $\frac{\sqrt{3}}{2}$ (4) $-\frac{\sqrt{3}}{2}$

14. If $\sin (-A) = \frac{3}{5}$, then $\sin A$ is equal to

   (1) $\frac{4}{5}$ (2) $-\frac{4}{5}$ (3) $\frac{3}{5}$ (4) $-\frac{3}{5}$

15. The expression $\cos (90° + \theta)$ is equivalent to
   (1) $\sin \theta$ (2) $-\sin \theta$ (3) $\cos \theta$ (4) $-\cos \theta$
16. The value of $(\cos 67°30')(\cos 22°30') - (\sin 67°30')(\sin 22°30')$ is
   (1) 1   (2) $\frac{\sqrt{2}}{2}$ (3) $-\frac{\sqrt{2}}{2}$ (4) 0

17. If $\sin A = \frac{3}{5}$, $\angle A$ is in Quadrant I, $\cos B = -\frac{5}{13}$, and $\angle B$ is in Quadrant II, find:

   a. $\cos (A + B)$ **b.** $\cos (-B)$ **c.** $\sin (90° - A)$ **d.** $\sin (-A)$

18. If $\sin X = -\frac{1}{3}$, x is the measure of an angle in Quadrant III, $\cos y = -\frac{1}{5}$, and y is the measure of

   an angle in Quadrant II, find:
   a. $\cos (x + y)$ **b.** $\cos (-x)$ **c.** $\cos (90° - x)$

19-6 SINE OF THE SUM OR DIFFERENCE OF ANGLE MEASURES

We can combine the identities that we learned in Section 19-5 to find identities for the sine of the sum of two angle measures and for the sine of the difference of two angle measures.

☐   IDENTITY PROOF: $\sin (A + B) = \sin A \cos B + \cos A \sin B$

Use the identity $\sin \theta = \cos (90° - \theta)$, and let $\theta = A + B$.

Then: $\sin (A + B) = \cos (90° - (A + B))$

$= \cos (90° - A - B)$

$= \cos ((90° - A) - B)$

$= \cos (90° - A) \cos B + \sin (90° - A) \sin B$

$$\sin (A + B) = \sin A \cos B + \cos A \sin B$$

We can demonstrate this identity using familiar function values. For example:

☐   Show that $\sin 90° = 1$ by using $\sin (60° + 30°)$.

$$\sin (A + B) = \sin A \cos B \quad + \cos A \sin B$$

$$\sin (60° + 30°) = \sin 60° \cos 30° + \cos 60° \sin 30°$$

$$\sin 90° = \frac{\sqrt{3}}{2} \cdot \frac{\sqrt{3}}{2} \quad + \frac{1}{2} \cdot \frac{1}{2}$$

$$= \frac{3}{4} \quad\quad + \frac{1}{4}$$

$$\sin 90° = 1$$

☐   IDENTITY PROOF: $\sin (A - B) = \sin A \cos B - \cos A \sin B$

Use the identity proved above and written in the form $\sin (x + y)$, and let $x = A$ and $y = -B$.

Then: $\sin (x + y) = \sin x \cos y \quad + \cos x \sin y$

$$\sin (A + (-B)) = \sin A \cos (-B) + \cos A \sin (-B)$$

$$\sin (A - B) = \sin A \cos B \quad + \cos A(-\sin B)$$

$$\mathbf{\sin (A - B) = \sin A \cos B - \cos A \sin B}$$

EXAMPLES

1. Show that $\sin 120° = \frac{\sqrt{3}}{2}$ by using $\sin (180° - 60°)$.

Solution

$$\sin (A - B) = \sin A \cos B \quad - \cos A \sin B$$

$$\sin (180° - 60°) = \sin 180° \cos 60° \quad - \cos 180° \sin 60°$$

$$\sin 120° = 0 \cdot \frac{1}{2} \quad\quad - (-1) \cdot \frac{\sqrt{3}}{2}$$

$$= 0 \quad\quad\quad + \frac{\sqrt{3}}{2}$$

$$\sin 120° = \frac{\sqrt{3}}{2}$$

2. Use the identity for the sine of the sum of two angle measures to show that $\sin (180° + x) = -\sin x$.

How to Proceed: *Solution:*

(1) Write the identity. $\sin (A + B) = \sin A \cos B \quad + \cos A \sin B$

(2) Substitute 180° for A $\sin (180° + x) = \sin 180° \cos x + \cos 180° \sin x$
and x for B.

(3) Write the known $= 0 \cdot \cos x + (-1) \cdot \sin x$
function values, and $= 0 - \sin x$
simplify. $\sin (180° + x) = -\sin x$

EXERCISES WITH OPEN-RESPONSE PROBLEMS

1. Copy and complete the identity: $\sin (x + y) = \underline{\hspace{1cm}}$.
2. Copy and complete the identity: $\sin (x - y) = \underline{\hspace{1cm}}$.

In 3–6, use the identity for $\sin (A + B)$ or $\sin (A - B)$ to verify each statement.

3. $\sin (90° + x) = \cos x$ **4.** $\sin (90° - x) = \cos x$
5. $\sin (270° + x) = -\cos x$ **6.** $\sin (180° - x) = \sin x$

In 7–12, express each sine value in terms of $\sin \theta$ or $\cos \theta$ or both.

7. $\sin \left(\frac{\pi}{2} + \theta \right)$ **8.** $\sin (\theta - \pi)$ **9.** $\sin \left(\frac{\pi}{4} + \theta \right)$

10. $\sin \left(\theta - \frac{\pi}{2} \right)$ **11.** $\sin \left(\frac{\pi}{4} - \theta \right)$ **12.** $\sin (\pi + \theta)$

13. If $\sin x = \frac{4}{5}$, $\cos y = \frac{4}{5}$, and x and y are measures of angles in the first quadrant, find the value of $\sin (x + y)$.

14. If $\angle B$ is acute and $\sin B = \frac{12}{13}$, find the value of $\sin (90° - B)$.

In 15–20, use the identity for the sine of the sum or difference of two angle measures to find the exact value of each function.

15. $\sin 150° = \sin (60° + 90°)$ **16.** $\sin 90° = \sin (135° - 45°)$
17. $\sin 75° = \sin (45° + 30°)$ **18.** $\sin 75° = \sin (120° - 45°)$
19. $\sin 105° = \sin (135° - 30°)$ **20.** $\sin 105° = \sin (60° + 45°)$

In 21–24, select the *numeral* preceding the expression that best completes each sentence.

21. The expression $\sin 40° \cos 15° + \cos 40° \sin 15°$ is equivalent to
   (1) $\sin 55°$ (2) $\sin 25°$ (3) $\cos 55°$ (4) $\cos 25°$

22. The expression $\sin\left(\dfrac{\pi}{6} - x\right)$ is equivalent to

   (1) $\dfrac{1}{2} - \sin x$ (2) $\dfrac{\sqrt{3}}{2} - \sin x$ (3) $\dfrac{\sqrt{3}}{2}\cos x - \dfrac{1}{2}\sin x$ (4) $\dfrac{1}{2}\cos x - \dfrac{\sqrt{3}}{2}\sin x$

23. If $\sin(A - 30°) = \cos 60°$, the number of degrees in the measure of $\angle A$ is
   (1) 30   (2) 60   (3) 90   (4) 120

24. If x and y are the measures of positive acute angles, $\sin x = \dfrac{1}{2}$, and $\sin y = \dfrac{4}{5}$, then $\sin(x + y)$ equals

   (1) $\dfrac{3 + 4\sqrt{3}}{10}$ (2) $\dfrac{3 - 4\sqrt{3}}{10}$ (3) $\dfrac{\sqrt{3}}{4} + \dfrac{12}{25}$ (4) $\dfrac{\sqrt{3}}{4} - \dfrac{12}{25}$

25. If $\sin x = -\dfrac{1}{3}$, $\sin y = -\dfrac{\sqrt{5}}{3}$, and x and y are the measures of angles in the third quadrant, find:
   a. $\sin(x + y)$ **b.** $\sin(x - y)$ **c.** $\sin(y - x)$

26. If $\sin A = \dfrac{3}{5}$, $\angle A$ is in Quadrant I, $\cos B = -\dfrac{5}{13}$, and $\angle B$ is in Quadrant II, find:
   a. $\sin(A + B)$ **b.** $\sin(A - B)$ **c.** $\sin(B - A)$
   d. $\cos(A + B)$ **e.** $\cos(A - B)$ **f.** $\cos(B - A)$

19-7   TANGENT OF THE SUM OR DIFFERENCE OF ANGLE MEASURES

Since $\tan \theta = \dfrac{\sin \theta}{\cos \theta}$, we can use the identities for $\sin(A + B)$ and $\cos(A + B)$ to derive an identity for $\tan(A + B)$.

□ IDENTITY PROOF: $\tan(A + B) = \dfrac{\tan A + \tan B}{1 - \tan A \tan B}$

Use the identity $\tan(A + B) = \dfrac{\sin(A + B)}{\cos(A + B)}$.

$$\tan(A + B) = \dfrac{\sin A \cos B + \cos A \sin B}{\cos A \cos B - \sin A \sin B}$$

Then, to write the identity in terms of $\tan A$ and $\tan B$, multiply by a form of 1 so that each term in the right-hand expression is divided by $\cos A \cos B$.

$$\tan (A + B) = \frac{(\sin A \cos B + \cos A \sin B)}{(\cos A \cos B - \sin A \sin B)} \cdot \frac{\dfrac{1}{\cos A \cos B}}{\dfrac{1}{\cos A \cos B}}$$

$$= \frac{\dfrac{\sin A \cancel{\cos B}}{\cos A \cancel{\cos B}} + \dfrac{\cancel{\cos A} \sin B}{\cancel{\cos A} \cos B}}{\dfrac{\cancel{\cos A} \cancel{\cos B}}{\cancel{\cos A} \cancel{\cos B}} - \dfrac{\sin A \sin B}{\cos A \cos B}}$$

$$= \frac{\tan A \cdot 1 + 1 \cdot \tan B}{1 \cdot 1 - \tan A \tan B}$$

$$\mathbf{\tan (A + B) = \frac{\tan A + \tan B}{1 - \tan A \tan B}}$$

In a similar manner, using the identities for sin $(A - B)$ and cos $(A - B)$, we can derive the identity

$$\mathbf{\tan(A - B) = \frac{\tan A - \tan B}{1 + \tan A \tan B}}$$

These two identities are true for all replacements of the variables for which tan $(A \pm B)$, tan A, and tan B are defined. For example:

□   Show that tan $120° = -\sqrt{3}$ by using tan $(60° + 60°)$.

$$\tan (A + B) = \frac{\tan A + \tan B}{1 - \tan A \tan B}$$

$$\tan (60° + 60°) = \frac{\tan 60° + \tan 60°}{1 - \tan 60° \tan 60°}$$

$$\tan 120° = \frac{\sqrt{3} + \sqrt{3}}{1 - \sqrt{3} \cdot \sqrt{3}} = \frac{2\sqrt{3}}{1 - 3} = \frac{2\sqrt{3}}{-2} = -\sqrt{3}$$

Verification that $-\sqrt{3}$ is the function value for tan $120°$ can be obtained through two calculator entries.

Enter: (−) 2nd √ 3 ENTER   *Enter:* TAN 120 ENTER

Display: ⎢−1.732050808⎢   *Display:* ⎢−1.732050808⎢

It is also possible to apply this tangent identity to cases where the tangent is undefined, as shown in the following example:

☐   Show that tan 90° is undefined by using tan (60° + 30°).

$$\tan (60° + 30°) = \frac{\tan 60° + \tan 30°}{1 - \tan 60° \tan 30°}$$

$$\tan 90° = \frac{\sqrt{3} + \dfrac{\sqrt{3}}{3}}{1 - \sqrt{3} \cdot \dfrac{\sqrt{3}}{3}} = \frac{\dfrac{3\sqrt{3}}{3} + \dfrac{\sqrt{3}}{3}}{1 - \dfrac{3}{3}} = \frac{\dfrac{4\sqrt{3}}{3}}{1 - 1}$$

$$\tan 90° = \frac{\dfrac{4\sqrt{3}}{3}}{0} \qquad \text{(Division by 0 is undefined.)}$$

If either tan 90° or a division by 0 is entered on a calculator, the display will read ERROR .

EXAMPLES

1. Use the identity for the tangent of the sum of two angle measures to show that (tan 180° + x) = tan x.

How to Proceed:	*Solution:*
(1) Write the identity.	$\tan (A + B) = \dfrac{\tan A + \tan B}{1 - \tan A \tan B}$
(2) Substitute 180° for *A* and *x* for *B*.	$\tan (180° + x) = \dfrac{\tan 180° + \tan x}{1 - \tan 180° \tan x}$
(3) Substitute the value of tan 180°, and simplify.	$= \dfrac{0 + \tan x}{1 - 0 \cdot \tan x}$
	$= \dfrac{\tan x}{1 - 0}$
	$\tan (180° + x) = \tan x$

2. If $\tan A = \frac{5}{4}$ and $\tan B = \frac{1}{5}$, find tan (A − B).

Solution

$$\tan (A - B) = \frac{\tan A - \tan B}{1 + \tan A \tan B}$$

$$= \frac{\dfrac{5}{4} - \dfrac{1}{5}}{1 + \dfrac{5}{4} \cdot \dfrac{1}{5}} = \frac{\left(\dfrac{5}{4} - \dfrac{1}{5}\right)}{\left(1 + \dfrac{1}{4}\right)} \cdot \frac{20}{20} = \frac{25 - 4}{20 + 5} = \frac{21}{25}$$

Answer: tan (A − B) = $\frac{21}{25}$

EXERCISES WITH OPEN-RESPONSE PROBLEMS

1. Copy and complete the identity: $\tan(\theta + \phi) = $ _____.
2. Copy and complete the identity: $\tan(x - y) = $ _____.

In 3–6, use the identity for $\tan(A + B)$ or $\tan(A - B)$ to verify each statement.

3. $\tan(360° + x) = \tan x$

4. $\tan(180° - x) = -\tan x$

5. $\tan(45° + x) = \dfrac{1 + \tan x}{1 - \tan x}$

6. $\tan(315° + x) = \dfrac{-1 + \tan x}{1 + \tan x}$

In 7–9, express each tangent value in terms of $\tan \theta$.

7. $\tan(\pi + \theta)$

8. $\tan(2\pi - \theta)$

9. $\tan\left(\dfrac{3\pi}{4} - \theta\right)$

10. Prove that $\tan(-x) = -\tan x$. (*Hint:* Start with the identity for $\tan(A - B)$, and let $A = 0°$ and $B = x$.)

11. If $\tan A = 4$ and $\tan B = 3$, find: **a.** $\tan(A + B)$ **b.** $\tan(A - B)$

12. If $\tan \theta = -6$ and $\tan \phi = \frac{1}{2}$, find: **a.** $\tan(\theta + \phi)$ **b.** $\tan(\theta - \phi)$

13. If $\tan x = -\frac{2}{3}$ and $\tan y = \frac{9}{4}$, find: **a.** $\tan(x + y)$ **b.** $\tan(x - y)$

14. Let $\tan A = 2$ and $\tan B = 3$.   **a.** Find the value of $\tan(A + B)$.   **b.** One possible measure of $\angle(A + B)$ is   (1) $0°$ (2) $45°$ (3) $90°$ (4) $135°$

In 15–18, use the identity for $\tan(A + B)$ or for $\tan(A - B)$ to find the exact value of each function. Rationalize the denominator of the answer.

15. $\tan 75° = \tan(30° + 45°)$

16. $\tan 15° = \tan(45° - 30°)$

17. $\tan 105° = \tan(60° + 45°)$

18. $\tan 195° = \tan(135° + 60°)$

In 19–22, select the *numeral* preceding the expression that best completes each sentence.

19. The expression $\dfrac{\tan 40° + \tan 30°}{1 - \tan 40° \tan 30°}$ is equivalent to

(1) $\tan 70°$ (2) $\tan 10°$ (3) $\dfrac{\tan 40°}{1 - \tan 40°}$ (4) $\dfrac{\tan 70°}{1 - \tan 70°}$

20. The expression $\tan(x + y)$ is undefined when
(1) $\tan x \tan y = 0$ (2) $\tan x \tan y = 1$ (3) $\tan x \tan y = -1$ (4) $\tan x + \tan y = 0$

21. The expression $\tan(A - B)$ is undefined when $\tan A = \frac{1}{2}$ and $\tan B$ equals
(1) 1 (2) 2 (3) -2 (4) 0

22. Since $\tan 165° = \tan(135° + 30°)$, the exact value of $\tan 165°$ can be found to be
(1) $-2 + \sqrt{3}$ (2) $-2 - \sqrt{3}$ (3) $2 + \sqrt{3}$ (4) $2 - \sqrt{3}$

23. The accompanying diagram consists of three congruent squares, namely, *ABGH*, *BCFG*, and *CDEF*. The side of each square has a length of 1.

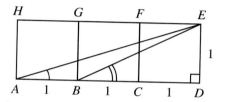

  a. Express the value of tan *A* as a fraction.
  b. Express the value of tan *B* as a fraction.
  c. Find the value of tan (*A* + *B*). Show your work.
  d. Based on the answer to part **c**, find the sum of the angle measures (m∠*A* + m∠*B*). Explain your answer.
  e. Find the value of the sum (m∠*AED* + m∠*BED*). Explain how you arrived at this answer.

19-8 FUNCTION VALUES OF DOUBLE ANGLES

Since *A* + *A* = 2*A*, we can derive an identity for the function value of an angle whose measure is twice that of a given angle. To do this, we start with the identity for the function value of the sum of two angle measures.

Sine of a Double Angle

☐ IDENTITY PROOF: $\sin 2A = 2 \sin A \cos A$

Use the identity $\sin (A + B) = \sin A \cos B + \cos A \sin B$, and let *B* = *A*.

Then: $\sin (A + A) = \sin A \cos A + \cos A \sin A$

$$\sin 2A = \sin A \cos A + \sin A \cos A$$

$$\mathbf{\sin 2A = 2 \sin A \cos A}$$

☐ To demonstrate this identity, let us show that sin 90° = 1 by using sin 2(45°).

$$\sin 2A = 2 \sin A \cos A$$

$$\sin 2(45°) = 2 \sin 45° \cos 45°$$

$$\sin 90° = 2 \cdot \frac{\sqrt{2}}{2} \cdot \frac{\sqrt{2}}{2} = \frac{4}{4} = 1$$

Cosine of a Double Angle

☐   IDENTITY PROOF: $\cos 2A = \cos^2 A - \sin^2 A$

Use the identity $\cos (A + B) = \cos A \cos B - \sin A \sin B$, and let $B = A$.

Then: $\cos (A + A) = \cos A \cos A - \sin A \sin A$

$$\cos 2A = \cos^2 A - \sin^2 A$$

By using the basic identity $\sin^2 A + \cos^2 A = 1$, we can write this identity in terms of $\cos A$ only or in terms of $\sin A$ only.

Use $\sin^2 A = 1 - \cos^2 A$:

$$\cos 2A = \cos^2 A - \sin^2 A$$
$$= \cos^2 A - (1 - \cos^2 A)$$
$$= \cos^2 A - 1 + \cos^2 A$$
$$\cos 2A = 2 \cos^2 A - 1$$

Use $\cos^2 A = 1 - \sin^2 A$:

$$\cos 2A = \cos^2 A \qquad - \sin^2 A$$
$$= (1 - \sin^2 A) - \sin^2 A$$
$$\cos 2A = 1 - 2 \sin^2 A$$

☐   Show that $\cos 60° = \frac{1}{2}$ by using $\cos 2(30°)$ in two ways.

$$\cos 2A = \cos^2 A - \sin^2 A$$
$$\cos 2(30°) = \cos^2 30° - \sin^2 30°$$
$$\cos 60° = \left(\frac{\sqrt{3}}{2}\right)^2 - \left(\frac{1}{2}\right)^2$$
$$\cos 60° = \frac{3}{4} - \frac{1}{4} = \frac{2}{4} = \frac{1}{2}$$

$$\cos 2A = 2 \cos^2 A - 1$$
$$\cos 2(30°) = 2 \cos^2 30° - 1$$
$$\cos 60° = 2\left(\frac{\sqrt{3}}{2}\right)^2 - 1$$
$$\cos 60° = 2\left(\frac{3}{4}\right) - 1 = \frac{3}{2} - 1 = \frac{1}{2}$$

Tangent of a Double Angle

☐   IDENTITY PROOF: $\tan 2A = \dfrac{2 \tan A}{1 - \tan^2 A}$

Use the identity $\tan (A + B) = \dfrac{\tan A + \tan B}{1 - \tan A \tan B}$, and let $B = A$.

Then: $\tan (A + A) = \dfrac{\tan A + \tan A}{1 - \tan A \tan A}$

$$\tan 2A = \dfrac{2 \tan A}{1 - \tan^2 A}$$

The following example uses the identity for a tangent of a double angle.

☐   Show $\tan 120° = -\sqrt{3}$ by using $\tan 2(60°)$.

$$\tan 2A = \frac{2 \tan A}{1 - \tan^2 A}$$

$$\tan 2(60°) = \frac{2 \tan 60°}{1 - \tan^2 60°}$$

$$\tan 120° = \frac{2(\sqrt{3})}{1 - (\sqrt{3})^2} = \frac{2\sqrt{3}}{1 - 3} = \frac{2\sqrt{3}}{-2} = -\sqrt{3}$$

Note that the identity is true for all values of A for which $\tan A$ and $\tan 2A$ are defined. If $A = 90°$, $\tan 2A = \tan 180° = 0$, but this value cannot be found by using the expression $\frac{2 \tan A}{1 - \tan^2 A}$.

EXAMPLE

$\text{Cos } A = -\frac{5}{13}$, and A is the measure of an angle in Quadrant II.   **a.** Find $\sin 2A$.
b. Find $\cos 2A$.   **c.** Find $\tan 2A$.   **d.** Determine the quadrant in which the angle whose measure is $2A$ lies.

How to Proceed:

a. (1) Find $\sin A$. Since A is the measure of an angle in Quadrant II, $\sin A$ is positive.

(2) Write the identity for $\sin 2A$.

(3) Substitute the values of $\sin A$ and $\cos A$, and simplify.

b. (1) Write the identity for $\cos 2A$.

(2) Substitute the values for $\sin A$ and $\cos A$, and simplify.

Solution:

$$\sin^2 A = 1 - \cos^2 A$$

$$= 1 - \left(-\frac{5}{13}\right)^2$$

$$= 1 - \frac{25}{169} = \frac{169}{169} - \frac{25}{169} = \frac{144}{169}$$

$$\sin A = \frac{12}{13}$$

$$\sin 2A = 2 \sin A \cos A$$

$$\sin 2A = 2\left(\frac{12}{13}\right)\left(-\frac{5}{13}\right)$$

$$= -\frac{120}{169}$$

$$\cos 2A = \cos^2 A - \sin^2 A$$

$$\cos 2A = \left(-\frac{5}{13}\right)^2 - \left(\frac{12}{13}\right)^2$$

$$= \frac{25}{169} - \frac{144}{169} = -\frac{119}{169}$$

c. (1) Find tan A.

$$\tan A = \frac{\sin A}{\cos A} = \frac{\frac{12}{13}}{-\frac{5}{13}} = \frac{\frac{12}{13}}{-\frac{5}{13}} \cdot \frac{13}{13} = -\frac{12}{5}$$

(2) Write the identity for tan $2A$.

$$\tan 2A = \frac{2 \tan A}{1 - \tan^2 A}$$

(3) Substitute the value of tan A, and simplify.

$$\tan 2A = \frac{2\left(-\frac{12}{5}\right)}{1 - \left(-\frac{12}{5}\right)^2}$$

$$= \frac{-\frac{24}{5}}{1 - \frac{144}{25}}$$

$$= \frac{-\frac{24}{5}}{-\frac{119}{25}} = +\frac{\frac{24}{5}}{\frac{119}{25}} \cdot \frac{25}{25} = \frac{120}{119}$$

Note: Tan $2A$ can also be found by using the answers to parts **a** and **b**:

$$\tan 2A = \frac{\sin 2A}{\cos 2A} = \frac{-\frac{120}{169}}{-\frac{119}{169}} = +\frac{\frac{120}{169}}{\frac{119}{169}} \cdot \frac{169}{169} = \frac{120}{119}$$

d. Since sin $2A$ and cos $2A$ are both negative, then $2A$ must be the measure of a Quadrant III angle.

Answers: **a.** $\sin 2A = -\frac{120}{169}$ **b.** $\cos 2A = -\frac{119}{169}$ **c.** $\tan 2A = \frac{120}{119}$ **d.** III

EXERCISES WITH OPEN-RESPONSE PROBLEMS

1. Copy and complete the identity: $\sin 2x = $ _____.
2. Copy and complete the identity: $\tan 2x = $ _____.

3. Write the identity for cos $2x$ in terms of:
   a. sin x and cos x **b.** cos x only   **c.** sin x only

4. If x is the measure of a positive acute angle and $\sin x = \frac{4}{5}$, find sin $2x$.

5. If $\sin A = -0.8$, what is the value of cos $2A$?
6. If $\cos \theta = 0.28$, express the value of cos 2θ in decimal form.

7. If $\cos A = -\frac{24}{25}$ and $\angle A$ is in Quadrant III, express, in fractional form, each value:

    a. $\sin A$ **b.** $\cos 2A$ **c.** $\sin 2A$

8. If $\tan A = \frac{1}{4}$, find $\tan 2A$.

9. Show that $\cos 90° = 0$ by using $\cos 2(45°)$.

10. Show that $\sin 180° = 0$ by using $\sin 2(90°)$.

11. Show that $\tan 360° = 0$ by using $\tan 2(180°)$.

12. Show that $\sin 270° = -1$ by using $\sin 2(135°)$.

13. If $\sin \theta = b$, express $\cos 2\theta$ in terms of b.

14. If $\cos \theta = a$, express $\cos 2\theta$ in terms of a.

15. If $\tan \theta = c$, express $\tan 2\theta$ in terms of c.

16. If $\sin A = -\frac{3}{5}$ and $\angle A$ is in Quadrant III, find:

    a. $\sin 2A$ **b.** $\cos 2A$ **c.** $\tan 2A$ **d.** the quadrant in which $\angle 2A$ terminates

17. If $\cos A = \frac{1}{3}$ and $\angle A$ is acute, find: **a.** $\sin 2A$ **b.** $\cos 2A$ **c.** $\tan 2A$

18. If $\cos \theta = -0.6$ and θ is the measure of an angle in Quadrant II, find:

    a. $\cos 2\theta$ **b.** $\sin 2\theta$ **c.** $\tan 2\theta$

    d. the quadrant in which the angle whose measure is 2θ terminates

In 19–22, select the *numeral* preceding the expression that best completes each sentence.

19. If $\cos \theta = \sin \theta$, then $\cos 2\theta$ is equal to

    (1) 1   (2) 0   (3) $2 \cos^2 \theta$ (4) $2 \sin^2 \theta$

20. The expression $(\sin x - \cos x)^2$ is equivalent to

    (1) 1   (2) $\sin^2 x - \cos^2 x$ (3) $1 - \cos 2x$ (4) $1 - \sin 2x$

21. If $\tan A = -1$, then $\tan 2A$

    (1) equals 1   (2) equals 2   (3) equals -2 (4) is undefined

22. If $\sin \theta$ is negative and $\sin 2\theta$ is positive, then $\cos \theta$

    (1) must be positive   (2) must be negative

    (3) must be 0   (4) may be positive or negative

23. a. *True* or *false*: The largest possible function value of $\sin x$ is 1, and the largest possible function value of $\sin 2x$ is 2.

    b. Explain your answer to part **a**.

19-9 FUNCTION VALUES OF HALF ANGLES

Since the angle measure θ is half of the angle measure 2θ, we can use the identities that were developed in the last section to derive identities for the function values of an angle whose measure is half that of a given angle.

Sine of a Half Angle

☐ IDENTITY PROOF: $\sin \frac{1}{2} A = \pm \sqrt{\dfrac{1 - \cos A}{2}}$

(1) Use the identity:

$$\cos 2\theta = 1 - 2 \sin^2 \theta$$

$$2 \sin^2 \theta = 1 - \cos 2\theta$$

(2) Solve for $\sin \theta$.
(*Note:* Since $\cos 2\theta \le 1$, then $1 - \cos 2\theta \ge 0$, and the right-hand member is a real number.)

$$\sin^2 \theta = \frac{1 - \cos 2\theta}{2}$$

$$\sin \theta = \pm \sqrt{\frac{1 - \cos 2\theta}{2}}$$

(3) Let $\theta = \frac{1}{2} A$.

Then, $2\theta = 2\left(\frac{1}{2} A\right) = A$.

$$\boldsymbol{\sin \frac{1}{2} A = \pm \sqrt{\frac{1 - \cos A}{2}}}$$

☐ Show that $\sin 30° = \frac{1}{2}$ by using $\sin \frac{1}{2} (60°)$.

$$\sin \frac{1}{2} A = \pm \sqrt{\frac{1 - \cos A}{2}}$$

$$\sin \frac{1}{2} (60°) = + \sqrt{\frac{1 - \cos 60°}{2}}$$

$$\sin 30° = \sqrt{\frac{1 - \frac{1}{2}}{2}} = \sqrt{\frac{\frac{1}{2}}{2}} = \sqrt{\frac{1}{2} \cdot \frac{2}{2}} = \sqrt{\frac{1}{4}} = \frac{1}{2}$$

Since $\frac{1}{2} (60°) = 30°$ is an acute-angle measure, the positive value was chosen for the sine.

Cosine of a Half Angle

In a similar way, we derive an identity for $\cos \frac{1}{2} A$ by starting with $\cos 2\theta$:

☐   IDENTITY PROOF: $\cos \frac{1}{2} A = \pm \sqrt{\dfrac{1 + \cos A}{2}}$

(1) Use the identity:

$$\cos 2\theta = 2 \cos^2 \theta - 1$$

$$2 \cos^2 \theta - 1 = \cos 2\theta$$

(2) Solve for $\cos \theta$.
(*Note:* Since $\cos 2\theta \geq -1$, then $1 + \cos 2\theta \geq 0$, and the right-hand side is a real number.)

$$2 \cos^2 \theta = 1 + \cos 2\theta$$

$$\cos^2 \theta = \frac{1 + \cos 2\theta}{2}$$

$$\cos \theta = \pm \sqrt{\frac{1 + \cos 2\theta}{2}}$$

(3) Let $\theta = \frac{1}{2} A$, $2\theta = 2\left(\frac{1}{2} A\right) = A$.

$$\mathbf{\cos \tfrac{1}{2} A = \pm \sqrt{\frac{1 + \cos A}{2}}}$$

☐   Show that $\cos 45° = \frac{\sqrt{2}}{2}$ by using $\cos \frac{1}{2} (90°)$.

$$\cos \tfrac{1}{2} A = \pm \sqrt{\frac{1 + \cos A}{2}}$$

$$\cos \tfrac{1}{2} (90°) = + \sqrt{\frac{1 + \cos 90°}{2}}$$

$$\cos 45° = \sqrt{\frac{1 + 0}{2}} = \sqrt{\frac{1}{2}} = \sqrt{\frac{1}{2} \cdot \frac{2}{2}} = \sqrt{\frac{2}{4}} = \frac{\sqrt{2}}{2}$$

The positive value was chosen for the function of an acute-angle measure.

Tangent of a Half Angle

Use the identities for $\sin \frac{1}{2} A$ and $\cos \frac{1}{2} A$ to derive an identity for $\tan \frac{1}{2} A$.

☐   IDENTITY PROOF: $\tan \frac{1}{2} A = \pm \sqrt{\dfrac{1 - \cos A}{1 + \cos A}}$

Use the identity $\tan \dfrac{1}{2} A = \dfrac{\sin \frac{1}{2} A}{\cos \frac{1}{2} A}$

$$= \pm \frac{\sqrt{\dfrac{1 - \cos A}{2}}}{\sqrt{\dfrac{1 + \cos A}{2}}} \cdot \frac{\sqrt{2}}{\sqrt{2}}$$

$$\mathbf{\tan \tfrac{1}{2} A = \pm \sqrt{\frac{1 - \cos A}{1 + \cos A}}}$$

☐ Show that $\tan 120° = -\sqrt{3}$ by using $\tan \frac{1}{2}(240°)$.

$$\tan \frac{1}{2} A = \pm\sqrt{\frac{1 - \cos A}{1 + \cos A}}$$

$$\tan \frac{1}{2}(240°) = -\sqrt{\frac{1 - \cos 240°}{1 + \cos 240°}}$$

$$\tan 120° = -\sqrt{\frac{1 - \left(-\frac{1}{2}\right)}{1 + \left(-\frac{1}{2}\right)}} = -\sqrt{\frac{\frac{3}{2}}{\frac{1}{2}}} = -\sqrt{\frac{\frac{3}{2}}{\frac{1}{2}} \cdot \frac{2}{2}} = -\sqrt{3}$$

Since $120°$ is the measure of an angle in Quadrant II, its tangent value is negative.

Choosing Signs for Function Values of Half Angles

In using each of the identities just derived for a function value of a half angle, we must be careful to choose the correct sign. For example:

- If $0° < x < 180°$, then $0° < \frac{1}{2}x < 90°$. Thus, $\frac{1}{2}x$ is the measure of an angle in Quadrant I, where $\sin \frac{1}{2}x$, $\cos \frac{1}{2}x$, and $\tan \frac{1}{2}x$ are positive.

- If $180° < x < 360°$, then $90° < \frac{1}{2}x < 180°$. Thus, $\frac{1}{2}x$ is the measure of an angle in Quadrant II, where $\sin \frac{1}{2}x$ is positive, and $\cos \frac{1}{2}x$ and $\tan \frac{1}{2}x$ are negative.

- If $360° < x < 540°$, then $180° < \frac{1}{2}x < 270°$. Thus, $\frac{1}{2}x$ is the measure of an angle in Quadrant III, where $\tan \frac{1}{2}x$ is positive, and $\sin \frac{1}{2}x$ and $\cos \frac{1}{2}x$ are negative.

- If $540° < x < 720°$, then $270° < \frac{1}{2}x < 360°$. Thus, $\frac{1}{2}x$ is the measure of an angle in Quadrant IV, where $\cos \frac{1}{2}x$ is positive, and $\sin \frac{1}{2}x$ and $\tan \frac{1}{2}x$ are negative.

EXAMPLES

1. If $\cos x = \frac{1}{9}$, what is the positive value of $\sin \frac{1}{2} x$?

Solution   Write the identity for the positive value of $\sin \frac{1}{2} x$. Substitute the given value for $\cos x$, and simplify.

$$\sin \frac{1}{2} x = \sqrt{\frac{1 - \cos x}{2}}$$

$$= \sqrt{\frac{1 - \frac{1}{9}}{2}} = \sqrt{\frac{\frac{8}{9}}{\frac{2}{1}} \cdot \frac{\frac{1}{2}}{\frac{1}{2}}} = \sqrt{\frac{4}{9}} = \frac{2}{3}$$

Answer: $\sin \frac{1}{2} x = \frac{2}{3}$

---

2. If $A = \text{Arc cos } \frac{1}{5}$, what is the value of $\tan \frac{A}{2}$?

How to Proceed:

(1) Write the identity for $\tan \frac{A}{2}$.

(2) If $A = \text{Arc cos } \frac{1}{5}$, then $\cos A = \frac{1}{5}$. Since $\cos A$ is positive and A is the principal value, $0° < A < 90°$. Thus, $0° < \frac{A}{2} < 45°$, and $\tan \frac{A}{2}$ is positive.

Solution:

$$\tan \frac{A}{2} = \pm\sqrt{\frac{1 - \cos A}{1 + \cos A}}$$

$$= \sqrt{\frac{1 - \frac{1}{5}}{1 + \frac{1}{5}}}$$

$$= \sqrt{\frac{\frac{4}{5}}{\frac{6}{5}}} = \sqrt{\frac{4}{5} \cdot \frac{5}{6}}$$

$$= \sqrt{\frac{2}{3} \cdot \frac{3}{3}} = \frac{\sqrt{6}}{3}$$

Answer: $\tan \frac{A}{2} = \frac{\sqrt{6}}{3}$

EXERCISES WITH OPEN-RESPONSE PROBLEMS

In 1–3, copy and complete each identity.

1. $\sin \frac{1}{2} x = $ _____.

2. $\cos \frac{1}{2} x = $ _____.

3. $\tan \frac{1}{2} x = $ _____.

4. If x is the measure of a positive acute angle and $\cos x = \frac{7}{32}$, find the value of $\sin \frac{1}{2} x$.

5. If $\cos A = \frac{1}{8}$ and $\angle A$ is positive and acute, find $\cos \frac{1}{2} A$.

6. If $A = \text{Arc} \cos \frac{1}{2}$, find the value of $\sin \frac{1}{2} A$.

7. If $B = \text{Arc} \cos \frac{24}{25}$, find the value of $\tan \frac{B}{2}$.

8. If $\cos x = -\frac{7}{18}$ and $180° < x < 270°$, find the value of $\sin \frac{1}{2} x$.

9. If $\cos y = -\frac{1}{2}$ and $180° < y < 270°$, find the value of $\cos \frac{y}{2}$.

10. If $\cos \theta = -\frac{15}{17}$ and $180° < \theta < 270°$, find the value of $\tan \frac{1}{2} \theta$.

11. Find $\cos \frac{1}{2} y$ if $y = \text{arc} \cos 0.28$ and $270° < y < 360°$.

12. Find $\sin \frac{1}{2} \theta$ if $\theta = \text{arc} \cos 0.68$ and $360° < \theta < 450°$.

13. Find $\tan \frac{1}{2} x$ if $x = \text{arc} \sin \frac{5}{13}$ and $90° < x < 180°$.

14. Find $\sin \frac{1}{2} B$ if $\tan B = \frac{3}{4}$ and $\angle B$ is acute.

15. Find the exact value of $\sin 60°$ by using $\sin \frac{1}{2} (120°)$.

16. Find the exact value of $\cos 225°$ by using $\cos \frac{1}{2} (450°)$.

17. Find the exact value of $\tan 135°$ by using $\tan \frac{1}{2} (270°)$.

18. If $\cos A = \frac{7}{25}$ and $\angle A$ is a positive acute angle, find: **a.** $\sin \frac{1}{2} A$ **b.** $\cos \frac{1}{2} A$ **c.** $\tan \frac{1}{2} A$

19. If $\cos B = \frac{5}{9}$ and $\angle B$ is a positive acute angle, find: **a.** $\sin \frac{1}{2} B$ **b.** $\cos \frac{1}{2} B$ **c.** $\tan \frac{1}{2} B$

20. If $\cos \theta = \frac{7}{8}$ and $0° < \theta < 90°$, find: **a.** $\sin \frac{\theta}{2}$ **b.** $\cos \frac{\theta}{2}$ **c.** $\tan \frac{\theta}{2}$

21. If $\sin A = 0.6$ and $\angle A$ is a positive acute angle, find:

a. $\sin \frac{1}{2} A$ **b.** $\cos \frac{1}{2} A$ **c.** $\tan \frac{1}{2} A$

In 22–27, select the *numeral* preceding the expression that best completes the sentence or answers the question.

22. Which of the following is *not* an identity?

(1) $\sin \frac{1}{2} x = \pm \sqrt{\frac{1 - \cos x}{2}}$

(2) $\cos^2 \frac{1}{2} x = \frac{1 + \cos x}{2}$

(3) $\tan 2x = \pm \sqrt{\frac{1 - \cos 4x}{1 + \cos 4x}}$

(4) $\sin \frac{1}{2} x = \frac{1}{2} \sin x$

23. The expression $\sqrt{\frac{1 - \cos 80°}{2}}$ is equivalent to

(1) $\cos 40°$ 　　　　(2) $\sin 40°$ 　　　　(3) $\frac{1}{2} - \cos 40°$ 　　　　(4) $\frac{1}{2}\sin 80°$

24. The expression $\frac{1 - \cos 100°}{1 + \cos 100°}$ is equivalent to

(1) $\tan 50°$ 　　　　(2) $-\cos 100°$ 　　　　(3) $\sqrt{\cos 50°}$ 　　　　(4) $\tan^2 50°$

25. The expression $2\sin^2 \frac{1}{2}\theta$ is equivalent to

(1) $1 - \cos\theta$ 　　　(2) $1 + \cos\theta$ 　　　(3) $\sin^2\theta$ 　　　(4) $2 - 2\cos\theta$

26. If $\cos\frac{1}{2}\theta = \frac{1}{3}$, then $\cos\theta$ equals

(1) $\frac{2}{3}$ 　　　　(2) $\frac{1}{6}$ 　　　　(3) $-\frac{7}{9}$ 　　　　(4) $\frac{7}{9}$

27. Using $\tan\frac{1}{2}(30°)$, we can find the exact value of $\tan 15°$ to be

(1) $2 + \sqrt{3}$ 　　　(2) $2 - \sqrt{3}$ 　　　(3) $\frac{2 + \sqrt{3}}{4}$ 　　　(4) $\frac{2 - \sqrt{3}}{4}$

19-10   SUMMARY OF IDENTITIES

Sum of Angle Measures	*Difference of Angle Measures*
$\sin(A + B) = \sin A \cos B + \cos A \sin B$	$\sin(A - B) = \sin A \cos B - \cos A \sin B$
$\cos(A + B) = \cos A \cos B - \sin A \sin B$	$\cos(A - B) = \cos A \cos B + \sin A \sin B$
$\tan(A + B) = \frac{\tan A + \tan B}{1 - \tan A \tan B}$	$\tan(A - B) = \frac{\tan A - \tan B}{1 + \tan A \tan B}$

Double-Angle Measures	*Half-Angle Measures*
$\sin 2A = 2\sin A \cos A$	$\sin\frac{1}{2}A = \pm\sqrt{\frac{1 - \cos A}{2}}$
$\cos 2A = \cos^2 A - \sin^2 A$	
$\cos 2A = 2\cos^2 A - 1$	$\cos\frac{1}{2}A = \pm\sqrt{\frac{1 + \cos A}{2}}$
$\cos 2A = 1 - 2\sin^2 A$	
$\tan 2A = \frac{2\tan A}{1 - \tan^2 A}$	$\tan\frac{1}{2}A = \pm\sqrt{\frac{1 - \cos A}{1 + \cos A}}$

These fundamental identities can be used to prove other identities. When proving an identity, we should express functions of a double angle, a half angle, or the sum or difference of angle measures in terms of functions of the same angle.

Although we usually try to transform the more complicated side of an identity, there are times when both sides look complex. As shown in the following example, either side of an identity can be transformed into the expression on the other side. It is always helpful to write the expression in terms of sines and cosines.

EXAMPLE

Prove the identity $\dfrac{2 \cos 2\theta}{\sin 2\theta} = \cot \theta - \tan \theta$.

Solution   Transform the left-hand side of the identity. Notice that other replacements can be made for $\cos 2\theta$.

$$\frac{2 \cos 2\theta}{\sin 2\theta} = \cot \theta - \tan \theta$$

$$\frac{2(\cos^2 \theta - \sin^2 \theta)}{2 \sin \theta \cos \theta} =$$

$$\frac{2 \cos^2 \theta - 2 \sin^2 \theta}{2 \sin \theta \cos \theta} =$$

$$\frac{2 \cos^2 \theta}{2 \sin \theta \cos \theta} - \frac{2 \sin^2 \theta}{2 \sin \theta \cos \theta} =$$

$$\frac{\cos \theta}{\sin \theta} - \frac{\sin \theta}{\cos \theta} =$$

$$\cot \theta - \tan \theta = \cot \theta - \tan \theta$$

Alternative Solution   Transform the right-hand side of the identity. Notice that the expressions are stated in terms of sines and cosines.

$$\frac{2 \cos 2\theta}{\sin 2\theta} = \cot \theta - \tan \theta$$

$$= \frac{\cos \theta}{\sin \theta} - \frac{\sin \theta}{\cos \theta}$$

$$= \frac{\cos \theta}{\sin \theta} \cdot \frac{\cos \theta}{\cos \theta} - \frac{\sin \theta}{\cos \theta} \cdot \frac{\sin \theta}{\sin \theta}$$

$$= \frac{\cos^2 \theta}{\sin \theta \cos \theta} - \frac{\sin^2 \theta}{\sin \theta \cos \theta}$$

$$= \frac{\cos^2 \theta - \sin^2 \theta}{\sin \theta \cos \theta}$$

$$= \frac{2}{2} \cdot \frac{\cos^2 \theta - \sin^2 \theta}{\sin \theta \cos \theta}$$

$$= \frac{2(\cos^2 \theta - \sin^2 \theta)}{2 \sin \theta \cos \theta}$$

$$\frac{2 \cos 2\theta}{\sin 2\theta} = \frac{2 \cdot \cos 2\theta}{\sin 2\theta}$$

EXERCISES WITH OPEN-RESPONSE PROBLEMS

In 1–26, in each case, prove the identity.

1. $\sin 2\theta \sec \theta = 2 \sin \theta$

2. $\sin 2\theta \csc \theta = 2 \cos \theta$

3. $\sin \theta = \frac{\sin 2\theta}{2 \cos \theta}$

4. $\frac{2 \cos \theta}{\sin 2\theta} = \csc \theta$

5. $\frac{\cos 2\theta}{\sin \theta} + \sin \theta = \frac{\cot \theta}{\sec \theta}$

6. $\tan \theta + \cot \theta = \frac{2}{\sin 2\theta}$

7. $\sin 2\theta = \frac{2 \tan \theta}{1 + \tan^2 \theta}$

8. $\cos 2\theta = \frac{1 - \tan^2 \theta}{1 + \tan^2 \theta}$

9. $\sin 2\theta \sec^2 \theta = 2 \tan \theta$

10. $2 - \sec^2 \theta = \cos 2\theta \sec^2 \theta$

11. $(\cos \theta - \sin \theta)^2 = 1 - \sin 2\theta$

12. $(\cos \theta + \sin \theta)^2 = 1 + \sin 2\theta$

13. $\frac{2 \sin^2 \theta}{\sin 2\theta} + \cot \theta = \sec \theta \csc \theta$

14. $\cos 2\theta = \frac{\cot^2 \theta - 1}{\cot^2 \theta + 1}$

15. $\frac{\cos 2\theta}{\sin \theta} + \sin \theta = \csc \theta - \sin \theta$

16. $\frac{2 \tan \theta - \sin 2\theta}{2 \sin^2 \theta} = \tan \theta$

17. $2 \cos \theta - \frac{\cos 2\theta}{\cos \theta} = \sec \theta$

18. $\frac{\cos 2\theta + \cos \theta + 1}{\sin 2\theta + \sin \theta} = \cot \theta$

19. $\frac{\sin \theta + \sin 2\theta}{\sec \theta + 2} = \sin \theta \cos \theta$

20. $\frac{1 + \cos 2\theta}{1 - \cos 2\theta} = \cot^2 \theta$

21. $\sin\left(\frac{\pi}{6} - \theta\right) + \sin\left(\frac{\pi}{6} + \theta\right) = \cos \theta$

22. $\cos\left(\frac{\pi}{4} - \theta\right) - \cos\left(\frac{\pi}{4} + \theta\right) = \sqrt{2} \sin \theta$

23. $\sin\left(\frac{\pi}{2} + \theta\right) - \sin\left(\frac{\pi}{2} - \theta\right) = 0$

24. $\sin\left(\frac{\pi}{4} + \theta\right) + \cos\left(\frac{\pi}{4} + \theta\right) = \sqrt{2} \cos \theta$

25. $\frac{\tan\left(\frac{\pi}{4} + \theta\right)}{\tan\left(\frac{3\pi}{4} - \theta\right)} = -1$

26. $\frac{\sin\left(\frac{\pi}{4} + \theta\right)}{\cos\left(\frac{\pi}{4} - \theta\right)} = 1$

27. a. Prove the identity $\frac{\sin 2A}{1 + \cos 2A} = \tan A$.

b. Use part **a** and let $A = \frac{1}{2}\theta$ to write an identity for $\tan \frac{1}{2}\theta$ in terms of $\sin \theta$ and $\cos \theta$.

c. Prove the identity $\pm\sqrt{\frac{1 - \cos \theta}{1 + \cos \theta}} = \frac{\sin \theta}{1 + \cos \theta}$.

19-11   FIRST-DEGREE TRIGONOMETRIC EQUATIONS

A ***trigonometric equation*** is an equation in which the variable is expressed in terms of a trigonometric function value. Compare these equations:

Algebraic Equation	*Trigonometric Equation*
$2x - 1 = 0$	$2 \cos \theta - 1 = 0$

To find the values of θ that make $2 \cos \theta - 1 = 0$ true, we first find a value or values for $\cos \theta$. To do this, we use the same procedure that we used to solve algebraic equations.

Solving an Algebraic Equation	*Solving a Trigonometric Equation*

$$\begin{array}{rcl} 2x - 1 &=& 0 \\ \underline{+1 \quad\quad +1} & & \\ 2x &=& 1 \\ \dfrac{2x}{2} &=& \dfrac{1}{2} \\ x &=& \dfrac{1}{2} \end{array} \qquad\qquad \begin{array}{rcl} 2 \cos \theta - 1 &=& 0 \\ \underline{+1 \quad\quad +1} & & \\ 2 \cos \theta &=& 1 \\ \dfrac{2 \cos \theta}{2} &=& \dfrac{1}{2} \\ \cos \theta &=& \dfrac{1}{2} \end{array}$$

There is one value of x that makes $2x - 1 = 0$ true, namely, $x = \frac{1}{2}$. There is also one value of $\cos \theta$ that makes $2 \cos \theta - 1 = 0$ true, namely, $\cos \theta = \frac{1}{2}$. When $\cos \theta = \frac{1}{2}$, however, there are infinitely many values of θ that make the equation $2 \cos \theta - 1 = 0$ true.

Replacement Sets and Solutions

Given $2 \cos \theta - 1 = 0$, we showed above that $\cos \theta = \frac{1}{2}$. The solution for θ depends upon the replacement set or domain being used. For example:

- In terms of degree measure, if the domain is $0° \leq \theta \leq 360°$ and $\cos \theta = \frac{1}{2}$, then $\theta = 60°$ or $\theta = 300°$.

- In terms of radian measure, if the domain is $0 \leq \theta \leq 2\pi$ and $\cos \theta = \frac{1}{2}$, then $\theta = \frac{\pi}{3}$ or $\theta = \frac{5\pi}{3}$.

- If θ is any real number and $\cos \theta = \frac{1}{2}$, then any value of θ that differs from $\frac{\pi}{3}$ or $\frac{5\pi}{3}$ by a multiple of 2π is also a solution. Thus, in terms of radian measure, the general solution of $\cos \theta = \frac{1}{2}$ is $\theta = \frac{\pi}{3} + 2\pi k$ or $\theta = \frac{5\pi}{3} + 2\pi k$ for any integer k.

When we solve an algebraic equation, the replacement set is usually the set of all real numbers. When we solve a trigonometric equation, the replacement set for $\sin \theta$ or $\cos \theta$ is the set of numbers between -1 and 1 inclusive, and the replacement set for $\tan \theta$ is the set of all real numbers.

For example, let us compare the solutions for three equations.

$3x - 5 = 7$	$3 \sin \theta - 5 = 7$	$3 \tan \theta - 5 = 7$
$3x = 12$	$3 \sin \theta = 12$	$3 \tan \theta = 12$
$x = 4$	$\sin \theta = 4$	$\tan \theta = 4$
Solution: {4}	*Solution:* { } or $\varnothing$	*Solution:* {arc tan 4}
		If $0° \leq \theta \leq 360°$ and θ is given to the nearest degree, {arc tan 4} = {76°, 256°}.

Calculators and Trigonometric Equations

The same techniques that we use to simplify an algebraic equation are applied to simplify a trigonometric equation. Once we arrive at a function value, however, we may use a calculator and keys such as $\boxed{\text{SIN}^{-1}}$, $\boxed{\text{COS}^{-1}}$, and $\boxed{\text{TAN}^{-1}}$ to identify the basic reference angle for the given function. For example, with a degree (Degree) setting on a calculator, reference angles are found by using the entries shown below.

$\boxed{\text{Degree}}$

$$2 \cos \theta - 1 = 0$$
$$\cos \theta = \tfrac{1}{2}$$

Enter: $\boxed{\text{2nd}}$ $\boxed{\text{COS}^{-1}}$
1 $\boxed{\div}$ 2 $\boxed{\text{ENTER}}$

Display: $\boxed{ 60.}$

$$3 \tan \theta - 5 = 7$$
$$\tan \theta = 4$$

Enter: $\boxed{\text{2nd}}$ $\boxed{\text{TAN}^{-1}}$ 4 $\boxed{\text{ENTER}}$

Display: $\boxed{75.96375653}$

To the nearest degree: 76°

In the examples shown above, since the function values are positive, each equation has a solution in Quadrant I. To find values of θ in other quadrants, we use the rules relating to reference angles.

Since cosine is positive in Quadrants I and IV,

In I: $\theta = 60°$
In IV: $\theta = 360° - 60° = 300°$

Since tangent is positive in Quadrants I and III,

In I: $\theta = 76°$
In III: $\theta = 180° + 76° = 256°$

If the solution in radian measure for a trigonometric equation can be expressed in terms of π, the calculator will display this solution as an approximate rational value. For example, in Quadrant I, the solution for $\cos \theta = \tfrac{1}{2}$ is $\theta = \tfrac{\pi}{3}$. With a radian (Radian) setting on the calculator, however, we observe:

$\boxed{\text{Radian}}$

Enter: $\boxed{\text{2nd}}$ $\boxed{\text{COS}^{-1}}$ 1 $\boxed{\div}$ 2 $\boxed{\text{ENTER}}$

Display: $\boxed{1.047197551}$

Although 1.047197551 is a rational approximation of $\frac{\pi}{3}$, it is preferable to give the *exact* value of a solution. For this reason, we usually do not use the calculator to find solutions that are multiples or fractional parts of π radians.

EXAMPLES

1. a. Solve for $\cos \theta$: $\cos \theta = 3 \cos \theta + 1$.   **b.** Find all values of θ in the interval $0 \leq \theta < 2\pi$ that satisfy the equation in part **a**.

Solutions   **a.**

$$\cos \theta = 3 \cos \theta + 1$$
$$\underline{-3 \cos \theta = -3 \cos \theta}$$
$$-2 \cos \theta = \qquad 1$$
$$\frac{-2 \cos \theta}{-2} = \frac{1}{-2}$$
$$\cos \theta = -\frac{1}{2}$$

b. (1) Since $\cos \frac{\pi}{3} = \frac{1}{2}$, the reference angle is an angle of $\frac{\pi}{3}$ radians.

(2) Since $\cos \theta$ is negative, θ is an angle in Quadrant II or III.

$$\text{In II: } \theta = \pi - \frac{\pi}{3} = \frac{2\pi}{3}$$
$$\text{In III: } \theta = \pi + \frac{\pi}{3} = \frac{4\pi}{3}$$

Answers: **a.** $\cos \theta = -\frac{1}{2}$ **b.** $\theta = \frac{2\pi}{3}$ or $\theta = \frac{4\pi}{3}$

---

2. Solve for θ in the interval $0° \leq \theta \leq 360°$: $5(\sin \theta + 3) = \sin \theta + 12$.
  a. Find θ to the *nearest degree.*   **b.** Find θ to the *nearest minute.*

How to Proceed:

a. (1) Solve for $\sin \theta$.

Solution:

$$5(\sin \theta + 3) = \sin \theta + 12$$
$$5 \sin \theta + 15 = \sin \theta + 12$$
$$\underline{-\sin \theta - 15 \quad -\sin \theta - 15}$$
$$4 \sin \theta \qquad = \qquad -3$$
$$\sin \theta = -\frac{3}{4} \text{ or } -0.75$$

(2) Since $\sin \theta = -0.75$, there is no solution for θ in Quadrant I. Find the reference angle for which $\sin \theta = +0.75$.

Enter: [2nd] [SIN⁻¹] .75 [ENTER]

Display: [48.59037789]

To the nearest degree, the reference angle measures 49°.

(3) Use the reference angle to find θ in Quadrants III and IV.

In III: $\theta = 180° + 49° = 229°$

In IV: $\theta = 360° - 49° = 311°$

b. To find θ to the *nearest minute* when $\sin \theta = -\frac{3}{4}$ or -0.75:

(1) Start with the reference angle. This angle contains 48°.

Enter: | 2nd | SIN⁻¹ | .75 | ENTER |

Display: | 48.59037789 |

(2) Convert 48° to minutes. Round to the nearest minute.

Enter: | 2nd | ANGLE | 4 | ENTER |

Display: | 48°35′25.36″ |

To the nearest minute, the reference angle measures 48°35′.

(3) Use the reference angle to find θ in Quadrants III and IV.

In III: $\theta = 180° + 48°35′ = 228°35′$

In IV: $\theta = 360° - 48°35′$
$= 359°60′ - 48°35′ = 311°25′$

Answers: **a.** {229°, 311°}   **b.** {228°35′, 311°25′}

---

3. Find to the *nearest degree* the measure of the positive acute angle that satisfies the equation $3(\csc \theta - 1) = \csc \theta + 2$.

How to Proceed:

(1) Solve the equation for $\csc \theta$.

(2) Write the reciprocal of each side of the equation, and use the identity $\frac{1}{\csc \theta} = \sin \theta$.

(3) Use a calculator to solve for θ, where $\sin \theta = 0.4$, and round to the nearest degree.

Solution:

$$3(\csc \theta - 1) = \csc \theta + 2$$
$$3 \csc \theta - 3 = \csc \theta + 2$$
$$2 \csc \theta = 5$$
$$\csc \theta = \frac{5}{2}$$

$$\frac{1}{\csc \theta} = \frac{2}{5}$$

$$\sin \theta = \frac{2}{5} \text{ or } 0.4$$

Enter: | 2nd | SIN⁻¹ | .4 | ENTER |

Display: | 23.57817848 |

To the nearest degree, $\theta = 24°$.

Answer: 24°

EXERCISES WITH OPEN-RESPONSE PROBLEMS

In 1–6, in each case, solve for θ in the interval $0° \leq \theta \leq 360°$.

1. $2 \sin \theta - 1 = 0$　　　　**2.** $2 \sin \theta - \sqrt{3} = 0$　　　　**3.** $3 \cos \theta + 1 = 1$
4. $\sqrt{3} \tan \theta - 3 = 0$　　　**5.** $8 \sin \theta + 1 = -3$　　　**6.** $3 \tan \theta - 2 = \tan \theta$

In 7–12, in each case, solve for θ in the interval $0 \leq \theta \leq 2\pi$.

7. $4(\cos \theta + 1) = 0$　　　　　　　**8.** $3 \cos \theta - \sqrt{3} = \cos \theta$
9. $2(\sin \theta + \sqrt{2}) = \sqrt{2}$　　　　**10.** $3 \cos \theta - 1 = 1 - \cos \theta$
11. $5 \tan \theta + 2 = 3 \tan \theta$　　　　**12.** $2(\sin \theta + 1) = \sin \theta + 3$

In 13–18, in each case, find θ to the *nearest degree* in the interval $0° \leq \theta \leq 360°$.

13. $5 \cos \theta - 1 = 0$　　　　　　　**14.** $2 \tan \theta + 3 = 7$
15. $6 \sin \theta + 2 = \sin \theta$　　　　　**16.** $10(\cos \theta + 1) = 6$
17. $\csc \theta + 8 = 3 \csc \theta$　　　　**18.** $3 \tan \theta + 2 = 7 - \tan \theta$

In 19–24, in each case, find to the *nearest minute* the measure of the acute angle that satisfies the equation.

19. $\sin \theta + 5 = 9 \sin \theta$　　　　　　**20.** $2 + \cos \theta = 2.734$
21. $2(\tan \theta - 4) = 5(\tan \theta - 6)$　　　**22.** $2 \sec \theta - 3 = \sec \theta$
23. $\csc \theta = 3(\csc \theta - 5)$　　　　**24.** $\cot \theta + 60 = 4 \cot \theta$

In 25–30, in each case, find to the *nearest minute* all values of θ in the interval $0° \leq \theta \leq 360°$.

25. $7 \cos \theta = 8 - 3 \cos \theta$　　　　　**26.** $6 \sin \theta = 7 - 2 \sin \theta$
27. $3(\tan \theta - 7) = \tan \theta$　　　　　**28.** $8(\cos \theta + 2) = 5 \cos \theta + 14$
29. $25(\sin \theta + 1) = 2$　　　　　　　**30.** $\tan \theta - 3 = 5 \tan \theta + 2$

In 31–34, select the *numeral* preceding the expression that best completes each sentence.

31. One root of the equation $2 \cos \theta + \sqrt{3} = 0$ is

(1) $\dfrac{2\pi}{3}$　　　　　(2) $\dfrac{\pi}{3}$　　　　　(3) $\dfrac{5\pi}{6}$　　　　　(4) $\dfrac{\pi}{6}$

32. One root of the equation $\tan x - 1 = 2 \tan x$ is

(1) $\dfrac{\pi}{4}$　　　　　(2) π　　　　　(3) $\dfrac{5\pi}{4}$　　　　　(4) $\dfrac{7\pi}{4}$

33. If $0° \leq \theta \leq 360°$, the solution set of $3 \tan \theta + \sqrt{3} = 2\sqrt{3}$ is
(1) $\{60°, 120°\}$　　　(2) $\{60°, 240°\}$　　　(3) $\{30°, 210°\}$　　　(4) $\{30°, 150°\}$
34. If $0° \leq \theta \leq 360°$, the solution set of $\sin \theta + 1 = 3$ is
(1) $\{90°, 270°\}$　　　(2) $\{30°, 150°\}$　　　(3) $\{0°, 180°\}$　　　(4) $\{\ \}$

19-12   SECOND-DEGREE TRIGONOMETRIC EQUATIONS

Solution by Factoring

A second-degree equation of the form $ax^2 + bx + c = 0$ $(a \neq 0)$ is called a quadratic equation. If a quadratic equation has rational roots, its solution can be found by factoring and setting each factor equal to 0. This procedure is used to solve the equation $x^2 - 3x - 4 = 0$, shown below.

☐   *Algebraic Equation.* Solve for x:

$$x^2 - 3x - 4 = 0$$

$$(x + 1)(x - 4) = 0$$

$$x + 1 = 0 \quad | \quad x - 4 = 0$$

$$x = -1 \quad | \quad x = 4$$

An equation such as $\tan^2 \theta - 3 \tan \theta - 4 = 0$ is a second-degree equation in terms of $\tan \theta$. To find the values of θ that make this equation true, we first solve the equation for $\tan \theta$, applying the same method we would use to solve $x^2 - 3x - 4 = 0$. Then, as shown below, we use the values of $\tan \theta$ to determine solutions for θ.

☐   *Trigonometric Equation.* Solve for θ, to the *nearest degree*, in the interval $0° \leq \theta \leq 360°$.

$$\tan^2 \theta - 3 \tan \theta - 4 = 0$$

$$(\tan \theta + 1)(\tan \theta - 4) = 0$$

$$\tan \theta + 1 = 0 \quad | \quad \tan \theta - 4 = 0$$

$$\tan \theta = -1 \quad | \quad \tan \theta = 4$$

Tan θ is negative in Quadrants II and IV; the reference angle is 45°.

Tan θ is positive in Quadrants I and III; use a calculator.

In II: $\theta = 180° - 45° = 135°$

In IV: $\theta = 360° - 45° = 315°$

In I: $\theta = 76°$

In III: $\theta = 180° + 76° = 256°$

Answer: For $0° \leq \theta \leq 360°$, the solution set of θ, to the *nearest degree*, is

$$\{76°, 135°, 256°, 315°\}.$$

If the replacement set for θ is the set of all real numbers, then, to the *nearest degree*, θ can be any measure that differs from one of the measures just found by a multiple of 360°; that is, for k an integer:

$$\theta = 135° + 360°k \qquad \theta = 76° + 360°k$$

$$\theta = 315° + 360°k \qquad \theta = 256° + 360°k$$

Solution by the Quadratic Formula

Any quadratic equation can be solved by using the quadratic formula. Notice the similarities and then compare the solutions for the algebraic equation and the trigonometric equation that follows.

☐ *Algebraic Equation:* Given $3x^2 - 5x - 4 = 0$, find x to the *nearest hundredth.*

Here, $a = 3$, $b = -5$, $c = -4$.

$$x = \frac{-b \pm \sqrt{b^2 - 4ac}}{2a}$$

$$= \frac{-(-5) \pm \sqrt{(-5)^2 - 4(3)(-4)}}{2(3)} = \frac{5 \pm \sqrt{25 + 48}}{6} = \frac{5 \pm \sqrt{73}}{6}$$

Evaluate $x = \frac{5 + \sqrt{73}}{6}$.

> *Enter:*   (5 + 2nd √ 73)) ÷ 6 ENTER
>
> *Display:*   2.257333958

To the *nearest hundredth:* $x = 2.26$

Evaluate $x = \frac{5 - \sqrt{73}}{6}$.

> *Enter:*   (5 − 2nd √ 73)) ÷ 6 ENTER
>
> *Display:*   −.5906672909

To the *nearest hundredth:* $x = -0.59$

Answer: $x = 2.26$ or $x = -0.59$, or $\{2.26, -0.59\}$

☐ *Trigonometric Equation:* Given $3 \cos^2 \theta - 5 \cos \theta - 4 = 0$, find θ to the *nearest degree* in the interval $0° \leq \theta \leq 360°$.

Here, $a = 3$, $b = -5$, $c = -4$.

$$\cos \theta = \frac{-b \pm \sqrt{b^2 - 4ac}}{2a}$$

$$= \frac{-(-5) \pm \sqrt{(-5)^2 - 4(3)(-4)}}{2(3)} = \frac{5 \pm \sqrt{25 + 48}}{6} = \frac{5 \pm \sqrt{73}}{6}$$

We evaluate the two roots to find approximations for $\cos \theta$. Then, if $-1 \leq \cos \theta \leq 1$, we use the approximate function value of $\cos \theta$ to solve for θ. If $\cos \theta < -1$ or $\cos \theta > 1$, there are no values for θ. Solutions are shown on the following page.

Given $3 \cos^2 \theta - 5 \cos \theta - 4 = 0$, then $\cos \theta = \frac{5 \pm \sqrt{73}}{6}$.

Evaluate $\cos \theta = \frac{5 + \sqrt{73}}{6}$.

Enter: `(` `(` 5 `+` `2nd` `√` 73 `)` `)` `÷` 6 `ENTER`

Display: `2.257333958`

(There is no solution for this value of $\cos \theta$.)

Evaluate $\cos \theta = \frac{5 - \sqrt{73}}{6}$.

Enter: `(` `(` 5 `−` `2nd` `√` 73 `)` `)` `÷` 6 `ENTER`

Display: `-.5906672909`

Enter: `2nd` `cos⁻¹` `(−)` `2nd` `ANS` `ENTER`

Display: `53.7956245`

The reference angle $= 54°$ to the *nearest degree*; $\cos \theta$ is negative:

$$\text{In II: } \theta = 180° - 54° = 126°$$
$$\text{In III: } \theta = 180° + 54° = 234°$$

Answer: $\theta = 126°$ or $\theta = 234°$, or $\{126°, 234°\}$

A Third Approach for Special Quadratics

For a quadratic equation $ax^2 + bx + c = 0$, where $b = 0$ and c is negative or $c = 0$, a solution can be found by using square roots, as shown below.

☐ Solve for θ in the interval $0° \leq \theta \leq 360°$: $\tan^2 \theta - 3 = 0$.

$$\tan^2 \theta - 3 = 0$$
$$\tan^2 \theta = 3$$
$$\tan \theta = \pm \sqrt{3}$$

$\tan \theta = \sqrt{3}$	$\tan \theta = -\sqrt{3}$
In I: $\theta = 60°$	In II: $\theta = 180° - 60° = 120°$
In III: $\theta = 180° + 60° = 240°$	In IV: $\theta = 360° - 60° = 300°$

Answer: $\{60°, 120°, 240°, 300°\}$

If the roots of the quadratic equation are rational, $b = 0$, and c is negative, all three methods can be used to find a solution. These three methods, as shown in the following example, include factoring, square root, and the quadratic formula.

☐ Given $\sin^2 \theta - 1 = 0$: **a.** Solve for $\sin \theta$.
b. Solve for θ in the interval $0 \le \theta \le 2\pi$.

a. METHOD 1. *Factoring*

$$\sin^2 \theta - 1 = 0$$

$$(\sin \theta - 1)(\sin \theta + 1) = 0$$

$\sin \theta - 1 = 0$	$\sin \theta + 1 = 0$
$\sin \theta = 1$	$\sin \theta = -1$

METHOD 2. *Square root*

$$\sin^2 \theta - 1 = 0$$

$$\sin^2 \theta = 1$$

$$\sin \theta = \pm 1$$

METHOD 3. *Quadratic Formula*

$$\sin^2 \theta - 1 = 0$$

Here, $a = 1, b = 0, c = -1$.

$$\sin \theta = \frac{-b \pm \sqrt{b^2 - 4ac}}{2a}$$

$$= \frac{0 \pm \sqrt{0^2 - 4(1)(-1)}}{2(1)} = \frac{0 \pm \sqrt{0 + 4}}{2} = \frac{\pm\sqrt{4}}{2} = \pm\frac{2}{2} = \pm 1$$

b. When $\sin \theta = 1$, $\theta = \frac{\pi}{2}$. When $\sin \theta = -1$, $\theta = \frac{3\pi}{2}$.

Answers: **a.** $\sin \theta = +1$ or -1 **b.** $\theta = \frac{\pi}{2}$ or $\frac{3\pi}{2}$

EXAMPLES

1. Solve the equation $2 \cos^2 \theta = \cos \theta$ for all values of θ in the interval $0° \le \theta \le 360°$.

How to Proceed:	*Solution:*
(1) Write the quadratic equation in standard form.	$2 \cos^2 \theta = \cos \theta$ $2 \cos^2 \theta - \cos \theta = 0$
(2) Factor.	$\cos \theta \, (2 \cos \theta - 1) = 0$

(3) Let each factor equal 0, and solve for $\cos \theta$.	$\cos \theta = 0$ | $2 \cos \theta - 1 = 0$
	   | $2 \cos \theta = 1$
	   | $\cos \theta = \frac{1}{2}$

(4) For each $\cos \theta$, find the value of θ in the given interval.	$\theta = 90°$ | $\theta = 60°$ or $270°$ | or $300°$

Answer: $\{60°, 90°, 270°, 300°\}$

2. In the interval $0° \le \theta < 360°$, find to the *nearest degree* all values of θ that satisfy the equation $3 \sin \theta + 4 = \frac{1}{\sin \theta}$.

How to Proceed:	*Solution:*

(1) Write an equivalent equation without fractions by multiplying each side by $\sin \theta$.

$$3 \sin \theta + 4 = \frac{1}{\sin \theta}$$

$$3 \sin^2 \theta + 4 \sin \theta = 1$$

(2) Write the equation in standard form, and solve by using the quadratic formula.

$$3 \sin^2 \theta + 4 \sin \theta - 1 = 0$$

$$a = 3, b = 4, c = -1$$

$$\sin \theta = \frac{-b \pm \sqrt{b^2 - 4ac}}{2a}$$

$$= \frac{-(4) \pm \sqrt{4^2 - 4(3)(-1)}}{2(3)}$$

$$= \frac{-4 \pm \sqrt{16 + 12}}{6}$$

$$= \frac{-4 \pm \sqrt{28}}{6}$$

(3) Evaluate $\sin \theta = \frac{-4 + \sqrt{28}}{6}$ and, if possible, find θ.

Enter:

Display: $\boxed{.215250437}$

Enter:
2nd	**SIN⁻¹**	**2nd**
ANS	**ENTER**	

Display: $\boxed{12.4302203}$

To the nearest degree, $\theta = 12°$

Also, in II: $\theta = 180° - 12° = 168°$

(4) Evaluate $\sin \theta = \frac{-4 - \sqrt{28}}{6}$ and, if possible, find θ.

Enter:

Display: $\boxed{-1.54858377}$

(There is no solution for this value of $\sin \theta$.)

Answer: $\theta = 12°$ or $\theta = 168°$, or $\{12°, 168°\}$

EXERCISES WITH OPEN-RESPONSE PROBLEMS

In 1–8, find all values of θ in the interval $0° \leq \theta < 360°$ that satisfy each equation.

1. $\sin^2 \theta - \sin \theta = 0$

2. $3 \tan^2 \theta - 1 = 0$

3. $2 \cos^2 \theta - 1 = 0$

4. $\cos^2 \theta - \cos \theta = 2$

5. $2 \sin^2 \theta - \sin \theta = 1$

6. $3 \sec^2 \theta + 5 \sec \theta = 2$

7. $2 \sin \theta + 1 = \frac{1}{\sin \theta}$

8. $\tan \theta = \frac{1}{\tan \theta}$

9. Find the measure of the smallest positive acute angle for which $2 \sin^2 \theta - 3 \sin \theta + 1 = 0$.

10. Find a value of x in the interval $0° \leq x < 360°$ that satisfies $\sin^2 x - 3 \sin x - 4 = 0$.

11. How many solutions to the equation $2 \sin^2 \theta - 3 \sin \theta + 1 = 0$ are there in the interval $0° \leq \theta \leq 90°$?

12. How many solutions to the equation $2 \cos^2 \theta + 3 \cos \theta + 1 = 0$ are there in the interval $0° \leq \theta \leq 90°$?

13. How many solutions to the equation $4 \cos^2 x + 3 \cos x - 1 = 0$ are there in the interval $0° \leq x < 180°$?

14. How many solutions to the equation $9 \sin^2 x - 6 \sin x + 1 = 0$ are there in the interval $0° \leq x < 360°$?

In 15–19, select the *numeral* preceding the expression that best completes each sentence.

15. The solution set of $\cos^2 \theta - \cos \theta - 2 = 0$ for $0° \leq \theta < 360°$ is

(1) $\{0°\}$ (2) $\{180°\}$ (3) $\{0°, 180°\}$ (4) $\{60°, 180°, 300°\}$

16. The smallest positive measure for which $2 \cos^2 \theta = \cos \theta$ is

(1) $0°$ (2) $30°$ (3) $60°$ (4) $90°$

17. A value of θ that is *not* a solution of $\cos^2 \theta - \cos \theta = 0$ is

(1) 0 (2) $\frac{\pi}{2}$ (3) π (4) $\frac{3\pi}{2}$

18. A value of θ that is a solution of the equation $\sec \theta = \frac{1}{\sec \theta}$ is

(1) 0 (2) $\frac{\pi}{4}$ (3) $\frac{\pi}{2}$ (4) $\frac{3\pi}{2}$

19. A value of θ that is a solution of the equation $2 \cos^2 \theta + \cos \theta = 0$ is

(1) $60°$ (2) $-60°$ (3) $0°$ (4) $240°$

In 20–23, use factoring to find to the *nearest degree* all values of θ in the interval $0° \leq \theta < 360°$ that satisfy each equation.

20. $\tan^2 \theta - 5 \tan \theta + 6 = 0$

21. $4 \sin^2 \theta - 3 \sin \theta - 1 = 0$

22. $3 \cos^2 \theta - 7 \cos \theta + 2 = 0$

23. $5 \sin^2 \theta + 4 \sin \theta = 0$

In 24–27, find to the *nearest degree* all values of θ in the interval $0° \leq \theta \leq 360°$ that satisfy each equation.

24. $25 \sin^2 \theta - 1 = 0$

25. $\tan^2 \theta = 16$

26. $2 \tan \theta - 7 = \dfrac{4}{\tan \theta}$

27. $\dfrac{2}{\cos \theta} = 5 \cos \theta + 3$

In 28–35, use the quadratic formula to find to the *nearest degree* all values of θ in the interval $0° \leq \theta < 360°$ that satisfy each equation.

28. $4 \sin^2 \theta - 2 \sin \theta - 3 = 0$

29. $2 \tan^2 \theta - \tan \theta - 2 = 0$

30. $9 \cos^2 \theta - 6 \cos \theta = 2$

31. $3 \sin^2 \theta - 1 = \sin \theta$

32. $5 \cos^2 \theta - 2 = 4 \cos \theta$

33. $8(\sin^2 \theta - \sin \theta) = 1$

34. $1 - 4 \cos \theta = 2 \cos^2 \theta$

35. $\tan^2 \theta = 8 \tan \theta - 5$

36. If $0° \leq x < 360°$, find all values of x for which $4 \sin^3 x - \sin x = 0$.

In 37–52, use any method to find to the *nearest minute* all values of θ that satisfy each equation in the interval $0° \leq \theta < 360°$. (*Note.* In at least one case, and perhaps more, the solution is the empty set, $\varnothing$.)

37. $3 \cos^2 \theta - 8 \cos \theta - 3 = 0$

38. $\sin^2 \theta + 2 \sin \theta - 5 = 0$

39. $49 \sin^2 \theta - 4 = 0$

40. $8 \cos^2 \theta + \cos \theta = 7$

41. $3 \tan^2 \theta + \tan \theta = 4$

42. $9 \cos^2 \theta - 37 \cos \theta + 4 = 0$

43. $3 \sin^2 \theta + \sin \theta = 10$

44. $2 \tan^2 \theta - 3 \tan \theta - 4 = 0$

45. $7 \cos^2 \theta = 5 \cos \theta + 1$

46. $6 \sin^2 \theta + 7 \sin \theta = 10$

47. $5 \sin^2 \theta + 9 \sin \theta + 4 = 0$

48. $2 \sin^2 \theta + 5 \sin \theta = 12$

49. $\cos^2 \theta = 5 + 8 \cos \theta$

50. $15 \sin^2 \theta + 2 = 11 \sin \theta$

51. $4 \tan \theta (6 - 5 \tan \theta) = 7$

52. $\sin \theta (\sin \theta + 1) = 1$

19-13   EQUATIONS INVOLVING MORE THAN ONE FUNCTION

Different Functions

To solve a trigonometric equation that contains two or more functions of a variable, such as $2 \cos^2 \theta - \sin \theta = 1$, we will find it useful to express each variable term as the same function of the same variable. To do this in the given equation, we need to express $\cos^2 \theta$ in terms of $\sin \theta$, or $\sin \theta$ in terms of $\cos \theta$.

Since $\sin^2 \theta + \cos^2 \theta = 1$, we could replace $\cos^2 \theta$ with $1 - \sin^2 \theta$. Alternatively, since $\sin^2 \theta = 1 - \cos^2 \theta$ and $\sin \theta = \pm\sqrt{1 - \cos^2 \theta}$, we could replace $\sin \theta$ with $\pm\sqrt{1 - \cos^2 \theta}$. It is simpler to use the first substitution and to avoid the radical expression.

☐ Solve for θ in the interval $0° \leq \theta < 360°$: $\quad 2\cos^2\theta - \sin\theta = 1$.

$$2\cos^2\theta - \sin\theta = 1$$
$$2(1 - \sin^2\theta) - \sin\theta = 1$$
$$2 - 2\sin^2\theta - \sin\theta = 1$$
$$-2\sin^2\theta - \sin\theta + 1 = 0$$
$$2\sin^2\theta + \sin\theta - 1 = 0$$
$$(2\sin\theta - 1)(\sin\theta + 1) = 0$$

$2\sin\theta - 1 = 0$	$\sin\theta + 1 = 0$
$2\sin\theta = 1$	$\sin\theta = -1$
$\sin\theta = \frac{1}{2}$	$\theta = 270°$
$\theta = 30°$ or $150°$	

Answer: $\{30°, 150°, 270°\}$

Equations that contain two different functions can sometimes be solved without substitution if the two functions can be separated by factoring, as shown in the next example.

☐ If $0 \leq \theta \leq \frac{\pi}{2}$, find θ when $2\cos\theta\sin\theta - \cos\theta = 0$.

How to Proceed:	*Solution:*
(1) Factor the left-hand side.	$2\cos\theta\sin\theta - \cos\theta = 0$
	$\cos\theta\,(2\sin\theta - 1) = 0$
(2) Set each factor equal to 0. Notice that each factor contains only one function.	$\cos\theta = 0 \quad\bigm|\quad 2\sin\theta - 1 = 0$
	$\theta = \frac{\pi}{2} \quad\bigm|\quad 2\sin\theta = 1$
	$\sin\theta = \frac{1}{2}$
	$\theta = \frac{\pi}{6}$

Answer: $\left\{\dfrac{\pi}{6}, \dfrac{\pi}{2}\right\}$

Different Angle Measures

In a similar way, if an equation contains function values of two different but related angle measures, such as θ and 2θ, we write the equation in terms of a single function of a single variable. For example:

☐ Find to the *nearest degree* the measure of the positive acute angle that satisfies the equation $\cos 2\theta - 2 \sin \theta + 2 = 0$.

There are three identities that express $\cos 2\theta$ in terms of function values of θ. Since the equation also has a term in $\sin \theta$, we will choose the identity for $\cos 2\theta$ that uses $\sin \theta$; that is, $\cos 2\theta = 1 - 2 \sin^2 \theta$.

$$\cos 2\theta - 2 \sin \theta + 2 = 0$$
$$1 - 2 \sin^2 \theta - 2 \sin \theta + 2 = 0$$
$$-2 \sin^2 \theta - 2 \sin \theta + 3 = 0$$

Here, $a = -2$, $b = -2$, $c = 3$.

$$\sin \theta = \frac{-b \pm \sqrt{b^2 - 4ac}}{2a}$$
$$= \frac{-(-2) \pm \sqrt{(-2)^2 - 4(-2)(3)}}{2(-2)} = \frac{2 \pm \sqrt{28}}{-4}$$

Evaluate $\sin \theta = \dfrac{2 + \sqrt{28}}{-4}$ and, if possible, find θ.

Enter: (2 + 2nd √ 28)) ÷ (−) 4 ENTER

Display: −1.822875656

(There is no solution for this value of $\sin \theta$.)

Evaluate $\sin \theta = \dfrac{2 - \sqrt{28}}{-4}$ and, if possible, find θ.

Enter: (2 − 2nd √ 28)) ÷ (−) 4 ENTER

Display: .8228756555

Enter: 2nd SIN⁻¹ 2nd ANS ENTER

Display: 55.37370265

To the *nearest degree*: 55°

Answer: To the *nearest degree* $\theta = 55°$.

KEEP IN MIND _____

To solve trigonometric equations:

1. If the equation involves different but related angle measures, use identities to write all functions in terms of the same angle measure.
2. If the equation involves different functions, separate the functions by factoring if possible, or use identities to express different functions in terms of the same function.

EXAMPLES

1. Find all values of θ in the interval $0° \leq \theta < 360°$ that satisfy the equation $2(\sin \theta + \csc \theta) = 5$.

How to Proceed:	*Solution:*
(1) Replace $\csc \theta$ by $\frac{1}{\sin \theta}$.	$2(\sin \theta + \csc \theta) = 5$ $$2\left(\sin \theta + \frac{1}{\sin \theta}\right) = 5$$
(2) Simplify the left-hand side by multiplication.	$2 \sin \theta + \frac{2}{\sin \theta} = 5$
(3) Clear fractions; multiply both sides by $\sin \theta$.	$2 \sin^2 \theta + 2 = 5 \sin \theta$
(4) Write the quadratic equation in standard form. Solve for $\sin \theta$ by factoring or by using the quadratic formula.	$2 \sin^2 \theta - 5 \sin \theta + 2 = 0$ $(2 \sin \theta - 1)(\sin \theta - 2) = 0$

$$
\begin{array}{c|c}
2 \sin \theta - 1 = 0 & \sin \theta - 2 = 0 \\
2 \sin \theta = 1 & \sin \theta = 2 \\
\sin \theta = \frac{1}{2} &
\end{array}
$$

| (5) Find the values of θ in the given interval. | $\theta = 30°$ or $\theta = 150°$ | (There is no solution for this value of $\sin \theta$.) |

Answer: $\theta = 30°$ or $\theta = 150°$, or $\{30°, 150°\}$

2. Solve for θ in the interval $0 \leq \theta < 2\pi$: $2 \sin \theta = \tan \theta$.

How to Proceed:	*Solution:*
(1) Write the equation in terms of sines and cosines.	$2 \sin \theta = \tan \theta$ $2 \sin \theta = \dfrac{\sin \theta}{\cos \theta}$
(2) Write an equivalent equation with one member equal to 0.	$2 \sin \theta - \dfrac{\sin \theta}{\cos \theta} = 0$
(3) Factor.	$\sin \theta \left(2 - \dfrac{1}{\cos \theta} \right) = 0$

(4) Set each factor equal to 0, and solve the resulting equations.

$$\sin \theta = 0 \qquad \left| \qquad 2 - \frac{1}{\cos \theta} = 0 \right.$$

$$\theta = 0 \text{ or } \pi \qquad \left| \qquad 2 = \frac{1}{\cos \theta} \right.$$

$$2 \cos \theta = 1$$

$$\cos \theta = \frac{1}{2}$$

$$\theta = \frac{\pi}{3} \text{ or } \frac{5\pi}{3}$$

Answer: $\left\{ 0, \dfrac{\pi}{3}, \pi, \dfrac{5\pi}{3} \right\}$

EXERCISES WITH OPEN-RESPONSE PROBLEMS

In 1–10, find all values of θ in the interval $0° \leq \theta \leq 360°$ that satisfy each equation.

1. $4 \sin^2 \theta + 4 \cos \theta = 5$
2. $2 \cos^2 \theta + 3 \sin \theta - 3 = 0$
3. $\sec^2 \theta - \tan \theta - 1 = 0$
4. $2 \cos \theta + 1 = \sec \theta$
5. $2 \sin^2 \theta + 3 \cos \theta = 0$
6. $\cos^2 \theta + \sin \theta = 1$
7. $\tan \theta = 3 \cot \theta$
8. $2 \sin \theta = \csc \theta$
9. $\cos \theta = \sec \theta$
10. $\sin 2\theta = \tan \theta$

In 11–14, find all values of θ in the interval $0 \leq \theta < 2\pi$ that satisfy each equation.

11. $\cos 2\theta + \cos \theta + 1 = 0$
12. $2 \sin^2 \theta - \cos 2\theta = 0$
13. $\cos 2\theta + \sin \theta = 0$
14. $\cos 2\theta + 3 \cos \theta + 2 = 0$

In 15–30, find to the *nearest degree* the values of θ in the interval $0° \leq \theta < 360°$ that satisfy each equation.

15. $5 \sin^2 \theta + 3 \cos \theta = 3$
16. $5 \cos^2 \theta - 4 \sin \theta - 4 = 0$
17. $\sec^2 \theta + \tan \theta - 7 = 0$
18. $2 \sec^2 \theta + 7 \tan \theta - 6 = 0$
19. $5 \cos \theta + 4 = \sec \theta$
20. $7 \sin \theta + 1 = 6 \csc \theta$
21. $\tan \theta + 5 = 6 \cot \theta$
22. $\cot \theta - 2 \tan \theta - 1 = 0$
23. $3 \sin^2 \theta + 5 \cos \theta - 4 = 0$
24. $\cos^2 \theta + \sin \theta = 0$
25. $3 \cos^2 \theta + 2 \sin \theta - 1 = 0$
26. $2 \sec^2 \theta - 3 \tan \theta - 1 = 0$
27. $\cos \theta + 1 = \sec \theta$
28. $3 \cos 2\theta + 8 \sin \theta + 5 = 0$
29. $3 \cos 2\theta + 5 \cos \theta + 2 = 0$
30. $2 \cos 2\theta + \cos \theta = 0$

In 31–36, in each case: **a.** Express θ in inverse trigonometric form.   **b.** Find the principal values of θ.

31. $2 \sin \theta \cos \theta + \sin \theta = 0$ **32.** $\sec \theta \tan \theta - 2 \tan \theta = 0$

33. $\cot \theta + \cot \theta \cos \theta = 0$ **34.** $2 \sin \theta \cos \theta + \sqrt{2} \cos \theta = 0$

35. $\sin 2\theta + \cos \theta = 0$ **36.** $\sin \theta - \sin 2\theta = 0$

37. Solve the equation $1 + \sin x = 2 \cos^2 x$ for the measure of a positive acute angle.

In 38 and 39, select the *numeral* preceding the expression that best completes each sentence.

38. For values of θ in the interval $0° \leq \theta < 360°$, the solution set of $\dfrac{2 \sin 2\theta}{\cos \theta} - \dfrac{1}{\sin \theta} = 0$ is

     (1) $\{60°, 300°\}$ (2) $\{30°, 150°\}$

     (3) $\{60°, 120°\}$ (4) $\{30°, 150°, 210°, 330°\}$

39. One value of θ that satisfies the equation $\sin \theta = \cos 2\theta$ is

     (1) $0°$ (2) $30°$ (3) $90°$ (4) $210°$

CHAPTER SUMMARY

An *identity* is an equation whose solution set is the set of all possible replacements of the variable for which each member of the equation is defined.

To prove that an equation is an identity:

(1) transform one side of the equality into the form of the other side, *or*

(2) transform both sides of the equality separately into some common form.

Common techniques used to prove an identity include transforming terms to those of sines and cosines, and using these basic identities:

Reciprocal Identities	*Quotient Identities*	*Pythagorean Identities*
$\sec \theta = \dfrac{1}{\cos \theta}$	$\tan \theta = \dfrac{\sin \theta}{\cos \theta}$	$\sin^2 \theta + \cos^2 \theta = 1$
$\csc \theta = \dfrac{1}{\sin \theta}$	$\cot \theta = \dfrac{\cos \theta}{\sin \theta}$	$\tan^2 \theta + 1 = \sec^2 \theta$
$\cot \theta = \dfrac{1}{\tan \theta}$		$1 + \cot^2 \theta = \csc^2 \theta$

For angle measures θ, A, and B, the following identities were proved in this chapter:

$\sin \theta = \cos (90° - \theta)$ $\cos \theta = \sin (90° - \theta)$	$\sin (-\theta) = -\sin \theta$ $\cos (-\theta) = \cos \theta$
Sums of Angle Measures $\sin (A + B) = \sin A \cos B + \cos A \sin B$ $\cos (A + B) = \cos A \cos B - \sin A \sin B$ $\tan (A + B) = \frac{\tan A + \tan B}{1 - \tan A \tan B}$	**Differences of Angle Measures** $\sin (A - B) = \sin A \cos B - \cos A \sin B$ $\cos (A - B) = \cos A \cos B + \sin A \sin B$ $\tan (A - B) = \frac{\tan A - \tan B}{1 + \tan A \tan B}$
Double-Angle Measures $\sin 2A = 2 \sin A \cos A$ $\cos 2A = \cos^2 A - \sin^2 A$ $\cos 2A = 2 \cos^2 A - 1$ $\cos^2 A = 1 - 2 \sin^2 A$ $\tan 2A = \frac{2 \tan A}{1 - \tan^2 A}$	**Half-Angle Measures** $\sin \tfrac{1}{2} A = \pm \sqrt{\dfrac{1 - \cos A}{2}}$ $\cos \tfrac{1}{2} A = \pm \sqrt{\dfrac{1 + \cos A}{2}}$ $\tan \tfrac{1}{2} A = \pm \sqrt{\dfrac{1 - \cos A}{1 + \cos A}}$

A ***trigonometric equation*** is an equation in which the variable is expressed in terms of a trigonometric function value. The procedures used to simplify a trigonometric equation are the same as those used to simplify any algebraic equation.

If an equation contains two or more different trigonometric functions, either separate the functions by factoring or express the different functions in terms of the same function. If different but related angle measures, such as θ and 2θ, appear in the same equation, use identities to write all functions in terms of the same angle measure.

VOCABULARY

19-1	Identity	Conditional equation
19-11	Trigonometric equation	

REVIEW EXERCISES WITH OPEN-RESPONSE PROBLEMS

In 1–6, prove each identity.

1. $\csc \theta = \dfrac{\sec \theta}{\tan \theta}$

2. $\sin \theta \tan \theta + \cos \theta = \sec \theta$

3. $\dfrac{1 + \cos 2\theta}{\sin 2\theta} = \cot \theta$

4. $\dfrac{2 \tan \theta - \sin 2\theta}{2 \tan \theta} = \sin^2 \theta$

5. $\sin 2\theta = \dfrac{2}{\tan \theta + \cot \theta}$

6. $\dfrac{1}{1 + \sin \theta} + \dfrac{1}{1 - \sin \theta} = 2 \sec^2 \theta$

In 7–10, solve each equation for θ in the interval $0° \le \theta \le 360°$.

7. $3 - 3 \sin \theta - 2 \cos^2 \theta = 0$

8. $\sin 2\theta + 2 \cos \theta = 0$

9. $\sec^2 \theta - \tan \theta - 1 = 0$

10. $\cos 2\theta + \sin^2 \theta - 1 = 0$

In 11–14, find to the *nearest degree* the values of θ that satisfy each equation in the interval $0° \le \theta \le 360°$.

11. $3 \cos 2\theta + \cos \theta + 2 = 0$

12. $7 \cos^2 \theta - 4 \sin \theta = 4$

13. $2 \tan \theta - 2 \cot \theta - 3 = 0$

14. $9 \sin^2 \theta + 6 \cos \theta - 8 = 0$

15. Find the three factors of $9 \cos^3 \theta - \cos \theta$.
16. Find the three factors of $\cos \theta - \cos \theta \sin^2 \theta$.
17. Find the smallest positive value of θ for which $3 \tan^2 \theta - 1 = 0$.
18. Find the measure, θ, of the smallest acute angle that is a solution of the equation $2 \cos^2 \theta - 5 \cos \theta + 2 = 0$.

19. If x is the measure of an acute angle and $\cos x = \frac{1}{2}$, find $\sin \frac{1}{2} x$.

20. If θ is the measure of an obtuse angle and $\cos \theta = -\frac{8}{17}$, find $\tan \frac{1}{2} \theta$.

21. If x is the measure of an acute angle and $\sin x = 0.9716$, find the value of $\sin (\pi + x)$.

22. If θ is the measure of an acute angle and $\sin \theta = \frac{1}{3}$, find $\cos 2\theta$.

23. If x is the measure of an angle in Quadrant III and $\cos x = -\frac{3}{5}$, find $\sin 2x$.

In 24–37, select the *numeral* preceding the expression that best completes the sentence or answers the question.

24. The expression $\sin 2\theta \csc \theta$ is equivalent to
   (1) $\sin^2 2\theta$ (2) $\sin^2 \theta$ (3) $2 \sin \theta$ (4) $2 \cos \theta$
25. The expression $\cos^2 2\theta + \sin^2 2\theta$ is equivalent to
   (1) 1 (2) 2 (3) $\cos \theta$ (4) $\cos 4\theta$

26. Which of the following is *not* an identity?
(1) $\sin(-x) = -\sin x$
(2) $\cos(-x) = -\cos x$
(3) $\tan(-x) = -\tan x$
(4) $\cot(-x) = -\cot x$

27. If $\tan x = -\frac{1}{4}$ and $\tan y = 2$, then the value of $\tan(x + y)$ is

(1) $\frac{9}{2}$ (2) $\frac{7}{2}$ (3) $\frac{9}{6}$ (4) $\frac{7}{6}$

28. The expression $\cos 40° \cos 30° - \sin 40° \sin 30°$ is equivalent to
(1) $\sin 70°$ (2) $\sin 10°$ (3) $\cos 70°$ (4) $\cos 10°$

29. The value of $\sin 10° \cos 20° + \cos 10° \sin 20°$ is

(1) $\frac{\sqrt{3}}{2}$ (2) $\frac{1}{2}$ (3) $\frac{\sqrt{2}}{2}$ (4) $\frac{\sqrt{3}}{3}$

30. The expression $\cos(x - 90°)$ is equivalent to
(1) $-\cos x$ (2) $\cos x$ (3) $-\sin x$ (4) $\sin x$

31. The expression $\sin\left(x - \frac{3\pi}{2}\right)$ is equivalent to

(1) $-\cos x$ (2) $\cos x$ (3) $-\sin x$ (4) $\sin x$

32. How many solutions to the equation $2\cos^2 \theta + 3\cos \theta + 1 = 0$ are there in the interval $0° \leq \theta \leq 360°$?
(1) 0   (2) 2   (3) 3   (4) 4

33. How many solutions to the equation $\cos^2 \theta - 5\cos \theta + 6 = 0$ are there in the interval $0° \leq \theta \leq 360°$?
(1) 1   (2) 2   (3) 3   (4) 0

34. If $\cos(\theta - 40°) = \sin 50°$, then the value in degrees of θ is
(1) 40   (2) 50   (3) 80   (4) 90

35. If $\tan x = \frac{1}{2}$ and $\tan y = \frac{1}{3}$, then $\tan(x + y)$ equals

(1) 1   (2) $\frac{5}{6}$ (3) $\frac{6}{5}$ (4) $\frac{5}{7}$

36. If $\cos \theta = \frac{1}{8}$ and $270° < \theta < 360°$, then $\cos \frac{1}{2}\theta$ equals

(1) $\frac{3}{4}$ (2) $\frac{\sqrt{7}}{4}$ (3) $-\frac{3}{4}$ (4) $-\frac{\sqrt{7}}{4}$

37. If $A = \text{Arc cos } \frac{5}{13}$, what is the value of $\tan \frac{A}{2}$?

(1) $\frac{2}{3}$ (2) $\frac{6}{5}$ (3) $\frac{3}{2}$ (4) $\frac{12}{5}$

38. If $\sin \frac{1}{2}\theta = \frac{\sqrt{5}}{3}$, find $\cos\theta$.

39. If x and y are the measures of acute angles, $\sin x = \frac{5}{13}$, and $\cos y = \frac{3}{5}$, find:

    a. $\sin(x+y)$ **b.** $\cos(x-y)$ **c.** $\tan 2x$ **d.** $\cos\frac{1}{2}y$ **e.** $\sin\left(\frac{\pi}{2}+x\right)$

    f. $\tan(-x)$

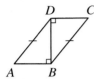

40. Diagonal $\overline{BD}$ of quadrilateral $ABCD$ is perpendicular to $\overline{AB}$ and to $\overline{DC}$, $AD = BC$, and $m\angle A = 2\,m\angle DBC$.
    a. Find $m\angle DBC$ and $m\angle A$.
    b. Prove: $ABCD$ is a parallelogram.
    (*Hint:* Express BD as function values of $\angle A$ and $\angle DCB$.)

CUMULATIVE REVIEW WITH OPEN-RESPONSE PROBLEMS

1. Write a statement that is logically equivalent to "If today is Saturday or Sunday, then I do not have to go to school."

2. In the diagram $\ell_1 \parallel \ell_2$ and $\ell_2 \parallel \ell_3$.
    a. What postulate can be used to prove that $\ell_1 \parallel \ell_3$?
    b. If $m\angle 1 = 65$, determine $m\angle 2$.

3. Solve for x: $7x - 5 > 10x + 7$

4. *Given:* $\triangle ABC$ with $\overline{AC} \cong \overline{BC}$ and $m\angle ACB < 90$.
    Prove: $m\angle A > 45$.

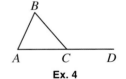

Ex. 4

5. Points $A(1, 0)$, $B(5, 0)$, and $C(8, 4)$ are the vertices of parallelogram $ABCD$. What are the coordinates of D?

6. Prove that the length of the line segment joining the midpoints of the two nonparallel sides of a trapezoid is equal to one-half the sum of the lengths of the parallel sides.

7. Simplify: $\dfrac{(a^2b)^{-1}}{a^{-4}b^2}$.

8. Between what two consecutive integers does $\dfrac{\sqrt{2}-4}{\sqrt{2}+1}$ lie?

9. A tangent line, $\overleftrightarrow{PA}$, intersects circle O at A and a secant, $\overline{PBC}$, intersects circle O at B and C. If $PA = 5$ and $PB:BC = 1:3$, find:
    a. PB **b.** PC

10. If $f(x) = \sqrt{x-1}$, find: **a.** the domain of f   **b.** the range of f   **c.** $f^{-1}(x)$
   d. the domain of $f^{-1}(x)$ **e.** the range of $f^{-1}(x)$

11. a. Sketch the graph of $y = \sin 2x$ in the interval $-\pi \le x \le \pi$.
   b. On the same set of axes, sketch the graph of $y = x$.
   c. Using the graphs drawn in parts **a** and **b**, determine the number of solutions of the equation $\sin 2x = x$.

Exploration

Express in terms of r, θ, and ϕ, the coordinates of A', which is the image of $A(r \cos \theta, r \sin \theta)$ under a rotation of ϕ about the origin.
   Find to the *nearest tenth* the coordinates of B', the image of $B(-3, 4)$ under a rotation of $50°$ about the origin.

Chapter 20

The Complex Numbers

In the world of animals, a horse, a lion, and an eagle are real. Many centuries ago, mythology and fables introduced animals that are not real; such *imaginary* creatures include the griffin, the unicorn, and the dragon. A griffin is a beast with the head and wings of an eagle and the body of a lion. A unicorn is portrayed as a horse with a single spiraled horn projecting from its forehead. A dragon is represented as a giant reptile, often having a serpent's tail, lion's claws, wings, and a scaly body.

In the world of mathematics, we have studied the *real* number system, starting with counting numbers only, then 0 and negative numbers, and eventually rational and irrational numbers. Are there numbers that are not real? And, if so, do these numbers have any use?

Rafaello Bombelli, an Italian mathematician, wrote of numbers that are not real, called *imaginary* numbers, in his *Algebra* (1572). Complex numbers, formed by adding real and imaginary numbers, were later displayed on a two-dimensional plane by mathematician Carl Friedrich Gauss. In this chapter, we will study both imaginary and complex numbers. Imaginary numbers, unlike imaginary creatures, play a significant role in our world, particularly in applications involving electricity and engineering.

20-1   IMAGINARY NUMBERS

We have learned how to solve quadratic equations having real roots. Some real roots, such as 2 and -2, are rational; other real roots, such as $\sqrt{3}$ and $-\sqrt{3}$, are irrational.

Solve: $\quad x^2 - 4 = 0$	*Solve:* $\quad x^2 - 3 = 0$
$x^2 = 4$	$x^2 = 3$
$x = \pm 2$	$x = \pm\sqrt{3}$
Answer: $x = 2$ or $x = -2$	*Answer:* $x = \sqrt{3}$ or $x = -\sqrt{3}$

There are quadratic equations, however, that have no roots in the set of real numbers. For example, to solve $x^2 + 1 = 0$, we write the equivalent equation, $x^2 = -1$. But the square of a real number is either positive or 0; that is, the square of a real number cannot be negative.

The equation $x^2 + 1 = 0$ will have two roots only if we agree to *extend our number system beyond the set of real numbers* to include numbers such as $\sqrt{-1}$ and $-\sqrt{-1}$.

Solve: $\qquad x^2 + 1 = 0$
$$x^2 = -1$$
$$x = \pm\sqrt{-1}$$
Answer: $x = \sqrt{-1}$ or $x = -\sqrt{-1}$

The numbers $\sqrt{-1}$ and $-\sqrt{-1}$ are *not* real numbers. Early mathematicians called these numbers *imaginary* because the numbers certainly are *not real*.

To simplify notation, we use i to represent the square root of -1. Therefore:

$$i = \sqrt{-1} \qquad \text{and} \qquad -i = -\sqrt{-1}$$

The number i, or the number $\sqrt{-1}$, is called the **imaginary unit** because it is the basis upon which a new set of numbers, called *imaginary numbers*, is built.

● **DEFINITION.** A **pure imaginary number** is any number that can be expressed in the form bi, where b is a real number such that $b \neq 0$, and i is the imaginary unit $\sqrt{-1}$.

Examples of pure imaginary numbers include $\sqrt{-25}$, $\sqrt{-7}$, $-2\sqrt{-9}$, and $\sqrt{-12}$ because:

1. $\sqrt{-25} = \sqrt{25}\sqrt{-1} = 5\sqrt{-1} = 5i$. (Although $5\sqrt{-1}$ and $5i$ indicate the same number, we will write the number in the form $5i$ in this book.)
2. $\sqrt{-7} = \sqrt{7}\sqrt{-1} = \sqrt{7}i = i\sqrt{7}$. (By writing $\sqrt{-7}$ as $i\sqrt{7}$, we make it clear that i is not a term under the radical sign.)
3. $-2\sqrt{-9} = -2\sqrt{9}\sqrt{-1} = -2 \cdot 3i = -6i$.
4. $\sqrt{-12} = \sqrt{12}\sqrt{-1} = \sqrt{4}\sqrt{3}\sqrt{-1} = 2\sqrt{3}i = 2i\sqrt{3}$.

● **In general, for any real number b, where $b > 0$:**

$$\sqrt{-b^2} = \sqrt{b^2}\sqrt{-1} = bi$$

Note: By the zero property of multiplication, $0i = 0 \cdot i = 0$, a real number.

Calculator Limitations

A scientific calculator is capable of displaying rational values only. For example, we know that the irrational number $\sqrt{3}$ is displayed as the rational approximation 1.732050808.

As shown below, any attempt to display an imaginary number on a calculator will result in an ERROR message.

$$\sqrt{-1} \to \textit{Enter:} \quad \boxed{\text{2nd}} \; \boxed{\sqrt{}} \; \boxed{(-)} \; 1 \; \boxed{\text{ENTER}}$$

$$\textit{Display:} \quad \boxed{\text{ERR: NONREAL ANS}}$$

For this reason, the study of any values involving an imaginary number will rely on algebraic techniques, not on calculator usage.

Powers of *i*

Since the solution of $x^2 = -1$ is $x = \sqrt{-1}$ or $x = -\sqrt{-1}$, it follows that:

$$(\sqrt{-1})^2 = -1 \qquad \text{and} \qquad (-\sqrt{-1})^2 = -1$$

Or, by substitution:

$$(i)^2 = -1 \qquad \text{and} \qquad (-i)^2 = -1$$

Using $i = \sqrt{-1}$ and $i^2 = -1$, we can build a table of the powers of i.

$$i = \sqrt{-1} \text{ or } i$$

$$i^2 = i \cdot i = -1$$

$$i^3 = i \cdot i \cdot i = i^2 \cdot i = -1\sqrt{-1} = -\sqrt{-1}, \text{ or simply } -i$$

$$i^4 = i \cdot i \cdot i \cdot i = i^2 \cdot i^2 = (-1)(-1) = 1$$

Let us see what happens now:

$$i^5 = i^4 \cdot i = 1 \cdot i = i$$

$$i^6 = i^4 \cdot i^2 = 1(-1) = -1$$

$$i^7 = i^4 \cdot i^3 = 1(-i) = -i$$

$$i^8 = i^4 \cdot i^4 = 1 \cdot 1 = 1$$

The powers of i repeat in a definite cycle: i, -1, $-i$, 1. By definition, $i^0 = 1$. Therefore:

$i^0 = 1$	$i^1 = i$	$i^2 = -1$	$i^3 = -i$
$i^4 = 1$	$i^5 = i$	$i^6 = -1$	$i^7 = -i$
$i^8 = 1$	$i^9 = i$	$i^{10} = -1$	$i^{11} = -i$

- **In general, for any power of i where k is a whole number:**

$$i^{4k} = 1 \qquad i^{4k+1} = i \qquad i^{4k+2} = -1 \qquad i^{4k+3} = -i$$

By moving in a clockwise direction within the circle at the right, we see that the powers of i behave exactly like a clock 4 system. In fact, when a whole number exponent is divided by 4, its remainder must be 0, 1, 2, or 3 (the same numbers as on a clock 4). Powers of i

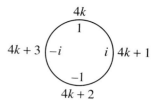

can be simplified by using the rules stated above or the remainders 0, 1, 2, 3. For example:

☐   Write i^{82} in simplest terms:

METHOD 1. *Use the rule.*

Since $i^{82} = i^{4(20)+2}$
and $i^{4k+2} = -1$,

then $i^{82} = i^{4(20)+2} = -1$.

Answer: $i^{82} = -1$

METHOD 2. *Use remainders.*

Since $82 \div 4 = 20$ with a *remainder of 2*,
then i^{82} is equivalent to i^2. Thus:

$$i^{82} = i^2 = -1.$$

Properties and Operations

Many familiar properties are true for the set of imaginary numbers, including the *commutative* and *associative* properties of both addition and multiplication, and the *distributive* property of multiplication over addition. These properties are used in performing operations with imaginary numbers. In each of the following examples, numbers are first expressed in terms of i, and then operations are performed.

Addition:
$$\sqrt{-16} + \sqrt{-9} = \sqrt{16}\sqrt{-1} + \sqrt{9}\sqrt{-1}$$
$$= 4i + 3i = (4 + 3)i = 7i$$

Subtraction:
$$\sqrt{-16} - \sqrt{-16} = \sqrt{16}\sqrt{-1} - \sqrt{16}\sqrt{-1}$$
$$= 4i - 4i = (4 - 4)i = 0i = 0$$

Multiplication:
$$\sqrt{-16}\sqrt{-9} = \sqrt{16}\sqrt{-1} \cdot \sqrt{9}\sqrt{-1}$$
$$= 4i \cdot 3i$$
$$= (4 \cdot 3)(i \cdot i)$$
$$= 12i^2 = 12(-1) = -12$$

Note: It is incorrect to use the rule $\sqrt{a}\sqrt{b} = \sqrt{ab}$ with pure imaginary numbers since this rule is true only when $a \geq 0$ and $b \geq 0$.

Division: $\sqrt{-16} \div \sqrt{-9} = \dfrac{\sqrt{-16}}{\sqrt{-9}} = \dfrac{\sqrt{16}\sqrt{-1}}{\sqrt{9}\sqrt{-1}} = \dfrac{4i}{3i} = \dfrac{4}{3}$

The examples just studied illustrate that:

1. The sum, or the difference, of two pure imaginary numbers is a *pure imaginary number*, except when the result is $0i = 0$.

2. The product, or the quotient, of two pure imaginary numbers is always a *real number*.

EXAMPLE

Express in terms of i the sum $4\sqrt{-18} + \sqrt{-50}$.

How to Proceed: *Solution:*

(1) Write each number in simplest radical form and in terms of i.

$$4\sqrt{-18} \quad + \sqrt{-50}$$
$$= 4\sqrt{9}\sqrt{2}\sqrt{-1} + \sqrt{25}\sqrt{2}\sqrt{-1}$$
$$= 4 \cdot 3\sqrt{2} \cdot i \quad + 5\sqrt{2} \cdot i$$
$$= 12i\sqrt{2} \quad\quad + 5i\sqrt{2}$$

(2) Use the distributive property to simplify the expression.

$$= (12 + 5)i\sqrt{2}$$
$$= 17i\sqrt{2}$$

Answer: $17i\sqrt{2}$

EXERCISES WITH OPEN-RESPONSE PROBLEMS

In 1–25, express each number in terms of i, and simplify.

1. $\sqrt{-36}$ **2.** $\sqrt{-100}$ **3.** $-\sqrt{-81}$ **4.** $2\sqrt{-49}$ **5.** $\frac{1}{8}\sqrt{-64}$

6. $-\frac{2}{3}\sqrt{-9}$ **7.** $\frac{3}{4}\sqrt{-144}$ **8.** $\frac{1}{3}\sqrt{-25}$ **9.** $\sqrt{-\frac{1}{4}}$ **10.** $\sqrt{-\frac{16}{25}}$

11. $4\sqrt{-\frac{49}{64}}$ **12.** $\frac{3}{5}\sqrt{-\frac{100}{9}}$ **13.** $\sqrt{-3}$ **14.** $\sqrt{-29}$ **15.** $3\sqrt{-11}$

16. $-\sqrt{-10}$ **17.** $\sqrt{-20}$ **18.** $-\sqrt{-28}$ **19.** $2\sqrt{-75}$ **20.** $5\sqrt{-8}$

21. $\frac{2}{3}\sqrt{-72}$ **22.** $-\frac{1}{2}\sqrt{-300}$ **23.** $-\sqrt{-\frac{1}{3}}$ **24.** $4\sqrt{-\frac{1}{8}}$ **25.** $\sqrt{-0.72}$

In 26–35, write each given power of i in simplest terms as 1, i, -1, or $-i$.

26. i^{12} **27.** i^{7} **28.** i^{49} **29.** i^{72} **30.** i^{54}

31. i^{99} **32.** i^{300} **33.** i^{246} **34.** i^{91} **35.** i^{2001}

In 36–57, write each number in terms of i, perform the indicated operation, and write the answer in simplest terms.

36. $\sqrt{-64} + \sqrt{-36}$ **37.** $3\sqrt{-4} + \sqrt{-121}$ **38.** $\sqrt{-100} - \sqrt{-9}$

39. $\sqrt{-16} - 2\sqrt{-4}$ **40.** $\sqrt{-45} + \sqrt{-5}$ **41.** $8\sqrt{-3} - \sqrt{-12}$

42. $\frac{1}{2}\sqrt{-200} - \sqrt{-32}$ **43.** $-2\sqrt{-18} - \frac{1}{5}\sqrt{-50}$ **44.** $\sqrt{-196} - \sqrt{-225}$

45. $\sqrt{-289} + \sqrt{-169}$ **46.** $\sqrt{-49} \cdot \sqrt{-1}$ **47.** $\sqrt{-81} \cdot \sqrt{-25}$

48. $\sqrt{-2} \cdot \sqrt{-18}$ **49.** $\sqrt{-5} \cdot \sqrt{-80}$ **50.** $-4\sqrt{-3} \cdot \sqrt{-3}$

51. $-3\sqrt{-10} \cdot 2\sqrt{-10}$ **52.** $6\sqrt{-6} \cdot \frac{2}{3}\sqrt{-6}$ **53.** $\frac{2}{3}\sqrt{-7} \cdot \sqrt{-63}$

54. $\dfrac{\sqrt{-400}}{\sqrt{-25}}$ **55.** $\dfrac{\sqrt{-98}}{\sqrt{-2}}$ **56.** $\dfrac{-\sqrt{-48}}{4\sqrt{-3}}$ **57.** $\dfrac{-\sqrt{-20}}{\sqrt{-180}}$

58. Express in terms of i the sum $\sqrt{-81} + 3\sqrt{-25} + \sqrt{-4}$.

59. Express in terms of i the sum $\sqrt{-72} + \sqrt{-32} + 3\sqrt{-8}$.

In 60–67, select the *numeral* preceding the expression that best completes the sentence or answers the question.

60. The expression $\sqrt{-192}$ is equivalent to
 (1) $-8\sqrt{3}$ (2) $8\sqrt{3}$ (3) $8i\sqrt{3}$ (4) $-8i\sqrt{3}$

61. If $\sqrt{-60}$ is subtracted from $\sqrt{-135}$, the difference is
 (1) $\sqrt{-75}$ (2) $i\sqrt{15}$ (3) $-i\sqrt{15}$ (4) i

62. The product $i^8 \cdot i^9 \cdot i^{10}$ equals
 (1) 1 (2) i (3) -1 (4) $-i$

63. The product of $2i^2 \cdot 3i^3$ is
 (1) 6 (2) $6i$ (3) -6 (4) $-6i$

64. The value of $(3i^3)^2$ is
 (1) 6 (2) -6 (3) 9 (4) -9

65. The sum of $5i^5$ and i^9 is
 (1) $6i$ (2) $5i$ (3) -5 (4) -6

66. The solution set of $x^2 + 9 = 0$ is
 (1) $\{-3\}$ (2) $\{3, -3\}$ (3) $\{3i, -3i\}$ (4) $\{i, -i\}$

67. Which expression is equal to 0?
 (1) $i^2 \cdot i^2$ (2) $i^2 + i^2$ (3) $i^4 \cdot i^2$ (4) $i^4 + i^2$

In 68–70, solve each equation, and express its roots in terms of i.

68. $x^2 + 64 = 0$ **69.** $x^2 = 2x^2 + 16$ **70.** $2x^2 + 10 = 0$

71. a. Is the set of pure imaginary numbers closed under addition? Explain your answer.
   b. Is there an identity element for addition in the set of pure imaginary numbers? Explain your answer.

72. Give as many reasons as possible to indicate why the set of pure imaginary numbers is *not* a group under multiplication.

20-2 COMPLEX NUMBERS

The discovery of the set of pure imaginary numbers enables us to define still another set of numbers, called the *complex numbers*.

- **DEFINITION.** A *complex number* is any number that can be expressed in the form $a + bi$, where a and b are real numbers and i is the imaginary unit.

In other words, a complex number is a real number *a*, a pure imaginary number *bi*, or the sum of a real number and a pure imaginary number *a* + *bi*. Examples of complex numbers include $2 + 5i$, $-3 + 0i = -3$, $0 + 2i = 2i$, and $0 + 0i = 0$.

Mathematician Carl Friedrich Gauss gave a physical meaning to complex numbers by representing them on a two-dimensional plane. The *real number line* is drawn horizontally, and the *pure imaginary number line* is drawn vertically, as shown at the right. Since $0i = 0$, it is natural that these number lines intersect at a point that represents 0 on the real number line and $0i$ on the imaginary number line. Therefore, this point of intersection represents the complex number $0 + 0i$.

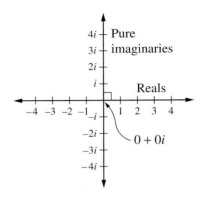

These two axes are used to form the ***complex number plane***. The real number axis is the *x*-axis, and the pure imaginary number axis is called the *yi*-axis.

The complex number plane is similar to the rectangular coordinate system studied earlier. In the same way that we located point $(x, y) = (2, 5)$, we now locate the point for the complex number $x + yi = 2 + 5i$. In other words, as shown at the right, we use the rectangular grid to locate the point of intersection of the real component 2 and the imaginary component 5*i*.

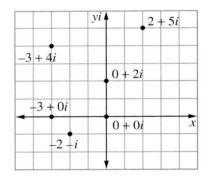

By studying other points on the complex number plane, we observe:

1. *Any complex number a + bi, where b = 0, is a real number.*

    For example, $-3 + 0i = -3$, represented by a point on the real number axis. Conversely, every real number can be expressed as a complex number, as in $5 = 5 + 0i$.

2. *Any complex number a + bi, where a = 0 and b ≠ 0, is a pure imaginary number.*

    For example, $0 + 2i = 2i$, represented by a point on the pure imaginary axis. Conversely, every pure imaginary number can be expressed as a complex number, as in $-4i = 0 - 4i$.

3. *Any complex number a + bi, where b ≠ 0, is an imaginary number.*

    For example, the complex numbers $-3 + 4i$, $-2 - i$, $2 + 5i$, and $0 + 2i$ can simply be called imaginary numbers. Notice that these numbers are represented by points in the complex number plane that are *not on the real number axis*. Of the imaginary numbers cited as examples, only $0 + 2i = 2i$ is a pure imaginary number.

● **The set of real numbers and the set of imaginary numbers are subsets of the set of complex numbers.**

Complex Numbers, Points, and Vectors

We have seen that a complex number can be represented by a *point* in the complex number plane, such as point C representing $3 + 2i$ in the first diagram.

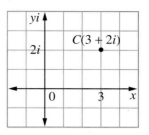

A point

The same complex number, $3 + 2i$, can also be represented as a *vector* in the complex number plane, as shown in the second diagram. Let $\overrightarrow{OA}$ represent 3, and $\overrightarrow{OB}$ represent $2i$. We will define the sum of two vectors, such as $\overrightarrow{OA} + \overrightarrow{OB}$, to be the resultant vector $\overrightarrow{OC}$ (that is, the diagonal in parallelogram $OACB$ determined by $\overrightarrow{OA}$ and $\overrightarrow{OB}$). Thus, $\overrightarrow{OC}$ is a vector representing the complex number $3 + 2i$. From this example, we observe:

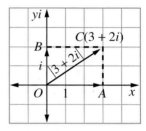

A vector

- **Every complex number can be represented as a point or as a vector in the complex number plane.**

Recall that on the real-number line the absolute value of a real number is the difference between the graphs of the number and 0. The absolute value of a complex number $a + bi$, represented by $|a^2 + b^2|$, is $\sqrt{a^2 + b^2}$ by the Pythagorean Theorem.

In the vector diagram above, the **magnitude** or length of the vector $\overrightarrow{OC}$ can be represented by $|3 + 2i| = \sqrt{3^2 + 2^2} = \sqrt{9 + 4} = \sqrt{13}$.

Equality of Complex Numbers

Two complex numbers are equal if and only if their real components are equal and their imaginary components are equal. In symbols, $a + bi = c + di$ if and only if $a = c$ and $bi = di$.

For example, $x + 3i = -5 + yi$ if and only if $x = -5$ and $3i = yi$ (or $y = 3$).

EXERCISES WITH OPEN-RESPONSE PROBLEMS

In 1–6, in each case: **a.** Write the complex number represented by the vector drawn in the accompanying diagram. **b.** Find the length of each vector.

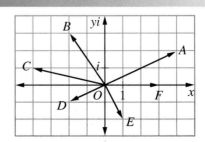

1. $\overrightarrow{OA}$ **2.** $\overrightarrow{OB}$ **3.** $\overrightarrow{OC}$

4. $\overrightarrow{OD}$ **5.** $\overrightarrow{OE}$ **6.** $\overrightarrow{OF}$

In 7–12, in each case, write the real numbers a and b that will make the equation true.

7. $a + bi = 7 + 2i$

8. $a - 6i = 4 + bi$

9. $a + \sqrt{-16} = 16 + bi$

10. $a + bi = 12 + i - 3$

11. $3i = a + bi$

12. $-\sqrt{25} = a + bi$

In 13–16, in each case: **a.** Tell whether the statement is true or false. **b.** If the statement is false, explain why.

13. The set of real numbers is a subset of the set of complex numbers.

14. If $b = 0$, then the number $a + bi$ is a real number.

15. If $a = 0$, then the number $a + bi$ is a pure imaginary number.

16. Every point on the complex number plane that does not represent a real number must represent an imaginary number.

In 17 and 18, select the *numeral* preceding the expression that best answers the question: Which number is included in the shaded area?

17. (1) $-1.5 + 3.5i$
    (2) $1.5 - 3.5i$
    (3) 3.5
    (4) $4.5i$

18. (1) $4 + 0.5i$
    (2) $-4 - 0.5i$
    (3) $2.5i$
    (4) $2.4 - i$

Ex. 17

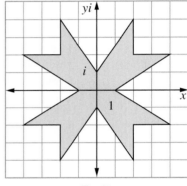

Ex. 18

20-3 ADDITION AND SUBTRACTION OF COMPLEX NUMBERS

Addition

It seems natural to treat the sum of two complex numbers as the sum of two binomials. By adding like terms, we find the sum of the real components and the sum of the pure imaginary components. At the right, an addition is performed in a vertical format. This addition may also be written in a horizontal format:

Add:
$2 + 3i$
$5 + \ i$
$7 + 4i$

$$(2 + 3i) + (5 + i) = (2 + 5) + (3i + i) = 7 + 4i$$

We can use vector addition to add the same two complex numbers. In the diagram on the next page, we let $\overrightarrow{OA}$ represent the complex number $2 + 3i$, and let $\overrightarrow{OB}$ represent $5 + i$. The sum of the vectors $\overrightarrow{OA}$ and $\overrightarrow{OB}$ is the resultant vector $\overrightarrow{OC}$ (that is, the diagonal in the parallelogram $OACB$ determined by $\overrightarrow{OA}$ and $\overrightarrow{OB}$). Thus, $\overrightarrow{OC}$ represents the complex number $7 + 4i$, and this geometric demonstration verifies the sum found above by algebraic methods.

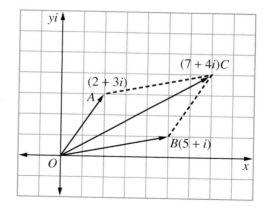

In general, whether we treat complex numbers as binomials or as vectors, we define the addition of complex numbers to be:

$$(a + bi) + (c + di) = (a + c) + (b + d)i$$

Addition Properties

The set of complex numbers under addition, or (Complex numbers, +), can be shown to have the following properties:

1. *Closure.* By the definition of addition, the sum of two complex numbers is a complex number. Thus, (Complex numbers, +) is closed.

2. *Associativity.* (Complex numbers, +) is associative. In symbols:

$$[(a + bi) + (c + di)] + (e + fi) = (a + bi) + [(c + di) + (e + fi)]$$

3. *Identity.* The identity element for the addition of real numbers is 0. However, $0 = 0 + 0i$. By this extension, we state that the identity element for (Complex numbers, +) is $0 + 0i$. This is true because

$$(a + bi) + (0 + 0i) = a + bi \qquad \text{and} \qquad (0 + 0i) + (a + bi) = a + bi$$

4. *Inverses.* The addition inverse of the complex number $a + bi$ is $-a - bi$ because

$$(a + bi) + (-a - bi) = 0 + 0i \qquad \text{and} \qquad (-a - bi) + (a + bi) = 0 + 0i$$

5. *Commutativity.* (Complex numbers, +) is commutative. In symbols:

$$(a + bi) + (c + di) = (c + di) + (a + bi)$$

Since these five properties are true, it follows that:

- **(Complex numbers, +) is a commutative group.**

Subtraction

Subtraction has been defined as the addition of an additive inverse. As shown below, to subtract $3 + 2i$, we add its inverse, $-3 - 2i$.

$$(1 + 3i) - (3 + 2i)$$
$$= (1 + 3i) + (-3 - 2i) = (1 - 3) + (3i - 2i) = -2 + i$$

Let us use vectors to demonstrate this subtraction. In the diagram, we let $\overrightarrow{OA}$ represent $1 + 3i$, and let $\overrightarrow{OB}$ represent $3 + 2i$. Since $-(3 + 2i) = -3 - 2i$, the additive inverse of $\overrightarrow{OB}$ is $\overrightarrow{OB'}$, or $-3 - 2i$.

Therefore, the subtraction of vectors, $\overrightarrow{OA} - \overrightarrow{OB}$, is treated as an addition of vectors. $\overrightarrow{OA} + \overrightarrow{OB'}$, where $\overrightarrow{OB'}$ is the additive inverse of $\overrightarrow{OB}$. The resultant $\overrightarrow{OC}$ represents $-2 + i$, which is the difference $\overrightarrow{OA} - \overrightarrow{OB}$:

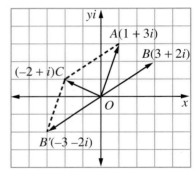

$$\overrightarrow{OA} - \overrightarrow{OB} = \overrightarrow{OA} + \overrightarrow{OB'} = \overrightarrow{OC}$$

$$(1 + 3i) - (3 + 2i)$$

In general, subtraction of complex numbers is defined as follows:

$$(a + bi) - (c + di) = (a - c) + (b - d)i$$

We note that the additive inverse of a complex number presented graphically is equivalent to moving the complex number through a point reflection in the origin, or a rotation of 180° about the origin.

EXAMPLES

1. Express the sum of $(5 + \sqrt{-36})$ and $(3 - \sqrt{-16})$ in the form $a + bi$.

Solution
$$(5 + \sqrt{-36}) + (3 - \sqrt{-16}) = (5 + 6i) + (3 - 4i)$$
$$= (5 + 3) + (6i - 4i)$$
$$= 8 + 2i$$

Answer: $8 + 2i$

---

2. Subtract $6 - 2i\sqrt{3}$ from $5 - 3i\sqrt{3}$.

Solution To subtract $6 - 2i\sqrt{3}$, add its inverse, $-6 + 2i\sqrt{3}$.
$$(5 - 3i\sqrt{3}) - (6 - 2i\sqrt{3}) = (5 - 3i\sqrt{3}) + (-6 + 2i\sqrt{3})$$
$$= (5 - 6) + (-3i\sqrt{3} + 2i\sqrt{3})$$
$$= -1 - i\sqrt{3}$$

Answer: $-1 - i\sqrt{3}$

EXERCISES WITH OPEN-RESPONSE PROBLEMS

In 1–14, in each case, perform the indicated operation and express the result in the form $a + bi$.

1. $(10 + 3i) + (5 + 8i)$
2. $(7 - 2i) + (3 - 6i)$
3. $(4 - 2i) + (-3 + 2i)$
4. $(6 + 3i) - (2 + i)$
5. $(-8 + 5i) - (5 - 7i)$
6. $(9 - 2i) - (9 - 5i)$
7. $(1.3 + 4i) + (2.9 - 1.7i)$
8. $(3.1 - 0.6i) - (4.8 - 0.4i)$
9. $\left(\frac{2}{3} - \frac{i}{4}\right) + \left(\frac{1}{6} - \frac{i}{2}\right)$
10. $\left(\frac{4}{5} + \frac{3}{8}i\right) - \left(\frac{3}{10} + \frac{3}{4}i\right)$
11. $(8 + \sqrt{-9}) - (10 + \sqrt{-4})$
12. $(-2 + \sqrt{-12}) + (8 + \sqrt{-27})$
13. $(-1 - \sqrt{-80}) - (3 + \sqrt{-20})$
14. $(5 - \sqrt{-128}) + (-5 - \sqrt{-98})$

15. Add: $5 + i, 7 - 3i, 12 + 6i, -10 - 8i$, and $-14 + 4i$.
16. Subtract $2 - 13i$ from $7 - 5i$.
17. From the sum of $3 - i$ and $-2 - 2i$, subtract $4 - 5i$.
18. Express the sum of $9 + \sqrt{-9}$ and $5 - \sqrt{-16}$ in the form $a + bi$.
19. Express the difference $(5 - \sqrt{-50}) - (-2 + \sqrt{-162})$ in the form $a + bi$.

In 20–25, in each case: **a.** Express the indicated sum or difference in the form $a + bi$. **b.** Demonstrate how this sum or difference is found using *vectors* in a complex number plane. (*Hint:* The parallelogram rule does not apply in Exercises 24 and 25.)

20. $(2 + 3i) + (3 - 2i)$
21. $(-3 - i) - (1 + 4i)$
22. $(-2 - i) - (-2 + 4i)$
23. $(5 - 4i) - (2 + 0i)$
24. $(3 + i) + (6 + 2i)$
25. $(6 - 4i) - (3 - 2i)$

26. *True* or *False*: The sum of any complex number and its additive inverse is a real number. Explain your answer.

20-4 MULTIPLICATION OF COMPLEX NUMBERS

The product of two complex numbers can be treated as the product of two binomials. Since i^2 can be replaced by -1, as shown in the following example, the product can then be written in the form of a complex number. For example:

☐ Find the product of $(3 + 2i)$ and $(2 + i)$.

METHOD 1. *The Distributive Property*

$(3 + 2i)(2 + i) = 3(2 + i) + 2i(2 + i)$

$\qquad = 6 + 3i + 4i + 2i^2$

$\qquad = 6 + 3i + 4i + 2(-1)$

$\qquad = 6 + 3i + 4i - 2$

$\qquad = 4 + 7i$

Answer: $4 + 7i$

METHOD 2. *Mental Arithmetic*

$(3 + 2i)(2 + i) = 6 + 7i + 2i^2$

$\qquad = 6 + 7i + 2(-1)$

$\qquad = 6 + 7i - 2$

$\qquad = 4 + 7i$

We may use either method to prove the following statement:

● **The product of two complex numbers is a complex number.**

Proof:
$$(a + bi)(c + di) = a(c + di) + bi(c + di)$$
$$= ac + adi + bci + bdi^2$$
$$= ac + adi + bci + bd(-1)$$
$$= ac + adi + bci - bd$$
$$= (ac - bd) + (adi + bci)$$

Thus: $$(a + bi)(c + di) = (ac - bd) + (ad + bc)i$$

In this proof, since $(a + bi)$ and $(c + di)$ are complex numbers, then a, b, c, and d are reals. By the closure properties of addition and multiplication, both $(ac - bd)$ and $(ad + bc)$ are real numbers. Therefore, the product $(ac - bd) + (ad + bc)i$ is a complex number by definition.

Multiplication, Transformations, and Vectors

To understand the multiplication of complex numbers from a graphic point of view, we will multiply $(3 + 2i)(2 + i)$ in a step-by-step manner, using transformations in these steps.

Since $(3 + 2i)(2 + i) = 3(2 + i) + 2i(2 + i)$, let $\overrightarrow{OA}$ represent $(2 + i)$ in each step.

Step 1: $3(2 + i) = 6 + 3i$
$$3 \cdot \overrightarrow{OA} = \overrightarrow{OA'}$$

Multiplication by 3 is equivalent to D_3, a *dilation of 3* with the origin as the center of dilation.

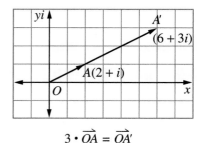

$3 \cdot \overrightarrow{OA} = \overrightarrow{OA'}$

Step 2: $i(2 + i) = 2i + i^2$
$$= 2i + (-1)$$
$$= -1 + 2i$$
$$i \cdot \overrightarrow{OA} = \overrightarrow{OB}$$

Multiplication by i is equivalent to $R_{90°}$, a *counterclockwise rotation of 90°* about the origin.

$i \cdot \overrightarrow{OA} = \overrightarrow{OB}$

Step 3: $2i(2 + i) = 4i + 2i^2$

$$= 4i - 2$$

$$= -2 + 4i$$

$$2i \cdot \overrightarrow{OA} = \overrightarrow{OB}', \text{ or}$$

$$2(\overrightarrow{OB}) = \overrightarrow{OB}'$$

Since multiplication by 2 is equivalent to D_2 and multiplication by i is equivalent to $R_{90°}$, *multiplication by 2i is equivalent to the composition of* $D_2 \circ R_{90°}$.

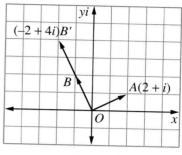

$$2i \cdot \overrightarrow{OA} = \overrightarrow{OB}'$$
$$\text{or} \quad 2(\overrightarrow{OB}) = \overrightarrow{OB}'$$

Step 4: Vector addition is used to find the resultant $\overrightarrow{OC}$. The graph includes steps 1, 2, and 3.

$$(3 + 2i)(2 + i)$$

$$= 3(2 + i) + 2i(2 + i)$$

$$= 3 \cdot \overrightarrow{OA} + 2i \cdot \overrightarrow{OA}$$

$$= \overrightarrow{OA}' + \overrightarrow{OB}'$$

$$= \overrightarrow{OC}$$

$$= 4 + 7i$$

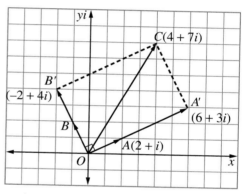

$$3 \cdot \overrightarrow{OA} + 2i \cdot \overrightarrow{OA} = \overrightarrow{OC} \quad \text{or} \quad \overrightarrow{OA}' + \overrightarrow{OB}' = \overrightarrow{OC}$$

Conjugates

The *conjugate* of the complex number $a + bi$ is the complex number $a - bi$. For example, the conjugate of $5 + 2i$ is $5 - 2i$. Similarly, $3 - i$ and $3 + i$ are conjugates of each other. Consider the following products:

$$(5 + 2i)(5 - 2i) = 25 + 10i - 10i - 4i^2 \qquad\qquad (3 - i)(3 + i) = 9 - 3i + 3i - i^2$$

$$= 25 + 10i - 10i + 4 \qquad\qquad\qquad\qquad = 9 - 3i + 3i + 1$$

$$= 29 + 0i \qquad\qquad\qquad\qquad\qquad\qquad = 10 + 0i$$

$$= 29 \qquad\qquad\qquad\qquad\qquad\qquad\qquad = 10$$

It is true that the product of two complex numbers is a complex number. However, when we multiply complex numbers that are conjugates, the imaginary component in the product is $0i$, which equals 0. We may now say:

● **The product of two complex numbers that are conjugates is a real number.**

Proof:
$$(a + bi)(a - bi) = a^2 + abi - abi - b^2i^2$$
$$= a^2 + abi - abi + b^2$$
$$= (a^2 + b^2) + (abi - abi)$$
$$= (a^2 + b^2) + (ab - ab)i$$
$$= (a^2 + b^2) + 0i$$

Thus: $$(a + bi)(a - bi) = a^2 + b^2$$

Since $(a + bi)$ and $(a - bi)$ are complex numbers, a and b are real. By the closure properties of multiplication and addition, the product $a^2 + b^2$ must also be a real number.

In the next section, we will study properties involving the multiplication of complex numbers. For the present, let us practice working with the operation.

EXAMPLES

1. Express the product of $(3 + 7i)$ and $(1 - 2i)$ in the form $a + bi$.

Solution Use either method. Let $i^2 = -1$, and simplify.

METHOD 1. *The Distributive Property*

$$(3 + 7i)(1 - 2i) = 3(1 - 2i) + 7i(1 - 2i)$$
$$= 3 - 6i + 7i - 14i^2$$
$$= 3 - 6i + 7i - 14(-1)$$
$$= 3 - 6i + 7i + 14$$
$$= 17 + 1i$$

METHOD 2. *Mental Arithmetic*

$$(3 + 7i)(1 - 2i) = 3 + 1i - 14i^2$$
$$= 3 + i - 14(-1)$$
$$= 3 + i + 14$$
$$= 17 + i$$

Answer: $17 + 1i$ or $17 + i$

2. Express the number $(4 - i)^2 - 8i^3$ in simplest terms.

How to Proceed:

Perform the operations. Reduce terms so that the highest power of i is i^1 or i. (Thus, $i^3 = -i$.)
Note: In simplest form, $a + 0i = a$.

Solution:

$$(4 - i)^2 - 8i^3 = (4 - i)(4 - i) - 8i^3$$
$$= 16 - 8i + i^2 - 8i^2 \cdot i$$
$$= 16 - 8i + (-1) - 8(-1)i$$
$$= 16 - 8i - 1 + 8i$$
$$= 15 + 0i$$
$$= 15$$

Answer: 15

EXERCISES WITH OPEN-RESPONSE PROBLEMS

In 1–13, in each case, write the product of the numbers in the form $a + bi$.

1. $(3 + i)(4 + i)$
4. $(4 - 5i)(2 + i)$
7. $(1 - 3i)(5 - 3i)$
10. $(8 + \sqrt{-25})(2 + \sqrt{-1})$
12. $(2 + \sqrt{-9})(3 - \sqrt{-4})$

2. $(5 - i)(3 + i)$
5. $(7 - i)(1 - 2i)$
8. $(6 - i)(6 + i)$
11. $(3 - \sqrt{-49})(2 + \sqrt{-16})$
13. $(5 - \sqrt{-36})(2 - \sqrt{-100})$

3. $(1 + 3i)(2 - i)$
6. $(8 - 5i)(3 - i)$
9. $(2 - i)(4 + 2i)$

In 14–19, multiply each pair of conjugates and express their product as a real number.

14. $(4 + i)(4 - i)$
17. $(7 - 2i)(7 + 2i)$

15. $(9 - i)(9 + i)$
18. $(\sqrt{5} + i)(\sqrt{5} - i)$

16. $(1 + 5i)(1 - 5i)$
19. $(\sqrt{6} - 3i)(\sqrt{6} + 3i)$

20. a. Express the product of $(2 + i)$ and $(3 + i)$ in the form $a + bi$.

   b. Find the product $(2 + i)(3 + i)$ using graphic methods.

   (*Hint:* Let $\overrightarrow{OA}$ represent $(3 + i)$. Use $2\,\overrightarrow{OA} + i\,\overrightarrow{OA}$ to find the product.)

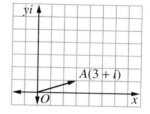

21. a. Express the product $(1 + 2i)(2 + 5i)$ in the form $a + bi$.

   b. Find the product $(1 + 2i)(2 + 5i)$ by using graphic methods.

In 22–29, in each case, raise the complex number to the indicated power, and write the answer in the form $a + bi$.

22. $(6 + i)^2$
26. $(2 + 5i)^2$

23. $(8 - i)^2$
27. $(1 + i)^3$

24. $(3 - 2i)^2$
28. $(2 - 2i)^3$

25. $(5 - 4i)^2$
29. $\left(3 - \frac{2}{3}i\right)^2$

In 30–53, in each case, perform the indicated operations, and write the answer in simplest terms. In other words, whenever possible, write the complex number answer as a real number or a pure imaginary number.

30. $(10 + i)(10 - i)$
33. $(2 + 5i)(5 + 2i)$
36. $(7 - 10i)(1 + 0i)$
39. $i(4 + i) - 4i$
42. $5(2 - i) - 5i^3$
45. $3i^3 - 3(2 - i)$
48. $(2 + i)^2 - 3$
51. $(2.5 - 0.4i)^2$

31. $(3 + 5i)(3 - 5i)$
34. $(9 + 3i)(6 - 2i)$
37. $(8 + 9i)(1 + 0i)$
40. $i(9 - 2i) - 2$
43. $(8 + i)(8 - i)$
46. $6i^3 + 2(7 + 3i)$
49. $(3 - 4i)^2 + 7$
52. $(5 - 0.1i)^2$

32. $(1 + 6i)(6 + i)$
35. $(4 - 3i)(3 - 4i)$
38. $(2 + 0i)(8 - 5i)$
41. $i(1 + i) + i^3$
44. $8 + i(8 - i)$
47. $i^3 + i(10 - i)$
50. $(1 + i)^2 - 2i$
53. $(1.5 - 0.6i)^2$

54. Express the product of $2 + i\sqrt{5}$ and its conjugate in simplest terms.

In 55 and 56, select the *numeral* preceding the expression that best completes each sentence.

55. The product $(3 + 3i)(3 - 3i)$ equals
   (1) 0   (2) 9   (3) 18   (4) $9 - 9i$
56. The complex number $i^3 - i(5 - i)$ is equivalent to
   (1) $1 - 6i$ (2) $-1 - 6i$ (3) $-1 - 4i$ (4) $-5 + i$

20-5 MULTIPLICATIVE INVERSES AND DIVISION OF COMPLEX NUMBERS

Multiplicative Identity and Inverses

As we define the multiplicative identity and inverses in the complex number system, let us recall these elements in the real number system.

Real Numbers	Complex Numbers
The identity element for multiplication is 1 because, for any real number n: $n \cdot 1 = n$ and $1 \cdot n = n$	The *identity element for multiplication* is $1 + 0i$ because, for any complex number $a + bi$: $(a + bi)(1 + 0i) = a + bi$ and $(1 + 0i)(a + bi) = a + bi$

Since $1 + 0i = 1$, we will often use this simpler form of the identity when working with complex numbers. Let us now consider inverses.

Real Numbers	Complex Numbers
The multiplicative inverse of a real number n is $\frac{1}{n}$, where $n \neq 0$, because: $n \cdot \frac{1}{n} = 1$ and $\frac{1}{n} \cdot n = 1$	The *multiplicative inverse* of a complex number $a + bi$ is $\frac{1}{a + bi}$, where $a + bi \neq 0 + 0i$, because: $(a + bi) \cdot \frac{1}{a + bi} = 1$ and $\frac{1}{a + bi} \cdot (a + bi) = 1$

There is a problem, however, in stating that $\frac{1}{a + bi}$ is the multiplicative inverse of $a + bi$. For example, the multiplicative inverse of $3 - i$ is $\frac{1}{3 - i}$, but $\frac{1}{3 - i}$ is not written in the form of a complex number.

To find the complex number that is equivalent to $\frac{1}{3 - i}$, we must *rationalize the denominator*. To do this, we multiply both numerator and denominator by the *conjugate* $3 + i$, an operation that, in effect, multiplies the fraction by the identity element 1. Therefore:

$$\frac{1}{3 - i} = \frac{1}{(3 - i)} \cdot \frac{(3 + i)}{(3 + i)} = \frac{3 + i}{9 - i^2} = \frac{3 + i}{9 + 1} = \frac{3 + i}{10}, \text{ or } \frac{3}{10} + \frac{1}{10}i$$

It can be shown that $(3 - i)$ and $\left(\frac{3}{10} + \frac{1}{10} i\right)$ are multiplicative inverses because their product is the identity element $1 + 0i$, or 1.

$$\textit{Check:}\quad (3 - i)\left(\frac{3}{10} + \frac{1}{10} i\right) = \frac{9}{10} + \frac{3}{10} i - \frac{3}{10} i - \frac{1}{10} i^2$$

$$= \frac{9}{10} + \frac{3}{10} i - \frac{3}{10} i + \frac{1}{10}$$

$$= \left(\frac{9}{10} + \frac{1}{10}\right) + \left(\frac{3}{10} i - \frac{3}{10} i\right)$$

$$= \frac{10}{10} \qquad + \quad 0i \quad = 1 + 0i = 1$$

Multiplication Properties

The identity and inverses are only two properties of the complex number system under multiplication. Let us list some important properties for (Complex numbers, $\cdot$).

1. *Closure.* We recall that $(a + bi)(c + di) = (ac - bd) + (ad + bc)i$. Since the product of two complex numbers is a complex number, it follows that (Complex numbers, $\cdot$) is closed.

2. *Associativity.* (Complex numbers, $\cdot$) is associative. In symbols:

$$[(a + bi) \cdot (c + di)] \cdot (e + fi) = (a + bi) \cdot [(c + di) \cdot (e + fi)]$$

3. *Identity.* The identity element in (Complex numbers, $\cdot$) is $1 + 0i$, which may be written in simplest terms as 1.

4. *Inverses.* To find the multiplicative inverse of a complex number $a + bi$, where $a + bi \neq 0 + 0i$, we write a fraction and rationalize its denominator:

$$\frac{1}{a + bi} = \frac{1}{(a + bi)} \cdot \frac{(a - bi)}{(a - bi)} = \frac{a - bi}{a^2 - b^2 i^2} = \frac{a - bi}{a^2 + b^2} = \frac{a}{a^2 + b^2} - \frac{bi}{a^2 + b^2}$$

In the final form of the inverse, the denominator $a^2 + b^2$ cannot equal 0. However, there is only one complex number, namely, $0 + 0i$, where $a^2 + b^2 = 0^2 + 0^2 = 0$. Therefore, every complex number except $0 + 0i$ has an inverse under multiplication.

●   **The multiplicative inverse of $a + bi$, where $a + bi \neq 0 + 0i$, is**

$$\frac{a - bi}{a^2 + b^2} \qquad \text{or} \qquad \frac{a}{a^2 + b^2} - \frac{bi}{a^2 + b^2}$$

5. *Commutativity.* (Complex numbers, $\cdot$) is commutative. In symbols:

$$(a + bi)(c + di) = (c + di)(a + bi)$$

By excluding the element $0 + 0i$, we can show that the remaining complex numbers under multiplication are still closed, associative, and commutative. The set of complex numbers less $0 + 0i$ contains the identity element $1 + 0i$ and inverses under multiplication. Therefore:

●   **(Complex numbers/$\{0 + 0i\}$, $\cdot$) is a commutative group.**

Division

Division by a number is equivalent to multiplication by the reciprocal (or multiplicative inverse) of that number; that is, $x \div y = x \cdot \frac{1}{y}$, or $\frac{x}{y} = x \cdot \frac{1}{y}$. For example, for the problem 6 divided by 2:

$$6 \div 2 = 6 \cdot \frac{1}{2} = 3 \qquad \text{or} \qquad \frac{6}{2} = 6 \cdot \frac{1}{2} = 3$$

We may extend this definition of division to the set of complex numbers. As seen in the following example, however, it now seems natural to rationalize the denominator once the division is written in fractional form. For example:

◻ Divide $8 + i$ by $2 - i$.

How to Proceed:	*Solution:*
(1) Write the division problem in fractional form.	$(8 + i) \div (2 - i) = \frac{8 + i}{2 - i}$
(2) To rationalize the denominator, multiply the fraction by a form of the identity element 1; that is, multiply by $\frac{2 + i}{2 + i}$, where $2 + i$ is the conjugate of the denominator $2 - i$. Then, simplify.	$= \frac{(8 + i)}{(2 - i)} \cdot \frac{(2 + i)}{(2 + i)}$ $= \frac{16 + 10i + i^2}{4 - i^2}$ $= \frac{16 + 10i - 1}{4 + 1}$ $= \frac{15 + 10i}{5} = \frac{15}{5} + \frac{10i}{5}$ $= 3 + 2i$

Answer: $3 + 2i$

A check is performed for a division problem by using multiplication. For example, to check that $6 \div 2 = 3$ or $\frac{6}{2} = 3$, we multiply $3 \cdot 2 = 6$. The product of the quotient, 3, and the divisor, 2, is equal to the dividend, 6. Let us use this process to check the division problem just performed with complex numbers.

If $\frac{8 + i}{2 - i} = 3 + 2i$, it should be true that $(3 + 2i)(2 - i) = 8 + i$.

$$\begin{aligned} \textit{Check:} \quad (3 + 2i)(2 - i) &= 6 + 4i - 3i - 2i^2 \\ &= 6 + 4i - 3i + 2 \\ &= 8 + i \quad \text{(True)} \end{aligned}$$

EXAMPLES

1. Prove that $1 + i$ and $\frac{1}{2} - \frac{1}{2}i$ are multiplicative inverses.

Solution   Two numbers are multiplicative inverses if their product is 1.

$$(1 + i)\left(\frac{1}{2} - \frac{1}{2}i\right) = \frac{1}{2} - \frac{1}{2}i + \frac{1}{2}i - \frac{1}{2}i^2$$

$$= \frac{1}{2} - \frac{1}{2}(-1) = \frac{1}{2} + \frac{1}{2} = 1$$

2. Write the multiplicative inverse of $2 + 4i$ in the form $a + bi$. Simplify, if possible.

Solution   (1) Write the multiplicative inverse as a fraction: $\frac{1}{2 + 4i}$.

(2) Rationalize the denominator. Since $2 - 4i$ is the conjugate of the denominator $2 + 4i$, multiply the fraction by $\frac{2 - 4i}{2 - 4i}$.

$$\frac{1}{2 + 4i} = \frac{1}{(2 + 4i)} \cdot \frac{(2 - 4i)}{(2 - 4i)} = \frac{2 - 4i}{4 - 16i^2} = \frac{2 - 4i}{4 + 16} = \frac{2 - 4i}{20}$$

(3) This inverse may be simplified by various methods.

$$\frac{2 - 4i}{20} = \frac{\overset{1}{2}(1 - 2i)}{\underset{10}{20}} = \frac{1 - 2i}{10} \qquad \text{or} \qquad \frac{2 - 4i}{20} = \frac{\overset{1}{2}}{\underset{10}{20}} - \frac{\overset{1}{4}i}{\underset{5}{20}} = \frac{1}{10} - \frac{i}{5}$$

Answer: $\dfrac{1 - 2i}{10}$ or $\dfrac{1}{10} - \dfrac{i}{5}$ or $\dfrac{1}{10} - \dfrac{1}{5}i$

3. Divide and check: $(3 + 12i) \div (4 - i)$.

Solution $(3 + 12i) \div (4 - i) = \dfrac{3 + 12i}{4 - i}$

$$= \frac{(3 + 12i)}{(4 - i)} \cdot \frac{(4 + i)}{(4 + i)}$$

$$= \frac{12 + 51i + 12i^2}{16 - i^2} = \frac{12 + 51i - 12}{16 + 1}$$

$$= \frac{0 + 51i}{17} = \frac{0}{17} + \frac{51i}{17}$$

$$= 0 + 3i = 3i$$

Check

$$\frac{3 + 12i}{4 - i} \overset{?}{=} 3i$$

$$3i(4 - i) \overset{?}{=} 3 + 12i$$

$$12i - 3i^2 \overset{?}{=} 3 + 12i$$

$$12i + 3 \overset{?}{=} 3 + 12i$$

$$3 + 12i = 3 + 12i \ \checkmark$$

Answer: $3i$ or $0 + 3i$

EXERCISES WITH OPEN-RESPONSE PROBLEMS

In 1–12, write the multiplicative inverse of each complex number in the form $a + bi$. Simplify, if possible.

1. $3 + i$

2. $6 - i$

3. $1 + 5i$

4. $4 - 3i$

5. $9 - 2i$

6. $7 + 5i$

7. $4 - 4i$

8. $5 + 5i$

9. $3 + 6i$

10. $8 - 4i$

11. $\sqrt{5} + i$

12. $2 - i\sqrt{3}$

In 13–19, in each case: **a.** Perform the indicated division. **b.** Check the answer.

13. $(4 - 2i) \div (1 + i)$

14. $(3 - i) \div (2 + i)$

15. $(5 + 5i) \div (3 - i)$

16. $\frac{5 - 3i}{1 - i}$

17. $\frac{7 - 4i}{1 - 2i}$

18. $\frac{21 + i}{5 - i}$

19. $\frac{18 + i}{2 + 3i}$

In 20–27, perform each indicated division.

20. $\frac{4 + i}{2 - 3i}$

21. $\frac{6 + i}{6 - i}$

22. $\frac{1 - 3i}{2 - 7i}$

23. $\frac{5 + i}{5 - i}$

24. $\frac{7 - i}{7 + i}$

25. $\frac{1 + 3i}{2 + 4i}$

26. $\frac{3 - 5i}{i}$

27. $\frac{7 + 2i}{4i}$

28. For each description of a complex number in Column 1 find the corresponding value in Column 2.

Column 1	*Column 2*
1. The additive inverse of $2 - i$	a. $2 + i$
2. The conjugate of $2 - i$	b. $2 - i$
3. The multiplicative inverse of $2 - i$	c. $1 + 0i$
4. The additive inverse of $-2 + i$	d. $0 + 0i$
5. The conjugate of $-2 + i$	e. $-2 + i$
6. The multiplicative inverse of $2 + i$	f. $-2 - i$
7. The identity for (Complex numbers, +)	g. $\frac{2}{5} + \frac{1}{5} i$
8. The identity for (Complex numbers/$\{0 + 0i\}$, ·)	h. $\frac{2}{5} - \frac{1}{5} i$

In 29 and 30, select the *numeral* preceding the expression that best completes each sentence.

29. The multiplicative inverse of $\frac{1}{2} - \frac{1}{2} i$ is

(1) $\frac{1}{2} + \frac{1}{2} i$

(2) $\frac{1}{2} - \frac{1}{2} i$

(3) $1 + i$

(4) $2 + 2i$

30. The expression $\frac{1}{7 - 3i}$ is equivalent to

(1) $\frac{7 + 3i}{40}$

(2) $\frac{7 + 3i}{58}$

(3) $\frac{7 - 3i}{40}$

(4) $\frac{7 - 3i}{58}$

31. a. What is the conjugate of $(0.6 - 0.8i)$?
  b. Express the product of $(0.6 - 0.8i)$ and its conjugate as a complex number.
  c. What is the multiplicative inverse of $(0.6 - 0.8i)$? (*Hint:* See part **b.**)

In 32–35, in each case, tell whether the statement is true or false. If it is false, explain why.

32. The conjugate of $\left(\frac{5}{13} + \frac{12}{13}i\right)$ is $\left(\frac{5}{13} - \frac{12}{13}i\right)$, and $\left(\frac{5}{13} + \frac{12}{13}i\right)\left(\frac{5}{13} - \frac{12}{13}i\right) = 1 + 0i$.

33. The conjugate of $\left(\frac{\sqrt{3}}{2} - \frac{i}{2}\right)$ is $\left(\frac{\sqrt{3}}{2} + \frac{i}{2}\right)$, and $\left(\frac{\sqrt{3}}{2} - \frac{i}{2}\right)\left(\frac{\sqrt{3}}{2} + \frac{i}{2}\right) = 1 + 0i$.

34. The conjugate of $\left(\frac{1}{3} - \frac{2}{3}i\right)$ is $\left(\frac{1}{3} + \frac{2}{3}i\right)$, and $\left(\frac{1}{3} - \frac{2}{3}i\right)\left(\frac{1}{3} + \frac{2}{3}i\right) = 1 + 0i$.

35. For any complex number, its conjugate is equal to its multiplicative inverse.

36. For what value of $a^2 + b^2$ does the conjugate of $a + bi$ equal the multiplicative inverse of $a + bi$?

20-6   THE FIELD OF COMPLEX NUMBERS

The Field Properties

A system that consists of a set of elements and two operations, usually addition and multiplication, is a *field* if eleven properties are true. We have studied ten field properties involving complex numbers in preceding sections of this chapter; the last property, which is the distributive property, is also true. Therefore:

- **(Complex numbers, +, ·) is a field because:**
  1. **(Complex numbers, +) is a commutative group.**
     These *five* properties were studied in Section 20-3.
  2. **(Complex numbers/{0 + 0i}, ·) is a commutative group.**
     These *five* properties were studied in Section 20-5.
  3. **Multiplication is distributive over addition.** In symbols:

$$(a + bi)[(c + di) + (e + fi)] = (a + bi)(c + di) + (a + bi)(e + fi)$$

In this statement of the distributive property, it can be proved that both numbers of the equation equal the same complex number, namely:

$$(ac + ae - bd - bf) + (ad + af + bc + be)i$$

Complex Numbers Cannot Be Ordered

In an *ordered field*, there are fifteen properties: the eleven properties of a field and four other properties that relate to order. One of the properties of an ordered field is the ***trichotomy property***, namely: For any elements a and b, one and only one of the following statements is true:

$$a > b \quad \textbf{or} \quad a = b \quad \textbf{or} \quad a < b$$

☐ In the ordered field (Rational numbers, $+, \cdot, <$), let us consider -4 and 3. By the trichotomy property:

$$-4 > 3 \text{ (False)} \quad \text{or} \quad -4 = 3 \text{ (False)} \quad \text{or} \quad -4 < 3 \text{ (True)}$$

☐ In the ordered field (Real numbers, $+, \cdot, <$), let us consider $\sqrt{5}$ and 2. By the trichotomy property:

$$\sqrt{5} > 2 \text{ (True)} \quad \text{or} \quad \sqrt{5} = 2 \text{ (False)} \quad \text{or} \quad \sqrt{5} < 2 \text{ (False)}$$

Any complex number of the form $x + 0i$ equals the real number x. Since the set of real numbers can be ordered, complex numbers of the form $x + 0i$ can be ordered. However, it is true that:

● **Complex numbers that are *not* real *cannot* be ordered.**

For example, consider the complex numbers $2 + 3i$ and $3 + 2i$, represented by vectors $\overrightarrow{OA}$ and $\overrightarrow{OB}$, respectively, in the diagram at the right. These vectors are not equal because they have different directions. Also, $2 + 3i \neq 3 + 2i$ by the definition of equality of complex numbers. However, it is *not* possible to say that one of these numbers is greater than the other.

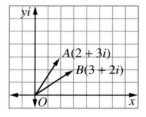

Let us study some convincing arguments about elements in an ordered field that will lead us to conclusions about complex numbers.

Argument 1: In an ordered field, the square of any number is greater than or equal to 0; that is:

If n is an element of an ordered field, then $n^2 \geq 0$.

The contrapositive of this statement must also be true:

*If $n^2 \ngeq 0$, then n is **not** an element of an ordered field.*

Now, let us consider a complex number, $0 + i$, which is simply i. Since $i^2 = -1$, and $-1 < 0$, it follows that $i^2 < 0$. Therefore, $i^2 \ngeq 0$. The squares of many complex numbers are neither greater than nor equal to 0. We conclude:

● **(Complex numbers, $+, \cdot$) is *not* an ordered field.**

Argument 2: In an ordered field, if a number is positive ($n > 0$) or if a number is negative ($n < 0$), then its square is greater than 0; that is:

$$\text{If } n > 0 \text{ or } n < 0, \text{ then } n^2 > 0.$$

But we have seen that $i^2 = -1$. Thus, $i^2 \not> 0$. By the contrapositive of the original statement, it is true that:

$$\text{If } n^2 \not> 0, \text{ then } n \not> 0 \text{ and } n \not< 0.$$

Since $i^2 \not> 0$, it follows that $i \not> 0$ and $i \not< 0$. We conclude:

- ● *i* **is not a positive number, and** *i* **is not a negative number.**

In the same way, any complex number of the form $a + bi$, where $b \neq 0$, is neither a positive number nor a negative number.

EXERCISES WITH OPEN-RESPONSE PROBLEMS

1. List the eleven field properties of (Complex numbers, $+$, $\cdot$).
2. **a.** What complex number is equal to $(4 - i)[(3 + 2i) + (1 - 4i)]$?
   b. What complex number is equal to $(4 - i)(3 + 2i) + (4 - i)(1 - 4i)$?
   c. If the answers to parts **a** and **b** are equal, what field property is illustrated by this equality?

In 3–10, in each case identify the property of the complex numbers that is illustrated by the statement.

3. $(7 - 4i) + (0 + 0i) = 7 - 4i$
4. $(2 + i)(8 - i) = (8 - i)(2 + i)$
5. $(2 + i)\left(\frac{2}{5} - \frac{1}{5}i\right) = 1 + 0i$
6. $(-3 + i) + (3 - i) = 0 + 0i$
7. $(17 - 9i)(1 + 0i) = 17 - 9i$
8. $(6 - i) + (8 + 5i) = (8 + 5i) + (6 - i)$
9. $(10 + 4i) + [(3 + 7i) + (2 - 6i)] = [(10 + 4i) + (3 + 7i)] + (2 - 6i)$
10. $(3 + 2i)[(3 + 7i) + (-2 - 6i)] = (3 + 2i)(3 + 7i) + (3 + 2i)(-2 - 6i)$

In 11–17, in each case, tell whether the statement is true or false. If the statement is false, explain why.

11. (Complex numbers, $+$, $\cdot$) is a field.
12. (Complex numbers, $+$, $\cdot$, $<$) is an ordered field.
13. In the set of complex numbers, $(8 + 6i) > (3 + 2i)$.
14. For the complex numbers i and $(1 - i)$, it is true that $i > (1 - i)$ or $i = (1 - i)$ or $i < (1 - i)$.
15. Every complex number has an additive inverse.
16. Every complex number has a multiplicative inverse.
17. The square of a complex number is greater than or equal to 0.

20-7 SOLVING QUADRATIC EQUATIONS WITH IMAGINARY ROOTS

In Section 10-11, we defined a **quadratic equation** as an equation of the form $ax^2 + bx + c = 0$, where a, b, and c are real numbers, and $a \neq 0$. We also solved quadratic equations with real roots by using the **quadratic formula**:

$$x = \frac{-b \pm \sqrt{b^2 - 4ac}}{2a}$$

Furthermore, in Section 10-11, we stated that, when the *discriminant* $b^2 - 4ac$ is a negative number, the roots of the quadratic equation are not real. Now that we have extended the number system from the real numbers to the complex numbers, let us attempt to solve a quadratic equation whose discriminant is negative. For example:

☐ Use the domain of complex numbers to solve the equation $x^2 - 8x + 17 = 0$. Check the solution.

How to Proceed: *Solution:*

(1) Compare the equation to $ax^2 + bx + c = 0$ to determine a, b, and c.

$x^2 - 8x + 17 = 0$
$a = 1, b = -8, c = 17$

(2) Substitute the values of a, b, and c in the quadratic formula, and simplify.

$x = \dfrac{-b \pm \sqrt{b^2 - 4ac}}{2a}$

$= \dfrac{-(-8) \pm \sqrt{(-8)^2 - 4(1)(17)}}{2(1)}$

$= \dfrac{8 \pm \sqrt{64 - 68}}{2}$

(*Note:* If $b^2 - 4ac$ is negative, then $\sqrt{b^2 - 4ac}$ is an imaginary number.)

$= \dfrac{8 \pm \sqrt{-4}}{2} = \dfrac{8 \pm \sqrt{4}\sqrt{-1}}{2}$

$= \dfrac{8 \pm 2i}{2} = \dfrac{8}{2} \pm \dfrac{2i}{2}$

$= 4 \pm i$

(3) Check both roots in the original equation only.

Check for $x = 4 + i$

$x^2 - 8x \qquad + 17 = 0$

$(4 + i)(4 + i) - 8(4 + i) + 17 \overset{?}{=} 0$

$16 + 8i + i^2 - 32 - 8i + 17 \overset{?}{=} 0$

$16 + \cancel{8i} - 1 - 32 - \cancel{8i} + 17 \overset{?}{=} 0$

$0 = 0$

Check for $x = 4 - i$

$x^2 - 8x \qquad + 17 = 0$

$(4 - i)(4 - i) - 8(4 - i) + 17 \overset{?}{=} 0$

$16 - 8i + i^2 - 32 - 8i + 17 \overset{?}{=} 0$

$16 - \cancel{8i} - 1 - 32 + \cancel{8i} + 17 \overset{?}{=} 0$

$0 = 0$

Answer: $x = 4 \pm i$ or $\{4 + i, 4 - i\}$

It is true that $4 + i$ and $4 - i$ are complex numbers. However, any number of the form $a + bi$, where $b \neq 0$, can also be called an *imaginary* number. Therefore, the roots $4 \pm i$ are imaginary.

In the next section, we will discuss the nature of the roots of any quadratic equation. For the present, however, we will restrict the equations in the exercises that follow to those having imaginary roots only.

EXAMPLES

1. a. Solve the equation $\frac{x^2}{2} = x - 5$, and express its roots in the form $a + bi$.

   b. Check the roots of the equation.

a.

How to Proceed:	*Solution:*
(1) Write the equation.	$\frac{x^2}{2} = x - 5$
(2) Multiply both sides by the L.C.D. to clear fractions.	$2 \cdot \dfrac{x^2}{2} = 2(x - 5)$
	$x^2 = 2x - 10$
(3) Transform the equation so that one side is 0.	$x^2 - 2x + 10 = 0$
(4) Compare the equation to $ax^2 + bx + c = 0$ to determine a, b, and c.	$a = 1, b = -2, c = 10$
(5) Substitute the values of a, b, and c in the quadratic formula and simplify. Remember: the domain is now the set of complex numbers.	$x = \dfrac{-b \pm \sqrt{b^2 - 4ac}}{2a}$
	$= \dfrac{-(-2) \pm \sqrt{(-2)^2 - 4(1)(10)}}{2(1)}$
	$= \dfrac{2 \pm \sqrt{4 - 40}}{2}$
	$= \dfrac{2 \pm \sqrt{-36}}{2} = \dfrac{2 \pm \sqrt{36}\sqrt{-1}}{2}$
	$= \dfrac{2 \pm 6i}{2} = \dfrac{2}{2} \pm \dfrac{6i}{2}$
	$= 1 \pm 3i$

b. Check both roots in the original equation only.

<table>
<tr><td align="center">Check for $x = 1 + 3i$</td><td align="center">Check for $x = 1 - 3i$</td></tr>
<tr><td align="center">$\frac{x^2}{2} = x - 5$</td><td align="center">$\frac{x^2}{2} = x - 5$</td></tr>
<tr><td align="center">$\frac{(1 + 3i)(1 + 3i)}{2} \overset{?}{=} (1 + 3i) - 5$</td><td align="center">$\frac{(1 - 3i)(1 - 3i)}{2} \overset{?}{=} (1 - 3i) - 5$</td></tr>
<tr><td align="center">$\frac{1 + 6i + 9i^2}{2} \overset{?}{=} 1 + 3i - 5$</td><td align="center">$\frac{1 - 6i + 9i^2}{2} \overset{?}{=} 1 - 3i - 5$</td></tr>
<tr><td align="center">$\frac{1 + 6i - 9}{2} \overset{?}{=} -4 + 3i$</td><td align="center">$\frac{1 - 6i - 9}{2} \overset{?}{=} -4 - 3i$</td></tr>
<tr><td align="center">$\frac{-8 + 6i}{2} \overset{?}{=} -4 + 3i$</td><td align="center">$\frac{-8 - 6i}{2} \overset{?}{=} -4 - 3i$</td></tr>
<tr><td align="center">$-4 + 3i = -4 + 3i$ ✔</td><td align="center">$-4 - 3i = -4 - 3i$ ✔</td></tr>
</table>

Answers: **a.** $x = 1 \pm 3i$ or $\{1 + 3i, 1 - 3i\}$ **b.** See checks.

---

2. Express the roots of $x^2 + 12 = 0$ in $a + bi$ form.

Solution

METHOD 1	METHOD 2
$x^2 + 12 = 0$	$x^2 + 12 = 0$
$x^2 = -12$	$a = 1, b = 0, c = 12$
$x = \pm\sqrt{-12}$	$x = \dfrac{0 \pm \sqrt{0^2 - 4(1)(12)}}{2(1)}$
$= \pm\sqrt{4} \cdot \sqrt{-1} \cdot \sqrt{3}$	$= \dfrac{0 \pm \sqrt{-48}}{2}$
$= \pm 2i\sqrt{3}$	$= \dfrac{0 \pm \sqrt{16} \cdot \sqrt{-1} \cdot \sqrt{3}}{2}$
	$= \dfrac{0 \pm 4i\sqrt{3}}{2} = 0 \pm 2i\sqrt{3}$

Answer: $x = \pm 2i\sqrt{3}$ or $x = 0 \pm 2i\sqrt{3}$

EXERCISES WITH OPEN-RESPONSE PROBLEMS

In 1–12, in each case: **a.** Solve the equation, and express the roots in the form $a + bi$.
b. Check the roots of the equation.

1. $x^2 - 4x + 5 = 0$ **2.** $x^2 - 6x + 25 = 0$ **3.** $x^2 + 26 = 2x$ **4.** $x^2 + 29 = 10x$

5. $x^2 = 8x - 25$ **6.** $3x^2 = 6(x - 1)$ **7.** $\frac{x^2}{3} = 4x - 15$ **8.** $\frac{x^2}{2} + 3x + 5 = 0$

9. $\frac{x^2 + 21}{4} = 1 - 2x$ **10.** $2x^2 + 72 = 0$ **11.** $\frac{x^2}{5} + 5 = 0$ **12.** $\frac{x^2}{8} + 10 = 2$

In 13–24, express the roots of each equation in $a + bi$ form.

13. $9x^2 - 6x + 2 = 0$

14. $2x^2 + 17 = 6x$

15. $4x(x - 2) + 5 = 0$

16. $x^2 + 36 = 7 - 10x$

17. $4x(x + 5) + 29 = 0$

18. $x^2 + 3 = 2x$

19. $x^2 + 20x = 2x - 86$

20. $13 = 4x(3 - x)$

21. $\frac{25x}{3} + \frac{3}{x} = 0$

22. $\frac{x - 4}{10} = \frac{x - 5}{x}$

23. $\frac{x - 2}{x} = \frac{x + 27}{17}$

24. $\frac{x - 3}{x} = \frac{x + 19}{15}$

In 25–27, select the *numeral* preceding the expression that best completes each sentence.

25. The roots of $x^2 - x + 5 = 0$ are

(1) $\frac{1 \pm i\sqrt{19}}{2}$

(2) $\frac{1 \pm i\sqrt{21}}{2}$

(3) $\frac{1 \pm 19i}{2}$

(4) $\frac{1 \pm 21i}{2}$

26. The roots of $2x^2 + x + 6 = 0$ are

(1) $\frac{1 \pm i\sqrt{47}}{2}$

(2) $\frac{-1 \pm i\sqrt{47}}{2}$

(3) $\frac{1 \pm i\sqrt{47}}{4}$

(4) $\frac{-1 \pm i\sqrt{47}}{4}$

27. The roots of $3x^2 + 2x + 1 = 0$ are

(1) $-\frac{1}{3} \pm \frac{1}{3} i$

(2) $-\frac{1}{3} \pm \frac{2}{3} i$

(3) $-\frac{1}{3} \pm \frac{i\sqrt{2}}{3}$

(4) $-1 \pm i\sqrt{2}$

20-8   THE NATURE OF THE ROOTS OF ANY QUADRATIC EQUATION

We begin with a word of caution. The coordinate plane and the complex plane are *not* the same plane. In the *coordinate plane*, each point represents a pair of real numbers, such as $(x, y) = (2, 3)$. In the *complex plane*, each point represents a complex number, such as $A = 2 + 3i$.

The discussion that follows in this section involves graphs and points on the coordinate plane only.

Coordinate plane

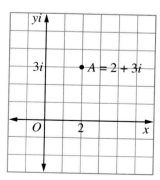

Complex plane

Quadratic Equations and Graphs

We have learned that the graph of any quadratic equation of the form $ax^2 + bx + c = y$, where a, b, and c are real numbers and $a \neq 0$, is a **parabola**. A parabola contains an infinite number of points, and each point represents some ordered pair (x, y) in the coordinate plane.

If the coefficient a is positive ($a > 0$), then the parabola contains a minimum turning point and opens upward.

If the coefficient a is negative ($a < 0$), then the parabola contains a maximum turning point and opens downward.

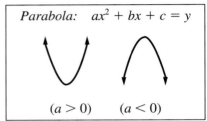

Let us imagine that a parabola crosses the x-axis at two points. We can use substitution to find the equation of this intersection, as follows:

Equation of the parabola:	$ax^2 + bx + c = y$
Equation of the x-axis:	$y = 0$
Equation of the intersection of the parabola and the x-axis:	$ax^2 + bx + c = 0$

Therefore, a *quadratic equation* is an equation of the form $ax^2 + bx + c = 0$, where a, b, and c are real numbers and $a \neq 0$. When the parabola crosses the x-axis at two points, the roots of the equation $ax^2 + bx + c = 0$ are the x-coordinates of the two points of intersection.

> *Quadratic Equation:* $ax^2 + bx + c = 0$
> (Intersection of parabola and x-axis)
>
> Roots of $ax^2 + bx + c = 0$ are x_1 and x_2.

If these points of intersection represent the ordered pairs $(x_1, 0)$ and $(x_2, 0)$, then the roots of the equation $ax^2 + bx + c = 0$ are x_1 and x_2. As we will see in the examples that follow, the parabola may be tangent to the x-axis and in some cases may not intersect the x-axis at all.

The Discriminant

By the quadratic formula, the two roots of $ax^2 + bx + c = 0$ are

$$x_1 = \frac{-b + \sqrt{b^2 - 4ac}}{2a} \quad \text{and} \quad x_2 = \frac{-b - \sqrt{b^2 - 4ac}}{2a}$$

The **discriminant** $b^2 - 4ac$, which is the expression under the radical sign, determines the nature of the roots of a quadratic equation when a, b, and c are rational numbers. Let us study possible values for the discriminant and, at the same time, examine the quadratic equation graphically.

Case 1. If $b^2 - 4ac > 0$ and $b^2 - 4ac$ is a perfect square, then the roots of the equation $ax^2 + bx + c = 0$ are *real*, *rational*, and *unequal*.

Solve: $x^2 - 2x - 3 = 0$.

$$a = 1, b = -2, c = -3$$

$$x = \frac{-b \pm \sqrt{b^2 - 4ac}}{2a}$$

$$= \frac{-(-2) \pm \sqrt{(-2)^2 - 4(1)(-3)}}{2(1)}$$

$$= \frac{2 \pm \sqrt{4 + 12}}{2}$$

$$= \frac{2 \pm \sqrt{16}}{2} = \frac{2 \pm 4}{2}$$

$$x_1 = \frac{2 + 4}{2} = \frac{6}{2} \quad \bigg| \quad x_2 = \frac{2 - 4}{2} = \frac{-2}{2}$$

$$= 3 \qquad\qquad\quad = -1$$

Graph: $x^2 - 2x - 3 = y$.

x	y
-2	5
-1	0
0	-3
1	-4
2	-3
3	0
4	5

Roots -1 and 3 of $x^2 - 2x - 3 = 0$ can be read directly from the graph.

Observation: The discriminant $b^2 - 4ac = 16$, a positive number that is a perfect square. The parabola intersects the x-axis at -1 and 3. Roots, -1 and 3, of $x^2 - 2x - 3 = 0$ are real, rational, and unequal.

Case 2. If $b^2 - 4ac > 0$ and $b^2 - 4ac$ is *not* a perfect square, then the roots of the equation $ax^2 + bx + c = 0$ are *real*, *irrational*, and *unequal*.

Solve: $x^2 - 6x + 7 = 0$.

$$a = 1, b = -6, c = 7$$

$$x = \frac{-b \pm \sqrt{b^2 - 4ac}}{2a}$$

$$= \frac{-(-6) \pm \sqrt{(-6)^2 - 4(1)(7)}}{2(1)}$$

$$= \frac{6 \pm \sqrt{36 - 28}}{2} = \frac{6 \pm \sqrt{8}}{2}$$

$$= \frac{6 \pm 2\sqrt{2}}{2} = \frac{\cancel{2}(3 \pm \sqrt{2})}{\cancel{2}}$$

$$x_1 = 3 + \sqrt{2} \qquad \text{or} \qquad x_2 = 3 - \sqrt{2}$$

Graph: $x^2 - 6x + 7 = y$.

x	y
1	2
2	-1
3	-2
4	-1
5	2

Although the roots $3 \pm \sqrt{2}$ cannot be read exactly from the graph, we can use $\sqrt{2} \approx 1.4$ to approximate their values:

$$3 + \sqrt{2} \approx 3 + 1.4 = 4.4$$
$$3 - \sqrt{2} \approx 3 - 1.4 = 1.6$$

Observation: The discriminant $b^2 - 4ac = 8$, a positive number that is not a perfect square. The parabola intersects the x-axis at $3 + \sqrt{2}$ and $3 - \sqrt{2}$. The roots, $3 \pm \sqrt{2}$, of $x^2 - 6x + 7 = 0$ are real, irrational, and unequal.

***Case 3.* If $b^2 - 4ac = 0$, then the roots of the equation $ax^2 + bx + c = 0$ are *real*, *rational*, and *equal*.**

Solve: $x^2 - 4x + 4 = 0$.

$a = 1, b = -4, c = 4$

$$x = \frac{-b \pm \sqrt{b^2 - 4ac}}{2a}$$

$$= \frac{-(-4) \pm \sqrt{(-4)^2 - 4(1)(4)}}{2(1)}$$

$$= \frac{4 \pm \sqrt{16 - 16}}{2} = \frac{4 \pm \sqrt{0}}{2}$$

$x_1 = \frac{4 + 0}{2} = \frac{4}{2}$ $x_2 = \frac{4 - 0}{2} = \frac{4}{2}$

$\quad = 2$ $\quad = 2$

Graph: $x^2 - 4x + 4 = y$.

x	y
0	4
1	1
2	0
3	1
4	4

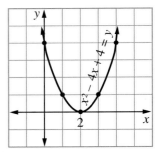

The parabola is tangent to the x-axis at $x = 2$. Each of the two roots of $x^2 - 4x + 4 = 0$ is equal to 2.

Observation: The discriminant $b^2 - 4ac = 0$. The parabola is tangent to the x-axis at 2. The roots of $x^2 - 4x + 4 = 0$ are 2 and 2; that is, the roots are real, rational, and equal.

***Case 4.* If $b^2 - 4ac < 0$, then the roots of the equation $ax^2 + bx + c = 0$ are imaginary.**

Solve: $x^2 - 4x + 5 = 0$.

$a = 1, b = -4, c = 5$

$$x = \frac{-b \pm \sqrt{b^2 - 4ac}}{2a}$$

$$= \frac{-(-4) \pm \sqrt{(-4)^2 - 4(1)(5)}}{2(1)}$$

$$= \frac{4 \pm \sqrt{16 - 20}}{2} = \frac{4 \pm \sqrt{-4}}{2}$$

$$= \frac{4 \pm 2i}{2} = \frac{2(2 \pm i)}{2}$$

$x_1 = 2 + i$ or $x_2 = 2 - i$

Graph: $x^2 - 4x + 5 = y$.

x	y
0	5
1	2
2	1
3	2
4	5

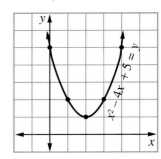

The minimum point of the parabola occurs at $(2, 1)$, and the parabola opens upward. Thus, the parabola does not intersect the x-axis at all.

Observation: The discriminant $b^2 - 4ac = -4$, a negative number. The parabola does not intersect the x-axis. Therefore, the equation $x^2 - 4x + 5 = 0$ has no real roots. By the quadratic formula, however, it is shown that the roots of $x^2 - 4x + 5 = 0$ are $2 + i$ and $2 - i$; that is, the roots are imaginary.

Thus, when a, b, and c are rational numbers, we observe:
If $b^2 - 4ac \geq 0$, the roots of $ax^2 + bx + c = 0$ are real numbers.
If $b^2 - 4ac < 0$, the roots of $ax^2 + bx + c = 0$ are imaginary.
The following table summarizes the findings in the cases studied above.

Value of Discriminant	Nature of Roots of $ax^2 + bx + c = 0$
$b^2 - 4ac > 0$, and $b^2 - 4ac$ is a perfect square.	real, rational, unequal
$b^2 - 4ac > 0$, and $b^2 - 4ac$ is not a perfect square.	real, irrational, unequal
$b^2 - 4ac = 0$	real, rational, equal
$b^2 - 4ac < 0$	imaginary

EXAMPLES

1. Find the largest integral value of k for which the roots of the equation $2x^2 + 7x + k = 0$ are real.

Solution　First, for equation $2x^2 + 7x + k = 0$:　$a = 2, b = 7, c = k$.
Next, if the roots of the quadratic equation are real, then $b^2 - 4ac \geq 0$.
Substitute the given values in $b^2 - 4ac \geq 0$, and solve for k.

METHOD 1	METHOD 2
$b^2 - 4ac \geq 0$	$b^2 - 4ac \geq 0$
$(7)^2 - 4(2)k \geq 0$	$(7)^2 - 4(2)k \geq 0$
$49 - 8k \geq 0$	$49 - 8k \geq 0$
$49 \geq 8k$	$-8k \geq -49$
$\dfrac{49}{8} \geq \dfrac{8k}{8}$	$\dfrac{-8k}{-8} \leq \dfrac{-49}{-8}$
$6\frac{1}{8} \geq k$	$k \leq 6\frac{1}{8}$

Since the largest integral value of k means the largest *integer* for which $6\frac{1}{8} \geq k$, or $k \leq 6\frac{1}{8}$, the integer is 6, or $k = 6$.

Answer: 6

Check both $k = 6$ and $k = 7$ (the next-larger integer).
If $k = 6$, then $b^2 - 4ac = 1$ and the roots of $2x^2 + 7x + 6 = 0$ are real.
If $k = 7$, then $b^2 - 4ac = -7$ and the roots of $2x^2 + 7x + 7 = 0$ are imaginary.

In 2 and 3, select the *numeral* preceding the choice that best completes each sentence.

2. The roots of the equation $2x^2 + 6x + 3 = 0$ are

    (1) real, rational, and unequal   (2) real, rational, and equal

    (3) real, irrational, and unequal   (4) imaginary

Solution   First, compare $2x^2 + 6x + 3 = 0$ to $ax^2 + bx + c = 0$ to find that $a = 2$, $b = 6$, and $c = 3$.

Then, the discriminant $b^2 - 4ac = (6)^2 - 4(2)(3) = 36 - 24 = 12$.

Since $b^2 - 4ac > 0$ and $b^2 - 4ac$ is *not* a perfect square, the roots of the equation are irrational as well as real and unequal.

Answer: (3)

---

3. The graph of $y = -x^2 - 6$

    (1) is tangent to the x-axis   (2) intersects the x-axis at two points

    (3) lies entirely above the x-axis   (4) lies entirely below the x-axis

Solution   (1) Compare $-x^2 - 6$ to $ax^2 + bx + c$ to find that $a = -1$, $b = 0$, $c = -6$.

    (2) The discriminant $b^2 - 4ac = (0)^2 - 4(-1)(-6) = 0 - 24 = -24$. Since $b^2 - 4ac < 0$, the roots of $-x^2 - 6 = 0$ are imaginary, and the parabola $y = -x^2 - 6$ does not intersect the x-axis.

    (3) Since the coefficient $a = -1$ (or $a < 0$), the parabola opens downward. Select choice (4).

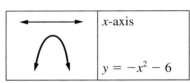

Alternative Solution   Graph the parabola $y = -x^2 - 6$.

x	-2	-1	0	1	2
y	-10	-7	-6	-7	-10

The maximum point of this parabola is $(0, -6)$. Select choice (4): The graph of $y = -x^2 - 6$ lies entirely below the x-axis.

Answer: (4)

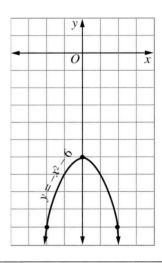

EXERCISES WITH OPEN-RESPONSE PROBLEMS

In 1–12, for each equation: **a.** Evaluate the discriminant $b^2 - 4ac$.   **b.** Using the value of $b^2 - 4ac$, select the choice below that describes the nature of the roots of the equation:

(1) real, rational, and unequal
(2) real, rational, and equal
(3) real, irrational, and unequal
(4) imaginary

1. $x^2 + 3x - 5 = 0$
4. $x^2 - 10x + 25 = 0$
7. $x^2 = 7x - 6$
10. $x^2 + 9 = 2x^2 + x$

2. $x^2 + 3x - 10 = 0$
5. $x^2 + 8x + 17 = 0$
8. $2x^2 + 3x = 4$
11. $x - 8 = x^2 - 2x$

3. $x^2 + 3x + 4 = 0$
6. $x^2 + 7x - 30 = 0$
9. $4x^2 + 9 = 12x$
12. $x^2 + 6 = 3x^2 + x$

In 13–21, in each case, select the choice below that describes the graph of the parabola:

(1) It is tangent to the x-axis.
(2) It intersects the x-axis at 2 points.
(3) It lies entirely above the x-axis.
(4) It lies entirely below the x-axis.

13. $y = x^2 - 2x - 8$
16. $y = x^2 - 6$
19. $y = 10x^2$

14. $y = x^2 - 2x + 1$
17. $y = 2x^2 - 5x + 4$
20. $y = -x^2 + 3x - 7$

15. $y = x^2 + 3$
18. $y = -x^2 - 10$
21. $y = 12 - x^2$

In 22–33, in each case, solve the quadratic equation, and check both roots.

22. $x^2 - 6x + 5 = 0$
25. $x^2 = 2x - 10$
28. $9x^2 + 4 = 0$
31. $x - x^2 = \frac{1}{4}$

23. $x^2 - 6x + 13 = 0$
26. $x^2 + 20x = 6x - 49$
29. $3x^2 + 11x = 4$
32. $\frac{x^2}{2} = x - 2$

24. $x^2 = 2x + 6$
27. $x^2 + 4x = x$
30. $x^2 + 10x + 26 = 0$
33. $\frac{x-2}{2} = \frac{x-1}{x}$

In 34–41, select the *numeral* preceding the expression that best completes each sentence.

34. The roots of $x^2 + 2x + k = 0$ are equal when k is
(1) 1   (2) 2   (3) 3   (4) 4

35. The roots of $x^2 + kx + 3 = 0$ are real when k is
(1) 1   (2) 2   (3) 3   (4) 4

36. The roots of $x^2 + bx + 8 = 0$ are imaginary when b equals
(1) 8   (2) −7   (3) 6   (4) −5

37. The roots of $ax^2 + 6x + 4 = 0$ are imaginary if a equals
(1) 1   (2) 2   (3) 3   (4) −1

38. If the graph of $y = ax^2 + bx + c$ is tangent to the x-axis, then the roots of $ax^2 + bx + c = 0$ are

    (1) rational and unequal   (2) rational and equal

    (3) irrational and unequal   (4) imaginary

39. The graph of $y = ax^2 + bx + c$ where $a \neq 0$ lies entirely above the x-axis. The roots of $ax^2 + bx + c = 0$ are

    (1) rational and unequal   (2) rational and equal

    (3) irrational   (4) imaginary

40. The graph of $y = x^2$ is symmetric with respect to

    (1) the x-axis   (2) the y-axis

    (3) the line $y = x$ (4) point $(0, 0)$

41. If the roots of $x^2 + bx + 16 = 0$ are equal, then b is

    (1) 8, only   (2) -8, only   (3) 8 or -8 (4) neither 8 nor -8

In 42–44, in each case, find the largest integral value of k such that the roots of the equation are real.

42. $x^2 + 6x + k = 0$ **43.** $2x^2 + 5x + k = 0$ **44.** $kx^2 - 7x + 3 = 0$

In 45–47, in each case, find the smallest integral value of k such that the equation has imaginary roots.

45. $x^2 - 3x + k = 0$ **46.** $kx^2 - 2x + 5 = 0$ **47.** $x^2 + 4x + k = 0$

48. If $a \neq 0$, $c = a$, and $b = 2a$, describe the nature of the roots of the equation $ax^2 + bx + c = 0$.

49. If $a \neq 0$, $b = a$, and $c = a$, describe the nature of the roots of the equation $ax^2 + bx + c = 0$.

20-9 USING GIVEN CONDITIONS TO WRITE A QUADRATIC EQUATION

Certain quadratic equations contain polynomial expressions that are factorable. If we factor such an expression and set each factor equal to 0, we can find the roots of the equation. For example:

Solve: $x^2 + 3x - 10 = 0$

$$(x - 2)(x + 5) = 0$$

$$x - 2 = 0 \quad | \quad x + 5 = 0$$

$$x = 2 \quad | \quad x = -5$$

Solution: $\{2, -5\}$

Let us now apply the strategy of *working backwards*.

Reverse Factoring Technique

If we are given the roots of a quadratic equation, we can reverse the process just illustrated to find the equation. This new procedure, which we will call the *reverse factoring technique*, is demonstrated in the following problem. For example:

☐ Write a quadratic equation whose roots are 3 and −7.

How to Proceed:	*Solution:*
(1) Write the roots.	$x = 3 \quad \mid \quad x = -7$
(2) Transform each equation so that one side is 0.	$x - 3 = 0 \quad \mid \quad x + 7 = 0$
	$(x - 3)(x + 7) = 0$
(3) Multiply the binomials, showing that their product is 0.	$x^2 + 4x - 21 = 0$

Answer: $x^2 + 4x - 21 = 0$

To check that the roots of $x^2 + 4x - 21 = 0$ are 3 and −7, substitute these values in the equation.

Check for $x = 3$	*Check* for $x = -7$
$x^2 + 4x - 21 = 0$	$x^2 + 4x - 21 = 0$
$(3)^2 + 4(3) - 21 \overset{?}{=} 0$	$(-7)^2 + 4(-7) - 21 \overset{?}{=} 0$
$9 + 12 - 21 \overset{?}{=} 0$	$49 - 28 - 21 \overset{?}{=} 0$
$0 = 0 ✔$	$0 = 0 ✔$

In the next example, we extend the reverse factoring technique to the general case.

☐ Write a quadratic equation whose roots are r_1 and r_2.

Solution:
$$x = r_1 \quad \mid \quad x = r_2$$
$$x - r_1 = 0 \quad \mid \quad x = r_2 = 0$$
$$(x - r_1)(x - r_2) = 0$$
$$x^2 - r_1 x - r_2 x + r_1 r_2 = 0$$

Answer:
$$x^2 - (r_1 + r_2)x + r_1 r_2 = 0$$

Observe these terms: $(r_1 + r_2)$ is the sum of the roots. $r_1 r_2$ is the product of the roots.

The Sum and the Product of the Roots of a Quadratic Equation

Let us discover some rules involving the sum and the product of the roots of a quadratic equation. Two proofs are offered here.

Proof 1:

(1) Write the general quadratic equation, $ax^2 + bx + c = 0$ $(a \neq 0)$, and multiply each side by $\frac{1}{a}$.

$$ax^2 + bx + c = 0$$

$$\tfrac{1}{a}(ax^2 + bx + c) = \tfrac{1}{a}(0)$$

$$x^2 + \tfrac{b}{a}x + \tfrac{c}{a} = 0$$

(2) Write the quadratic equation whose roots are r_1 and r_2, shown in the example above.

$$\updownarrow \qquad \updownarrow$$

$$x^2 - (r_1 + r_2)x + r_1 r_2 = 0$$

(3) Compare the coefficients of the corresponding terms of the equations in steps 1 and 2.

$$-(r_1 + r_2) = \tfrac{b}{a}$$

or

$$(r_1 + r_2) = \tfrac{-b}{a} \qquad\qquad r_1 r_2 = \tfrac{c}{a}$$

$$\textbf{Sum of the roots} = \tfrac{-b}{a} \quad \Big| \quad \textbf{Product of the roots} = \tfrac{c}{a}$$

Proof 2 (An Alternative Approach):

(1) If r_1 and r_2 are the roots of the quadratic equation $ax^2 + bx + c = 0$, where $a \neq 0$, it follows by the quadratic formula that

$$r_1 = \frac{-b + \sqrt{b^2 - 4ac}}{2a} \qquad \text{and} \qquad r_2 = \frac{-b - \sqrt{b^2 - 4ac}}{2a}$$

(2) Add: $r_1 + r_2 = \dfrac{-b + \sqrt{b^2 - 4ac} - b - \sqrt{b^2 - 4ac}}{2a} = \dfrac{-2b}{2a} = \dfrac{-b}{a}$

$$\textbf{Sum of the roots} = \tfrac{-b}{a}.$$

(3) Multiply: $r_1 r_2 = \left(\dfrac{-b + \sqrt{b^2 - 4ac}}{2a}\right)\left(\dfrac{-b - \sqrt{b^2 - 4ac}}{2a}\right)$ Notice that the numerators are conjugates.

$$r_1 r_2 = \frac{+b^2 - (b^2 - 4ac)}{4a^2} = \frac{b^2 - b^2 + 4ac}{4a^2} = \frac{4ac}{4a \cdot a} = \frac{c}{a}$$

$$\textbf{Product of the roots} = \tfrac{c}{a}.$$

The rules for the sum and the product of the roots can be used to help us find a quadratic equation to fit certain given information. In fact, if we are given roots that are irrational or imaginary and we are asked to find the quadratic equation that contains these roots, these rules are especially useful, as shown in the next example.

☐   Write a quadratic equation whose roots are $3 + \sqrt{5}$ and $3 - \sqrt{5}$.

Solution   (1) The sum of the roots $= (3 + \sqrt{5}) + (3 - \sqrt{5}) = 6$. Thus, $\frac{-b}{a} = 6$.

(2) The product of the roots $= (3 + \sqrt{5})(3 - \sqrt{5}) = 9 - 5 = 4$. Thus, $\frac{c}{a} = 4$.

(3) Let $a = 1$. $\quad\Big|\quad$ Then, $\frac{-b}{a} = 6$, or $\frac{-b}{1} = 6$ $\quad\Big|\quad$ Also, $\frac{c}{a} = 4$, or $\frac{c}{1} = 4$

$$-b = 6 \qquad\qquad c = 4$$
$$b = -6$$

(4) Substitute $a = 1$, $b = -6$, and $c = 4$ in the equation $ax^2 + bx + c = 0$.

Answer: $x^2 - 6x + 4 = 0$

To *check* that $x^2 - 6x + 4 = 0$ is a correct equation, apply the quadratic formula and find the roots of the equation.

$$x = \frac{-b \pm \sqrt{b^2 - 4ac}}{2a} = \frac{-(-6) \pm \sqrt{(-6)^2 - 4(1)(4)}}{2(1)} = \frac{6 \pm \sqrt{36 - 16}}{2}$$

$$= \frac{6 \pm \sqrt{20}}{2} = \frac{6 \pm \sqrt{4}\sqrt{5}}{2} = \frac{6 \pm 2\sqrt{5}}{2} = \frac{6}{2} \pm \frac{2\sqrt{5}}{2} = 3 \pm \sqrt{5} \quad ✔$$

KEEP IN MIND ───────────────

For any quadratic equation $ax^2 + bx + c = 0$, $a \neq 0$:

The sum of the roots $= -\frac{b}{a}$.

The product of the roots $= \frac{c}{a}$.

EXAMPLES

1. For the quadratic equation $2x^2 + 5x + 8 = 0$, find:
   a. the sum of its roots   **b.** the product of its roots

Solutions   For the quadratic equation $2x^2 + 5x + 8 = 0$: $a = 2$, $b = 5$, $c = 8$.

a. Sum of the roots $= \frac{-b}{a}$ $\quad\Big|\quad$ **b.** Product of the roots $= \frac{c}{a}$

$$= \frac{-5}{2} \qquad\qquad\qquad = \frac{8}{2} = 4$$

Answers: **a.** $\frac{-5}{2}$ **b.** 4

2. Write a quadratic equation whose roots are $\frac{1}{2}$ and -2.

Solution METHOD 1. Use the reverse factoring technique. To clear the fraction in $x = \frac{1}{2}$, multiply each member of the equation by 2.

$$
\begin{array}{c|c}
x = \frac{1}{2} & x = -2 \\
2x = 1 & \\
2x - 1 = 0 & x + 2 = 0
\end{array}
$$

$$(2x - 1)(x + 2) = 0$$
$$2x^2 + 3x - 2 = 0$$

METHOD 2. Use the rules for the sum and the product of the roots. In step 3, notice that coefficient a may take on different values.

(1) The sum of the roots $= \frac{1}{2} + (-2) = -\frac{3}{2}$. Thus, $-\frac{b}{a} = -\frac{3}{2}$.

(2) The product of the roots $= \left(\frac{1}{2}\right)(-2) = -1$. Thus, $\frac{c}{a} = -1$.

(3) Let $a = 1$.

$$-\frac{b}{a} = -\frac{3}{2}, \text{ or } -\frac{b}{1} = -\frac{3}{2}$$

$$b = \frac{3}{2}$$

$$\frac{c}{a} = -1, \text{ or } \frac{c}{1} = -1$$

$$c = -1$$

(3) Alternative: Let $a = 2$.

$$-\frac{b}{a} = -\frac{3}{2}, \text{ or } -\frac{b}{2} = -\frac{3}{2}$$

$$-b = -3$$

$$b = 3$$

$$\frac{c}{a} = -1, \text{ or } \frac{c}{2} = -1$$

$$c = -2$$

(4) Thus, $ax^2 + bx + c = 0$ can be written as

$$x^2 + \frac{3}{2}x - 1 = 0.$$

(4) Thus, $ax^2 + bx + c = 0$ can be written as

$$2x^2 + 3x - 2 = 0.$$

Note: If the members of $x^2 + \frac{3}{2}x - 1 = 0$ are multiplied by 2, the equivalent equation, $2x^2 + 3x - 2 = 0$, is formed. Both equations are correct answers because they are *equivalent* equations; that is, they have the same roots.

Answer: $2x^2 + 3x - 2 = 0$, or any equivalent equation

3. Write a quadratic equation whose roots are $5i$ and $-5i$.

Solution   METHOD 1. Use the reverse factoring technique, extended to include the set of imaginary numbers.

$$x = 5i \qquad x = -5i$$
$$x - 5i = 0 \qquad x + 5i = 0$$
$$(x - 5i)(x + 5i) = 0$$
$$x^2 - 25i^2 = 0$$
$$x^2 - 25(-1) = 0$$
$$x^2 + 25 = 0$$

METHOD 2. Use the rules for the sum and the product of the roots of a quadratic equation.

(1) The sum of the roots $= 5i + (-5i) = 0$. Thus, $-\frac{b}{a} = 0$.

(2) The product of the roots $= (5i)(-5i) = -25i^2 = 25$. Thus, $\frac{c}{a} = 25$.

(3) Let $a = 1$.

$-\frac{b}{a} = 0$, or $-\frac{b}{1} = 0$	$\frac{c}{a} = 25$, or $\frac{c}{1} = 25$
$-b = 0$	$c = 25$
$b = 0$	

(4) Substitute $a = 1$, $b = 0$, and $c = 25$ in $ax^2 + bx + c = 0$ to form the equation $1x^2 + 0x + 25 = 0$, or $x^2 + 25 = 0$.

Answer: $x^2 + 25 = 0$

---

4. a. If one root of a quadratic equation is $3 + 2i$, what is its other root?
  b. Write a quadratic equation having these roots.

Solutions   **a.** If a quadratic equation with rational coefficients has imaginary roots, the roots are conjugates. Thus, if one root is $3 + 2i$, the other root is $3 - 2i$.

b. (1) The sum of the roots $= (3 + 2i) + (3 - 2i) = 6$. Thus, $-\frac{b}{a} = 6$.

(2) The product of the roots $= (3 + 2i)(3 - 2i)$

$$= 9 - 4i^2 = 9 + 4 = 13. \text{ Thus, } \frac{c}{a} = 13.$$

(3) Let $a = 1$.

$-\frac{b}{a} = 6$, or $-\frac{b}{1} = 6$	$\frac{c}{a} = 13$, or $\frac{c}{1} = 13$
$-b = 6$	$c = 13$
$b = -6$	

(4) By substitution, $ax^2 + bx + c = 0$ is $x^2 - 6x + 13 = 0$.

Answers: **a.** $3 - 2i$ **b.** $x^2 - 6x + 13 = 0$

---

5. If one root of $x^2 - 6x + k = 0$ is 4, find the other root.

Solution	METHOD 1	METHOD 2

METHOD 1

1. In $x^2 - 6x + k = 0$, $a = 1$, $b = -6$.

2. Let root $r_1 = 4$.

3. $r_1 + r_2 = -\frac{b}{a}$

$$4 + r_2 = \frac{-(-6)}{1}$$

$$= 6$$

$$r_2 = 2$$

METHOD 2

1. Substitute 4 for x:

$$x^2 - 6x + k = 0$$
$$4^2 - 6(4) + k = 0$$
$$16 - 24 + k = 0$$
$$-8 + k = 0$$
$$k = 8$$

2. Solve the equation: $x^2 - 6x + 8 = 0$

$$(x - 2)(x - 4) = 0$$

$$\begin{array}{c|c} x - 2 = 0 & x - 4 = 0 \\ x = 2 & x = 4 \end{array}$$

Answer: The second root is 2.

EXERCISES WITH OPEN-RESPONSE PROBLEMS

In 1–12, for each quadratic equation, find: **a.** the sum of its roots **b.** the product of its roots

1. $x^2 - 2x - 15 = 0$ **2.** $x^2 + 9x + 5 = 0$ **3.** $2x^2 - 7x + 3 = 0$ **4.** $4x^2 + x - 3 = 0$
5. $x^2 + 6x = 16$ **6.** $3x^2 + 9x = 2$ **7.** $2x^2 = 3x - 6$ **8.** $x^2 + 9 = 0$
9. $4x^2 - 8x = 0$ **10.** $2m^2 + 2 = 5m$ **11.** $5k - 10 = 2k^2$ **12.** $y^2 + 2y = 2$

In 13–18, in each case, write a quadratic equation whose roots have the indicated sum and product.

13. sum = 4, product = 3   **14.** sum = 16, product = -80
15. sum = -3, product = -10 **16.** sum = -6, product = 8
17. $r_1 + r_2 = 8$, $r_1 r_2 = 25$ **18.** $r_1 + r_2 = -\frac{5}{2}$, $r_1 r_2 = 1$

In 19–39, in each case, write a quadratic equation that has the given roots.

19. $-3, 5$ **20.** 2, 10   **21.** $-4, -6$ **22.** $-8, 8$

23. 7, 0   **24.** $\sqrt{3}, -\sqrt{3}$ **25.** $\frac{1}{2}, 4$ **26.** $-2, \frac{3}{2}$

27. $-\frac{1}{3}, -\frac{2}{3}$ **28.** $i, -i$ **29.** $4i, -4i$ **30.** $2 + i, 2 - i$

31. $6 - i, 6 + i$ **32.** $2 + \sqrt{3}, 2 - \sqrt{3}$ **33.** $1 - \sqrt{7}, 1 + \sqrt{7}$
34. $5 + 3i, 5 - 3i$ **35.** $-4 + 5i, -4 - 5i$ **36.** $7 + i, 7 - i$
37. $-2 + i\sqrt{5}, -2 - i\sqrt{5}$ **38.** $6 + 3i\sqrt{2}, 6 - 3i\sqrt{2}$ **39.** $4 + 2i\sqrt{3}, 4 - 2i\sqrt{3}$

In 40–47, for each quadratic equation, one root, r_1, is given. In each case, find the second root, r_2, of the equation.

40. $x^2 - 11x + k = 0$; $r_1 = 5$

41. $x^2 - x + k = 0$; $r_1 = -4$

42. $x^2 + 9x + k = 0$; $r_1 = -2$

43. $x^2 + kx + 18 = 0$; $r_1 = 6$

44. $x^2 + kx - 16 = 0$; $r_1 = -8$

45. $x^2 + kx + 4 = 0$; $r_1 = 12$

46. $2x^2 + kx - 12 = 0$; $r_1 = \frac{3}{2}$

47. $3x^2 - x + k = 0$; $r_1 = -\frac{5}{3}$

48. If the roots of the equation $x^2 - 4x + c = 0$ are $2 + 3i$ and $2 - 3i$, what is the value of c?

49. If the roots of the equation $x^2 + kx + 6 = 0$ are $4 + \sqrt{10}$ and $4 - \sqrt{10}$, what is the value of k?

50. a. If one root of a quadratic equation with rational coefficients is $4 - i$, what is the other root?
   b. Write a quadratic equation having these roots.

51. a. If one root of a quadratic equation with rational coefficients is $3 + \sqrt{7}$, what is the other root?
   b. Write a quadratic equation having these roots.

52. a. Find the roots of the equation $x^2 - 6x + 34 = 0$.
   b. Demonstrate that the sum of these roots is 6.
   c. Demonstrate that the product of these roots is 34.

In 53 and 54, select the *numeral* preceding the expression that best completes each sentence.

53. A quadratic equation having the roots 0 and -2 is
   (1) $x^2 - 2 = 0$
   (2) $x^2 - 2x = 0$
   (3) $x^2 + 2x = 0$
   (4) $x^2 + 2 = 0$

54. A quadratic equation with roots $7 + i$ and $7 - i$ is
   (1) $x^2 - 14x + 50 = 0$
   (2) $x^2 - 14x + 48 = 0$
   (3) $x^2 + 14x + 50 = 0$
   (4) $x^2 + 14x + 48 = 0$

55. Write, in simplest form, a quadratic equation whose roots are k and $-k$.

56. Write, in simplest form, a quadratic equation whose roots are $e + fi$ and $e - fi$.

57. The roots of $x^2 - 5x + c = 0$ differ by 3.
   a. What are the roots of the equation?   **b.** What is the value of c?

58. The roots of $x^2 - 6x + c = 0$ differ by $2\sqrt{3}$.
   a. What are the roots of the equation?   **b.** What is the value of c?

59. The roots of $x^2 + 2x + c = 0$ differ by $4i$.
   a. What are the roots of the equation?   **b.** What is the value of c?

20-10 SOLUTION OF SYSTEMS OF EQUATIONS

In Math A, we learned how to solve a system of linear equations by algebraic and graphic methods. If the equations are consistent, the graphs will be intersecting lines and there will be one solution. For example:

Solve $x - 2y = 4$
$\qquad y = 3 - 2x.$

Algebraic Solution	*Graphic Solution*

Algebraic Solution

$$x - 2y = 4$$
$$y = 3 - 2x$$
$$x - 2(3 - 2x) = 4$$
$$x - 6 + 4x = 4$$
$$5x = 10$$
$$x = 2$$
$$y = 3 - 2x$$
$$ = 3 - 2(2)$$
$$ = 3 - 4$$
$$ = -1$$

Answer: $(x, y) = (2, -1)$

or

$$x = 2, y = -1$$

Graphic Solution

On the same set of axes, graph both equations. The coordinates of the point of intersection are the solution of the system.

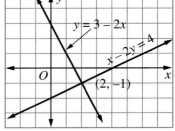

Answer: $(x, y) = (2, -1)$

Recall that parallel lines have the same slope and perpendicular lines have slopes that are negative reciprocals, that is, their product is -1.

In the equations above, the lines can be shown to be perpendicular by finding and comparing their slopes. Since $y = mx + b$,

$$x - 2y = 4 \qquad\qquad y = 3 - 2x$$
$$-2y = -x + 4 \qquad y = -2x + 3$$
$$y = \tfrac{1}{2}x - 2 \qquad\quad m = -2$$
$$m = \tfrac{1}{2}$$

The lines are perpendicular since their slopes are negative reciprocals.

These same procedures are used to solve a **quadratic-linear system**. In the graphic solution, the graphs may intersect in two points, one point, or no point. Since the points in the coordinate plane correspond to the set of ordered pairs of real numbers, these intersections indicate pairs of real numbers. As shown in the following graphs, there may be two real solutions, one real solution, or no real solution.

Two real solutions

One real solution

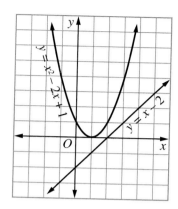

No real solution

When a quadratic-linear system has *no* solution in the set of real numbers, two complex roots can often be found by solving algebraically, as shown in the following example.

EXAMPLE

The quadratic-linear system graphed at the right has no real solution.

Solve this system of equations algebraically and check:

$$y = x^2 - 2x + 3$$
$$2x - y = 2.$$

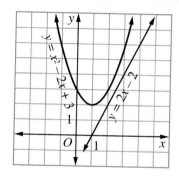

How to Proceed:

(1) Solve the linear equation for one of the variables.

(2) Substitute the value of y, $2x - 2$, for y in the quadratic equation.

(3) Write the resulting equation in standard form, and solve by using the quadratic formula.

Solution:

$$2x - y = 2$$
$$-y = -2x + 2$$
$$y = 2x - 2$$

$$y = x^2 - 2x + 3$$
$$2x - 2 = x^2 - 2x + 3$$
$$0 = x^2 - 4x + 5$$

$$x = \frac{4 \pm \sqrt{16 - 20}}{2}$$

$$= \frac{4 \pm 2i}{2} = 2 \pm i$$

(4) Substitute each value of x in the linear equation of the system to find y.

$$x = 2 + i$$
$$y = 2x - 2$$
$$= 2(2 + i) - 2$$
$$= 4 + 2i - 2$$
$$= 2 + 2i$$

$$x = 2 - i$$
$$y = 2x - 2$$
$$= 2(2 - i) - 2$$
$$= 4 - 2i - 2$$
$$= 2 - 2i$$

(5) Write the solution. (*Note:* Although the graphs of the equations have no point of intersection in the coordinate plane and thus no real solution, these equations have complex roots in common.)

$$(x_2, y_1) = (2 + i, 2 + 2i),$$
$$(x_2, y_2) = (2 - i, 2 - 2i)$$

or

$$x = 2 + i \qquad x = 2 - i$$
$$y = 2 + 2i \qquad y = 2 - 2i$$

(6) Check each ordered pair in both equations.

Checks for $(2 + i, 2 + 2i)$

$$y = x^2 - 2x + 3$$
$$2 + 2i \overset{?}{=} (2 + i)^2 - 2(2 + i) + 3$$
$$2 + 2i \overset{?}{=} 4 + 4i + i^2 - 4 - 2i + 3$$
$$2 + 2i \overset{?}{=} 4 + 4i - 1 - 4 - 2i + 3$$
$$2 + 2i = 2 + 2i \quad \text{(True)}$$

$$2x - y = 2$$
$$2(2 + i) - (2 + 2i) \overset{?}{=} 2$$
$$4 + 2i - 2 - 2i \overset{?}{=} 2$$
$$2 = 2$$
$$\text{(True)}$$

Checks for $(2 - i, 2 - 2i)$

$$y = x^2 - 2x + 3$$
$$2 - 2i \overset{?}{=} (2 - i)^2 - 2(2 - i) + 3$$
$$2 - 2i \overset{?}{=} 4 - 4i + i^2 - 4 + 2i + 3$$
$$2 - 2i \overset{?}{=} 4 - 4i - 1 - 4 + 2i + 3$$
$$2 - 2i = 2 - 2i \quad \text{(True)}$$

$$2x - y = 2$$
$$2(2 - i) - (2 - 2i) \overset{?}{=} 2$$
$$4 - 2i - 2 + 2i \overset{?}{=} 2$$
$$2 = 2$$
$$\text{(True)}$$

Answer: $(x_1, y_1) = (2 + i, 2 + 2i),$

or

$(x_2, y_2) = (2 - i, 2 - 2i)$

$x = 2 + i, y = 2 + 2i$

$x = 2 - i, y = 2 - 2i$

EXERCISES WITH OPEN-RESPONSE PROBLEMS

1. Name the maximum number of points of intersection for:
   a. a line and a circle
   b. a line and a parabola
   c. a line and a hyperbola
   d. a line and an ellipse

2. What does it mean if the two graphs of a system do *not* intersect?

3. The equations of two linear functions are

$$2x - y = -4$$
$$ky = 4x - 2$$

a. Determine k so that the graphs of the functions will be perpendicular lines. State the domain and the range of each function and graph the lines.

b. Determine k so that the graphs of the functions will be parallel lines. State the domain and the range of each function and graph the lines.

4. a. Draw the graph of $y = x^2 - 4x + 5$ for $-1 \le x \le 5$.

b. On the same set of axes, draw the graph of $y = 5 - x$.

c. Determine from the graphs drawn in parts **a** and **b** the solution of the system. Check in both equations.

In 5–12, solve each system of equations graphically and check.

5. $2x - y = 5$
$\quad 3x + 2y = 4$

6. $x^2 + y^2 = 10$
$\quad y = 3x$

7. $9x^2 + y^2 = 9$
$\quad 3x - y = 3$

8. $y = x^2 - 4x + 3$
$\quad y = x - 1$

9. $x^2 - y^2 = 9$
$\quad y = 4$

10. $xy = 8$
$\quad y = x + 2$

11. $y = -x^2 + 4$
$\quad y = x + 2$

12. $x^2 + y^2 = 8$
$\quad x + y = 4$

In 13–20, solve each system of equations algebraically and check.

13. $x^2 + 4y^2 = 4$
$\quad x = 2y - 2$

14. $y = x^2 - 3$
$\quad x + y = -1$

15. $y = 2 - x^2$
$\quad y = 2x + 4$

16. $x^2 + y^2 = 16$
$\quad x - y = 4$

17. $xy = -6$
$\quad x + 3y = 3$

18. $9x^2 - 4y^2 = 36$
$\quad y = 3x - 6$

19. $x^2 + y^2 = 18$
$\quad x + y = 6$

20. $x^2 - 2y^2 = 11$
$\quad y = x + 1$

In 21–28, for each quadratic-linear system of equations:

a. Solve graphically. (If the graphs do not intersect, write "No real roots.")

b. Solve algebraically, whether the roots are real or imaginary.

c. Check the roots in both equations.

21. $y = x^2 + x - 4$
$\quad y = 2x - 2$

22. $y = x^2$
$\quad 2x + y = -2$

23. $x^2 + y^2 = 25$
$\quad y = x - 1$

24. $xy = 12$
$\quad y = 2x + 2$

25. $y = 2x - x^2$
$\quad y = 2x + 1$

26. $y = x^2 + 4x + 1$
$\quad y = 2x + 1$

27. $x + y = 2$
$\quad xy = 12$

28. $x^2 + (y - 2)^2 = 4$
$\quad x = -3$

29. a. Draw the graphs of $25x^2 + 4y^2 = 100$ and $y = 2x + 5$ on the same set of axes.

b. How many solutions does this system have?

c. Solve the system algebraically to obtain the exact values of the roots.

d. Use a calculator to check the solution you obtained in part **c**.

20-11 QUADRATIC INEQUALITIES

Graphic Interpretation

We have learned that certain quadratic equations can be solved by graphic methods. For example, the graph of the parabola $y = x^2 - 1$ crosses the x-axis at 1 and -1, as shown at the right. Since the equation of the x-axis is $y = 0$, the intersection of $y = x^2 - 1$ (the parabola) and $y = 0$ (the x-axis) is the equation $x^2 - 1 = 0$. As shown in the graph of the number line also seen at the right, the solution set of $x^2 - 1 = 0$ is $x = -1$ or $x = 1$.

The set of points that form the parabola $y = x^2 - 1$ separates the plane into two regions, or *open half-planes*, named by the inequalities

Coordinate plane:	
Number line:	The solution set of $x^2 - 1 = 0$ is $\{-1, 1\}$

$$y > x^2 - 1 \qquad \text{and} \qquad y < x^2 - 1$$

In the coordinate graphs shown below, each shaded region is an open half-plane, and the points of the parabola $y = x^2 - 1$ are drawn as a dashed line to show that they are not points in the open half-plane.

The intersection of each open half-plane and the x-axis (that is, $y = 0$) is the graph of the solution set of a ***quadratic inequality*** on a number line.

At the left, the intersection of

$y > x^2 - 1$ and $y = 0$ is

$0 > x^2 - 1$ or $x^2 - 1 < 0$

At the right, the intersection of

$y < x^2 - 1$ and $y = 0$ is

$0 < x^2 - 1$ or $x^2 - 1 > 0$

Coordinate plane:		*Coordinate plane:*	
Number line:	The solution set of $x^2 - 1 < 0$ is $\{x \mid -1 < x < 1\}$	*Number line:*	The solution set of $x^2 - 1 > 0$ is $\{x \mid x < -1 \text{ or } x > 1\}$

Algebraic Interpretation

Now let us examine the same three quadratic relationships from an algebraic point of view. Since $x^2 - 1$ is factorable, a principle involving factors is applied to each situation. In each principle, we use logic, specifically concepts involving *and* and *or*. For example:

☐ **1.** Solve the quadratic equation $x^2 - 1 = 0$.

Since the product of two factors is 0, the first factor is 0 *or* the second factor is 0. Thus, we use this principle:

$$\textbf{If } \textit{ab} = \textbf{0, then } \textit{a} = \textbf{0 } \textit{or } \textit{b} = \textbf{0.}$$
$$x^2 - 1 = 0$$
$$(x + 1)(x - 1) = 0$$
$$x + 1 = 0 \ \textit{or} \ x - 1 = 0$$
$$x = -1 \ \textit{or} \ x = 1$$

Answer: $\{-1, 1\}$

☐ **2.** Solve the quadratic inequality $x^2 - 1 < 0$.

Here, the product of two factors is less than 0; that is, the product is negative. Therefore, the first factor is negative *and* the second factor is positive, *or* the first factor is positive *and* the second factor is negative. This principle is stated as follows:

$$\textbf{If } \textit{ab} < \textbf{0, then } \textit{a} < \textbf{0 } \textit{and } \textit{b} > \textbf{0, } \textit{or } \textit{a} > \textbf{0 } \textit{and } \textit{b} < \textbf{0.}$$
$$x^2 - 1 < 0$$
$$(x + 1)(x - 1) < 0$$

$x + 1 < 0$	*and*	$x - 1 > 0$	*or*	$x + 1 > 0$	*and*	$x - 1 < 0$
$x < -1$	*and*	$x > 1$		$x > -1$	*and*	$x < 1$

There are no numbers that are less than -1 *and* greater than 1 at the same time. Since this intersection is empty, *disregard* this case.

Answer: $\{x \mid -1 < x < 1\}$

The numbers that are greater than -1 *and* less than 1 are in the intersection

$$\{x \mid -1 < x < 1\}$$

☐ **3.** Solve the quadratic inequality $x^2 - 1 > 0$.

Here, the product of two factors is greater than 0; that is, the product is positive. Therefore, both factors are negative *or* both factors are positive. This principle is stated as follows:

If $ab > 0$, then $a < 0$ and $b < 0$, or $a > 0$ and $b > 0$.

$$x^2 - 1 > 0$$

$$(x + 1)(x - 1) > 0$$

$x + 1 < 0$ and $x - 1 < 0$		$x + 1 > 0$ and $x - 1 > 0$
$x < -1$ and $x < 1$	*or*	$x > -1$ and $x > 1$

The word *and* indicates an intersection of sets. The numbers that are less than -1 *and* also less than 1 form the intersection

The word *and* indicates an intersection of sets. The numbers that are greater than -1 *and* also greater than 1 form the intersection

$$x < -1 \qquad or \qquad x > 1$$

Answer: $\{x \mid x < -1 \text{ or } x > 1\}$

Caution: In Section 20-6, we learned that imaginary numbers cannot be ordered; that is, the relations $>$ and $<$ are meaningless for imaginary numbers.

Therefore, quadratic inequalities cannot have solutions that are imaginary numbers. In other words:

● **Solution sets of quadratic inequalities are restricted to the sets of real numbers only.**

Summary

The three examples we have just studied serve as illustrations of the following general cases, where roots r_1 and r_2 are real numbers, $r_1 \neq r_2$, and $a > 0$:

Quadratic Relation:	$ax^2 + bx + c = 0$	$ax^2 + bx + c < 0$	$ax^2 + bx + c > 0$
Graph:	●———● r_1 r_2	○———○ r_1 r_2	○———○ r_1 r_2
Solution Set:	$\{r_1, r_2\}$	$\{x \mid r_1 < x < r_2\}$	$\{x \mid x < r_1 \text{ or } x > r_2\}$

An equality can be combined with an inequality to form a quadratic relationship involving $\leq$ or $\geq$, as shown below.

Relation:	$ax^2 + bx + c \leq 0$	$ax^2 + bx + c \geq 0$
Graph:	●———● r_1 r_2	●———● r_1 r_2
Solution Set:	$\{x \mid r_1 \leq x \leq r_2\}$	$\{x \mid x \leq r_1 \text{ or } x \geq r_2\}$

Let us consider *two exceptions* to these general cases:

1. Roots r_1 and r_2 of the quadratic equation are *imaginary*. Here, the parabola does not intersect the *x*-axis. The solution of any related quadratic inequality is either the set of all real numbers or the empty set.
    For example, the roots of $x^2 + 1 = 0$ are i and $-i$.

Thus: For $x^2 + 1 > 0$, the solution = Real numbers
              For $x^2 + 1 < 0$, the solution = { } or $\varnothing$

2. Roots r_1 and r_2 of the quadratic equation are *equal*. Since $r_1 = r_2$, the parabola intersects the *x*-axis in one point only. The solution of any related quadratic inequality is either the set of real numbers less r_1 or the empty set.
    For example, the single root of $(x - 2)^2 = 0$ is 2.

Thus: For $(x - 2)^2 > 0$, the solution = Real numbers/{2}
              For $(x - 2)^2 < 0$, the solution = { } or $\varnothing$

EXAMPLES

1. Which is the graph of the solution set of $x^2 + 2x - 8 > 0$?

(1) ←—∘———∘—→   (2) ←—∘———∘—→   (3) ←—∘———∘—→   (4) ←—∘———∘—→
    −4   2   −4   2   −2   4   −2   4

Solution   Use this principle:
    If $ab > 0$, then $a < 0$ *and* $b < 0$, *or* $a > 0$ *and* $b > 0$.

$$x^2 + 2x - 8 > 0$$
$$(x + 4)(x - 2) > 0$$

$x + 4 < 0$ and $x - 2 < 0$		$x + 4 > 0$ and $x - 2 > 0$
$x < -4$ and $x < 2$	*or*	$x > -4$ and $x > 2$
This intersection is		This intersection is
$x < -4$		$x > 2$

The solution set is $\{x \mid x < -4 \text{ or } x > 2\}$, graphed in choice (2).

Answer: (2)

---

2. Graph the solution set of $x^2 - 4x - 5 < 0$.

Solution   (1) Factor the quadratic *equation* to find its roots. These roots are the critical points on the number-line graph.

$$x^2 - 4x - 5 = 0$$
$$(x + 1)(x - 5) = 0$$

$$x + 1 = 0 \quad \bigg| \quad x - 5 = 0$$
$$x = -1 \quad \bigg| \quad x = 5$$

(2) Use the quadratic *inequality* to test a value from each of the three regions created on the number line.

Test $x < -1$.	Test $-1 < x < 5$.	Test $x > 5$.
$x^2 - 4x - 5 < 0$	$x^2 - 4x - 5 < 0$	$x^2 - 4x - 5 < 0$
$(-2)^2 - 4(-2) - 5 \overset{?}{<} 0$	$(0)^2 - 4(0) - 5 \overset{?}{<} 0$	$(8)^2 - 4(8) - 5 \overset{?}{<} 0$
$4 + 8 - 5 \overset{?}{<} 0$	$0 - 0 - 5 \overset{?}{<} 0$	$64 - 32 - 5 \overset{?}{<} 0$
$7 < 0$	$-5 < 0$	$27 < 0$
(False)	(True)	(False)

(3) The inequality is true only when $-1 < x < 5$.
Graph this region on the number line.

$\leftarrow\!\!\overset{\circ}{\rule{0pt}{0pt}}\!\!\rule[3pt]{18pt}{1pt}\!\!\overset{\circ}{\rule{0pt}{0pt}}\!\!\rightarrow$
   $-1\quad\ \ 5$

Alternative Solution   Use this principle:
   If $ab < 0$, then $a < 0$ *and* $b > 0$, *or* $a > 0$ *and* $b < 0$.

$$x^2 - 4x - 5 < 0$$
$$(x + 1)(x - 5) < 0$$

$x + 1 < 0$ and $x - 5 > 0$		$x + 1 > 0$ and $x - 5 < 0$
$x < -1$ and $x > 5$	*or*	$x > -1$ and $x < 5$

Since this intersection is empty, disregard this set.

The intersection is $\{x \mid -1 < x < 5\}$

$\leftarrow\!\!\overset{\circ}{\rule{0pt}{0pt}}\!\!\rule[3pt]{18pt}{1pt}\!\!\overset{\circ}{\rule{0pt}{0pt}}\!\!\rightarrow$
   $-1\quad\ \ 5$

Answer: $\leftarrow\!\!\overset{\circ}{\rule{0pt}{0pt}}\!\!\rule[3pt]{18pt}{1pt}\!\!\overset{\circ}{\rule{0pt}{0pt}}\!\!\rightarrow$
      $-1\quad\ \ 5$

---

3. Graph the solution set of $x^2 - 4x - 5 \le 0$.

Solution   Use the solution from Example 2 above, but replace $<$ with $\le$, and replace $>$ with $\ge$, since the equality is included. Here the number-line graph includes -1 and 5 because of the equality.

Answer: $\leftarrow\!\!\bullet\!\!\rule[3pt]{18pt}{1pt}\!\!\bullet\!\!\rightarrow$
      $-1\quad\ \ 5$

EXERCISES WITH OPEN-RESPONSE PROBLEMS

In 1–7, select the *numeral* preceding the expression that best completes the sentence or answers the question.

1. The solution of $x^2 - 4 < 0$ is
   (1) $-2 < x < 2$ (2) $-4 < x < 4$ (3) $x < -2$ or $x > 2$ (4) $x < -4$ or $x > 4$

2. The solution of $x^2 - 9 > 0$ is
   (1) $-3 < x < 3$ (2) $-9 < x < 9$ (3) $x < -3$ or $x > 3$ (4) $x < -9$ or $x > 9$

3. Which is the graph of the solution set of $x^2 + 3x - 4 > 0$?

(1)
−4   1

(2)
−1   4

(3)
−4   1

(4)
−1   4

4. Which is the graph of the solution set of $x^2 - 8x + 12 < 0$?

(1)
2   6

(2)
−6 −2

(3)
2   6

(4)
−6 −2

5. If $x^2 - 3x \leq 0$, which is the graph of the solution set?

(1)
0   3

(2)
0   3

(3)
−3   0

(4)
−3   0

6. The graph of the solution set of $x^2 - 4x \geq 0$ is

(1)
0   4

(2)
0   4

(3)
−4   0

(4)
−4   0

7. Which of the following is a quadratic inequality whose solution is graphed at the right?

$-\sqrt{3}$ $\sqrt{3}$

(1) $x^2 - 3 < 0$ (2) $x^2 - 3 > 0$

(3) $x^2 - 3 \leq 0$ (4) $x^2 - 3 \geq 0$

In 8–23, for each quadratic inequality: **a.** Write the solution set. **b.** Graph the solution set.

8. $x^2 - 16 < 0$
9. $x^2 - 25 > 0$
10. $2x^2 - 8 > 0$
11. $x^2 - 4x \geq 0$
12. $x^2 + 7x \leq 0$
13. $x^2 - 7x + 10 < 0$
14. $x^2 - x - 6 > 0$
15. $x^2 - 5x - 24 \leq 0$
16. $x^2 + 8x + 7 \geq 0$
17. $x^2 > 8x + 20$
18. $x^2 + 2x < 15$
19. $x^2 + 27 < 12x$
20. $4x^2 - 9 \geq 0$
21. $2x^2 - 11x + 5 \geq 0$
22. $3x^2 + 10x \leq 8$
23. $9x^2 + 4 \leq 15x$

24. The quadratic inequality $x^2 - 14x + 49 \leq 0$ has a solution set consisting of only one number.
  a. Find the solution set.   **b.** Explain why the solution set is limited to one number.
25. Explain why the solution set of $x^2 + 16 < 0$ is empty.
26. Explain why the solution set of $x^2 + 9 > 0$ is the set of all real numbers.

In 27–34, write the solution set of each quadratic inequality.

27. $x^2 - 6x + 9 > 0$
28. $x^2 - 6x + 9 < 0$
29. $x^2 - 6x + 9 \geq 0$
30. $x^2 - 6x + 9 \leq 0$
31. $4x^2 + 1 < 4x$
32. $4x^2 + 1 > 4x$
33. $4x^2 + 1 \leq 4x$
34. $4x^2 + 1 \geq 4x$

CHAPTER SUMMARY

The number i, or $\sqrt{-1}$, is called the **imaginary unit**. A **pure imaginary number** is any number of the form bi, where b is a real number such that $b \neq 0$, and i is the imaginary unit $\sqrt{-1}$. In general, for any power of i where k is a whole number:

$$i^{4k} = 1 \qquad i^{4k+1} = i \qquad i^{4k+2} = -1 \qquad i^{4k+3} = -i$$

A **complex number** is any number of the form $a + bi$, where a and b are real numbers, and i is the imaginary unit $\sqrt{-1}$. The **complex number plane** is formed by drawing the pure imaginary number line perpendicular to the real number line, with these lines intersecting at the origin, $0 + 0i$, or 0.

Every complex number can be represented as a point or as a *vector* in the complex plane. Vector addition may be used to add two complex numbers where the sum is the *resultant vector*, or the diagonal of a parallelogram whose sides are the addends. As shown at the right:

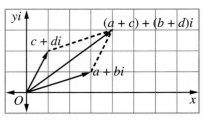

$$(a + bi) + (c + di) = (a + c) + (b + d)i$$

The distance from O to $a + bi$ or the **magnitude** of the vector is $|a + bi| = \sqrt{a^2 + b^2}$.

Although the complex numbers cannot be ordered, (Complex numbers, $+$, $\cdot$) is a **field** because:

1. (Complex numbers, $+$) is a commutative group.

2. (Complex numbers/$\{0 + 0i\}$, $\cdot$) is a commutative group.

3. Multiplication is distributive over addition.

A **quadratic equation**, $ax^2 + bx + c = 0$, where a, b, and c are real numbers and $a \neq 0$, may be solved by using the **quadratic formula**:

$$x = \frac{-b \pm \sqrt{b^2 - 4ac}}{2a}$$

In this formula, when a, b, and c are rational, the value of the **discriminant**, $b^2 - 4ac$, indicates the nature of the roots of the quadratic equation:

If $b^2 - 4ac > 0$ and $b^2 - 4ac$ is a perfect square, the roots are real, rational, and unequal.

If $b^2 - 4ac > 0$ and $b^2 - 4ac$ is not a perfect square, the roots are real, irrational, and unequal.

If $b^2 - 4ac = 0$, the roots are real, rational, and equal.

If $b^2 - 4ac < 0$, the roots are imaginary.

For every quadratic equation, $ax^2 + bx + c = 0$ ($a \neq 0$), the sum of the two roots is $\frac{-b}{a}$ and the product of the roots is $\frac{c}{a}$.

Quadratic-linear systems are usually solved by algebraic or graphing techniques. If the graphs of a quadratic equation and a linear equation have no points in common, the system has *no real* roots. In these cases, however, two *complex* roots are often found as solutions to the system by using algebraic methods.

The solution of a **quadratic inequality** may be graphed on a number line:

$ax^2 + bx + c < 0$ $(a > 0)$	$ax^2 + bx + c > 0$ $(a > 0)$
solution $= \{x\mid r_1 < x < r_2\}$	solution $= \{x\mid x < r_1 \;\; \text{or} \;\; x > r_2\}$

VOCABULARY

20-1   Imaginary unit   Pure imaginary number
20-2   Complex number   Complex number plane   Magnitude
20-4   Conjugate (of a complex number)
20-5   Identity element for multiplication   Multiplicative inverse
           Rationalize the denominator
20-6   Field   Trichotomy property
20-7   Quadratic equation   Quadratic formula
20-8   Discriminant
20-10   Quadratic-linear system
20-11   Quadratic inequality

REVIEW EXERCISES WITH OPEN-RESPONSE PROBLEMS

In 1–4, in each case, write each number in terms of i, perform the indicated operations, and write the answer in simplest terms.

1. $\sqrt{-49} + 3\sqrt{-25}$

3. $5\sqrt{-5} \cdot \sqrt{-20}$

2. $\sqrt{-18} + \sqrt{-2} - \sqrt{-32}$

4. $\sqrt{-300} - 2\sqrt{-75} + \sqrt{-48}$

In 5–10, in each case, perform the indicated operations, and express the result in the form $a + bi$.

5. $(7 - 3i) + (5 + 8i)$

7. $(2 + 5i)(3 - 7i)$

9. $(5 + \sqrt{-16})(2 - \sqrt{-9})$

6. $(4 - 10i) - (23 - 6i)$

8. $(4 - 3i)^2$

10. $(6 + 7i) \div (2 - i)$

In 11–16, in each case, perform the indicated operations and write the answer in simplest terms.

11. $(5 - i)(10 + 2i)$

13. $(1 + i)^4$

15. $(9 - i\sqrt{2})(9 + i\sqrt{2})$

12. $3i(2 - i) - 3(i + 1)$

14. $(1 - 3i)^2 + 6i$

16. $(1 - i) \div (3 - i)$

17. *True* or *False*: (Complex numbers, $+$, $\cdot$) is a field.

18. *True* or *False*: Every complex number has a multiplicative inverse.

In 19–24, find, in $a + bi$ form, the roots of each equation.

19. $x^2 - 6x + 10 = 0$

20. $x^2 + 10x + 26 = 0$

21. $x^2 + 29 = 4x$

22. $\frac{x^2}{4} = 3x - 10$

23. $2x^2 = 6x - 5$

24. $\frac{16x}{7} + \frac{7}{x} = 0$

25. Find the largest integral value of k such that the roots of $2x^2 + 7x + k = 0$ are real.

26. What is the sum of the roots of $3x^2 - 12x + 10 = 0$?

27. If the roots of $x^2 - 6x + k = 0$ are $3 + \sqrt{7}$ and $3 - \sqrt{7}$, find k.

In 28–31, in each case, write a quadratic equation for the given roots.

28. $6i, -6i$ **29.** $-8, 3$ **30.** $\frac{4}{3}, -\frac{2}{3}$ **31.** $2 + 4i, 2 - 4i$

In 32–43, select the *numeral* preceding the choice that best completes each sentence.

32. The complex number $5i^3 - 2i^2$ is equivalent to
(1) $-2 + 5i$ (2) $-2 - 5i$ (3) $2 - 5i$ (4) $2 + 5i$

33. The product $4i^3 \cdot 2i^2$ is
(1) 8 (2) $8i$ (3) -8 (4) $-8i$

34. The number $3 + i(3 + i)$ is equivalent to
(1) 8 (2) $2 + 3i$ (3) $8 + 6i$ (4) $4 + 3i$

35. The expression $\sqrt{-192}$ equals
(1) $8\sqrt{3}$ (2) $3\sqrt{8}$ (3) $8i\sqrt{3}$ (4) $3i\sqrt{8}$

36. The product of $5 - 2i$ and its conjugate is
(1) 21 (2) 29 (3) $21 - 20i$ (4) $29 - 20i$

37. The multiplicative identity for the set of complex numbers is
(1) $1 + 0i$ (2) $1 + 1i$ (3) $0 + 1i$ (4) $0 + 0i$

38. The multiplicative inverse of $3 - i$ is
(1) $3 + i$ (2) $\frac{3 + i}{10}$ (3) $\frac{3 + i}{8}$ (4) $\frac{3 - i}{10}$

39. If $x + yi = 1 + 2i + 3i^2$, then
(1) $x = 1, y = 2$ (2) $x = -2, y = 2$
(3) $x = 2, y = 2$ (4) $x = 4, y = 2$

40. The roots of $x^2 - 16x + 61 = 0$ are
(1) real, rational, and equal   (2) real, rational, and unequal
(3) real, irrational, and unequal   (4) imaginary

41. The graph of the parabola $y = x^2 + 8$
(1) is tangent to the x-axis   (2) intersects the x-axis at 2 points
(3) lies entirely above the x-axis   (4) lies entirely below the x-axis

42. The roots of $2x^2 + bx + 1 = 0$ are imaginary when b equals
(1) -4 (2) -2 (3) 3 (4) 4

43. The graph of the solution set of $x^2 - 9x + 14 < 0$ is

(1) ⟵ ∘—∘ ⟶
  $\;\;$ 2 $\;\;$ 7

(2) ⟵ ∘ $\;\;$ ∘ ⟶
  $\;\;$ 2 $\;\;$ 7

(3) ⟵ ∘—∘ ⟶
  $\;$ -7 -2

(4) ⟵ ∘ $\;\;$ ∘ ⟶
  $\;$ -7 -2

44. Which number is included in the shaded region?
(1) $-1 + i$
(2) $-2 + 2.5i$
(3) $1 - 2i$
(4) $2 - 2.5i$

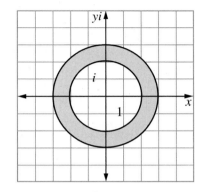

45. For the following linear functions:
  a. Determine k so that the graphs of the functions will be perpendicular lines. State the domain and the range of each function and graph the lines.
  b. Determine k so that the graphs of the functions will be parallel lines. State the domain and the range of each function and graph the lines.

$$3x - y = 4$$
$$ky = 3x - 6$$

In 46–48, for each quadratic-linear system of equations:
a. Solve graphically. (If the graphs do not intersect, write "No real roots.")
b. Solve algebraically.   **c.** Check.

46. $x^2 - 2x = 2 - y$
   $y = 2x + 1$

47. $xy = -4$
   $x + 2y = 2$

48. $x^2 + 4y^2 = 4$
   $x = 6$

49. In an ordered field, the following conditional statement is true:

$$\textit{If } x > y, \textit{ then } x - y > 0.$$

  a. Write the contrapositive of the given conditional statement.
  b. Let $x = 5i$, $y = 4i$, and $x - y = 5i - 4i = i$. Since it has been proved that $i \not> 0$ or that $x - y \not> 0$, what conclusion must be true?
    (1) $5i > 4i$ (2) $5i \not> 4i$ (3) $i < 0$ (4) $i = 0$

CUMULATIVE REVIEW WITH OPEN-RESPONSE PROBLEMS

1. A trapezoid has three congruent sides and a fourth side whose length is twice that of each of the congruent sides.
  a. Find the measures of the base angles of the trapezoid.
  b. Show that the trapezoid can be separated into three congruent equilateral triangles.

2. If $A(3, 0)$ and $B(5, 3)$ are on $\overleftrightarrow{AB}$, find, to the nearest degree, the measure of the acute angle that $\overleftrightarrow{AB}$ makes with the *x*-axis.

3. In right triangle *ABC*, m$\angle C$ = 90, m$\angle A$ = 56, and *AB* = 7.5. Find the length of the shortest side of the triangle to the *nearest tenth*.

4. Points $A(1, 1)$ and $C(7, 7)$ are the endpoints of the diagonal of square *ABCD*. Find the coordinates of *B* and *D*.

5. Do $A(-1, 5)$, $B(1, 4)$, and $C(8, 0)$ lie on a line? Explain your answer.

6. **a.** *Given:* Right triangle *ABC*, m$\angle C$ = 90.

   $\overline{DE} \perp \overline{AB}$ at *E*.

   Prove: $\triangle ABC \sim \triangle ADE$.
   b. If *D* is the midpoint of $\overline{CA}$,
   AE = 6 centimeters, and
   AB = 24 centimeters, find:
   (1) DA (2) CA (3) DE (4) BC

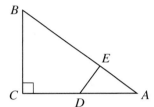

7. Under a rotation of 30° about the origin, the image of $A\left(\frac{\sqrt{5}}{3}, \frac{2}{3}\right)$ is A'. Find the coordinates of A'.

8. Express $\log \frac{a^2}{\sqrt{b}}$ in terms of $\log a$ and $\log b$.

9. If $f(x) = 3^x$ and $g(x) = 2x$, find: **a.** $f \circ g(x)$ **b.** $g \circ f(x)$

10. Find to the *nearest tenth* of a meter the length of the longer diagonal of a parallelogram if the lengths of two sides are 13.6 meters and 24.5 meters and the measure of one angle is 24°30'.

11. Find all values of *x* in the interval $0° \leq x \leq 360°$ that are solutions of the equation $\sin 2x + \cos x = 0$.

Exploration

The *polar form* of the complex number $a + bi$ is $r(\cos \theta + i \sin \theta)$ where $r = \sqrt{a^2 + b^2}$, $a = r \cos \theta$, and $b = r \sin \theta$.

a. Show that $(a + bi)^2 = r^2(\cos 2\theta + i \sin 2\theta)$
b. Find $(2 + 2i)^2$ using $a + bi$ form.
c. Write $2 + 2i$ in polar form.
d. Find $(2 + 2i)^2$ using the polar form found in part **c** and the identity in part **a**.
e. Compare the answers found in parts **b** and **d**.

Chapter 21
Statistics

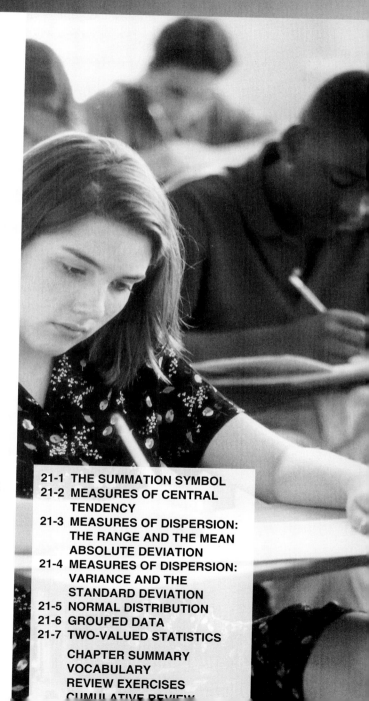

Every year, colleges receive applications for admission, often many more than the number of students that can be admitted in the coming year. To choose the applicants who are most likely to succeed in the academic programs that a particular college offers, admission officers spend months examining resumes that include the candidates' academic records.

Comparable grades from different high schools, however, may not reflect the same level of achievement. For this reason, colleges often take into account the scores received by students on national standardized tests. Statistical measures concerning these tests provide the persons who must choose prospective students with reliable, although not conclusive, standards for comparing applicants.

Standardizing testing is just one way in which statistics are used. The collection and interpretation of data are vital steps in decision making in research, business, industry, government, and politics, as well as in our personal lives.

21-1   THE SUMMATION SYMBOL

In statistics, we often work with sums. The **summation symbol** is the Greek capital letter sigma, Σ, used to indicate the sum of related terms. For example, $\sum_{i=1}^{6} i$ means the sum of the integers, symbolized by i, from $i = 1$ to $i = 6$. Therefore:

$$\sum_{i=1}^{6} i = 1 + 2 + 3 + 4 + 5 + 6 = 21$$

In the preceding example, the letter i is called the **index**; and when the indicated sum is evaluated, i is replaced by a series of consecutive integers, starting with the lower limit of summation and ending with the upper limit of summation.

The **lower limit of summation** is the value of the index placed below the summation symbol, and the **upper limit of summation** is the value of the index placed above the summation symbol. In $\sum_{i=1}^{6} i$, the lower limit is 1, and the upper limit is 6.

Any letter can serve as an index; but i, j, k, and n are the most frequently used letters. Since an index acts as a placeholder, an index of i is *not* equal to the imaginary unit, $\sqrt{-1}$.

The meaning of the summation symbol is shown in the following equations:

$$\sum_{k=0}^{5} 3^k = 3^0 + 3^1 + 3^2 + 3^3 + 3^4 + 3^5 = 1 + 3 + 9 + 27 + 81 + 243 = 364$$

$$\sum_{j=3}^{6} j^2 = 3^2 + 4^2 + 5^2 + 6^2 = 9 + 16 + 25 + 36 = 86$$

Use of Subscripts

If a variable quantity is denoted by x, then successive values of that variable can be indicated by using a **subscript**, as in x_1, x_2, x_3 (read as x sub-1, x sub-2, x sub-3). The use of sigma notation and subscripted variables is shown in the following examples.

☐ Mr. Cook teaches five classes. The numbers of students absent from his classes today are 3, 1, 2, 0, and 1. Mr. Cook records the number of student absences using subscripted variables:

$$x_1 = 3, \qquad x_2 = 1, \qquad x_3 = 2, \qquad x_4 = 0, \qquad x_5 = 1$$

The total number of absentees from Mr. Cook's classes for the day can be written as follows in sigma notation:

$$\sum_{i=1}^{5} x_i = x_1 + x_2 + x_3 + x_4 + x_5 = 3 + 1 + 2 + 0 + 1 = 7$$

When the summation symbol is used without an index and without upper and lower limits of summation, Σ designates the sum of *all* values of the given variable under consideration. Summation symbols without an index are used in the following example.

Reports x	Frequency f	xf
5	1	5
4	5	20
3	8	24
2	7	14
1	4	4
0	2	0

☐   Mrs. Gallagher, a science teacher, has completed five laboratory sessions with her class. In the frequency distribution at the right, she has recorded the number of students who have completed 0, 1, 2, 3, 4, or 5 lab reports. The sum of the frequencies equals the number of students in the class. Therefore:

$$\text{Number of students in class} = \Sigma f = 1 + 5 + 8 + 7 + 4 + 2 = 27$$

To find the total number of reports completed, we first, for each row, multiply the number of completed reports, x, by the number of students who have completed that many reports, f. The sum of these products, Σxf, is the total number of reports completed.

$$\begin{aligned}
\Sigma xf &= 5(1) + 4(5) + 3(8) + 2(7) + 1(4) + 0(2) \\
&= 5 \quad + 20 \ \ + 24 \ \ + 14 \ \ + 4 \quad + 0 \ \ = 67
\end{aligned}$$

Therefore, 67 lab reports have been completed.

Calculator Applications

Graphing calculators have the capability of storing data and displaying sums. On the TI-81, TI-82, and TI-83, we use the functions given in the [STAT] menu. Throughout this chapter, we will display key sequences for the TI-83, which can be adapted to other graphing calculators that have similar capabilities. On the TI-82 and TI-83, data sets are stored in lists. If a set of data has been previously entered into the lists, it is necessary to clear these lists before entering new data.

Enter: [2nd] [MEM] 4 [ENTER]

Now we will list the number of reports, x, in L1; the frequency, f, in L2; and the product, xf, in L3. We need only to enter the information in L1 and L2. The calculator will compute the values for L3 the product of the corresponding entries in L1 and L2, and complete the list.

Enter:

Next, we want to determine the number of students in the class by finding Σf, the sum of the data in L2. We will enter the STAT menu, use the right arrow key to move to CALC , and press ENTER to choose 1-Var Stats. The calculator will copy 1-Var Stats to the home screen. We then enter L2 to tell the calculator to use the data in that list.

Enter: STAT ▶ ENTER 2nd L2 ENTER

Display:
1-Var Stats
$\bar{x} = 4.5$
$\Sigma x = 27$
$\Sigma x^2 = 159$
$Sx = 2.738612788$
$\sigma x = 2.5$
↓ n = 6

The display shown above gives several different statistical values related to this set of data. The third line tells us that the sum of the frequencies that were entered in L2 is 27. We will study the meaning of the other information given in the display in Sections 21-2 and 21-4.

Finally, we learn the total number of lab reports completed by finding Σxf, the sum of the data in L3.

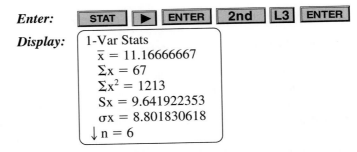

Enter: STAT ▶ ENTER 2nd L3 ENTER

Display:
1-Var Stats
$\bar{x} = 11.16666667$
$\Sigma x = 67$
$\Sigma x^2 = 1213$
$Sx = 9.641922353$
$\sigma x = 8.801830618$
↓ n = 6

The display tells us that the sum of the data in L3, that is, the total number of completed reports, is 67.

EXAMPLES

1. In parts **a** and **b**, in each case, evaluate the sum.

a. $\displaystyle\sum_{k=1}^{5} 3k$ **b.** $3 \displaystyle\sum_{k=1}^{5} k$

Solutions   **a.** $\displaystyle\sum_{k=1}^{5} 3k = 3(1) + 3(2) + 3(3) + 3(4) + 3(5)$

$= 3 + 6 + 9 + 12 + 15 = 45$ *Answer*

b. $3 \sum_{k=1}^{5} k = 3(1 + 2 + 3 + 4 + 5) = 3(15) = 45$ *Answer*

Note: $\sum_{k=1}^{5} 3k = 3 \sum_{k=1}^{5} k.$

Example 1 illustrates a general statement that is proved in Example 2.

---

2. If c is a constant, show that $\sum_{j=1}^{n} cj = c \sum_{j=1}^{n} j.$

Solution

$$\sum_{j=1}^{n} cj = c(1) + c(2) + c(3) + \cdots + c(n)$$

$$= c(1 + 2 + 3 + \cdots + n) \text{ by the distributive property}$$

$$= c \sum_{j=1}^{n} j$$

---

3. Using the summation symbol, write an expression that equals $1 + \frac{1}{4} + \frac{1}{9} + \frac{1}{16}.$

Solution $1 + \frac{1}{4} + \frac{1}{9} + \frac{1}{16}$ $=$ $\frac{1}{1^2} + \frac{1}{2^2} + \frac{1}{3^2} + \frac{1}{4^2}$ $=$ $\sum_{i=1}^{4} \frac{1}{i^2}$ *Answer*

Note: Other answers also exist. For example:

$$1 + \frac{1}{4} + \frac{1}{9} + \frac{1}{16} = \sum_{n=0}^{3} \frac{1}{(n + 1)^2}$$

EXERCISES WITH OPEN-RESPONSE PROBLEMS

In 1–15, find the value indicated by each summation symbol.

1. $\sum_{k=0}^{6} 2k$

2. $\sum_{i=1}^{5} (i + 1)$

3. $\sum_{j=0}^{4} j^2$

4. $\sum_{n=2}^{5} (n - 2)^2$

5. $\sum_{j=1}^{3} j^3$

6. $\sum_{n=0}^{3} 2^n$

7. $\sum_{n=1}^{4} \frac{1}{n}$

8. $\sum_{k=0}^{5} (10 - k)$

9. $\sum_{i=3}^{7} (2 - i)^2$

10. $5 \sum_{n=1}^{4} (n - 1)$

11. $\sum_{k=1}^{3} 3k^2$

12. $\sum_{k=1}^{3} k^{k-1}$

13. $\sum_{n=0}^{2} \cos(n\pi)$

14. $\sum_{n=1}^{3} \sin\left(\frac{n\pi}{2}\right)$

15. $\sum_{k=0}^{4} \cos\left(\frac{k\pi}{2}\right)$

In 16–21, in each case, use the summation symbol to write an expression to indicate the sum.

16. $2(1) + 2(2) + 2(3) + 2(4) + 2(5)$

17. $0 + 1 + 4 + 9 + 16$

18. $\frac{1}{3} + \frac{1}{6} + \frac{1}{9} + \frac{1}{12} + \frac{1}{15}$

19. $\frac{1}{2} + \frac{2}{3} + \frac{3}{4} + \frac{4}{5}$

20. $1^1 + 2^2 + 3^3 + 4^4 + 5^5 + 6^6$

21. $2(1) + 3(2) + 4(3)$

In 22–25, find the value of each indicated sum when $x_1 = 12$, $x_2 = 5$, $x_3 = 4$, $x_4 = 8$, and $x_5 = 7$.

22. $\displaystyle\sum_{i=1}^{5} x_i$

23. $\displaystyle\sum_{k=3}^{5} x_k$

24. $3\displaystyle\sum_{j=1}^{3} x_j$

25. $\displaystyle\sum_{n=2}^{4} 5x_n$

In 26–29, select the *numeral* preceding the choice that best completes each sentence.

26. The value of $3\displaystyle\sum_{k=1}^{5} (k - 1)$ is

(1) 10   (2) 15   (3) 30   (4) 45

27. The value of $\displaystyle\sum_{n=1}^{3} \tan \frac{(2n - 1)\pi}{4}$ is

(1) 1   (2) 2   (3) 3   (4) -1

28. $\displaystyle\sum_{n=0}^{2} \left(\text{Arc sin} \frac{n}{2}\right)$ equals

(1) $60°$ (2) $90°$ (3) $120°$ (4) $150°$

29. The sum $1 + 8 + 27 + 64$ is *not* equal to

(1) $\displaystyle\sum_{i=1}^{4} i^3$ (2) $\displaystyle\sum_{k=0}^{4} (k + 1)^3$ (3) $\displaystyle\sum_{n=0}^{3} (n + 1)^3$ (4) $\displaystyle\sum_{j=2}^{5} (j - 1)^3$

30. Represent the sum $5 + 10 + 15 + 20 + 25 + 30$ by *three* different expressions, each involving the summation symbol.

31. In a–d, evaluate each expression.

a. $\displaystyle\sum_{n=4}^{7} (3n + 2)$ **b.** $3\displaystyle\sum_{n=4}^{7} (n + 2)$ **c.** $\displaystyle\sum_{n=4}^{7} (3n + 6)$ **d.** $3\displaystyle\sum_{n=4}^{7} (n + 6)$

e. Which expressions, if any, in parts **a–d** represent the same sum?

32. Show that $\displaystyle\sum_{k=1}^{n} 7k = 7\displaystyle\sum_{k=1}^{n} k$.

33. If b is a constant, show that $\displaystyle\sum_{n=1}^{6} bn = b\displaystyle\sum_{n=1}^{6} n$.

34. Show that $\displaystyle\sum_{k=1}^{n} (k - 1) = \displaystyle\sum_{k=0}^{n-1} k$.

35. Evaluate $\displaystyle\sum_{n=1}^{100} n$. (*Hint:* Add $1 + 100$, add $2 + 99$, etc.)

21-2 MEASURES OF CENTRAL TENDENCY

In analyzing data, we often find it useful to represent all collected values by a single number called a ***measure of central tendency***. Each measure of central tendency is a number that in some way can be used to designate all of the numbers in a particular set of data. In Math A, we have studied three measures of central tendency: the *mean*, the *median*, and the *mode*.

The Mean

The ***mean***, or ***arithmetic mean***, of a set of n numbers is the sum of the numbers divided by n. The symbol for mean is $\bar{x}$, read as *x*-bar. Therefore, for a set of data, $x_1, x_2, x_3, \ldots, x_n$:

$$\text{Mean} = \bar{x} = \frac{\sum_{i=1}^{n} x_i}{n} = \frac{x_1 + x_2 + x_3 + \cdots + x_n}{n}$$

For example, a cabdriver collected the following fares one afternoon: $7.50, $6.00, $9.50, $8.75, $14.00, $10.50, $6.25, $8.75, $9.25, and $11.00. To find the mean of these 10 fares, we first find their sum and then divide by 10.

$$\bar{x} = \frac{\sum_{i=1}^{10} x_i}{10} = \frac{\$91.50}{10} = \$9.15$$

The mean is often called the ***average***. If the cabdriver had collected $9.15 from each of the 10 fares, the total amount collected would have been the same, that is, $91.50.

The Median

When a set of data values is arranged in numerical order, the middle value is called the ***median***. Therefore, in an ordered set, the number of values that precede the median is equal to the number of values that follow it. We will consider two cases: one in which there is an odd number of values in the set of data, and the other in which there is an even number of scores.

CASE 1: Kurt's grades on his report card are 88, 81, 91, 83, and 86. To find Kurt's median grade, we follow these two steps:

1. Arrange the grades in numerical order.   81, 83, 86, 88, 91

2. Mark off equal numbers of grades from the top and   81, 83, 86, 88, 91
   from the bottom.
   The middle number is the median.   Median = 86

Alternative Method: If the number of data values, n, is an odd number, the median is the value that is $\frac{n+1}{2}$ from the bottom or from the top when the values are arranged in order. Since there are five grades on Kurt's report card, find $\frac{n+1}{2} = \frac{5+1}{2} = 3$. The median grade is therefore third from the top and third from the bottom. This grade is 86.

CASE 2: Sarah's grades on her report card are 88, 90, 85, 84, 83, and 88. To find Sarah's median grade, we follow these three steps:

1. Arrange the grades in numerical order.   90, 88, 88, 85, 84, 83
2. Mark off equal numbers of grades from the top   90, 88, 88, 85, 84, 83
   and from the bottom, leaving two in the middle.
3. Find the mean of the two middle grades. $\frac{88 + 85}{2} = \frac{173}{2} = 86.5$

   The mean of the middle numbers is the   Median = 86.5
   median.

Alternative Method: If the number of data values, n, is an even number, the median is the mean (average) of the values that are $\frac{n}{2}$ and $\frac{n+2}{2}$ from the bottom or from the top when the values are arranged in order. Since there are six grades on Sarah's report card, find $\frac{n}{2} = \frac{6}{2} = 3$ and $\frac{n+2}{2} = \frac{6+2}{2} = 4$. The median grade is therefore the mean of the third and fourth grades from the top or from the bottom. This grade is 86.5.

The Mode

The *mode* is the value that appears most often in a set of data. For example, in Case 2 above, Sarah's grades were 90, 88, 88, 85, 84, and 83. Since the grade of 88 occurs twice and every other grade only once, the mode for Sarah's grades is 88.

When a set of data is arranged in a table as a frequency distribution, the mode is the entry with the highest frequency. The table at the right shows the number of children in each of 20 families that answered a survey. The mode for this set of data is 2, the entry with the highest frequency.

Number of Children	Frequency
6	1
5	0
4	2
3	4
2	8
1	5

For some sets of data, there may be more than one mode, and, for some other sets, no mode whatsoever.

1. The ages of employees at a fast-food restaurant are 17, 17, 17, 18, 18, 19, 19, 19, 21, 23, and 37. This set of data contains *two* modes: 17 and 19. When two modes appear, the set of data is said to be *bimodal*, and both modes are reported. We do *not* take an average of these modes, since a mode tells us where most values occur.

2. Mrs. Mangold found the following numbers of spelling errors on compositions that she graded: 0, 0, 0, 1, 2, 2, 3, 4, 4, 4, 5, 5, 5, 6, 7, 7, 8, 9, 9, and 12. This set of data has *three* modes: 0, 4, and 5.

3. On his last five trips to Sound Beach, Mr. Fernandes caught the following numbers of fish: 3, 1, 5, 0, 2. Since no number appears more often than others, this set of data has *no* mode.

Quartiles

When a set of data is arranged in numerical order, the median (also called the *second quartile*) separates the data into two equal parts. The data values below the mean are separated into two equal parts by a value called the ***lower*** or ***first quartile***. Similarly, the data values above the mean are separated into two equal parts by a value called the ***upper*** or ***third quartile***. In this way, quartiles separate a set of data into four equal parts.

To find the quartiles, we begin by finding the median. For example, the heights, in inches, of 17 children are given below. The median is the ninth height in the ordered list.

$$45, 47, 47, 48, 49, 50, 50, 50, \underset{\underset{\text{median}}{\uparrow}}{51,} 51, 52, 53, 53, 55, 55, 56, 58$$

The median separates the data into two equal groups with eight heights in each group. The lower quartile is the middle value of the heights that are below the median, and the upper quartile is the middle value of the heights that are above the median. Since there are eight heights in each of these sets of data, the middle values are the averages of the fourth and fifth heights in each group.

$$45, 47, 47, 48, \underset{\underset{48.5}{\uparrow}}{} 49, 50, 50, 50, \quad 51, \underset{\underset{51}{\uparrow}}{} 51, 52, 53, 53, \underset{\underset{54}{\uparrow}}{} 55, 55, 56, 58$$

lower quartile	median	upper quartile
first quartile	second quartile	third quartile

A ***box-and-whisker plot*** is a graph that displays the quartile values as well as the smallest and largest numbers in a set of data. To draw a box-and-whisker plot for the set of heights given above, we choose a scale that includes all of the heights, 45 to 58, in the set of data. Then we place dots above the numbers that are the lowest value, 45; the first quartile, 48.5; the median, 51; the third quartile, 54; and the largest value, 58.

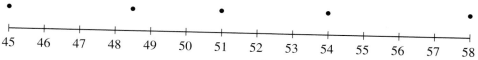

Next we draw a box between the dots that represent the lower and the upper quartiles, and a vertical line in the box at the median.

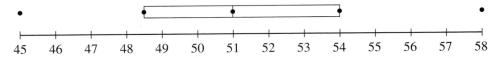

Finally, we draw the whiskers, a line segment connecting the lowest value and the first quartile, and a line segment connecting the upper quartile and the largest value.

Calculator Applications

On any calculator, the mean of Sarah's grades (Case 2 on page 984) can be found by adding the grades and dividing the sum by 6 using the following key sequence:

Therefore, Sarah's mean grade is $86.\overline{3} = 86\frac{1}{3}$.

Some graphing calculators can find both mean and median. We begin by removing any data that may be stored in L1 of the graphing calculator. We enter Sarah's grades, and then we display 1-Var Stats for L1.

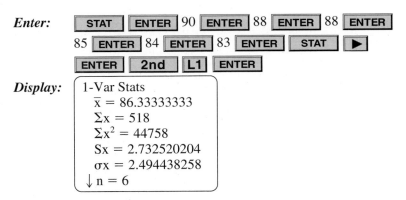

Display:

1-Var Stats
$\overline{x} = 86.33333333$
$\Sigma x = 518$
$\Sigma x^2 = 44758$
$Sx = 2.732520204$
$\sigma x = 2.494438258$
$\downarrow n = 6$

The second line of the display tells us that the mean, $\overline{x}$, is 86.33333333. The arrow pointing down next to $n = 6$ in the bottom line tells us that more information can be obtained by pressing the ▼ key, so we press this key until the remaining information about this set of data is displayed.

Display:

1-Var Stats
↑n = 6
minX = 83
Q1 = 84
Med = 86.5
Q3 = 88
maxX = 90

The fifth line of this display tells us that the median is 86.5. The fourth and sixth lines give the first quartile, 84, and the third quartile, 88. We note that the first quartile, the median, and the third quartile separate the set of six grades into four equal quarters with one grade in each quarter.

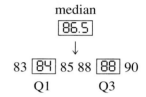

median
86.5
↓
83 84 85 88 88 90
Q1   Q3

The graphing calculator will also draw a box-and-whisker plot for Sarah's grades. With the data entered in L1, we use **STATPLOT**, which is the second function of the **Y=** key, to turn on plot 1, and choose the box plot using the data in L1 and a frequency of 1 for each entry in L1.

Enter: **2nd** **STATPLOT** **ENTER** **ENTER** **▼** **▶** **▶**
▶ **▶** **ENTER** **▼** **2nd** **L1** **▼** **ALPHA** 1

Now we must set the **WINDOW** to a range of values of *x* that include the data values. We will use values from 80 to 92.

Enter: **WINDOW** 80 **ENTER** 92 **ENTER** 1 **ENTER** 0 **ENTER**
5 **ENTER** 1 **ENTER** 1 **ENTER** **GRAPH**

Display:

If we press **TRACE**, the calculator will place the cursor at the vertical line that indicates the median and will display the median value, 86.5. The left arrow key will move the cursor to the first quartile value, 84, and to the smallest value, 83. The right arrow key will move the cursor to the third quartile value, 88, and to the largest value, 90.

EXAMPLES

1. Mrs. Taggart bought a new car. She kept a record of the number of miles that she drove per gallon of gas for each of the first six times she filled the tank. Her record showed the following numbers of miles per gallon: 29, 32, 32, 33, 35, 37. Find:
a. the mean **b.** the median **c.** the mode **d.** the first and third quartiles

Solutions **a.** $\bar{x} = \dfrac{\sum\limits_{i=1}^{n} x_i}{n} = \dfrac{29 + 32 + 32 + 33 + 35 + 37}{6} = \dfrac{198}{6} = 33$

b. There are six entries in this set of data. The median is the mean (average) of the entries that fall into positions 3 and 4 from the top or the bottom.

$$29, 32, 32, 33, 35, 37$$

$$\text{median} = \dfrac{32 + 33}{2}$$

$$= 32.5$$

c. The mode is the entry that occurs most often: 32.

d. The median separates the data into two sets, each of which contains three numbers:

$$\{29, 32, 32\} \text{ and } \{33, 35, 37\}$$

The first quartile is the middle number in the lower half, 32, and the third quartile is the middle number in the upper half, 35.

median

$$\boxed{32.5}$$

$$\downarrow$$

$$29, \boxed{32}, 32, 33, \boxed{35}, 37$$

first quartile   third quartile

Answers: **a.** Mean = 33 **b.** Median = 32.5 **c.** Mode = 32
d. First quartile = 32, Third quartile = 35

---

2. The ages of 25 students in a senior high school mathematics class are recorded in the frequency distribution table at the right. For these ages, find: **a.** the mean **b.** the median **c.** the mode

Age in years x	Frequency f
18	2
17	11
16	12

Solutions: **a.** (1) The total number of students in the class is $\Sigma f = n = 25$.

(2) To find the sum of the ages of the 25 students, add two 18's, eleven 17's, and twelve 16's. Each product of a frequency, f, and an age, x, is fx, the sum of the ages of all students of the same age. The sum of these products, Σfx, equals the sum of the ages of all 25 students. Here $\Sigma fx = 415$.

x	f	fx
18	2	36
17	11	187
16	12	192
—	$\Sigma f = 25$	$\Sigma fx = 415$

(3) The mean $= \bar{x} = \dfrac{\Sigma fx}{\Sigma f} = \dfrac{415}{25} = 16.6$

b. The median is the middle value.

For $n = 25$, the median is the value that is $\frac{n+1}{2} = \frac{25+1}{2} = 13$, that is, 13th from the top or 13th from the bottom. Therefore, the median age lies in the interval 17.

c. The age that appears most frequently is 16 because this interval has the highest frequency.

Answers: **a.** Mean = 16.6   **b.** Median = 17   **c.** Mode = 16

EXERCISES WITH OPEN-RESPONSE PROBLEMS

1. Find the mean grade for each of the following students. If necessary, round the mean to the *nearest tenth*.
  a. Peter: 90, 70, 88, 82, 70
  b. Maria: 80, 82, 93, 91, 94
  c. Elizabeth: 82, 75, 100, 83
  d. Thomas: 92, 91, 75, 93, 98
  e. Al: 80, 70, 92, 78, 78, 98
  f. Joanna: 90, 90, 61, 90

2. a. Mr. Katzel will give a grade of A on the report card to any student whose mean average is 90.0 or higher. Which student(s) listed in Exercise 1, if any, will receive a grade of A?
  b. If Mr. Katzel omits the lowest test grade for each student listed in Exercise 1, which student(s) will then receive a grade of A?

3. For each set of student grades in Exercise 1, find the median grade.

In 4–11, find the mode for each distribution. If no mode exists, write "None."

4. 3, 3, 4, 5, 9   **5.** 4, 4, 5, 9, 9   **6.** 4, 4, 6, 6, 6
7. 3, 4, 7, 8, 9   **8.** 3, 8, 3, 8, 3   **9.** 5, 2, 2, 5, 2, 5
10. 1, 7, 4, 3, 2, 4, 3, 1, 7, 1   **11.** 5, 2, 7, 2, 8, 5, 9, 3

12. What is the median for the digits 0, 1, 2, . . . , 9?
13. The median age of four children is 9.5 years. If Jeanne is 11, Debbie is 8, and Jimmy is 5 years old, then Kathy's age *cannot* be
  (1) 10   (2) 11   (3) 13   (4) 16
14. The set of data 6, 8, 9, x, 9, 8 is given. Find all possible values of x such that: **a.** There is no mode because all scores appear an equal number of times.   **b.** There is only one mode.   **c.** There are two modes.

In 15–18, in each case, the scores of a student on four tests are recorded. Find the score needed by each student on a fifth test so that the mean average of all five tests is exactly 80, or explain why such an average is not possible.

15. Edna: 80, 75, 92, 85   **16.** Rosemary: 77, 81, 76, 83
17. Joe: 78, 72, 70, 75   **18.** Jerry: 68, 82, 79, 71

19. Alice Garr typed a seven-page report. She made the following numbers of typing errors, reported for successive pages of the report: 2, 0, 2, 1, 4, 5, 7.   **a.** For the number of errors per page, find: (*1*) the mean   (*2*) the median   (*3*) the mode   (*4*) the first quartile   (*5*) the third quartile
b. Draw a box-and-whisker plot for this set of data.

20. David enters bicycle races. His times to complete the last 10 races, each covering a distance of 20 miles, were recorded to the nearest minute as follows: 55, 58, 53, 50, 52, 50, 54, 55, 59, 55. For these recorded times, find: **a.** the mean   **b.** the median   **c.** the mode   **d.** the first quartile   **e.** the third quartile

21. In the last 12 times that Mary ran the 100-yard dash, her times to the nearest tenth of a second were 13.5, 13.2, 13.1, 13.3, 13.2, 13.0, 12.8, 13.1, 13.0, 13.1, 13.4, 13.1.   **a.** For these 12 times, find: (*1*) the mean   (*2*) the median   (*3*) the mode   (*4*) the first quartile   (*5*) the third quartile
b. Draw a box-and-whisker plot for this set of data.

22. The ages of 30 students enrolled in a health class are shown in the table.
a. Find the mean age to the *nearest tenth* of a year.
b. Find the median age.
c. For this set of data, which statement is true?
(1) median > mode
(2) median = mode
(3) median < mode
(4) median > mean

Ages x_i	Frequency f_i
18	2
17	12
16	14
15	2

In 23–27, for each given frequency distribution, find: **a.** the mean   **b.** the median   **c.** the mode.

23.

Measure x_i	Frequency f_i
10	3
11	5
12	2

24.

Index i	Measure x_i	Frequency f_i
1	100	3
2	90	3
3	80	4

25.

x_i	f_i
10	1
20	5
30	2
40	4

26.

x_i	f_i
5	5
4	5
3	2
2	3

27.

x_i	f_i
15	12
10	4
5	4
0	4

28. Eddie Dunn scored the following numbers of goals in his last seven hockey games: 3, 4, 0, 2, 3, 1, and 2. What is the least number of goals that Eddie must score in his next game to claim that his mean average number of goals per game is greater than 2?

21-3 MEASURES OF DISPERSION: THE RANGE AND THE MEAN ABSOLUTE DEVIATION

The mean is the measure of central tendency most frequently used to describe statistical data. The mean, however, does not give us sufficient information about the data to draw conclusions.

Frequency diagrams for four sets of data are given in Figures 1–4. The pictures clearly show us that these sets of data are very different.

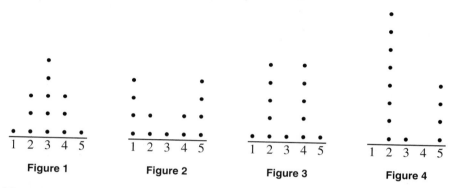

Figure 1   **Figure 2**   **Figure 3**   **Figure 4**

Nevertheless, for each set of data displayed here, *the mean is 3*. For example, using the data in Figure 4, we can complete the frequency table at the right and find sums. It follows that:

x_i	f_i	$f_i x_i$
1	0	0
2	8	16
3	1	3
4	0	0
5	4	20
—	$n = 13$	$\Sigma f_i x_i = 39$

$$\text{Mean} = \bar{x} = \frac{\Sigma f_i x_i}{n} = \frac{39}{13} = 3$$

Since each of these sets of data has a mean of 3, we need another measure to show how the sets are different. The new measure should indicate how individual values are scattered, or distributed, about the mean. A number that indicates the spread, or variation, of data values about the mean is called a ***measure of dispersion***.

In this section, we will study two other measures of dispersion: the *range* and the *mean absolute deviation*. In the next section, we will study two other measures of dispersion, *variance* and *standard deviation*.

The Range

The simplest of the measures of dispersion is the range. The ***range*** is the difference between the highest value and the lowest value in a set of data.

For example, if Eve Lucano's grades for this marking period are 97, 94, 92, 89, and 87, the range of Eve's grades is 97 − 87 or 10.

Since the range is dependent on only the highest and lowest values in a distribution, the range is *often unreliable* as a measure of dispersion. Let us consider the following cases in which we compare data.

Comparison 1. For each set of data in Figures 5 and 6, the mean is 6 and the range = 10 − 2 = 8.

Although these frequency diagrams are very different, the range does not help us in comparing the distribution of data in these sets.

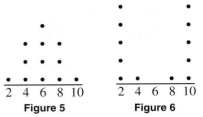

Figure 5   Figure 6

Comparison 2. The test scores for two students are shown below.

Heidi:	75, 88, 91, 92, 95, 99	Range = 99 − 75 = 24
Eric:	87, 88, 91, 92, 95, 99	Range = 99 − 87 = 12

While the range of Heidi's scores is twice the range of Eric's scores, the individual scores of these two students are exactly the same, except for one extreme score, 75, in Heidi's set. In fact, both students have averages in the low nineties. Here, the sets of data are very much alike, but we have been led to believe that they are different because of the differences in the ranges.

The Mean Absolute Deviation

Let us study a more useful measure of dispersion, based on the information in the accompanying table.

1. The data values in column 1 are used to find the mean:

$$\bar{x} = \frac{\Sigma x_i}{n} = \frac{516}{6} = 86$$

x_i	$\bar{x}$	$x_i - \bar{x}$	$|x_i - \bar{x}|$
93	86	7	7
90	86	4	4
89	86	3	3
87	86	1	1
85	86	−1	1
72	86	−14	14
Σx_i 516	—	$\Sigma(x_i - \bar{x})$ 0	$\Sigma|x_i - \bar{x}|$ 30

2. The mean of 86 is entered in every row of column 2.

3. The difference between each entry, x_i, in the sample and the mean, $\bar{x}$, is recorded in column 3. We note that the sum of these differences is 0; that is, $\Sigma(x_i - \bar{x}) = 0$. If the differences had been reversed, it would still be true that $\Sigma(\bar{x} - x_i) = 0$. This example illustrates the fact that *the sum of the differences between each entry in a sample and the mean of that sample is always equal to 0.*

4. In column 4, however, by taking the absolute value of the deviation of each entry from the mean, we see that the sum of these absolute values is usually a number other than 0. Here, $\Sigma|x_i - \bar{x}| = 30$.

5. By definition, the *mean absolute deviation* $= \dfrac{\sum\limits_{i=1}^{n} |x_i - \bar{x}|}{n} = \dfrac{30}{6} = 5.$

- **DEFINITION. If $\bar{x}$ is the mean of a set of numbers denoted by x_i, then the *mean absolute deviation*, or simply the *mean deviation*, is**

$$\frac{\sum\limits_{i=1}^{n} |x_i - \bar{x}|}{n} \qquad \textbf{or} \qquad \frac{1}{n}\sum_{i=1}^{n} |x_i - \bar{x}|$$

Since $|a - b| = |b - a|$, it is also correct to write the formula for the mean absolute deviation as follows:

$$\frac{\sum\limits_{i=1}^{n} |\bar{x} - x_i|}{n} \quad \text{or} \quad \frac{1}{n} \sum\limits_{i=1}^{n} |\bar{x} - x_i|$$

EXAMPLES

1. Two students in a computer course have the same average, based on the grades received by each student for six computer programs.

Thomas: 90, 70, 85, 100, 80, 85   (mean = 85)
Robert: 100, 90, 65, 90, 65, 100   (mean = 85)

a. For each set of grades, find the mean absolute deviation to the *nearest tenth.*
b. Which student has more widely dispersed grades? Explain why.

Solutions   **a.** For each student, organize the data in a table, find $\Sigma|x_i - \bar{x}|$, and find the mean absolute deviation.

Thomas

x_i	$\bar{x}$	$|x_i - \bar{x}|$
100	85	15
90	85	5
85	85	0
85	85	0
80	85	5
70	85	15

$$\Sigma|x_i - \bar{x}| = 40$$

$$\text{mean deviation} = \frac{\Sigma|x_i - \bar{x}|}{n}$$

$$= \frac{40}{6} = 6.66$$

$$= 6.7 \quad Answer$$

Robert

x_i	$\bar{x}$	$|x_i - \bar{x}|$
100	85	15
100	85	15
90	85	5
90	85	5
65	85	20
65	85	20

$$\Sigma|x_i - \bar{x}| = 80$$

$$\text{mean deviation} = \frac{\Sigma|x_i - \bar{x}|}{n}$$

$$= \frac{80}{6} = 13.33$$

$$= 13.3 \quad Answer$$

b. Robert has more widely dispersed grades because the mean deviation of his grades, 13.3, is about twice as great as the mean deviation, 6.7, for Thomas.   *Answer*

2. George Goldstein is a business student. His last six scores on tests in accounting were 87, 76, 93, 83, 84, and 81. For these scores, find:
a. the range   **b.** the mean deviation

Solutions   **a.** The range is the difference between the highest and the lowest scores. Here, the range = $93 - 76 = 17$.

b. (1) Organize the data in column 1 of a table.

(2) Find the mean:

$$\bar{x} = \frac{\Sigma x_i}{n} = \frac{504}{6} = 84$$

(3) After the mean is entered in every row of column 2, find the values of $x_i - \bar{x}$ in column 3 and $|x_i - \bar{x}|$ in column 4.

x_i	$\bar{x}$	$x_i - \bar{x}$	$|x_i - \bar{x}|$
93	84	9	9
87	84	3	3
84	84	0	0
83	84	−1	1
81	84	−3	3
76	84	−8	8
Σx_i 504	—	—	$\Sigma|x_i - \bar{x}|$ 24

(4) Find the mean deviation:

$$\frac{\Sigma|x_i - \bar{x}|}{n} = \frac{24}{6} = 4$$

Answers: **a.** Range = 17
b. Mean deviation = 4

EXERCISES WITH OPEN-RESPONSE PROBLEMS

In 1–6, for each set of student grades, find the range.

1. Ann: 83, 87, 92, 92, 95

2. Barbara: 94, 90, 86, 86, 85

3. Bill: 78, 97, 82, 86, 90

4. Cathy: 88, 81, 90, 74, 72

5. Stephen: 91, 65, 92, 94, 98

6. Tom: 90, 90, 90, 90, 90

7. If each student in Mr. Pedersen's class is either 16 or 17 years old, what is the range of student ages in the class?

8. The most expensive item in Dale Singer's shopping basket is meat at $5.60, and the least expensive item is fruit at $0.39. What is the range of the prices of items in the shopping basket?

9. a. Anna has 14 grandchildren. If the oldest is 18 and the youngest is 3, what is the range of ages of the grandchildren?

    b. If Andrea, Anna's fifteenth grandchild, is born today, what is now the range of ages of Anna's grandchildren?

10. For the data given in the accompanying table:

    a. Find the mean.

    b. Copy and complete the table.

    c. Find the mean absolute deviation.

x_i	$\bar{x}$	$x_i - \bar{x}$	$|x_i - \bar{x}|$
27			
26			
25			
22			
20			

11. "Curveball" Klopfer is a baseball pitcher. In his last six games, he struck out the following numbers of batters: 16, 20, 14, 13, 21, 12. For this set of data, find:

    a. the range   **b.** the mean   **c.** the mean deviation

12. *True* or *False*: For any set of data, $\frac{1}{n}\Sigma|x_i - \bar{x}| = \frac{1}{n}\Sigma|\bar{x} - x_i|$. Explain your answer.

13. Frances owns and manages a printing business. Over the last 6 days, she has processed the following numbers of jobs: 5, 8, 12, 7, 3, 4. For the number of jobs processed, find:

    a. the mean (*Hint:* The mean is not an integer.)   **b.** the mean absolute deviation

14. Last week, Florence kept a log of the number of hours that she watched television each day. The times, recorded to the nearest half hour, are 5, 4, 3, 5, 2, 1.5, and 0. For these times:

    a. Find the mean to the *nearest tenth*.   **b.** Using the mean from part **a**, find the mean deviation to the *nearest hundredth*.

15. Three sets of data (Set I, Set II, and Set III) are displayed in the following frequency diagrams.

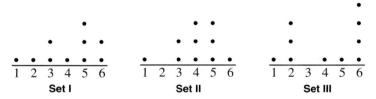

    a. For each set of data, find: (*1*) the range (*2*) the mean (*3*) the mean deviation

    b. By using the mean deviations found, tell: (*1*) which set of data is most closely grouped about the mean (*2*) which set of data is most widely dispersed

16. Two students in a mathematics class are comparing their grades.

        Mary Murray: 87, 98, 82, 96, 99, 84
       Thea Olmstead: 95, 92, 79, 94, 90, 96

    a. For Mary's grades, find: (*1*) the range (*2*) the mean (*3*) the mean deviation to the *nearest tenth*

    b. For Thea's grades, find: (*1*) the range (*2*) the mean (*3*) the mean deviation to the *nearest tenth*

    c. Which student has more widely dispersed grades? Explain why.

17. The data sets below show the highest daily temperatures, recorded in degrees Celsius, for two weeks in the summer. Each week had the same mean daily reading.

Week 1:   37, 35, 34, 30, 32, 36, 34   (mean = 34)
Week 2:   37, 36, 40, 33, 31, 30, 31   (mean = 34)

a. For each week's data, find the mean deviation to the *nearest tenth*.
b. Using part **a**, tell which week had the more consistent readings.

18. The set of data 3, 4, 4, 5, 5, 5, 6, 6, 7 contains nine numbers and has a range of 4 and a mean of 5. Write three more sets of data for which $n = 9$, the range = 4, and the mean = 5.

21-4 MEASURES OF DISPERSION: VARIANCE AND THE STANDARD DEVIATION

To find the mean absolute deviation, we used the absolute value of the deviation of each element of the data set from the mean to change negative differences to positive numbers. Negative differences can also be changed to positive values by squaring the differences. For example:

$$(5 - 7)^2 = (-2)^2 = 4 \qquad \text{and} \qquad (1 - 7)^2 = (-6)^2 = 36$$

The Variance

A measure of dispersion that uses the squares of the deviations from the mean gives greatest weight to the scores that are farthest from the mean.

- **DEFINITION. The *variance*, v, of a set of data is the average of the squares of the deviations from the mean.**

$$v = \frac{\sum_{i=1}^{n} (x_i - \bar{x})^2}{n} \qquad \text{or} \qquad v = \frac{1}{n} \sum_{i=1}^{n} (x_i - \bar{x})^2$$

A method for finding variance can be demonstrated by the following example:

☐   On five mathematics tests taken this month, Fred earned grades of 92, 86, 95, 84, and 78. Find the variance of this set of grades.

To solve this problem, follow steps 1–4 to organize the data in a table, and then step 5 to use the entries in the table to find the variance as shown on the following page.

1. In column 1, write the data in numerical order.

2. Find the mean of the data:

$$\bar{x} = \frac{\Sigma x_i}{n} = \frac{435}{5} = 87$$

Write the mean in each row of column 2.

3. In column 3, write the difference of each entry, x_i, minus the mean, $\bar{x}$.

4. In column 4, write the square of each difference shown in column 3.

5. Add the entries in column 4, and divide this sum, $\Sigma(x_i - \bar{x})^2$, by 5, the number of grades.

x_i	$\bar{x}$	$x_i - \bar{x}$	$(x_i - \bar{x})^2$
95	87	8	64
92	87	5	25
86	87	-1	1
84	87	-3	9
78	87	-9	81
435 Σx_i	—	—	180 $\Sigma(x_i - \bar{x})^2$

$$\nu = \frac{\sum_{i=1}^{5}(x_i - \bar{x})^2}{5} = \frac{180}{5} = 36$$

Answer: The variance of Fred's grades is 36.

The Standard Deviation

Some people object to variance as a measure of dispersion because it contains a distortion that results from squaring the differences. To overcome this objection, we can find the square root of the variance and thus obtain a measure of dispersion that has the same units as the given data. This measure, called the *standard deviation*, is the most important and widely used measure of dispersion in the world today.

● **DEFINITION. The *standard deviation*, σ, of a set of data is equal to the square root of the variance.**
The symbol for standard deviation is σ, the lowercase Greek letter sigma.

$$\sigma = \sqrt{\nu} = \sqrt{\frac{\sum_{i=1}^{n}(x_i - \bar{x})^2}{n}} \quad \text{or} \quad \sigma = \sqrt{\frac{1}{n}\sum_{i=1}^{n}(x_i - \bar{x})^2}$$

☐ Find the standard deviation of Fred's five mathematics grades: 92, 86, 95, 84, and 78.

1–5. Find the variance, using steps 1–5 of the preceding example.

$$\nu = \frac{\sum_{i=1}^{5}(x_i - \bar{x})^2}{5} = 36$$

6. Find the square root of the variance.

$$\sigma = \sqrt{\nu} = \sqrt{36} = 6$$

Answer: The standard deviation of Fred's grades is 6.

Calculator Applications

The standard deviation can be displayed on most graphing calculators. In Section 21-2 we learned that, after data had been entered into a list, the 1-Var Stats screen displayed a variety of statistical measures. We can find the standard deviation of Fred's grades by using the following steps on a TI-83 or similar steps on other graphing calculators:

Step 1. Clear list 1.

Enter:

Step 2. Enter the new data to L1.

Enter:

Step 3. Display the 1-Var Stats screen.

Enter: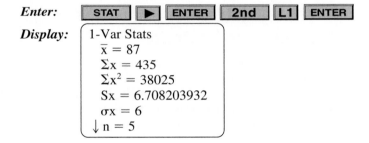

Display:

1-Var Stats
$\bar{x} = 87$
$\Sigma x = 435$
$\Sigma x^2 = 38025$
$Sx = 6.708203932$
$\sigma x = 6$
$\downarrow n = 5$

In the display above, the second line tells us the mean ($\bar{x} = 87$) and the sixth line tells us the standard deviation ($\sigma x = 6$) for this set of data.

Even if a calculator does not have standard deviation capability, it will be useful in finding the differences, squares, sums, and square roots that must be computed to find the standard deviation.

EXAMPLE

The times, in minutes, required by five students to complete a test were as follows: 35, 27, 30, 25, and 38. For this set of data, find:

a. the mean   **b.** the standard deviation to the *nearest tenth*

Solutions **a.** $\bar{x} = \dfrac{\Sigma x_i}{n} = \dfrac{38 + 35 + 30 + 27 + 25}{5}$

$= \dfrac{155}{5} = 31$

x_i	$\bar{x}$	$x_i - \bar{x}$	$(x_i - \bar{x})^2$
38	31	7	49
35	31	4	16
30	31	−1	1
27	31	−4	16
25	31	−6	36
155 Σx_i	—	—	118 $\Sigma(x_i - \bar{x})^2$

b. To find the standard deviation, construct a table.

(1) In column 1, write the data, x_i, in numerical order.

(2) In each row of column 2, write the mean, $\bar{x}$.

(3) In column 3, write the deviations from the mean, $x_i - \bar{x}$.

(4) In column 4, write the squares of the deviations and find the sum, $\Sigma(x_i - \bar{x})^2$.

(5) Use the rule for standard deviation and round to the *nearest tenth*, 4.9.

$$\sigma = \sqrt{\frac{1}{n}\sum_{i=1}^{n}(x_i - \bar{x})^2}$$

$$= \sqrt{\frac{1}{5}(118)}$$

$$= \sqrt{23.6} = 4.85$$

Calculator Solutions Enter the data in L1.

Enter: STAT ENTER 38 ENTER 35
ENTER 30 ENTER 27 ENTER 25
ENTER

Display the 1-Var Stats screen to find the mean and the standard deviation.

Enter: STAT ▶ ENTER 2nd L1
ENTER

Display:
```
1-Var Stats
 x̄ = 31
 Σx = 155
 Σx² = 4923
 Sx = 5.431390246
 σx = 4.857983121
↓ n = 5
```

To the nearest tenth: $\sigma x = 4.9$

Answers: **a.** Mean = 31 **b.** Standard deviation = 4.9

Caution: A graphing calculator may ease the computation involved in finding statistical measures such as mean and standard deviation, but a genuine understanding of these measures and a good number sense are required to know when answers are reasonable and when they are not. Since one wrong keystroke will result in incorrect statistical measures, it is important to know how to find these values using basic operations only. A calculator approach using the STAT key can then serve as a check.

EXERCISES WITH OPEN-RESPONSE PROBLEMS

1. For the data given in the accompanying table:
   a. Find the mean.
   b. Copy and complete the table.
   c. Find the standard deviation to the *nearest tenth*.

x_i	$\bar{x}$	$x_i - \bar{x}$	$(x_i - \bar{x})^2$
30			
29			
26			
23			
12			

2. The scores of six students on an IQ test are listed below.

   Fred: 130   Toni: 127   Lee: 125
   Paul: 122   Lynn: 128   John: 118

   For these scores, find: a. the mean   b. the standard deviation

3. The highest number of points that a student can score in a mathematics competition is 5. In the last six competitions, Jennifer's scores were 2, 1, 4, 2, 4, 5. For these scores, calculate:
   a. the mean   b. the standard deviation to the *nearest tenth*

4. On his last five fishing trips, Jim caught the following numbers of fish: 6, 5, 12, 3, 9. For this set of data, find: a. the mean   b. the standard deviation to the *nearest tenth*

5. On a test, five students received scores of 63, 60, 59, 57, and 56. For these scores, find:
   a. the mean   b. the standard deviation to the *nearest tenth*

6. The heights, in centimeters, of five players on the basketball team are listed at the right. For these heights, find:
   a. the mean   b. the standard deviation to the *nearest tenth*

Player	Height (cm)
R. Melendy	192
C. Cronin	189
D. Schmeling	187
M. Natale	184
R. Weinrich	183

7. Two students are comparing their grades on their report cards.

   Sean O'Brien: 83, 92, 79, 65, 82, 85
   Eddy Capobianco: 83, 75, 78, 86, 77, 87

   a. Which student, if either, has the higher mean average?
   b. For Sean's grades, calculate the standard deviation to the *nearest tenth*.
   c. For Eddy's grades, calculate the standard deviation to the *nearest tenth*.
   d. Which student has the greater dispersion in grades?

8. During a 5-day work week, Helen worked the following numbers of hours per day: 8, 10, 9, 11, 10. For this set of data, calculate: a. the mean   b. the standard deviation to the *nearest tenth*

9. Dave worked the following numbers of hours at a fast-food restaurant over a period of 7 days: 5, 4, 0, 9, 7, 0, 3. Using $n = 7$, find: a. the mean number of hours worked per day   b. the standard deviation to the *nearest tenth*

10. Over the last 7 days, Mr. Kavanagh spent the following number of hours reading a novel: 3, 1.5, 2, 1.5, 4, 2.5, 3. For these times, find: **a.** the mean **b.** the standard deviation to the *nearest tenth*

11. In a statistical study, if the variance is 64, the standard deviation is
(1) 6.4 (2) 16 (3) 8 (4) 64

12. If the standard deviation for a set of data is 2.5, find the value of the variance.

13. In a statistical study, variance and standard deviation are usually not equal. For what two numerical values would these measures be equal?

21-5 NORMAL DISTRIBUTION

In most statistical studies, the number of data values or scores to be considered is large, and these values are organized into groups. For example, 10 coins are tossed, and the number of heads obtained is recorded. The table that follows shows the results after 100 trials of tossing 10 coins.

Number of heads	0	1	2	3	4	5	6	7	8	9	10
Frequency	1	2	4	11	20	24	20	11	4	2	1

The *histogram* for the distribution of the number of heads is the bar graph, shown below. The *frequency polygon* is the line graph, determined by connecting the midpoints of the upper edges of all the bars, as shown in the same diagram.

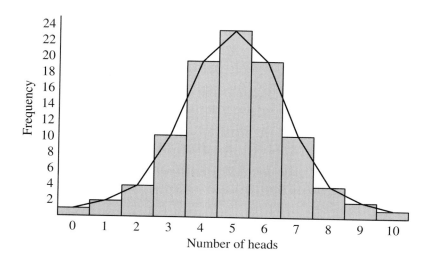

If we draw a smooth curve through the points that determine the frequency polygon as shown on page 1001, the curve would be shaped somewhat like a bell. In fact, by increasing the number of trials, as well as the number of coins tossed in each trial, the frequency polygon would more closely resemble a *bell-shaped curve* called the ***normal curve***.

In a normal curve, the greatest frequency occurs at a data value in the center of the distribution. This center value is the *mean*, $\bar{x}$. A vertical line drawn through the mean serves as an axis of symmetry for the normal curve. Since half the values in the distribution lie below the mean and half lie above it, this

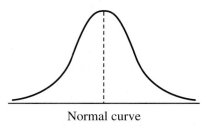

Normal curve

center value is also the *median*. Moreover, since this center value has the greatest frequency in the distribution, it is also the *mode*.

As we move further to the right or to the left of the mean in a normal curve, the frequencies decrease. The normal curve is essentially a theoretical model that is used to study sets of data. For example, a frequency polygon of the heights of thousands of high school juniors would closely approximate the normal curve. So too would data involving weights, clothing sizes, numerical test grades, and the like.

Standard Deviation and the Normal Curve

The distribution of data represented by the normal curve is called a ***normal distribution***. In a normal distribution, the pattern of data values described below and diagrammed on page 1003 will occur, correct to the nearest 0.5%.

1. *Of the data values, 68% lie within one standard deviation of the mean.* In other words, 68%, or slightly more than two-thirds of the values, lie in the interval from $\bar{x} - \sigma$ to $\bar{x} + \sigma$, or from one standard deviation below the mean to one standard deviation above the mean. Because the curve is symmetrical, 34% of the scores lie in the interval from $\bar{x} - \sigma$ to $\bar{x}$, and 34% lie in the interval from $\bar{x}$ to $\bar{x} - \sigma$.

2. *Of the data values, 95% lie within two standard deviations of the mean.* Thus, 47.5% of the values lie in the interval from $\bar{x} - 2\sigma$ to $\bar{x}$, and 47.5% lie in the interval from $\bar{x}$ to $\bar{x} + 2\sigma$. By arithmetic, we can show that each interval, $\bar{x} - 2\sigma$ to $\bar{x} - \sigma$ and $\bar{x} + \sigma$ to $\bar{x} + 2\sigma$, contains 13.5% of the values.

3. *Of the data values, 99.5% lie within three standard deviations of the mean.*

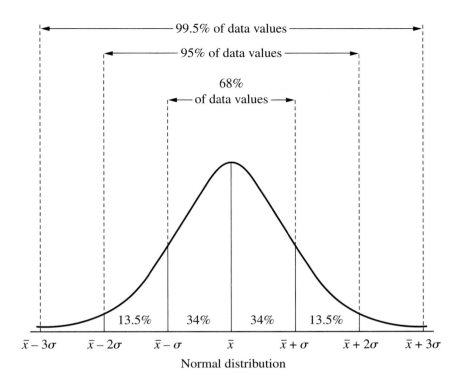

Normal distribution

Let us see how these concepts are used in a statistical study in the following example.

In a normal distribution, the mean height of 10-year-old children is 138 centimeters and the standard deviation is 5 centimeters. Find the heights that are: **a.** exactly one standard deviation above and below the mean **b.** two standard deviations above and below the mean

a, b. Sketch and label the normal curve as an aid.

$$\bar{x} = 138 \qquad \text{and} \qquad \sigma = 5$$

Then:

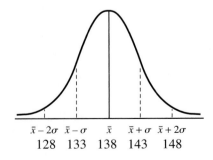

$$\bar{x} + 2\sigma = 138 + 2(5) = 148$$

$$\bar{x} + \sigma = 138 + 5 \quad = 143$$

$$\bar{x} - \sigma = 138 - 5 \quad = 133$$

$$\bar{x} - 2\sigma = 138 - 2(5) = 128$$

Answers: **a.** 143 and 133 centimeters **b.** 148 and 128 centimeters

A ***percentile*** of a score or a measure indicates what percent of the total frequency scored at or below that measure.

By using the percents of the data that are expected to lie one, two, or three standard deviations from the mean, we can list the percentiles for five important measures in a normal distribution, as shown in the diagram at the right. For example, the mean, $\bar{x}$, is at the 50th percentile because 50% of the values lie at or below the mean. Similarly, the value that lies one standard deviation above the mean, $\bar{x} + \sigma$, is at the 84th percentile because 84% of the values lie at or below $\bar{x} + \sigma$.

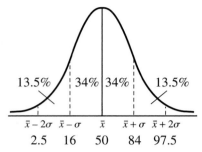

Percentiles in a normal distribution

Now let us combine the values from the statistical study involving heights of 10-year-old children with the percents and percentiles of a normal distribution. Many interesting observations can be made, only a few of which are listed below.

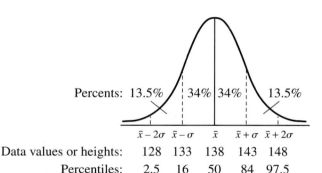

1. Of the children, 68% are between 133 centimeters and 143 centimeters tall.
2. Of the children, 95% are between 128 centimeters and 148 centimeters tall.
3. Of the children, 34% are between 138 centimeters and 143 centimeters tall.
4. A 10-year-old child who is 133 centimeters tall is at the 16th percentile; that is, 16% of 10-year-old children are 133 centimeters or shorter in height.
5. A 10-year-old child who is 148 centimeters tall is at the 97.5 percentile; that is, only 2.5% of 10-year-old children are taller than 148 centimeters.
6. If the height of a 10-year-old child is at the 90th percentile, then the child is somewhere between 143 and 148 centimeters tall.
7. A height of 137 centimeters is above the 16th percentile but less than the 50th percentile for this population.
8. Heights that would occur *less than* 5% of the time for these children are heights less than 128 centimeters and heights greater than 148 centimeters.

In higher mathematics courses, statistical tables are provided that allow us to be very precise when assigning percentiles to data values. For now, let us simply remember the percents and percentiles that occur in a normal distribution for these key measures: $\bar{x}$, $\bar{x} \pm \sigma$, and $\bar{x} \pm 2\sigma$.

EXAMPLES

1. Scores on the Preliminary Scholastic Aptitude Test (PSAT) range from 20 to 80. For a certain population of students, the mean is 52 and the standard deviation is 9.

   a. A score at the 65th percentile might be (1) 49 (2) 56 (3) 64 (4) 65
   b. Which of the following scores can be expected to occur *less than* 3% of the time? (1) 39 (2) 47 (3) 65 (4) 71

Solutions   Sketch a normal curve. Place appropriate scores and percentiles at $\bar{x}$, $\bar{x} \pm \sigma$, and $\bar{x} \pm 2\sigma$.

$$\text{Let } \bar{x} = 52 \text{ and } \sigma = 9. \text{ Then: } \bar{x} + 2\sigma = 52 + 2(9) = 70$$
$$\bar{x} + \sigma = 52 + 9 \quad = 61$$
$$\bar{x} - \sigma = 52 - 9 \quad = 43$$
$$\bar{x} - 2\sigma = 52 - 2(9) = 34$$

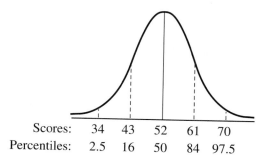

Scores:	34	43	52	61	70
Percentiles:	2.5	16	50	84	97.5

a. The 65th percentile lies in the interval from the 50th percentile to the 84th percentile, that is, from $\bar{x}$ to $\bar{x} + \sigma$. The scores in this interval range from 52 to 61. Of the four choices given, only (2), a score of 56, lies within the interval.

b. The score of 70 lies at the 97.5 percentile. Since 71 is greater than 70, then 71 is above the 97.5 percentile, and this score should occur less than 3% of the time. Therefore, select (4) 71.

Answers: **a.** (2)   **b.** (4)

2. In the diagram, the shaded area represents approximately 68% of the scores in a normal distribution. If the scores range from 12 to 40 in this interval, find the standard deviation.

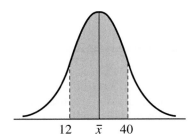

Solution   Since 68% of the scores in a normal distribution lie in the interval from $\bar{x} - \sigma$ to $\bar{x} + \sigma$, write and solve the equation $(\bar{x} + \sigma) - (\bar{x} - \sigma) = 40 - 12$.

$$(\bar{x} + \sigma) - (\bar{x} - \sigma) = 40 - 12$$
$$\bar{x} + \sigma - \bar{x} + \sigma = 40 - 12$$
$$2\sigma = 28$$
$$\sigma = 14$$

Answer: 14

EXERCISES WITH OPEN-RESPONSE PROBLEMS

In 1–4, in each case, write the number that makes the sentence true.

1. In a normal distribution, the mean is at the _____ percentile.

2. Approximately _____% of the values in a normal distribution lie within one standard deviation of the mean.

3. A value that is one standard deviation below the mean in a normal distribution is at the _____ percentile.

4. In a normal distribution, about _____% of the values lie in the interval from $\bar{x} - 2\sigma$ to $\bar{x} + 2\sigma$.

5. For the scores on a standardized test, the mean is 82 and the standard deviation is 6. Find the scores for: **a.** $\bar{x} + 2\sigma$ **b.** $\bar{x} + \sigma$ **c.** $\bar{x} - \sigma$ **d.** $\bar{x} - 2\sigma$

In 6–12, select the *numeral* preceding the choice that best completes the statement or answers the question.

6. On a standardized test, the mean score is 70 and the standard deviation is 10. If Rita Keane scored 90 on this test, her score is at the
   (1) 84th percentile   (2) 90th percentile
   (3) 95th percentile   (4) 97.5 percentile

7. If the mean score of an IQ test is 104 and the standard deviation is 7, then 68% of the scores are
   (1) less than 104   (2) between 90 and 104
   (3) between 97 and 111   (4) greater than 104

8. Mr. Noren bowls regularly, and his average score is 182. His bowling scores approximate a normal distribution with a standard deviation of 8.5. He can expect to bowl between 182 and 199
   (1) about 47.5% of the time (2) about 34% of the time
   (3) more than 50% of the time (4) less than 16% of the time

9. The lengths of time for telephone calls approximate a normal distribution. If the mean length is 4.3 minutes with a standard deviation of 1.4 minutes, about 84% of the calls are
   (1) 4.3 minutes or less   (2) 5.7 minutes or less
   (3) from 2.9 to 5.7 minutes (4) 4.3 minutes or more

10. For a certain group of students, the mean score on a college aptitude test was 430 with a standard deviation of 108.
    a. Which of the following interval of scores should occur most frequently?
       (1) below 322   (2) between 214 and 332
       (3) between 322 and 538   (4) above 430
    b. Which of the following scores might be at the 70th percentile?
       (1) 505   (2) 540   (3) 590   (4) 700

11. Ms. Surber owns a real-estate business. Sale prices of homes in her area approximate a normal distribution, with a mean of $72,000 and a standard deviation of $7,600. A home that sells for $87,600 would rank:
    (1) below the 75th percentile   (2) between the 75th and 85th percentiles
    (3) between the 85th and 95th percentiles (4) above the 95th percentile

12. In a contest, the mean time for pianists to play the "Minute Waltz" was 56 seconds, with a standard deviation of 3 seconds. The times approximated a normal distribution. If Al Cavallaro played the "Minute Waltz" in 50 seconds, his time was faster than what percent of the population?
    (1) 2.5%   (2) 16%   (3) 84%   (4) 97.5%

13. In a large school district, the years of service for the teaching staff approximate a normal distribution. The mean is 16 years of teaching, and the standard deviation is 7.4 years. Four teachers, and the number of years of service for each, are listed below.

Robert Novak: 16 years   Mabel Oestrich: 35 years
Samuel Backer: 21 years   Nancy Garbowski: 12 years

According to years of service, name the teacher(s), if any, who might possibly rank at the:
a. 10th percentile   **b.** 35th percentile   **c.** 50th percentile
d. 70th percentile   **e.** 90th percentile   **f.** 99th percentile

14. In the diagram, about 95% of the data values fall in the shaded area. If the distribution is normal and these values range from 25 to 51, find:
a. the standard deviation
b. the mean

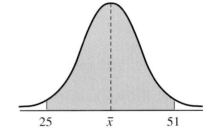

In 15–18, in each case, assume a normal distribution. Using the given information, find:
a. the standard deviation   **b.** the mean

15. $\bar{x} - \sigma = 75$ and $\bar{x} + \sigma = 109$
16. $\bar{x} - \sigma = 4.5$ and $\bar{x} + 2\sigma = 25.5$
17. Values within one standard deviation of the mean range from 9.2 to 14.
18. About 2.5% of the values are at or below 45, and 2.5% are above 77.

19. In a normal distribution, $\bar{x} = 27.9$, and 16% of the values are at or below 25.2. Find:
a. σ **b.** $\bar{x} + 2\sigma$

21-6 GROUPED DATA

Most statistical studies involve a large number of data values in which the same value may be repeated many times. We can work efficiently with such sets of data by grouping together data values that are equal and noting the *frequency* of each value, that is, the number of times that the value occurs.

Intervals of Length 1

When we work with grouped data, the measures of dispersion are found by applying the rules developed in Sections 21-3 and 21-4, but we must use the frequency of each data value when evaluating these formulas. We begin by examining intervals of length 1.

The following example shows how frequency is used in organizing data and in finding standard deviation. For example:

☐   Mrs. Fowler, an English teacher, recorded the number of misspelled words in each of 25 student-written book reports as follows:

$$12, 7, 7, 7, 6, 6, 5, 5, 5, 5, 5, 5, 4, 4, 4, 3, 3, 3, 2, 2, 2, 2, 1, 0, 0, 0$$

Find the mean and the standard deviation to the *nearest hundredth*.

1. Record the data, using numerical order, in a table. Write each different number of misspelled words in column 1 and the frequency of that number in column 2.

2. Find the number of reports, Σf_i or n.

3. In column 3, find each product, $f_i x_i$, and the sum of these products, $\Sigma f_i x_i$.

Col. 1	Col. 2	Col. 3	Col. 4	Col. 5	Col. 6
Measure x_i	**Frequency** f_i	$f_i x_i$	$x_i - \bar{x}$	$(x_i - \bar{x})^2$	$f_i(x_i - \bar{x})^2$
12	1	12	8	64	$1 \cdot 64 = 64$
7	3	21	3	9	$3 \cdot 9 = 27$
6	2	12	2	4	$2 \cdot 4 = 8$
5	5	25	1	1	$5 \cdot 1 = 5$
4	3	12	0	0	$3 \cdot 0 = 0$
3	3	9	-1	1	$3 \cdot 1 = 3$
2	4	8	-2	4	$4 \cdot 4 = 16$
1	1	1	-3	9	$1 \cdot 9 = 9$
0	3	0	-4	16	$3 \cdot 16 = 48$
—	25 $\Sigma f_i = n$	100 $\Sigma f_i x_i$	—	—	180 $\Sigma f_i(x_i - \bar{x})^2$

4. Find the mean: $\bar{x} = \dfrac{\Sigma f_i x_i}{\Sigma f_i}$ or $\bar{x} = \dfrac{\Sigma f_i x_i}{n} = \dfrac{100}{25} = 4$.

5. In column 4, write the values of $x_i - \bar{x}$, the deviations from the mean, which are found by subtracting the mean, 4, from each x_i.

6. In column 5, write the squares of the deviations from the mean, $(x_i - \bar{x})^2$.

7. Multiply each square in column 5 by the corresponding frequency in column 2, and write the products, $f_i(x_i - \bar{x})^2$, in column 6.

8. Find the sum of the numbers in column 6, $\Sigma f_i(x_i - \bar{x})^2$.

9. Find the standard deviation by using the formula

$$\sigma = \sqrt{\frac{\Sigma f_i(x_i - \bar{x})^2}{\Sigma f_i}} \quad \text{or} \quad \sigma = \sqrt{\frac{\Sigma f_i(x_i - \bar{x})^2}{n}} = \sqrt{\frac{180}{25}} = \sqrt{7.2} \approx 2.68$$

Answer: Mean $= 4$, and standard deviation $= 2.68$.

To see how closely this set of data approximates a normal distribution, we will find the boundaries for the intervals that are one and two standard deviations above and below the mean.

$$\bar{x} - 2\sigma = 4 - 2(2.7) = -1.4 \qquad \bar{x} - \sigma = 4 - 2.7 = 1.3$$
$$\bar{x} + \sigma = 4 + 2.7 = 6.7 \qquad \bar{x} + 2\sigma = 4 + 2(2.7) = 9.4$$

1. In Mrs. Fowler's class, 17 students have 2, 3, 4, 5, or 6 misspelled words. Thus, from 1.3 to 6.7, or within one standard deviation of the mean, exactly $\frac{17}{25}$ or 68% of the population is found.

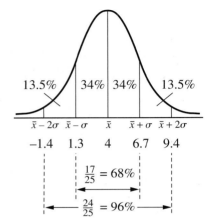

2. Every student except one is found in the interval from -1.4 to 9.4. Thus, $\frac{24}{25}$ or 96% of the population lies within two standard deviations of the mean.

3. The one student with 12 spelling errors is found outside the interval from -1.4 to 9.4. This student represents $\frac{1}{25}$ or 4% of the population. We expect scores in a normal distribution to fall outside the interval from $\bar{x} - 2\sigma$ to $\bar{x} + 2\sigma$ less than 5% of the time.

Although the number, $n = 25$, is relatively small in this study, the percents that we have just found indicate that this set of data closely approximates a normal distribution.

Calculator Applications

The table at the left shows the number of misspelled words in 25 book reports. For this set of data, find the mean and the standard deviation to the *nearest hundredth*.

x_i	f_i
12	1
7	3
6	2
5	5
4	3
3	3
2	4
1	1
0	3
—	25

The data values, x_i, are entered in one list, and the frequencies, f_i, in another. After the data values have been entered, the names of the lists in which the data and the frequencies are stored are entered after 1-Var Stats is copied to the home screen.

Step 1. Copy the data values to L1 and the frequencies to L2.

Step 2. Calculate the statistical values for this set of data.

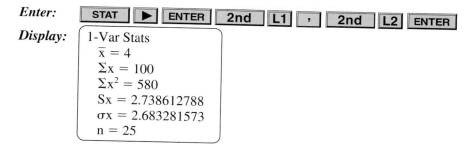

Enter: | STAT | | ▶ | | ENTER | | 2nd | | L1 | , | 2nd | | L2 | | ENTER |

Display:
```
1-Var Stats
  x̄ = 4
  Σx = 100
  Σx² = 580
  Sx = 2.738612788
  σx = 2.683281573
  n = 25
```

The mean, $\bar{x} = 4$, and the standard deviation, $\sigma = 2.683281573$, can be read from the calculator display shown above.

Intervals of Length Greater Than 1

If the range of a set of data is large, it is useful to group the data into intervals that include more than one data value. The *length* to an interval is the difference between the lower limits of two consecutive intervals. All intervals must have the same length. Usually, the number of intervals for grouped data should not be less than 5 or greater than 15.

For example, the following set of data gives the grades of 25 students:

56, 60, 65, 67, 70, 72, 74, 77, 78, 78, 80, 81, 82,
82, 84, 84, 84, 87, 87, 87, 88, 89, 92, 93, 95

Since the range of the grades is $95 - 56 = 39$, a convenient grouping can consist of eight intervals, each with a length of 5. We let the *midpoint of each interval* be x_i. For example, in the interval 81–85, the midpoint is 83 and the frequency is 6. The actual sum of the six grades in this interval, $81 + 82 + 82 + 84 + 84 + 84$, is 497, which is close to $f_i x_i = 6(83) = 498$, the product of the frequency of this interval, 6, and its midpoint, 83. If we compare the sum of all of the given data with $\Sigma f_i x_i$, the sum of the products of the midpoint of an interval times the frequency of that interval for each interval, we see that the sums are very close. Thus, using the midpoint in place of each data value in an interval simplifies computation and does not significantly change the results.

Therefore, for data grouped in intervals with midpoint x_i and frequency f_i:

Interval	x_i	f_i
91–95	93	3
86–90	88	5
81–85	83	6
76–80	78	4
71–75	73	2
66–70	68	2
61–65	63	1
56–60	58	2

$$\text{Mean} = \bar{x} = \frac{\Sigma f_i x_i}{\Sigma f_i} \quad \text{or} \quad \bar{x} = \frac{\Sigma f_i x_i}{n}$$

$$\text{Standard deviation} = \sigma = \sqrt{\frac{\Sigma f_i (x_i - \bar{x})^2}{\Sigma f_i}} \quad \text{or} \quad \sigma = \sqrt{\frac{\Sigma f_i (x_i - \bar{x})^2}{n}}$$

EXAMPLE

The test scores of 50 students are grouped into intervals as shown in the accompanying table.

For this set of grouped data, find:

a. the mean
b. the standard deviation to the *nearest hundredth*

Interval	Frequency
96–100	2
91–95	4
86–90	10
81–85	14
76–80	10
71–75	6
66–70	4

Solutions

a. To find the mean, use columns 1–4 in the table shown below.
  (1) In column 2, let each measure, x_i, represent the midpoint of the interval.
  (2) In column 4, find the products, $f_i x_i$, and their sum, $\Sigma f_i x_i$.
  (3) Determine the mean:

$$\bar{x} = \frac{\Sigma f_i x_i}{\Sigma f_i} = \frac{4{,}100}{50} = 82$$

	Col. 1	Col. 2	Col. 3	Col. 4	Col. 5	Col. 6	Col. 7
	Interval	**Measure** x_i	**Frequency** f_i	$f_i x_i$	$x_i - \bar{x}$	$(x_i - \bar{x})^2$	$f_i(x_i - \bar{x})^2$
	96–100	98	2	196	16	256	512
	91–95	93	4	372	11	121	484
	86–90	88	10	880	6	36	360
	81–85	83	14	1,162	1	1	14
	76–80	78	10	780	−4	16	160
	71–75	73	6	438	−9	81	486
	66–70	68	4	272	−14	196	784
	—	—	50 Σf_i	4,100 $\Sigma f_i x_i$	—	—	2,800 $\Sigma f_i(x_i - \bar{x})^2$

b. To find the standard deviation, continue to use the table shown above.
  (1) To obtain the numbers in column 5, headed $x_i - \bar{x}$, subtract the mean, 82, from each measure, x_i. Then, in column 6, square these deviations from the mean. For example, $98 - 82 = 16$, and $(16)^2 = 256$.
  (2) In column 7, multiply the square of each deviation by its corresponding frequency. For example, $2 \cdot 256 = 512$.
  (3) Add the entries in the last column, and find the standard deviation.

$$\sigma = \sqrt{\frac{\Sigma f_i(x_i - \bar{x})^2}{\Sigma f_i}} = \sqrt{\frac{2{,}800}{50}} = \sqrt{56} \approx 7.48$$

Calculator Solutions **a, b.**

Step 1. Copy the data values to L1 and the frequencies to L2.

Enter:

Step 2. Calculate the statistical values for this set of data.

Enter: STAT ▶ ENTER 2nd L1 , 2nd L2
ENTER

Display:

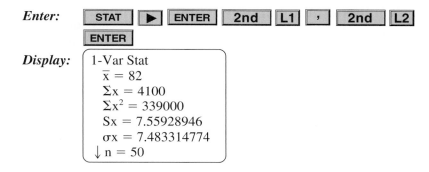

```
1-Var Stat
 x̄ = 82
 Σx = 4100
 Σx² = 339000
 Sx = 7.55928946
 σx = 7.483314774
↓n = 50
```

Answers: **a.** Mean = 82   **b.** Standard deviation ≈ 7.48

EXERCISES WITH OPEN-RESPONSE PROBLEMS

1. The set of data 12, 15, 12, 10, 9, 12, 9, 10, 12, 9 has been organized into the table that follows. For this set of grouped data: **a.** Find the mean.   **b.** Copy and complete the table.   **c.** Find the standard deviation to the *nearest tenth*.

Measure (x_i)	Frequency (f_i)	f_ix_i	$x_i - \bar{x}$	$(x_i - \bar{x})^2$	$f_i(x_i - \bar{x})^2$
15	1				
12	4				
10	2				
9	3				

In 2–4, for each set of grouped data, find: **a.** the mean   **b.** the standard deviation to the *nearest hundredth*

2.

Measure x_i	Frequency f_i
31	1
25	5
22	2
20	2

3.

Measure x_i	Frequency f_i
40	4
30	10
20	4
10	2

4.

Measure x_i	Frequency f_i
10	4
8	2
7	2
5	7

5. In her last 10 mathematics tests, Karla Adasse scored 90, 100, 80, 100, 100, 70, 90, 80, 90, and 100. Organize these test grades into a table of grouped data, and find: **a.** the mean grade   **b.** the standard deviation

6. Anita Falk kept a record of the number of miles that she drove each day during the last week: 20, 20, 15, 20, 10, 40, and 15. Organize the record of her mileage into a table of grouped data, and find: **a.** the mean   **b.** the standard deviation to the *nearest tenth*

7. Ten high-school juniors were chosen at random. Their nonverbal scores on the PSAT were 68, 65, 70, 70, 68, 58, 65, 68, 70, and 68. Find the standard deviation of these scores to the *nearest hundredth*.

8. Mr. McEntee is a guidance counselor. During the last 8 school days, he saw the following numbers of students: 12, 8, 10, 12, 15, 10, 10, and 3. For this set of data, find the standard deviation to the *nearest tenth*.

9. Mrs. Cerulli drives to work. Of her last 10 trips, 5 trips took 20 minutes each, 4 trips took 18 minutes each, and 1 trip took 38 minutes. For these times, find: **a.** the range   **b.** the median   **c.** the mode   **d.** the mean   **e.** the standard deviation to the *nearest tenth*

10. The test scores of 50 students are grouped into intervals as shown in the table at the right. For this set of grouped data, find:

a. the mean

b. the standard deviation

Interval	Frequency
96–100	2
91–95	8
86–90	8
81–85	5
76–80	11
71–75	10
66–70	5
61–65	1

Ex. 10

11. Ten Speedo cars tested at random were found to average the following numbers of miles per gallon: 30, 31, 31, 29, 32, 30, 23, 31, 32, and 31.   **a.** Find the mean for this set of data.   **b.** Find the standard deviation to the *nearest tenth*.   **c.** Mr. Pappas owns the car that averages 23 miles per gallon. Does his car have a rate within two standard deviations of the mean?

12. Ms. Kandybowicz analyzed the scores on a test given to 30 students in her class. Using the accompanying table, find: **a.** the mean score   **b.** the standard deviation to the *nearest tenth*

Interval	Midpoint x_i	Frequency f_i
94–100	97	2
87–93	90	5
80–86	83	15
73–79	76	7
66–72	69	1

Ex. 12

13. Elizabeth Connolly organized her grades on 20 lab reports into the accompanying table. For this set of data, find:

a. the mean grade

b. the standard deviation to the *nearest tenth*

x_i	f_i
100	8
90	9
80	2
70	1

Ex. 13

14. The ages of 10 mathematics teachers are 58, 21, 34, 28, 41, 41, 34, 38, 41, and 34 years. For this set of data, find: **a.** the mean **b.** the standard deviation to the *nearest tenth*

15. A group of children grew string beans. For 1 week, they recorded the number of beans on each of their 20 plants. For the grouped data in the table:
a. Find the mean. **b.** Find the standard deviation to the *nearest hundredth*. **c.** Joanna grew the plant that had the greatest number of string beans, and Zack grew the plant having the least. Whose plant, if any, lies outside the interval that is two standard deviations from the mean?

Interval	Midpoint x_i	Frequency f_i
45–49		1
40–44		0
35–39		5
30–34		8
25–29		6

21-7 TWO-VALUED STATISTICS

Scatter Plots

The relationship between two different sets of data can be studied using graphs. For example, a doctor might use a chart that compares height and weight to recommend a goal weight for a dieter. A businessperson might compare the cost of manufacturing a product to the selling price in order to predict future costs and pricing. Each of these cases involves **two-valued statistics** that can be displayed and investigated using a **scatter plot**.

EXAMPLE

The table below shows the heights and shoe sizes for a male gym class.

Shoe size	Height in inches	Shoe size	Height in inches	Shoe size	Height in inches	Shoe size	Height in inches
11	68	7	60	13	76	10	66
8	60	10	70	11	70	8	62
10	64	9	64	7.5	62	12	68
13	78	11	72	10	68	9.5	66
12.5	74	13	74	14	76	12	76
14	78	12	72	13	72	14	80
11	74	13.5	78	12	70	15	78

Use a graphing calculator to represent the data with a scatter plot. Enter the data for shoe size in List 1 and the data for height in List 2. Set the STAT PLOT for a scatter plot. Adjust the window to clearly display the data and graph.

Enter: `ZOOM` 9

Your graph should be similar to the one shown below.

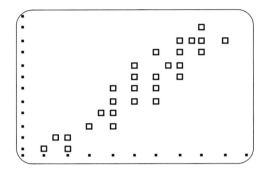

Correlation Coefficient

The graph shows that, in general, as the heights increase, the shoe sizes increase. This represents a *positive correlation* between the data sets. If the graph shows one data set increasing while the other decreases, a *negative correlation* is represented. If there is no obvious relationship between the data sets, it can be said that there is *no correlation*.

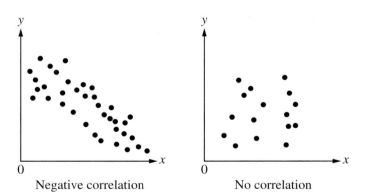

Negative correlation   No correlation

The **correlation coefficient**, r, is a number between -1 and $+1$ that tells whether or not there is a linear relationship between the two variables. The more positive the correlation, the closer the correlation coefficient is to $+1$. If there is a strong negative correlation, the correlation coefficient is close to -1. If there is a moderate correlation, the coefficient would be close to -0.5 or 0.5 depending on whether the correlation is negative or positive. When there is no correlation, the correlation coefficient is 0.

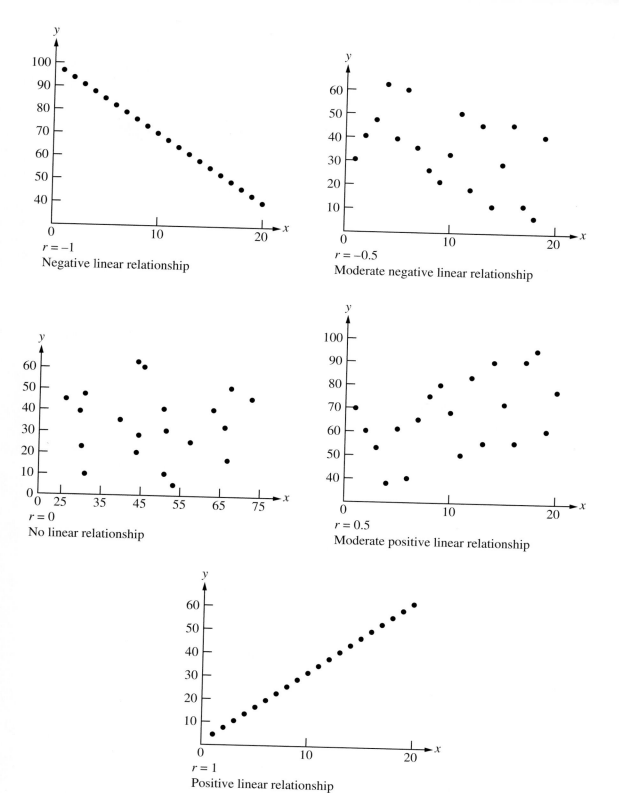

$r = -1$
Negative linear relationship

$r = -0.5$
Moderate negative linear relationship

$r = 0$
No linear relationship

$r = 0.5$
Moderate positive linear relationship

$r = 1$
Positive linear relationship

For the example showing shoe sizes and heights, the correlation appears to be close to a positive linear correlation. You can check your assumption with a graphing calculator.

Enter: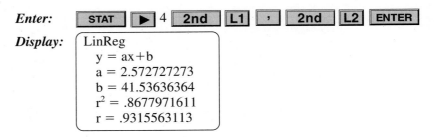

Display:
> LinReg
> y = ax+b
> a = 2.572727273
> b = 41.53636364
> r^2 = .8677971611
> r = .9315563113

r = .93, to the *nearest hundredth* or close to 1.

Line of Best Fit

You can draw a line that approximates or models the relationship shown in the graph of shoe sizes and heights. To draw the line

- find the mean of the shoe sizes (x) and the mean of the heights (y).
- plot the point (x, y) on the same axes with the scatter plot.
- draw a straight line through the point that best represents the data.

This line is called a **line of best fit** or a **trend line**. It is one of many lines that can be used to model this situation. In this case, $x \approx 11$ and $y \approx 70$.

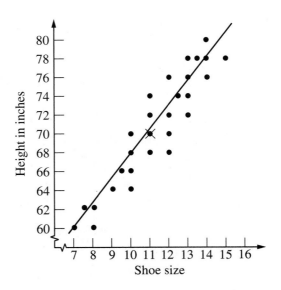

A graphing calculator can be used to check the equation of the line of best fit.

Enter: | Y= | VARS | 5 | ▶ | ▶ | ENTER | ZOOM | 9

Display:

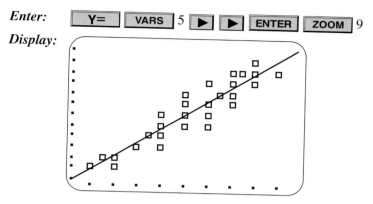

You can use the points (11, 70) and (10, 68) to write an equation of the line drawn. First approximate the slope of the line.

$$\text{Slope} = \frac{70 - 68}{11 - 10} = \frac{2}{1} = 2$$

Then, using the point (10, 68) and the slope 2, apply the point-slope form of a line to find an equation.

$$(y - 68) = 2(x - 10)$$
$$y - 68 = 2x - 20$$
$$y = 2x + 48$$

This line can also be used to approximate values that are not points on the graph. For example, about how tall would a man be that wears a size $8\frac{1}{2}$ shoe?

$$y = 2x + 48 = 2(8.5) + 48 = 17 + 48 = 65 \text{ inches}$$

The line shows that the man would be about 65 inches tall. Keep in mind that this is a prediction and not a fact. Not every man that wears a size $8\frac{1}{2}$ shoe is 65 inches tall.

Note that this is only one of many possible equations that can be used to approximate the height of a man in this group, given his shoe size.

EXAMPLE

A tourist has a pamphlet that contains the following list of taxi fares for various distances. How much should the tourist expect to pay for a cab ride of 18.4 miles?

Miles driven	1	3	5	12
Cost ($)	1.75	3.80	6.50	12.00

Solution   Step 1. Clear the lists and enter the miles driven in L1 and the cost in L2.

Step 2. Find the line of best fit.

> ***Enter:***   STAT   ▶   4   ENTER

Step 3. Enter the equation in Y=.

> ***Enter:***   Y=   VARS   5   ▶   ▶   ENTER   ZOOM   9

Step 4. Make a prediction using the linear model. Change the window to be greater than 18.4, so that the required value will be shown.

> ***Enter:***   2nd   CALC   ENTER   18.4   ENTER

The cost of an 18.4-mile taxi ride is $18.14, to the *nearest cent*.

Curve Fitting

In some cases, the appropriate model for a set of data is not a line but a curve. There are various models that can be fitted to sets of data using the graphing calculator STAT key and CALC section. A line, a quadratic, a cubic, a logarithmic, an exponential, or a power equation can be fitted to the data entered into two lists.

EXAMPLE

Which model best fits the data about the planets given in the table?

Planet	Orbital Speed (km/s)	Distance from Sun (millions of km)
Venus	34.8	108.2
Earth	29.6	149.6
Mars	23.9	227.9
Jupiter	12.9	778
Saturn	9.6	1427

Enter the data in L1 and L2 and draw a scatter plot. Then use the STAT key and the CALC section to graph a linear model ($ax + b$).

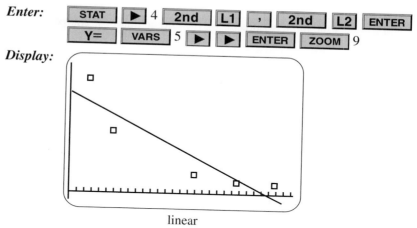

linear

The linear model does not really fit the data. Repeat the procedure for the quadratic, logarithmic, exponential, and power models. Be sure to clear the linear model, the co-efficients, and the equation (Y=) before testing each model. You can read the equation for each model from the Y= screen. From the displays, it appears that the power model is the best fit.

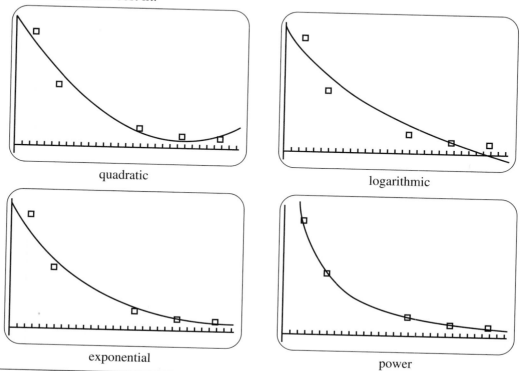

quadratic

logarithmic

exponential

power

EXERCISES WITH OPEN-RESPONSE PROBLEMS

In 1 and 2, select the *numeral* preceding the choice that best completes the sentence.

1. The relationship of the number of weeks since planted to the height of a seedling, in inches, is given in the accompanying table.

Weeks	1	2	3	4
Height (in.)	0	0.25	1	1.50

The linear correlation coefficient for this relationship is

(1) −1 (2) 0 (3) 0.5 (4) 1

2. The points in the scatter plot represent the normal temperatures of a northern U.S. city during the months July through December. Based on this scatter plot, it would be reasonable to conclude:
   (1) month and temperature have a coefficient of correlation that is less than zero.
   (2) month and temperature have a coefficient of correlation that is equal to zero.
   (3) month and temperature have a coefficient of correlation that is between zero and 0.5.
   (4) month and temperature have a coefficient of correlation that is greater than 0.5.

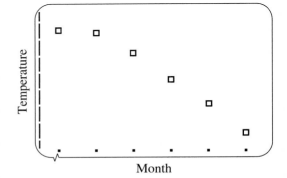

3. The table below shows the number of cellular phone users in the United States for the last several years.

Year	Cellular Telephone Subscribers in U.S. (in millions)	Year	Cellular Telephone Subscribers in U.S. (in millions)
1985	0.3	1993	16.0
1986	0.7	1994	24.1
1987	1.2	1995	33.8
1988	2.0	1996	44.0
1989	3.5	1997	55.3
1990	5.3	1998	69.2
1991	7.6	1999	86.0
1992	11.0		

a. Create a scatter plot for the data. Let the horizontal axis represent the year and the vertical axis represent the number of cell phone subscribers. To simplify the data, use 0 for 1985.
b. Determine the relationship between the sets of data. Justify your answer.
c. Find the coefficient of correlation for the data.
d. Predict the number of cellular telephone subscribers there will be in the year 2004.

4. The data in the accompanying table shows the total number of daily papers published over a period of 77 years.
   a. Create a scatter plot for the data and find a curve of best fit.
   b. Use the answer to **a** to predict the total dailies in 2004.

Year	Total dailies	Year	Total dailies	Year	Total dailies
1920	2,042	1950	1,772	1980	1,747
1930	1,942	1960	1,763	1990	1,611
1940	1,878	1970	1,748	1997	1,509

5. The 1999–2000 win-loss statistics for the Eastern Conference, Atlantic Division, of the National Hockey League are shown in the accompanying table.
   a. Find the mean for the number of wins, $\overline{W}$, and the mean for the number of losses, $\overline{L}$.
   b. Determine if the point $(\overline{W}, \overline{L})$ is a point on the line of best fit. Justify your answer.

	Wins	Losses
Philadelphia	45	25
New Jersey	45	29
Pittsburgh	37	37
N.Y. (1)	29	41
N.Y. (2)	24	49

6. The accompanying table shows the number of recorded music and music videos shipped, in millions, in the years indicated. Find the mean for the years, $\overline{Y}$, and the mean for the number of units shipped, $\overline{S}$, and determine if the point $(\overline{Y}, \overline{S})$ is a point on the line of best fit. Justify your answer.

Year	Units Shipped (in millions)
1991	801.1
1992	895.5
1993	955.6
1994	1,122.7
1995	1,112.7
1996	1,137.2
1997	1,063.4
1998	1,124.3
1999	1,160.6

CHAPTER SUMMARY

The sum of related terms can be symbolized by the Greek capital letter Σ. The notation $\sum_{i=1}^{n} i^2$ means the sum of the squares of the integers from 1 to n. The ***index*** is the variable that is replaced by consecutive integers starting with the ***lower limit of summation***, written below the ***summation symbol***, and ending with the ***upper limit of summation***, written above the summation symbol.

Measures of central tendency are used to represent all data values by a single number. The ***mean***, ***median***, and ***mode*** are measures of central tendency.

Quartiles separate an ordered list of data into four equal parts. The ***first*** or ***lower quartile*** separates the data below the median, or ***second quartile***, into two equal parts; the ***third*** or ***upper quartile*** separates the data above the median into two equal parts. A ***box-and-whisker plot*** displays the smallest value, the quartile values, and the largest value of a set of data. A ***percentile*** of a score or measure indicates the percent of the total frequency at or below that measure.

A number that indicates the variation within a set of data is a ***measure of dispersion***. The four formulas that follow define different measures of dispersion in which $\bar{x}$ is the mean of a set of n numbers, x_i is the interval measure (or midpoint of an interval whose length is greater than 1), and $\Sigma f_i = n$:

1. ***Range*** = difference between the highest and the lowest value in a data set.

2. ***Mean absolute deviation*** $= \dfrac{\sum_{i=1}^{n} f_i |x_i - \bar{x}|}{n}$.

3. ***Variance*** $= v = \dfrac{\sum_{i=1}^{n} f_i(x_i - \bar{x})^2}{n}$ or $\dfrac{\sum_{i=1}^{n} f_i(x_i - \bar{x})^2}{\Sigma f_i}$.

4. ***Standard deviation*** $= \sigma = \sqrt{v} = \sqrt{\dfrac{\sum_{i=1}^{n} f_i(x_i - \bar{x})^2}{n}}$ or $\sqrt{\dfrac{\sum_{i=1}^{n} f_i(x_i - \bar{x})^2}{\Sigma f_i}}$.

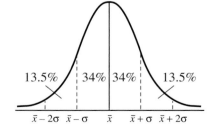

The ***normal curve*** is a bell-shaped curve that is a theoretical model used to study sets of data. In a ***normal distribution***:

68% of the data values lie between $\bar{x} - \sigma$ and $\bar{x} + \sigma$,

95% of the data values lie between $\bar{x} - 2\sigma$ and $\bar{x} + 2\sigma$,

99.5% of the data values lie between $\bar{x} - 3\sigma$ and $\bar{x} + 3\sigma$.

In two-valued statistics, a relationship between two different sets of data is studied and can be graphed in a *scatter plot*. In some, but not all, cases, one or more straight lines may be found and a linear equation may be written to approximate the relationship between data sets. This line is often called the *line of best fit* or a *trend line*. In some cases, a quadratic, logarithmic, exponential, or power model better fits the data. The degree of the relationship between sets of data can be expressed as the *correlation coefficient*, *r*, which is a number between -1 and $+1$ where -1 is a negative relationship and $+1$ is a positive relationship.

VOCABULARY

21-1 Summation symbol   Index   Lower limit of summation
Upper limit of summation   Subscript

21-2 Measure of central tendency   Mean (second quartile)
Median   Mode   First (lower) quartile   Third (upper) quartile
Box-and-whisker plot

21-3 Measure of dispersion   Range
Mean absolute deviation (mean deviation)

21-4 Variance   Standard deviation

21-5 Frequency polygon   Normal curve   Normal distribution
Percentile

21-7 Two-valued statistics   Scatter plot   Correlation coefficient
Line of best fit   Trend line

REVIEW EXERCISES WITH OPEN-RESPONSE PROBLEMS

In 1–4, find the value indicated by each summation symbol.

1. $\displaystyle\sum_{n=1}^{3} n^n$ **2.** $\displaystyle\sum_{i=2}^{4} (5-i)^2$ **3.** $\displaystyle\sum_{k=0}^{4} 3(k+1)$ **4.** $\displaystyle\sum_{n=0}^{2} \sin(n\pi)$

5. Which statistical term represents the data value that occurs most often in a distribution?

6. If Sal's test grades are 73, 90, 87, 98, and 92, what is the range of his grades?

7. The hours that Carol worked over the last 8 weeks are recorded in the table at the right. For these hours, find:
   a. the mean   **b.** the median   **c.** the mode

Measure x_i	Frequency f_i
34	1
32	4
30	1
28	2

In 8–11, select the *numeral* preceding the choice that best answers the question or completes the sentence.

8. For the grouped data in the accompanying table, which is true?
(1) The mean equals the median.
(2) The mean exceeds the median by 3.
(3) The median exceeds the mean by 3.
(4) The mean equals the mode.

Index i	Measure x_i	Frequency f_i
1	40	4
2	25	2
3	20	3
4	10	1

9. In a class, 15 students are 17 years old and 10 students are 16 years old. The mean age, in years, of these students is
(1) 16.3   (2) 16.5   (3) 16.6   (4) 16.8

10. The weights of a group of people approximate a normal distribution. If the mean weight is 64 kilograms and the standard deviation is 4.8, which weight, in kilograms, is expected to occur less than 3% of the time?
(1) 56   (2) 59.3   (3) 69.8   (4) 74

11. On a standardized exam, the mean score is 83 and the standard deviation is 5.5. Which score might be assigned to a student at the 70th percentile?
(1) 70   (2) 77.5   (3) 86   (4) 90

12. Two players at a miniature golf course had the same average for the first nine holes of golf.

> Len: 3, 2, 5, 3, 3, 1, 5, 3, 2   (mean = 3)
> Stan: 3, 2, 5, 3, 3, 3, 2, 3, 3   (mean = 3)

a. Find the mean absolute deviation for each player, expressed as a fraction.
b. Which player had more widely dispersed scores?

13. In the diagram, about 68% of the data values fall in the shaded area. If the distribution is normal and the values range from 55 to 80, find:
a. the standard deviation
b. the mean
c. the value at $\bar{x} + 2\sigma$

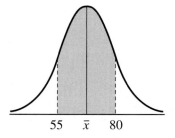

55    $\bar{x}$ 80

14. Over the last 5 days, Mrs. Tountas received the following numbers of letters in the mail: 7, 4, 9, 2, 3. For these data, find: **a.** the mean   **b.** the standard deviation to the *nearest tenth*.

15. The scores earned by six students on the PSAT are 62, 57, 55, 54, 51, and 50. For these scores, calculate to the *nearest tenth*:   **a.** the mean   **b.** the standard deviation

16. For the grouped data in the accompanying table, find:
   a. the mean   **b.** the median   **c.** the mode
   d. the standard deviation to the *nearest tenth*

Measure (x_i)	Frequency (f_i)
60	12
55	30
50	34
45	54

17. Doris scored the following grades on her last 10 science tests: 85, 100, 90, 90, 100, 85, 80, 90, 100, and 90. Organize these grades into a table of grouped data, and find: **a.** the mean   **b.** the standard deviation to the *nearest tenth*

18. The data in the table below shows the number of students per computer for the school years 1983 to 1999.

School Year	Students per Computer in U.S. Public Schools
1983–1984	125
1985–1986	50
1986–1987	37
1987–1988	32
1988–1989	25
1989–1990	22
1990–1991	20
1991–1992	18
1992–1993	16
1993–1994	14
1994–1995	10.5
1995–1996	10
1996–1997	7.8
1997–1998	6.1
1998–1999	5.7

   a. Create a scatter plot for the data and determine whether there is a relationship between the sets of data. Justify your answer.
   b. Find the equation of the line or curve of best fit.
   c. Use the answer to **b** to predict the number of students per computer in the school year 2003–2004.

CUMULATIVE REVIEW WITH OPEN-RESPONSE PROBLEMS

1. **a.** In the figure, the bisector of ∠DAB and the bisector of ∠EBA intersect at F. If m∠C = 100, find m∠F.
   b. If m∠C = x, express m∠F in terms of x.

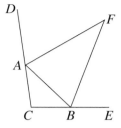

2. **a.** The image of A(x, y) under a reflection in the line y = x is B, and the image of B under a reflection in the y-axis is C. What are the coordinates of C?
   b. The image of A(x, y) under a reflection in the y-axis is D, and the image of D under a reflection in the line y = x is E. What are the coordinates of E?
   c. Under what transformation is E the image of C?

3. The slope of $\overleftrightarrow{AB}$ is $\frac{1}{2}$. If the coordinates of A are (0, 1) and the coordinates of B are (3, c), find the value of c.

4. Write the equation(s) of the locus of points equidistant from the x- and y-axes.

5. **a.** Solve the following system of equations graphically.
$$y = x^2 + 2x - 1$$
$$y = 2x + 8$$
   b. Solve the system of equations algebraically and check.

6. Quadrilateral ABCD is separated into two triangles by diagonal $\overline{BD}$. The lengths of the sides of the quadrilateral in meters are AB = 450, BC = 162, CD = 216, and DA = 360. The length of the diagonal $\overline{BD}$ is 270 meters.

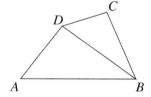

   a. Show that each of the triangles is a right triangle.
   b. Find, to the nearest degree, the measure of ∠A.
   c. Find, to the nearest degree, the measure of ∠DBC.
   d. Are the triangles similar? Explain your answer.

7. Prove the identity: $\frac{2 \cos 2A}{\sin 2A} = \cot A - \tan A$.

8. The functions f and g are defined by the following tables:

x	0	1	2	3	4
f(x)	1	3	9	27	81

x	1	2	3	4	5
g(x)	0	1	2	3	4

Find: **a.** g ∘ f(1)   **b.** f ∘ g(1)

9. Forces of 135 pounds and 217 pounds act on a body to produce a resultant force of 318 pounds. Find to the *nearest tenth* the degree measure of the angle between the forces.

10. Write an expression for x in terms of a and b if $\log x = 2 \log a + \log b$.

11. Solve for x: $8 - \sqrt{3x - 2} = 3$.

12. Write $\frac{1 - i}{1 + i}$ in $a + bi$ form.

Exploration

Show that if each number in a set of data is increased by a constant c, the mean is increased by c and the standard deviation is unchanged.

Chapter 22

Probability, Sequences, and the Binomial Theorem

No prescription is guaranteed to be 100% effective in combating an infection. Last week, three patients with the same ailment visited Dr. Beth Deaner, who, after examining them, prescribed the same medication for all three. This medicine is known to be 98% effective in treating the infection from which these patients suffer; that is, the probability is .98 that the medication will destroy the infection.

What is the probability that the medicine will be effective for all three patients? This probability is *not* .98. Do you think the probability is higher or lower than .98?

What is the probability that the medicine will be effective for *at least two* of the patients? For *at least one* patient? In either case, the probability is, once again, *not* .98. Why is this so?

In this chapter, we will review some basic concepts of probability and then extend this study to find the probabilities that a given outcome will occur in specified numbers of trials. Once these concepts are learned, the questions posed on this page can be answered.

22-1 PERMUTATIONS AND COMBINATIONS

Permutations of the Form $_nP_n$; Factorials

A bank contains 4 coins: a penny, a nickel, a dime, and a quarter, represented by P, N, D, and Q, respectively. If 1 coin is taken out of the bank at random, there are 4 possible outcomes. The *sample space*, *s*, or the set of all possible outcomes, is $\{P, N, D, Q\}$.

If a coin is tossed, there are 2 possible outcomes, heads and tails, represented by H and T, respectively. This sample space is $\{H, T\}$.

Therefore, if 1 of the 4 coins is taken out of the bank and tossed, the sample space becomes

$$\{(P, H), (P, T), (N, H), (N, T), (D, H), (D, T), (Q, H), (Q, T)\}$$

This sample space is represented on the graph at the right. We see that there are $4 \cdot 2$ or 8 possible outcomes. The result illustrates the *counting principle*.

- **The Counting Principle. If one activity can occur in any of *m* ways and, following this, a second activity can occur in any of *n* ways, then both activities can occur in the order given in $m \cdot n$ ways.**

The 4 coins in the bank are to be drawn out 1 at a time without replacement. There are 4 possible outcomes for the first draw. Then, since 3 coins remain in the bank, there are 3 possible coins to be drawn and $4 \cdot 3$ ways in

Draw	Number of Coins in Bank	Number of Possible Outcomes
1st	4	4
2nd	3	$4 \cdot 3$
3rd	2	$4 \cdot 3 \cdot 2$
4th	1	$4 \cdot 3 \cdot 2 \cdot 1$

which the first 2 coins could be removed. On the third draw there are 2 coins left to be selected and $4 \cdot 3 \cdot 2$ ways in which the first 3 coins could be removed. On the last draw 1 coin is left to be selected, and there are $4 \cdot 3 \cdot 2 \cdot 1$ or 24 possible orders in which the coins could have been drawn.

A *permutation* is an arrangement of objects in some specific order. The symbol $_4P_4$ is read as "the number of permutations of 4 things taken 4 at a time."

$$_4P_4 = 4 \cdot 3 \cdot 2 \cdot 1 = 24$$

There are 24 permutations of the 4 coins.

We have learned that, for any natural number n, we define **n factorial**, or **factorial n**, as

$$n! = n(n-1)(n-2) \cdots 3 \cdot 2 \cdot 1$$

Therefore, $4! = 4 \cdot 3 \cdot 2 \cdot 1$ and $_4P_4 = 4!$

- **In general, the number of permutations of *n* things taken *n* at a time is**

$$_nP_n = n! = (n-1)(n-2)\cdots 2\cdot 1$$

To evaluate a factorial on a calculator, we may use repeated multiplication or the *factorial key*, $\boxed{\text{x!}}$, which is usually accessed by first pressing $\boxed{\text{MATH}}$ $\boxed{\blacktriangleright}$ $\boxed{\blacktriangleright}$ $\boxed{\blacktriangleright}$ 4 or $\boxed{\text{2nd}}$ or $\boxed{\text{INV}}$ or $\boxed{\text{SHIFT}}$. As shown below, 4! = 24.

Repeated Multiplication   *Factorial Key*

Enter: 4 $\boxed{\times}$ 3 $\boxed{\times}$ 2 $\boxed{\times}$ 1 $\boxed{=}$ ***Enter:*** $\boxed{\text{MATH}}$ $\boxed{\blacktriangleright}$ $\boxed{\blacktriangleright}$ $\boxed{\blacktriangleright}$ 4

                                          $\boxed{\text{ENTER}}$

Display: $\boxed{\text{24.}}$ ***Display:*** $\boxed{\text{24.}}$

Since factorial numbers grow very large very quickly, calculator displays of factorials are often given in scientific notation. For example, 15! is displayed as $1.307674368 \times 10^{12}$, which equals 1,307,674,368,000.

Enter: 15 $\boxed{\text{MATH}}$ $\boxed{\blacktriangleright}$ $\boxed{\blacktriangleright}$ $\boxed{\blacktriangleright}$ 4 $\boxed{\text{ENTER}}$

Display: $\boxed{\text{1.307674368 E12}}$

Permutations of the Form $_nP_r$ $(r \le n)$

Let us imagine that a bank contains 5 coins (a penny, a nickel, a dime, a quarter, and a half-dollar), and 2 of these coins are to be drawn. There are 5 ways in which the first coin can be selected and 4 ways in which the second coin can be selected. Therefore, there are $5 \cdot 4$ or 20 orders in which these coins can be selected. The symbol $_5P_2$ is read as "the number of permutations of 5 things taken 2 at a time."

$$_5P_2 = 5\cdot 4 = 20$$

An alternative approach to evaluating $_5P_2$ makes use of factorials:

$$_5P_2 = \frac{5!}{(5-2)!} = \frac{5!}{3!} = \frac{5\cdot 4\cdot \cancel{3}\cdot \cancel{2}\cdot \cancel{1}}{\cancel{3}\cdot \cancel{2}\cdot \cancel{1}} = 20$$

- **In general, the number of permutations of *n* things taken *r* at a time is**

$$_nP_r = \underbrace{n(n-1)(n-2)\cdots}_{r \text{ factors}} \qquad \text{or} \qquad _nP_r = \frac{n!}{(n-r)!}$$

To evaluate any permutation $_nP_r$ $(r \le n)$ on a calculator, common approaches include multiplication, factorials, and use of the *permutation key*, $\boxed{\text{nPr}}$, which is usually accessed by first pressing $\boxed{\text{MATH}}$ $\boxed{\blacktriangleright}$ $\boxed{\blacktriangleright}$ $\boxed{\blacktriangleright}$ 2 or $\boxed{\text{2nd}}$. In each of the methods shown below, $_5P_2 = 20$.

METHOD 1: *Using the Multiplication Key,* $\boxed{\times}$

      Enter: 5 $\boxed{\times}$ 4 $\boxed{\text{ENTER}}$

      Display: $\boxed{\text{20.}}$

METHOD 2: *Using the Permutation Key,* $\boxed{\text{nPr}}$

Enter: 5 $\boxed{\text{MATH}}$ $\boxed{\blacktriangleright}$ $\boxed{\blacktriangleright}$ $\boxed{\blacktriangleright}$ 2 2 $\boxed{\text{ENTER}}$

Display: $\boxed{\qquad 20.}$

METHOD 3: *Using the Factorial Key,* $\boxed{\text{x!}}$

Enter: 5 $\boxed{\text{2nd}}$ $\boxed{\text{x!}}$ $\div$ $\boxed{(}$ 5 $\boxed{-}$ 2 $\boxed{)}$ $\boxed{\text{2nd}}$ $\boxed{\text{x!}}$ $\boxed{=}$

Display: $\boxed{\qquad 20.}$

The order of keystrokes shown here may not be correct for every calculator; the correct sequence for a particular calculator can be found in the calculator manual or by experimenting with different keystrokes.

Permutations with Repetition

A bank contains 6 coins: a penny, a nickel, a dime, and 3 quarters. In how many different orders can the 6 coins be removed from the bank?

If the coins are considered to be all different, then the number of orders is

$$_6P_6 = 6! = 6 \cdot 5 \cdot 4 \cdot 3 \cdot 2 \cdot 1 = 720$$

But within any given order, such as $P\,N\,Q\,D\,Q\,Q$, there are 3! or 6 permutations of the 3 quarters that produce this arrangement of coins. These permutations are indicated by using subscripts:

$$P\,N\,Q_1\,D\,Q_2\,Q_3 \qquad P\,N\,Q_2\,D\,Q_1\,Q_3 \qquad P\,N\,Q_3\,D\,Q_1\,Q_2$$
$$P\,N\,Q_1\,D\,Q_3\,Q_2 \qquad P\,N\,Q_2\,D\,Q_3\,Q_1 \qquad P\,N\,Q_3\,D\,Q_2\,Q_1$$

We can divide the 720 arrangements of coins into groups of 6 that are the same. Therefore, the number of different orders of the 6 coins, 3 of which are quarters, is

$$\frac{6!}{3!} = \frac{6 \cdot 5 \cdot 4 \cdot 3 \cdot 2 \cdot 1}{3 \cdot 2 \cdot 1} = \frac{720}{6} = 120$$

- **In general, the number of permutations of n things taken n at a time when r are identical is $\frac{n!}{r!}$.**

Combinations, $_nC_r$ ($r \leq n$)

A bank contains 4 coins: a penny, a nickel, a dime, and a quarter. Two coins are to be drawn from the bank, and the sum of the values noted. The number of ways in which 2 coins can be drawn from the bank, one after another, is a permutation: $_4P_2 = 4 \cdot 3 = 12$. Here, order is important, and the 12 permutations can be written as 12 ordered pairs.

Let us now find the number of possible *sums of the values* of the 2 coins selected. If the penny is drawn first and then the dime, the sum is 11 cents. If the dime is drawn first and then the penny, the sum is again 11 cents. Here, the order of the coins drawn is *not* important in finding the sum. A selection in which order is not important is called a ***combination***.

For any 2 coins selected, such as the penny and the dime, there are $2! = 2 \cdot 1 = 2$ orders. Therefore, to find the number of combinations of 4 things taken 2 at a time, we divide the number of permutations of 4 things taken 2 at a time by the 2! orders:

Permutations	Combinations
$(P, D)(D, P) \longrightarrow$	$\{P, D\}$
$(P, N)(N, P) \longrightarrow$	$\{P, N\}$
$(P, Q)(Q, P) \longrightarrow$	$\{P, Q\}$
$(N, D)(D, N) \longrightarrow$	$\{N, D\}$
$(N, Q)(Q, N) \longrightarrow$	$\{N, Q\}$
$(D, Q)(Q, D) \longrightarrow$	$\{D, Q\}$

$$_4C_2 = \frac{_4P_2}{2!} = \frac{4 \cdot 3}{2 \cdot 1} = 6$$

In the box shown above, each of the six combinations listed has a unique sum; these sums are 11¢, 6¢, 26¢, 15¢, 30¢, and 35¢, respectively. By comparing the listed permutations and combinations, we see that:

1. *Permutations* are regarded as *ordered* elements, such as the ordered pairs (P, D) and (D, P).

2. *Combinations* are regarded as *sets*, such as $\{P, D\}$, in which order is not important.

If, from a class of 23 students, 4 are to represent the class in a science contest, the order in which the students are chosen is not important. This is a combination, $_{23}C_4$, which may also be written as $\binom{23}{4}$.

$$_{23}C_4 = \frac{_{23}P_4}{4!} = \frac{23 \cdot 22 \cdot 21 \cdot 20}{4 \cdot 3 \cdot 2 \cdot 1} = 8{,}855$$

● **In general, the number of combinations of *n* things taken *r* at a time is**

$$_nC_r = \frac{_nP_r}{r!} \qquad \text{or} \qquad \binom{n}{r} = \frac{_nP_r}{r!}$$

Note: The alternative symbol for the combination, $\binom{n}{r}$, is *not* the fraction $\left(\frac{n}{r}\right)$.

Since most scientific calculators have a ***combination key***, ▐ **nCr** ▐, which is usually accessed by first pressing the ▐ **MATH** ▐ ▶ ▶ ▶ 3 or ▐ **2nd** ▐ key, the calculator may be used to evaluate the combination $_{23}C_4$.

Enter: 23 ▐ **MATH** ▐ ▶ ▶ ▶ 3 4 ▐ **ENTER** ▐

Display: ▐   8855.   ▐

The order of keystrokes may vary for different calculators.

Relationships Involving Combinations

Certain relationships with combinations can be shown to be true:

1. There is only 1 way to select a 3-person committee from a group of 3 people, and a 4-person committee from a group of 4 people.

$$_3C_3 = \frac{_3P_3}{3!} = \frac{3 \cdot 2 \cdot 1}{3 \cdot 2 \cdot 1} = 1 \qquad \text{and} \qquad \binom{4}{4} = \frac{_4P_4}{4!} = \frac{4 \cdot 3 \cdot 2 \cdot 1}{4 \cdot 3 \cdot 2 \cdot 1} = 1$$

- **In general, for any counting number n:**

$$_nC_n = 1 \qquad \text{or} \qquad \binom{n}{n} = 1$$

2. There is only 1 way to take 0 object from a set of n objects.

- **In general, for any counting number n:**

$$_nC_0 = 1 \qquad \text{or} \qquad \binom{n}{0} = 1$$

3. Since $_7C_2 = \frac{7 \cdot 6}{2 \cdot 1}$ and $_7C_5 = \frac{7 \cdot 6 \cdot 5 \cdot 4 \cdot 3}{5 \cdot 4 \cdot 3 \cdot 2 \cdot 1} = \frac{7 \cdot 6}{2 \cdot 1}$, then $_7C_2 = {_7C_5}$.

- **In general, for any whole numbers n and r, when $r \le n$:**

$$_nC_r = {_nC_{n-r}} \qquad \text{or} \qquad \binom{n}{r} = \binom{n}{n-r}$$

EXAMPLES

1. In how many different orders can the program for a music recital be arranged if 7 students are to perform?

Solution   This is a permutation of 7 things taken 7 at a time.

$$_7P_7 = 7 \cdot 6 \cdot 5 \cdot 4 \cdot 3 \cdot 2 \cdot 1 = 5,040$$

Calculator Solutions   METHOD 1: *Enter:*   7 [MATH] [▶] [▶] [▶] 2 7 [ENTER]

METHOD 2: *Enter:*   7 [MATH] [▶] [▶] [▶] 4 [ENTER]

Display: [5040.]

Answer: 5,040 orders

2. In how many ways can 1 junior and 1 senior be selected from a group of 8 juniors and 6 seniors?

Solution Use the counting principle. The junior can be selected in 8 ways, and the senior can be selected in 6 ways. Therefore, there are $8 \cdot 6 = 48$ possible selections.

Answer: 48 ways

---

3. How many 5-letter arrangements can be made from the letters in the word BOOKS?

Solution This is a permutation of 5 things taken 5 at a time when 2 are identical.

$$\frac{_5P_5}{2!} = \frac{5!}{2!} = \frac{5 \cdot 4 \cdot 3 \cdot 2 \cdot \cancel{1}}{2 \cdot \cancel{1}} = 60$$

Calculator Solution

Enter: 5 [MATH] [▶] [▶] [▶] 2 5 [÷] 2 [MATH] [▶] [▶] [▶] 4 [ENTER]

Display: [60.]

Answer: 60 arrangements

---

4. A reading list gives the titles of 20 novels and 12 biographies from which each student is to choose 3 novels and 2 biographies to read. How many different combinations of titles can be chosen?

How to Proceed:	*Solution:*
(1) Find the number of ways in which 3 novels can be chosen.	$\binom{20}{3} = \frac{20 \cdot 19 \cdot 18}{3 \cdot 2 \cdot 1}$ $= 1{,}140$
(2) Find the number of ways in which 2 biographies can be chosen.	$\binom{12}{2} = \frac{12 \cdot 11}{2 \cdot 1}$ $= 66$
(3) Use the counting principle to find the number of possible choices of novels and biographies.	$1{,}140 \cdot 66 = 75{,}240$

Calculator Solution Evaluate $_{20}C_3 \cdot {}_{12}C_2$.

Enter: 20 [MATH] [▶] [▶] [▶] 3 3 [×] 12 [MATH] [▶] [▶] [▶] 3 2 [ENTER]

Display: [75240.]

Answer: 75,240 combinations

EXERCISES WITH OPEN-RESPONSE PROBLEMS

In 1–18, evaluate each expression.

1. $_6P_6$

2. $_8P_4$

3. $_{12}P_2$

4. $_8C_5$

5. $_8C_3$

6. $_{12}C_{12}$

7. $_{12}C_0$

8. $4!$

9. $\binom{13}{4}$

10. $\binom{17}{15}$

11. $\frac{_5P_3}{3!}$

12. $\frac{_6P_2}{2!}$

13. $\frac{30!}{26!\,4!}$

14. $_{18}C_5$

15. $\frac{_{18}P_5}{5!}$

16. $_{14}P_{14}$

17. $_{91}C_{89}$

18. $_{50}C_{48}$

19. In how many different ways can 6 runners be assigned to 6 lanes at the start of a race?

20. In how many different ways can a hand of 5 cards be dealt from a deck of 52 cards?

21. There are 7 students in a history club.   **a.** In how many ways can a president, a vice-president, and a treasurer be elected from the members of the club?   **b.** In how many ways can a committee of 3 club members be selected to plan a visit to a museum?

22. There are 5 red and 4 white marbles in a jar. A marble is drawn from the jar and is not replaced. Then, a second marble is drawn.   **a.** In how many ways can a red marble and a white marble be drawn in that order?   **b.** In how many ways can a red marble and a white marble be drawn in either order?

In 23–28, in each case, find the number of "words" (arrangements of letters) that can be formed from the letters of the given word, using all letters in each arrangement.

23. axis

24. circle

25. identity

26. parabola

27. abscissa

28. minimum

29. From a standard deck of 52 cards, 2 cards are drawn without replacement.   **a.** How many combinations of 2 hearts are possible?   **b.** How many combinations of 2 kings are possible?

30. Each week, Mark does the dishes on 4 days and Lisa does them on the remaining 3 days. In how many different orders can they choose to do the dishes? (*Hint:* This is an arrangement of 7 things with repetition.)

31. Each week, Albert does the dishes on 3 days, Rita does them on 2 days, and Marie does them on the remaining 2 days. In how many different orders can they choose to do the dishes?

32. There are 4 boys and 5 girls who are members of a chess club.
   a. How many games must be played if each member is to play every other member once?
   b. In how many ways can 1 boy and 1 girl be selected to play a demonstration game?
   c. In how many ways can a group of 3 members be selected to represent the club at a regional meet?
   d. In how many ways can 2 boys and 2 girls be selected to attend the state tournament?

22-2 PROBABILITY

A sample space is the set of all possible outcomes or results of an activity. An **event, E,** is a subset of a sample space. For example, if a die is rolled, the sample space is {1, 2, 3, 4, 5, 6}. The event of rolling a number less than 3 is {1, 2}.

If the die is fair, or unbiased, each outcome is equally likely to occur. The probability of rolling a number less than 3 is the ratio of the number of elements in the set, {1, 2}, to the number of elements in the sample space, {1, 2, 3, 4, 5, 6}:

$$P(\text{rolling a number less than 3}) = \frac{2}{6} = \frac{1}{3}$$

● **The *theoretical probability* of an event is the number of ways that an event can occur divided by the total number of possible outcomes when each outcome is equally likely to occur.**

If $P(E)$ represents the probability of an event E,
   $n(E)$ represents the number of ways that E can occur, and
   $n(S)$ represents the number of possible outcomes in the sample space S, then:

$$P(E) = \frac{n(E)}{n(S)}$$

Consider the following examples:

☐   What is the probability of drawing a red queen from a standard deck of 52 cards?

Use counting.

(1) The sample space S = {cards in the deck}. $\longrightarrow n(S) = 52$

(2) The event E = {queen of hearts, queen of diamonds} $\longrightarrow n(E) = 2$

(3) Substitute these values in the formula: $\qquad P(\text{red queen}) = \frac{n(E)}{n(S)} = \frac{2}{52} = \frac{1}{26}$

Answer: $P(\text{red queen}) = \frac{1}{26}$

The number of outcomes in the sample space and in the event can often be determined by using permutations or combinations, as seen in the next example.

☐ Two cards are to be drawn from a standard deck of 52 cards without replacement. What is the probability that both cards will be red?

Since order is not required, use combinations.

(1) The total number of outcomes is $_{52}C_2 = \frac{52 \cdot 51}{2 \cdot 1} = 26 \cdot 51$.

(2) The number of favorable outcomes is $_{26}C_2 = \frac{26 \cdot 25}{2 \cdot 1} = 13 \cdot 25$.

(3) Substitute these values in the formula: $P(E) = \frac{n(E)}{n(S)}$

$$P(2 \text{ red cards}) = \frac{n(E)}{n(S)} = \frac{_{26}C_2}{_{52}C_2} = \frac{\overset{1}{13} \cdot 25}{\underset{2}{26} \cdot 51} = \frac{25}{102}$$

Answers: $P(2 \text{ red cards}) = \frac{25}{102}$

Numerical values are assigned to probabilities such that:

1. The probability of an event that is ***certain*** is 1. For example, the probability of rolling a number less than 7 on a single roll of a die is $\frac{6}{6}$ or 1.

2. The probability of an ***impossible*** event is 0. For example, the probability of rolling a number greater than 7 on a single roll of a die is $\frac{0}{6} = 0$.

3. The probability of any event is greater than or equal to 0 and less than or equal to 1.

$$0 \le P(E) \le 1$$

4. Since $P(E) + P(\text{not } E) = 1$, it follows that:

$$\text{If } P(E) = p, \text{ then } P(\text{not } E) = 1 - p$$

For example, if $P(\text{rain}) = .40$, then $P(\text{not rain}) = 1 - .40 = .60$.

EXAMPLES

1. A choral group is composed of 6 juniors and 8 seniors. If a junior and a senior are chosen at random to sing a duet at the spring concert, what is the probability that the choices are Emira, who is a junior, and Jean, who is a senior?

Solution (1) Since there are 6 ways of choosing the junior and 8 ways of choosing the senior, there are $6 \cdot 8 = 48$ possible choices.

(2) There is 1 choice that includes Emira and Jean.

(3) $P(\text{Emira and Jean}) = \frac{n(E)}{n(S)} = \frac{1}{48}$.

Alternative Solution   Since the choices are independent events, use the counting principle for probabilities.

$$P(\text{choosing Emira}) = \frac{1}{6}, \text{ and } P(\text{choosing Jean}) = \frac{1}{8}$$

Therefore, $P(\text{choosing Emira and Jean}) = \frac{1}{6} \cdot \frac{1}{8} = \frac{1}{48}.$

Answer: $P(\text{choosing Emira and Jean}) = \frac{1}{48}$

---

2. From the set of two-digit numbers, $\{00, 01, 02, \ldots, 99\}$, a number is selected at random. What is the probability that both digits in the number are even?

Solution   Even digits are 0, 2, 4, 6, 8; odd digits are 1, 3, 5, 7, 9.

$$P(\text{first digit even}) = \frac{5}{10}, \text{ and } P(\text{second digit even}) = \frac{5}{10}$$

By the counting principle for probabilities:

$$P(\text{both even}) = P(\text{first even}) \cdot P(\text{second even}) = \frac{5}{10} \cdot \frac{5}{10} = \frac{1}{2} \cdot \frac{1}{2} = \frac{1}{4}$$

Calculator Solution   Evaluate $P(\text{both even}) = \frac{5}{10} \cdot \frac{5}{10}.$

> **Enter:**   5 ÷ 10 × 5 ÷ 10 **ENTER**
> **Display:**   .25

Answer: $P(\text{both digits even}) = \frac{1}{4}$ or .25

---

3. What is the probability that a 3-letter word formed from the letters of the word COINAGE consists of all vowels?

How to Proceed:	*Solution:*
(1) Find $n(S)$, the number of 3-letter permutations of the 7 letters in the word COINAGE.	$n(S) = {}_7P_3 = 7 \cdot 6 \cdot 5$ $= 210$
(2) Find $n(E)$, the number of 3-letter permutations of the 4 vowels (O, I, A, E) in the word.	$n(E) = {}_4P_3 = 4 \cdot 3 \cdot 2$ $= 24$
(3) Find the probability of event E.	$P(E) = \frac{n(E)}{n(S)} = \frac{24}{210} = \frac{4}{35}$

Answer: $P(\text{all vowels}) = \frac{4}{35}$

Note: The evaluation of $P(E) = \frac{_4P_3}{_7P_3}$ on a calculator serves to illustrate why it is preferable to use fractions in finding a probability.

Enter: 4 [MATH] [▶] [▶] [▶] 2 3 ÷ 7 [MATH] [▶] [▶] [▶] 2 3
[ENTER]

Display: [.1142857143]

This display is a rational *approximation*, not equal to the exact probability, $\frac{4}{35}$.

EXERCISES WITH OPEN-RESPONSE PROBLEMS

1. What is the probability of getting a number less than 5 on a single throw of a fair die?
2. If 1 letter of the word ELEMENT is chosen at random, what is the probability that the vowel *e* is chosen?
3. A bag contains only 5 red marbles and 3 blue marbles. If 1 marble is drawn at random from the bag, what is the probability that it is blue?
4. If the letters of the word *equal* are rearranged at random, what is the probability that the first letter of the new arrangement is a vowel?
5. If 2 coins are tossed, what is the probability that both show heads?
6. If 2 coins are tossed, what is the probability that neither shows heads?
7. If a card is drawn from a standard deck of 52 cards, what is the probability that the card is a queen?
8. If 2 cards are drawn from a standard deck of 52 cards without replacement, what is the probability that both cards are queens?
9. A bank contains 4 coins: a penny, a nickel, a dime, and a quarter. One coin is removed at random and tossed. **a.** What is the probability that the dime is removed? **b.** What is the probability that the coin shows heads? **c.** What is the probability that the coin is a quarter that shows heads? **d.** What is the probability that the coin has a value less than 20 cents and shows heads?
10. The weather report gives the probability of rain on Saturday as 20% and the probability of rain on Sunday as 10%. **a.** What is the probability that it will *not* rain on Saturday? **b.** What is the probability that it will *not* rain on Sunday? **c.** What is the probability that it will *not* rain either day?
11. A seed company advertises that, if its geranium seed is properly planted, the probability that the seed will grow is 90%. **a.** What is the probability that a geranium seed that has been properly planted will fail to grow? **b.** If 5 geranium seeds are properly planted, what is the probability that all will fail to grow?
12. Of the 5 sandwiches that Mrs. Muth made for her children's lunches, 2 contain tuna fish and 3 contain peanut butter and jelly. Her son, Tim, took 2 sandwiches at random. What is the probability that these 2 sandwiches contain peanut butter and jelly?
13. Mrs. Gillis' small son, Brian, tore all the labels off the soup cans on the kitchen shelf. If Mrs. Gillis knows that she bought 4 cans of tomato soup and 2 cans of vegetable soup, what is the probability that the first 2 cans of soup she opens are both tomato?

14. Of the 15 students in Mrs. Barney's mathematics class, 10 take Spanish. If 2 students are absent from Mrs. Barney's class on Monday, what is the probability that both of these students take Spanish?

15. At a card party, 2 door prizes are to be awarded by drawing 2 names at random from a box. The box contains the names of 40 persons, including Patricia Sullivan and Joe Ramirez.   **a.** What is the probability that Joe's name is *not* drawn for either prize?   **b.** What is the probability that Patricia wins 1 of the prizes?

22-3 PROBABILITY WITH TWO OUTCOMES

In Section 22-2, some exercises were solved by using the counting principle with probabilities. In this section, we will study applications of this principle in greater detail.

In the spinner at the left, the arrow can land on 1 of 3 equally likely regions, numbered 1, 2, and 3. If the arrow lands on a line, the spin is not counted, and the arrow is spun again.

Let us define an experiment with 2 outcomes for this spinner as either obtaining an odd number or obtaining an even number. Therefore:

$$P(\text{odd}) = P(O) = \tfrac{2}{3} \quad \text{and} \quad P(\text{even}) = P(E) = \tfrac{1}{3}$$

When the arrow is spun several times, the result of each spin is independent of the results of the other spins. To find the probability of getting an odd number each time in several spins, we can use the ***counting principle with probabilities***.

● **If E and F are independent events, and if the probability of E is m $(0 \leq m \leq 1)$ and the probability of F is n $(0 \leq n \leq 1)$, then the probability of E and F occurring jointly is $m \cdot n$ $(0 \leq m \cdot n \leq 1)$.**

If the arrow is spun twice:

$$P(2 \text{ odd numbers in 2 spins}) = \tfrac{2}{3} \cdot \tfrac{2}{3} = \tfrac{4}{9}$$

If the arrow is spun 3 times:

$$P(3 \text{ odd numbers in 3 spins}) = \tfrac{2}{3} \cdot \tfrac{2}{3} \cdot \tfrac{2}{3} = \tfrac{8}{27}$$

If the arrow is spun 4 times:

$$P(4 \text{ odd numbers in 4 spins}) = \tfrac{2}{3} \cdot \tfrac{2}{3} \cdot \tfrac{2}{3} \cdot \tfrac{2}{3} = \tfrac{16}{81}$$

We can also apply the counting principle with probabilities to situations where the arrow is spun n times and an odd number is obtained *less than* n times, as shown in the following examples.

☐ Find the probability of obtaining *exactly 1 odd* number on 4 spins of the arrow.

Consider getting an odd number on the first spin and an even number on each of the other 3 spins.

$$P(\text{odd on first spin only}) = \frac{2}{3} \cdot \frac{1}{3} \cdot \frac{1}{3} \cdot \frac{1}{3} = \frac{2}{81}$$

As seen in each row of the chart at the right, however, the odd number could appear on the second spin, or on the third spin, or on the fourth spin. Then:

O	E	E	E
E	O	E	E
E	E	O	E
E	E	E	O

$$P(\text{odd on second spin only}) = \frac{1}{3} \cdot \frac{2}{3} \cdot \frac{1}{3} \cdot \frac{1}{3} = \frac{2}{81}$$

$$P(\text{odd on third spin only}) = \frac{1}{3} \cdot \frac{1}{3} \cdot \frac{2}{3} \cdot \frac{1}{3} = \frac{2}{81}$$

$$P(\text{odd on fourth spin only}) = \frac{1}{3} \cdot \frac{1}{3} \cdot \frac{1}{3} \cdot \frac{2}{3} = \frac{2}{81}$$

Since there are 4 possible ways to spin exactly 1 odd number, each with a probability of $\left(\frac{2}{3}\right)^1 \cdot \left(\frac{1}{3}\right)^3$ or $\frac{2}{81}$, it follows that:

$$P(\text{exactly 1 odd on 4 spins}) = 4 \cdot \left(\frac{2}{3}\right)^1 \cdot \left(\frac{1}{3}\right)^3 = \frac{8}{81}$$

Answer: $P(\text{exactly 1 odd on 4 spins}) = \frac{8}{81}$

☐ Find the probability of obtaining *exactly 2 odd* numbers on 4 spins of the arrow.

Consider the case in which the first 2 spins are odd and the last 2 spins are even.

$$P(\text{odd on first 2 spins only}) = \frac{2}{3} \cdot \frac{2}{3} \cdot \frac{1}{3} \cdot \frac{1}{3} = \left(\frac{2}{3}\right)^2 \cdot \left(\frac{1}{3}\right)^2 = \frac{4}{81}$$

The chart at the right, however, shows that there are 6 possible ways to spin exactly 2 odd numbers. This is a *combination* of 2 odd numbers out of 4 spins, obtained by the formula $_4C_2 = \frac{4 \cdot 3}{2 \cdot 1} = 6$. Thus:

O	O	E	E
O	E	O	E
O	E	E	O
E	O	O	E
E	O	E	O
E	E	O	O

$$P(\text{exactly 2 odds on 4 spins}) = {_4C_2} \cdot \left(\frac{2}{3}\right)^2 \cdot \left(\frac{1}{3}\right)^2$$

$$= 6 \cdot \frac{4}{9} \cdot \frac{1}{9} = \frac{24}{81} \text{ or } \frac{8}{27}$$

Answer: $P(\text{exactly 2 odds on 4 spins}) = \frac{24}{81}$ or $\frac{8}{27}$

◻   Find the probability of obtaining *exactly 3 odd* numbers on 4 spins of the arrow.

Consider the case in which the first 3 spins are odd and the last spin is even.

$$P(\text{odd on only the first 3 spins}) = \frac{2}{3} \cdot \frac{2}{3} \cdot \frac{2}{3} \cdot \frac{1}{3}$$

$$= \left(\frac{2}{3}\right)^3 \cdot \left(\frac{1}{3}\right)^1 = \frac{8}{81}$$

Since the number of possible ways to obtain exactly 3 odd numbers on 4 spins of the arrow is a combination, $_4C_3$, it follows that:

$$P(\text{exactly 3 odds on 4 spins}) = {_4C_3} \cdot \left(\frac{2}{3}\right)^3 \cdot \left(\frac{1}{3}\right)^1$$

$$= \frac{4 \cdot \cancel{3} \cdot \cancel{2}}{\cancel{3} \cdot \cancel{2} \cdot 1} \cdot \frac{8}{27} \cdot \frac{1}{3} = \frac{32}{81}$$

Answer: $P(\text{exactly 3 odds on 4 spins}) = \frac{32}{81}$

The patterns seen in the solutions shown above enable us to determine the probability of exactly r successes in n independent trials of an experiment with *exactly two outcomes*, called a ***Bernoulli experiment*** or ***binomial probability***.

A Bernoulli experiment, such as tossing a coin, has two outcomes: heads and tails. Other experiments, such as tossing a die, can also be thought of as having two outcomes, for example, rolling a one and not rolling a one. If an event E, such as rolling a one on a die, is to occur exactly r times in n trials, then the event *not E*, that is, rolling a number that is *not* one, must occur $n - r$ times in n trials.

- **In general, for a given experiment, if the probability of success is p and the probability of failure is $1 - p = q$, then the probability of exactly r successes in n independent trials is**

$$_nC_r p^r q^{n-r}$$

EXAMPLES

1. If a fair coin is tossed 10 times, what is the probability that it falls tails exactly 6 times?

Solution   In 1 toss of a fair coin: probability of success $p = P(\text{tails}) = \frac{1}{2}$

and probability of failure $q = P(\text{heads}) = \frac{1}{2}$

Here, the number of trials, n, is 10, and the number of successes, r, is 6. Use the formula for a Bernoulli experiment:

$$_nC_r \quad p^r \quad q^{n-r}$$

$$_{10}C_6 \left(\frac{1}{2}\right)^6 \left(\frac{1}{2}\right)^{10-6} = \frac{10 \cdot 9 \cdot 8 \cdot 7 \cdot 6 \cdot 5}{6 \cdot 5 \cdot 4 \cdot 3 \cdot 2 \cdot 1} \left(\frac{1}{2}\right)^6 \left(\frac{1}{2}\right)^4$$

$$= 210 \cdot \frac{1}{64} \cdot \frac{1}{16} = \frac{210}{1,024} = \frac{105}{512}$$

Answer: P(exactly 6 tails in 10 tosses) $= \dfrac{105}{512}$

---

2. If 5 fair dice are tossed, what is the probability that they show exactly 3 fours?

Solution

For this set of data:

$$p = P(4) = \frac{1}{6}$$

$$q = P(\text{not } 4) = \frac{5}{6}$$

$$n = 5 \text{ trials}$$

$$r = 3 \text{ successes}$$

$$n - r = 2 \text{ failures}$$

Use the formula: $_nC_r p^r q^{n-r}$

$$P(3 \text{ fours in 5 trials}) = {}_5C_3 \left(\frac{1}{6}\right)^3 \left(\frac{5}{6}\right)^2$$

$$= \frac{5 \cdot 4 \cdot 3}{3 \cdot 2 \cdot 1} \cdot \frac{1}{216} \cdot \frac{25}{36}$$

$$= 10 \cdot \frac{1}{216} \cdot \frac{25}{36}$$

$$= \frac{250}{7,776} = \frac{125}{3,888}$$

Answer: P(3 fours in 5 trials) $= \dfrac{125}{3,888}$

Calculator Solution

Use binompdf, found under the DISTR menu and enter (n, p, r).

Enter: | 2nd | | DIST | 0 5 | , | | (| 1 | ÷ | 6 |) | | , | 3 | ENTER |

Display: | .0321502058 |

Answer: P(3 fours in 5 trials) $\approx .032 \approx \dfrac{125}{3,888}$

EXERCISES WITH OPEN-RESPONSE PROBLEMS

1. A fair coin is tossed 4 times.   **a.** Find the probability of tossing:
(*1*) exactly 4 tails   (*2*) exactly 3 tails   (*3*) exactly 2 tails
(*4*) exactly 1 tail   (*5*) exactly 0 tails
b. What is the sum of the probabilities found in part **a**?

2. A fair coin is tossed 5 times. Find the probability of tossing:
a. exactly 2 heads   **b.** exactly 3 heads   **c.** exactly 4 heads

3. If 4 fair dice are tossed, find the probability of getting:
a. exactly 3 fives   **b.** exactly 4 fives   **c.** exactly 2 fives

4. If 4 fair dice are tossed, find the probability of getting:
   a. exactly 3 even numbers   **b.** exactly 2 odd numbers   **c.** no odd number

5. Jan's record shows that her probability of success on a basketball free throw is $\frac{3}{5}$. Find the probability that Jan will be successful on 2 out of 3 shots.

6. The probability that the Wings will win a baseball game is $\frac{2}{3}$. State the probability that the Wings will win:
   a. exactly 2 out of 4 games   **b.** exactly 3 out of 4 games   **c.** their next 4 games

In 7 and 8, select the *numeral* preceding the choice that best answers each question.

7. What is the probability of getting a number less than 3 on 6 out of 10 tosses of a fair die?

   (1) $6\left(\frac{1}{3}\right)^6$ (2) $210\left(\frac{1}{3}\right)^6$ (3) $6\left(\frac{1}{3}\right)^6\left(\frac{2}{3}\right)^4$ (4) $210\left(\frac{1}{3}\right)^6\left(\frac{2}{3}\right)^4$

8. A coin is loaded so that the probability of heads is $\frac{1}{4}$. What is the probability of getting exactly 3 heads on 8 tosses of the coin?

   (1) $_8C_3\left(\frac{1}{4}\right)^3$ (2) $_8C_3\left(\frac{1}{4}\right)^3\left(\frac{3}{4}\right)^5$ (3) $_8C_3\left(\frac{1}{4}\right)^3\left(\frac{1}{4}\right)^5$ (4) $3\left(\frac{1}{4}\right)^3\left(\frac{3}{4}\right)^5$

In 9–13, answers may be expressed in exponential form, as in the choices for Exercises 7 and 8.

9. The probability that a flashbulb is defective is found to be $\frac{1}{20}$. What is the probability that a package of 6 flashbulbs has only 1 defective bulb?

10. A multiple-choice test gives 5 possible choices for each answer, of which 1 is correct. The probability of selecting the correct answer by guessing is $\frac{1}{5}$.
    a. What is the probability of getting 5 out of 10 questions correct by guessing?
    b. What is the probability of getting only 1 out of 10 questions correct by guessing?
    c. What is the probability of getting 9 correct answers out of 10 by guessing?

11. Mrs. Shusda gave a true-false test of 10 questions. The probability of selecting the correct answer by guessing is $\frac{1}{2}$.
    a. What is the probability that Fred, who guessed at every answer, will get 9 out of 10 correct?
    b. What is the probability that Fred will get 10 out of 10 correct?
    c. What is the probability that Fred will get either 9 or 10 out of 10 correct?

12. In a group of 100 persons who were born in June, what is the probability that exactly 2 were born on June 1? (Assume that a person born in June is equally likely to have been born on any 1 of the 30 days.)

13. In a box there are 4 red marbles and 5 white marbles. Marbles are drawn 1 at a time and replaced after each drawing. What is the probability of drawing:
    a. exactly 2 red marbles when 3 marbles are drawn?
    b. exactly 3 white marbles when 5 marbles are drawn?
    c. exactly 7 red marbles when 12 marbles are drawn?

22-4 *AT LEAST* AND *AT MOST*

When we are anticipating success on repeated trials of an experiment, we often require *at least* a given number. For example, in a game, David rolls 5 dice. To win, *at least* 3 of the 5 dice that David rolls must be "ones." Therefore, David will win if he rolls 3, 4, or 5 "ones." In general:

● **At least r successes in n trials means $r, r + 1, r + 2, \ldots, n$ successes.**

If a manufacturer considers *at most* 2 defective parts in a lot of 100 parts to be an acceptable standard, then there can be 2, 1, or 0 defective parts in every 100 parts.

● **At most r successes in n trials means $r, r - 1, r - 2, \ldots, 0$ successes.**

The examples that follow show how these concepts are applied to probability.

EXAMPLES

1. Rose is the last person to compete in a basketball free-throw contest. To win, Rose must be successful in at least 4 out of 5 throws. If the probability that Rose will be successful on any single throw is $\frac{3}{4}$, what is the probability that Rose will win the contest?

Solution To be successful in at least 4 out of 5 throws means to be successful in 4 or in 5 throws.

On 1 throw, $P(\text{success}) = \frac{3}{4}$ and $P(\text{failure}) = 1 - \frac{3}{4} = \frac{1}{4}$. Then:

(1) $P(\text{4 out of 5 successes}) = {}_5C_4\left(\frac{3}{4}\right)^4\left(\frac{1}{4}\right)^1$

$$= \frac{5 \cdot 4 \cdot 3 \cdot 2}{4 \cdot 3 \cdot 2 \cdot 1} \cdot \frac{81}{4^4} \cdot \frac{1}{4^1} = \frac{405}{4^5} = \frac{405}{1,024}$$

(2) $P(\text{5 out of 5 successes}) = {}_5C_5\left(\frac{3}{4}\right)^5\left(\frac{1}{4}\right)^0 = 1 \cdot \frac{243}{4^5} \cdot 1 = \frac{243}{1,024}$

(3) $P(\text{at least 4 out of 5 successes})$:

$$= P(\text{4 out of 5 successes}) + P(\text{5 out of 5 successes})$$
$$= \frac{405}{1,024} + \frac{243}{1,024} = \frac{648}{1,024} = \frac{81}{128}$$

Answer: $P(\text{at least 4 out of 5 successes}) = \frac{81}{128}$

2. A family of 5 children is chosen at random. What is the probability that there are at most 2 boys in this family of 5 children?

Solution To have at most 2 boys means to have 0, 1, or 2 boys. Let us assume that $P(\text{boy}) = \frac{1}{2}$ and $P(\text{girl}) = \frac{1}{2}$. Then:

(1) $P(0 \text{ boys in 5 children}) = {}_5C_0\left(\frac{1}{2}\right)^5\left(\frac{1}{2}\right)^0 = 1 \cdot \left(\frac{1}{2}\right)^5 \cdot 1 = \frac{1}{32}$

(2) $P(1 \text{ boy in 5 children}) = {}_5C_1\left(\frac{1}{2}\right)^1\left(\frac{1}{2}\right)^4 = 5 \cdot \frac{1}{2} \cdot \frac{1}{16} = \frac{5}{32}$

(3) $P(2 \text{ boys in 5 children}) = {}_5C_2\left(\frac{1}{2}\right)^2\left(\frac{1}{2}\right)^3 = \frac{5 \cdot 4}{2 \cdot 1} \cdot \frac{1}{4} \cdot \frac{1}{8} = \frac{10}{32}$

(4) $P\left(\begin{array}{c}\text{at most 2 boys}\\ \text{in 5 children}\end{array}\right) = P(0 \text{ boys}) + P(1 \text{ boy}) + P(2 \text{ boys})$

$$= \frac{1}{32} \qquad + \frac{5}{32} \qquad + \frac{10}{32} \qquad = \frac{16}{32} = \frac{1}{2}$$

Answer: $P(\text{at most 2 boys in family of 5 children}) = \frac{1}{2}$

---

3. A coin is loaded so that the probability of heads is 4 times the probability of tails.
  a. What is the probability of heads on a single throw?
  b. What is the probability of at least 1 tail in 5 throws?

Solutions **a.** Let $P(\text{tails}) = q$ and $P(\text{heads}) = 4q$.

$$q + 4q = 1$$
$$5q = 1$$
$$q = \frac{1}{5}, \text{ or } P(\text{tails}) = \frac{1}{5}$$

Then $4q = 4 \cdot \frac{1}{5} = \frac{4}{5}$, and $P(\text{heads}) = \frac{4}{5}$

b. $P(\text{at least 1 tail in 5 throws})$

$= P(1 \text{ tail}) \quad + P(2 \text{ tails}) \quad + P(3 \text{ tails}) \quad + P(4 \text{ tails}) \quad + P(5 \text{ tails})$

$= {}_5C_1\left(\frac{1}{5}\right)^1\left(\frac{4}{5}\right)^4 + {}_5C_2\left(\frac{1}{5}\right)^2\left(\frac{4}{5}\right)^3 + {}_5C_3\left(\frac{1}{5}\right)^3\left(\frac{4}{5}\right)^2 + {}_5C_4\left(\frac{1}{5}\right)^4\left(\frac{4}{5}\right)^1 + {}_5C_5\left(\frac{1}{5}\right)^5$

$= 5 \cdot \frac{256}{3,125} \quad + 10 \cdot \frac{64}{3,125} \quad + 10 \cdot \frac{16}{3,125} \quad + 5 \cdot \frac{4}{3,125} \quad + 1 \cdot \frac{1}{3,125}$

$= \frac{1,280}{3,125} \quad + \frac{640}{3,125} \quad + \frac{160}{3,125} \quad + \frac{20}{3,125} \quad + \frac{1}{3,125}$

$= \frac{2,101}{3,125}$

Alternative Solution   There is one way to fail to get at least 1 tail in 5 throws, that is, to get 5 heads in 5 throws.

$$P(\text{failure}) = P(5 \text{ heads})$$

$$= {}_5C_0\left(\frac{4}{5}\right)^5$$

$$= 1 \cdot \frac{1{,}024}{3{,}125}$$

$$= \frac{1{,}024}{3{,}125}$$

Then, $P(\text{success}) = 1 - P(\text{failure})$

$$= 1 - \frac{1{,}024}{3{,}125}$$

$$= \frac{3{,}125}{3{,}125} - \frac{1{,}024}{3{,}125}$$

$$= \frac{2{,}101}{3{,}125}$$

Answers: **a.** $P(\text{heads}) = \frac{4}{5}$ **b.** $P(\text{at least 1 tail in 5 throws}) = \frac{2{,}101}{3{,}125}$

The **probability distribution** for an event is a list of *all* possible outcomes in the event and their probabilities. For Example 3 on page 1048, the list would include the data shown in the table. The probability plot of the data is also shown.

Successes	Probability (rounded)
0	.3277
1	.4096
2	.2048
3	.0512
4	.0064
5	.0003

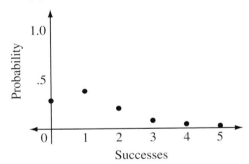

If n is very large and the probability of success is not close to 0 or 1, the normal curve gives a close approximation of the binomial probability distribution.

EXERCISES WITH OPEN-RESPONSE PROBLEMS

1. A fair coin is tossed 4 times. Find the probability of tossing:
   a. exactly 3 heads   **b.** exactly 4 heads   **c.** at least 3 heads
   d. exactly 0 heads   **e.** exactly 1 head   **f.** at most 1 head
2. If a fair coin is tossed 6 times, find the probability of obtaining at most 2 heads.
3. If 5 fair coins are tossed, what is the probability that at least 2 tails are obtained?
4. A fair die is rolled 3 times. Find the probability of rolling:
   a. exactly 1 five   **b.** no fives   **c.** at most 1 five
   d. at least 2 sixes   **e.** at most 2 fours   **f.** at most 1 even
   g. exactly 1 even   **h.** at most 1 number less than three
   i. at least 1 even   **j.** at least 1 number greater than four
5. If a fair die is tossed 5 times, find the probability of obtaining at most 2 ones.
6. If 4 fair dice are rolled, what is the probability that at least 2 are fives?

In 7–18, an arrow can land on one of 5 equally likely regions on a spinner, numbered 1, 2, 3, 4, and 5. If the arrow lands on a line, the spin is not counted and the arrow is spun again.

In 7–16, for the spinner described, find each probability.

7. P(even number)   **8.** P(odd number)

9. P(both even on 2 spins)   **10.** P(both odd on 2 spins)

11. P(at least 1 even on 2 spins)   **12.** P(at least 1 odd on 2 spins)

13. P(exactly 2 evens on 3 spins)   **14.** P(at least 2 evens on 3 spins)

15. P(exactly 2 odds on 4 spins)   **16.** P(at most 2 odds on 4 spins)

Ex. 7–18

17. *True* or *False*: If the arrow is spun on the spinner as described, then P(at least 3 evens on 5 spins) = P(at most 2 odds on 5 spins). Explain your answer.

18. For the spinner described: **a.** Find $P(2)$.   **b.** If the arrow is spun 5 times, will a "2" appear exactly once? Support your answer by finding P(exactly one "2" on 5 spins).

19. A coin is weighted so that the probability of heads is $\frac{4}{5}$.
  a. What is the probability of getting at least 3 heads when the weighted coin is tossed 4 times?
  b. What is the probability of getting at most 2 tails when the weighted coin is tossed 5 times?

20. Each evening the members of the Sanchez family are equally likely to watch the news on any one of 3 possible TV channels: 5, 8, and 13.   **a.** What is the probability that they watch the news on channel 8 on at least 3 out of 5 evenings?   **b.** What is the probability that they watch the news on channel 13 on at most 2 out of 5 evenings?

21. In a game, the probability of winning is $\frac{1}{5}$ and the probability of losing is $\frac{4}{5}$. If 3 games are played, what is the probability of winning at least 2 games?

22. In each game that the school basketball team plays, the probability that the team will win is $\frac{2}{3}$. What is the probability that the team will win at least 3 of the next 4 games?

23. A die is loaded so that the probability of rolling a one is $\frac{3}{4}$. What is the probability of rolling at least 2 ones when the die is tossed 3 times?

24. If a family of 4 children is selected at random, what is the probability that at most 3 of the children are boys?

In 25 and 26, an electronic game contains 9 keys. As shown at the right, 5 keys have numbers, and 4 keys have colors. Each key is equally likely to be pressed on each move.

Red	1	Blue
2	3	4
Green	5	Yellow

25. If one key is pressed at random in the electronic game, find:
  a. P(number key)   **b.** P(color key)

26. If 3 keys are pressed at random in the electronic game, find the probability of selecting:
  a. exactly 1 color key   **b.** at least 2 color keys   **c.** at most 1 color key
  d. all color keys   **e.** exactly 1 number key   **f.** at least 1 number key

In 27–31, answers may be expressed in exponential form.

27. Of last year's graduates, 3 out of 5 are enrolled in college. If the names of 10 of last year's graduates are chosen at random, what is the probability that at least 8 out of 10 are in college?

28. A coin is loaded so that the probability of heads on a single throw is 3 times the probability of tails.
  a. What is the probability of heads and the probability of tails on a single throw?
  b. What is the probability of at most 3 heads when the coin is tossed 6 times?

29. A license number consists of 5 letters of the alphabet selected at random. Each letter can be selected any number of times.
  a. What is the probability that the license number has at most 2 Q's?
  b. What is the probability that the license number has at least 4 X's?

30. A manufacturer tests her product and finds that the probability of a defective part is .02. What is the probability that out of 5 parts selected at random at most 1 will be defective?

31. A seed company advertises that, if its seeds are properly planted, 95% of them will germinate. What is the probability that, when 20 seeds are properly planted, at least 15 will germinate?

32. *Calculator exercise: Express each answer as a six-place decimal.* Three patients with the same ailment visited a doctor who, after examining them, prescribed the same medication for all three. This medicine is known to be 98% effective in combating the observed illness; that is, the probability is .98 that the medicine will destroy the infection. Find, for these patients, the probability that the medication will destroy the infection for:
  a. all 3   **b.** exactly 2   **c.** exactly 1   **d.** none
  e. at least 2   **f.** at least 1   **g.** at most 1   **h.** at most 2

22-5 ARITHMETIC SEQUENCES AND SERIES

Understanding the Meaning of a Sequence

Observe that there is a simple pattern in the number arrangement 4, 8, 12, 16, ... If this pattern is extended, the next two terms are 20 and 24. A set of ordered numbers such as 4, 8, 12, 16, 20, 24 is called a *sequence*.

The sequence 4, 8, 12, 16 may be extended by setting up a one-to-one correspondence between the four terms of the given sequence and the first four members of the set of positive integers as follows:

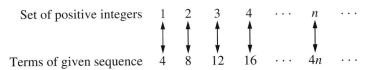

Observe that each term of the given sequence is 4 times the positive integer with which it is paired. If this pattern is applied to find new terms, the fifth term is 4(5) or 20; the sixth term is 4(6) or 24; and, in general, the nth term is $4n$.

A sequence such as 4, 8, 12, 16, which has a first term and a last term, is called a *finite sequence*. A sequence such as 4, 8, 12, 16, . . . in which, after each term of the sequence there is another term, is called an *infinite sequence*.

In the sequence whose terms are $a_1, a_2, a_3, \ldots, a_n, \ldots, a_1$ represents the first term, a_3 represents the third term, and a_n represents the nth term. The subscript in a term represents the place of the term in the sequence.

The expression that represents the general term of a sequence, a_n, is the rule that may be used to find any term of the sequence. For example, in the sequence 4, 8, 12, 16, ..., $4n$, ..., the nth term is represented by $4n$. Therefore, $a_n = 4n$ is the rule for forming the sequence. Each term of the sequence may be found by substituting a positive integer for n. For example, to find the 8th term, substitute 8 for n. Hence, the 8th term, $a_8 = 4(8)$ or 32.

Finding the General Term of an Arithmetic Sequence

In the sequence 2, 5, 8, 11, each term after the first term, 2, is the sum of the preceding term and a constant, 3. Such a sequence is an *arithmetic sequence*.

- **DEFINITION.** An *arithmetic sequence* is a sequence in which each term after the first is the sum of the preceding term and a constant.

Thus, in the sequence 2, 5, 8, 11, the term $5 = 2 + 3$ and the term $11 = 8 + 3$. Note that the constant 3 may be found by subtracting any term from its successor; for example, $5 - 2 = 3$, $8 - 5 = 3$, and $11 - 8 = 3$. Hence, the constant 3 is the *common difference* in the arithmetic sequence 2, 5, 8, 11.

PROCEDURE. To find the common difference in an arithmetic sequence, subtract any term from its successor.

Thus, in the decreasing arithmetic sequence 15, 12, 9, 6, the common difference is -3 since $12 - 15 = -3$.

In general, in an arithmetic sequence, if d represents the common difference, and a_{n-1} and a_n represent two consecutive terms, then $d = a_n - a_{n-1}$. Keep in mind that the common difference is positive in an increasing sequence such as 2, 5, 8, 11; it is negative in a decreasing sequence such as 15, 12, 9, 6; it is zero in the sequence 5, 5, 5, 5.

We can graph an arithmetic sequence with the numbers of the terms as the n-values and the terms as the a-values. The graph is a linear function with the domain the positive integers and the slope the common difference.

2, 5, 8, 11

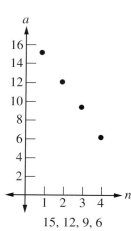

15, 12, 9, 6

If a_1 represents the first term of an arithmetic sequence and d represents the common difference, then the sequence may be written as follows:

Number of term   1   2   3   4   5   . . . , n

Terms of sequence $a_1,\ a_1 + d,\ a_1 + 2d,\ a_1 + 3d,\ a_1 + 4d, \ldots , a_1 + (n-1)d$

Note that the fourth term of the sequence is $a_1 + 3d$ and the fifth term is $a_1 + 4d$. In general, the nth term $= a_1 + (n-1)d$; that is, the nth term is the sum of the first term and $(n-1)$ common differences.

● **In general, if the nth term of an arithmetic sequence is represented by a_n, then**

$$a_n = a_1 + (n-1)d$$

For example, in the sequence 2, 5, 8, 11, . . . , the 51st term is $a_{51} = 2 + 50(3) = 2 + 150 = 152$. Also, in the sequence 15, 10, 5, . . . , the 25th term is $a_{25} = 15 + 24(-5) = 15 - 120 = -105$.

Finding the Sum of an Arithmetic Series

A **series** is the indicated sum of the terms of a sequence. Thus, $2 + 5 + 8 + 11$ is an example of a *finite series* and $2 + 5 + 8 + 11 + \cdots$ is an example of an *infinite series*.

In general, $a_1 + a_2 + a_3 + \cdots + a_n$ represents a finite series and $a_1 + a_2 + a_3 + \cdots + a_n + \cdots$ represents an infinite series.

Be careful to note that a series is an *indicated sum* of the terms of a sequence, not the sum itself. Do not confuse the series $2 + 5 + 8 + 11$ with its sum, 26. The series $2 + 5 + 8 + 11$ cannot be represented by 26.

● **DEFINITION.** An *arithmetic series* is the indicated sum of the terms of an arithmetic sequence.

Hence, since 5, 8, 11, 14, 17 is an arithmetic sequence, then $5 + 8 + 11 + 14 + 17$ is an arithmetic series. Since $5 + 8 + 11 + 14 + 17 = 55$, we say that the *sum* of this series is 55.

In an arithmetic series, if a_1 is the first term, n is the number of terms, a_n is the nth term, and d is the common difference, then S_n, the sum of the arithmetic series, is given by the following formulas:

$$S_n = \frac{n}{2}\,(a_1 + a_n)$$

$$S_n = \frac{n}{2}\,[2a_1 + (n-1)d]$$

EXAMPLES

1. a. Write a rule that can be used in forming a sequence 1, 4, 9, 16, ...
   b. Use the rule found in part **a** to write the next three terms of the sequence.

Solutions **a.** Set up a one-to-one correspondence between the members of the set of positive integers and the terms of the given sequence.

$$\begin{array}{ccccccc} \text{Set of positive integers} & 1 & 2 & 3 & 4 & \cdots & n & \cdots \\ & \updownarrow & \updownarrow & \updownarrow & \updownarrow & & \updownarrow & \\ \text{Terms of given sequence} & 1 & 4 & 9 & 16 & \cdots & n^2 & \cdots \end{array}$$

Since each term of the sequence is the square of the positive integer with which it is paired, the rule $a_n = n^2$ is a rule that can be used to form the sequence.

Answer: $a_n = n^2$

b. Use the rule which forms the sequence $a_n = n^2$ to find the next three terms of the sequence as follows:
The fifth term, $a_5 = 5^2$ or 25.
The sixth term, $a_6 = 6^2$ or 36.
The seventh term, $a_7 = 7^2$ or 49.

Answer: 25, 36, 49

---

2. Write the first five terms of the sequence where the nth term is represented by $n + 2$.

Solution To find the first five terms of the sequence represented by $n + 2$: In $n + 2$, replace n by the positive integers 1, 2, 3, 4, and 5 respectively.

$$a_1 = 1 + 2 \text{ or } 3 \quad a_2 = 2 + 2 \text{ or } 4 \quad a_3 = 3 + 2 \text{ or } 5$$
$$a_4 = 4 + 2 \text{ or } 6 \quad a_5 = 5 + 2 \text{ or } 7$$

Answer: 3, 4, 5, 6, 7

---

3. Find the 12th term of the arithmetic sequence 3, 8, 13, 18, ...

Solution First find the common difference by subtracting the first term from the second. Then find the 12th term.

$$d = 8 - 3 = 5$$
$$a_n = a_1 + (n - 1)d \qquad a_1 = 3, n = 12, d = 5$$
$$a_n = 3 + (12 - 1)5$$
$$= 3 + (11)5$$
$$= 3 + 55 = 58$$

Answer: The 12th term is 58.

---

4. Write the first seven terms of an arithmetic sequence in which the third term is 7 and the seventh term is 15.

Solution

When $n = 7$, $a_n = a_7 = 15$. Hence,

When $n = 3$, $a_n = a_3 = 7$. Hence,

Subtract:

$$a_n = a_1 + (n - 1)d$$
$$15 = a_1 + 6d$$
$$7 = a_1 + 2d$$
$$\overline{\phantom{7 = {}}8 = \phantom{a_1 + {}}4d}$$
$$2 = d$$

Since the third term is 7:

Substitute $d = 2$:

$$7 = a_1 + 2d$$
$$7 = a_1 + 2(2)$$
$$7 = a_1 + 4$$
$$3 = a_1$$

Answer: The terms are 3, 5, 7, 9, 11, 13, 15.

---

5. Find the sum of ten terms of an arithmetic sequence whose first term is 5 and whose tenth term is -13.

Solution

$S_n = \frac{n}{2}(a_1 + a_n)$ $a_1 = 5, a_{10} = -13, n = 10$

$S_n = \frac{10}{2}[5 + (-13)]$

$ = 5(-8)$

$ = -40$ *Answer*

---

6. Find the sum of the first 50 terms of the arithmetic series $3 + 5 + 7 + 9 + \cdots$

Solution

METHOD 1	METHOD 2

METHOD 1

Using $S_n = \frac{n}{2}(a_1 + a_n)$:

First, find the 50th term.

$a_1 = 3, d = 2, n = 50$

$a_n = a_1 + (n - 1)d$

$a_{50} = 3 + (50 - 1)2$

$\phantom{a_{50}} = 3 + (49)2$

$\phantom{a_{50}} = 101$

Then find the sum of 50 terms.

$S_n = \frac{n}{2}(a_1 + a_n)$

$S_{50} = \frac{50}{2}(3 + 101)$

$\phantom{S_{50}} = 25(104) = 2,600$ *Answer*

METHOD 2

Using $S_n = \frac{n}{2}[2a_1 + (n - 1)d]$:

$a_1 = 3, d = 2, n = 50$

$S_n = \frac{n}{2}[2a_1 + (n - 1)d]$

$S_{50} = \frac{50}{2}[2(3) + (50 - 1)2]$

$\phantom{S_{50}} = 25[6 + (49)2]$

$\phantom{S_{50}} = 25(6 + 98)$

$\phantom{S_{50}} = 25(104)$

$\phantom{S_{50}} = 2,600$ *Answer*

7. A man wishes to pay off a debt of \$1,160 by making monthly payments in which each payment after the first is \$4 more than that of the preceding month. According to this plan, how long will it take him to pay the debt if the first payment is \$20 and no interest is charged?

Solution Let n = the number of payments.
The payments form an arithmetic sequence 20, 24, 28, ...

$$S_n = \frac{n}{2}[2a_1 + (n-1)d] \qquad S_n = 1160,\ a_1 = 20,\ d = 4$$

$$1160 = \frac{n}{2}[40 + (n-1)4]$$

$$1160 = \frac{n}{2}(40 + 4n - 4)$$

$$1160 = \frac{n}{2}(4n + 36)$$

$$1160 = 2n^2 + 18n$$

$$0 = 2n^2 + 18n - 1160$$

$$0 = n^2 + 9n - 580$$

$$0 = (n + 29)(n - 20)$$

$$n + 29 = 0 \ \big| \ n - 20 = 0$$

$$n = -29 \ \big| \ n = 20$$

Reject

Answer: 20 payments

EXERCISES WITH OPEN-RESPONSE PROBLEMS

In 1–4: **a.** Write a rule (that is, a formula for the general term a_n) that can be used in forming a sequence. **b.** Use the rule found in part **a** to write the next three terms of the sequence.

1. 4, 5, 6, 7, . . .   **2.** 2, 4, 6, 8, . . .   **3.** $1, \frac{1}{2}, \frac{1}{3}, \frac{1}{4}, \ldots$ **4.** $-1, 0, 1, 2, \ldots$

In 5–12, write the first four terms of the sequence defined by the given rule.

5. $a_n = 5n$ **6.** $a_n = n + 5$ **7.** $a_n = 3n - 4$ **8.** $a_n = n^2$

9. $a_n = 3^n$ **10.** $a_n = 2^{n-1}$ **11.** $a_n = n(n + 1)$ **12.** $a_n = \frac{2n}{2n + 1}$

In 13–20, find the common difference of the arithmetic sequence. Then find the next two terms.

13. 5, 7, 9, . . .   **14.** $x + 1, x + 4, x + 7, \ldots$ **15.** 7, 2, −3, . . .   **16.** $2\frac{1}{2}, 3, 3\frac{1}{2}, \ldots$

17. $2x, 3x, 4x, \ldots$ **18.** $5\frac{2}{3}, 5\frac{1}{3}, 5, \ldots$ **19.** .3, .5, .7, . . .   **20.** 1.02, 1.04, 1.06, . . .

In 21–24, find a_n in an arithmetic sequence that has the given values for a_1, d, and n.

21. $a_1 = 6, d = 4, n = 8$ **22.** $a_1 = 9, d = -2, n = 10$

23. $a_1 = \frac{5}{2}, d = -\frac{1}{2}, n = 7$ **24.** $a_1 = -\frac{4}{5}, d = -\frac{2}{5}, n = 28$

In 25–30, find the sum of the terms of the arithmetic sequence that has the given data.

25. $a_1 = 7, a_{12} = 29, n = 12$

26. $a_1 = -14, a_5 = 30, n = 5$

27. $a_1 = 2, a_{14} = 54, n = 14$

28. $a_1 = 20, a_9 = -6, n = 9$

29. $a_1 = 5, d = 3, n = 15$

30. $a_1 = -12, d = -2, n = 10$

In 31–36, find the sum of the indicated number of terms of the arithmetic sequence.

31. 1, 8, 15, . . . (first 10 terms)

32. 20, 17, 14, . . . (first 16 terms)

33. $8, 7\frac{1}{2}, 7, \ldots$ (first 20 terms)

34. 5, 1, −3, . . . (first 13 terms)

35. −3, −5, −7, . . . (first 18 terms)

36. −12, −10, −8, . . . (first 12 terms)

37. Find the sum of all the positive odd integers less than 100.

38. Find the sum of all the even integers from 2 to 100 inclusive.

39. Which term of the arithmetic sequence 7, 13, 19, . . . is 133?

40. If the first term of an arithmetic sequence is 7 and the twenty-fifth term is 79, what is the common difference?

41. The first term of an arithmetic sequence is 10 and the thirtieth term is −77. Find the common difference.

42. In an arithmetic sequence, $a_1 = \frac{2}{3}$ and $a_{12} = 19$. Find the common difference.

43. Find the number of terms in the arithmetic sequence 4, 7, 10, . . . , 40.

44. Find the number of terms in the arithmetic sequence 84, 82, 80, . . . , 20.

45. The second and fourth terms of an arithmetic sequence are 15 and 21. Find the third term.

46. Jared accepted a job which pays $28,000 the first year with yearly increases of $1,400. Find his salary during his tenth year on the job.

47. In a theater, the front row of the orchestra has 30 seats. Each row after the first row has 6 seats more than the previous row. Find the number of seats in the 15th row.

48. Brianna saved $4,000 during her first year on the job. In each of the following years, she saved $1,500 more than she had saved the previous year. During which year will her savings for the year amount to $16,000?

49. **a.** Find x so that the numbers $4x - 1$, $2x + 2$, and $2x - 3$ form an arithmetic sequence.
   b. Find the fifth term of the sequence.

50. An object falls 16.08 feet, 48.24 feet, 80.40 feet in successive seconds.
   a. How far will it fall in the tenth second?
   b. How far will it fall in 15 seconds?

51. In an arithmetic sequence, $S_n = 210$, $a_n = 24$, and $n = 14$. Find a_1.

52. In an arithmetic sequence, $d = 5$, $n = 14$, $S_n = 651$. Find a_1 and a_n.

53. A sum of money is to be distributed among 10 prize winning contestants in such a way that each one after the first receives $10 more than the preceding person. The largest prize awarded is three times the smallest. Let a represent the smallest prize.
   a. Express the largest prize in terms of a.
   b. Using the formula for the last term of an arithmetic sequence, find a.
   c. Find the amount distributed in prizes.

22-6 GEOMETRIC SEQUENCES AND SERIES

Finding the General Term of a Geometric Sequence

In the sequence 2, 6, 18, 54, each term after the first term, 2, is the product of the preceding term and a constant 3. Such a sequence is a *geometric sequence*.

- **DEFINITION.** A *geometric sequence* is a sequence in which each term after the first is the product of the preceding term and a constant.

Thus, in the sequence 2, 6, 18, 54, the term $6 = 2(3)$ and the term $54 = 18(3)$. Note that the constant 3 may be found by dividing any term by its predecessor. Thus, $\frac{6}{2} = 3$, $\frac{18}{6} = 3$, and $\frac{54}{18} = 3$. Hence, the constant 3 is the **common ratio** in the geometric sequence 2, 6, 18, 54.

PROCEDURE. To find the common ratio in a geometric sequence, divide any term by its predecessor, the term that immediately precedes it.

Thus, in the geometric sequence 5, -25, 125, -625, the common ratio is -5 since $\frac{-25}{5} = -5$.

- **In general, in a geometric sequence, if r represents the common ratio and a_{n-1} and a_n represent two consecutive terms, then**

$$r = \frac{a_n}{a_{n-1}}$$

Note that the common ratio may be positive or negative, but not 0.

If a_1 represents the first term of a geometric sequence and r represents the common ratio, then the sequence may be written as follows:

Number of term	1	2	3	4	5	...,	n
Terms of sequence	a_1,	a_1r,	a_1r^2,	a_1r^3,	a_1r^4,	...,	a_1r^{n-1}

Note that the fourth term of the sequence is a_1r^3 and the fifth term is a_1r^4. In general, the nth term $= a_1r^{n-1}$; that is, the nth term is the product of the first term, and the common ratio raised to the $(n - 1)$ power.

Thus, the ninth term of 2, 20, 200, 2000, . . . is $2(10^8) = 200,000,000$.

- **In general, if the nth term of a geometric sequence is represented by a_n, then**

$$a_n = a_1r^{n-1}$$

For example, in the sequence 8, 4, 2, 1, . . . , $a_6 = 8\left(\frac{1}{2}\right)^5 = 8\left(\frac{1}{32}\right) = \frac{1}{4}$. Also, in the sequence 12, -6, 3, $-1\frac{1}{2}$, . . . , $a_6 = 12\left(-\frac{1}{2}\right)^5 = 12\left(-\frac{1}{32}\right) = -\frac{3}{8}$.

We can graph a geometric sequence with the numbers of the terms as the n-values and the terms as the a-values. The graph is an exponential function with the domain the positive integers.

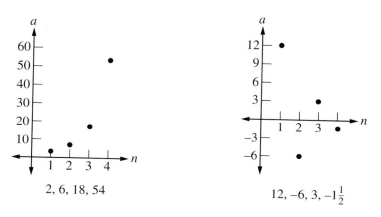

2, 6, 18, 54   12, -6, 3, $-1\frac{1}{2}$

Finding the Sum of a Geometric Series

● **DEFINITION.** A *geometric series* is the indicated sum of the terms of a geometric sequence.

Since 5, 10, 20, 40, 80 is a geometric sequence, $5 + 10 + 20 + 40 + 80$ is a geometric series. Since $5 + 10 + 20 + 40 + 80 = 155$, we say that the sum of this series is 155.

In general, a geometric series is represented by $a_1 + a_1 r + a_1 r^2 + \cdots a_1 r^{n-1}$, in which a_1 is the first term, n is the number of terms, a_n is the nth term, and r is the common ratio. The sum of the geometric series, S_n, is given by the following formulas:

$$S_n = \frac{a_1 - a_1 r^n}{1 - r} \quad \text{or} \quad S_n = \frac{a_1 - a_n r}{1 - r}, r \neq 1$$

Finding the Sum of an Infinite Geometric Series

We have learned that if the number of terms in a sequence increases without limit, the sequence is called an *infinite sequence*. Also, if the number of terms in a series increases without limit, we call the series an *infinite series*.

Thus, 1, $\frac{1}{2}$, $\frac{1}{4}$, $\frac{1}{8}$, $\frac{1}{16}$, $\frac{1}{32}$, ... is an infinite geometric sequence. Also, $1 + \frac{1}{2} + \frac{1}{4} + \frac{1}{8} + \frac{1}{16} + \frac{1}{32} + \cdots$ is an infinite geometric series.

Consider the infinite geometric series $1 + 2 + 4 + 8 + 16 + 32 + \cdots$.
Let us find the sums of different numbers of terms of this series.

$$S_1 = 1 \text{ (We define } S_1 \text{ as the first term, 1.)}$$
$$S_2 = 1 + 2 = 3$$
$$S_3 = 1 + 2 + 4 = 7$$
$$S_4 = 1 + 2 + 4 + 8 = 15$$
$$S_5 = 1 + 2 + 4 + 8 + 16 = 31$$

In general, $S_n = 1 + 2 + 4 + 8 + 16 + \cdots$ to n terms.

We can see that as we increase the number of terms that are being added in the series, the individual terms become larger and larger. Furthermore, the sums S_1, S_2, S_3, and so on, also become larger and larger. In fact, we can make S_n as large as we please by adding a sufficiently large number of terms. There is no limit to the value of S_n. We say that the sum of the terms of this infinite series is not finite. Such an infinite series is said to be a ***divergent series***.

Other examples of infinite geometric series that are divergent are

$$-1 - 2 - 4 - 8 - 16 - 32 - \cdots \text{ and } 1 - 2 + 4 - 8 + 16 - 32 + \cdots$$

In general, an infinite geometric series is a divergent series if the absolute value of the common ratio, r, is greater than or equal to 1; that is, $|r| \geq 1$.

On the other hand, consider the infinite geometric series

$$1 + \tfrac{1}{2} + \tfrac{1}{4} + \tfrac{1}{8} + \tfrac{1}{16} + \tfrac{1}{32} + \cdots$$

Let us find the sums of different numbers of terms of this series.

$$S_1 = 1 \text{ (We define } S_1 \text{ as the first term, 1.)}$$
$$S_2 = 1 + \tfrac{1}{2} = 1\tfrac{1}{2}, \text{ or } 1.5$$
$$S_3 = 1 + \tfrac{1}{2} + \tfrac{1}{4} = 1\tfrac{3}{4}, \text{ or } 1.75$$
$$S_4 = 1 + \tfrac{1}{2} + \tfrac{1}{4} + \tfrac{1}{8} = 1\tfrac{7}{8}, \text{ or } 1.875$$
$$S_5 = 1 + \tfrac{1}{2} + \tfrac{1}{4} + \tfrac{1}{8} + \tfrac{1}{16} = 1\tfrac{15}{16}, \text{ or } 1.9375$$

In general, $S_n = 1 + \tfrac{1}{2} + \tfrac{1}{4} + \tfrac{1}{8} + \tfrac{1}{16} + \cdots$ to n terms.

We can see that as we increase the number of terms in the series, the individual terms are becoming smaller and smaller. Although the sums $S_1, S_2, S_3, \ldots$ are becoming larger, there is a limit to the value of S_n. The value of S_n gets closer and closer to 2, but is never equal to 2. We can obtain a value of S_n as close to 2 as we wish by adding a sufficiently large number of terms. For example, to obtain a value of S_n within $\frac{1}{1000}$ of 2, we would add 12 terms. However, there is no value of n for which the value of S_n is equal to 2. We say that the value of S_n "approaches" the number 2 as a limit, and for that reason we also say that the sum of an infinite number of terms of this series is 2. Such a series, in which the infinite sequence $S_1, S_2, S_3, \ldots$ approaches a limit, is called a ***convergent series***.

Other examples of infinite geometric series that are convergent are

$$-1 - \frac{1}{2} - \frac{1}{4} - \frac{1}{8} - \frac{1}{16} - \frac{1}{32} - \cdots \text{ and } 1 - \frac{1}{2} + \frac{1}{4} - \frac{1}{8} + \frac{1}{16} - \frac{1}{32} + \cdots$$

In general, an infinite geometric series is a convergent series if the absolute value of the common ratio, r, is less than 1; that is, $|r| < 1$.

In order to find the limit of the sum of an infinite convergent geometric series, we can use the following formula:

$$S = \frac{a_1}{1-r}, |r| < 1$$

For example, in the series $1 + \frac{1}{2} + \frac{1}{4} + \frac{1}{8} + \cdots$, $a_1 = 1$ and $r = \frac{1}{2}$. Hence,

$$S = \frac{a_1}{1-r} = \frac{1}{1 - \frac{1}{2}} = \frac{1}{\frac{1}{2}} = 2$$

For verbal problems involving geometric sequences, the following ideas may be helpful in writing the equations that can be used in solving the problems:

1. The ratio of any term of a geometric sequence to its preceding term is equal to the ratio of any other term to its preceding term.

2. Apply the formulas for a_n and S_n in a geometric sequence.

EXAMPLES

1. Find the seventh term of the geometric progression $32, -16, 8, \ldots$.

Solution   First find the common ratio by dividing the second term by the first. Then find the seventh term.

$$r = (-16) \div (32) = -\frac{1}{2}$$

$$a_n = a_1 r^{n-1} \qquad\qquad a_1 = 32, n = 7, r = -\frac{1}{2}$$

$$= 32\left(-\frac{1}{2}\right)^6$$

$$= 32\left(\frac{1}{64}\right)$$

$$= \frac{1}{2} \quad \textit{Answer}$$

2. Find the sum of the first five terms of the geometric sequence $5, 15, 45, \ldots$.

Solution   Step 1. Find the common ratio, r, by dividing the second term, 15, by the first term, 5.
$r = 15 \div 5$, or $r = 3$.

Step 2. Find the sum of the first five terms of the series $5 + 15 + 45 + \cdots$.

$$S_n = \frac{a_1 - a_1 r^n}{1 - r} \qquad a_1 = 5, r = 3, n = 5$$

$$S_5 = \frac{5 - 5(3)^5}{1 - 3}$$

$$= \frac{5 - 1215}{-2} = \frac{-1210}{-2} = 605 \quad Answer$$

---

3. There are three numbers such that the second is two more than the first and the third is nine times the first. The numbers form a geometric sequence. Find the numbers.

Solution Let x = the first number. Then $x + 2$ = the second number and $9x$ = the third number. The numbers $x, x + 2, 9x$ are numbers in a geometric sequence.

In a geometric sequence of three terms, the middle term is the mean proportional between the first and the last terms. Hence,

$$\frac{x}{x + 2} = \frac{x + 2}{9x}$$

$$9x^2 = (x + 2)^2$$

$$9x^2 = x^2 + 4x + 4$$

$$8x^2 - 4x - 4 = 0$$

$$2x^2 - x - 1 = 0$$

$$(x - 1)(2x + 1) = 0$$

$$x - 1 = 0 \;\Big|\; 2x + 1 = 0$$

$$x = 1 \;\Big|\; x = -\frac{1}{2}$$

If $x = 1$, the geometric sequence is 1, 3, 9. If $x = -\frac{1}{2}$, the geometric sequence is $-\frac{1}{2}, 1\frac{1}{2}, -4\frac{1}{2}$.

Answer: $1, 3, 9$ or $-\frac{1}{2}, 1\frac{1}{2}, -4\frac{1}{2}$

---

4. Find the sum of the infinite series $4 + \frac{4}{3} + \frac{4}{9} + \frac{4}{27} + \cdots$.

Solution First, find the ratio by dividing the second term by the first term. Then find the sum.

$$r = \left(\frac{4}{3}\right) \div (4) = \frac{4}{3} \times \frac{1}{4} = \frac{1}{3}$$

$$S = \frac{a_1}{1 - r} \qquad \text{Substitute: } a_1 = 4, r = \frac{1}{3}$$

$$= \frac{4}{1 - \frac{1}{3}} = \frac{4}{\frac{2}{3}} = 6 \quad Answer$$

---

5. Find the sum of the terms of the infinite geometric sequence $2, -1, \frac{1}{2}, -\frac{1}{4}, \ldots$.

Solution $r = (-1) \div (2) = -\frac{1}{2}$

$$S = \frac{a_1}{1-r} \qquad a_1 = 2, r = -\frac{1}{2}$$

$$= \frac{2}{1 - \left(-\frac{1}{2}\right)} = \frac{2}{1 + \frac{1}{2}} = \frac{2}{\frac{3}{2}} = \frac{4}{3} \quad Answer$$

---

6. Find the value of the repeating decimal $0.535353\ldots$.

Solution $0.535353\ldots = 0.53 + 0.0053 + 0.000053 + \cdots$

In this infinite geometric series, the common ratio $r = 0.0053 \div 0.53 = 0.01$. Since $a_1 = 0.53$ and $r = 0.01$, then $S = \frac{a_1}{1-r} = \frac{0.53}{1 - 0.01} = \frac{0.53}{0.99} = \frac{53}{99}$.

Answer: $\frac{53}{99}$

EXERCISES WITH OPEN-RESPONSE PROBLEMS

In 1–6, find the common ratio of the geometric sequence and the next two terms.

1. $5, 10, 20, \ldots$

2. $-3, 6, -12, \ldots$

3. $-3, -9, -27, \ldots$

4. $9, 3, 1, \ldots$

5. $4x, 16x, 64x, \ldots$

6. $\frac{1}{2}, \frac{1}{2}y, \frac{1}{2}y^2, \ldots$

In 7–9, write the first four terms of a geometric sequence in which a_1 and r have the given values.

7. $a_1 = 5, r = -2$

8. $a_1 = 6, r = \frac{1}{3}$

9. $a_1 = 4, r = x$

In 10–12, write the last four terms of a geometric sequence in which a_n and r have the given values.

10. $a_n = 243, r = 3$

11. $a_n = 12, r = \frac{1}{2}$

12. $a_n = 368, r = -2$

In 13–18, find the indicated term of the geometric sequence.

13. $1, 2, 4, \ldots$ (7th term)

14. $12, 6, 3, \ldots$ (8th term)

15. $-3, 6, -12, \ldots$ (6th term)

16. $4, 1, \frac{1}{4}, \ldots$ (5th term)

17. $3, \frac{3}{2}, \frac{3}{4}, \ldots$ (8th term)

18. $-\frac{3}{2}, 3, -6, \ldots$ (9th term)

In 19–24, find the sum of the indicated number of terms of the geometric sequence. (In Exercise 24, $y \neq 0, y \neq 1$.)

19. $1, 3, 9, \ldots$ (first 6 terms)

20. $8, 4, 2, \ldots$ (first 6 terms)

21. $-3, -15, -75, \ldots$ (first 5 terms)

22. $3, -6, 12, \ldots$ (first 5 terms)

23. $\frac{1}{27}, \frac{1}{9}, \frac{1}{3}, \ldots$ (first 5 terms)

24. $1, y, y^2, \ldots$ (first 10 terms)

In 25–28, find the first term and the common ratio of the infinite geometric series and state whether the series diverges or converges.

25. $20 + 10 + 5 + 2\frac{1}{2} + \cdots$

26. $3 + 12 + 48 + 192 + \cdots$

27. $8 - 2 + \frac{1}{2} - \frac{1}{8} + \cdots$

28. $2 - 6 + 18 - 54 + \cdots$

In 29–34, find the sum of the terms of the infinite geometric sequence.

29. $4, 2, 1, \ldots$

30. $5, \frac{5}{2}, \frac{5}{4}, \ldots$

31. $3, -1, \frac{1}{3}, \ldots$

32. $12, 8, 5\frac{1}{3}, \ldots$

33. $0.4, 0.04, 0.004, \ldots$

34. $0.23, 0.0023, 0.000023, \ldots$

In 35–37, find the sum of the infinite geometric sequence in which a_1 and r have the given values.

35. $a_1 = 7, r = \frac{1}{2}$

36. $a_1 = 8, r = -\frac{1}{4}$

37. $a_1 = 0.7, r_1 = 0.1$

In 38–46, find the sum of the infinite series.

38. $6 + 2 + \frac{2}{3} + \cdots$

39. $12 + 3 + \frac{3}{4} + \cdots$

40. $200 + 50 + 12\frac{1}{4} + \cdots$

41. $8 + 4 + 2 + \cdots$

42. $\frac{7}{10} + \frac{7}{100} + \frac{7}{1,000} + \cdots$

43. $\frac{1}{5} + \frac{1}{10} + \frac{1}{20} + \cdots$

44. $-2 - \frac{1}{4} - \frac{1}{32} - \cdots$

45. $9 - 6 + 4 - \cdots$

46. $\frac{1}{2} - \frac{1}{3} + \frac{2}{9} - \cdots$

In 47–50, find the sum of the indicated number of terms of the geometric series.

47. $8 + 16 + 32 + \cdots$ (first 5 terms)

48. $81 + 27 + 9 + \cdots$ (first 6 terms)

49. $\frac{1}{8} + \frac{1}{4} + \frac{1}{2} + \cdots$ (first 7 terms)

50. $1 - 5 + 25 - 125 + \cdots$ (first 8 terms)

In 51–54: **a.** Write the geometric series. **b.** Find the sum of the series.

51. $\sum_{i=1}^{4} 2^i$

52. $\sum_{i=1}^{3} \left(\frac{1}{3}\right)^i$

53. $\sum_{j=1}^{5} 2(3)^{j-1}$

54. $\sum_{k=-1}^{3} (-5)(4)^{k+1}$

In 55–62, represent the repeating decimal as an equivalent fraction.

55. 0.888888 . . .   **56.** 0.131313 . . .   **57.** 0.363636 . . .   **58.** 0.484848 . . .

59. 0.727272 . . .   **60.** 0.838383 . . .   **61.** 0.125125 . . .   **62.** 0.431431 . . .

63. In a lottery, the first ticket drawn paid a prize of $50,000,000. Every succeeding ticket paid half as much as the preceding one. Four tickets were drawn. How much did the fourth ticket pay?

64. A house which was built at a cost of $150,000 depreciates each year by an amount equal to 4% of its value at the beginning of the year. Find the value of this house at the end of 5 years.

22-7 THE BINOMIAL THEOREM

Any binomial may be represented by $(x + y)$, where x represents the first term and y represents the second term. If a binomial is raised to a positive integral power, the result is a polynomial called the **expansion of the binomial**. Here is the expansion of the first four powers of $(x + y)$:

$$(x + y)^0 = 1$$
$$(x + y)^1 = 1x + 1y$$
$$(x + y)^2 = (x + y)(x + y) = 1x^2 + 2xy + 1y^2$$
$$(x + y)^3 = (x + y)(x + y)^2 = (x + y)(x^2 + 2xy + y^2)$$
$$= x^3 + 2x^2y + xy^2 + x^2y + 2xy^2 + y^3$$
$$= 1x^3 + 3x^2y + 3xy^2 + 1y^3$$
$$(x + y)^4 = (x + y)(x + y)^3 = (x + y)(x^3 + 3x^2y + 3xy^2 + y^3)$$
$$= x^4 + 3x^3y + 3x^2y^2 + xy^3 + x^3y + 3x^2y^2 + 3xy^3 + y^4$$
$$= 1x^4 + 4x^3y + 6x^2y^2 + 4xy^3 + 1y^4$$

Different patterns emerge as the products that equal the binomial expansions are shown below on the left.

One pattern involves only the *coefficients* of the terms in the expansions. This display, called **Pascal's triangle**, is shown below on the right.

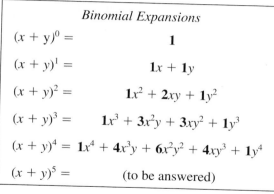

Binomial Expansions

$(x + y)^0 =$ **1**

$(x + y)^1 =$ $\mathbf{1}x + \mathbf{1}y$

$(x + y)^2 =$ $\mathbf{1}x^2 + \mathbf{2}xy + \mathbf{1}y^2$

$(x + y)^3 =$ $\mathbf{1}x^3 + \mathbf{3}x^2y + \mathbf{3}xy^2 + \mathbf{1}y^3$

$(x + y)^4 = \mathbf{1}x^4 + \mathbf{4}x^3y + \mathbf{6}x^2y^2 + \mathbf{4}xy^3 + \mathbf{1}y^4$

$(x + y)^5 =$ (to be answered)

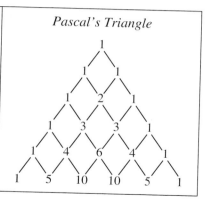

Pascal's Triangle

In Pascal's triangle, elements inside the triangle can also be obtained by adding a pair of adjacent entries from the row above. Thus, the elements of the fifth row (1-4-6-4-1) are added to find the elements of the sixth row, which are 1-5-10-10-5-1.

Coefficients

Other patterns found in the binomial expansions involve the *factors* or *powers* of x and y. In any expansion $(x + y)^n$, the first term is x^n or $x^n y^0$. Then, in each successive term, the exponent of x decreases by 1 as the exponent of y increases by 1 until the last term, $x^0 y^n$, or simply y^n, is reached.

For example, terms in the expansion $(x + y)^5$ include factors or powers of x and y beginning with x^5 (or $x^5 y^0$) and ending with y^5 (or $x^0 y^5$).

$$x^5 y^0, \ x^4 y^1, \ x^3 y^2, \ x^2 y^3, \ x^1 y^4, \ x^0 y^5$$

Powers or factors

These patterns involving coefficients and factors enable us to write

$$(x + y)^5 = 1x^5 + 5x^4 y + 10x^3 y^2 + 10x^2 y^3 + 5xy^4 + 1y^5$$

Since $(x + y)^5 = (x + y)(x + y)(x + y)(x + y)(x + y)$, we can think of the expansion of $(x + y)^5$ as the result of choosing all possible combinations of either x or y from each of 5 factors.

1. We can choose x from 5 factors and y from 0 factors: $_5C_0 x^5 y^0$.
   The number of ways of doing this is $_5C_0$.

2. We can choose x from 4 factors and y from 1 factor: $_5C_1 x^4 y^1$.
   The number of ways of doing this is $_5C_1$.

3. We can choose x from 3 factors and y from 2 factors: $_5C_2 x^3 y^2$.
   The number of ways of doing this is $_5C_2$.

4. We can choose x from 2 factors and y from 3 factors: $_5C_3 x^2 y^3$.
   The number of ways of doing this is $_5C_3$.

5. We can choose x from 1 factor and y from 4 factors: $_5C_4 x^1 y^4$.
   The number of ways of doing this is $_5C_4$.

6. We can choose x from 0 factors and y from 5 factors: $_5C_5 x^0 y^5$.
   The number of ways of doing this is $_5C_5$.

Therefore:

$$(x + y)^5 = {}_5C_0 x^5 y^0 + {}_5C_1 x^4 y^1 + {}_5C_2 x^3 y^2 + {}_5C_3 x^2 y^3 + {}_5C_4 x^1 y^4 + {}_5C_5 x^0 y^5$$

or

$$(x + y)^5 = \binom{5}{0} x^5 y^0 + \binom{5}{1} x^4 y^1 + \binom{5}{2} x^3 y^2 + \binom{5}{3} x^2 y^3 + \binom{5}{4} x^1 y^4 + \binom{5}{5} x^0 y^5$$

or

$$(x + y)^5 = 1x^5 + 5x^4 y + 10x^3 y^2 + 10x^2 y^3 + 5xy^4 + 1y^5$$

- **In general:**

$$(x + y)^n = {}_nC_0 x^n y^0 + {}_nC_1 x^{n-1} y^1 + {}_nC_2 x^{n-2} y^2 + \cdots + {}_nC_{n-1} x^1 y^{n-1} + {}_nC_n x^0 y^n$$

or

$$(x + y)^n = \binom{n}{0} x^n y^0 + \binom{n}{1} x^{n-1} y^1 + \binom{n}{2} x^{n-2} y^2 + \cdots + \binom{n}{n-1} x^1 y^{n-1} + \binom{n}{n} x^0 y^n$$

The examples that follow show how this general form is used to expand any binomial. Other observations based on patterns tell us that:

1. For any binomial expansion $(x + y)^n$, there are $n + 1$ terms.

2. In general, the rth term of the expansion is

$$_nC_{r-1} x^{n-r+1} y^{r-1}$$

EXAMPLES

1. Write the expansion of $(b^2 - 3)^3$.

Solution   Write the general expansion of $(x + y)^3$, and let $x = b^2$ and $y = -3$.

$$(x + y)^3 = {}_3C_0 x^3 y^0 + {}_3C_1 x^2 y^1 + {}_3C_2 x^1 y^2 + {}_3C_3 x^0 y^3$$

Then:

$$(b^2 - 3)^3 = 1 \cdot (b^2)^3 (-3)^0 + 3 \cdot (b^2)^2 (-3)^1 + 3 \cdot (b^2)^1 (-3)^2 + 1 \cdot (b^2)^0 (-3)^3$$
$$= 1 \cdot b^6 \cdot 1 \qquad + 3 \cdot b^4 \cdot (-3) \quad + 3 \cdot b^2 \cdot 9 \qquad + 1 \cdot 1 \cdot (-27)$$
$$= b^6 \qquad\qquad - 9b^4 \qquad\qquad + 27b^2 \qquad\qquad - 27$$

Answer: $(b^2 - 3)^3 = b^6 - 9b^4 + 27b^2 - 27$

---

2. Compute $(2k - 1)^4$ by using the binomial expansion formula.

Solution   Write the general formula for $(x + y)^4$, and let $x = 2k$ and $y = -1$.

$$(x + y)^4 = \binom{4}{0} x^4 y^0 + \binom{4}{1} x^3 y^1 + \binom{4}{2} x^2 y^2 + \binom{4}{3} x^1 y^3 + \binom{4}{4} x^0 y^4$$

Then:

$$(2k - 1)^4$$
$$= 1(2k)^4 (-1)^0 + 4(2k)^3 (-1) + 6(2k)^2 (-1)^2 + 4(2k)^1 (-1)^3 + 1(2k)^0 (-1)^4$$
$$= 1 \cdot 16k^4 \cdot 1 \ + 4 \cdot 8k^3 (-1) + 6 \cdot 4k^2 \cdot 1 \quad + 4 \cdot 2k(-1) \ + 1 \cdot 1 \cdot 1$$
$$= 16k^4 - 32k^3 + 24k^2 - 8k \ + 1$$

Answer: $(2k - 1)^4 = 16k^4 - 32k^3 + 24k^2 - 8k + 1$

---

3. Write the *eleventh term* of the expansion of $(2a - 1)^{12}$.

How to Proceed:	*Solution:*
(1) Write the general formula for the rth term of a binomial expansion.	$_nC_{r-1}x^{n-r+1}y^{r-1}$
(2) To find the 11th term of $(2a - 1)^{12}$, let $n = 12$, $r = 11$, $x = 2a$, and $y = -1$. Substitute these values in the formula, and simplify.	$_{12}C_{11-1}(2a)^{12-11+1}(-1)^{11-1}$ $= {}_{12}C_{10} \cdot (2a)^2 \cdot (-1)^{10}$ $= {}_{12}C_2 \cdot (2a)^2 \cdot (-1)^{10}$ $= 66 \cdot 4a^2 \cdot 1$ $= 264a^2$

Answer: $264a^2$

EXERCISES WITH OPEN-RESPONSE PROBLEMS

In 1–8, write the expansion of each binomial.

1. $(x + y)^6$
5. $(3a - 1)^3$

2. $(x + y)^7$
6. $(x - 2)^4$

3. $(x + y)^{10}$
7. $(1 - b^3)^5$

4. $(x - 1)^8$
8. $(2a^2 - b^3)^3$

In 9–16, in each case, write in simplest form the *third term* of the expansion.

9. $(a + b)^4$
13. $(a - 7)^6$

10. $(k + 2)^5$
14. $(2 + y)^7$

11. $(x - 3y)^5$
15. $(2x - 1)^6$

12. $(k - 5)^3$
16. $(4x + 3)^7$

In 17–20, in each case, write in simplest form the *fourth term* of the expansion.

17. $(5 - b)^4$
18. $(2a - 3)^5$
19. $(k^2 + 1)^7$
20. $\left(2x - \frac{1}{2}\right)^6$

21. Write in expanded form the volume of a cube if the measure of each edge is represented by $(2x - 3)$.

22. a. Find the value of $(1.01)^4$ by using the expansion of $(1 + 0.01)^4$.
  b. Use a calculator to evaluate $(1.01)^4$.
  c. State one advantage and one disadvantage to evaluating $(1.01)^{12}$ by:
    (*1*) using the binomial expansion (*2*) using a calculator

In 23–26, evaluate each power by using the expansion of a binomial.

23. $(1.01)^5$
24. $(1.2)^3$
25. $(1.02)^4$
26. $(1.05)^3$

In 27–30, select the *numeral* preceding the choice that best completes each sentence.

27. The third term of the expansion of $(a + 2b)^4$ is
  (1) $2a^2b^2$ (2) $4a^2b^2$ (3) $12a^2b^2$ (4) $24a^2b^2$

28. The eighth term of the expansion of $(2r - 1)^8$ is
    (1) $16r$ (2) $-16r$ (3) 1 (4) -1

29. The middle term of the expansion of $(x - 2y)^4$ is
    (1) $12x^2y^2$ (2) $-12x^2y^2$ (3) $24x^2y^2$ (4) $-24x^2y^2$

30. The last term in the expansion of $(6 - y)^9$ is
    (1) $54y^9$ (2) $-54y^9$ (3) y^9 (4) $-y^9$

CHAPTER SUMMARY

A *sample space*, *S*, is the set of all possible outcomes of an activity, and an *event*, *E*, is any subset of the sample space. If each outcome is equally likely to occur, the *theoretical probability* of an event *E* is the number of outcomes in *E*, divided by the number of outcomes in sample space *S*.

$$P(E) = \frac{n(E)}{n(S)}$$

The probability of an *impossible* event is 0, the probability of a *certain* event is 1, and all other probabilities lie between these values, that is $0 \le P(E) \le 1$.

The number of outcomes in a sample space or in an event is determined by using the counting principle, permutations, and/or combinations.

1. The *counting principle* states that, if one activity occurs in *m* ways and is followed by a second activity that occurs in *n* ways, then both activities occur in the given order in $m \cdot n$ ways. This principle may be extended to probabilities.

2. A *permutation* is an arrangement of objects in some specific order. The permutation of *n* objects taken *n* at a time, $_nP_n$, is equal to *factorial n*.

$$_nP_n = n! = n \cdot (n - 1) \cdot (n - 2) \cdot \ldots \cdot 3 \cdot 2 \cdot 1$$

The permutation of *n* objects taken *r* at a time ($r \le n$) can be found by the formulas:

$$_nP_r = \underbrace{n \cdot (n - 1) \cdot (n - 2) \cdot \ldots}_{r \text{ factors}} \qquad \text{and} \qquad _nP_r = \frac{n!}{(n - r)!}$$

3. A *combination* is a set of objects in which order is *not* important, such as a committee. The formula for the combination of *n* objects taken *r* at a time ($r \le n$) is

$$_nC_r = \frac{_nP_r}{r!}$$

By definition: $_nC_n = 1$ $_nC_0 = 1$ and $_nC_r = {_nC_{n-r}}$

A **Bernoulli experiment** has exactly two outcomes. For an experiment consisting of n independent trials, if r is the number of successes, then $n - r$ is the number of failures. If we let the probability of a success $= p$ and the probability of a failure $= q = 1 - p$, then the probability of exactly r successes in n independent trials is

$$_nC_r p^r q^{n-r}$$

At least r successes in n trials means $r, r + 1, r + 2, \ldots, n$ successes.

At most r successes in n trials means $r, r - 1, r - 2, \ldots, 0$ successes.

An **arithmetic sequence** is a sequence in which each term after the first is the sum of the preceding term and a constant. It can be represented by

$$a_1, a_1 + d, a_1 + 2d, a_1 + 3d, a_1 + 4d, \ldots, a_1 + (n - 1)d$$

where a_1 represents the first term of an arithmetic sequence and d represents the common difference. If the nth term of the sequence is a_n, $a_n = a_1 + (n - 1)d$.

An **arithmetic series** is the indicated sum of the terms of an arithmetic sequence. The sum of an arithmetic series can be found by the formulas:

$$S_n = \frac{n}{2}(a_1 + a_n)$$
$$S_n = \frac{n}{2}[2a_1 + (n - 1)d]$$

where a_1 is the first term, n is the number of terms, a_n is the nth term, and d is the common difference.

A **geometric sequence** is a sequence in which each term after the first is the product of the preceding term and a constant. It can be represented by

$$a_1, a_1r, a_1r^2, a_1r^3, a_1r^4, \ldots, a_1r^{n-1}$$

A **geometric series** is the indicated sum of the terms of a geometric sequence. The sum of a geometric series can be found by the formulas:

$$S_n = \frac{a_1 - a_1r^n}{1 - r} \quad or \quad S_n = \frac{a_1 - a_nr}{1 - r}, r \neq 1$$

An infinite series is said to be a **divergent series** if the sum of its terms is not finite. An infinite series whose sequence approaches a limit is called a **convergent series**.

Every binomial $(x + y)$ can be expanded to the nth power by using the formula

$$(x + y)^n = {_nC_0}x^n y^0 + {_nC_1}x^{n-1}y^1 + {_nC_2}x^{n-2}y^2 + \cdots + {_nC_{n-1}}x^1y^{n-1} + {_nC_n}x^0y^n$$

or

$$(x + y)^n = \binom{n}{0}x^n y^0 + \binom{n}{1}x^{n-1}y^1 + \binom{n}{2}x^{n-2}y^2 + \cdots + \binom{n}{n-1}x^1y^{n-1} + \binom{n}{n}x^0y^n$$

In the binomial expansion of $(x + y)^n$, there are $n + 1$ terms and, in general, the rth term of the expansion is $_nC_{r-1}x^{n-r+1}y^{r-1}$.

VOCABULARY

22-1 Sample space, S Counting principle   Permutation
Factorial n (n factorial)   Factorial key, $\boxed{!}$
Permutation key, $\boxed{\text{nPr}}$ Combination   Combination key, $\boxed{\text{nCr}}$

22-2 Event, E Theoretical probability   Certain   Impossible

22-3 Counting principle with probabilities   Bernoulli experiment
Binomial probability

22-4 Probability distribution

22-5 Sequence   Finite sequence   Infinite sequence   Arithmetic sequence
Common difference   Finite series   Infinite series   Arithmetic series

22-6 Geometric sequence   Common ratio   Geometric series
Divergent series   Convergent series

22-7 Expansion of the binomial   Pascal's triangle

REVIEW EXERCISES WITH OPEN-RESPONSE PROBLEMS

In 1–10, evaluate each expression.

1. $_5P_5$ **2.** $_6P_3$ **3.** $_6C_3$ **4.** $_7C_0$ **5.** $_{20}C_{20}$

6. $\binom{12}{5}$ **7.** $\frac{_4P_4}{2!}$ **8.** $\frac{7!}{6!}$ **9.** $\frac{20!}{17!\,3!}$ **10.** $_{62}C_{59}$

11. a. In how many ways can first, second, and third prize be awarded in an art contest if 6 entries are being considered for these prizes?
b. In how many ways can 3 honorable-mention awards be given in an art contest if 9 entries are being considered for these awards?

12. How many different sums of money can be obtained by taking 2 coins from a purse containing a half-dollar, a quarter, a dime, a nickel, and a penny?

13. From a standard deck of 52 cards, 4 cards are drawn without replacement.
a. How many combinations of 4 cards are possible?
b. How many combinations of 4 hearts are possible?
c. What is the probability that the 4 cards are all hearts?

In 14–16, tell the number of ways in which the letters in each word can be rearranged.

14. chef   **15.** career   **16.** bookkeeper

17. If 6 fair coins are tossed, find the probability of obtaining:
a. exactly 5 heads   **b.** exactly 6 heads   **c.** at least 5 heads
d. exactly 3 heads   **e.** at most 3 heads   **f.** at least 3 heads

18. In a basketball free-throw contest, the probability that Eric will be successful on each shot is $\frac{4}{5}$. Find the probability that Eric will be successful in:

a. exactly 2 out of 3 shots   **b.** at least 2 out of 3 shots
c. at most 1 out of 3 shots   **d.** exactly 2 out of 4 shots

In 19–22: **a.** Write a rule that can be used in forming a sequence.   **b.** Use the rule found in part **a** to write the next three terms of the sequence.

19. 6, 7, 8, 9, . . .   **20.** −2, −1, 0, 1, . . .
21. 4, 12, 36, 108, . . .   **22.** −2, 0, 2, 4, . . .

In 23 and 24, find the indicated term of the arithmetic sequence.

23. 7, 11, 15, . . . (15th term)   **24.** 1.05, 1.10, 1.15, . . . (12th term)

25. Find the sum of all the positive numbers less than 200 that are exactly divisible by 3.

In 26–28, find the missing term of the geometric sequence.

26. 4, 12, 36, . . . , 324   **27.** 2, 3, $4\frac{1}{2}$, . . . , $10\frac{1}{8}$ **28.** 6, −2, $\frac{2}{3}$, . . . , $\frac{9}{27}$

29. A rubber ball is dropped from a height of 18 feet. It rebounds $\frac{2}{3}$ of the distance from which it fell previously. This process continues until the ball comes to rest. Find the total distance through which the ball moved.

In 30–33, write the expansion of each binomial.

30. $(x + y)^8$ **31.** $(1 + 3x)^4$ **32.** $(5 - b)^3$ **33.** $\left(a - \frac{1}{a}\right)^5$

In 34–37, write in simplest form the *fifth term* of each expansion.

34. $(x + y)^{10}$ **35.** $(5 - y^2)^5$ **36.** $(3 - 2a)^6$ **37.** $(x^2 + 1)^9$

38. A calculator has 10 number keys and 5 operation keys.
   a. If one key is pressed at random, what is the probability that the key pressed is: (*1*) a number key? (*2*) an operation key?
   b. When 5 keys are pressed at random, what is the probability that:
   (*1*) exactly 3 are operation keys? (*2*) at least 3 are operation keys?
   (*3*) at most 2 are number keys?

In 39–43, in each case, select the *numeral* preceding the choice that best completes the sentence or answers the question.

39. When a certain machine makes parts, the probability that 1 part is defective is $\frac{1}{20}$. In a sample of 50 parts, the probability that exactly 5 are defective is

   (1) $\left(\frac{1}{20}\right)^5\left(\frac{19}{20}\right)^{45}$ (2) $_{45}C_5\left(\frac{1}{20}\right)^5\left(\frac{19}{20}\right)^{45}$

   (3) $_{50}C_5\left(\frac{1}{20}\right)^5\left(\frac{19}{20}\right)^{50}$ (4) $_{50}C_5\left(\frac{1}{20}\right)^5\left(\frac{19}{20}\right)^{45}$

40. What is the probability of getting exactly 7 fours when 10 dice are rolled?

   (1) $\left(\frac{1}{6}\right)^7\left(\frac{5}{6}\right)^{10}$ (2) $\left(\frac{1}{6}\right)^7\left(\frac{5}{6}\right)^3$ (3) $_{10}C_3\left(\frac{1}{6}\right)^7\left(\frac{5}{6}\right)^3$ (4) $_7C_3\left(\frac{1}{6}\right)^7\left(\frac{5}{6}\right)^3$

41. The normal distribution can be used to approximate the probability of
    (1) rolling a 12 with a pair of dice.
    (2) picking a king and a queen from a deck of cards.
    (3) spinning an odd number on a spinner numbered 1 to 5.
    (4) obtaining at least 6 heads on 10 tosses of a fair coin.

42. The fourth term of the expansion of $(1 - y^3)^7$ is
    (1) $35y^6$ (2) $35y^9$ (3) $-35y^6$ (4) $-35y^9$

43. The middle term of the expansion of $(a + b)^8$ is
    (1) a^4b^4 (2) $56a^4b^4$ (3) $70a^4b^4$ (4) $56a^5b^3$

CUMULATIVE REVIEW

1. List the following in order, starting with the smallest: $9^{150}, 5^{200}, 20^{100}$.

2. The map and graph describe a car trip from Albany to Skaneatales along Route 90, city streets in Syracuse, and Route 20.

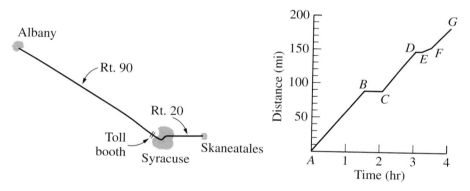

    a. Describe the trip, making use of both the map and the graph to explain the progress of the journey.
    b. Draw a graph that shows the speed at which the car traveled during the trip. Let the horizontal axis represent time in hours and the vertical axis represent speed in miles per hour.

3. Solve the following system of equations.   **a.** graphically   **b.** algebraically
$$y = x^2 - 4x - 1$$
$$3x + y = 1$$

4. The length of a rectangle is 12 centimeters longer than the width. The area of the rectangle is 100 square centimeters.
    a. Find the width of the rectangle in simplest radical form.
    b. Express the width of the rectangle to the *nearest hundredth* of a centimeter.
    c. Find the length of the rectangle to the *nearest hundredth* of a centimeter.

5. Evaluate $\displaystyle\sum_{n=3}^{5} \frac{n-1}{2}$.

6. Find the roots of $x^2 - 6x + 13 = 0$.

7. The table shows the numbers of pounds lost by forty persons who participated in a weight-loss program. For this set of data, find:

    a. the mean   **b.** the standard deviation

Number of Pounds x_i	Frequency f_i	Number of Pounds x_i	Frequency f_i
35–39	1	15–19	10
30–34	3	10–14	4
25–29	8	5–9	1
20–24	12	0–4	1

8. The ratio of the measures of the sides of a triangle is $3:6:7$. Find the measure of the smallest angle of the triangle to the *nearest tenth* of a degree.

9. Factor completely: $a^3 + 3a^2b - ab^2 - 3b^3$

10. Solve for x: $\log_5(x-1) - \log_5(x+3) = -1$.

Exploration

a. When is the probability of exactly 8 successes in 10 trials equal to the probability of exactly 2 successes in 10 trials?

b. When is the probability of 8 successes in 10 trials less than the probability of 2 successes in 10 trials?

c. Write general rules to compare the probability of r successes in n trials to the probability of $n - r$ successes in n trials.

Summary of Formulas

Functions of the Sum of Two Angles

$\sin (A + B) = \sin A \cos B + \cos A \sin B$

$\cos (A + B) = \cos A \cos B - \sin A \sin B$

$\tan (A + B) = \dfrac{\tan A + \tan B}{1 - \tan A \tan B}$

Functions of the Difference of Two Angles

$\sin (A - B) = \sin A \cos B - \cos A \sin B$

$\cos (A - B) = \cos A \cos B + \sin A \sin B$

$\tan (A - B) = \dfrac{\tan A - \tan B}{1 + \tan A \tan B}$

Functions of the Double Angle

$\sin 2A = 2 \sin A \cos A$

$\cos 2A = \cos^2 A - \sin^2 A$

$\cos 2A = 2 \cos^2 A - 1$

$\cos 2A = 1 - 2 \sin^2 A$

$\tan 2A = \dfrac{2 \tan A}{1 - \tan^2 A}$

Functions of the Half Angle

$\sin \frac{1}{2} A = \pm \sqrt{\dfrac{1 - \cos A}{2}}$

$\cos \frac{1}{2} A = \pm \sqrt{\dfrac{1 + \cos A}{2}}$

$\tan \frac{1}{2} A = \pm \sqrt{\dfrac{1 - \cos A}{1 + \cos A}}$

Law of Sines

$\dfrac{a}{\sin A} = \dfrac{b}{\sin B} = \dfrac{c}{\sin C}$

Law of Cosines

$a^2 = b^2 + c^2 - 2bc \cos A$

Area of Triangle

$K = \frac{1}{2} ab \sin C$

Normal Curve
Standard Deviation

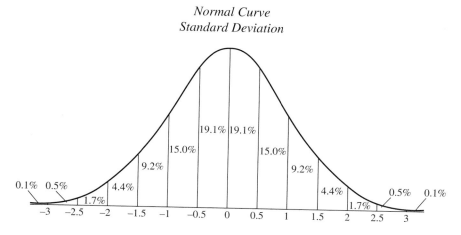

0.1%   0.5%   1.7%   4.4%   9.2%   15.0%   19.1%   19.1%   15.0%   9.2%   4.4%   1.7%   0.5%   0.1%

−3   −2.5   −2   −1.5   −1   −0.5   0   0.5   1   1.5   2   2.5   3

Index

linear, 505
logarithmic. *See* Logarithmic functions
notation for, 502
one-to-one, 549, 564
periodic, 708
period of, 708
polynomial, 506
product, 542
quadratic, 506
restricted domains and, 490–491
step, 508
sum, 542
transformations of plane as, 564
trigonometric. *See* Trigonometric
    functions
vertical-line test for, 489–490
wrapping, 704–705
Function values
choosing signs for, for half angles, 892
of coterminal angles, 628
of double angles, 885–888
finding remaining trigonometric, of
    angle when one function value
    is known, 685–690
of half angles, 890–893
as lengths of line segments, 675–677
of special angles, 631–634

G

Gauss, Carl Friedrich, 920, 926
General quadrilateral, 246
Geometric inequalities, 178–200
Geometric sequences, 1058–1063
defined, 1058
finding the general term of, 1058–1059
Geometric series
defined, 1059
finding the sum of, 1059
finding the sum of an infinite,
    1059–1061
Geometry
analytic, 1
coordinate, 1
Euclidean, 1
    definitions in, 95–96
proportions in, 321–322
proving statements in, 92–140
Geometry proofs, 100
comparing, to logic proof, 98–99
connection between logic proofs and,
    99–100
Glide reflections, 585–588, 592
Graphing
conjunctions, 385–388
disjunctions, 385–388
inverse variation, 540
parabolas, 515–519
solution sets involving one variable
    on a number line, 385–388

Graphing calculators, 314–316
combination key, 1034
conversion keys on, 640–641, 649
finding trigonometric function values
    on, 635–642
grouped data on, 1010–1011
log key on, 799
measures of central tendency on,
    986–987
permutation key, 1032–1033
standard deviation on, 998
statistics on, 979–980
test key of, 314
trace key on, 316
trigonometric equations and,
    899–900
Graphs
of functions, 489–490, 706
of reciprocal functions, 728–730
relating, to life situations, 496–497
trigonometric, 703–750
of $y = \cos x$, 711–713
of $y = \sin x$, 706–709
of $y = \tan x$, 725–727
Greatest common monomial factor,
    334
Greatest-integer function, 508
Grouped data, 1008–1013
intervals of length 1, 1008–1010
intervals of length greater than 1,
    1011–1013
Groups, 298
properties under composition,
    544–545
of transformations, 603–604

H

Half angles
choosing signs for function values of,
    892
cosine of, 891
function values of, 890–893
sine of, 890
tangent of, 891–892
Half-line, 13
Hexagon, 237
Hidden conditionals, 52
Histogram, 1001
Horizontal asymptote, 774
Horizontal lines, 282
slope of, 28, 33
Hyperbola, 528–531
defined, 528, 536
inverse variation, 539–540
transverse axis of, 530
Hypotenuse, 21, 612
in proving right triangles congruent,
    231–233
Hypothesis, 41, 98

I

i (imaginary unit), 921
multiplication by, 932
powers of, 922–923
Identify element, 297
Identities, 603–604, 857, 929, 937
algebraic, 858
defined, 681, 858
Pythagorean, 674–675, 680–683, 860
quotient, 674–675, 683, 860
reciprocal, 672, 683, 860
summary of, 895–896
trigonometric, 858
Identity function, 544
Identity proofs, guidelines for, 866
if and only if, 40
if . . . then, 40
Image, 560
Imaginary numbers, 920, 921–924
calculator limitations, 922
powers of, 922–923
properties and operations, 923
pure, 921, 923
Imaginary roots, solving quadratic
    equations with, 944–946
Imaginary unit, 921
powers of, 922–923
Implication, 41
Index, 398
dividing radicals with same, 415–417
multiplying radicals with same,
    411–414
statistics and, 989
Indirect proof, 107–108
Inductive reasoning, 93
Inequalities, 179
absolute-value, 393–396
addition properties of, 308
defined, 312
geometric, 178–200
involving exterior angle of triangle,
    189–191
involving lengths of sides of triangle,
    187–188
involving sides and angles in triangle,
    194–198
multiplication properties of, 308
quadratic, 966–970
substitution postulate for, 180–181
transitive property of, 180–181, 308
Inequality postulates, 179–181
involving addition and subtraction,
    183
involving multiplication and division,
    185
substitution, 180–181
transitive, 180
trichotomy, 180